HUMAN BIOLOGY

SEVENTEENTH EDITION

SYLVIA S. MADER
MICHAEL WINDELSPECHT

Mc
Graw
Hill

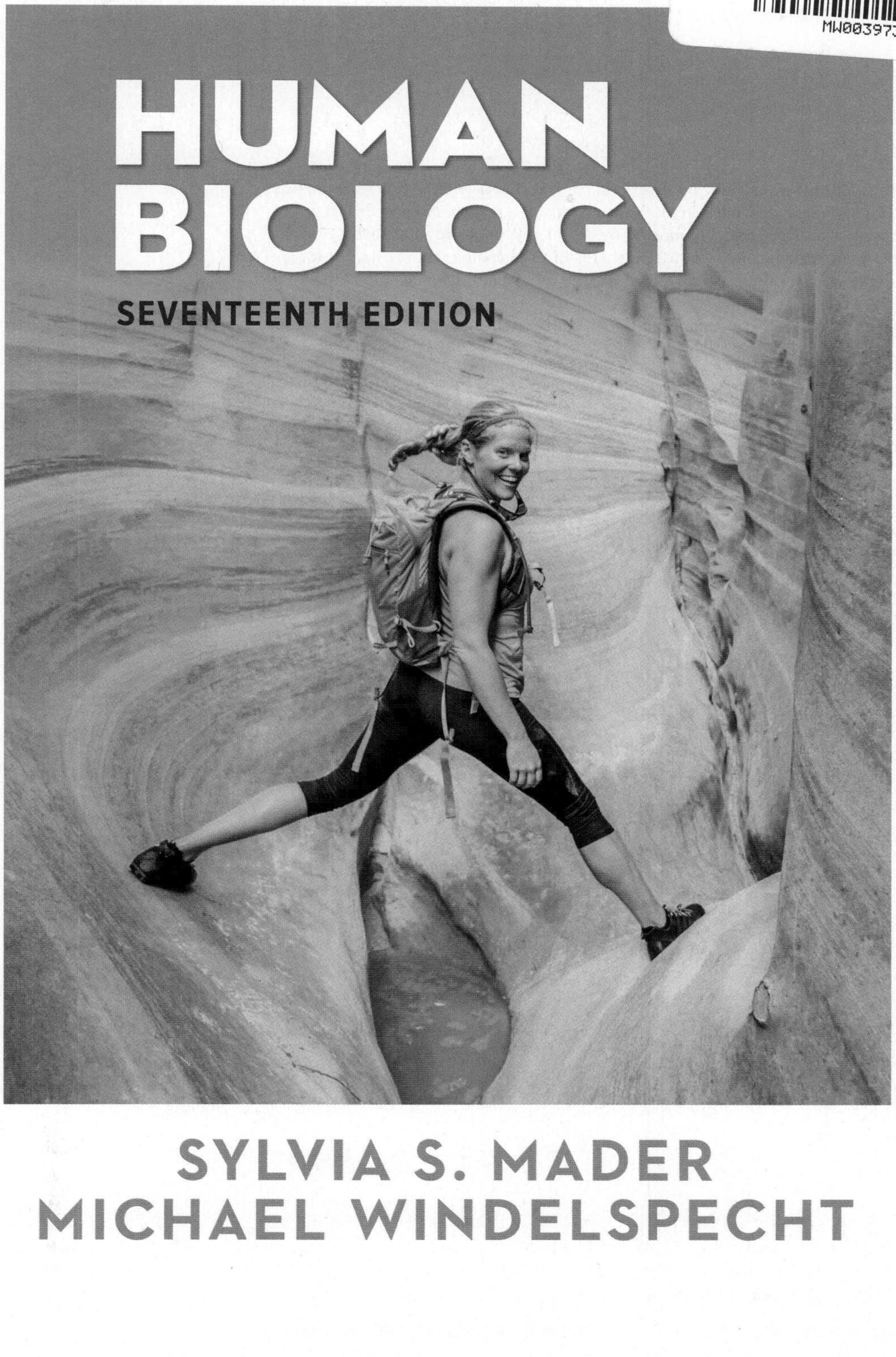

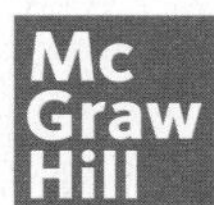

HUMAN BIOLOGY

Published by McGraw Hill LLC, 1325 Avenue of the Americas, New York, NY 10019.

This book is printed on acid-free paper.

1 2 3 4 5 6 7 8 9 LWI 27 26 25 24 23 22

ISBN 978-1-265-25006-5
MHID 1-265-25006-5

Cover Images: *Suzanne Stroeer/Aurora Photos/Getty Images*

mheducation.com/highered

ABOUT THE AUTHORS

Courtesy of Sylvia S. Mader

Sylvia S. Mader

Sylvia S. Mader has authored several nationally recognized biology texts published by McGraw Hill. Educated at Bryn Mawr College, Harvard University, Tufts University, and Nova Southeastern University, she holds degrees in both biology and education. Over the years, she has taught at University of Massachusetts, Lowell; Massachusetts Bay Community College; Suffolk University; and Nathan Mayhew Seminars. Her ability to reach out to science-shy students led to the writing of her first text, *Inquiry into Life*. Highly acclaimed for her crisp and entertaining writing style, her books have become models for others who write in the field of biology.

Ricochet Creative Productions, LLC

Michael Windelspecht

As an educator, Dr. Windelspecht has taught introductory biology, genetics, and human genetics in the online, traditional, and hybrid environments at community colleges, comprehensive universities, and military institutions. For over a decade he served as the introductory biology coordinator at Appalachian State University, where he directed a program that enrolled over 4,500 students annually.

He received degrees from Michigan State University (BS, zoology–genetics) and the University of South Florida (PhD, evolutionary genetics), and has published papers in areas as diverse as science education, water quality, and the evolution of insecticide resistance. His current interests are in the analysis of data from digital learning platforms for the development of personalized microlearning assets and next-generation publication platforms. He is currently a member of the National Association of Science Writers and several science education associations. He has served as the keynote speaker on the development of multimedia resources for online and hybrid science classrooms. In 2015, he won the DevLearn HyperDrive competition for a strategy to integrate student data into the textbook revision process.

As an author and editor, Dr. Windelspecht has over 30 reference textbooks and multiple print and online lab manuals to his credit. He has founded several science communication companies, including Ricochet Creative Productions, which actively develops and assesses new technologies for the science classroom, and Inspire-EdVentures, which provides experiential learning opportunities online and in Belize. You can learn more about Dr. Windelspecht by visiting his website at www.windelspectrum.com.

Courtesy of Dave Cox

Contributor

Dave Cox serves as professor of biology at Lincoln Land Community College, in Springfield, Illinois. He was educated at Illinois College and Western Illinois University. As an educator, Professor Cox teaches introductory biology for nonmajors in the traditional classroom format, as well as in a hybrid format. He also teaches biology for majors, and marine biology and biological field studies as study-abroad courses in Belize. He is the co-owner of Howler Publications, a company that specializes in scientific study abroad courses. Professor Cox has served as a contributor to multiple McGraw Hill titles over the past 12 years. He also develops educational resources for the ecotourism industry in Belize.

Students: Get Learning that Fits You

Effective tools for efficient studying

Connect is designed to help you be more productive with simple, flexible, intuitive tools that maximize your study time and meet your individual learning needs. Get learning that works for you with Connect.

Study anytime, anywhere

Download the free ReadAnywhere app and access your online eBook, SmartBook 2.0, or Adaptive Learning Assignments when it's convenient, even if you're offline. And since the app automatically syncs with your Connect account, all of your work is available every time you open it. Find out more at **www.mheducation.com/readanywhere**

"I really liked this app—it made it easy to study when you don't have your textbook in front of you."

- Jordan Cunningham,
Eastern Washington University

Calendar: owattaphotos/Getty Images

Everything you need in one place

Your Connect course has everything you need—whether reading on your digital eBook or completing assignments for class, Connect makes it easy to get your work done.

Learning for everyone

McGraw Hill works directly with Accessibility Services Departments and faculty to meet the learning needs of all students. Please contact your Accessibility Services Office and ask them to email accessibility@mheducation.com, or visit **www.mheducation.com/about/accessibility** for more information.

Top: Jenner Images/Getty Images, Left: Hero Images/Getty Images, Right: Hero Images/Getty Images

PREFACE

Goals of the Seventeenth Edition

Humans are a naturally inquisitive species. As children, we become fascinated with our bodies, and life in general, at a very early age. We want to know how our bodies work, why there are differences, and similarities, between ourselves and the other children around us. In other words, at a very early age we are all biologists.

In many ways, today's students in the science classroom face some of the same challenges their parents did decades ago. The abundance of new terms often overwhelms even the best-prepared student, and the study of biological processes and methods of scientific thinking may convince some students that "science isn't their thing." The study of human biology creates an opportunity for teachers to instruct their students using the ultimate model organism—their own bodies. Whether this is their last science class or the first in a long career in allied health, the study of human biology is pertinent to everyone.

Students in today's world are being exposed, almost on a daily basis, to exciting new discoveries and insights that, in many cases, were beyond our predictions even a few short years ago—from revolutionary new techniques to develop vaccines to stop pandemics, to the impacts of climate change on their local environments and advances in medical techniques to fight diseases such as cancer. Therefore, it is important that we know not only why we are different, but how we are the same as the species we share the planet with. It is our task, as instructors, not only to make these findings available to our students but to enlighten students as to why these discoveries are important to their lives and society. At the same time, we must provide students with a firm foundation in those core principles on which biology is founded, and in doing so, provide them with the background to better understand the many discoveries still to come.

As educators, the authors of this text understand the needs of our colleagues in developing curricula that increasingly focus on relevancy and delivery in the online environment. McGraw Hill Education has long been an innovator in the development of educational resources, and the *Human Biology* text is at the forefront in integrating these resources and digital technologies into the science classroom. In this edition, that involved the following:

- Making the content more relevant to the current generation of students by updating chapter openers and themed readings to focus on issues and topics important to the discussions that students are hearing in the world around them.
- Integrating relevancy modules to supplement the format of a traditional textbook and provide another avenue for students to engage with the content.
- Redesigning the artwork to ensure it transitions to the digital world of mobile devices.
- Developing a new Featured Reading Series, The Diversity of Science, to emphasize the contributions of unrecognized scientists to our understanding of biology.

Virtual Labs and Lab Simulations

While the biological sciences are hands-on disciplines, instructors today are often asked to deliver some of their lab content online, as full online replacements, supplements to prepare for in-person labs, or make-up labs. These simulations help each

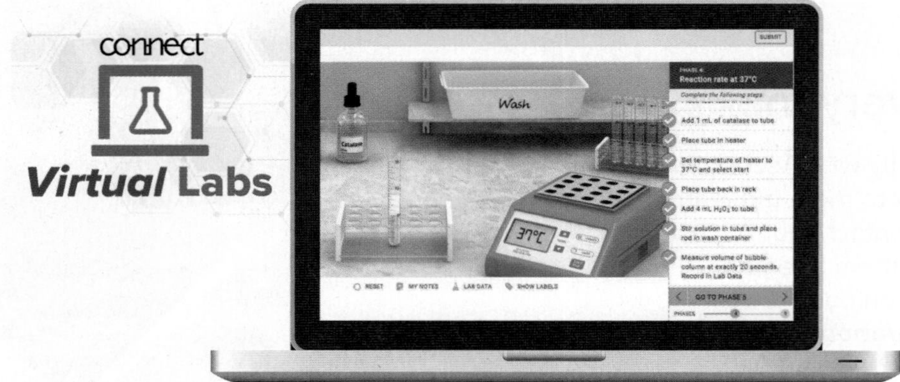

student learn the practical and conceptual skills needed, and then let them check their understanding of the lessons by providing feedback. With adaptive pre-lab and post-lab assessments available, instructors can customize each assignment.

From the instructor's perspective, these simulations may be used in the lecture environment to help students visualize complex scientific processes, such as DNA technology or Gram staining, while at the same time providing a valuable connection between the lecture and lab environments.

Relevancy

The use of real-world examples to demonstrate the importance of biology in the lives of students is widely recognized as an effective teaching strategy for the introductory biology classroom. Students want to learn about the topics they are interested in. The development of relevancy-based resources is a major focus for the authors of the Mader series of texts. Some examples of how we have increased the relevancy content of this edition are explained in the following paragraphs.

Relevancy Modules

A series of relevancy modules have been designed to accompany each unit in *Human Biology.* These modules demonstrate the connections between biological content and topics that are of interest to society as a whole. Each module consists of an introductory video, an overview of basic scientific concepts, and then a closer look at the application of these concepts to the topic. An infographic at the end of each module may be easily used in the lecture environment to initiate discussion of the topic. Discussion and assessment questions, specific to the modules, are available at the end of the module, and for automatic assessment in the Connect platform. Below is a list of our current relevancy modules.

These modules are available as a supplementary eBook to the existing text within Connect, and may be assigned by the instructor for use in a variety of ways in the classroom.

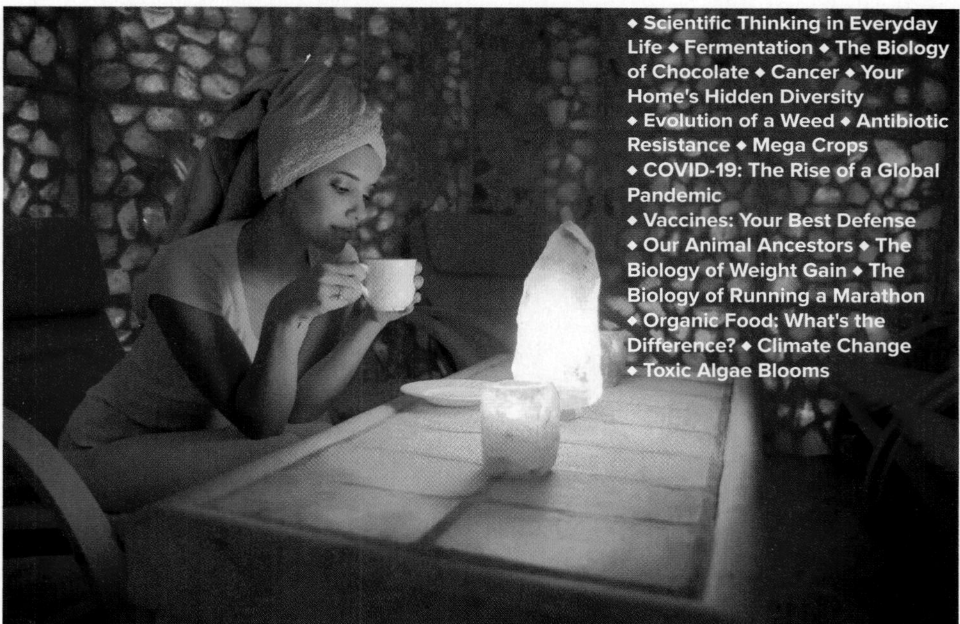

◆ Scientific Thinking in Everyday Life ◆ Fermentation ◆ The Biology of Chocolate ◆ Cancer ◆ Your Home's Hidden Diversity
◆ Evolution of a Weed ◆ Antibiotic Resistance ◆ Mega Crops
◆ COVID-19: The Rise of a Global Pandemic
◆ Vaccines: Your Best Defense
◆ Our Animal Ancestors ◆ The Biology of Weight Gain ◆ The Biology of Running a Marathon
◆ Organic Food: What's the Difference? ◆ Climate Change
◆ Toxic Algae Blooms

Slavica/E+/Getty Images

BioNOW Videos

The BioNOW series of videos, narrated and produced by educator Jason Carlson, provide a relevant, applied approach that allows your students to feel they can actually learn biology on their own. While tying directly to the content of your course, the videos help students relate their daily lives to the biology you teach, and lets them connect what they learn back to their lives.

Each video provides an engaging and entertaining story about applying the science of biology to a real situation or problem. Attention is taken to use tools and techniques that the average person would have access to, so your students see the science as something they could do and understand.

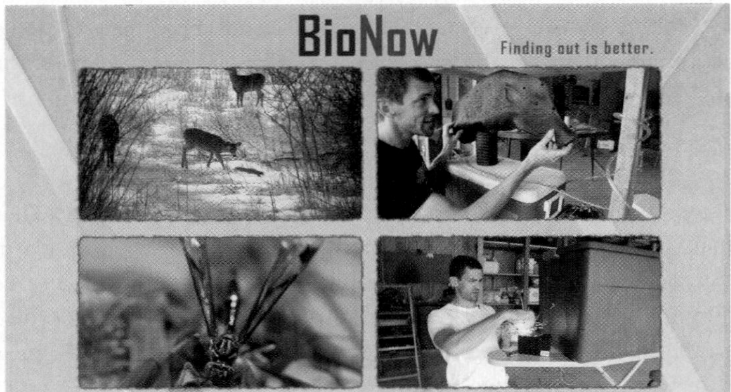

Photos: McGraw Hill

Ricochet Science Website

The website https://ricochetscience.com, managed by Michael Windelspecht, provides updates on news and stories that are interesting to science and nonscience majors alike. The PopScience articles on this site provide an excellent focus for classroom discussions on topics that are currently being debated in society. The site also features videos and tutorial animations to assist the students in recognizing the relevance of what they are learning in the classroom.

ACKNOWLEDGMENTS

Dr. Sylvia Mader is one of the icons of science education. Her dedication to her students, coupled with her clear, concise writing style, has benefited the education of thousands of students over the past four decades. As an educator, it is an honor to continue her legacy and to bring her message to the next generation of students.

As always, I had the privilege to work with a phenomenal group of people on this edition. I would especially like to thank you, the numerous instructors who have shared emails with me or have invited me into your classrooms, both physically and virtually, to discuss your needs as instructors and the needs of your students. You are all dedicated and talented teachers, and your energy and devotion to quality teaching is what drives a textbook revision.

Many dedicated and talented individuals assisted in the development of this edition of *Human Biology*. I am very grateful for the help of so many professionals at McGraw Hill who were involved in bringing this book to fruition. Therefore, I would like to thank the following:

- My product developer, Anne Winch, for her incredible ability to manage all aspects of this project simultaneously.
- Portfolio director Michelle Vogler and portfolio manager Lora Neyens, for their guidance and for reminding me why what we do is important.
- My marketing manager, Erin Martin, for placing me in contact with great instructors, on campus and virtually, throughout this process.
- My content project manager, Jessica Portz, and lead content project manager, Kelly Hart, for guiding this project throughout the publication process.
- Content licensing specialist, Lori Hancock, and photo specialist, David Tietz, for the photos within this text. Biology is a visual science, and their contributions are evident on every page.
- Michael McGee and Sharon O'Donnell, who acted as my copyeditor and proofreader, respectively, for this edition.
- Jane Peden, for her behind-the-scenes work that keeps us all functioning.

As both an educator and an author, communicating the importance of science represents one of my greatest passions. Our modern society is based largely on advances in science and technology over the past few decades. As I present in this text, there are many challenges facing humans, and an understanding of how science can help analyze, and offer solutions to, these problems is critical to our species' health and survival. The only solution to these problems is an increase in scientific literacy, and more importantly, a greater appreciation for the roles of scientists in society. It is my hope that this text helps with that process.

I also want to acknowledge my family and friends for all of their support. My family team of Sandy, Devin, and Kayla have always been my motivation and encouragement. And for my dearest friends, who have never wavered in their support, thank you for believing.

Michael Windelspecht, PhD
Blowing Rock, NC

BRIEF CONTENTS

CONTENTS

Unit 7 Human Evolution and Ecology

READINGS

BIOLOGY TODAY ▶ Diversity in Science

BIOLOGY TODAY ▶ Health

BIOLOGY TODAY ▶ Science

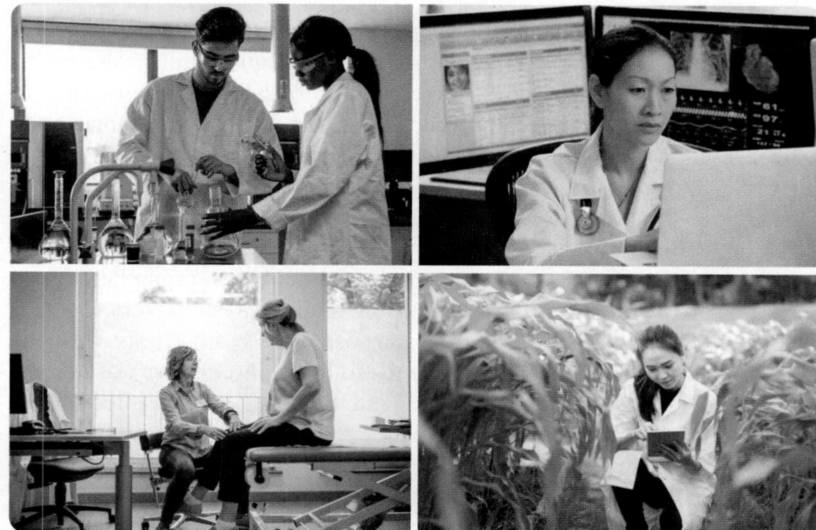

(top left): Daniel Allan/Image Source; (top right): Ariel Skelley/Getty Images; (bottom left): Luis Alvarez/Digital Vision/Getty Images; (bottom right): Tatomm/iStock/Getty Images

CHAPTER 1

Exploring Life and Science

Diversity in Science

Our planet is home to a staggering diversity of life. Our species, *Homo sapiens,* is just one of the estimated 8.7 million different species (not counting bacteria) that inhabit the globe. Life may be found everywhere, from the deepest ocean trenches to the tops of the highest mountains. Biology is the area of scientific study that focuses on understanding all aspects of living organisms. Human biology focuses not only on the biology of our species but also its interactions with other species on the planet. This diversity of life is important to humans, because it provides us with food, medicines, and the raw materials needed to manufacture the millions of items that make our way of life possible.

Equally as important as our planet's biodiversity is the diversity of the people who study biology. Scientists rely upon their own experiences to ask questions, develop hypotheses, and design experiments or models to explain natural phenomena. Therefore, in order for the scientific community to ably address the challenges facing human society, from climate change to emerging diseases, we need a diverse population of individuals, with unique experiences and viewpoints, to contribute their ideas and opinions. As we will see throughout this text, there are many ways to study our world, and our diversity is a major strength in developing solutions.

As you read through the chapter, think about the following questions:

1. What are some of the many ways a scientist can study biology?
2. Why would diversity in the scientific community play an important role in addressing how science can address the needs of society?

CHAPTER OUTLINE

1.1 The Characteristics of Life

LEARNING OUTCOMES

Upon completion of this section, you should be able to

1. Explain the basic characteristics common to all living organisms.
2. Describe the levels of organization of life.
3. Explain why the study of evolution is important in understanding life.

The science of **biology** is the study of living organisms and the environments they live in. All living organisms (Fig. 1.1) share several basic characteristics. They (1) are organized, (2) acquire materials and energy, (3) are homeostatic, (4) respond to stimuli, (5) reproduce and have the potential for growth, and (6) have an evolutionary history.

Life Is Organized

Life can be organized in a hierarchy of levels (Fig. 1.2). Note that, at the very base of this organization, **atoms** join together to form the **molecules,** which in turn make up a cell. A **cell** is the smallest structural and functional unit of an organism. Some organisms, such as bacteria, are single-celled organisms. Humans are multicellular, because they are composed of many different types of cells. For example, the structure of nerve cells in the human body allows these cells to conduct nerve impulses.

A **tissue** is a group of similar cells that perform a particular function. Nervous tissue is composed of millions of nerve cells that transmit signals to all parts of the body. An **organ** is made up of several types of tissues, and each organ belongs to an **organ system.** The organs of an organ system work together to accomplish a common purpose. The brain works with the spinal cord to send commands to body parts by way of nerves. **Organisms,** such as trees and humans, are a collection of organ systems.

The levels of biological organization extend beyond the individual. All the members of one **species** (a group of interbreeding organisms) in a particular area belong to a **population.** A tropical grassland may have a population of zebras, acacia trees, and humans, for example. The interacting populations of the grasslands make up a **community.** The community of populations interacts with the physical environment to form an **ecosystem.** Finally, all the Earth's ecosystems collectively make up the **biosphere** (Fig. 1.2, *top*).

Figure 1.1 All life shares common characteristics.
From the simplest one-celled organisms to complex plants and animals, all life shares several basic characteristics.
(student group): FatCamera/E+/Getty Images; (mushrooms): IT Stock/age fotostock; (bacteria): Paul Gunning/Science Photo Library/Getty Images; (gorilla): Mike Price/Shutterstock; (sunflower): MedioImages/PunchStock/Getty Images; (*Giardia*): Dr. Stan Erlandsen/CDC

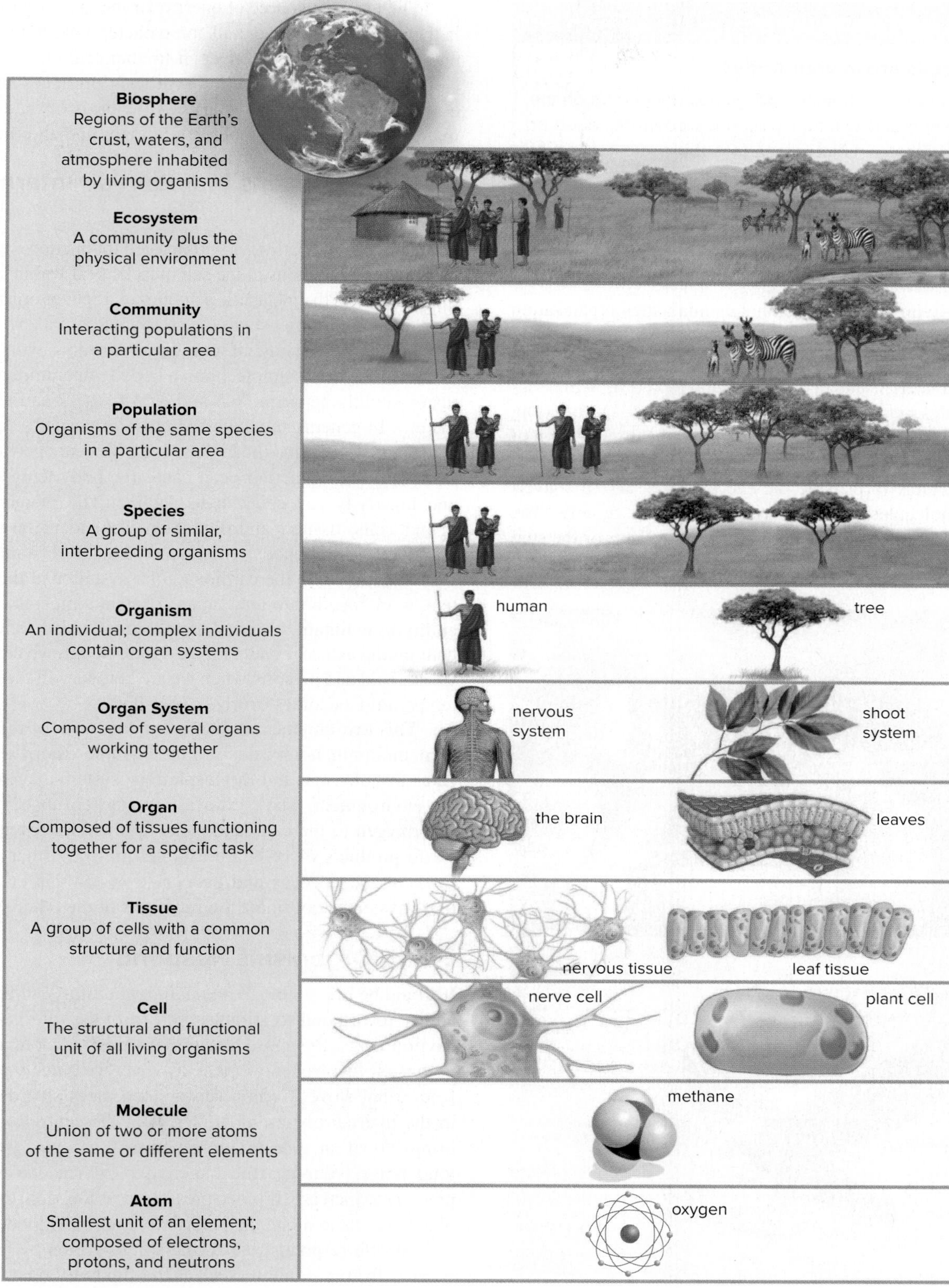

Biosphere
Regions of the Earth's crust, waters, and atmosphere inhabited by living organisms
Ecosystem
A community plus the physical environment
Community
Interacting populations in a particular area
Population
Organisms of the same species in a particular area
Species
A group of similar, interbreeding organisms
Organism
An individual; complex individuals contain organ systems
human
tree
Organ System
Composed of several organs working together
nervous system
shoot system
Organ
Composed of tissues functioning together for a specific task
the brain
leaves
Tissue
A group of cells with a common structure and function
nervous tissue
leaf tissue
Cell
The structural and functional unit of all living organisms
nerve cell
plant cell
Molecule
Union of two or more atoms of the same or different elements
methane
Atom
Smallest unit of an element; composed of electrons, protons, and neutrons
oxygen

Figure 1.2 Levels of biological organization.
Life is connected from the atomic level to the biosphere. The cell is the basic unit of life, and it comprises molecules and atoms. The sum of all life on the planet is called the biosphere.

BIOLOGY IN YOUR LIFE

How many cells are in your body?

The number of cells in a human body varies depending on the size of the person and whether cells have been damaged or lost. However, most estimates suggest there are well over 30 trillion cells in a human body. To put this into perspective, there are only an estimated 3 trillion trees on Earth.

Life Requires Materials and Energy

Humans, like all living organisms, cannot maintain their organization or carry on life's activities without an outside source of materials and energy. **Energy** is the capacity to do work. Like other animals, humans acquire materials and energy by eating food (Fig. 1.3).

Food provides nutrient molecules, which are used as building blocks or for energy. It takes energy to maintain the organization of the cell and the organism itself. Some nutrient molecules are broken down completely to provide the energy necessary to convert other nutrient molecules into the parts and products of cells. The breakdown of food is a component of our **metabolism,** or the sum of all the chemical reactions that occur within a cell or organism.

a.

b.

Figure 1.3 Humans and other animals must acquire energy. All life, including humans (**a**) and other animals, such as this eagle (**b**), must acquire energy to survive. The method by which organisms acquire energy is dependent on the species.

(a): Ariel Skelley/Blend Images/Getty Images; (b): Brian E Kushner/Shutterstock

The ultimate source of energy for the majority of life on Earth is the sun. Plants, algae, and some bacteria are able to harvest the energy of the sun and convert it to chemical energy by a process called **photosynthesis.** Photosynthesis produces organic molecules, such as sugars, that serve as the basis of the food chain for many other organisms, including humans and all other animals.

Living Organisms Maintain an Internal Environment

For the metabolic pathways within a cell to function correctly, the environmental conditions of the cell must be kept within strict operating limits. Many of the metabolic activities of a cell, or organism, function in maintaining **homeostasis**—a constant internal environment.

In humans, many of our organ systems work to maintain homeostasis. For example, human body temperature normally fluctuates slightly between 36.5 and 37.5°C (97.7 and 99.5°F) during the day. In general, the lowest temperature usually occurs between 2 A.M. and 4 A.M., and the highest usually occurs between 6 P.M. and 10 P.M. However, activity can cause the body temperature to rise, and inactivity can cause it to decline. The metabolic activities of our cells, tissues, and organs are dependent on maintaining a relatively constant body temperature. Therefore, a number of body systems, including the cardiovascular system and the nervous system, work together to maintain a constant temperature. The body's ability to maintain a normal temperature is also somewhat dependent on the external temperature. Even though we can shiver when we are cold and perspire when we are hot, we will die if the external temperature becomes overly cold or hot.

This text emphasizes how all the systems of the human body help maintain homeostasis. For example, the digestive system takes in nutrients, and the respiratory system exchanges gas with the environment. The cardiovascular system distributes nutrients and oxygen to the cells and picks up their wastes. The metabolic waste products of cells are excreted by the urinary system. The work of the nervous and endocrine systems is critical, because these systems coordinate the functions of the other systems.

Living Organisms Respond

It would be impossible to maintain homeostasis without the body's ability to respond to stimuli, both from the internal and external environments. Response to external stimuli is more apparent to us, because it involves movement, as when we quickly remove a hand from a hot stove. Certain sensory receptors also detect a change in the internal environment, and then the central nervous system brings about an appropriate response. When you are startled by a loud noise, your heartbeat increases, which causes your blood pressure to increase. If blood pressure rises too high, the brain directs blood vessels to dilate, helping restore normal blood pressure.

All life responds to external stimuli, often by moving toward or away from a stimulus, such as the sight of food. Organisms may use a variety of mechanisms to move, but movement in humans and other animals is dependent on their nervous and musculoskeletal systems. The leaves of plants track the passage of the sun during the day; when a houseplant is placed near a window, its stems bend to face the sun. The movement of an animal, whether self-directed

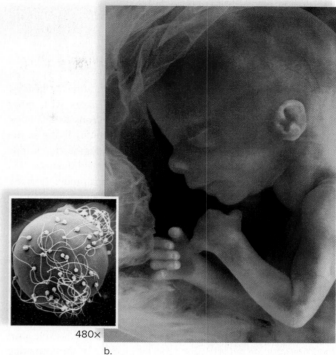

Figure 1.4 Growth and development define life.
a. A small acorn becomes a tree, and (**b**) following fertilization an embryo becomes a fetus by the process of growth and development.
(a) (seedling): bogdan ionescu/Shutterstock; (a) (tree): Frank Krahmer/Photographer's Choice/Getty Images; (b) (sperm/egg): David M. Phillips/Science Source; (b) (fetus): Steve Allen/Brand X Pictures/Getty Images

or in response to a stimulus, constitutes a large part of its *behavior*. Some behaviors help us acquire food and reproduce.

Living Organisms Reproduce and Develop

Reproduction is a fundamental characteristic of life. Cells come into being only from preexisting cells, and all living organisms have parents. When organisms **reproduce,** they pass on their genetic information to the next generation. Following the fertilization of an egg by a sperm cell, the resulting zygote undergoes a rapid period of growth and development. This is common in most forms of life. Figure 1.4*a* illustrates that an acorn progresses to a seedling before it becomes an adult oak tree. In humans, growth occurs as the fertilized egg develops into a fetus (Fig. 1.4*b*). **Growth,** recognized by an increase in size and often in the number of cells, is a part of development. In multicellular organisms, such as humans, the term **development** is used to indicate all the changes that occur from the time the egg is fertilized until death. Therefore, it includes all the changes that occur during childhood, adolescence, and adulthood. Development also includes the repair that takes place following an injury.

The genetic information of all life is **DNA (deoxyribonucleic acid).** DNA contains the hereditary information that directs not only the structure of each cell but also its function. The information in DNA is contained within **genes,** short sequences of hereditary material that specify the instructions for a specific trait. Before reproduction occurs, DNA is replicated so an exact copy of each gene may be passed on to the offspring. When humans reproduce, a sperm carries genes contributed by a male into the egg, which contains genes contributed by a female. The genes direct both growth and development so that the organism will eventually resemble the parents. Sometimes **mutations,** minor variations in these genes, can cause an organism to be better suited for its environment. These mutations are the basis of evolutionary change.

Organisms Have an Evolutionary History

Evolution is the process by which a population changes over time. The mechanism by which evolution occurs is **natural selection** (see Section 23.2). When a new variation arises that allows certain members of a population to capture more resources, these members tend to survive and have more offspring than the other, unchanged members. Therefore, each successive generation will include more members with the new variation, which represents an **adaptation** to the environment. Consider, for example, populations of humans who live at high altitudes, such as the cultures living at elevations of over 4,000 meters (m) (14,000 ft) in the Tibetan Plateau. This environment is very low in oxygen. As the Science feature "Adapting to Life at High Elevations" investigates, these populations have evolved an adaptation that reduces the amount of hemoglobin, the oxygen-carrying pigment in the blood. As the feature explains, this adaptation makes life at these altitudes possible.

Evolution, which has been going on since the origin of life and will continue as long as life exists, explains both the unity and diversity of life. All organisms share the same characteristics of life because their ancestry can be traced to the first cell or cells. Organisms are diverse because they are adapted to different ways of life.

BIOLOGY TODAY ▶ Science

Adapting to Life at High Elevations

Humans, like all other organisms, have an evolutionary history. This not only means we share common ancestors with other animals, but over time we demonstrate adaptations to changing environmental conditions. One study of populations living in the high-elevation mountains of Tibet (Fig. 1A) demonstrates how the processes of evolution and adaptation influence humans.

Normally, when a person moves to a higher altitude, the body may respond by making more hemoglobin, the component of blood that carries oxygen, which in turn thickens the consistency of the blood. For minor elevation changes, this does not present much of a problem. But for people who live at extreme elevations (some people in the Himalayas can live at elevations of over 13,000 ft, or close to 4,000 m), excess hemoglobin can present a number of health problems, including chronic mountain sickness, a disease that affects people who live at high altitudes for extended periods of time. The problem is that, as the amount of hemoglobin increases, the blood thickens and becomes more viscous. This can cause elevated blood pressure, or hypertension, and an increase in the formation of blood clots, both of which have negative physiological effects.

Figure 1A **High-elevation adaptations.**
Individuals living at high elevations, such as Tibetans, have become adapted to their high-elevation environment.
Michael Freeman/Corbis

Because high hemoglobin levels would be a detriment to people at high elevations, it makes sense that natural selection would favor individuals who produce less hemoglobin at high elevations. Such is the case with the Tibetans in this study. Researchers have identified an allele of a gene that reduces hemoglobin production at high elevations. Comparisons between Tibetans at both high and low elevations strongly suggest that selection has played a role in the prevalence of the high-elevation allele.

The gene is *EPSA1,* located on chromosome 2 of humans. *EPSA1* produces a transcription factor that basically regulates which genes are turned on and off in the body, a process called gene expression. The transcription factor produced by *EPSA1* has a number of functions in the body. For example, in addition to controlling the amount of hemoglobin in the blood, this transcription factor also regulates other genes that direct how the body uses oxygen.

When the researchers examined the variations in *EPSA1* in the Tibetan population, they discovered that the Tibetan version greatly reduces the production of hemoglobin. Therefore, the Tibetan population has lower hemoglobin levels than people living at lower altitudes, allowing these individuals to escape the consequences of thick blood.

How long did it take for the original population to adapt to living at higher elevations? Initially, the comparison of variations in these genes between high-elevation and low-elevation Tibetan populations suggested that the event may have occurred over a 3,000-year period. But researchers were skeptical of those data because they suggested a relatively rapid rate of evolutionary change. Additional studies of genetic databases yielded an interesting finding—the *EPSA1* gene in Tibetans was identical to a similar gene found in an ancient group of humans called the Denisovans (see Section 23.5). Scientists now believe that the *EPSA1* gene entered the Tibetan population around 40,000 years ago, either through interbreeding between early Tibetans and Denisovans, or from one of the immediate ancestors of this now-lost group of early humans.

Questions to Consider

1. What other environments do you think could be studied to look for examples of human adaptation?
2. In addition to hemoglobin levels, do you think people at high elevations may exhibit other adaptations?

CHECK YOUR PROGRESS 1.1

1. List the basic characteristics of life.
2. Summarize the levels of biological organization.
3. Explain the relationship between adaptations and evolutionary change.

CONNECTING THE CONCEPTS

Both homeostasis and evolution are central themes in the study of biology. For more examples of homeostasis and evolution, refer to the following discussions:

Section 4.8 explains how body temperature is regulated.

Section 11.4 explores the role of the kidneys in fluid and salt homeostasis.

Section 23.3 examines the evolutionary history of humans.

1.2 Humans Are Related to Other Animals

LEARNING OUTCOMES

Upon completion of this section, you should be able to

1. Summarize the place of humans in the overall classification of living organisms.
2. Understand that humans have a cultural heritage.
3. Describe the relationship between humans and the biosphere.

Biologists classify all life as belonging to one of three **domains.** The evolutionary relationships of these domains are presented in Figure 1.5.

Two of these domains, domain Bacteria and domain Archaea, contain prokaryotes, single-celled organisms that lack a nucleus (Fig. 1.6). Organisms in the third domain, Eukarya, all contain cells that possess a nucleus. Some of these organisms are single-celled; others are multicellular. Humans are an example of multicelled Eukarya.

Historically, domain Eukarya was divided into one of four **kingdoms** (Fig. 1.6). However, the development of improved techniques in analyzing the DNA of organisms suggests that not all of the Protistas (the earliest eukaryotes) share the same evolutionary lineage, meaning that the evolution of the eukaryotes has occurred along several paths. A new taxonomic group, called a **supergroup,** was developed to explain these evolutionary relationships. There are currently six supergroups for domain Eukarya. Over the past several years, changes have been made to the supergroup classification as new research unveils relationships between these organisms. While these relationships are still being studied and analyzed, current thinking places the animals in the same supergroup (the Opisthikonts) as the fungi.

The traditional kingdom level of classification within domain Eukarya is still widely used, and is often placed beneath the

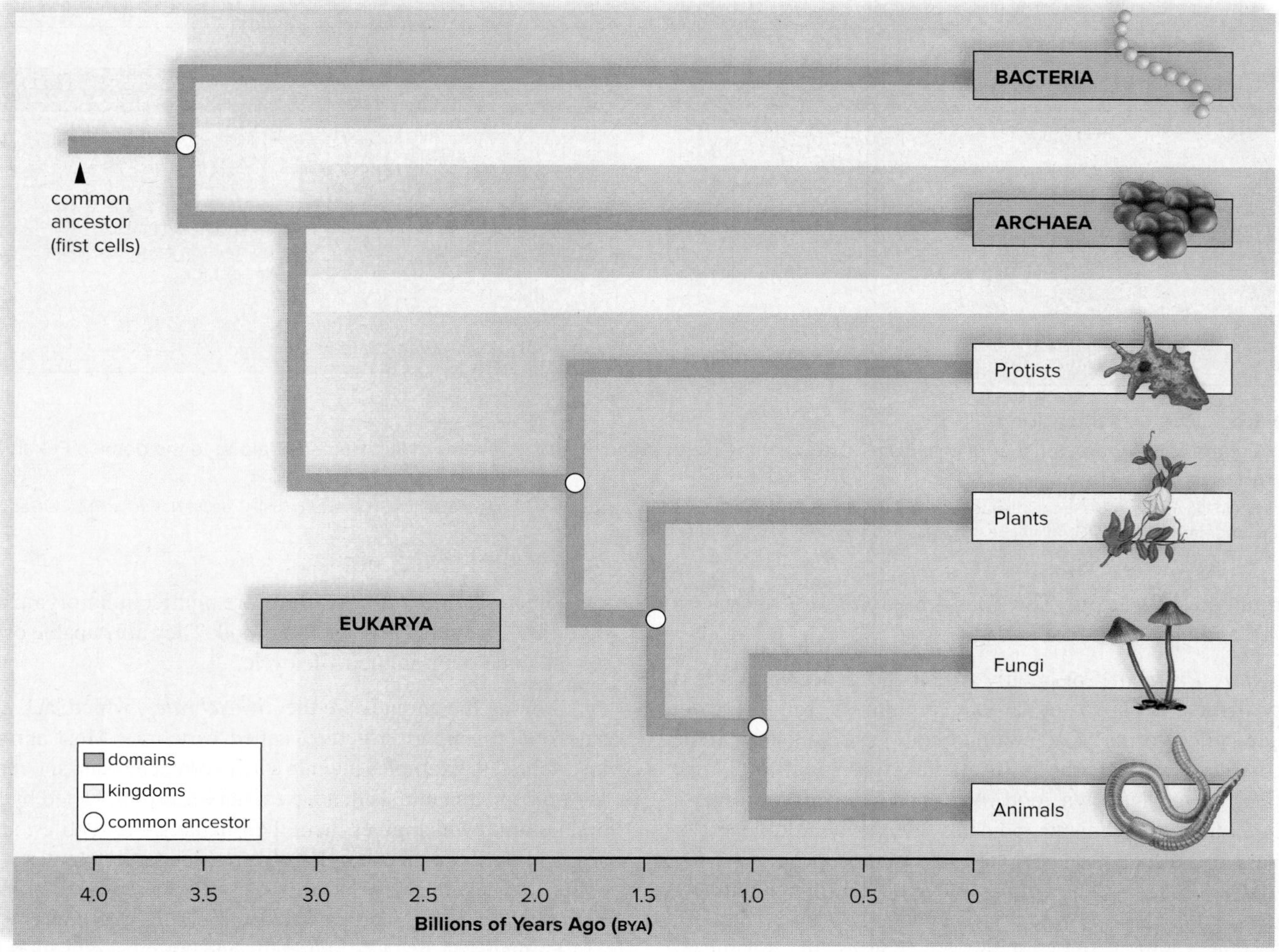

Figure 1.5 **The evolutionary relationships of the three domains of life.**
Living organisms are classified into three domains: Bacteria, Archaea, and Eukarya. The Eukarya are further divided into kingdoms (see Fig. 1.6).

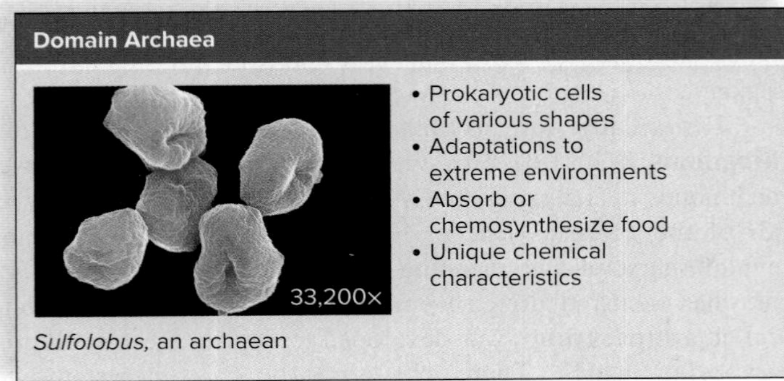

Domain Archaea
• Prokaryotic cells of various shapes
• Adaptations to extreme environments
• Absorb or chemosynthesize food
• Unique chemical characteristics
33,200×
Sulfolobus, an archaean

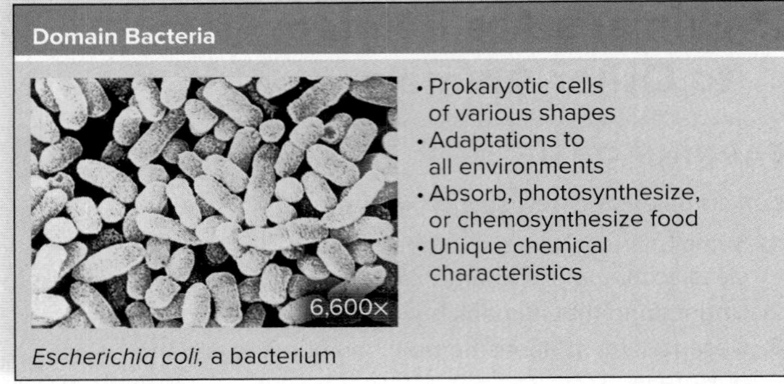

Domain Bacteria
• Prokaryotic cells of various shapes
• Adaptations to all environments
• Absorb, photosynthesize, or chemosynthesize food
• Unique chemical characteristics
6,600×
Escherichia coli, a bacterium

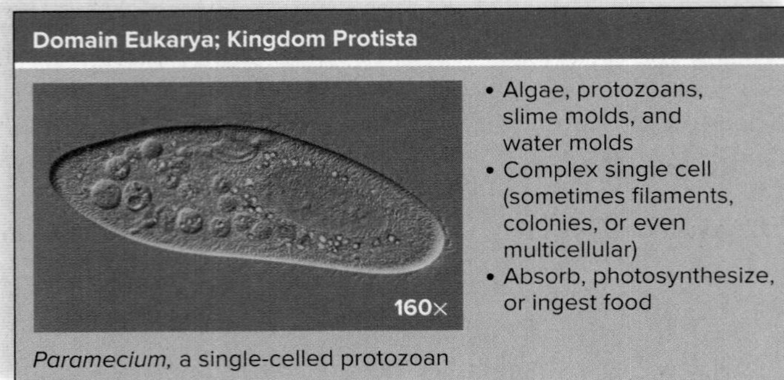

Domain Eukarya; Kingdom Protista
• Algae, protozoans, slime molds, and water molds
• Complex single cell (sometimes filaments, colonies, or even multicellular)
• Absorb, photosynthesize, or ingest food
160×
Paramecium, a single-celled protozoan

Domain Eukarya: Kingdom Plantae
• Certain algae, mosses, ferns, conifers, and flowering plants
• Multicellular, usually with specialized tissues, containing complex cells
• Photosynthesize food
Ophrys apifera, bee orchid

Domain Eukarya: Kingdom Fungi
• Molds, mushrooms, yeasts, and ringworms
• Mostly multicellular filaments with specialized, complex cells
• Absorb food
Amanita muscaria, a mushroom

Domain Eukarya: Kingdom Animalia
• Sponges, worms, insects, fishes, frogs, turtles, birds, and mammals
• Multicellular with specialized tissues containing complex cells
• Ingest food
Buteo jamaicensis, red-tailed hawk

Figure 1.6 **The classification of life.**
This figure offers some characteristics of organisms in each of the major domains and kingdoms of life. Humans belong to the domain Eukarya and kingdom Animalia.
(archaea): Eye of Science/Science Source; (bacteria): A. Barry Dowsett/Science Source; (paramecium): M.I. Walker/Science Source; (orchids): CreativeNature_nl/iStock/Getty Images; (mushrooms): Ingram Publishing/Getty Images; (hawk): Keneva Photography/Shutterstock

supergroup classification. The four kingdoms are shown in Figure 1.6 and include the following:

- *Kingdom Protista*. Commonly called the **protists,** this is a very diverse group of eukaryotic organisms, ranging from single-celled forms to a few multicellular organisms. Some protists use photosynthesis to manufacture food, and some must acquire their own food. As we mentioned, the diverse nature of these organisms indicates they have multiple evolutionary origins, and thus belong to different supergroups.
- *Kingdom Plantae*. The **plants** are multicellular, photosynthetic organisms.
- *Kingdom Fungi*. **Fungi** are the familiar molds and mushrooms that help decompose dead organisms. Some fungi are parasites of plants and animals.
- *Kingdom Animalia*. **Animals** are multicellular organisms that must ingest and process their food. They are capable of motion at some point in their life cycle.

Among the animals are the *invertebrates,* which lack an internal skeletal support structure, called vertebrae. Most animals are invertebrates. Examples include earthworms, insects, and mollusks. *Vertebrates* are animals that have a nerve cord protected by a vertebral column, which gives them their name. Fish, reptiles, amphibians, and birds are all examples of vertebrates. Vertebrates with hair or fur and mammary glands are classified as *mammals*. Humans, raccoons, seals, and meerkats are examples of mammals.

Humans are *primate* mammals and are most closely related to apes. We are distinguished from apes by our (1) highly developed brains, (2) completely upright stance, (3) creative language, and

(4) ability to use a wide variety of tools. Humans did not evolve from apes; apes and humans share a common, apelike ancestor. Today's apes are our evolutionary cousins. Our relationship to apes is analogous to you and your first cousin being descended from your grandparents. We could not have evolved directly from our cousins, because we are contemporaries—living on Earth at the same time.

Humans Have a Cultural Heritage

Humans have a cultural heritage in addition to a biological heritage. *Culture* encompasses human activities and products passed on from one generation to the next outside of direct biological inheritance. Among animals, only humans have a language that allows us to communicate information and experiences symbolically. We are born without knowledge of an accepted way to behave, but we gradually acquire this knowledge by adult instruction and the imitation of role models. Members of the previous generation pass on their beliefs, values, and skills to the next generation. Many of the skills involve tool use, which can vary from how to hunt in the wild to how to use a computer. Human skills have also produced a rich heritage in the arts and sciences. However, a society highly dependent on science and technology has its drawbacks as well. Unfortunately, this cultural development may mislead us into believing that humans are somehow not part of the natural world surrounding us.

Humans Are Members of the Biosphere

All life on Earth is part of the biosphere, the living network that spans the surface of the Earth into the atmosphere and down into the soil and seas. Although humans can raise animals and crops for food, we depend on the environment for many services. Without microorganisms that decompose, the waste we create would soon cover the Earth's surface. Some species of bacteria help us by cleaning up pollutants like heavy metals and pesticides.

Freshwater ecosystems, such as rivers and lakes, provide fish to eat, water to drink, and water to irrigate crops. Many of our crops and prescription drugs were originally derived from plants that grew naturally in an ecosystem. Some human populations around the globe still depend on wild animals as a food source. The water-holding capacity of forests prevents flooding, and the ability of forests and other ecosystems to retain soil prevents soil erosion. For many people, these forests provide a place for recreational activities like hiking and camping.

BIOLOGY IN YOUR LIFE

How many humans are there?

In 2021, it was estimated there were over 7.9 billion humans on the planet. Each human needs food, shelter, clean water and air, and materials to maintain a healthy lifestyle. Our species adds an additional 83 million people per year—that is like adding the population of ten New York Cities annually! This makes human population growth one of the greatest threats to the biosphere.

CHECK YOUR PROGRESS 1.2

1. Define the term *biosphere*.
2. Define *culture*.
3. Explain why humans belong to the domain Eukarya and kingdom Animalia.

CONNECTING THE CONCEPTS

To learn more about the preceding material, refer to the following discussions:

Chapter 23 examines recent developments in the study of human evolution.

Chapter 24 provides a more detailed look at ecosystems.

Chapter 25 explores how humans interact with the biosphere.

1.3 Science as a Process

LEARNING OUTCOMES

Upon completion of this section, you should be able to

1. Describe the general process of the scientific method.
2. Distinguish between a control group and an experimental group in a scientific test.
3. Recognize the importance of scientific journals in the reporting of scientific information.
4. Recognize the importance of statistical analysis to the study of science.

Science is a way of knowing about the natural world. When scientists study the natural world, they aim to be objective, rather than subjective. Objective observations are supported by factual information, whereas subjective observations involve personal judgment. For example, the fat content of a particular food would be an objective observation of a nutritional study. Reporting about the good or bad taste of the food would be a subjective observation. It is difficult to make objective observations and conclusions, because we are often influenced by our prejudices. Scientists must keep in mind that scientific conclusions can change because of new findings. New findings are often made because of recent advances in techniques or equipment.

Religion, aesthetics, ethics, and science are all ways in which humans seek order in the natural world. The nature of scientific inquiry differs from these other ways of knowing and learning, because the scientific process employs the **scientific method,** a standard series of steps used in gaining new knowledge that is widely accepted among scientists. The scientific method (Fig. 1.7) acts as a guideline for scientific studies.

The approach of individual scientists to their work is as varied as the scientists. However, much of the scientific process is descriptive. For example, an observation of a new disease may lead a scientist to describe all the aspects of the disease, such as the environment, the age of onset, and the characteristics of the disease. Some areas of biology, such as the study of biodiversity in the

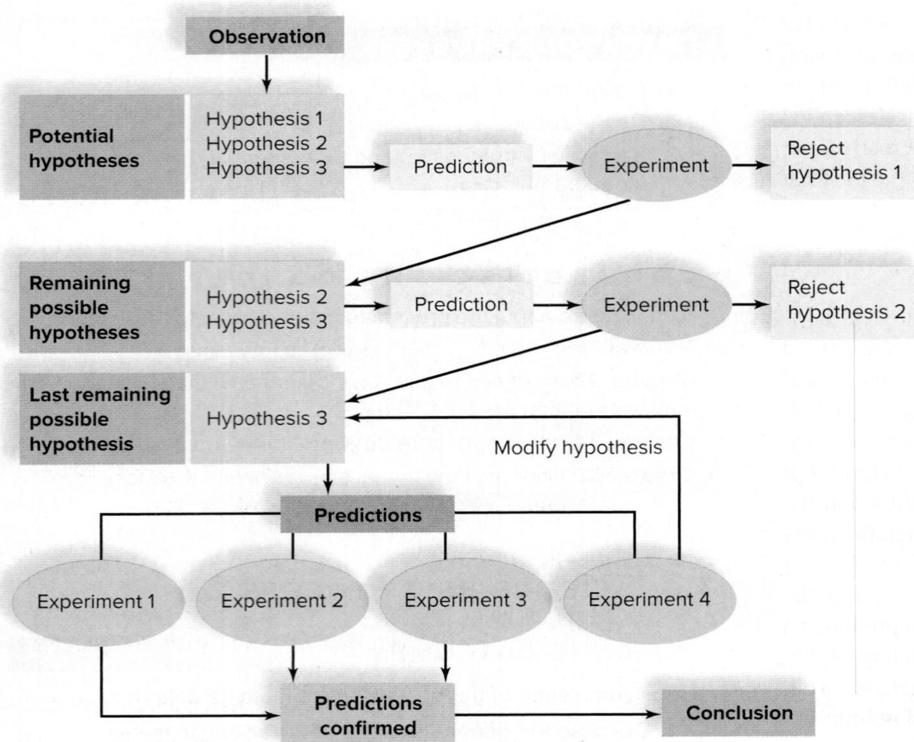

Figure 1.7 The scientific method. On the basis of new and/or previous observations, a scientist formulates a hypothesis. The hypothesis is used to develop predictions to be tested by further experiments and/or observations, and new data either support or do not support the hypothesis. Following an experiment, a scientist often chooses to retest the same hypothesis or to test a related hypothesis. Conclusions from many different but related experiments may lead to the development of a scientific theory. For example, studies pertaining to development, anatomy, and fossil remains all support the theory of evolution.

ecological sciences (see Section 1.4), lend themselves more to this descriptive approach. Regardless of their area of study, most scientists spend a considerable amount of time performing a descriptive analysis of their observation before proceeding into the steps of the scientific method. Scientists often modify or adapt the process to suit their particular field of study, but for the sake of discussion, it is useful to think of the scientific method as consisting of certain logical steps.

Start with an Observation

Scientists believe that nature is orderly and measurable—that natural laws, such as the law of gravity, do not change with time—and that a natural event, or *phenomenon,* can be understood more fully through **observation**—a formal way of watching the natural world.

Observations may be made with the senses, such as sight and smell, or with instruments; for example, a microscope enables us to see objects that could never be seen by the naked eye. Scientists may expand their understanding even further by taking advantage of the knowledge and experiences of other scientists. For instance, they may look up past studies on the Internet or at the library, or they may write or speak to others who are researching similar topics.

Develop a Hypothesis

After making observations and gathering knowledge about a phenomenon, a scientist uses inductive reasoning. **Inductive reasoning** occurs whenever a person uses creative thinking to combine isolated facts into a cohesive whole. Chance alone can help a scientist arrive at an idea. The most famous case pertains to the antibiotic penicillin, which was discovered in 1928. While examining a petri dish of bacteria that had accidentally become contaminated with the mold *Penicillium,* Alexander Fleming observed an area around the mold that was free of bacteria. Fleming had long been interested in finding cures for human diseases caused by bacteria, and he was very knowledgeable about antibacterial substances. So when Fleming saw the dramatic effect of *Penicillium* mold on bacteria, he reasoned that the mold might be producing an antibacterial substance.

We call such a possible explanation for a natural event a **hypothesis.** A hypothesis is based on existing knowledge, so it is much more informed than a mere guess. Fleming's hypothesis was supported by further study, but sometimes a hypothesis is not supported and must be either modified and subjected to additional study or rejected. When thinking about how to test the hypothesis, the scientist may make a **prediction,** or an expected outcome, based on knowledge of the factors involved in the observation.

All of a scientist's past experiences, no matter what they might be, may influence the formation of a hypothesis. But a scientist considers only hypotheses that can be tested by experiments or further observations. Moral and religious beliefs, although very important to our lives, differ among cultures and through time and are not always testable.

Test the Hypothesis

Scientists often perform an **experiment,** which is a series of procedures, to test a hypothesis. To determine how to test a hypothesis, a scientist uses deductive reasoning. **Deductive reasoning** involves "if . . . then" logic.

The manner in which a scientist intends to conduct an experiment is called the **experimental design.** A good experimental design

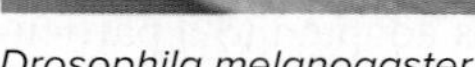

Drosophila melanogaster

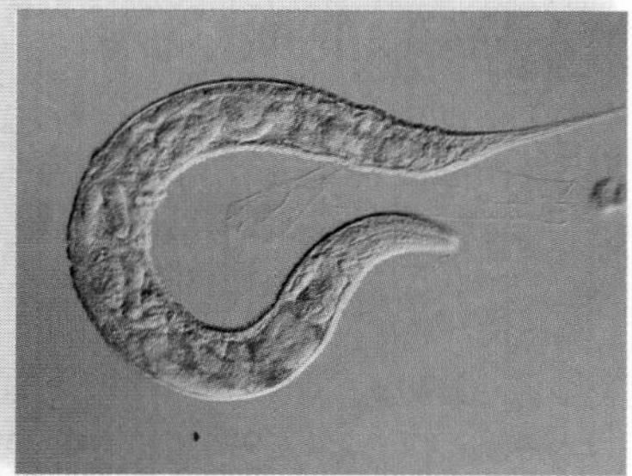

Caenorhabditis elegans 64×

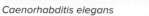

Arabidopsis thaliana

Mus musculus

Figure 1.8 Model organisms used in scientific studies. *Drosophila melanogaster* is used as a model organism in the study of genetics. *Mus musculus* is used in the study of medicine. *Caenorhabditis elegans* is used by developmental biologists, and *Arabidopsis thaliana* is used by botanists to understand plant genetics.

(*Drosophila*): janeff/iStockphoto/Getty Images; (*C. elegans*): Sinclair Stammers/Science Source; (*Arabidopsis*): Wildlife GmbH/Alamy Stock Photo; (*M. musculus*): Redmond Durrell/Alamy Stock Photo

ensures that scientists are examining the contribution of a specific variable, called the **experimental variable,** to the observation. The result is termed the **responding variable,** or dependent variable, because it is due to the experimental variable.

To ensure the results will be meaningful, an experiment contains both test groups and a **control group.** A test group is exposed to the experimental variable, but the control group is not. If the control group and test groups show the same results, the experimenter knows that the hypothesis predicting a difference between them is not supported.

Scientists often use **model** organisms and model systems to test a hypothesis. Some common model organisms are shown in Figure 1.8. Model organisms are chosen because they allow the researcher to control aspects of the experiment, such as age and genetic background. Cell biologists may use mice for modeling the effects of a new drug. Like model organisms, model systems allow the scientist to control specific variables and environmental conditions in a way that may not be possible in the natural environment. For example, ecologists may use computer programs to model how human activities will affect the climate of a specific ecosystem. While models provide useful information, they do not always answer the original question completely. For example, medicine that is effective in mice ideally should be tested in humans, and ecological experiments conducted using computer simulations need to be verified by actual field experiments.

Collect and Analyze the Data

The **data,** or results, from scientific experiments may be presented in a variety of formats, including tables and graphs. A graph shows the relationship between two quantities. In many graphs, the experimental variable is plotted on the *x*-axis (horizontal), and the result is plotted along the *y*-axis (vertical). Graphs are useful tools to summarize data in a clear and simplified manner. For example, the line graph in Figure 1.9 shows the variation in the concentration of blood cholesterol over a 4-week study. The bar above and below each data point represents the variation, or standard error, in the results. The title and labels can assist you in reading a graph; therefore, when looking at a graph, first check the two axes to determine what the graph pertains to. By looking at this graph, we know the blood cholesterol levels were highest during week 2, and we can see to what degree the values varied over the course of the study.

Statistical Data

Most scientists who publish research articles use statistics to help them evaluate their experimental data. In statistics, the standard error, or standard deviation, tells us how uncertain a particular value is. Suppose you predict how many hurricanes Florida will have next year by calculating the average number during the past 10 years. If the number of hurricanes per year varies widely, your standard error will be larger than if the number per year is usually about the same. In other words, the standard error tells you how far off the average could be. If the average number of hurricanes is four and the standard error is ±2, then your prediction of four hurricanes is between two and six hurricanes. In Figure 1.9, the standard error is represented by the bars above and below each data point. This provides a visual indication of the statistical analysis of the data.

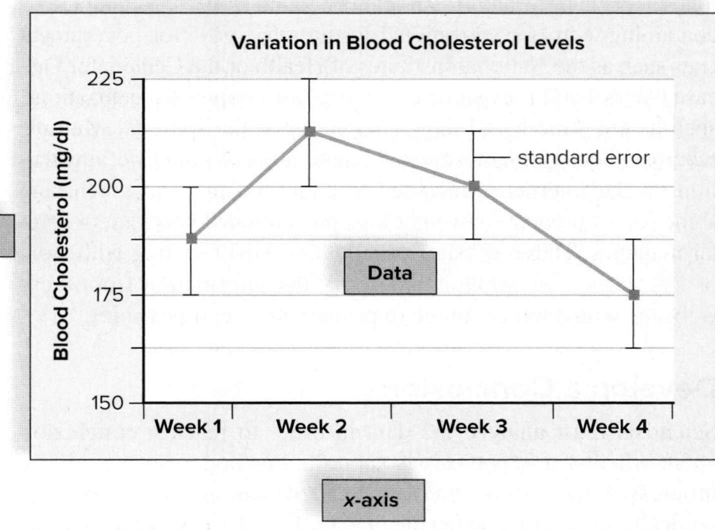

Figure 1.9 The presentation of scientific data. This line graph shows the variation in the concentration of blood cholesterol over a 4-week study. The bars above and below the data points represent the variation, or standard error, in the results.

Statistical Significance

When scientists conduct an experiment, there is always the possibility that the results are due to chance or to some factor other than the experimental variable. Investigators take into account several factors when they calculate the probability value (p) that their results were due to chance alone. If the probability value is low, researchers describe the results as statistically significant. A probability value of less than 5% (usually written as $p < 0.05$) is acceptable; even so, keep in mind that the lower the p value, the less likely it is that the results are due to chance. Therefore, the lower the p value, the greater the confidence the investigators and you can have in the results. Depending on the type of study, most scientists like to have a p value of < 0.05, but p values of < 0.001 are common in many studies.

Scientific Publications

Scientific studies are customarily published in scientific journals, such as *Science* or *Nature,* so that all aspects of a study are available to the scientific community. Before information is published in scientific journals, it is typically reviewed by experts, who ensure that the research is credible, accurate, unbiased, and well executed. Another scientist should be able to read about an experiment in a scientific journal, repeat the experiment in a different location, and get the same (or very similar) results. Some articles are rejected for publication by reviewers when they believe there is something questionable about the design of an experiment or the manner in which it was conducted. This process of rejection is important in science because it causes researchers to critically review their hypotheses, predictions, and experimental designs, so that their next attempt will more adequately address their hypothesis. Often, it takes several rounds of revision before research is accepted for publication in a scientific journal.

People should be especially careful about scientific information available on the Internet, which is not well regulated. Reliable, credible scientific information can often be found at websites with URLs containing .edu (for educational institution), .gov (for government sites such as the National Institutes of Health or the Centers for Disease Control and Prevention), and .org (for nonprofit organizations, such as the American Lung Association or the National Multiple Sclerosis Society). Unfortunately, quite a bit of scientific information on the Internet is intended to entice people into purchasing some sort of product for weight loss, prevention of hair loss, or similar maladies. These websites usually have URLs ending with .com or .net. It pays to question and verify the information from these websites with another source (a primary source, if possible).

Develop a Conclusion

Scientists must analyze the data in order to reach a **conclusion** about whether a hypothesis is supported or not. Because science progresses, the conclusion of one experiment can lead to the hypothesis for another experiment (see Fig. 1.9). In other words, results that do not support one hypothesis can often help a scientist formulate another hypothesis to be tested. Scientists report their findings in scientific journals, so that their methodology and data are available to other scientists.

Scientific Theory

The ultimate goal of science is to understand the natural world in terms of **scientific theories,** which are accepted explanations for how the world works. Some of the basic theories of biology are the cell theory, which says that all organisms are composed of cells; the gene theory, which says that inherited information in a gene contributes to the form, function, and behavior of organisms; and the theory of evolution, which says that all organisms have a common ancestor and that each organism is adapted to a particular way of life.

The theory of evolution is considered the unifying concept of biology, because it pertains to many different aspects of organisms. For example, the theory of evolution enables scientists to understand the history of life, the variety of organisms, and the anatomy, physiology, and development of organisms. The theory of evolution has been a very fruitful scientific theory, meaning it has helped scientists generate new testable hypotheses. Because this theory has been supported by so many observations and experiments for over 100 years, some biologists refer to the theory of evolution as the **principle** of evolution, a term sometimes used for theories that are generally accepted by an overwhelming number of scientists. Others prefer the term **law** instead of *principle*.

An Example of a Controlled Study

As presented in the Science feature "Discovering the Cause of Ulcers," we now know that most stomach and intestinal ulcers (open sores) are caused by the bacterium *Helicobacter pylori.*

Experimental Design

Let's say investigators want to determine which of two antibiotics is best for the treatment of an ulcer. When clinicians do an experiment, they try to vary just the experimental variables—in this case, the medications being tested. Each antibiotic is administered to an independent test group. The control group is not given an antibiotic. If by chance the control group shows the same results as one of the test groups, the investigators may conclude that the antibiotic in that test group is ineffective, because it does not show a result that is significantly different from that of the control group. The study depicted in Figure 1.10*a* shows how investigators may study this hypothesis:

Hypothesis: Newly discovered antibiotic B is a better treatment for ulcers than antibiotic A, which is in current use.

In any experiment, it is important to reduce the number of possible variables (differences). In this experiment, those variables may include factors such as differences in the subjects' sex, weight, and previous illnesses. Therefore, the investigators *randomly* divide a large group of volunteers equally into experimental groups. The hope is that any differences will be distributed evenly among the three groups. The larger the number of volunteers (the sample size), the greater the chance of reducing the influence of external variables. This is why many medical studies involve thousands of individuals.

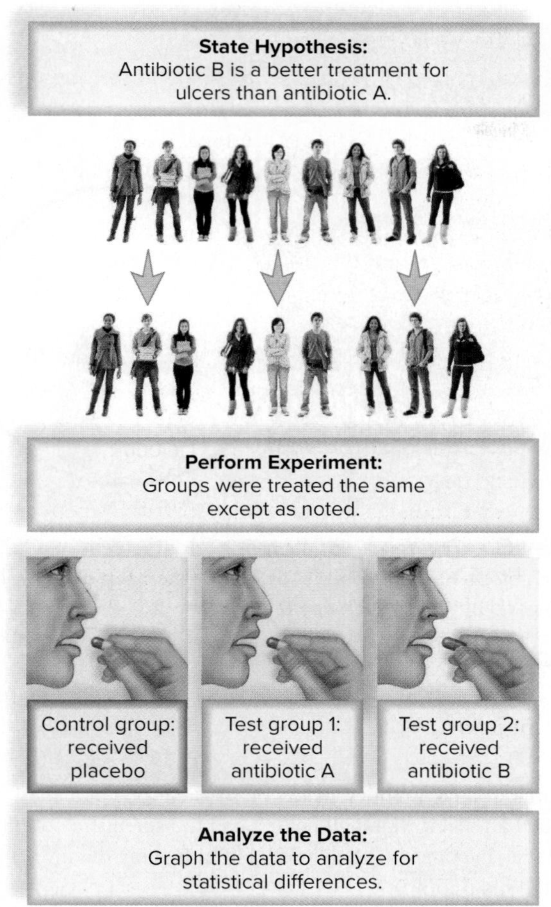
State Hypothesis:
Antibiotic B is a better treatment for ulcers than antibiotic A.
Perform Experiment:
Groups were treated the same except as noted.
Control group: received placebo
Test group 1: received antibiotic A
Test group 2: received antibiotic B
Analyze the Data:
Graph the data to analyze for statistical differences.

a. Experimental design

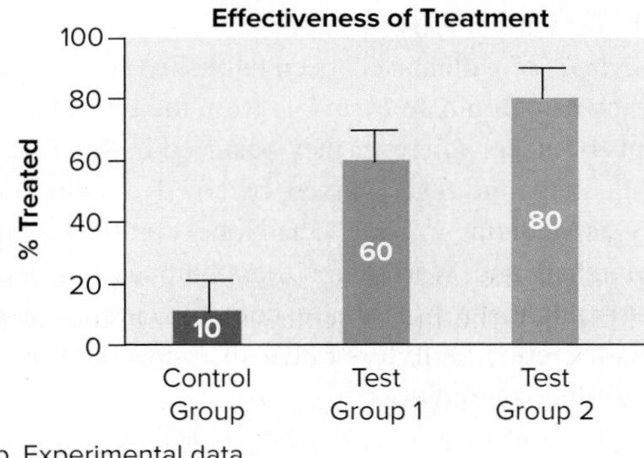
Effectiveness of Treatment
% Treated
100
80
60
40
20
0
10
60
80
Control Group
Test Group 1
Test Group 2

b. Experimental data

Figure 1.10 Example of a controlled study.
a. The experimental design of the controlled study. **b.** The experimental data displayed as a graph showing that medication B was a more effective treatment than medication A for the treatment of ulcers.
(students, all photos): René Mansi/E+/Getty Images

In this experiment, the researchers divide the individuals into three groups:

Control group: Subjects with ulcers are not treated with either antibiotic.
Test group 1: Subjects with ulcers are treated with antibiotic A.
Test group 2: Subjects with ulcers are treated with antibiotic B.

After the investigators have determined that all volunteers do have ulcers, they will want the subjects to think they are all receiving the *same* treatment. This is an additional way to protect the results from any influence other than the medication. To achieve this end, the subjects in the control group can receive a **placebo,** a treatment that appears to be the same as that administered to the other two groups but that actually contains no medication. In this study, the use of a placebo would help ensure that all subjects are equally dedicated to the study.

The Results and Conclusion

After 2 weeks of administering the same amount of medication (or placebo) in the same way, researchers examine the stomach and intestinal linings of each subject to determine if ulcers are still present. Endoscopy is one way to examine a patient for the presence of ulcers. This procedure, which is performed under sedation, involves inserting an endoscope—a small, flexible tube with a tiny camera on the end—down the throat and into the stomach and the upper part of the intestine. Then, the doctor can see the lining of these organs and can check for ulcers. Tests performed during an endoscopy can also determine if *Helicobacter pylori* is present.

Because endoscopy is somewhat subjective, it is probably best if the examiner is not aware of which group the subject is in; otherwise, examiner prejudice may influence the examination. When neither the patient nor the technician is aware of the specific treatment, it is called a *double-blind* study.

In this study, the investigators may decide to determine the effectiveness of the medication by the percentage of people who no longer have ulcers. So, if 20 people out of 100 still have ulcers, the medication is 80% effective. The difference in effectiveness is easily read in the graph portion of Figure 1.10*b*.

Conclusion: On the basis of their data, the investigators conclude that their hypothesis has been supported.

CHECK YOUR PROGRESS 1.3

1. Describe each step of the scientific method.
2. Explain why a controlled study is an important part of the experimental design.
3. List a few pros and cons of using a scientific journal versus other sources of information.
4. Summarize how the use of graphs and statistics aids in data analysis.

CONNECTING THE CONCEPTS

For more information on the topics presented in this section, refer to the following discussions:

Section 8.4 discusses how resistance to antibiotics occurs.
Section 9.3 provides more information on ulcers.
Figure 14.4 shows the relationship between an action potential and voltage across a plasma membrane.

BIOLOGY TODAY ▶ Science

Discovering the Cause of Ulcers

In 1974, Barry James Marshall (Fig. 1B) was a young resident physician at Queen Elizabeth II Medical Center in Perth, Australia. There he saw many patients who had bleeding stomach ulcers. A pathologist at the hospital, Dr. J. Robin Warren, told him about finding a particular bacterium, now called *Helicobacter pylori,* near the site of peptic ulcers. Marshall compiled data showing a possible correlation between the presence of *H. pylori* and the occurrence of both gastritis (inflammation of the stomach) and stomach ulcers. On the basis of these data, Marshall formulated a hypothesis: *H. pylori* is the cause of gastritis and ulcers.

Marshall decided to make use of Koch's postulates, the standard criteria that must be fulfilled to show that a pathogen (bacterium or virus) causes a disease:

- The suspected pathogen (virus or bacterium) must be present in every case of the disease.
- The pathogen must be isolated from the host and grown in a lab dish.
- The disease must be reproduced when a pure culture of the pathogen is inoculated into a healthy susceptible host.
- The same pathogen must be recovered again from the experimentally infected host.

By 1983, Marshall had fulfilled the first and second of Koch's criteria. He was able to isolate *H. pylori* from patients with ulcers and grow it in the laboratory. Despite Marshall's presentation of these findings to the scientific community, most physicians continued to believe that stomach acidity and stress were the causes of stomach ulcers. In those days, patients were usually advised to make drastic changes in their lifestyle to cure their ulcers. Many scientists believed that no bacterium would be able to survive the normal acidity of the stomach.

Marshall had a problem in fulfilling the third and fourth of Koch's criteria. He had been unable to infect guinea pigs and rats with the bacteria, because the bacteria did not flourish in the intestinal tracts of those animals. Marshall was not able to use human subjects because of ethical reasons. Marshall was so determined to support his hypothesis that in 1985 he decided to perform the experiment on himself! To the disbelief of those in the lab that day, he and another volunteer swallowed a foul-smelling, foul-tasting solution of *H. pylori.* Within the week, they felt lousy and were vomiting up their stomach contents. Examination by endoscopy showed that their stomachs were now inflamed, and biopsies of the stomach lining contained the suspected bacterium (Fig. 1B). Their symptoms abated without need for medication, and they never developed an ulcer. Marshall challenged the scientific community to refute his hypothesis. Many tried, but ultimately the investigators supported his findings.

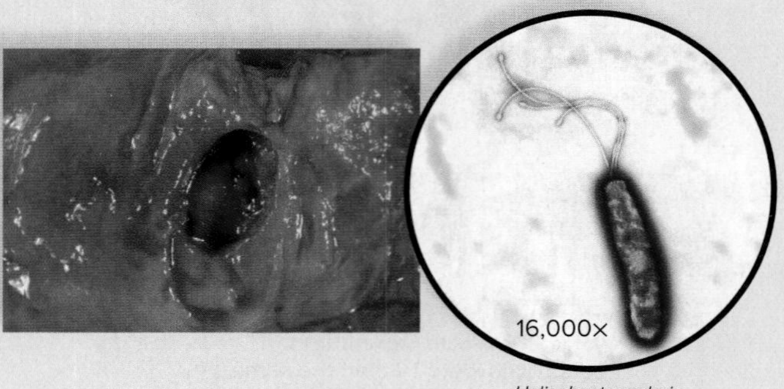

Figure 1B **The cause of stomach ulcers.**
Research by Dr. Barry Marshall showed that stomach ulcers (*left*) are often caused by *Helicobacter pylori* (*right*).
(ulcer): Dr. E. Walker/Science Source; (*H. pylori*): Heather Davies/Science Photo Library/Science Source

In science, many experiments, often involving a considerable number of subjects, are required before a conclusion can be reached. By the early 1990s, at least three independent studies involving hundreds of patients had been published showing that antibiotic therapy can eliminate *H. pylori* from the intestinal tract and cure patients of ulcers wherever they occurred in the tract.

Dr. Marshall and Dr. Warren received a Nobel Prize in Physiology or Medicine in 2005. The Nobel committee reportedly thanked Marshall and Warren for their "pioneering discovery," stating that peptic ulcer disease now could be cured with antibiotics and acid-secretion inhibitors rather than becoming a "chronic, frequently disabling condition."

Questions to Consider

1. Explain how Marshall's approach was similar to, and different from, the scientific method shown in Figure 1.7.
2. How could Marshall have done this experiment if he had an animal model to work with?

1.4 Science and the Challenges Facing Society

LEARNING OUTCOMES

Upon completion of this section, you should be able to

1. Distinguish between science and technology.
2. Summarize some of the major challenges facing science.

As we have learned in this chapter, science is a systematic way of acquiring knowledge about the natural world. Science is a slightly different endeavor than technology. **Technology** is the application of scientific knowledge to the interests of humans. Scientific investigations are the basis for the majority of our technological advances. As is often the case, a new technology, such as your cell phone or a new drug, is based on years of scientific investigations. In this section, we are going to explore some of the challenges facing science, technology, and society.

Climate Change

The overwhelming consensus within the scientific community is that the single greatest challenge facing science and society, and the greatest threat to both humans and the environment, is climate change. The term **climate change** refers to changes in the normal cycles of the Earth's climate that may be attributed to human activity. Climate change is primarily due to an imbalance in the chemical cycling of the element carbon. Normally, carbon is cycled within an ecosystem (see Section 24.3). However, due to human activities, more carbon dioxide is being released into the atmosphere than is being removed. In 1850, atmospheric CO_2 was at about 280 parts per million (ppm). Today, it is over 415 ppm (Fig. 1.11). This increase is largely due to the burning of fossil fuels and the destruction of forests to make way for farmland and pastures. The amount of carbon dioxide released into the atmosphere today is about twice the amount that remains in the atmosphere. It is believed that most of this dissolves in the oceans, which are increasing in acidity. The increased amount of carbon dioxide (and other gases) in the atmosphere is causing a rise in temperature called **global warming.** These gases allow the sun's rays to pass through them, but they then absorb and radiate heat back to Earth, a phenomenon called the *greenhouse effect.*

There is a consensus among scientists from around the globe that climate change and global warming are causing significant changes in many of the Earth's ecosystems and represent one of the greatest challenges of our time. Throughout this text, we will return to see how climate change is impacting humans, from the loss of biodiversity to increases in the rates of certain types of human disease. We will examine climate change in more detail in Chapters 24 and 25.

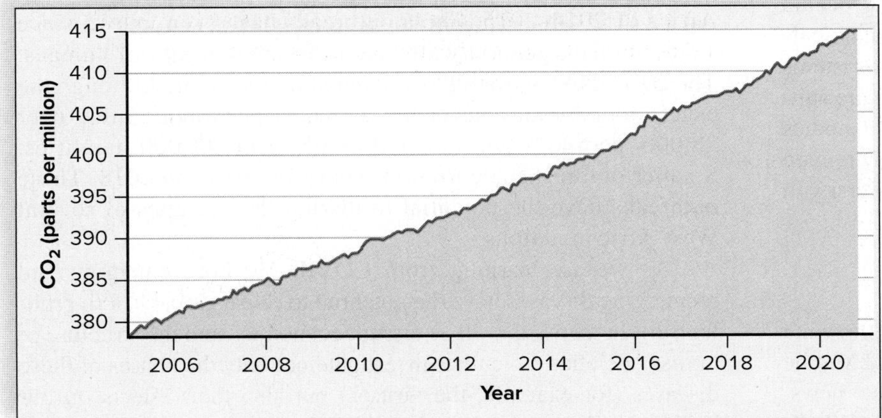

Figure 1.11 **Increases in atmospheric carbon dioxide concentrations.** The global average carbon dioxide (CO_2) concentration now exceeds 415 ppm and is the major contributing factor to climate change and global warming.

NOAA, "Global Climate Change: Facts." http://climate.nasa.gov/vital-signs/carbon-dioxide/.

Biodiversity and Habitat Loss

The term **biodiversity** represents the total number and relative abundance of species, the variability of their genes, and the different ecosystems in which they live. The biodiversity of our planet has been estimated to be around 8.7 million species (not counting bacteria), and so far, approximately 2.3 million have been identified and named. **Extinction** is the death of a species or larger classification category. It is estimated that presently we are losing hundreds of species every year due to human activities and that as much as 27% of all identified species, including most primates, birds, and amphibians, may be in danger of extinction before the end of the century. In many cases, these extinctions are accelerated by a combination of habitat loss and climate change (Fig. 1.12). Many biologists are alarmed about the present rate of extinction and hypothesize it may eventually rival the rates of the five mass extinctions that occurred during our planet's history. The last mass extinction, about 65 million years ago, caused many plant and animal species, including the dinosaurs, to become extinct.

The two most biologically diverse ecosystems—tropical rain forests and coral reefs—are home to many organisms. These ecosystems are also threatened by human activities. The canopy of the tropical rain forest alone supports a variety of organisms, including orchids, insects, and monkeys. Coral reefs, which are found just offshore of the continents and islands near the equator, are built up from calcium carbonate skeletons of sea animals called corals. Reefs provide a habitat for many animals, including jellyfish, sponges, snails, crabs, lobsters, sea turtles, moray eels, and some of the world's most colorful fishes. Like tropical rain forests, coral reefs are severely threatened as the human population increases in size. Some reefs are 50 million years old, yet in just a few decades, human activities have destroyed an estimated 25% of all coral reefs and seriously degraded another 30%. At this rate, nearly three-quarters could be destroyed within 40 years. Similar statistics are available for tropical rain forests.

Figure 1.12 **Loss of Biodiversity.**
Of the 111 known species of lemurs, all of which are found on the island of Madagascar, 105 are classified as endangered or threatened by extinction.
Gudkov Andrey/Shutterstock

The destruction of healthy ecosystems has many unintended effects. For example, we depend on them for food, medicines, and various raw materials. Draining of the natural wetlands of the Mississippi and Ohio Rivers and the construction of levees have worsened flooding problems, making once-fertile farmland undesirable. The destruction of South American rain forests has killed many species that may have yielded the next miracle drug and has decreased the availability of many types of lumber. We are only now beginning to realize that we depend on ecosystems even more for the services they provide. Just as chemical cycling occurs within a single ecosystem, so all ecosystems keep chemicals cycling throughout the biosphere. The workings of ecosystems ensure that the environmental conditions of the biosphere are suitable for the continued existence of humans. In fact, several studies show that ecosystems cannot function properly unless they remain biologically diverse. We will explore the concept of biodiversity in greater detail in later chapters of this text.

Emerging and Reemerging Diseases

Over the past decade, avian influenza (H5N1 and H7N9), swine flu (H1N1), severe acute respiratory syndrome (SARS), and Middle East respiratory syndrome (MERS) have been in the news. In 2020, a global pandemic called COVID-19 was caused by a new form of SARS virus named SARS-CoV-2. These are called **emerging diseases** because they are relatively new to humans.

Where do emerging diseases come from? Some of them may result from new and/or increased exposure to animals or insect populations that act as vectors for disease. Changes in human behavior and use of technology can also result in new diseases. For example, Legionnaires' disease emerged in 1976 due to bacterial contamination of a large air-conditioning system in a hotel. The bacteria thrived in the cooling tower used as the water source for the air-conditioning system. SARS is thought to have arisen in Guandong, China, due to the consumption of civets, a type of exotic cat considered a delicacy. The civets were possibly infected by exposure to horseshoe bats sold in open markets. While the source of SARS-CoV-2 is still being investigated, it is also thought to have resulted from human contact with, or consumption of, horseshoe bats.

In addition, globalization results in the transport all over the world of diseases previously restricted to isolated communities. The first SARS-CoV-2 cases were reported in Wuhan, China, in November 2019. By the end of March 2020, SARS-CoV-2, and the respiratory illness it caused, COVID-19, had spread globally and was found in every country and continent, except Antarctica, on the globe. As of this writing in 2021, COVID-19 had infected over 210 million people worldwide and resulted in over 4.4 million deaths.

Some pathogens mutate and change hosts, jumping from birds to humans, for example. Before 1997, avian flu was thought to affect only birds. A mutated strain jumped to humans in the 1997 outbreak. To control that epidemic, officials killed 1.5 million chickens to remove the source of the virus. New forms of avian influenza (bird flu) are being discovered every few years. As mentioned, the SARS-CoV-2 virus is believed to have jumped to humans from horseshoe bats, but other species, such as pangolins, may have been involved.

Reemerging diseases are also a concern. Unlike an emerging disease, a reemerging disease has been known to cause disease in humans for some time, but generally has not been considered a health risk due to a relatively low level of incidence in human populations. Even so, reemerging diseases can cause problems. One example is the Ebola outbreak in West Africa of 2014–2015. Ebola outbreaks have been known since 1976, but have generally affected only small groups of humans. The 2014–2015 outbreak was a much larger event. Although the exact numbers may never be known, it is estimated that over 28,000 people were infected, with over 11,000 fatalities. Smaller outbreaks occurred in Africa in 2016 and 2018. These outbreaks have the potential to disrupt the societies of several West African nations.

As we are learning from COVID-19, both emerging and reemerging diseases have the potential to cause global health problems for humans, as well as disrupt economies and the structure of human societies. Scientists investigate not only the causes of these diseases (for example, the viruses) but also their effects on our bodies and the mechanisms by which they are transmitted. We will take a closer look at pathogens, such as viruses, in Section 8.1, and emerging diseases in Section 8.2.

CHECK YOUR PROGRESS 1.4

1. Explain how a new technology differs from a scientific discovery.
2. Explain why the conservation of biodiversity is important to human society.
3. Summarize how emerging diseases and climate change have the potential to influence the entire human population.

CONNECTING THE CONCEPTS

For more information on these challenges facing human society, refer to the following discussions:

Section 8.3 provides additional information on emerging and reemerging diseases.

Section 24.3 examines the impact of climate change and global warming on ecosystems.

Section 25.3 explores the importance of preserving biodiversity.

CONCLUSION

In the beginning of this chapter, we introduced the importance of diversity to science. Throughout this chapter, you have explored some of the basic characteristics of life as we currently understand it, the processes by which science is performed, and the importance of science in addressing the needs of society. The diversity of backgrounds, opinions, and ideas that comes from a diverse scientific community will play an important role in making the study of biology relevant, and important, to all of human society.

SUMMARIZE

1.1 The Characteristics of Life

Biology is the study of life. All living organisms share common characteristics:

- They have levels of organization—**atoms, molecules, cells, tissues, organs, organ systems, organisms, species, populations, community, ecosystem,** and **biosphere.**
- They acquire materials and **energy** from the environment. **Metabolism** is the sum of the reactions involved in these processes. **Photosynthesis,** which occurs in organisms such as plants, is responsible for producing the organic molecules that serve as food for most organisms.
- They **reproduce** and experience **growth,** and in many cases **development.** The instructions for these processes are contained within the **DNA (deoxyribonucleic acid)** and are organized as **genes. Mutations** cause variations of those instructions.
- They maintain an internal environment, called **homeostasis,** that operates within a narrow range of environmental factors.
- They respond to stimuli.
- As species, they are influenced by **natural selection** as the process that results in **evolution** and **adaptation** to their environment over time.

1.2 Humans Are Related to Other Animals

The classification of living organisms mirrors their evolutionary relationships. Humans are animals that belong to the animal **kingdom** of the **domain** Eukarya. Other kingdoms include the **plants, protists,** and **fungi.** A new classification, called a **supergroup,** is being developed to describe evolutionary relationships based on DNA analyses.

In addition to their evolutionary history, humans have a cultural heritage in which language, tool use, values, and information are passed on from one generation to the next.

Like all life, humans are members of the biosphere. Humans depend on the biosphere for its many services, such as absorption of pollutants, sources of water and food, prevention of soil erosion, and natural beauty.

1.3 Science as a Process

When studying the natural world, scientists use a process called the **scientific method.**

- **Observations,** along with previous data, are used to formulate a hypothesis. **Inductive reasoning** allows a scientist to combine facts into a **hypothesis.**
- New observations and/or experiments are carried out in order to test the hypothesis. Through **deductive reasoning,** scientists can develop a **prediction** of what may occur as a result of the experiment. A good **experimental design** includes an **experimental variable** and a **control group.** Scientists may use **models** and model organisms in their experimental design.
- The **data** from the experimental and observational results are analyzed, often using statistical methods. The results are often presented in tables or graphs for ease of interpretation.
- A conclusion is made as to whether the results support the hypothesis or do not support the hypothesis.
- The results may be submitted to a scientific publication for review by the scientific community.
- Over time, multiple conclusions in a particular area may allow scientists to arrive at a **theory** (or **principle** or **law**), such as the cell theory or the theory of evolution. The theory of evolution is a unifying concept of biology.

1.4 Science and the Challenges Facing Society

While science investigates the principles of the natural world, **technology** applies this knowledge to the needs of society. Some challenges that scientists are investigating include:

- The impact of **climate change** and **global warming.**
- The loss of **biodiversity** and habitats such as coral reefs and rain forests. This often results in the **extinction** of species.
- **Emerging diseases,** such as avian influenza and SARS, and reemerging diseases, such as Ebola.

ENGAGE

BioNOW

Want to know how this science is relevant to your life? Check out the BioNOW video below:

- Characteristics of Life

McGraw Hill

Which step of the scientific method was represented in this video? How was it accomplished and which steps would follow?

THINKING CRITICALLY

1. Explain how climate change and loss of biodiversity may produce health threats for humans. Give an example of how scientists have already documented instances where this is occurring.
2. You are a scientist working at a pharmaceutical company and have developed a new cancer medication that has the potential for use in humans. Outline a series of experiments, including the use of a model, to test whether the cancer medication works.
3. Scientists have been exploring the possibility of life on other planets and moons of our solar system. If life is found to exist outside of Earth, will that change our definition of the basic characteristics of life? Will it change our definition of a biosphere?

MAKING IT RELEVANT

1. Why is it important for the scientific community to be diverse to address the needs facing society due to climate change?
2. How might a diverse scientific community be able to better address the loss of biodiversity at a local level?
3. Emerging diseases often occur in rural areas of the globe, where scientific education is minimal. What are some ways a diverse and global community of scientists can help reduce the risk of these diseases becoming a problem?

Find answers to all of the chapter questions at connect.mheducation.com

CHAPTER 2

Chemistry of Life

Jeff Mondragon/Alamy Stock Photo

Ocean Acidification

If you take a look at our planet from space, you will quickly notice we live on a water planet. In fact, not only is 71% of our planet's surface covered by water, but the physiology of every organism on the planet is based on water. While we historically have taken water for granted, the impact of climate change is beginning to increase our awareness of the importance of this resource on the health of many species, including our own.

The primary cause of climate change is the release of carbon dioxide (CO_2) gas into the atmosphere through the burning of fossil fuels by humans. Not only does that CO_2 contribute to global warming, it also dissolves very easily in water, forming carbonic acid. In the oceans of the world, the presence of carbonic acid increases the acidity of the aquatic environment.

So why is this important? The increase in acidity decreases the amount of another compound, called carbonate, in the oceans. Carbonate plays an important role in the formation of shells of organisms, such as crabs, lobsters, and clams. As the ocean acidifies, these organisms have a harder time forming shells and other hard structures. Marine biologists have already noticed a decline not only in the amount of carbonate in shellfish, but also their overall abundance in the ocean's ecosystem. Because these organisms are an important part of the food chain, the loss of carbonate has a ripple effect that ultimately affects humans.

In this chapter, we will explore the importance of water to life as we know it, as well as the atoms responsible for making up the compounds of life.

As you read through the chapter, think about the following questions:

1. What elements are common in all living organisms?
2. Why is water so important to life?
3. What is the difference between an acid and a base?

CHAPTER OUTLINE

BEFORE YOU BEGIN

Before beginning this chapter, take a few moments to review the following discussions:

Section 1.1 What are the basic characteristics of all living organisms?

Figure 1.2 What is the difference between an atom and a molecule?

2.1 From Atoms to Molecules

LEARNING OUTCOMES

Upon completion of this section, you should be able to

1. Distinguish between atoms and elements.
2. Describe the structure of an atom.
3. Define *isotope* and summarize its application in both medicine and biology.
4. Distinguish between ionic and covalent bonds.

Matter is anything that takes up space and has mass. Matter can exist in a number of forms, including as a solid, gas, liquid, or plasma. Not only are humans composed of matter, but so is the food we eat, the water we drink, and the air we breathe.

Elements

An **element** is one of the basic building blocks of matter, and cannot be broken down by chemical means. Considering the variety of living and nonliving organisms in the world, it's remarkable there are only 98 naturally occurring elements, although some of these exist in only very small quantities. It is even more surprising that over 90% of the human body is composed of just 4 elements: carbon, nitrogen, oxygen, and hydrogen. Even so, other elements, such as iron, are important to our health. If our diet is deficient in iron, then our bodies cannot manufacture a protein called hemoglobin, which serves as an important molecule in the transportation of oxygen (another element) to our cells.

Each element has a name and a symbol. For example, carbon has been assigned the atomic symbol C, and iron has been assigned the symbol Fe. Some of the symbols we use for elements are derived from Latin. For example, the symbol for sodium is Na because *natrium,* in Latin, means "sodium." Likewise, the symbol for iron is Fe because *ferrum* means "iron."

Chemists arrange the elements in a *periodic* table, so named because all the elements in a column show periodicity, meaning that all the elements in each column behave similarly during chemical reactions (Fig. 2.1). For example, all the elements in column VII (7) undergo the same types of chemical reactions, for reasons we will soon explore. A portion of the periodic table is shown in Figure 2.1. A complete table is available in Appendix.

BIOLOGY IN YOUR LIFE

You are made of old stars

We are all familiar with elements. *Iron, sodium, oxygen,* and *carbon* are all common terms in our lives, but where do elements originate from?

Normal chemical reactions do not produce elements. The majority of the heavier elements, such as iron, are produced only by the intense chemical reactions within stars. When these stars reach the end of their lives, they explode, producing supernovas. Supernovas scatter the heavier elements into space, where they are eventually involved in the formation of planets. The iron within your blood was formed by the explosions of stars. The astronomer Neil deGrasse Tyson once stated, "After all, what nobler thought can one cherish than that the universe lives within us all?"

(1 = atomic number; H = atomic symbol; 1.008 = atomic mass)

Periods	I	II	III	IV	V	VI	VII	VIII
1	1 H 1.008							2 He 4.003
2	3 Li 6.941	4 Be 9.012	5 B 10.81	6 C 12.01	7 N 14.01	8 O 16.00	9 F 19.00	10 Ne 20.18
3	11 Na 22.99	12 Mg 24.31	13 Al 26.98	14 Si 28.09	15 P 30.97	16 S 32.07	17 Cl 35.45	18 Ar 39.95
4	19 K 39.10	20 Ca 40.08	31 Ga 69.72	32 Ge 72.59	33 As 74.92	34 Se 78.96	35 Br 79.90	36 Kr 83.60

Groups

Figure 2.1 **A portion of the periodic table of elements.** The number on the top of each square is the atomic number, which increases from left to right. The letter symbols represent the elements; some are abbreviations of Greek or Latin names. Below the symbol is the value for the atomic mass. A complete periodic table can be found in Appendix.

Atoms

An **atom** is the smallest unit of an element that still retains the chemical and physical properties of the element. The same name is given to the element and the atoms of the element. Though it is possible to split an atom, it is the smallest unit to enter into chemical reactions. Physicists have identified a number of subatomic particles that make up atoms. The three best-known subatomic particles are positively charged **protons,** uncharged **neutrons,** and negatively charged **electrons.** Protons and neutrons are located within the nucleus of an atom, and electrons move about the nucleus. Figure 2.2 shows the arrangement of the subatomic particles of some common elements. In Figure 2.2, the circle around the nucleus of the atom represents an **electron shell,** which represents the average location of electrons. Notice that most of an atom is empty space. If we could draw an atom the size of a football stadium, the nucleus would be like a gumball in the center of the field, and the electrons would be tiny specks whirling about in the upper stands.

The Periodic Table

Atoms have not only an atomic symbol but also an atomic number and mass number. The **atomic number** represents the number of protons in the nucleus of an element. All atoms of an element have the same number of protons housed in the nucleus.

Each atom also has its own mass number, dependent on the number of subatomic particles in that atom. Protons and neutrons are assigned one atomic mass unit (AMU) each. Electrons are so small that their AMU is considered zero in most calculations

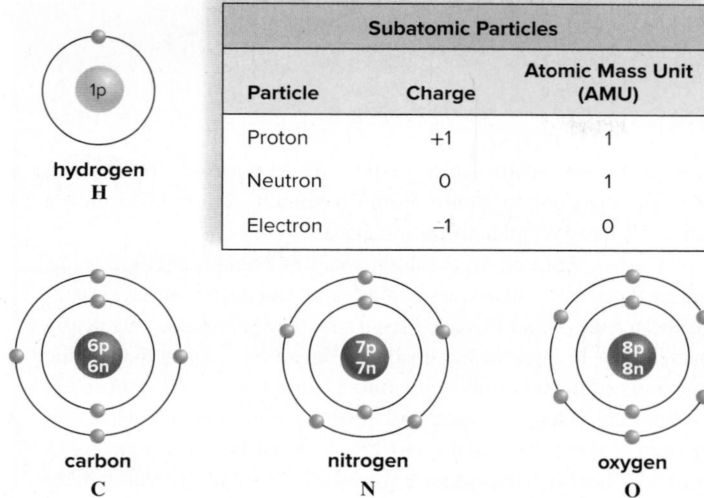

Subatomic Particles		
Particle	**Charge**	**Atomic Mass Unit (AMU)**
Proton	+1	1
Neutron	0	1
Electron	–1	0

Figure 2.2 **The atomic structure of select elements.** Notice that the protons (p) and neutrons (n) are located in the nucleus, while the electrons (blue dots) are found in shells around the nucleus.

(Fig. 2.2). Therefore, the **mass number** of an atom represents the sum of the protons and neutrons in the nucleus.

By convention, when an atom stands alone (and not in the periodic table, discussed next), the atomic number is written as a subscript to the lower left of the atomic symbol. The mass number is written as a superscript to the upper left of the atomic symbol. Regardless of position, the smaller number is always the atomic number, as shown here for carbon:

mass number — $^{12}_{6}C$ — atomic symbol
atomic number —

The atoms shown in the periodic table (see Fig. 2.1) are assumed to be electrically neutral. Therefore, the atomic number tells you not only the number of protons but also the number of electrons. The **atomic mass** (the number below the atomic symbol on the periodic table) is the average of the AMU for all the isotopes (discussed next) of that atom. To determine the number of neutrons, subtract the number of protons from the atomic mass, and take the closest whole number.

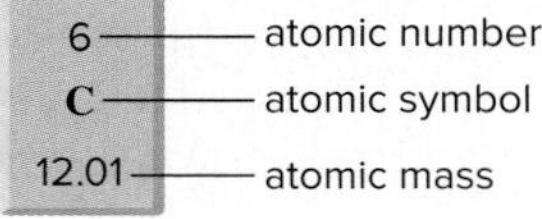

Isotopes

Isotopes of an atom have the same number of protons but different numbers of neutrons. Therefore, they have the same atomic number but their mass numbers are different. For example, the element carbon 12 (^{12}C) has six neutrons, carbon 13 (^{13}C) has seven neutrons, and carbon 14 (^{14}C) has eight neutrons, but all three have six protons. You can determine the number of neutrons for an isotope by subtracting the atomic number (see Fig. 2.1) from the mass number.

Unlike the other two isotopes of carbon, carbon 14 is unstable and breaks down over time. As carbon 14 decays, it releases various types of energy in the form of rays and subatomic particles; therefore, it is a **radioisotope.**

Our understanding of radioactivity largely stems from the work of Marie Curie, who not only coined the term, but also contributed much to its study (see the Diversity in Science feature "The Legacy of Marie Curie"). Today, biologists use radiation to date objects from our distant past, create images, treat diseases, and trace the movement of substances in the body. As we will see next, the radiation given off by radioisotopes can be detected in various ways.

Low Levels of Radiation

The importance of chemistry to biology and medicine is nowhere more evident than in the many uses of radioisotopes. A radioisotope behaves the same chemically as the stable isotopes of an element. This means you can put a small amount of radioisotope in a sample and it becomes a *tracer* by which to detect molecular changes.

Specific tracers are used in imaging the body's organs and tissues and can be used to diagnose the presence of tumors. For example, after a solution containing a minute amount of iodine 131 is swallowed by a patient, it becomes concentrated in the thyroid, which uses iodine to make the hormone thyroxine. After the thyroid has had some time to accumulate the iodine 131, an image may indicate whether it is healthy in structure and function (Fig. 2.3*a*).

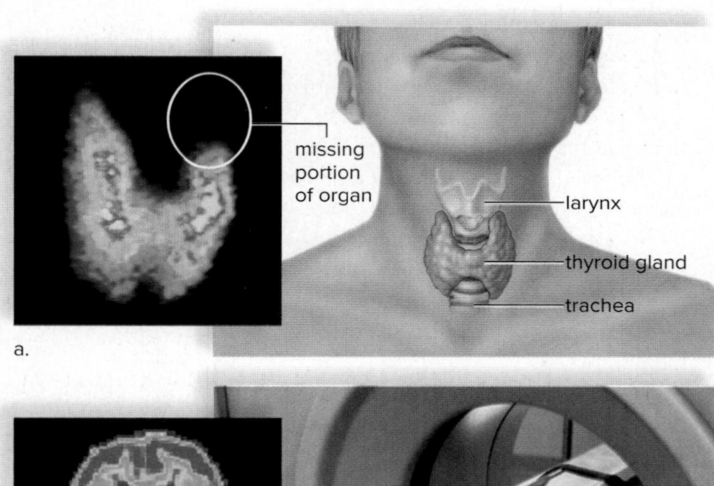

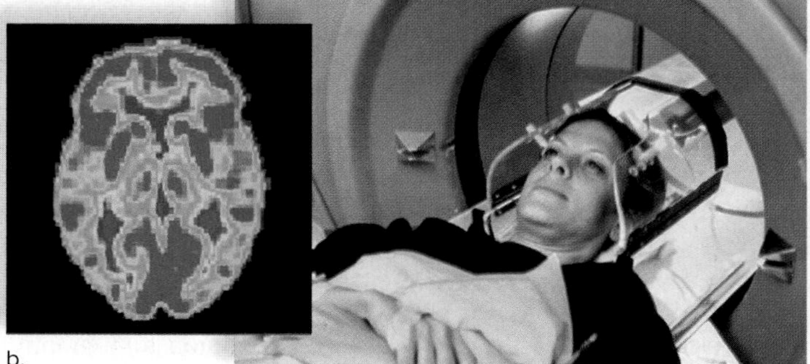

Figure 2.3 **Medical uses for low-level radiation.**
a. The missing area (indicated by the circle) in this thyroid scan indicates the presence of a tumor that does not take up radioactive iodine. **b.** A PET (positron-emission tomography) scan reveals which portions of the brain are most active (red surrounded by light green).
(photos) (a): Southern Illinois University/Science Source; (b, PET scan): Photo Researchers/Science History Images/Alamy Stock Photo; (b, patient): Courtesy of National Institutes of Health

BIOLOGY TODAY ▶ Diversity in Science

The Legacy of Marie Curie

Like many people, you may not have a favorable view of the word *radioactivity*. Yet, modern society relies heavily on the concept of radioactivity to provide us with electricity, safe food supplies, and the benefits of modern medicine. Our comprehension of biology is also dependent on the use of radioactivity to understand the inner workings of a cell, variations in genes, and how organisms and ecosystems process nutrients and energy.

Our understanding of radioactivity is largely based on the work of Marie Curie, a Polish scientist of the late nineteenth and early twentieth century (Fig. 2A). Yet her story, like the story of so many female scientists, was also one defined by overcoming barriers to her sex. Her life and research not only turned science on its head, but proved to those of her era that a woman could be just as brilliant and accomplished—if not more so—than her male peers, at a time when many women were not even permitted to study at a university.

Early in her career, the discovery of radioactivity by French scientist Henri Becquerel inspired Curie and her husband to study the phenomenon of radiation in their own lab. Working in cramped and often poorly ventilated conditions, they discovered that certain minerals containing uranium were, in fact, emitting far more radiation than they should have been. The two believed that this hinted at a new element, which Curie named polonium after her home country of Poland. Not five months later, Curie found an even more radioactive element than polonium, which she called radium.

Curie's research did more than discover new elements, she also proposed a new theory of radiation: that the "rays" emitted by elements such as uranium and polonium were the product of interactions within the atom itself. This challenged the then-widely accepted belief in the atom as the smallest particle in physics, opening the door to future atomic research. She even coined a name for these elements: "radio-active."

Figure 2A Marie Curie.
Marie Curie was one of the early pioneers in the discovery of radioactivity.
Science History Images/Alamy Stock Photo

Curie's research on radiation was immediately recognized as one of the greatest discoveries of its time. But when Curie was suggested for the Nobel Prize in Physics in 1903, her name was nearly passed over in favor of her husband. Because he was a man, some members of the committee attributed Curie's work to her husband instead, given that a woman had never been granted a Nobel Prize before. In the end—and in part due to intensive lobbying on her behalf by her husband—Marie Curie was awarded the Nobel Prize in Physics, alongside her husband and Henri Becquerel in 1903, becoming the first woman in history to achieve the Nobel Prize.

Not ten years later, in 1911, she received a second Nobel, this time in chemistry and wholly in her own name, making her the first person, or any gender, to win two Nobel Prizes.

Curie's research into radiation would go on to have several real-world applications still employed today. The use of radiation for medicine would go on to save lives in WW1, when *"petit Curies"*—mobile X-ray carriages—treated Allied soldiers on the Western Front. Today, modern medical radiotherapy used to combat cancer and tumors, originates from Curie's research, while her theories that challenged the indivisible nature of the atom would inspire future atomic scientists, giving way to nuclear power, as well as, less benevolently, the atomic bomb.

As we remember Curie's contributions, we must also recognize that her accomplishments were made in spite of the gender barriers placed against her—barriers still faced by women and underrepresented populations in the sciences, over 110 years later.

Another example is in the use of positron-emission tomography (PET) to determine the comparative activity of tissues. Radioactively labeled glucose, which emits a subatomic particle known as a positron, can be injected into the body. The radiation given off is detected by sensors and analyzed by a computer. The result is a color image that shows which tissues took up glucose and are metabolically active (red areas in Fig. 2.3*b*). A PET scan of the brain can help diagnose a brain tumor, Alzheimer's disease, and epilepsy and can determine whether a stroke has occurred.

High Levels of Radiation

Radioactive substances in the environment can harm cells, damage DNA, and cause cancer. The release of radioactive particles following a nuclear power plant accident, such as occurred at the Japanese Fukushima nuclear plant in 2011, can have far-reaching and long-lasting effects on human health.

However, the effects of radiation can also be put to good use. Radiation from radioisotopes has been used for many years to kill bacteria and viruses and to sterilize medical and dental products.

Increasingly, the technology is being used to increase the safety of our food supply. By using specific types of radiation, food can be sterilized without irradiating or damaging the food. Radiation can be used to ensure public safety against bacterial infection. It is used to sterilize the U.S. mail and other packages to free them of possible pathogens, such as anthrax spores.

The ability of radiation to kill cells is often applied to cancer cells. Radioisotopes can be introduced into the body in a way that allows radiation to destroy only cancer cells, with little risk to the rest of the body (Fig. 2.4). Another form of high-energy radiation, X-rays, can be used for medical diagnosis and cancer therapy.

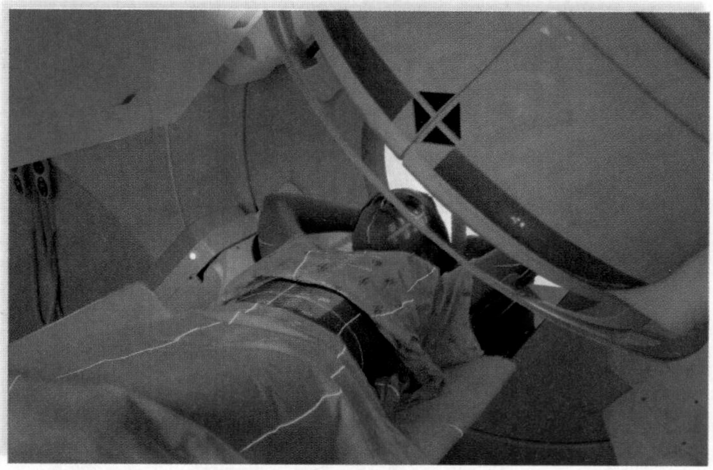

Figure 2.4 Using radiation to treat cancer.
Physicians can use radiation therapy to kill cancer cells.
Mark Kostich/E+/Getty Images

Molecules and Compounds

Atoms often bond with one another to form a chemical unit called a **molecule.** A molecule can contain atoms of the same type, as when an oxygen atom joins with another oxygen atom to form oxygen gas. Or the atoms can be different, as when an oxygen atom joins with two hydrogen atoms to form water. When the atoms are different, a **compound** is formed. Two types of bonds join atoms: ionic bonds and covalent bonds.

Ionic Bonding

Atoms with more than one shell are most stable when the outer shell, also called the **valence shell,** contains eight electrons. During an ionic reaction, atoms give up or take on an electron or electrons to achieve a stable valence shell.

Figure 2.5 depicts a reaction between a sodium (Na) atom and a chlorine (Cl) atom. Sodium, with one electron in the valence shell, reacts with a single chlorine atom. Why? Once the reaction

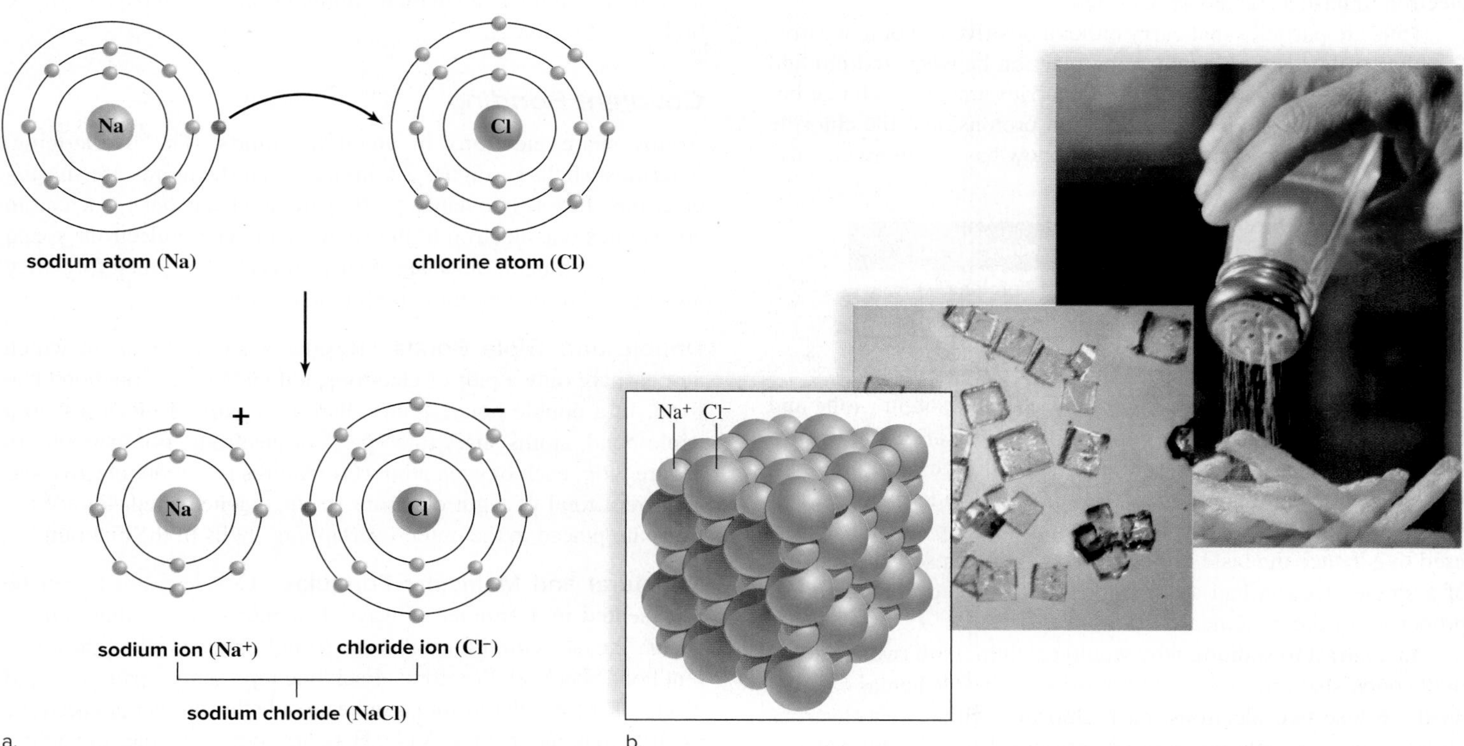

Figure 2.5 Formation of an ionic bond.
a. During the formation of sodium chloride, an electron is transferred from the sodium atom to the chlorine atom. At the completion of the reaction, each atom has eight electrons in its valence shell, but each also carries a charge as shown. **b.** In a sodium chloride crystal, ionic bonding between Na^+ and Cl^- causes the ions to form a three-dimensional lattice configuration, in which each sodium ion is surrounded by six chloride ions and each chloride ion is surrounded by six sodium ions.
(photos) (b, salt crystals): Evelyn Jo Johnson/McGraw Hill; (b, salt shaker): PM Images/Photodisc/Getty Images

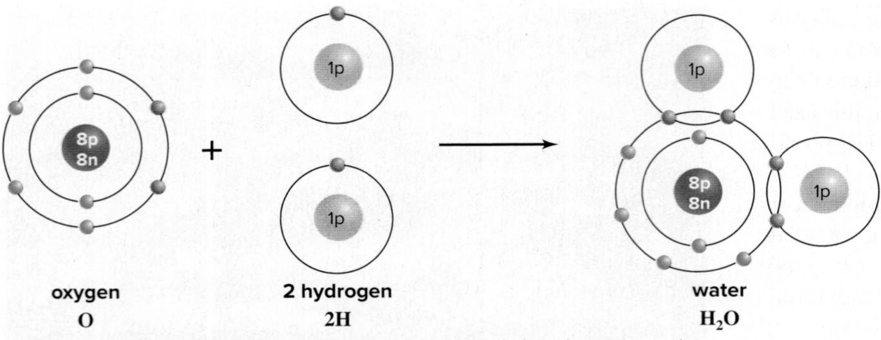

a. When an oxygen and two hydrogen atoms covalently bond, water results.

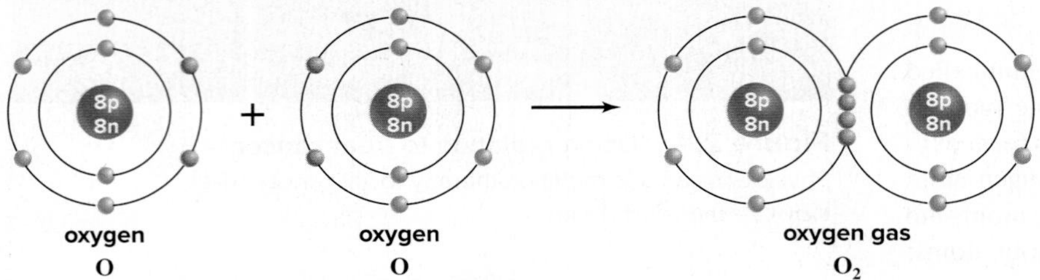

b. When two oxygen atoms covalently bond, oxygen gas results.

Figure 2.6 Covalent bonds.
Covalent bonds allow atoms to fill their valence shells by sharing electrons. Because the electrons are being shared, it is necessary to count the electrons in the outer shell as belonging to both bonded atoms. Hydrogen is most stable with two electrons in the valence shell; oxygen is most stable with eight electrons in the valence shell. Therefore, the molecular formula for water is (**a**) H_2O, and for oxygen gas it is (**b**) O_2.

is finished and sodium loses one electron to chlorine, sodium's valence shell will have eight electrons. Similarly, a chlorine atom, which has seven electrons already, needs to acquire only one more electron to have a stable valence shell.

Ions are particles that carry either a positive (+) or a negative (–) charge. For example, when the reaction between sodium and chlorine is complete, the sodium ion carries a positive charge because it now has one less electron than protons, and the chloride ion carries a negative charge because it now has one more electron than protons:

Sodium Ion (Na^+)	Chloride Ion (Cl^-)
11 protons (+)	17 protons (+)
10 electrons (–)	18 electrons (–)
One (+) charge	One (–) charge

The attraction between oppositely charged sodium ions and chloride ions forms an **ionic bond.** Sodium is a soft metal that reacts violently when placed in water, and chlorine is a toxic gas. However, the resulting compound, sodium chloride (NaCl), commonly known as table salt, has neither of these properties and is used to enhance the taste of our food. As you can see, the transfer of a single electron had a tremendous influence on the chemical properties of these elements.

In contrast to sodium, why would calcium, with two electrons in the outer shell, react with two chlorine atoms? Whereas calcium needs to lose two electrons, each chlorine, with seven electrons already, requires only one more electron to have a stable valence shell. The resulting salt ($CaCl_2$) is called calcium chloride. If you live in a northern climate, you are familiar with the use of calcium chloride as a de-icer.

The balance of various ions in the body is important to our health. Too much sodium in the blood can contribute to high blood pressure. Calcium deficiency leads to rickets (a bowing of the legs) in children. Too much or too little potassium results in heartbeat irregularities and can be fatal. Bicarbonate, hydrogen, and hydroxide ions are all involved in maintaining the acid-base balance of the body (see Section 2.2).

Covalent Bonding

Atoms share electrons in **covalent bonds.** The overlapping, outermost shells in Figure 2.6 indicate that the atoms are sharing electrons. Just as two hands participate in a handshake, each atom contributes one electron to the shared pair. These electrons spend part of their time in the valence shell of each atom; therefore, they are counted as belonging to both bonded atoms.

Double and Triple Bonds Besides a single bond, in which atoms share only a pair of electrons, a double or a triple bond can form. In a double bond, atoms share two pairs of electrons; in a triple bond, atoms share three pairs of electrons. For example, in Figure 2.6*b*, each oxygen atom (O) requires two more electrons to achieve a total of eight electrons in the valence shell. Four electrons are placed in the outer, overlapping shells in the diagram.

Structural and Molecular Formulas Covalent bonds can be represented in a number of ways. In contrast to the diagrams in Figure 2.6, structural formulas use straight lines to show the covalent bonds between the atoms. Each line represents a pair of shared electrons. Molecular formulas indicate only the number of each type of atom making up a molecule. Here are some examples of each:

Structural formula: H—O—H, O═O

Molecular formula: H_2O, O_2

What are the structural and molecular formulas for carbon dioxide? Carbon, with four electrons in the valence shell, requires four more electrons to complete its outer shell. Each oxygen, with six electrons in the valence shell, needs only two electrons to complete its outer shell. Therefore, carbon shares two pairs of electrons with each oxygen atom, and the formulas are as follows:

Structural formula: O=C=O

Molecular formula: CO_2

CHECK YOUR PROGRESS 2.1

1. List the number of electrons, neutrons, and protons in an atom of magnesium (Mg; see Fig. 2.1).
2. Determine the number of neutrons found in the isotopes of oxygen ^{16}O and ^{18}O (see Fig. 2.1).
3. Explain the beneficial uses of radioisotopes.
4. Summarize the differences between ionic and covalent bonds, and give an example of each.

CONNECTING THE CONCEPTS

The study of biology has a firm foundation in chemistry. To see this relationship in more detail, refer to the following discussions:

Section 3.3 describes how cells move ions across plasma membranes.

Section 11.3 explains how our urinary system uses ions to maintain homeostasis.

2.2 Water and Life

LEARNING OUTCOMES

Upon completion of this section, you should be able to

1. Describe the properties of water.
2. Explain the role of hydrogen bonds in the properties of water.
3. Summarize the structure of the pH scale and the importance of buffers to biological systems.

Water is the most abundant molecule in living organisms, usually making up about 60–70% of the total body weight. Furthermore, the physical and chemical properties of water make life as we know it possible.

In water molecules, the electrons spend more time circling the oxygen (O) atom than the hydrogens, because oxygen has a greater ability to attract electrons than do the hydrogen (H) atoms. The negatively charged electrons are closer to the oxygen atom, so the oxygen atom becomes slightly negative. In turn, the hydrogens are slightly positive. Therefore, water is a **polar** molecule; the oxygen end of the molecule has a slight negative charge (δ^-), while the hydrogen end has a slight positive charge (δ^+). The structure of a water molecule is shown in Figure 2.7*a*.

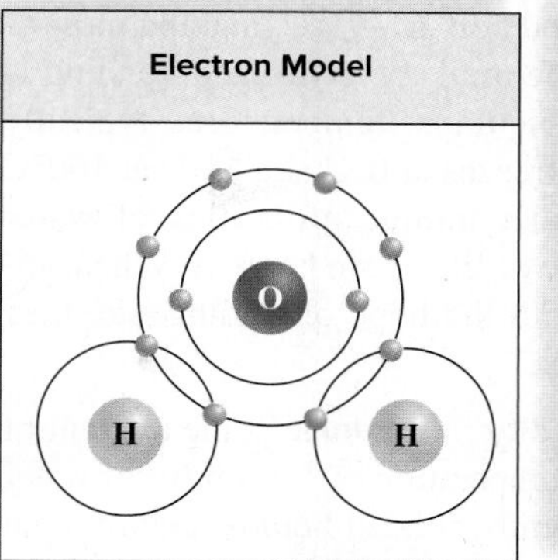

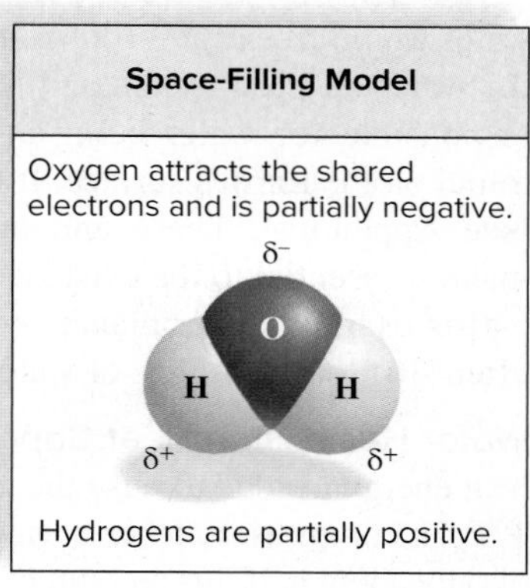

a. Water (H_2O)

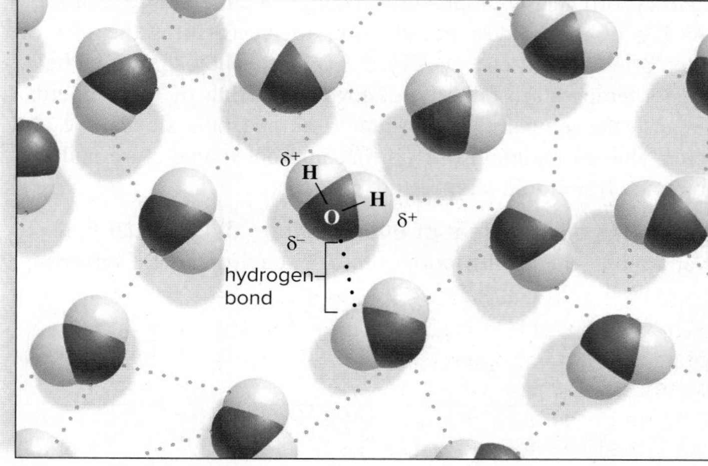

b. Hydrogen bonding between water molecules

Figure 2.7 **Hydrogen bonds and water molecules.**
a. Two models for the structure of water. The diagram on the *left* shows the sharing of electrons between the oxygen and hydrogen atoms. The diagram on the *right* illustrates that water is a polar molecule because electrons are not equally shared. Electrons move closer to oxygen, creating a partial negative charge δ^-, whereas hydrogen has a partial positive charge δ^+. **b.** The partial charges allow hydrogen bonds (dotted lines) to form temporarily between water molecules.

Hydrogen Bonds

A **hydrogen bond** is the attraction of a slightly positive, covalently bonded hydrogen to a slightly negative atom in the vicinity. These usually occur between a hydrogen and either an oxygen or a nitrogen atom. A hydrogen bond is represented by a dotted line because it is relatively weak and can be broken rather easily.

In Figure 2.7*b*, you can see that each hydrogen atom, being slightly positive, bonds to the slightly negative oxygen atom of another water molecule.

Properties of Water

The first cell(s) evolved in water, and all living organisms are 70–90% water. Because of hydrogen bonding, water molecules cling together, and this association gives water its unique chemical properties. Without hydrogen bonding between molecules, water would freeze at −100°C and boil at −91°C, making most of the water on Earth steam and life unlikely. Hydrogen bonding is responsible for water being a liquid at temperatures typically found on the Earth's surface. It freezes at 0°C and boils at 100°C (see Appendix). These and other unique properties of water make it essential to the existence of life as we know it. When scientists examine other planets with the hope of finding life, they often first look for signs of water.

Water Has a High Heat Capacity A **calorie** is the amount of heat energy needed to raise the temperature of 1 gram (g) of water 1°C. In comparison, other covalently bonded liquids require input of only about half this amount of energy to rise 1°C in temperature. The many hydrogen bonds that link water molecules together help water absorb heat without a great change in temperature. Converting 1 g of the coldest liquid water to ice requires the loss of 80 calories of heat energy (Fig. 2.8*a*). Water holds on to its heat, and its temperature falls more slowly than that of other liquids. Because the temperature of water rises and falls slowly, we are better able to maintain our normal internal temperature and are protected from rapid temperature changes.

Water Has a High Heat of Evaporation When water boils, it evaporates—that is, it vaporizes into the environment. Converting 1 g of the hottest water to a gas requires an input of 540 calories of energy. Water has a high heat of evaporation, because hydrogen bonds must be broken before water boils. Water's high heat of vaporization gives our bodies an efficient way to release excess body heat in a hot environment. When we sweat or get splashed with water, body heat is used to vaporize the water, thus cooling us (Fig. 2.8*b*). Because of water's high heat of vaporization and its ability to hold on to its heat, temperatures along the coasts are moderate. During the summer, the ocean absorbs and stores solar heat, and during the winter, the ocean releases it slowly. In contrast, the interior regions of continents experience abrupt changes in temperatures.

Water Is a Solvent Due to its polarity, water facilitates chemical reactions, both outside and within living systems. As a *solvent*, it dissolves a great number of substances, especially those that, like water, are polar. A *solution* contains dissolved substances, which are then called *solutes*. When ionic compounds—for example, sodium chloride (NaCl)—are put into water, the negative ends of the water molecules are attracted to the sodium ions, and the positive ends of the water molecules are attracted to the chloride ions. This attraction causes the sodium ions and the chloride ions to separate, or dissociate, in water.

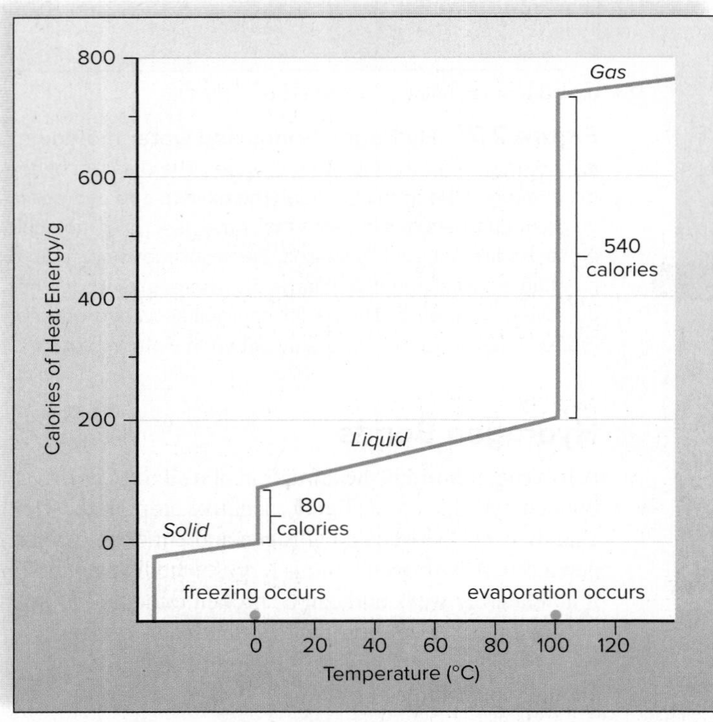

a. Calories lost when 1 g of liquid water freezes, and calories required when 1 g of liquid water evaporates.

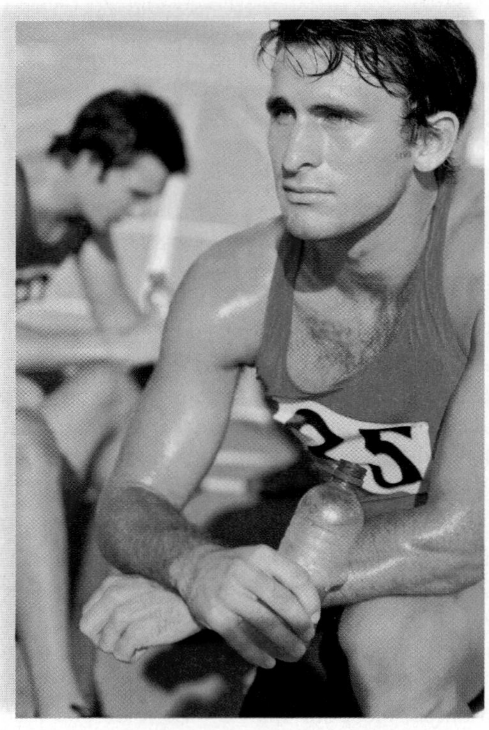

b. Water's high heat of evaporation is useful for cooling the body.

Figure 2.8 Temperature and water.

a. The high heat capacity of water resists a change from a liquid to a gaseous state. If water were a gas at a lower temperature, life could not exist.

b. Body heat vaporizes sweat. In this way, bodies cool when the temperature rises.

(b): Clerkenwell/Getty Images

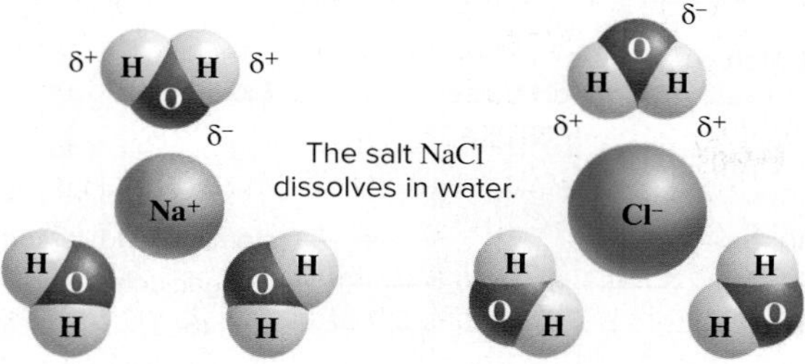

Molecules that can attract water are said to be **hydrophilic.** When ions and molecules disperse in water, they move about and collide, allowing reactions to occur. Molecules that cannot attract water are said to be **hydrophobic.** Hydrophilic molecules tend to attract other polar molecules. Similarly, hydrophobic substances usually associate with other **nonpolar** molecules. As we will see in Section 2.3, many oils, such as vegetable oils, are nonpolar, and therefore hydrophobic. This is why oil does not mix well with water.

Water Molecules Are Cohesive and Adhesive **Cohesion** refers to the ability of water molecules to cling to each other. This is due to the hydrogen bonds between water molecules. At any moment in time, a water molecule can form hydrogen bonds with at most four other water molecules. Because of cohesion, water exists as a liquid under the conditions of temperature and pressure present at the Earth's surface. The strong cohesion of water molecules is apparent, because water flows freely, yet water molecules do not separate from each other.

> **BIOLOGY IN YOUR LIFE**
>
> **The cohesion of water allows you to breathe**
>
> Every time you take a breath, you are experiencing the cohesive property of water. How? Because in your chest (thoracic) cavity, a thin film of water coats both the surface of the lungs and the inner chest wall. As our rib cage expands during inhalation, cohesion allows the lungs to stick to the chest wall, allowing them to open so we can breathe.

Adhesion refers to the ability of water molecules to cling to a surface. Because water is polar, it is attracted to other polar surfaces. Many animals, including humans, contain internal vessels in which water assists in the transport of nutrients and wastes, because the cohesion and adhesion of water allows blood to fill the tubular vessels of the cardiovascular system. For example, the liquid portion of our blood, which transports dissolved and suspended substances about the body, is 92% water. The water in our blood assists in the transport of nutrients and oxygen to our cells and in the removal of waste material from the cells.

Frozen Water Is Less Dense than Liquid Water As liquid water cools, the molecules come closer together. Water is most dense at 4°C, but the water molecules are still moving about (Fig. 2.9). At temperatures below 4°C, only vibrational movement occurs, and

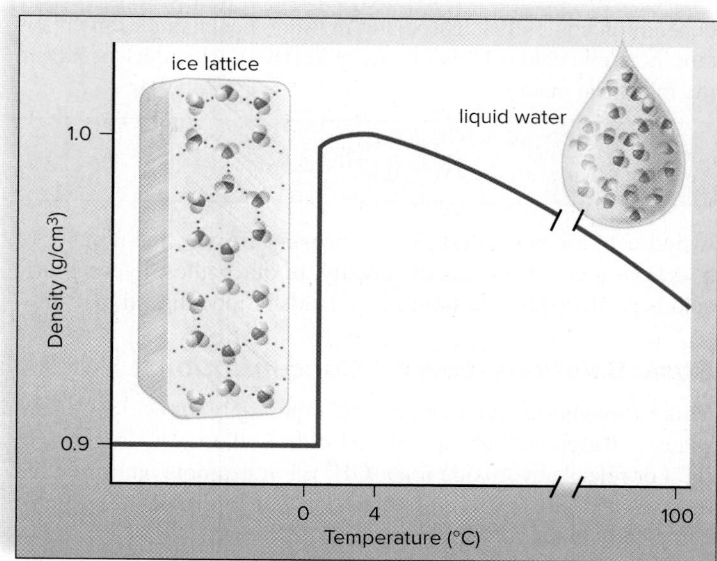

Figure 2.9 **Frozen water is less dense than liquid water.** Ice is less dense than water because the hydrogen bonds in ice are farther apart than the hydrogen bonds of liquid water.

hydrogen bonding becomes more rigid but also more open. This means that water expands as it reaches 0°C and freezes, which is why cans of soda burst when placed in a freezer and why frost heaves make northern roads bumpy in the winter. It also means that ice is less dense than liquid water, and therefore ice floats on liquid water.

This property of water plays an important role in many aquatic ecosystems. If ice did not float on water, it would sink to the bottom, and ponds, lakes, and perhaps even the ocean would freeze solid, making life impossible in the water, as well as on land. Instead, bodies of water always freeze from the top down. When a body of water freezes on the surface, the ice acts as an insulator to prevent the water below it from freezing. This allows aquatic organisms to survive the winter. As ice melts in the spring, it draws heat from the environment, helping prevent a sudden change in temperature that might be harmful to life.

Acids and Bases

When water molecules dissociate (break up), they release an equal number of hydrogen ions (H^+) and hydroxide ions (OH^-):

$$\underset{\text{water}}{H{-}O{-}H} \rightleftharpoons \underset{\text{hydrogen ion}}{H^+} + \underset{\text{hydroxide ion}}{OH^-}$$

Only a few water molecules at a time dissociate, and the actual number of H^+ or OH^- is 10^{-7} moles/liter. A **mole** is a unit of scientific measurement for atoms, ions, and molecules.

Acidic Solutions (High H^+ Concentrations)

Lemon juice, vinegar, tomatoes, and coffee are all acidic solutions. What do they have in common? **Acids** are substances that dissociate in water, releasing hydrogen ions (H^+). The acidity of a substance depends on how fully it dissociates in water. For example, an important inorganic acid is hydrochloric acid (HCl), which dissociates in the following manner:

$$HCl \longrightarrow H^+ + Cl^-$$

If hydrochloric acid is added to a beaker of water, the number of hydrogen ions (H^+) increases greatly. In our bodies, hydrochloric acid is produced by the stomach and aids in food digestion.

Basic Solutions (Low H^+ Concentrations)

Milk of magnesia and ammonia are commonly known basic substances. **Bases** are substances that either take up hydrogen ions (H^+) or release hydroxide ions (OH^-). For example, an important base is sodium hydroxide (NaOH), which dissociates almost completely in the following manner:

$$NaOH \longrightarrow Na^+ + OH^-$$

If sodium hydroxide is added to a beaker of water, the number of hydroxide ions increases. Sodium hydroxide (also called lye) is contained in many drain-cleaning products.

Some acids and bases are strong, meaning they donate a large number of H^+ or OH^- ions. You should not taste strong acids or bases, because they are destructive to cells. Many household cleansers, such as ammonia or bleach, have poison symbols and carry an important warning not to ingest the product.

pH Scale

The **pH scale** is used to indicate the acidity or basicity (alkalinity) of a solution. The pH scale (Fig. 2.10) ranges from 0 to 14. A pH of 7 represents a neutral state in which the hydrogen ion and hydroxide ion concentrations are equal. A pH below 7 is an acidic solution, because the hydrogen ion concentration is greater than the hydroxide concentration. A pH above 7 is basic, because the $[OH^-]$ is greater than the $[H^+]$. Further, as we move down the pH scale from pH 14 to pH 0, each unit is 10 times more acidic than the previous unit.[1] As we move up the scale from 0 to 14, each unit is 10 times more basic than the previous unit. Therefore, pH 5 is 100 times more acidic than pH 7 and 100 times more basic than pH 3.

The pH scale was devised to eliminate the use of cumbersome numbers. For example, the possible hydrogen ion concentrations of a solution are on the left of this listing and the pH is on the right:

$[H^+]$ (moles per liter)		pH
0.000001	$= 1 \times 10^{-6}$	6
0.0000001	$= 1 \times 10^{-7}$	7
0.00000001	$= 1 \times 10^{-8}$	8

[1]pH is defined as the negative log of the hydrogen ion concentration $[H^+]$.

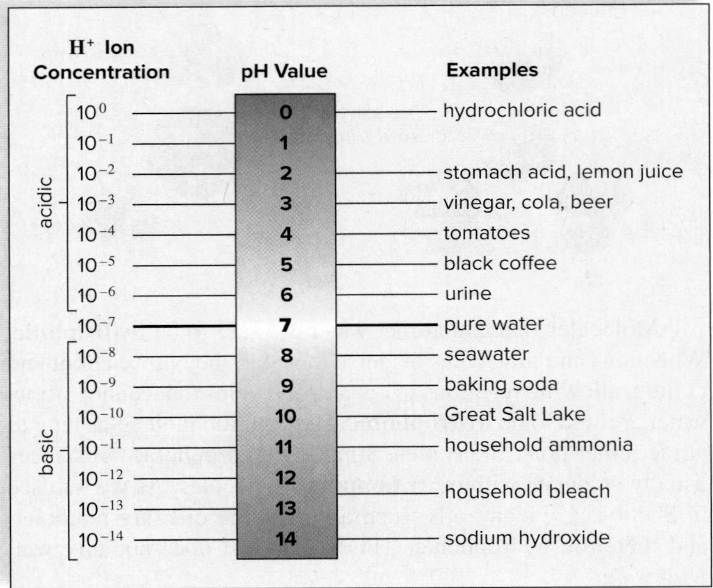

Figure 2.10 The pH scale.
The pH scale ranges from 0 to 14, with 0 being the most acidic and 14 being the most basic. A solution at pH 7 (neutral pH) has equal amounts of hydrogen ions (H^+) and hydroxide ions (OH^-). An acidic pH has more H^+ than OH^- and a basic pH has more OH^- than H^+. The pH of familiar solutions can be seen on the scale.

Buffers

From organisms to ecosystems, pH needs to be maintained within a narrow range to prevent negative consequences. Normally, pH stability is possible because the body and the environment have **buffers** to prevent pH changes. Buffers help keep the pH within normal limits, because they are chemicals or combinations of chemicals that take up excess hydrogen ions (H^+) or hydroxide ions (OH^-). For example, carbonic acid (H_2CO_3) is a weak acid that minimally dissociates and then re-forms in the following manner:

$$\underset{\text{carbonic acid}}{H_2CO_3} \underset{\text{dissociates}}{\overset{\text{re-forms}}{\rightleftarrows}} \underset{\text{hydrogen ion}}{H^+} + \underset{\text{bicarbonate ion}}{HCO_3^-}$$

The pH of our blood when we are healthy is always about 7.4—just slightly basic (alkaline). Blood always contains a combination of some carbonic acid and some bicarbonate ions. When hydrogen ions (H^+) are added to blood, the following reaction occurs:

$$H^+ + HCO_3^- \longrightarrow H_2CO_3$$

When hydroxide ions (OH^-) are added to blood, this reaction occurs:

$$OH^- + H_2CO_3 \longrightarrow HCO_3^- + H_2O$$

These reactions prevent any significant change in blood pH.

At the ecosystem level, a problem arises when precipitation in the form of rain or snow becomes so acidic that the environment runs out of natural buffers in the soil and water. Rain normally has a pH of about 5.7. However, in some regions, such as the Appalachian Mountains, rain with a pH of 2.6 has been recorded. Why is the pH of the rain so low? Rain becomes acidic because the burning of fossil fuels emits sulfur dioxides (SO_2) and nitrogen oxides (NO_2) into the atmosphere. They combine with water to produce sulfuric acid (H_2SO_4) and nitric acid (HNO_3). Acid deposition destroys statues and kills forests (see Section 24.3). It also leads to fish kills in lakes and streams.

CHECK YOUR PROGRESS 2.2

1. List the characteristics of water and explain how hydrogen bonds contribute to these properties.
2. Explain the difference between a solution with a pH of 5 and a solution with a pH of 3.
3. Contrast the hydrogen ion concentrations of acids and bases.

CONNECTING THE CONCEPTS

The properties of water play an important role in human physiology and the maintenance of homeostasis. For a few examples, refer to the following discussions:

Section 5.6 provides a description of how the body moves nutrients using the circulatory system.

Section 10.6 explores how the respiratory system helps regulate the pH of blood.

Section 11.4 examines how the kidneys maintain water and pH homeostasis in the body.

2.3 Molecules of Life

LEARNING OUTCOMES

Upon completion of this section, you should be able to

1. List the four classes of organic molecules found in cells.
2. Describe the processes by which the organic molecules are assembled and disassembled.

Four categories of **organic molecules**—carbohydrates, lipids, proteins, and nucleic acids—are unique to cells. In biology, "organic" doesn't refer to how food is grown; it refers to a molecule that contains carbon (C) and hydrogen (H) and is usually associated with living organisms.

Each type of organic molecule in cells is composed of subunits. When a cell constructs a **macromolecule,** a molecule that contains many subunits, it uses a **dehydration reaction,** a type of synthesis reaction. During a dehydration reaction, a —OH (hydroxyl group) and a —H (hydrogen atom), the equivalent of a water molecule, are removed as the molecule forms (Fig. 2.11*a*).

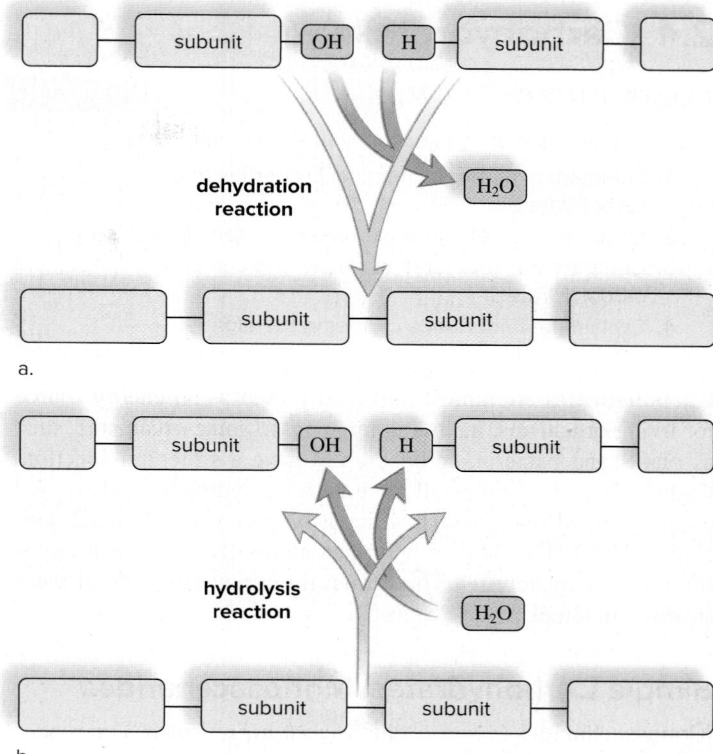

Figure 2.11 The breakdown and synthesis of macromolecules.
a. Subunits bond in a dehydration reaction. Water is given off and a macromolecule forms. **b.** In the reverse reaction, macromolecules are divided into subunits by hydrolysis.

The reaction is reminiscent of a train whose length is determined by how many boxcars it has hitched together. To break down macromolecules, the cell uses a **hydrolysis reaction** in which the components of water are added during the breaking of the bond between the molecules (Fig. 2.11*b*).

CHECK YOUR PROGRESS 2.3

1. Explain the difference between an organic and an inorganic molecule.
2. List the four classes of organic molecules.
3. Distinguish between a dehydration reaction and a hydrolysis reaction.

CONNECTING THE CONCEPTS

Organic nutrients not only play an important role in the building of cells but also serve as sources of energy. For more information, refer to the following discussions:

Section 3.6 explains how the body uses organic nutrients as energy sources.

Sections 9.1 to **9.4** explore how the digestive system processes organic nutrients and prepares them for transport.

2.4 Carbohydrates

LEARNING OUTCOMES

Upon completion of this section, you should be able to

1. Summarize the basic chemical properties of a carbohydrate.
2. State the roles of carbohydrates in human physiology.
3. Compare the structures of simple and complex carbohydrates.
4. Explain the importance of fiber in the diet.

Carbohydrates are almost universally used as an energy source for living organisms, including humans. In some organisms, such as plants and bacteria, carbohydrates have a structural function. Carbohydrate molecules all have carbon, hydrogen, and oxygen atoms grouped H—C—OH, which is why they are often abbreviated as CHO. The ratio of hydrogen atoms (H) to oxygen atoms (O) is approximately 2:1. This ratio is the same as the ratio in water (*hydros-* in Greek means "water").

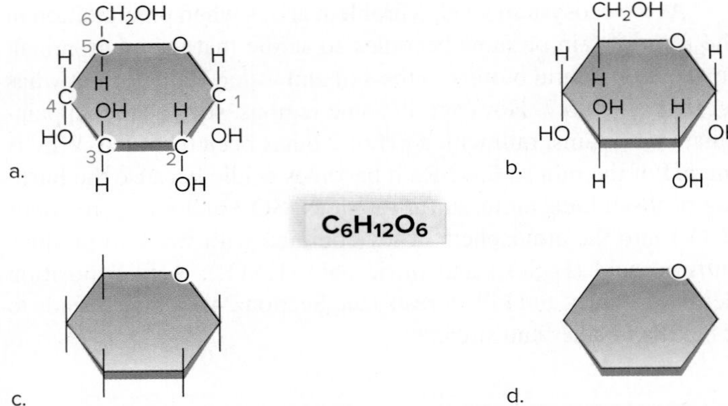

Figure 2.12 Glucose.
Glucose is the common form of monosaccharide that provides energy for cells. Each of these structural formulas is glucose. **a.** The carbon skeleton and all attached groups are shown. **b.** The carbon skeleton is omitted. **c.** The carbon skeleton and attached groups are omitted. **d.** Only the ring shape, which includes one oxygen atom, remains.

Simple Carbohydrates: Monosaccharides

Monosaccharides (*mono-,* "one"; *saccharide,* "sugar") consist of only a single sugar molecule and are commonly called simple sugars. A monosaccharide can have a carbon backbone of three to seven carbons. For example, pentoses are monosaccharides with five carbons, and hexoses are monosaccharides with six carbons. The most common monosaccharide, and the one our bodies use as an immediate source of energy, is the hexose **glucose.** There are several different ways a glucose molecule may be presented in a diagram (see Fig. 2.12).

Other common hexoses are *fructose,* found in fruits, and *galactose,* which is found in milk. Monosaccharides are the monomers used to build longer carbohydrate chains.

Disaccharides

A **disaccharide** (*di-,* "two"; *saccharide,* "sugar") is made by joining only two monosaccharides together by a dehydration reaction. *Maltose* is a disaccharide formed by a dehydration reaction between two glucose molecules (Fig. 2.13). When our hydrolytic digestive juices break down maltose, the result is two glucose molecules.

When glucose and fructose join, the disaccharide *sucrose* forms. Sucrose, ordinarily derived from sugarcane and sugar beets, is commonly known as table sugar. You may also have heard of *lactose,* a disaccharide found in milk. Lactose is glucose combined with galactose. Some people are lactose intolerant because they cannot break down lactose. This leads to unpleasant gastrointestinal symptoms when they consume dairy products.

Complex Carbohydrates: Polysaccharides

Long polymers such as starch, glycogen, and cellulose are **polysaccharides** (*poly-,* "many") that contain long chains of glucose subunits. Due to their length, they are sometimes referred to as complex carbohydrates.

The polysaccharides starch and glycogen are long polymers of glucose found in plants and animals, respectively. These chains may vary in length, but may contain several thousand glucose

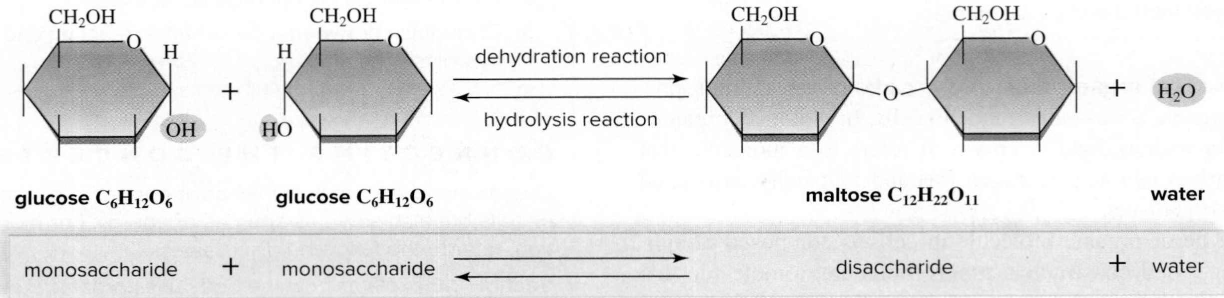

Figure 2.13 The synthesis and breakdown of a disaccharide.
Maltose, a disaccharide, is formed by a dehydration reaction between two glucose molecules. The breakdown of maltose occurs following a hydrolysis reaction and the addition of water.

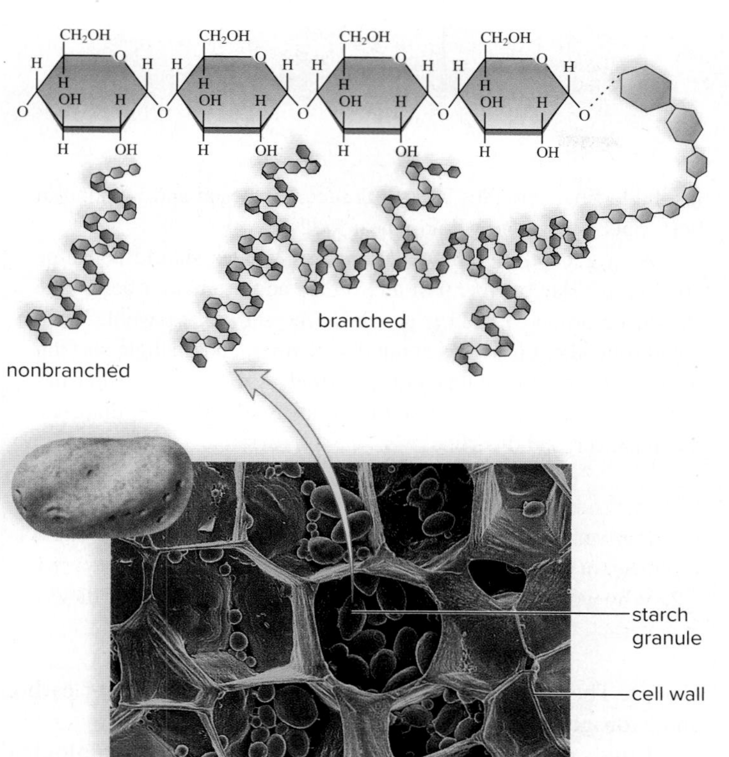

Figure 2.14 **Starch is a plant complex carbohydrate.** Starch has straight chains of glucose molecules. Some chains are also branched, as indicated. The electron micrograph shows starch granules in potato cells.
(photo): Dr. Jeremy Burgess/Science Source

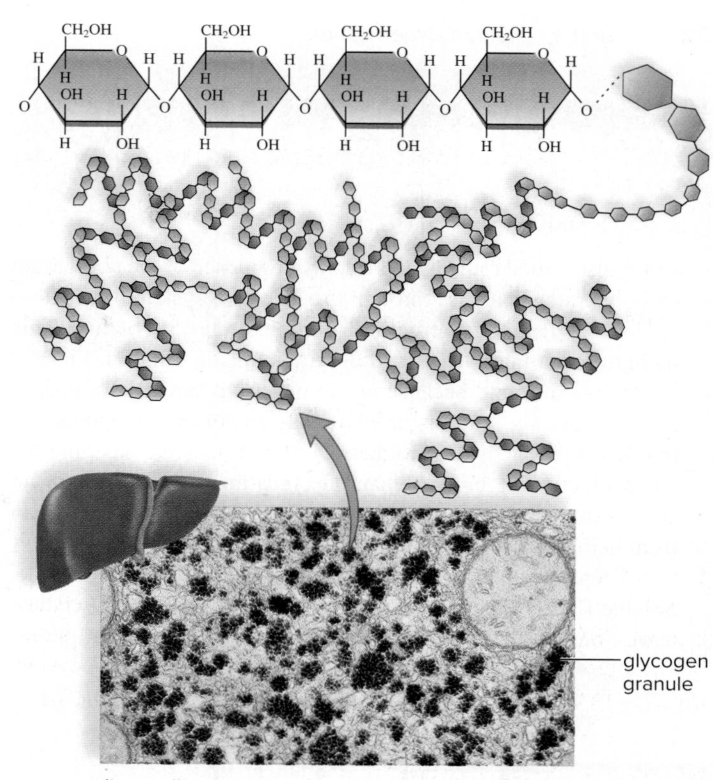

Figure 2.15 **Glycogen is an animal complex carbohydrate.** Glycogen is more branched than starch. The electron micrograph shows glycogen granules in liver cells.
(photo): Don W. Fawcett/Science Source

molecules. Both starch and glycogen are used to store glucose to meet the energy needs of the cell.

Plants store a large amount of glucose in the form of **starch.** Starch may have either a branched or unbranched structure (Fig. 2.14).

Animals store a large amount of glucose in the form of **glycogen.** In our bodies and those of other vertebrates, liver cells contain granules, where glycogen is stored until needed. The storage and release of glucose from liver cells are controlled by hormones. After we eat, the release of the hormone insulin from the pancreas promotes the storage of glucose as glycogen. Notice in Figure 2.15 that glycogen is even more branched than starch.

Because starches are the storage form of carbohydrates in plants, we typically find them in roots (such as potatoes) and in seeds, such as wheat.

The polysaccharide **cellulose,** commonly called fiber, is found in plant cell walls. In cellulose, the glucose units are joined by a slightly different type of linkage than that in starch or glycogen (Fig. 2.16). Though this might seem to be a technicality, it is important, because we are unable to digest foods containing this type of linkage; therefore, cellulose largely passes through our digestive tract as fiber, or roughage. The Health feature "Fiber in the Diet" examines the health benefits of fiber.

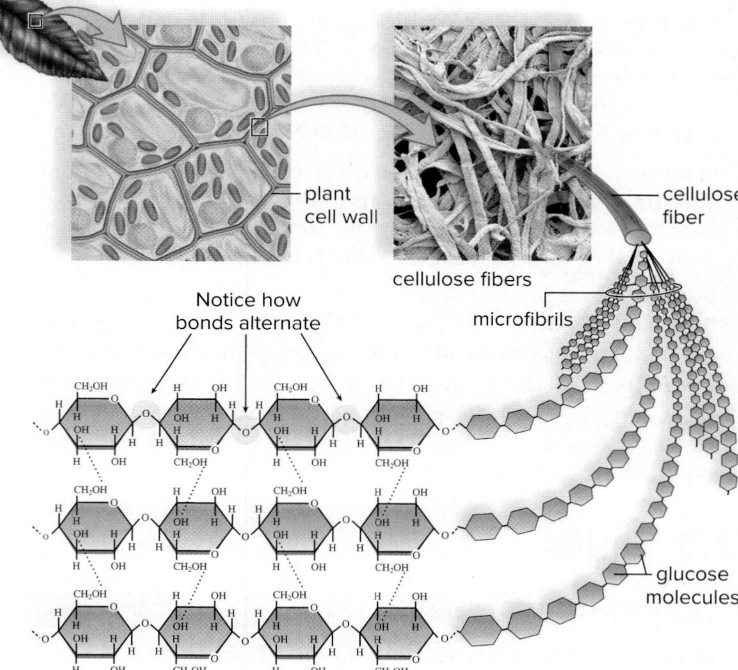

Figure 2.16 **Fiber is a plant complex carbohydrate.** Unlike starch, fiber does not supply us with energy. This is because of the arrangements of the chemical bonds in the fiber chains. However, fiber is an important component of our diet and helps keep our digestive system healthy.
(photo): Scimat/Science Source

BIOLOGY TODAY ▶ Health

Fiber in the Diet

Fiber, also called roughage, is mainly composed of the undigested carbohydrates that pass through the digestive system. Most fiber is derived from the structural carbohydrates of plants. This includes such material as cellulose, pectins, and lignin. Fiber is not truly a nutrient, because we do not use it directly for energy or cell building, but it is an extremely important component of our diet. Fiber adds bulk to material in the intestine, keeping the colon functioning normally, and it binds many types of harmful chemicals in the diet, including cholesterol, and prevents them from being absorbed.

There are two basic types of fiber—insoluble and soluble. Soluble fiber dissolves in water and acts in the binding of cholesterol. Soluble fiber is found in many fruits, as well as oat grains. Insoluble fiber provides bulk to the fecal material and is found in bran, nuts, seeds, and whole-wheat foods.

As a general recommendation, adult males should consume 30–38 g per day of fiber. For an average adult female, fiber intake should be around 21–25 g per day. One serving of whole-grain bread (one slice) provides about 3 g of fiber, and a single serving of beans (½ cup) contains 4–5 g of fiber. A diet high in fiber has been shown to reduce the risk of cardiovascular disease, diabetes, colon cancer, and diverticulosis.

Questions to Consider

1. How might a diet that is high in fiber also prevent a person from overeating?
2. Why would you want to vary the types of fiber in your diet?

CHECK YOUR PROGRESS 2.4

1. Explain the differences between a monosaccharide, a disaccharide, and a polysaccharide, and give an example of each.
2. Describe the difference in structure between a simple carbohydrate and a complex carbohydrate.
3. Explain why some complex carbohydrates can be used for energy but others cannot.

CONNECTING THE CONCEPTS

In humans, carbohydrates primarily serve as energy molecules, although fiber does act to ensure the health of the digestive system. For more information on the interaction of the human body with carbohydrates, refer to the following discussions:

Section 3.6 explores the use of carbohydrates for energy at the cellular level.

Section 9.3 examines how the digestive system processes carbohydrates.

Section 9.6 explains how fiber promotes the health of the digestive system.

2.5 Lipids

LEARNING OUTCOMES

Upon completion of this section, you should be able to

1. Compare the structures of fats, phospholipids, and steroids.
2. State the function of each class of lipids.

Lipids are diverse in structure and function, but they have a common characteristic: They do not dissolve in water. Their low solubility in water is due to an absence of hydrophilic polar groups. They contain little oxygen and consist mostly of carbon and hydrogen atoms.

Lipids contain more energy per gram than other biological molecules; therefore, fats in animals and oils in plants function well as energy storage molecules. Others (phospholipids) form a membrane so that the cell is separated from its environment and has inner compartments as well. Steroids are a large class of lipids that includes, among other molecules, the sex hormones.

Triglycerides: Fats and Oils

The most familiar lipids are called **triglycerides.** You may commonly know these as fats and oils. **Fats,** usually of animal origin (e.g., lard and butter), are solid at room temperature. **Oils,** usually of plant origin (e.g., corn oil and soybean oil), are liquid at room temperature. The term *triglyceride* refers to the three-part structure of the molecule. Triglycerides are formed when one glycerol molecule reacts with three fatty acid molecules (Fig. 2.17) using a dehydration synthesis reaction.

Triglycerides have several functions in the body. They are used for long-term energy storage, insulate against heat loss, and form a protective cushion around major organs.

Because triglycerides are hydrophobic, they do not readily interact with the water environment of our cells and bodies. Emulsifiers can cause triglycerides to mix with water. They contain molecules with a nonpolar end and a polar end. The molecules position themselves about an oil droplet so their polar ends project outward. The droplet *disperses* in water, which means that **emulsification** has occurred. In our bodies, emulsification occurs during the digestion of fatty foods. To assist in the breakdown of triglycerides, the liver manufactures bile. Bile is stored by the gallbladder and released into the small intestine following a meal. Bile emulsifies the triglycerides in the food, allowing greater access by the digestive enzymes.

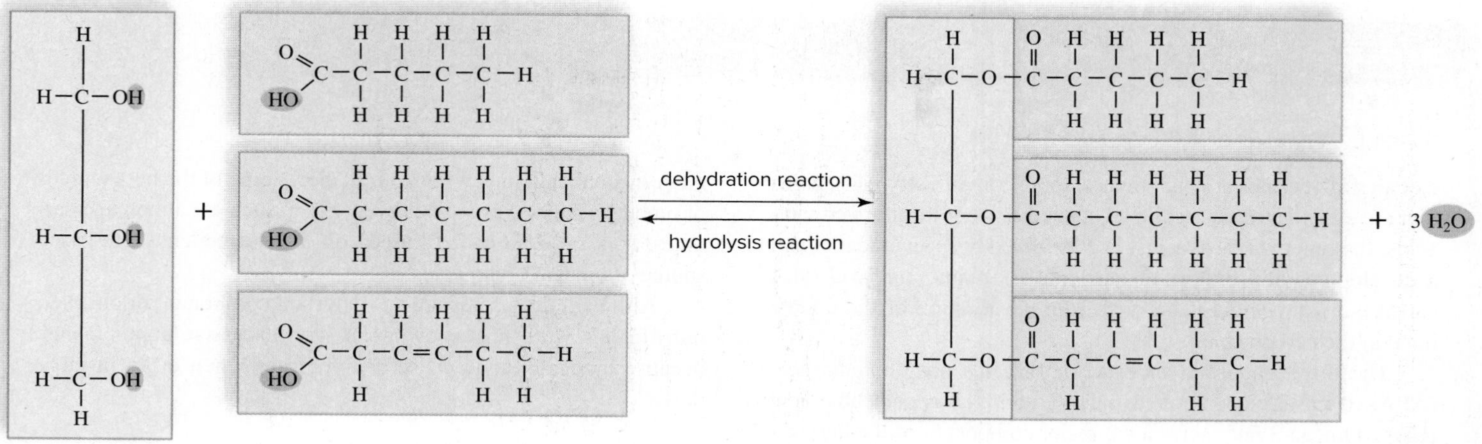

glycerol + 3 fatty acids ⇌ (dehydration reaction / hydrolysis reaction) fat molecule + 3 H_2O (3 water molecules)

Figure 2.17 **Structure of a triglyceride.**
Triglycerides are formed when three fatty acids combine with glycerol by dehydration synthesis reactions. The reverse reaction starts the digestion of fat; hydrolysis introduces water, and fatty acid–glycerol bonds are broken.

Waxes are molecules made up of one fatty acid combined with another single organic molecule, usually an alcohol (chemists refer to "alcohols" as an entire group of molecules that includes drinking alcohol and rubbing alcohol). Waxes prevent loss of moisture from body surfaces. Cerumen, or ear wax, is a very thick wax produced by glands lining the outer ear canal (see Section 15.5). It protects the ear canal from irritation and infection by trapping particles, bacteria, and viruses. When ear wax is completely washed away by swimming or diving, the result is a painful "swimmer's ear."

Saturated, Unsaturated, and Trans Fatty Acids

A **fatty acid** is a carbon–hydrogen chain that ends with the acidic group —COOH (Fig. 2.17, *top*). Most of the fatty acids in cells contain 16 or 18 carbon atoms per molecule, although smaller ones with fewer carbons are also known. Fatty acids are either saturated or unsaturated. **Saturated fatty acids** have no double bonds between the carbon atoms. The chain is saturated, so to speak, with all the hydrogens it can hold. **Unsaturated fatty acids** have double bonds in the carbon chain wherever the number of hydrogens is less than two per carbon (Fig. 2.18).

In general, oils, present in cooking oils and bottle margarines, are liquids at room temperature because the presence of a double bond creates a bend in the fatty acid chain (Fig. 2.18). Such kinks prevent close packing between the hydrocarbon chains and account for the fluidity of oils. On the other hand, butter, which contains saturated fatty acids and no double bonds, is a solid at room temperature.

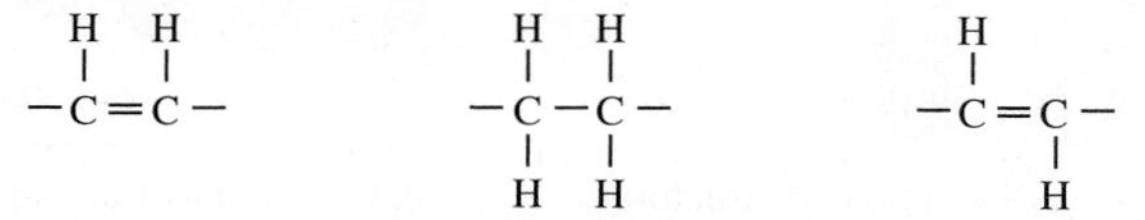

Unsaturated fats (oils) — **Saturated fats** (butter) — **Unsaturated trans fats** (hydrogenated oils)

Figure 2.18 **Comparison of fat saturation.**
Saturated fats have no double bonds between carbons in the fatty acid. Unsaturated fats have one or more double bonds in the fatty acid. For a fat to be a trans fat, the hydrogens need to be on opposite sides of the carbon–carbon double bond.

Saturated fats, in particular, contribute to the disease *atherosclerosis.* Atherosclerosis is caused by the formation of lesions, or *atherosclerotic plaques,* on the inside of blood vessels. The plaques narrow the blood vessel diameter, choking off blood and oxygen supply to tissues. Atherosclerosis is the primary cause of cardiovascular disease (heart attack and stroke) in the United States. Even more harmful than naturally occurring saturated fats are the **trans fats** (*trans-* in Latin means "across") (Fig. 2.18) created artificially from vegetable oils. Trans fats may be partially hydrogenated to make them semisolid. Complete hydrogenation of oils causes all double bonds to become saturated. Partial hydrogenation does not saturate all bonds. It reconfigures some double bonds, but some of the hydrogen atoms end up on different sides of the chain. This configuration makes these bonds difficult to break, allowing these trans fats to accumulate in the circulatory system. Trans fats were traditionally found in foods such as shortenings, solid margarines, and many processed foods (snack foods, baked goods, and fried foods). However, the level of these in processed foods has been decreasing over the past few years as we have begun to understand the negative health aspects of trans fats.

Current dietary guidelines from the American Heart Association (AHA) advise replacing trans fats with unsaturated oils. In particular, monounsaturated oils (such as olive oil, with one double bond in the carbon chain) are recommended. Polyunsaturated oils (many double bonds in the carbon chain), such as corn oil, canola oil, and safflower oil, also fit in the AHA guidelines.

Dietary Fat

For good health, the diet should include some fat; however, for the reasons stated, the first thing to do when looking at a nutrition label is to check the total amount of fat per serving. Historically,

BIOLOGY TODAY ▶ **Health**

The Omega-3 Fatty Acids

Not all triglycerides are bad. In fact, some contain fatty acid chains that are essential to our health. A special class of unsaturated fatty acids, the omega-3 fatty acids, is considered both an essential and a developmentally important nutrient. The name *omega-3* (also called *n-3 fatty acids*) is derived from the location of the double bond in the carbon chain.

The three important omega-3 fatty acids are linolenic acid (ALA), docosahexaenoic acid (DHA), and eicosapentaenoic acid (EPA). Omega-3 fatty acids are a major component of the fatty acids in the brain, and adequate amounts of them appear to be important in children and young adults. A diet rich in these fatty acids also offers protection against cardiovascular disease; research is ongoing with regard to other health benefits. DHA may also reduce the risk of Alzheimer's disease. DHA and EPA can be manufactured from ALA in small amounts within our bodies. Some of the best sources of omega-3 fatty acids are cold-water fish, such as salmon and sardines. Flax oil, also called linseed oil, is an excellent plant-based source of omega-3 fatty acids.

Although fatty acids are an important component of our diet, nutritionists warn not to overdo it with excessive supplements, because omega-3s may cause health issues when taken in large doses.

Questions to Consider

1. Why might a diet high in omega-3 fatty acids also be low in cholesterol?
2. Why would omega-3 fatty acids reduce the risk of cardiovascular disease?

the total recommended amount of fat in a 2,000-calorie diet was set at 65 grams. However, in 2015 these upper limits on fats in the diet were dropped as research indicated that what was important was not the total amount of fat in the diet but instead the types of fat in the diet (see the Health feature "The Omega-3 Fatty Acids"). Because of this, consumers will start to see changes in their food labels and recommended dietary intakes over the next few years (see Section 9.6).

Phospholipids

Phospholipids have a phosphate group (Fig. 2.19). They are constructed like fats, except that in place of the third fatty acid, there is a phosphate group or a grouping that contains both phosphate and nitrogen. These molecules are not electrically neutral, as are fats, because the phosphate and nitrogen-containing groups are ionized. They form the polar (hydrophilic) head of the molecule, and the rest of the molecule becomes the nonpolar (hydrophobic) tails. (Remember that *hydrophilic* means "water-loving" and *hydrophobic* is "water-fearing.")

Phospholipids are the primary components of the plasma membranes in cells. In a water environment, they spontaneously form a *bilayer* (a sort of molecular "sandwich") in which the hydrophilic heads (the sandwich "bread") face outward toward watery solutions, and the tails (the sandwich "filling") form the hydrophobic interior (Fig. 2.19*b*).

Steroids

Steroids are lipids that have an entirely different structure from those of fats. Steroid molecules have a backbone of four fused carbon rings. Each one differs primarily in the functional groups attached to the rings. One example of a steroid is cholesterol. Cholesterol is a component of an animal cell's plasma membrane and is the precursor of several other steroids, such as the sex hormones estrogen and testosterone. The liver usually makes all the cholesterol the body needs. While there are no "good" and "bad"

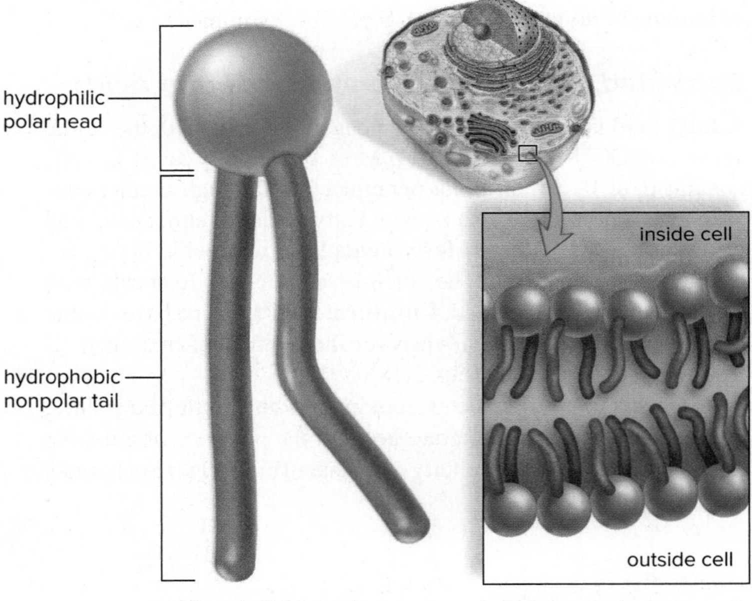

Figure 2.19 Structure of a phospholipid.
a. Phospholipids are structured like fats with one fatty acid replaced by a polar phosphate group. Therefore, the head is hydrophilic polar, whereas the tails are hydrophobic nonpolar. **b.** This causes the molecules to configure themselves in a "sandwich" arrangement when exposed to water: with polar phosphate groups on the outside of the layer, and nonpolar lipid tails on the inside of the layer.

BIOLOGY TODAY ▶ Health

Good and Bad Cholesterol

Blood tests to analyze your lipid profile are part of many annual medical exams. Suppose after your annual exam that your doctor tells you your total cholesterol is 210, your HDL value is low (34), and your LDL value is high (110). You know you need to get your total cholesterol below 200 (the threshold of a healthy diet), but like most people, you have no idea what the other two numbers mean. Then, you remember that LDL is commonly referred to as "bad" cholesterol, and HDL is called "good" cholesterol. In actuality, these molecules are not forms of cholesterol; they are types of proteins. The lipoproteins in the body serve as a form of fat and cholesterol carrier, moving these nutrients around as needed. An LDL is a lipoprotein that is full of triglycerides and cholesterol, whereas an HDL is basically empty. Thus, a high LDL value indicates your carriers are usually full, meaning your diet must be providing too many of these nutrients.

In the body, LDL lipoproteins are known to deposit some of their cholesterol along the smooth muscle tissues of the arteries, leading to the formation of atherosclerotic plaques (see Section 5.7). On the other hand, HDL lipoproteins tend to carry their cholesterol contents to the liver, where they are broken down and removed from the blood.

After additional research, you find out that other factors, such as your daily intake of unrefined carbohydrates, the amount of dietary fiber, daily exercise, and even genetics, can play a role in regulating "good" and "bad" levels of these lipoproteins. Furthermore, the numbers the doctor gave you were actually concentrations of these molecules in your blood (in milligrams per deciliter, or mg/dl). In today's world, it is important we all understand the terminology associated with our own medical history.

Questions to Consider

1. Why might physicians resort to calling HDLs and LDLs "good" and "bad"?
2. How might genetics play a role in the ratio of these lipoproteins?

forms of cholesterol (see the Health feature "Good and Bad Cholesterol"), dietary sources should be restricted because elevated levels of cholesterol, saturated fats, and trans fats are linked to atherosclerosis.

The male sex hormone testosterone is formed primarily in the testes; the female sex hormone estrogen is formed primarily in the ovaries. Testosterone and estrogen differ only by the functional groups attached to the same carbon backbone. However, they have a profound effect on the body and the sexuality of humans and other animals (Fig. 2.20). The taking of anabolic steroids, usually to build muscle strength, is illegal because the side effects are harmful to the body.

CHECK YOUR PROGRESS 2.5

1. State the function of triglycerides in the human body.
2. List the uses of phospholipids and steroids in the body.
3. Summarize why not all lipids should be avoided in the diet.

CONNECTING THE CONCEPTS

Fats and lipids have a variety of uses in the human body. To see how they interact with the systems of the body, refer to the following discussions:

Section 5.7 provides more information on atherosclerosis.

Section 9.3 explores the digestion and absorption of fats.

Section 16.1 examines how some lipids act as hormones in the body.

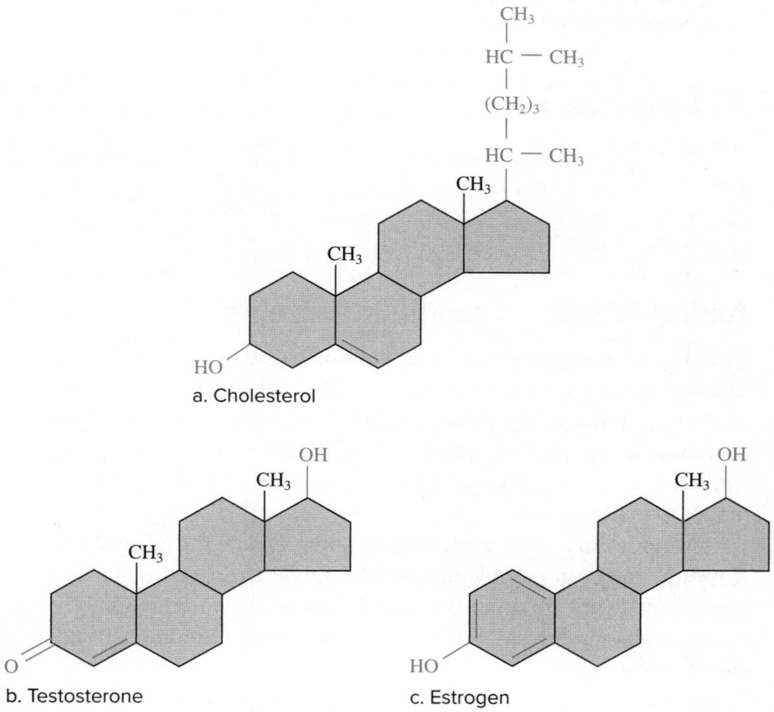

a. Cholesterol

b. Testosterone

c. Estrogen

Figure 2.20 **Examples of steroids.**
a. All steroids are made from cholesterol and have four carbon rings. Compare the structures of (**b**) testosterone and (**c**) estrogen, and notice the slight changes in their attached groups (shown in blue).

2.6 Proteins

LEARNING OUTCOMES

Upon completion of this section, you should be able to

1. Describe the structure of an amino acid.
2. Explain how amino acids are combined to form proteins.
3. Summarize the four levels of protein structure.

Proteins are of primary importance in the structure and function of cells. Some of their many functions in humans include:

- *Support:* Some proteins are structural proteins. Keratin, for example, makes up hair and nails. Collagen lends support to ligaments, tendons, and skin.
- *Enzymes:* Enzymes bring reactants together and thereby speed chemical reactions in cells. They are specific for one particular type of reaction and function only at body temperature.
- *Transport:* Channel and carrier proteins in the plasma membrane allow substances to enter and exit cells. Some other proteins transport molecules in the blood of animals; hemoglobin in red blood cells is a complex protein that transports oxygen.
- *Defense:* Antibodies are proteins. They combine with foreign substances, called antigens. In this way, they prevent antigens from destroying cells and upsetting homeostasis.
- *Hormones:* Hormones are regulatory proteins. They serve as intercellular messengers that influence the metabolism of cells. The hormone insulin regulates the content of glucose in the blood and in cells. The presence of growth hormone determines the height of an individual.
- *Motion:* The contractile proteins actin and myosin allow parts of cells to move and cause muscles to contract. Muscle contraction facilitates the movement of animals from place to place.

The structures and functions of vertebrate cells and tissues differ according to the type of proteins they contain. For example, muscle cells contain actin and myosin, red blood cells contain hemoglobin, and support tissues contain collagen.

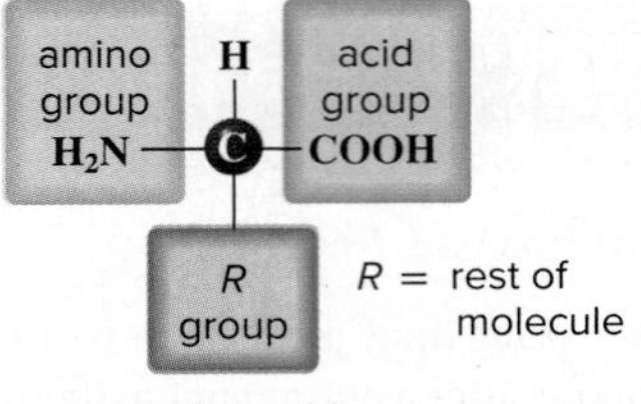

Amino acid

a. Structure of an amino acid

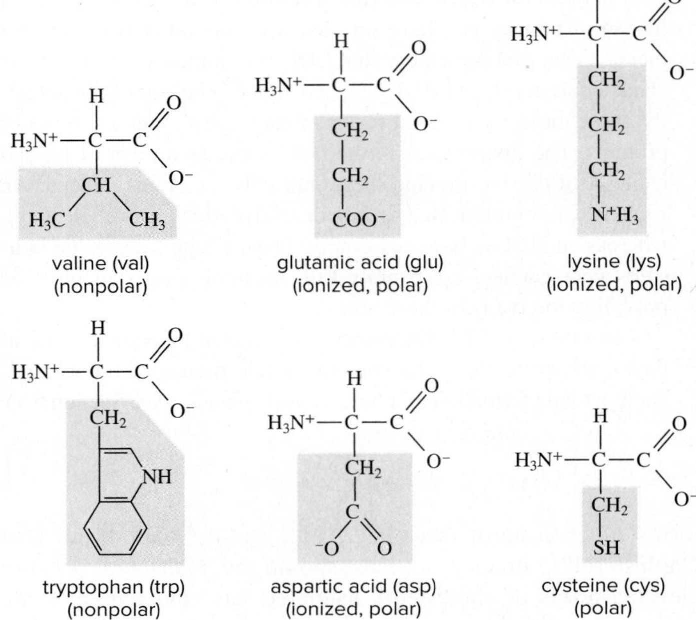

b. Examples of amino acids

Figure 2.21 The structure of amino acids.
a. Amino acids all have an amine group (H_3N^+), an acid group (COO^-), and an *R* group attached to the central carbon atom. **b.** A sample of some of the 20 amino acids used by humans. Notice that the *R* groups (screened in blue) are all different. Some *R* groups are nonpolar and hydrophobic; others are polar and hydrophilic. Still others are polar and charged (ionized).

Amino Acids: Subunits of Proteins

Proteins are macromolecules with **amino acid** subunits (Fig. 2.21*a*). The central carbon atom in an amino acid bonds to a hydrogen atom and to three other groups of atoms. The name *amino acid* is appropriate because one of these groups is an —NH_2 (amino group) and another is a —COOH (carboxyl group, an acid). The third group is the *R* group for an amino acid.

Amino acids differ according to their particular *R* group. The *R* groups range in complexity from a single hydrogen atom to a complicated ring compound. Some *R* groups are polar, while others are nonpolar. Several amino acids commonly found in cells are shown in Figure 2.21*b*.

Peptides

Figure 2.22 shows how two amino acids join by a dehydration reaction between the carboxyl group of one and the amino group of another. The covalent bond between two amino acids is called a **peptide bond.** When three or more amino acids are linked by peptide bonds, the chain that results is called a **polypeptide.**

The atoms associated with the peptide bond share the electrons unevenly, because oxygen attracts electrons more than nitrogen. Therefore, the hydrogen attached to the nitrogen has a slightly positive charge (δ^+), whereas the oxygen has a slightly negative charge (δ^-):

$O^{\delta-}$ — peptide bond
—C—N—
$H^{\delta+}$

δ^- = slightly negative
δ^+ = slightly positive

Shape of Proteins

The function of a protein is directly associated with its structure. Changes in this shape may have an impact on the effectiveness of

amino group | acidic group | peptide bond

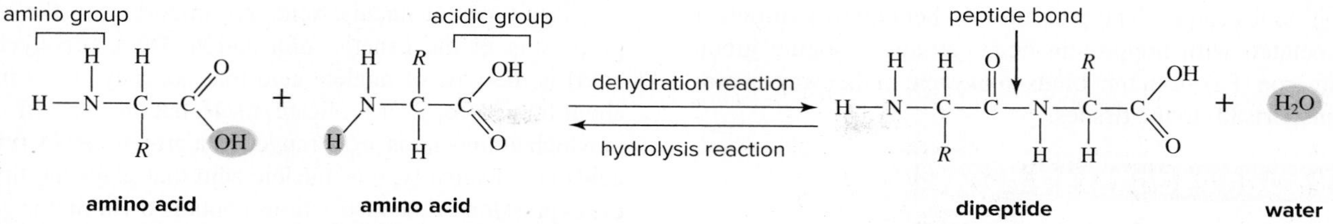

amino acid + amino acid ⇌ dipeptide + water (H_2O)

dehydration reaction →
← hydrolysis reaction

Figure 2.22 **Synthesis and breakdown of a protein.**
Amino acids join by peptide bonds using a dehydration reaction, and a water molecule is given off. In the reverse reaction, peptide bonds are broken by hydrolysis, and a water molecule is produced.

a protein to perform its function. For example, when proteins are exposed to extremes in heat and pH, they undergo an irreversible change in shape called **denaturation.** For example, you may be aware that the addition of vinegar (an acid) to milk causes curdling. This is due to a change in pH. Similarly, heating causes coagulation of egg whites, which contain a protein called albumin. Denaturation occurs because the normal bonding between the *R* groups has been disturbed. Once a protein loses its normal shape, it is no longer able to perform its usual function. Researchers recognize that a change in protein shape is responsible for diseases such as Alzheimer's disease and Creutzfeldt–Jakob disease (the human form of mad cow disease).

Levels of Protein Organization

The structure of a protein has at least three levels of organization, but can have four levels (Fig. 2.23). The first level, called the *primary structure,* is the linear sequence of the amino acids joined by peptide bonds. Each particular polypeptide has its own sequence of amino acids. This sequence of amino acids is determined by the information contained within the DNA of each organism (see Section 2.7).

The *secondary structure* of a protein comes about when the polypeptide takes on a certain orientation in space. Hydrogen bonding is possible between the C═O of one amino acid and the N—H of another amino acid in a polypeptide. Coiling of the chain results in an α (alpha) helix, or a right-handed spiral, and folding of the chain results in a β (beta) pleated sheet. Hydrogen bonding between peptide bonds holds the shape in place.

The *tertiary structure* of a protein is its final, three-dimensional shape. It is at this level of organization that many proteins establish their function. For example, in most enzymes, the hydrophobic portions are packed on the inside, while the hydrophilic portions are on the outside, where they can make contact with water. The tertiary structure of the enzymes determines the types of molecules with which they will interact. The tertiary shape of a polypeptide is maintained by various types of bonding between the *R* groups: covalent, ionic, and hydrogen bonding all occur. Environmental factors, such as pH and temperature, often disrupt the tertiary structure, causing the protein to denature.

Some proteins have only one polypeptide; others have more than one polypeptide, each with its own primary, secondary, and tertiary structures. These separate polypeptides are arranged to give these proteins a fourth level of structure, termed the *quaternary structure.* Many enzymes have a quaternary structure, as does

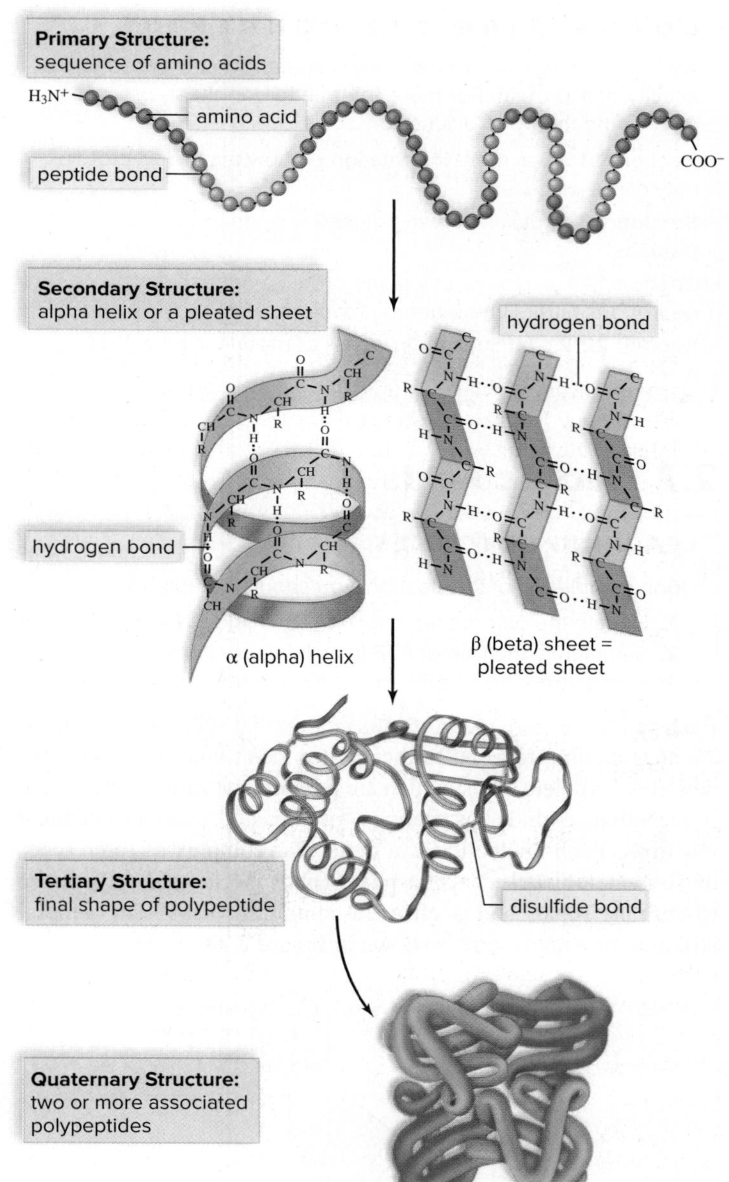

Figure 2.23 **Levels of protein structure.**
The structures of proteins can differ significantly. Primary structure, the sequence of amino acids, determines secondary and tertiary structure. Quaternary structure is created by assembling smaller proteins into a large structure.

the hemoglobin protein. The structure of hemoglobin allows it to be associated with nonprotein heme groups. A heme group contains an iron (Fe) atom that binds to oxygen; in that way, hemoglobin transports O_2 to the tissues.

CHECK YOUR PROGRESS 2.6

1. Describe the major functions of proteins.
2. Explain the structure of an amino acid.
3. List the four levels of protein structure and briefly explain the factors that contribute to each level.

CONNECTING THE CONCEPTS

Almost every function of the body is somehow connected to the activity of a protein. For more information on these processes, refer to the following discussions:

Section 8.1 gives more information on how misfolded proteins may cause disease.

Section 9.3 explains how the digestive system processes proteins.

Section 14.1 explores how some proteins are used as neurotransmitters in the nervous system.

Section 22.2 examines the process of protein synthesis in a cell.

2.7 Nucleic Acids

LEARNING OUTCOMES

Upon completion of this section, you should be able to

1. Explain the differences between RNA and DNA.
2. Summarize the role of ATP in cellular reactions.

Each cell has a storehouse of information that specifies how a cell should function, respond to the environment, and divide to make new cells. **Nucleic acids,** which are polymers of **nucleotides,** store information, include instructions for life, and conduct chemical reactions. Each nucleotide is a molecular complex of three types of subunit molecules: a phosphate (phosphoric acid), a pentose (5-carbon) sugar, and a nitrogen-containing base. The general structure of a nucleotide is shown in Figure 2.24.

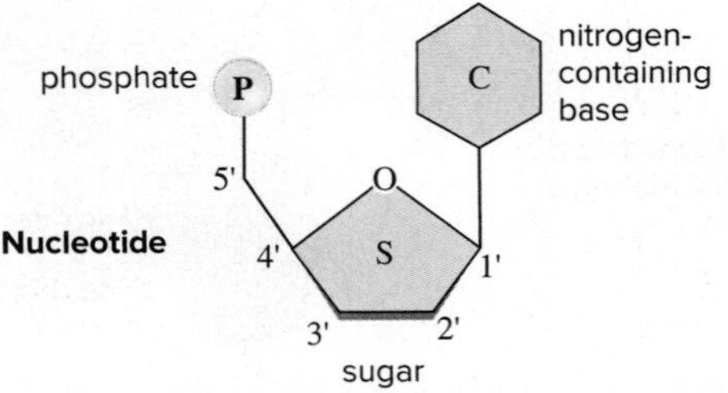

Figure 2.24 Structure of a nucleotide.
Nucleotides contain a nitrogenous base, a 5-carbon sugar, and a phosphate group. The numbers indicate the locations of the carbon atoms in the sugar group.

Two types of nucleic acids are important in the storage and processing of the genetic information. **DNA (deoxyribonucleic acid)** is the type of nucleic acid that not only stores information about how to copy, or replicate, itself, but also specifies the order in which amino acids are arranged in a protein. **RNA (ribonucleic acid)** is a diverse type of nucleic acid that plays multiple roles in the expression of the instructions contained within the genetic material. We will explore the various forms of RNA and their roles in gene expression in Section 22.2.

Not all nucleotides are made into DNA or RNA polymers. Some nucleotides are directly involved in metabolic functions in cells. For example, some are components of **coenzymes,** nonprotein organic molecules that help regulate enzymatic reactions. **ATP (adenosine triphosphate)** is a nucleotide that stores large amounts of energy needed for synthetic reactions and for various other energy-requiring processes in cells.

How the Structures of DNA and RNA Differ

Though both DNA and RNA are polymers of nucleotides, there are some small differences in the types of subunits each contains and in their final structure. These differences give DNA and RNA their unique functions in the body.

The nucleotides in DNA contain the sugar deoxyribose, and the nucleotides in RNA contain the sugar ribose; this difference accounts for their respective names. There are four different types of bases in DNA: **adenine (A), thymine (T), guanine (G),** and **cytosine (C)** (Table 2.1). The base can have two rings (adenine or guanine) or one ring (thymine or cytosine). In RNA, the base **uracil (U)** replaces the base thymine. These structures are called *bases* because their presence raises the pH of a solution.

The nucleotides link to make a polynucleotide called a strand, which has a backbone made up of phosphate–sugar–phosphate–sugar. The bases project to one side of the backbone. The nucleotides of a gene occur in a definite order, and so do the bases. After many years of work, researchers now know the sequence of the bases in human DNA—the human genome. This breakthrough has already led to improvements in genetic counseling, gene therapy, and medicines to treat the causes of many human illnesses.

DNA is double-stranded, with the two strands twisted about each other in the form of a *double helix* (see Fig. 2.25*a*). In DNA,

Table 2.1 DNA Structure Compared to RNA Structure

	DNA	RNA
Sugar	Deoxyribose	Ribose
Bases	Adenine, guanine, thymine, cytosine	Adenine, guanine, uracil, cytosine
Strands	Double-stranded with base pairing	Single-stranded
Helix	Yes	No

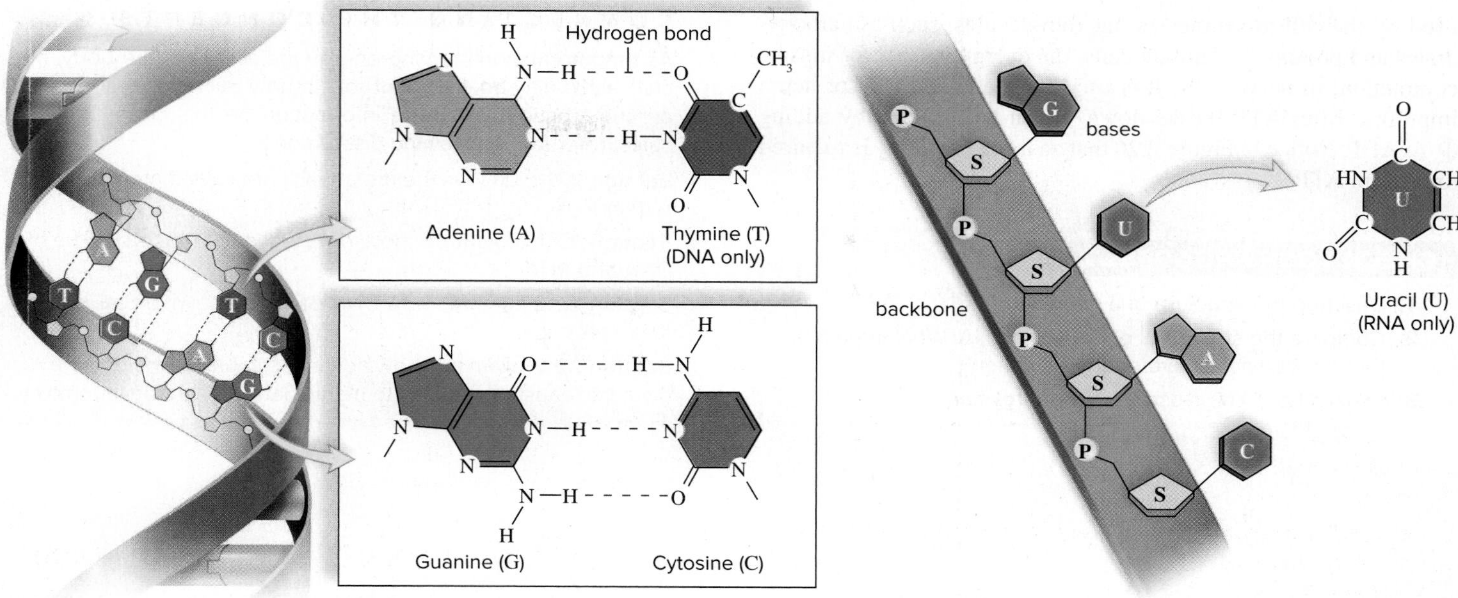

a. DNA structure with base pairs: A with T and G with C

b. RNA structure with bases G, U, A, C

Figure 2.25 **The structures of DNA and RNA.**
a. In DNA, adenine and thymine are a complementary base pair. Note the hydrogen bonds that join them (like the steps in a spiral staircase). Likewise, guanine and cytosine can pair. **b.** RNA has uracil instead of thymine, so complementary base pairing isn't possible.

the two strands are held together by hydrogen bonds between the bases. When coiled, DNA resembles a spiral staircase. When unwound, it resembles a stepladder. The uprights (sides) of the ladder are made entirely of phosphate and sugar molecules, and the rungs of the ladder exhibit **complementary base pairing.** Thymine (T) always pairs with adenine (A), and guanine (G) always pairs with cytosine (C). This complementary base pairing is what is responsible for the double-helix shape of the DNA molecule and allows for the DNA to be replicated during the process of cell division (see Section 19.2).

RNA is usually a single-stranded molecule. When RNA forms, complementary base pairing with one DNA strand passes the correct sequence of bases to RNA (Fig. 2.25*b*). RNA is the nucleic acid directly involved in protein synthesis.

ATP: An Energy Carrier

In addition to being the subunits of nucleic acids, nucleotides have metabolic functions. When adenosine (adenine plus ribose) is modified by the addition of three phosphate groups instead of one, it becomes ATP (adenosine triphosphate), which is an energy carrier in cells.

Structure of ATP Suits Its Function

ATP is a high-energy molecule, because the last two phosphate bonds are unstable and easily broken. Usually in cells, the last phosphate bond is hydrolyzed, leaving the molecule **ADP (adenosine diphosphate)** and a molecule of inorganic phosphate Ⓟ (Fig. 2.26). The energy released by ATP breakdown is

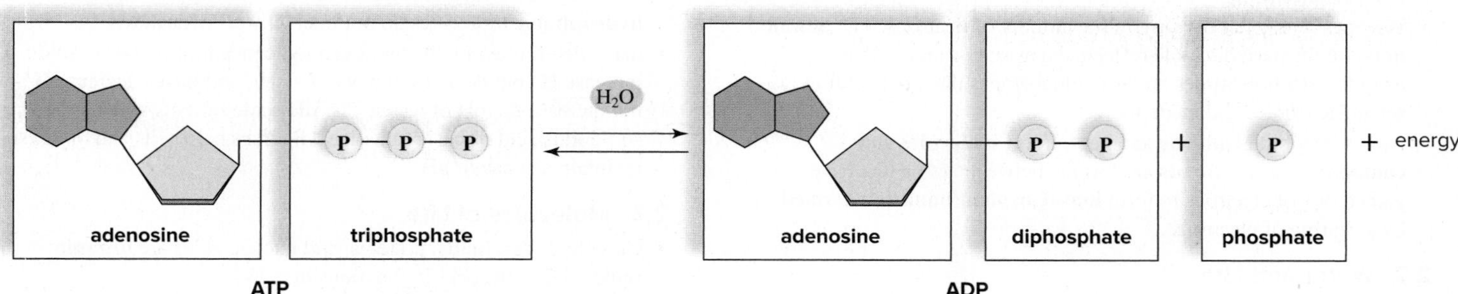

Figure 2.26 **ATP is the universal energy currency of cells.**
ATP is composed of the base adenosine and three phosphate groups (called a triphosphate). When cells need energy, ATP is hydrolyzed (water is added), forming ADP and Ⓟ. Energy is released. To recycle ATP, energy from food is required, and the reverse reaction occurs: ADP and Ⓟ join to form ATP, and water is given off.

used by the cell to synthesize macromolecules, such as carbohydrates and proteins. In muscle cells, the energy is used for muscle contraction; in nerve cells, it is used for the conduction of nerve impulses. After ATP breaks down, it can be recycled by adding Ⓟ to ADP. Notice in Figure 2.26 that an input of energy is required to re-form ATP.

CHECK YOUR PROGRESS 2.7

1. Describe the structure of a nucleotide.
2. Compare the structures of DNA and RNA. What impact do these differences have on their function?
3. Explain how ATP is used as an energy carrier.

CONNECTING THE CONCEPTS

As the information-carrying energy molecules of the body, nucleic acids play an important role in how our cells, tissues, and organs function. For more information on this class of molecules, refer to the following discussions:

Section 3.6 examines the metabolic pathways that generate ATP in a cell.

Section 22.1 provides a more detailed look at the structure of DNA and RNA.

Section 22.2 explores how DNA contains the information to make proteins.

Section 22.3 examines how advances in biotechnology are giving scientists the ability to manipulate DNA in the laboratory.

CONCLUSION

As far as we know, life is dependent on water, and water is one of the most important components of all living organisms. The cells of our body are all composed primarily of water, and water allows for the majority of chemical reactions to occur that define us as living organisms. Our search for life on other planets often focuses on the presence or absence of water, because we know life evolved on Earth from the oceans. Plus, human society and the majority of life on our planet is dependent on the health of our aquatic ecosystems. Thus, in many ways, water is the common factor that unites all life on our planet.

SUMMARIZE

2.1 From Atoms to Molecules

- **Matter** is composed of elements; each **element** is made up of just one type of **atom.** Elements are identified by an atomic symbol and an **atomic number,** which indicates the number of protons in an atom of an element. The **mass number** of an atom is based on the number of **protons** and **neutrons** in the nucleus.
- **Electrons** orbit the nucleus of an atom in **electron shells.** An atom's chemical properties depend on the number of electrons in its valence shell.
- **Isotopes** of an element vary in the number of neutrons. The **atomic mass** on the periodic table reflects the average mass of these isotopes. **Radioisotopes** are unstable isotopes that are useful in scientific studies and medicine.
- Atoms may bind with one another to form **molecules** and **compounds. Ionic bonds** are formed between atoms that have gained or lost electrons to form **ions. Covalent bonds** are formed by a sharing of electrons.

2.2 Water and Life

- The properties of water occur because water is a **polar** compound, resulting in the formation of **hydrogen bonds** between water molecules.
- Water is a liquid, instead of a gas, at room temperature. The energy needed to change the state of water is called a **calorie.**
- Water heats and freezes slowly, moderating temperatures and allowing bodies to cool by vaporizing water.
- Frozen water is less dense than liquid water, so ice floats on water.
- **Cohesion** is the ability of water molecules to attract one another. **Adhesion** is the attraction between water molecules and a surface.
- Water is the universal solvent because of its polarity. Polar **hydrophilic** molecules interact easily with water. **Nonpolar hydrophobic** molecules do not interact well with water.
- pH is determined by the hydrogen ion concentration (H^+). **Acids** increase H^+ but decrease the pH of water, and **bases** decrease H^+ but increase the pH of water. The **pH scale** reflects whether a solution is acid or basic (alkaline). **Buffers** help cells and organisms maintain a constant pH.

2.3 Molecules of Life

- Carbohydrates, lipids, proteins, and nucleic acids are **organic molecules** with specific functions in cells.
- **Dehydration reactions** form macromolecules from their building blocks. **Hydrolysis reactions** break down **macromolecules.**

Organic Molecules	Examples	Monomers	Functions
Carbohydrates	Monosaccharides, disaccharides, polysaccharides	CH_2OH, O, H, H, OH, H, HO, OH, H, OH **Glucose**	Immediate energy and stored energy; structural molecules
Lipids	Triglycerides, phospholipids, steroids	**Glycerol** **Fatty acid**	Long-term energy storage; membrane components
Proteins	Structural, enzymatic, carrier, hormonal, contractile	amino group H_2N — C — acid group COOH; H; *R* group **Amino acid**	Support, metabolic, transport, regulation, motion
Nucleic acids	DNA, RNA ATP	phosphate P, base C, O, S **Nucleotide**	Storage of genetic information, energy carrier

2.4 Carbohydrates

- **Carbohydrates** are short-term energy storage molecules.
- Simple carbohydrates are **monosaccharides** or **disaccharides. Glucose** is a monosaccharide used by cells for quick energy.
- Complex carbohydrates are **polysaccharides. Starch, glycogen,** and **cellulose** (fiber) are polysaccharides containing many glucose units.
- Plants store glucose as starch, whereas animals store glucose as glycogen. Cellulose forms plant cell walls. Cellulose is dietary fiber. Fiber plays an important role in digestive system health.

2.5 Lipids

- **Lipids** are nonpolar molecules that do not dissolve in water. **Fats,** also called **triglycerides,** and **oils** are lipids that act as long-term energy storage molecules.
- **Fatty acids** can be **saturated** or **unsaturated. Trans fats** are unsaturated fatty acids that have adverse effects on your health.
- Plasma membranes contain **phospholipids.**
- **Steroids** are complex lipids composed of four interlocking rings. Testosterone and estrogen are steroids. Cholesterol is a steroid that is transported by proteins called lipoproteins (LDLs and HDLs).

2.6 Proteins

- **Proteins** may be structural proteins (keratin, collagen), hormones, or enzymes that speed chemical reactions. Proteins account for cell movement (actin, myosin), enable muscle contraction (actin, myosin), or transport molecules in blood (hemoglobin).
- Proteins are macromolecules with **amino acid** subunits. A peptide is composed of two amino acids linked by a **peptide bond,** and a **polypeptide** contains many amino acids.
- A protein has levels of structure: A primary structure is determined by the sequence of amino acids that forms a polypeptide. A secondary structure is an α (alpha) helix. A tertiary structure occurs when the secondary structure forms a three-dimensional, globular shape. A quaternary structure occurs when two or more polypeptides join to form a single protein. **Denaturation** represents an irreversible change in the shape of a protein.

2.7 Nucleic Acids

- **Nucleic acids** are macromolecules composed of nucleotides. **Nucleotides** are composed of a sugar, a base, and a phosphate. DNA and RNA are polymers of nucleotides.
- **DNA (deoxyribonucleic acid)** contains the sugar deoxyribose; contains the bases **adenine (A), guanine (G), thymine (T),** and **cytosine (C);** is double-stranded; and forms a helix. The helix exhibits **complementary base pairing** between the strands of DNA.
- **RNA (ribonucleic acid)** contains the sugar ribose; contains the bases adenine, guanine, **uracil (U),** and cytosine; and does not form a helix.
- **ATP (adenosine triphosphate)** is a high-energy molecule because its bonds are unstable.
- ATP undergoes hydrolysis to **ADP (adenosine diphosphate)** + Ⓟ, which releases energy used by cells to do metabolic work.

ENGAGE

BioNOW

Want to know how this science is relevant to your life? Check out the BioNOW video below:

- Properties of Water

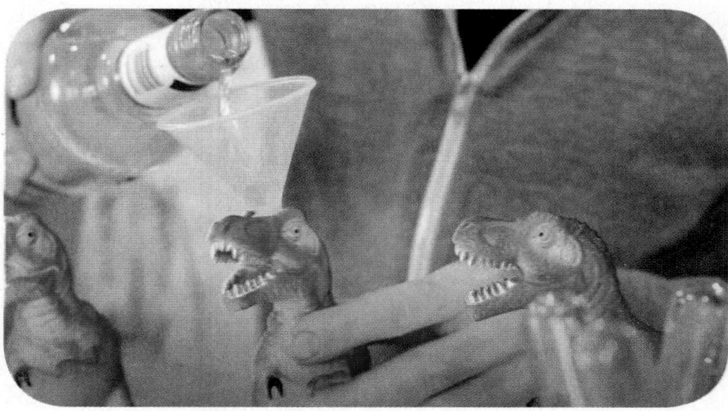

McGraw Hill

What chemical property allows water to have all the unique characteristics shown in the video?

THINKING CRITICALLY

1. On a hot summer day, you decide to dive into a swimming pool. Before you begin your dive, you notice the surface of the water is smooth and continuous. After the dive, you discover that some water droplets are clinging to your skin and that your skin temperature feels cooler. Explain these observations based on the properties of water.
2. In biology, structure equals function. How does the tremendous variability in the structure of proteins relate to their importance (function) in biological systems?
3. Explain why a radioactive isotope of an element reacts chemically the same as a nonradioactive isotope of the same element.

MAKING IT RELEVANT

1. If we were to choose an organism from each of the kingdoms of life and analyze them biochemically, which molecule would be common across all of the organisms?
2. Explain how a knowledge of the different saturation levels of triglycerides can help you make healthier choices in the grocery store.
3. As scientists continue to explore other planets in our solar system, they are looking for evidence that may indicate life has existed, or currently exists, on other planets and moons. Other than water, which molecules should scientists look for to reveal evidence of life on these other bodies?

Find answers to all of the chapter questions at connect.mheducation.com

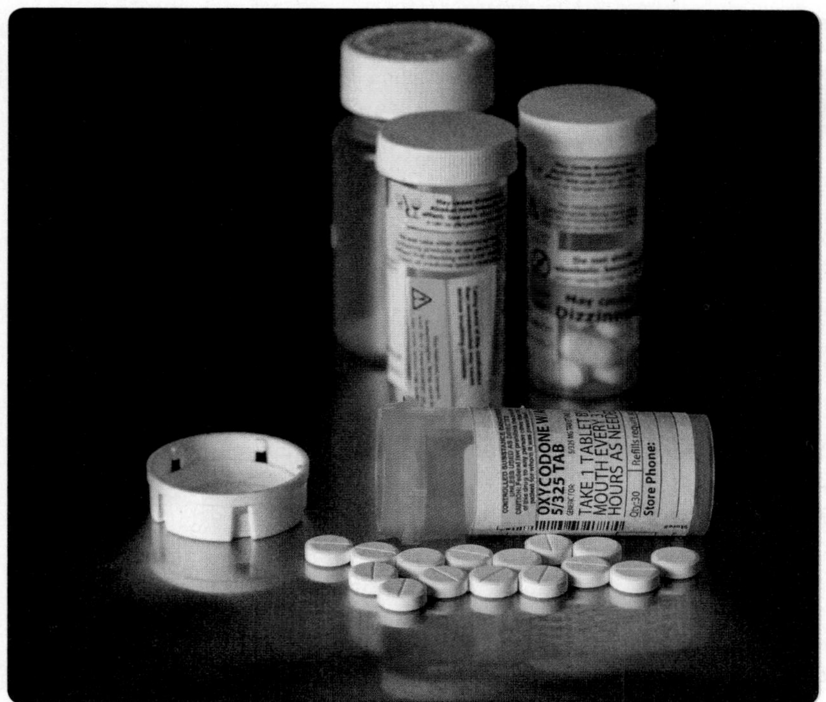

Steve Heap/Shutterstock

CHAPTER 3

Cell Structure and Function

The Opioid Crisis

Each day, approximately 130 people die from an opioid overdose in the United States. The addiction and misuse of opioids has become a national crisis that impacts the social and economic welfare of our country.

The opioid system is a component of the central nervous system, which within humans, controls pain, reward, and addictive behaviors. Opioid receptors belong to a group of transmembrane proteins found on the surface of cells. When the receptors are engaged by an opioid such as morphine or heroin, the pain pathway is altered and feelings of euphoria and pleasure can result. Three main receptors—mu, delta, and kappa—are responsible for enabling opioids to exert their effect. Mu receptors are molecular switches that trigger the brain reward system. Delta receptors appear to play a role in determining an individual's emotional state and kappa receptors are associated with pain relief.

Morphine is the most widely used opioid to control pain after surgery or for individuals who suffer from chronic pain. It acts on the mu receptor and therefore has the potential for abuse and addiction. A number of drugs may be prescribed to combat opioid abuse. These drugs bind to the opioid receptors on the plasma membrane and eliminate withdrawal symptoms.

In this chapter, we will explore the structure and function of cells and examine how the plasma membrane plays a central role in the function of a cell.

As you read through the chapter, think about the following questions:

1. What is the role of the plasma membrane in a cell?
2. How do transport and channel proteins function in a plasma membrane?

CHAPTER OUTLINE

BEFORE YOU BEGIN

Before beginning this chapter, take a few moments to review the following discussions:

Section 2.2 What properties of water make it a crucial molecule for life as we know it?

Sections 2.3 to **2.7** What are the basic roles of carbohydrates, fats, proteins, and nucleic acids in the cell?

Section 2.7 What is the role of ATP in a cell?

3.1 What Is a Cell?

LEARNING OUTCOMES

Upon completion of this section, you should be able to

1. State the basic principles of the cell theory.
2. Explain how the surface-area-to-volume ratio limits cell size.
3. Summarize the role of microscopy in the study of cells.

All organisms, including humans, are composed of cells. From single-celled bacteria to plants and complex animals such as ourselves, the cell is the fundamental unit of life. However, it took technological advances, namely in the invention of the microscope, to not only discover the existence of cells but to recognize their importance in the levels of biological organization shown in Figure 1.2.

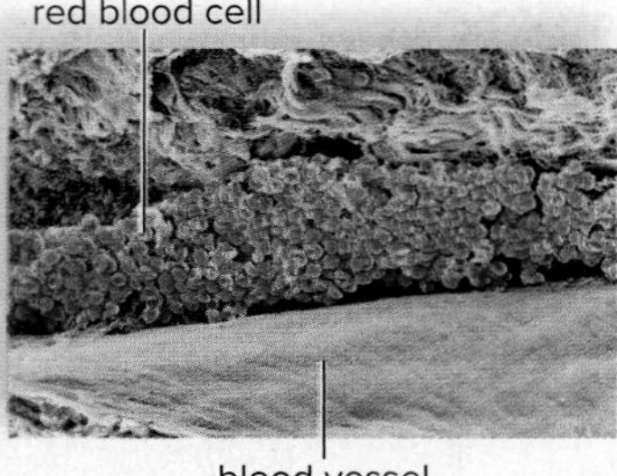

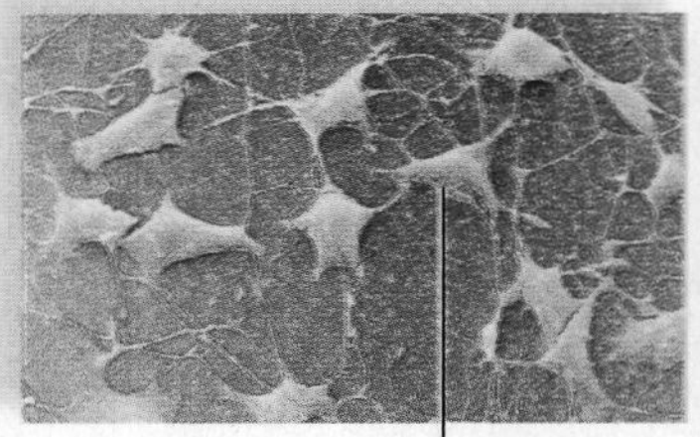

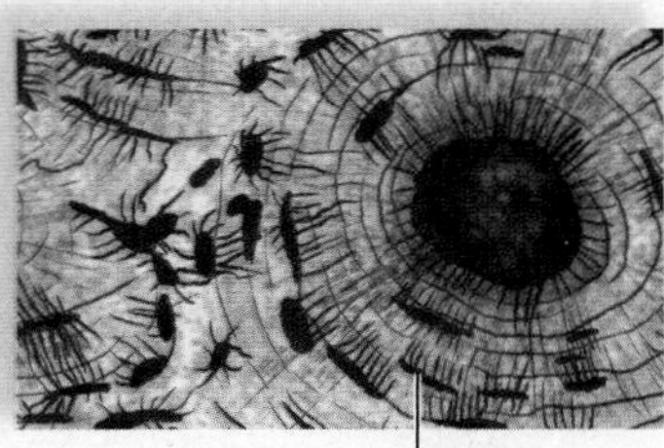

Figure 3.1 **Cells vary in structure and function.** A cell's structure is related to its function. Despite differences in appearance, all cells exchange substances with their environment.
(blood cell and blood vessel): STEVE GSCHMEISSNER/SPL/Getty Images; (nerve cell): SPL/Science Source; (osteocyte): Dennis Strete/McGraw Hill

The Cell Theory

The word *cell* didn't enter biology until the seventeenth century. The Dutch scientist Anton van Leeuwenhoek is recognized for making some of the earliest microscopes and observing things no one had seen before. Robert Hooke, an English scientist, confirmed van Leeuwenhoek's observations and was the first to use the term *cell.* The tiny chambers he observed in the honeycomb structure of cork reminded him of the rooms, or cells, in a monastery.

Over 150 years later—in the 1830s—a series of German naturalists not only discovered that plant and animal tissues were made of cells, but also proposed that cells all originate from other cells. These observations became the basis of the **cell theory,** which states that all organisms are made up of basic living units called cells, and that all cells come only from previously existing cells. Today, the cell theory is one of the fundamental theories of biology.

The cell theory states that:

- *A cell is the basic unit of life.* According to the cell theory, nothing smaller than a cell is considered to be alive. A single-celled organism exhibits the basic characteristics of life that were presented in Section 1.1. There is no smaller unit of life that is able to reproduce and grow, respond to stimuli, remain homeostatic, take in and use materials from the environment, and become adapted to the environment. In short, life has a cellular nature.
- *All living organisms are made up of cells.* While many organisms, such as bacteria, are single-celled, other organisms, including humans and plants, are multicellular. In multicellular organisms, cells are often organized as tissues, such as nervous tissue and connective tissue. Even bone consists of cells (called osteocytes) surrounded by the material they have deposited. Cells may differ in their appearance, as shown in the comparison of several cell types in Figure 3.1. However, despite these differences, they all have certain structures in common. In general, it is important to recognize that the structure of a cell is directly related to its function.
- *New cells arise only from preexisting cells.* Until the nineteenth century, most people believed in spontaneous generation: that nonliving objects could give rise to living organisms. For example, maggots were thought to arise from meat hung in the butcher shop. Maggots often appeared in meat to which flies had access. However, people did not realize that the living maggots did not spontaneously generate from the nonliving meat. A series of experiments by Francesco Redi in the seventeenth century demonstrated that meat that was placed within sealed containers did not generate maggots. In other words, life did not generate spontaneously. In 1864, the French scientist Louis Pasteur conducted a now-classic set of experiments using bacterial cells. His experiments proved conclusively that spontaneous generation of life from nonlife is not possible.

When animals, such as humans, reproduce, a sperm cell joins with an egg cell to form a zygote. By reproducing, parents pass a copy of their genetic information to their offspring. The zygote is the first cell of a new multicellular organism. Through the process of cell division, every cell in the new organism will contain a copy of the parents' genes.

Cell Size

Despite their importance, most cells are small and can be seen only under a microscope. The small size of cells means they are measured using the smaller units of the metric system, such as the *micrometer* (μm). A micrometer is 1/1,000 of a millimeter (mm). The micrometer is the common unit of measurement for people who use microscopes professionally (see Appendix for a complete list of metric units).

A few cells, such as the egg of a chicken or frog, are large enough to be seen by the naked eye. In comparison, a human egg cell is around 100 μm in size, placing it right at the limit of what can be viewed by our eyes. However, most cells are much smaller. The small size of cells is explained by considering the *surface-area-to-volume ratio* of cells. Nutrients enter a cell—and waste exits a

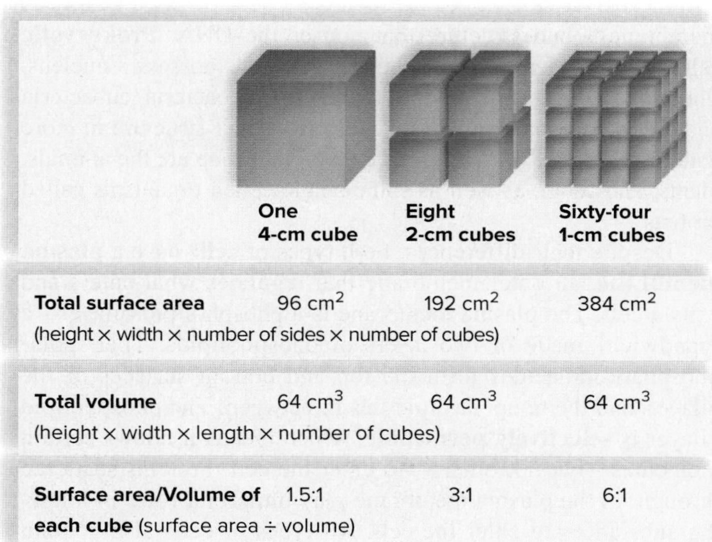

One 4-cm cube
Eight 2-cm cubes
Sixty-four 1-cm cubes
Total surface area 96 cm² 192 cm² 384 cm²
(height × width × number of sides × number of cubes)
Total volume 64 cm³ 64 cm³ 64 cm³
(height × width × length × number of cubes)
Surface area/Volume of each cube (surface area ÷ volume) 1.5:1 3:1 6:1

Figure 3.2 **Surface-area-to-volume ratio limits cell size.** As cell size decreases, the ratio of the surface area to volume increases.

cell—at its surface. Therefore, the greater the amount of surface, the greater the ability to get material into and out of the cell. A large cell requires more nutrients and produces more waste than a small cell. However, as cells become smaller in volume, the proportionate amount of surface area actually increases. You can see this by comparing the cubes in Figure 3.2.

We would expect, then, that there would be a limit to how large an actively metabolizing cell can become. An example is a chicken's egg. Once a chicken's egg is fertilized and starts metabolizing, it divides repeatedly without increasing in size. This increases the amount of surface area needed for adequate exchange of materials in these rapidly dividing cells.

Studying Cells: The Science of Microscopy

Microscopes provide scientists with a deeper look into how cells function. There are many types of microscopes, from compound light microscopes to powerful electron microscopes. The

Table 3.1 **Resolving Power of the Eye and Common Microscopes**

	Magnification	Resolving Power
Eye	N/A	0.1 mm (100 μm)
Light microscope	1,000×	0.0001 mm (0.1 μm)
Transmission electron microscope	100,000× (or greater)	0.000001 mm (0.01 μm)

magnification, or the ratio between the observed size of an image and its actual size, varies with the type of microscope. In addition, the resolution of the image varies between microscopes (Table 3.1). *Resolution* is the ability to distinguish between two adjacent points, and it represents the minimum distance between two objects that allows them to be seen as two different objects. Usually, the more powerful the microscope, the greater the resolution. Figure 3.3 illustrates images of a red blood cell taken by three different types of microscopes.

A *compound light microscope* (Fig. 3.3*a*) uses a set of glass lenses and light rays passing through the object to magnify objects. The image can be viewed directly by the human eye.

The *transmission electron microscope* makes use of a stream of electrons to produce magnified images (Fig. 3.3*b*). The human eye cannot see the image. Therefore, it is projected onto a fluorescent screen or photographic film to produce an image (called a *micrograph*) that can be viewed. The magnification and resolution produced by a transmission electron microscope is much higher than that of a light microscope. Therefore, this microscope has the ability to produce enlarged images with greater detail.

A *scanning electron microscope* provides a three-dimensional view of the surface of an object (Fig. 3.3*c*). A narrow beam of electrons is scanned over the surface of the specimen, which is coated with a thin layer of metal. The metal gives off secondary electrons, which are collected to produce a television-type picture of the specimen's surface on a screen.

In the laboratory, the light microscope is often used to view live specimens. However, this is not the case for electron

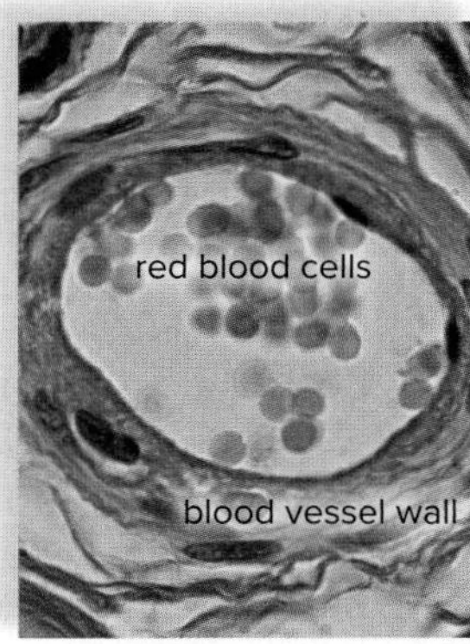

a. Light micrograph 250×

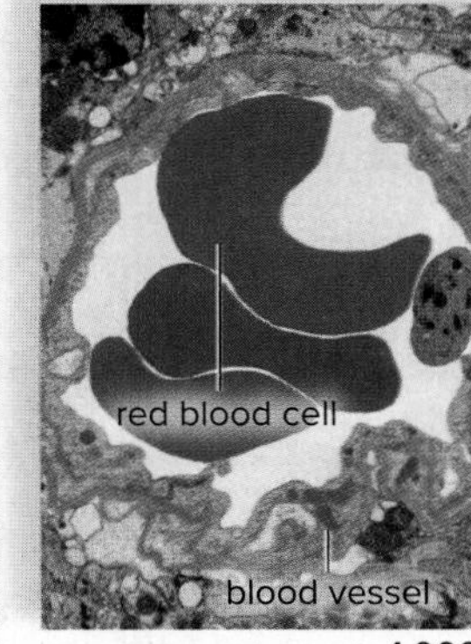

b. Transmission electron micrograph 4,000×

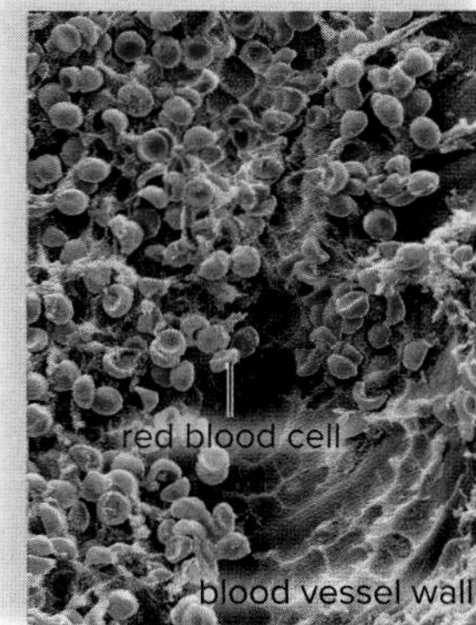

c. Scanning electron micrograph

Figure 3.3 **Micrographs of human red blood cells.**
a. Light micrograph (LM) of many cells in a large vessel (stained). **b.** Transmission electron micrograph (TEM) of just three cells in a small vessel (colored). **c.** Scanning electron micrograph (SEM) gives a three-dimensional view of cells and vessels (colored).
(a): Ed Reschke/Stone/Getty Images; (b, c): Steve Gschmeissner/Science Photo Library/Getty Images

microscopes. Because electrons cannot travel very far in air, a strong vacuum must be maintained along the entire path of the electron beam. Often, cells are treated before being viewed under a microscope. Because most cells are transparent, they are often stained with colored dyes before being viewed under a light microscope. Certain cellular components take up the dye more than other components, which enhances contrast. A similar approach is used in electron microscopy, except the sample is treated with electron-dense metals (such as gold) to provide contrast. The metals do not provide color, so electron micrographs may be colored after the micrograph is obtained. The expression "falsely colored" means the original micrograph was colored after it was produced. In addition, during electron microscopy, cells are treated so they do not decompose in the vacuum. Frequently, they are also embedded into a matrix, which allows a researcher to slice the cell into very thin pieces, providing cross-sections of the cell's interior.

CHECK YOUR PROGRESS 3.1

1. Summarize the cell theory and state its importance to the study of biology.
2. Explain how a cell's size relates to its function.
3. Compare and contrast the information that may be obtained from a light microscope and an electron microscope.

CONNECTING THE CONCEPTS

For more on the cells mentioned in this section, refer to the following discussions:

Section 6.2 discusses how red blood cells transport gases within the circulatory system.

Section 6.6 provides an overview of how red blood cells help maintain homeostasis in the body.

Section 18.1 examines the complex structure of a human egg cell.

3.2 How Cells Are Organized

LEARNING OUTCOMES

Upon completion of this section, you should be able to

1. Distinguish between the structure of a prokaryotic cell and that of a eukaryotic cell.
2. Identify the roles of the plasma membrane and the organelles of a eukaryotic cell.
3. Summarize how eukaryotic cells evolved from prokaryotic cells.

Biologists classify cells into two broad categories—the prokaryotes and eukaryotes. The primary difference between a prokaryotic cell and a eukaryotic cell is the presence or absence of a nucleus, a membrane-bound structure that houses the DNA. **Prokaryotic cells** lack a nucleus, whereas **eukaryotic cells** possess a nucleus. The prokaryotic group includes two groups of bacteria: eubacteria and archaebacteria. We will take a look at their structure in more detail in Section 8.1. Within the eukaryotic group are the animals, plants, and fungi, as well as some single-celled organisms called protists.

Despite their differences, both types of cells have a **plasma membrane,** an outer membrane that regulates what enters and exits a cell. The plasma membrane is a phospholipid bilayer—a "sandwich" made of two layers of phospholipids. Their polar phosphate molecules form the top and bottom surfaces of the bilayer, and the nonpolar lipid lies in between. The phospholipid bilayer is **selectively permeable,** which means it allows certain molecules—but not others—to enter the cell. Proteins scattered throughout the plasma membrane play important roles in allowing substances to enter the cell. All types of cells also contain **cytoplasm,** which is a semifluid medium containing *cytosol*, a mixture of water and various types of molecules, and organelles. The presence of proteins accounts for the semifluid nature of the cytoplasm.

The cytoplasm of a eukaryotic cell contains **organelles,** internal compartments that have specialized functions. Originally, the term *organelle* referred to only membranous structures, but we will use it to include any well-defined subcellular structure. Eukaryotic cells have many types of organelles (Fig. 3.4). Organelles allow for the compartmentalization of the cell. This keeps the various cellular activities separated from one another.

Evolution of the Eukaryotic Cell

The first cells on Earth were prokaryotic cells (see Section 23.1 for the evolutionary history of life). Today these cells are represented by bacteria and archaea, which differ mainly by their chemistry.

Early prokaryotic organisms, such as archaea, were well adapted to life on early Earth. The environment they evolved in contained conditions that would be instantly lethal to life today: The atmosphere contained no oxygen; instead it was filled with carbon monoxide and other poisonous gases; the temperature of the planet was above 200°F, and there was no ozone layer to protect organisms from damaging radiation from the sun.

Despite these conditions, prokaryotic life survived, and in doing so gradually adapted to Earth's environment. In the process, most of the archaebacteria went extinct. However, we now know that some are still around and can be found in some of the most inhospitable places on the planet, such as thermal vents and salty seas. The study of these ancient bacteria is still shedding light on the early origins of life.

Evidence widely supports the hypothesis that eukaryotic cells evolved from archaea. The internal structure of eukaryotic cells is believed to have evolved as the series of events shown in Figure 3.5. The nucleus could have formed by invagination of the plasma membrane, a process whereby a pocket is formed in the plasma membrane. The pocket would have enclosed the DNA of

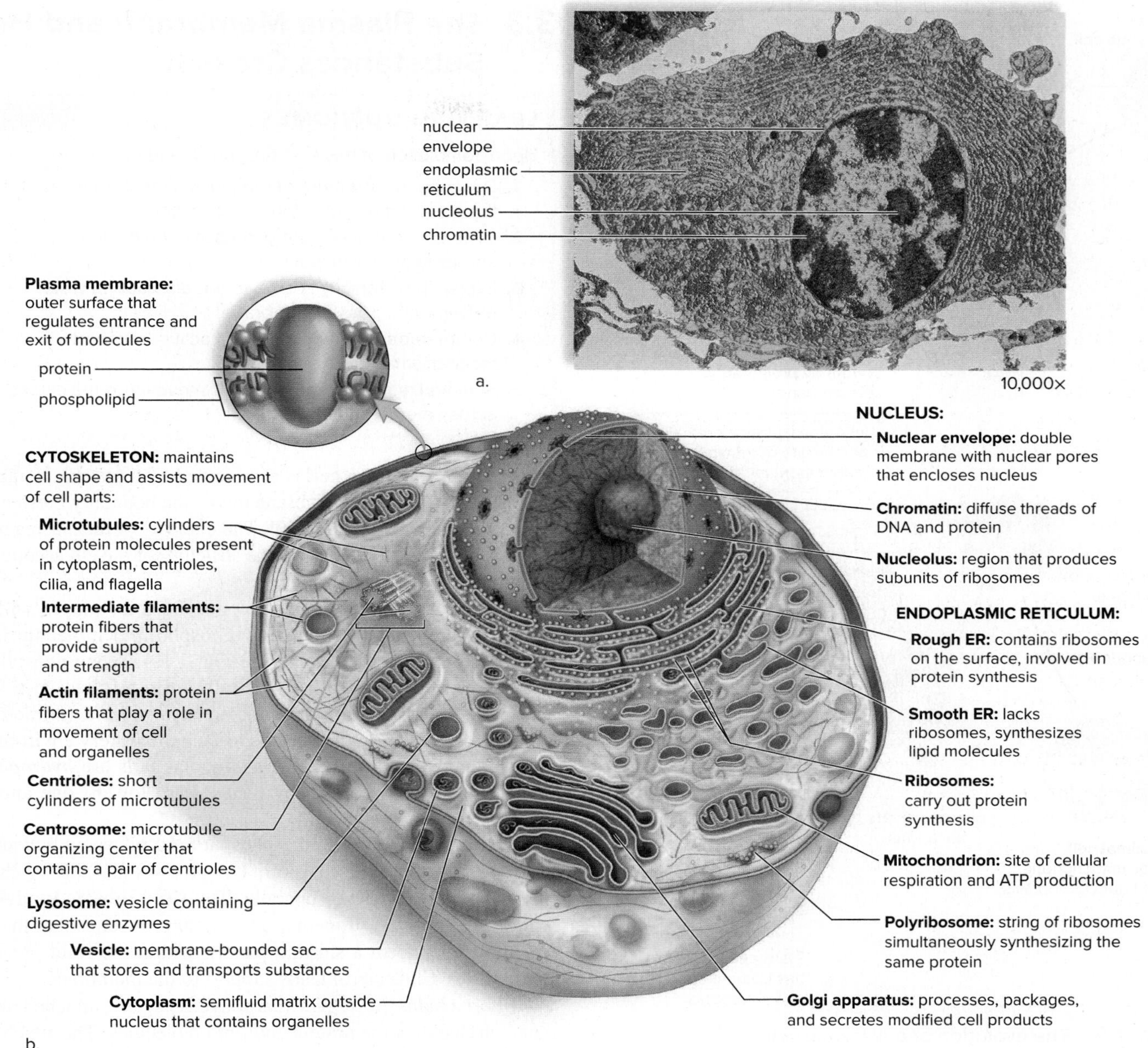

nuclear envelope
endoplasmic reticulum
nucleolus
chromatin
a.
10,000×
Plasma membrane: outer surface that regulates entrance and exit of molecules
protein
phospholipid
CYTOSKELETON: maintains cell shape and assists movement of cell parts:
Microtubules: cylinders of protein molecules present in cytoplasm, centrioles, cilia, and flagella
Intermediate filaments: protein fibers that provide support and strength
Actin filaments: protein fibers that play a role in movement of cell and organelles
Centrioles: short cylinders of microtubules
Centrosome: microtubule organizing center that contains a pair of centrioles
Lysosome: vesicle containing digestive enzymes
Vesicle: membrane-bounded sac that stores and transports substances
Cytoplasm: semifluid matrix outside nucleus that contains organelles
b.
NUCLEUS:
Nuclear envelope: double membrane with nuclear pores that encloses nucleus
Chromatin: diffuse threads of DNA and protein
Nucleolus: region that produces subunits of ribosomes
ENDOPLASMIC RETICULUM:
Rough ER: contains ribosomes on the surface, involved in protein synthesis
Smooth ER: lacks ribosomes, synthesizes lipid molecules
Ribosomes: carry out protein synthesis
Mitochondrion: site of cellular respiration and ATP production
Polyribosome: string of ribosomes simultaneously synthesizing the same protein
Golgi apparatus: processes, packages, and secretes modified cell products

Figure 3.4 **The structure of a typical animal eukaryotic cell.**
a. A transmission electron micrograph of the interior structures of an animal cell. **b.** The structure and function of the components of a eukaryotic cell.
(a): Alfred Pasieka/Science Source

the cell, thus forming its nucleus. Surprisingly, some of the organelles in eukaryotic cells may have arisen by engulfing prokaryotic cells. The engulfed prokaryotic cells were not digested; rather, they then evolved into different organelles. One of these events would have given the eukaryotic cell a mitochondrion. Mitochondria are organelles that carry on cellular respiration. Another such event may have produced the chloroplast. Chloroplasts are found in cells that carry out photosynthesis. This process is often called *endosymbiosis.*

CHECK YOUR PROGRESS 3.2

1. Summarize the role of the plasma membrane and organelles in a eukaryotic cell.
2. Describe the main differences between a eukaryotic and a prokaryotic cell.
3. Describe the possible evolution of the nucleus, mitochondria, and chloroplast.

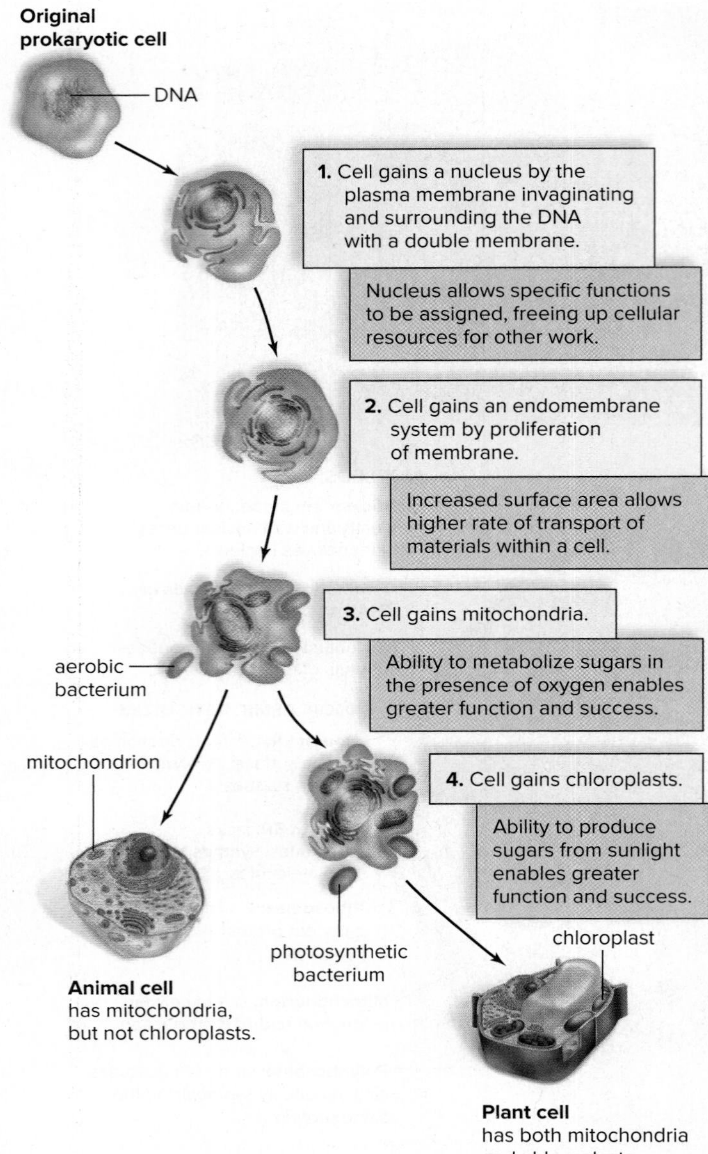
Original prokaryotic cell
DNA
1. Cell gains a nucleus by the plasma membrane invaginating and surrounding the DNA with a double membrane.
Nucleus allows specific functions to be assigned, freeing up cellular resources for other work.
2. Cell gains an endomembrane system by proliferation of membrane.
Increased surface area allows higher rate of transport of materials within a cell.
3. Cell gains mitochondria.
Ability to metabolize sugars in the presence of oxygen enables greater function and success.
aerobic bacterium
4. Cell gains chloroplasts.
Ability to produce sugars from sunlight enables greater function and success.
mitochondrion
chloroplast
photosynthetic bacterium
Animal cell has mitochondria, but not chloroplasts.
Plant cell has both mitochondria and chloroplasts.

Figure 3.5 **The evolution of eukaryotic cells.** Invagination of the plasma membrane of a prokaryotic cell could have created the nucleus. Later, the cell gained organelles, some of which may have been independent prokaryotes.

CONNECTING THE CONCEPTS

The material in this section summarizes some previous concepts of eukaryotic and prokaryotic cells and the role of phospholipids in the plasma membrane. For more information, refer to the following discussions:

Section 1.2 examines the difference in the classification of eukaryotic and prokaryotic organisms.

Section 8.1 provides more information on the structure of bacterial cells.

3.3 The Plasma Membrane and How Substances Cross It

LEARNING OUTCOMES

Upon completion of this section, you should be able to

1. Describe the structure of the plasma membrane and list the type of molecules found in the membrane.
2. Distinguish between the processes of diffusion, osmosis, and facilitated transport.
3. Explain how tonicity relates to the direction of water movement across a membrane.
4. Compare passive-transport and active-transport mechanisms.
5. Summarize how eukaryotic cells move large molecules across membranes.

Like all cells, a human cell is surrounded by a plasma membrane (Fig. 3.6). The plasma membrane marks the boundary between the outside and the inside of the cell. The integrity of the plasma membrane is necessary not only for the structure of the eukaryotic cell, but its function as well.

The plasma membrane is a phospholipid bilayer with attached or embedded proteins. A phospholipid molecule has a polar head and nonpolar tails (see Fig. 2.19). When phospholipids are placed in water, they naturally form a spherical bilayer. The polar heads, being charged, are *hydrophilic* (attracted to water). They position themselves to face the watery environment outside and inside the cell. The nonpolar tails are *hydrophobic* (not attracted to water). They turn inward toward one another, where there is no water.

At body temperature, the phospholipid bilayer is a liquid. It has the consistency of olive oil. The proteins are able to change their position by moving laterally. The **fluid-mosaic model** is a working description of membrane structure. It states that the protein molecules form a shifting pattern within the fluid phospholipid bilayer. Cholesterol lends support to the membrane.

Short chains of sugars (carbohydrates) are attached to the outer surface of some protein and lipid molecules. The attachment of a sugar produces a *glycoprotein*, while the attachment of a sugar to a lipid molecule creates a *glycolipid*. These molecules help mark the cell as belonging to a particular individual. This identification is called "self" and helps the body identify foreign cells that may cause infections. They also account for why people have different blood types.

Some plasma membrane proteins form channels through which certain substances can enter cells. Others are either enzymes that catalyze reactions or are carriers involved in the passage of molecules through the membrane.

Plasma Membrane Functions

The plasma membrane isolates the interior of the cell from the external environment. In doing so, it allows only certain molecules and ions to enter and exit the cytoplasm freely. Therefore, the plasma membrane is said to be selectively permeable (Fig. 3.7).

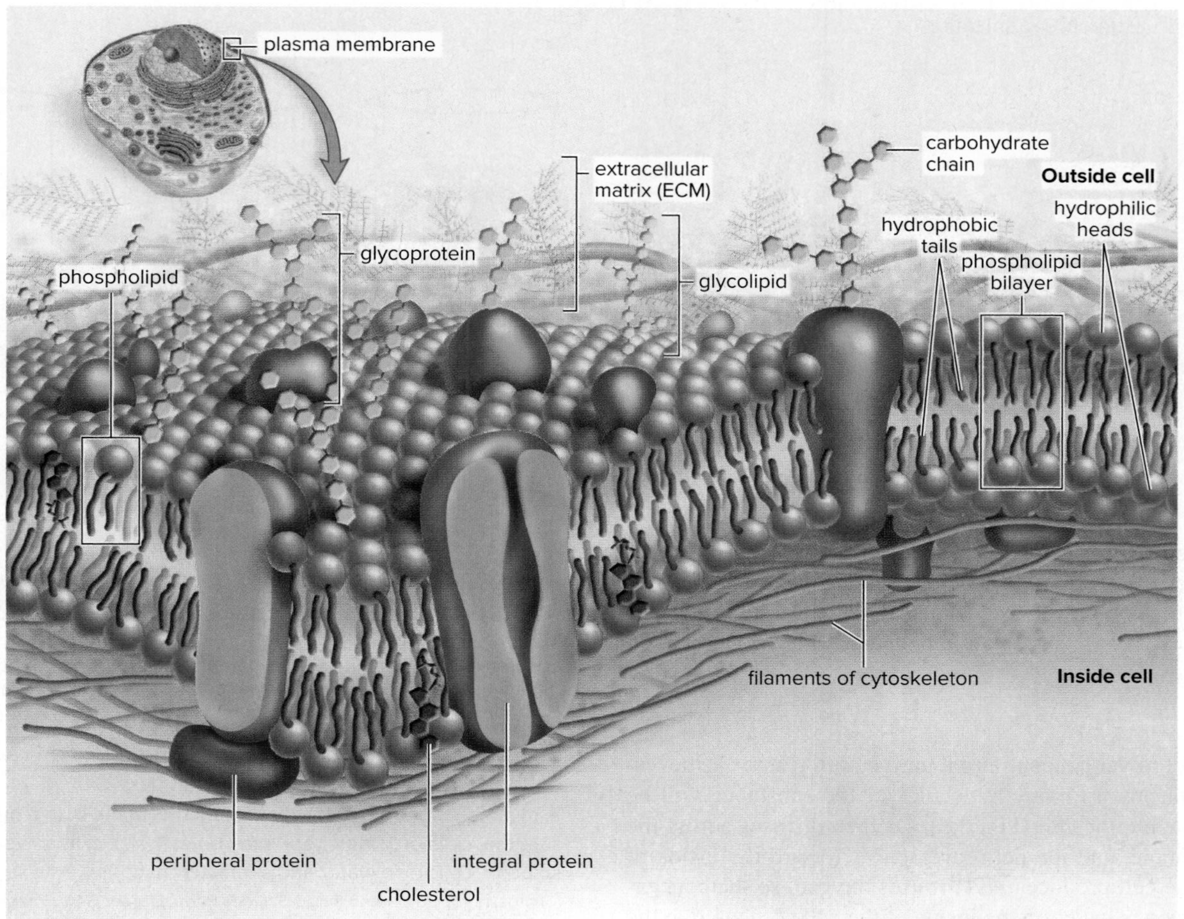

Figure 3.6 **Organization of the plasma membrane.**
The membrane is composed of a phospholipid bilayer in which proteins are embedded (integral proteins) or associated with the cytoplasmic side (peripheral proteins). Steroids (cholesterol) help regulate the fluidity of the membrane. Cytoskeleton filaments are attached to the inside surface by membrane proteins.

Small, lipid-soluble molecules, such as oxygen and carbon dioxide, can pass through the membrane easily. The small size of water molecules allows them to freely cross the membrane by using protein channels called *aquaporins.* Ions and large molecules cannot cross the membrane without more direct assistance, which will be discussed later.

Diffusion

Diffusion is the random movement of molecules from an area of higher concentration to an area of lower concentration, until they are equally distributed. Diffusion is a passive way for molecules to enter or exit a cell. No cellular energy is needed to bring it about.

Certain molecules can freely cross the plasma membrane by diffusion. When molecules can cross a plasma membrane, which way will they go? The molecules will move in both directions. But the *net movement* will be from the region of higher concentration

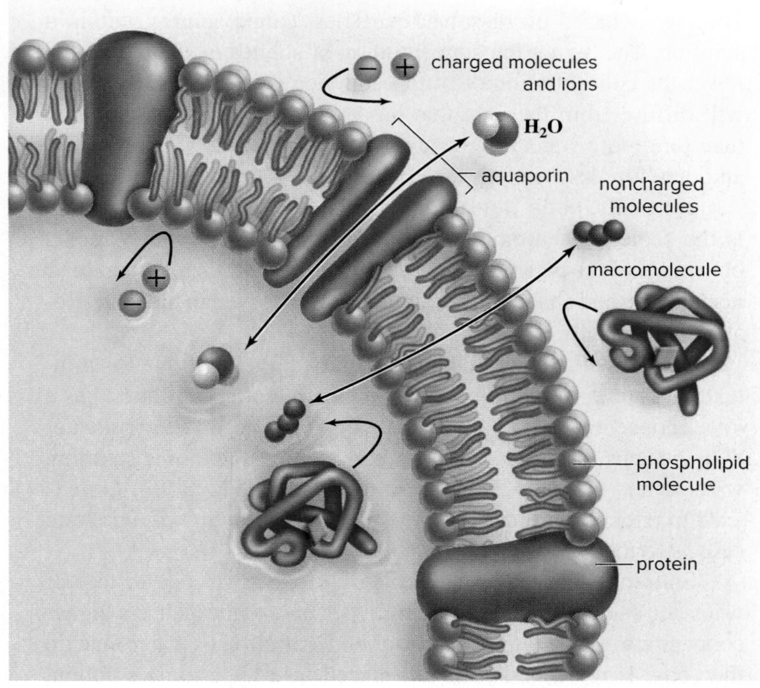

Figure 3.7 **Selective permeability of the plasma membrane.**
Small, uncharged molecules are able to cross the membrane, whereas large or charged molecules cannot. Water travels freely across membranes through aquaporins.

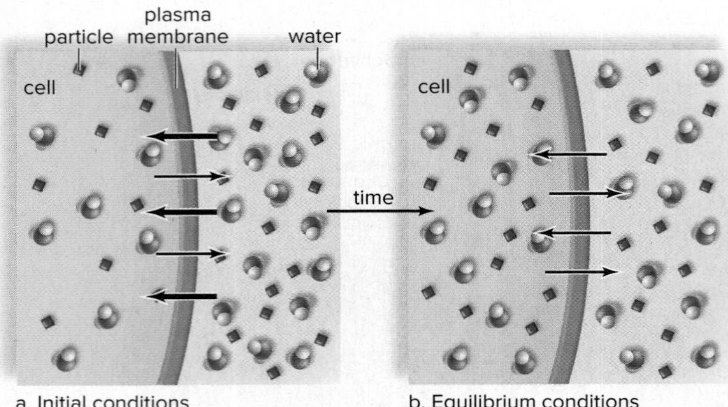

Figure 3.8 Diffusion across the plasma membrane.
a. When a substance can diffuse across the plasma membrane, it will move back and forth across the membrane, but the net movement will be toward the region of lower concentration. **b.** At equilibrium, equal numbers of particles and water cross in both directions, and there is no net movement.

Figure 3.9 Effects of changes in tonicity on red blood cells.
a. In an isotonic solution, cells remain the same. **b.** In a hypotonic solution, cells gain water and may burst (lysis). **c.** In a hypertonic solution, cells lose water and shrink (crenation).
(photos) (a–b): Power and Syred/Science Photo Library/Getty Images; (c): STEVE GSCHMEISSNER/Science Photo Library/Brand X Pictures/Getty Images

to the region of lower concentration, until equilibrium is achieved. At equilibrium, just as many molecules of the substance will be entering as leaving the cell (Fig. 3.8). Oxygen diffuses across the plasma membrane, and the net movement is toward the inside of the cell. As the cell produces ATP, it uses oxygen, so the concentration of oxygen is lower on the inside of the cell compared to the exterior environment.

Osmosis

Osmosis is the net movement of water across a selectively permeable membrane. The direction by which water will diffuse is determined by the tonicity of the solutions inside and outside the cell. Tonicity is based on dissolved particles, called solutes, within a solution. The higher the concentration of solutes in a solution, the lower the concentration of water, and vice versa. Typically, water will diffuse from the area that has less solute (low tonicity, and therefore more water) to the area with more solute (high tonicity, and therefore less water).

Normally, body fluids are *isotonic* to cells (Fig. 3.9*a*). There is the same concentration of nondiffusible solutes and water on both sides of the plasma membrane. Therefore, cells maintain their normal size and shape. Intravenous solutions given in medical situations are usually isotonic.

Solutions that cause cells to swell or even burst due to an intake of water are said to be *hypotonic.* A hypotonic solution has a lower concentration of solute and a higher concentration of water than the cells. If red blood cells are placed in a hypotonic solution, water enters the cells. They swell to bursting (Fig. 3.9*b*). *Lysis* is used to refer to the process of bursting cells. Bursting of red blood cells is termed *hemolysis.*

Solutions that cause cells to shrink or shrivel due to loss of water are said to be *hypertonic.* A hypertonic solution has a higher concentration of solute and a lower concentration of water than do the cells. If red blood cells are placed in a hypertonic solution, water leaves the cells; they shrink (Fig. 3.9*c*). The term *crenation* refers to red blood cells in this condition. These changes have occurred due to osmotic pressure. **Osmotic pressure** controls water movement in our bodies. For example, in the small and large intestines, osmotic pressure allows us to absorb the water in food and drink. In the kidneys, osmotic pressure controls water absorption as well.

BIOLOGY IN YOUR LIFE

Can you drink seawater?

Seawater is hypertonic to our cells. Seawater contains approximately 3.5% salt, whereas our cells contain 0.9%. Once salt has entered the blood, your cells would shrivel up and die as they lost water trying to dilute the excess salt. Your kidneys can only produce urine that is slightly less salty than seawater, so you would dehydrate providing the amount of water necessary to rid your body of the salt. In addition, salt water contains high levels of magnesium ions, which cause diarrhea and further dehydration.

Facilitated Transport

Many solutes do not simply diffuse across a plasma membrane. They are transported by means of protein carriers within the

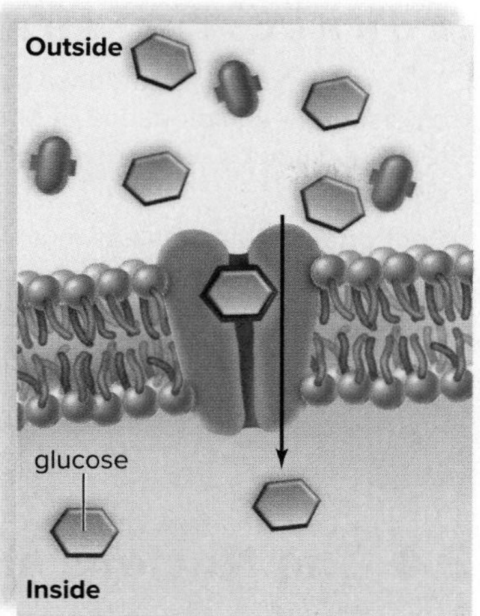

Figure 3.10 Facilitated transport across a plasma membrane.
This is a passive form of transport in which substances move down their concentration gradient through a protein carrier. In this example, glucose (green) moves into the cell by facilitated transport. The end result will be an equal distribution of glucose on both sides of the membrane.

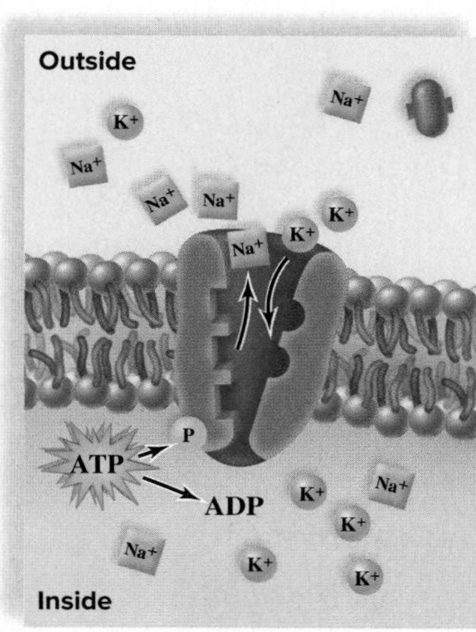

Figure 3.11 Active transport and the sodium–potassium pump.
This is a form of transport in which a molecule moves from low concentration to high concentration. It requires a protein carrier and energy. Na^+ exits, and K^+ enters, the cell by active transport, so Na^+ will be concentrated outside the cell and K^+ will be concentrated inside it.

membrane. During **facilitated transport,** a molecule is transported across the plasma membrane from the side of higher concentration to the side of lower concentration (Fig. 3.10). This is a passive means of transport, because the cell does not need to expend energy to move a substance down its concentration gradient. Each protein carrier, sometimes called a *transporter,* binds only to a specific molecule. For example, a glucose transporter will only move glucose molecules across the membrane. Type 2 diabetes results when cells lack a sufficient number of glucose transporters.

BIOLOGY IN YOUR LIFE

Why are transmembrane proteins important?

In 1989, scientists determined that defects in a gene on chromosome 7 are the cause of cystic fibrosis (CF). This gene, called *CFTR* (cystic fibrosis transmembrane conductance regulator), codes for a protein that is responsible for the movement of chloride ions across the membranes of cells that produce mucus, sweat, and saliva. Defects in this gene cause an improper water-salt balance in the excretions of these cells, which in turn leads to the symptoms of CF. Studies have indicated there are over 1,800 known mutations in the CF gene. which accounts for the differences in the disease's severity in individuals with CF.

Active Transport

During **active transport,** a molecule is moving from an area of *lower* concentration to one of *higher* concentration. Active transport in involved in a number of functions in the body, from the movement of iodine ions into the cells of the thyroid gland to the transport of sugar into the cells lining the small intestine. All active transport mechanisms require a protein carrier and the use of cellular energy obtained from the breakdown of ATP. When ATP is broken down, energy is released. In this case, the energy is used to carry out active transport.

Proteins involved in active transport often are called *pumps.* Just as a water pump uses energy to move water against the force of gravity, energy is used to move substances against their concentration gradients. One type of pump, called the **sodium–potassium pump,** is active in all the cells of the body for the movement of sodium ions (Na^+) outside, and potassium ions (K^+) inside, the cell (Fig. 3.11). This type of pump is associated especially with nerve and muscle cells.

The passage of salt (NaCl) across a plasma membrane is of primary importance in cells. First, sodium ions are pumped across a membrane. Then, chloride ions diffuse through channels that allow their passage. In cystic fibrosis, a mutation in these chloride ion channels causes them to malfunction. This leads to the symptoms of this inherited (genetic) disorder.

Bulk Transport

Cells use bulk transport to move large molecules, such as polysaccharides or polypeptides, across the membrane. These processes use vesicles rather than channel or transport proteins. During *endocytosis,* a portion of the plasma membrane invaginates, or forms a pouch, to envelop a substance and fluid. Then, the membrane pinches off to form an endocytic vesicle inside the cell (Fig. 3.12*a*). Some white blood cells are able to take up pathogens (disease-causing agents) by endocytosis. This process is given a special name: *phagocytosis.* If small molecules and fluid are being imported, then the process is called *pinocytosis* (Fig. 3.12*b*).

During *exocytosis,* a vesicle fuses with the plasma membrane as secretion occurs. Later in this chapter, we will see that a steady stream of vesicles moves between certain organelles, before finally fusing with the plasma membrane. This is the way that signaling molecules, called *neurotransmitters,* leave one nerve cell to excite the next nerve cell or a muscle cell.

One form of endocytosis uses a receptor, a form of membrane protein, on the surface of the cell to concentrate specific molecules of interest for endocytosis. This process is called *receptor-mediated endocytosis* (Fig. 3.12*c*). An inherited form of cardiovascular disease occurs when cells fail to take up a combined lipoprotein and cholesterol molecule from the blood by receptor-mediated endocytosis.

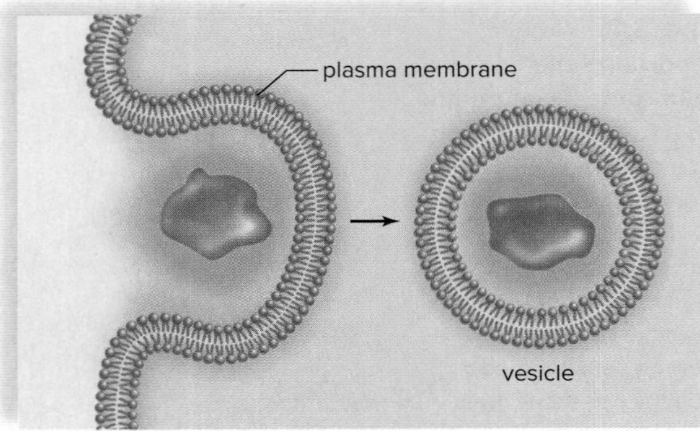

a. Phagocytosis

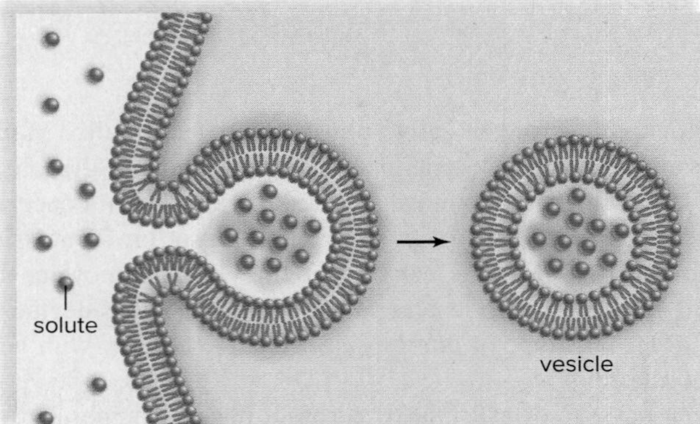

b. Pinocytosis

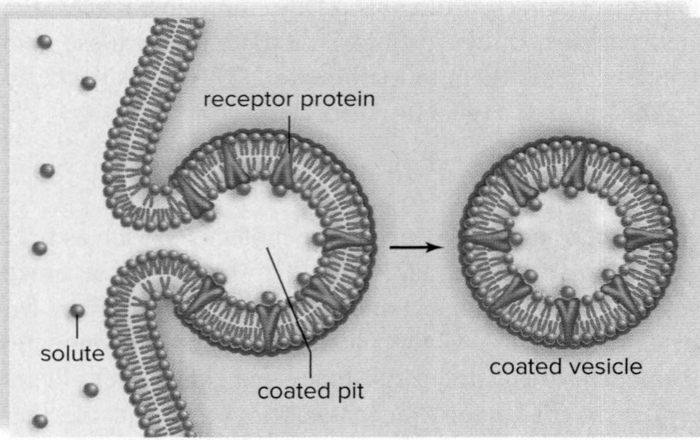

c. Receptor-mediated endocytosis

Figure 3.12 Examples of endocytosis.
a. Large substances enter a cell by phagocytosis. **b.** Small molecules and fluids enter a cell by pinocytosis. **c.** In receptor-mediated endocytosis, molecules first bind to specific receptors and are then brought into the cell by endocytosis.

CHECK YOUR PROGRESS 3.3

1. Summarize how the fluid-mosaic model describes the structure of the plasma membrane.
2. Compare and contrast diffusion, osmosis, facilitated transport, and active transport.
3. Discuss the various ways cells can move materials in bulk into and out of the cell.

CONNECTING THE CONCEPTS

The movement of materials across a plasma membrane is crucial to the maintenance of homeostasis for many organ systems in humans. For some examples, refer to the following discussions:

Section 9.3 examines how nutrients, including glucose, are moved into the cells of the digestive system.

Section 11.4 investigates how the movement of salts by the urinary system maintains blood homeostasis.

Section 21.2 explains the patterns of inheritance associated with cystic fibrosis.

3.4 The Nucleus and Endomembrane System

LEARNING OUTCOMES

Upon completion of this section, you should be able to

1. Describe the structure of the nucleus and explain its role as the storage place of genetic information.
2. Summarize the functions of the organelles of the endomembrane system.
3. Explain the role and location of the ribosomes.

The nucleus contains the genetic instructions necessary for the manufacture of the proteins involved in most cellular functions. The endomembrane system is a series of membranous organelles that function in the processing of materials for the cell.

The Nucleus

The presence of a nucleus is a defining characteristic of eukaryotic cells (Fig. 3.13). The function of the nucleus is to store the genetic information as long chains of DNA.

Within the nucleus is **chromatin,** a combination of DNA molecules and proteins. The chromatin is surrounded by a semi-fluid medium called the *nucleoplasm,* which differs in pH and composition from the cytoplasm outside the nucleus. During cell division, chromatin can coil tightly to form visible long linear structures called **chromosomes.** While uncoiled, the individual chromosomes cannot be distinguished; the chromatin appears grainy in electron micrographs of the nucleus. As we will see in Section 19.1, the chromosomes are responsible for transmitting genetic information from one generation to the next.

Located on the chromosome are collections of **genes,** which are segments of DNA that contain information for the production of specific proteins. These proteins have many functions in cells, and they help determine a cell's specificity. While every cell in the body contains the same genes, cells vary in which genes are turned on and off, and this enables them to perform their function in the tissue or organism.

Micrographs of a nucleus often show a dark region (or sometimes more than one) of chromatin. This is the **nucleolus,** where ribosomal RNA (rRNA) is produced. This is also where rRNA joins with proteins to form the subunits of ribosomes.

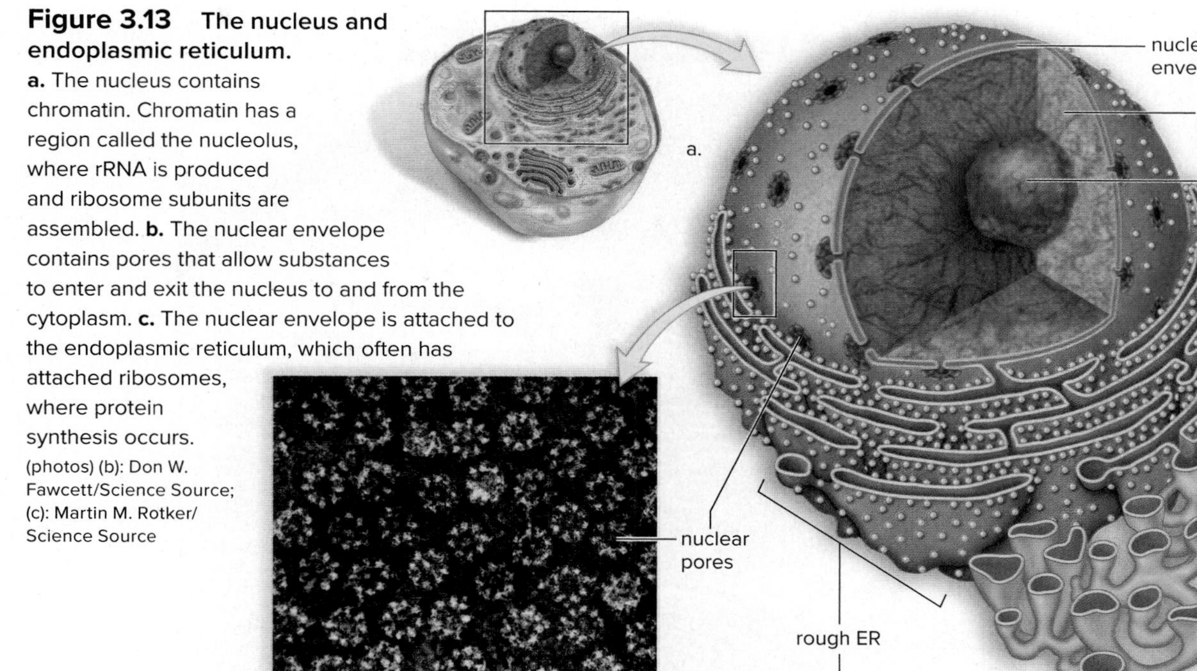

Figure 3.13 **The nucleus and endoplasmic reticulum.** **a.** The nucleus contains chromatin. Chromatin has a region called the nucleolus, where rRNA is produced and ribosome subunits are assembled. **b.** The nuclear envelope contains pores that allow substances to enter and exit the nucleus to and from the cytoplasm. **c.** The nuclear envelope is attached to the endoplasmic reticulum, which often has attached ribosomes, where protein synthesis occurs.
(photos) (b): Don W. Fawcett/Science Source; (c): Martin M. Rotker/ Science Source

The nucleus is separated from the cytoplasm by a double membrane known as the **nuclear envelope.** This is continuous with the endoplasmic reticulum (ER), a membranous system of membranous saccules and channels, discussed a little later in this section. The nuclear envelope has **nuclear pores** of sufficient size to permit the passage of ribosomal subunits out of the nucleus and proteins into the nucleus.

Ribosomes

Ribosomes are organelles composed of proteins and rRNA. Protein synthesis occurs at the ribosomes. Ribosomes are often attached to the endoplasmic reticulum, but they also may occur free within the cytoplasm, either singly or in groups called *polyribosomes.* Proteins synthesized at ribosomes attached to the endoplasmic reticulum have a different destination from that of proteins manufactured at ribosomes free in the cytoplasm.

The Endomembrane System

The **endomembrane system** consists of the nuclear envelope, the endoplasmic reticulum, the Golgi apparatus, lysosomes, and **vesicles** (tiny membranous sacs) (Fig. 3.14). This system compartmentalizes the cell so that chemical reactions are restricted to specific regions. The vesicles transport molecules from one part of the system to another.

The Endoplasmic Reticulum

The **endoplasmic reticulum (ER)** has two portions (see Fig. 3.13). *Rough ER* is studded with ribosomes on the side of the membrane that faces the cytoplasm. The proteins synthesized at these ribosomes enter the interior of the ER. Some of these proteins are incorporated into the plasma membrane (for example, channel proteins), whereas others are packed into vesicles and sent to the Golgi apparatus (see below) for additional processing and modifications. The *smooth ER* is continuous with the rough ER, but it does not have attached ribosomes. Smooth ER synthesizes the phospholipids and other lipids that occur in membranes. It also has various other functions, depending on the particular cell. For example, in the testes it produces testosterone, and it helps detoxify compounds (such as drugs) in the liver.

The ER forms transport vesicles in which large molecules are transported to other parts of the cell. Often, these vesicles are on their way to the plasma membrane or the Golgi apparatus.

The Golgi Apparatus

The **Golgi apparatus** is named for Camillo Golgi who discovered its presence in cells in the late nineteenth century. The Golgi apparatus consists of a stack of slightly curved saccules whose

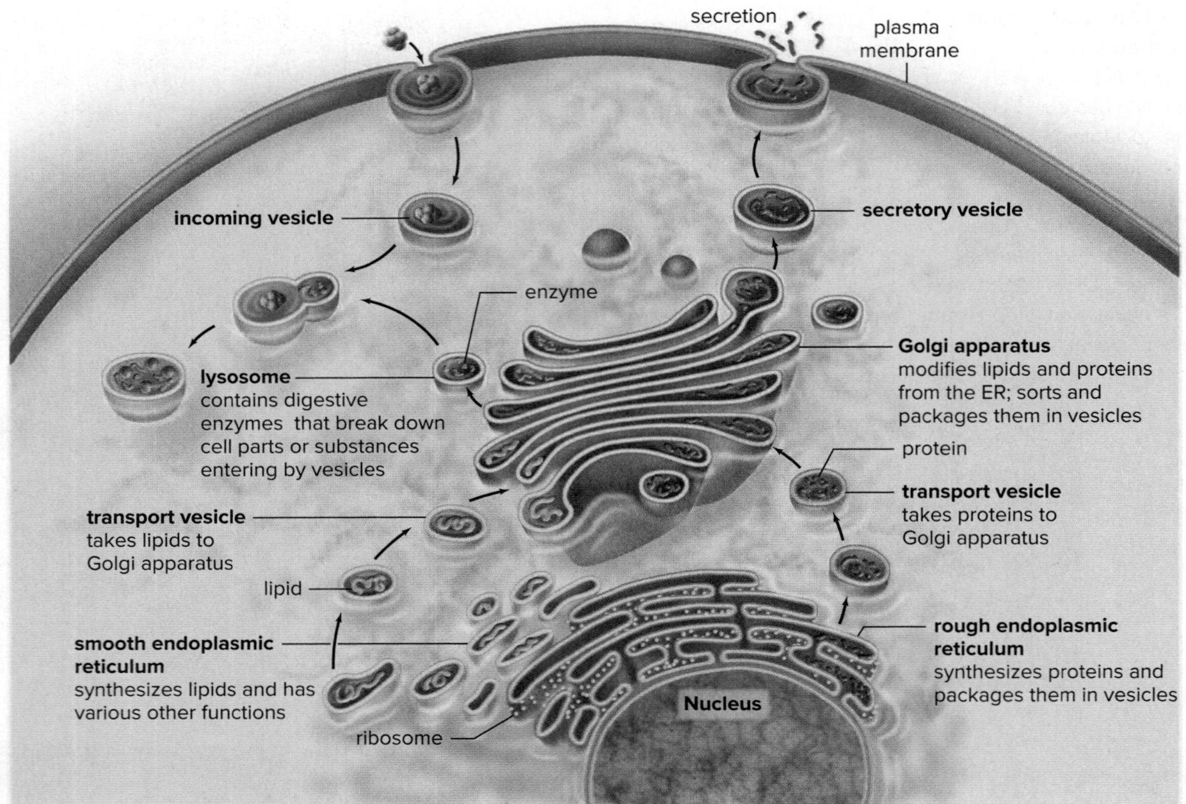

Figure 3.14 The endomembrane system.
The organelles in the endomembrane system work together to produce, modify, and secrete products for the cell. Some of these may be loaded into vesicles to produce lysosomes to digest incoming materials.

appearance can be compared to a stack of pancakes. Here, proteins and lipids received from the ER are modified. For example, a chain of sugars (carbohydrates) may be added to them, forming glycoproteins and glycolipids. These are then incorporated into the plasma membrane where they serve in the process of cellular identification.

The vesicles that leave the Golgi apparatus move to other parts of the cell. Some vesicles proceed to the plasma membrane where they discharge their contents. In all, the Golgi apparatus is involved in processing, packaging, and secretion.

Lysosomes

Lysosomes, membranous sacs produced by the Golgi apparatus, contain hydrolytic enzymes. Lysosomes are found in all cells of the body but are particularly numerous in white blood cells that engulf disease-causing microbes. When a lysosome fuses with such an endocytic vesicle, its contents are digested by hydrolytic enzymes into simpler subunits, which then enter the cytoplasm. In a process called autodigestion, parts of a cell may be broken down by the lysosomes. Some human diseases are caused by the lack of a particular enzyme in the lysosome. Tay-Sachs disease occurs due to an inactive enzyme in the lysosomes, which causes undigested lipids to collect in nerve cells, leading to developmental problems and death in early childhood.

CHECK YOUR PROGRESS 3.4

1. Describe the functions of the following organelles: endoplasmic reticulum, Golgi apparatus, and lysosomes.
2. Explain how the nucleus, ribosomes, and rough endoplasmic reticulum contribute to protein synthesis.
3. Describe the organelles of the endomembrane system involved in the export of a protein from the cell.

CONNECTING THE CONCEPTS

For a more detailed look at how the organelles of the endomembrane system function, refer to the following discussions:

Section 18.5 contains information on how aging is related to the breakdown of cellular organelles.

Section 21.2 explores the patterns of inheritance associated with Tay-Sachs disease.

Section 22.2 provides a more detailed look at how ribosomes produce proteins.

3.5 The Cytoskeleton, Cell Movement, and Cell Junctions

LEARNING OUTCOMES

Upon completion of this section, you should be able to

1. Explain the role of the cytoskeleton in the cell.
2. Summarize the major protein fibers in the cytoskeleton.
3. Describe the role of flagella and cilia in human cells.
4. Compare the functions of adhesion junctions, gap junctions, and tight junctions in human cells.

It took a high-powered electron microscope to discover that the cytoplasm of the cell is crisscrossed by several types of protein fibers, collectively called the **cytoskeleton** (see Fig. 3.4). The cytoskeleton helps maintain a cell's shape and either anchors the organelles or assists in their movement, as appropriate.

In the cytoskeleton, **microtubules** are cylinders that contain rows of a protein called tubulin. The regulation of microtubule assembly is under the control of a microtubule-organizing center called the **centrosome** (see Fig. 3.4). Microtubules help maintain the shape of the cell and act as tracks along which organelles move. During cell division, microtubules form spindle fibers, which assist in the movement of chromosomes. **Actin filaments,** made of a protein called actin, are long, extremely thin fibers that usually occur in bundles or other groupings. Actin filaments are involved in movement. Microvilli, which project from certain cells and can shorten and extend, contain actin filaments. **Intermediate filaments,** as their name implies, are intermediate in size between microtubules and actin filaments. Their structures and functions differ according to the type of cell.

Cilia and Flagella

Cilia (*sing.,* cilium) and **flagella** (*sing.,* flagellum) are involved in movement of materials along the plasma membrane, or cellular movement. The ciliated cells that line our respiratory tract sweep back up the throat the debris trapped within mucus. This helps keep the lungs clean. Similarly, ciliated cells move an egg along the uterine tube, where it may be fertilized by a flagellated sperm cell (Fig. 3.15). Motor molecules, powered by ATP, allow the microtubules in cilia and flagella to interact and bend and, thereby, move.

The importance of normal cilia and flagella is illustrated by the occurrence of a genetic disorder called ciliary dyskinesia. This is a recessive disorder (see Section 21.3) in which one of the genes associated with the production of a protein found in the microtubules of cilia and flagella is not formed correctly. The result is cilia and flagella that will not bend. Not surprisingly, these individuals suffer from recurrent and severe respiratory infections. The ciliated cells lining respiratory passages fail to keep their lungs clean. They are also unable to reproduce naturally due to the lack of ciliary action to move the egg in a female or the lack of flagella action by sperm in a male.

Extracellular Matrix

A protective **extracellular matrix (ECM)** is a meshwork of proteins and polysaccharides in close

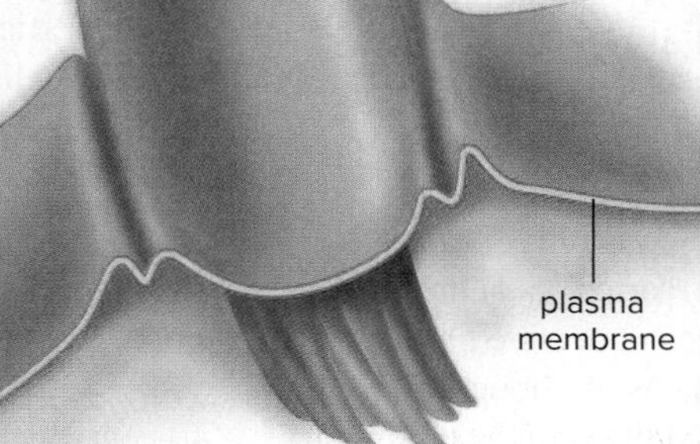

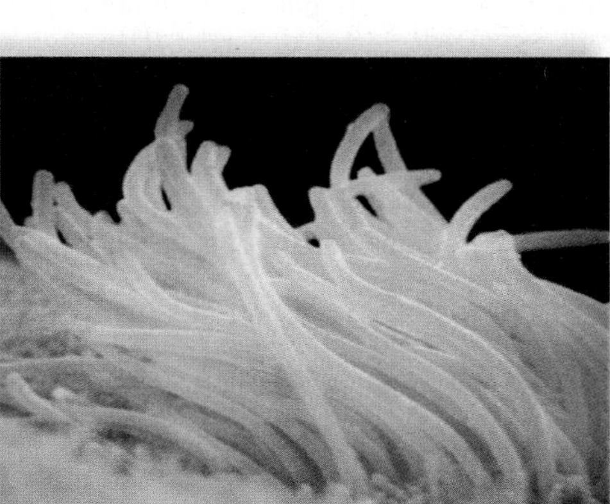

Figure 3.15 Structure and function of the flagella and cilia. **a.** Sperm are an example of a human cell with flagella. **b.** The structure of a flagellum (or cilium) contains microtubules. **c.** Cilia cover the surface of the cells of the respiratory system, where they beat upward to remove foreign matter.

(photos) (a): Dr. Tony Brain/Science Photo Library/Getty Images; (c): Dr. G. Moscoso/Science Source

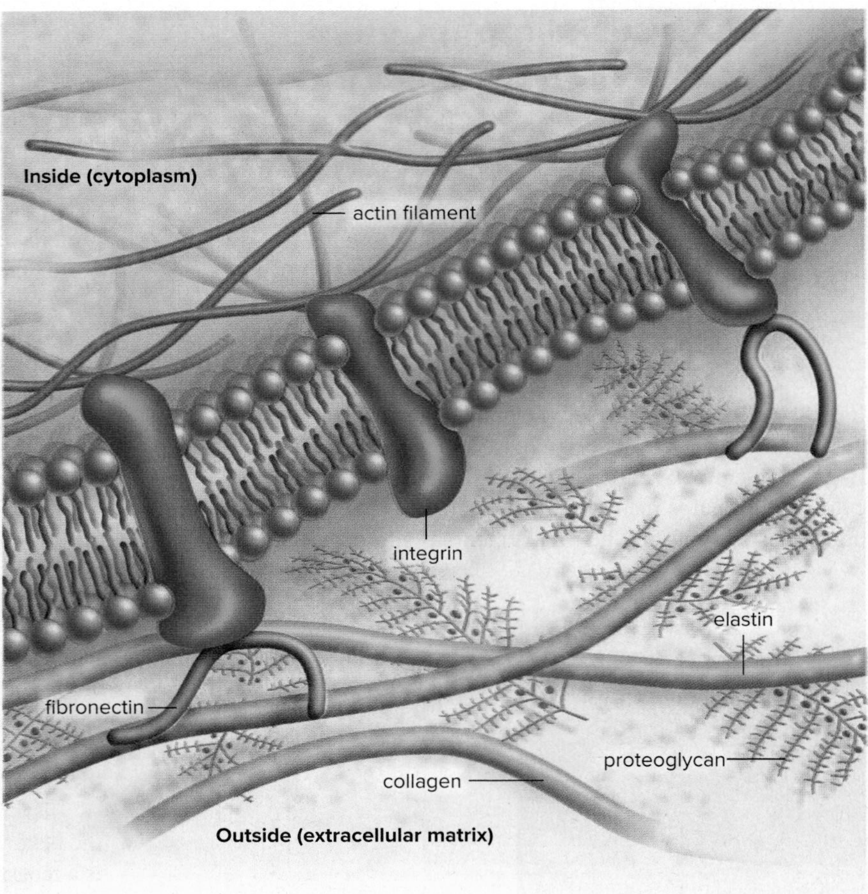

Figure 3.16 **Extracellular matrix.** In the extracellular matrix (ECM), collagen and elastin have a support function, whereas fibronectins bind to integrin, thus assisting communication between the ECM and the cytoskeleton.

association with the cell that produced them (Fig. 3.16). Collagen and elastin fibers are two well-known structural proteins in the ECM; collagen resists stretching, and elastin gives the ECM resilience.

Fibronectin is an adhesive protein (colored green in Fig. 3.16) that binds to a protein in the plasma membrane called integrin. Integrins are integral membrane proteins that connect to fibronectin externally and to the actin cytoskeleton internally. Through its connections with both the ECM and the cytoskeleton, integrin plays a role in cell signaling, permitting the ECM to influence the activities of the cytoskeleton and, therefore, the shape and activities of the cell. Proteoglycans (a combination of polysaccharides and proteins) interact with polysaccharides in the ECM to resist compression. Proteoglycans also influence the process of cell signaling by regulating the passage of molecules through the ECM to the plasma membrane, where receptors are located.

In Section 4.2, during the discussion of connective tissue, we will explore how the extracellular matrix varies in quantity and consistency: being quite flexible, as in loose connective tissue; semiflexible, as in cartilage; and rock solid, as in bone. The extracellular matrix of bone is hard because, in addition to the components mentioned, mineral salts, notably calcium salts, are deposited outside the cell.

Junctions Between Cells

As we will see in Section 4.1, human tissues are known to have junctions between their cells that allow them to function in a coordinated manner. Figure 3.17 illustrates the three main types of cell junctions in human cells.

Adhesion junctions mechanically attach adjacent cells. In these junctions, the cytoskeletons of two adjacent cells are interconnected. They are a common type of junction between skin cells. In *tight junctions,* connections between the plasma membrane proteins of neighboring cells produce a zipperlike barrier. These types of junctions are common in the digestive system and the kidney where it is necessary to contain fluids (digestive juices and urine) within a specific area. *Gap junctions* serve as communication portals between cells. In these junctions, channel proteins of the plasma membrane fuse, allowing easy movement between adjacent cells.

CHECK YOUR PROGRESS 3.5

1. List the three types of fibers in the cytoskeleton.
2. Describe the structure of cilia and flagella, and state the function of each.
3. List the types of junctions found between animal cells, and state a function for each.

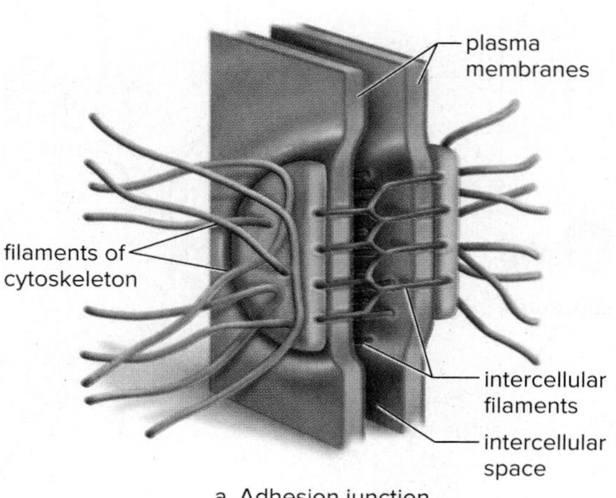

a. Adhesion junction

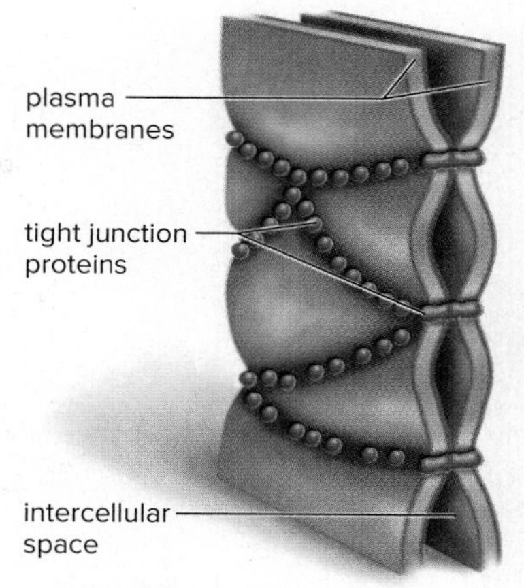

b. Tight junction

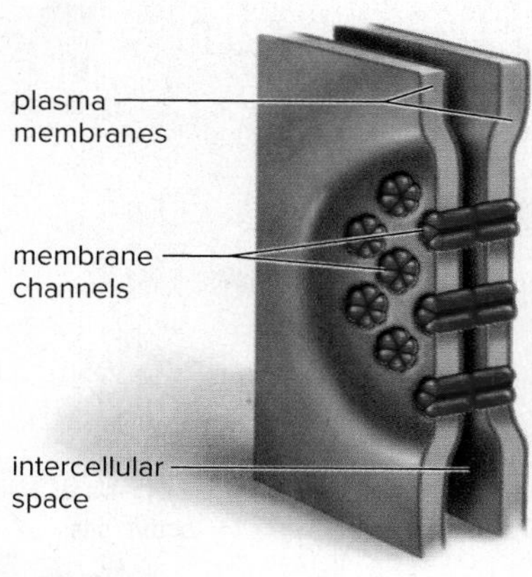

c. Gap junction

Figure 3.17 **Junctions between cells.**
a. Adhesion junctions mechanically connect cells. **b.** Tight junctions form barriers with the external environment. **c.** Gap junctions allow for communication between cells.

CONNECTING THE CONCEPTS

The cytoskeleton of the cell plays an important role in many aspects of our physiology. To explore this further, refer to the following discussions:

Section 10.1 investigates how the ciliated cells of the respiratory system function.

Section 17.2 explains the role of the flagellated sperm cell in reproduction.

Section 19.3 explores how the cytoskeleton is involved in cell division.

3.6 Metabolism and the Energy Reactions

LEARNING OUTCOMES

Upon completion of this section, you should be able to

1. Understand the relationship of products and reactants in a metabolic reaction.
2. Identify the role of an enzyme in a metabolic reaction.
3. Summarize the roles of the anaerobic and aerobic pathways in energy generation.
4. Illustrate the stages of the ATP cycle.

Metabolic Pathways

Metabolism is the sum of all the chemical reactions that occur within the body. The reactions, such as cellular respiration, occur at the cellular level and often involve metabolic pathways that are carried out by enzymes sequentially arranged in cells:

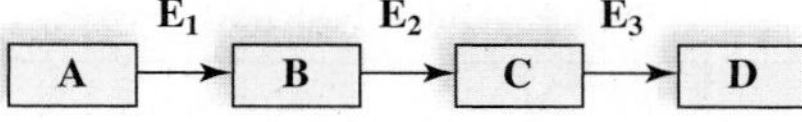

Metabolic pathways begin with a particular reactant (such as A in the diagram above) and end with a final product (D in the diagram). Many specific steps can be involved in a metabolic pathway, and each step is a chemical reaction catalyzed by an enzyme (E_1, E_2, E_3). The substrates for the first reaction are converted into products, and those products then serve as the substrates for the next enzyme-catalyzed reaction. One reaction leads to the next reaction in an organized, highly regulated manner.

Metabolic pathways are highly regulated by the cell. One type of regulation is *feedback inhibition.* In feedback inhibition, one of the end products of the metabolic pathway interacts with an enzyme early in the pathway. In most cases, this feedback slows down the pathway so that the cell does not produce more product than it needs.

Enzymes

Enzymes are metabolic assistants that speed up the rate of a chemical reaction. The reactant(s) that participate(s) in the reaction is/are called the enzyme's **substrate(s).** Enzymes are often named for their substrates. For example, lipids are broken down by lipase, maltose by maltase, and lactose by lactase.

The following equation is often used to indicate that an enzyme forms a complex with its substrate:

$$\underset{\text{substrate}}{S} + \underset{\text{enzyme}}{E} \longrightarrow \underset{\text{enzyme-substrate complex}}{ES} \longrightarrow E + \underset{\text{product}}{P}$$

Enzymes have a specific region, called an **active site,** where the substrates are brought together so they can react. An enzyme's specificity is caused by the shape of the active site. Here, the enzyme and its substrate(s) fit together in a specific way, much as the pieces of a jigsaw puzzle fit together (Fig. 3.18). After one reaction is complete, the product or products are released. The enzyme is then ready to be used again. Therefore, a cell requires only a small amount of a particular enzyme to carry out a reaction. It is important to note that enzymes are not destroyed in a chemical reaction, and therefore can be used over and over again.

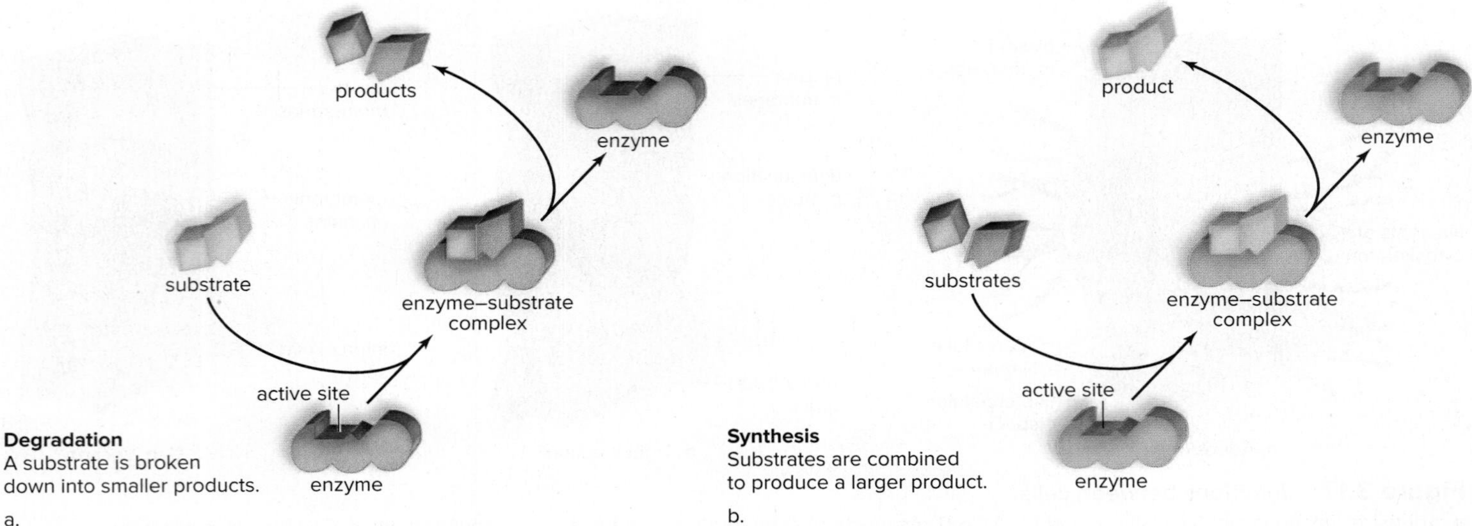

Figure 3.18 Action of an enzyme.
An enzyme has an active site, where the substrates and enzyme fit together in such a way that the substrates are oriented to react. Following the reaction, the products are released and the enzyme is free to act again. **a.** Some enzymes carry out degradation, in which the substrate is broken down into smaller products. **b.** Other enzymes carry out synthesis, in which the substrates are combined to produce a larger product.

Molecules frequently do not react with one another unless they are activated in some way. In the lab, for example, in the absence of an enzyme, activation is very often achieved by heating a reaction flask to increase the number of effective collisions between molecules. The energy that must be added to cause molecules to react with one another is called the **energy of activation (E_a)** (Fig. 3.19). Even though the reaction will proceed, the energy of activation must be overcome. The burning of firewood releases a tremendous amount of energy, but firewood in a pile does not spontaneously combust. The input of some energy, perhaps a lit match, is required to overcome the energy of activation.

Figure 3.19 shows E_a when an enzyme is not present compared to when an enzyme is present, illustrating that enzymes lower the amount of energy required for activation to occur. Nevertheless, the addition of the enzyme does not change the end result of the reaction. Notice that the energy of the products is less than the energy of the reactants. This indicates that the reaction will occur, but not until the energy of activation is overcome. Without the enzyme, the reaction rate will be very slow. By lowering the energy of activation, the enzyme increases the rate of the reaction.

Coenzymes are nonprotein molecules that assist the activity of an enzyme and may even accept or contribute atoms to the reaction. It is interesting that vitamins are often components of coenzymes. The vitamin niacin is a part of the coenzyme **NAD^+ (nicotinamide adenine dinucleotide),** which carries hydrogen (H) and electrons.

Mitochondria and Cellular Respiration

Mitochondria (*sing.,* mitochondrion) are often called the powerhouses of the cell. Just as a powerhouse burns fuel to produce electricity, the mitochondria convert the chemical energy of glucose products into the chemical energy of ATP molecules. In the process, mitochondria use up oxygen and give off carbon dioxide. Therefore, the process of producing ATP is called **cellular respiration.** The structure of mitochondria is appropriate to the task. Mitochondria are double-membrane organelles, with an outer plasma membrane and an inner membrane that is folded to form little shelves called *cristae*. These project into the matrix, an inner space filled with a gel-like fluid (Fig. 3.20). The matrix of a mitochondrion contains enzymes for breaking down glucose products.

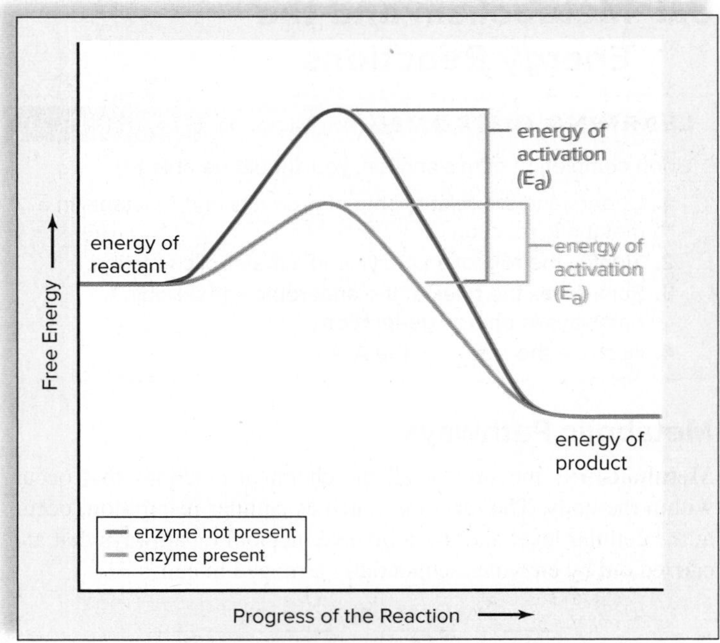

Figure 3.19 Energy of activation.
Enzymes accelerate the rate of a metabolic reaction by lowering the amount of energy of activation needed to start the reaction.

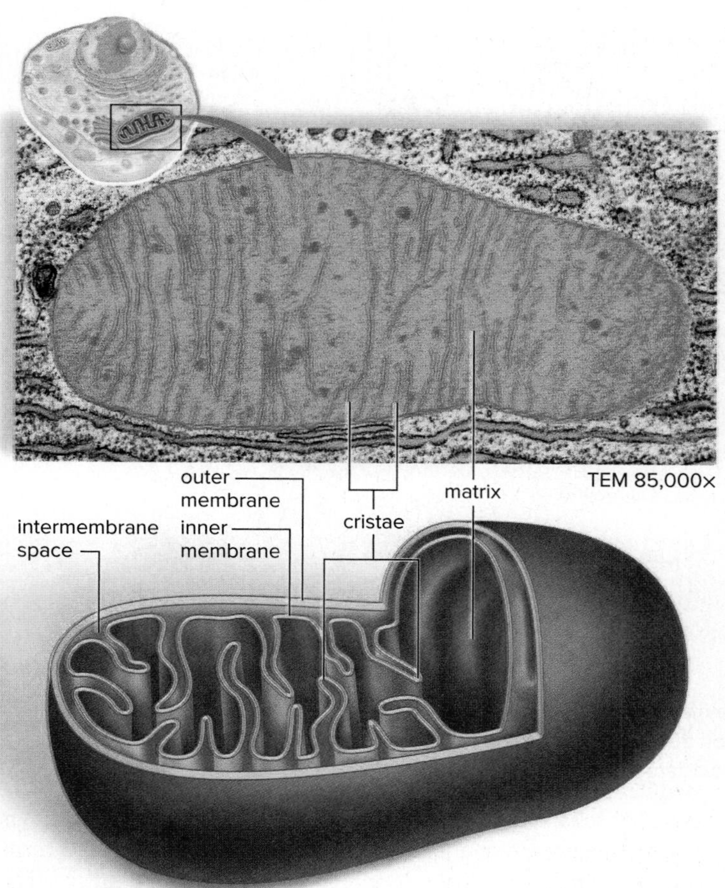

Figure 3.20 **The structure of a mitochondrion.**
A mitochondrion is bound by a double membrane, and the inner membrane folds into projections called cristae. The cristae project into a semifluid matrix that contains many enzymes.
(photo): Keith R. Porter/Science Source

ATP production then occurs at the cristae. Protein complexes that aid in the conversion of energy are located in an assembly-line fashion on these membranous shelves.

The structure of a mitochondrion supports the hypothesis that mitochondria were originally prokaryotes that became engulfed by a cell (see Fig. 3.5). Mitochondria are bound by a double membrane, as a prokaryote would be if it were taken into a cell by endocytosis. Even more interesting is the observation that mitochondria have their own genes—and they reproduce themselves!

ATP–ADP Cycle

ATP is the energy currency of the cell and is involved in a variety of cellular processes. The ATP (Fig. 3.21) resembles that of a rechargeable battery. The breakdown of glucose during cellular respiration is used to produce ATP from ADP and inorganic phosphate Ⓟ. This ATP is then used for the metabolic work of the cell. Muscle cells use ATP for contraction, and nerve cells use it for conduction of nerve impulses. ATP breakdown releases heat, ADP, and phosphate Ⓟ.

Cellular Respiration

After blood transports glucose and oxygen to cells, cellular respiration begins. Cellular respiration breaks down glucose to carbon dioxide and water. Three pathways are involved in the breakdown of glucose—glycolysis, the citric acid cycle, and the electron transport chain (Fig. 3.22). These metabolic pathways allow the energy in a glucose molecule to be slowly released, so that ATP can be gradually produced. Cells would lose a tremendous amount of energy, in the form of heat, if glucose breakdown occurred all at once. When humans burn wood or coal, the energy escapes all at once as heat. But a cell "burns" glucose gradually, and energy is captured as ATP.

Glycolysis **Glycolysis** means "sugar splitting." During glycolysis, glucose, a 6-carbon (C_6) molecule, is split so that the result is two 3-carbon (C_3) molecules of *pyruvate*. Glycolysis, which occurs in the cytoplasm, is found in most every type of cell. Therefore, this pathway is believed to have evolved early in the history of life.

Glycolysis is an **anaerobic** pathway because it does not require oxygen. This pathway can occur in microbes that live in bogs or swamps or in our intestinal tract where there is no oxygen. During glycolysis, hydrogens and electrons are removed from glucose,

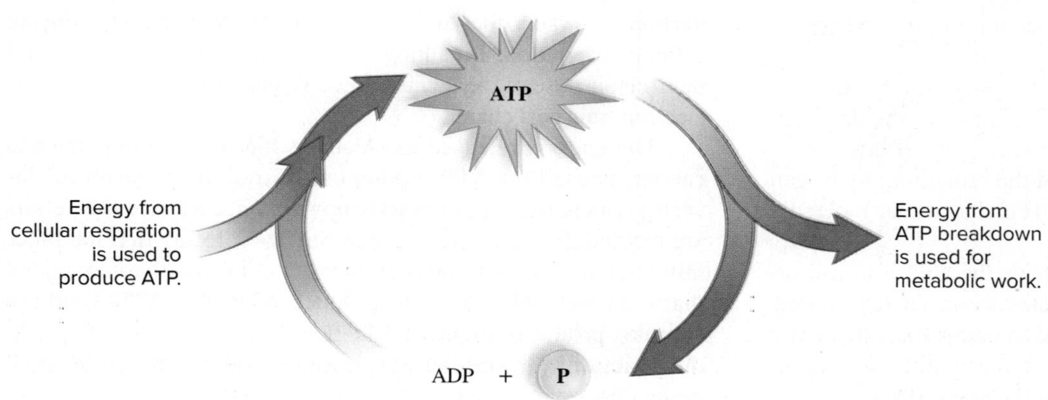

Figure 3.21 **The ATP cycle.**
The breakdown of organic nutrients, such as glucose, by cellular respiration transfers energy to form ATP. ATP is used for energy-requiring reactions, such as muscle contraction. ATP breakdown also gives off heat. Additional food energy rejoins ADP and Ⓟ to form ATP again.

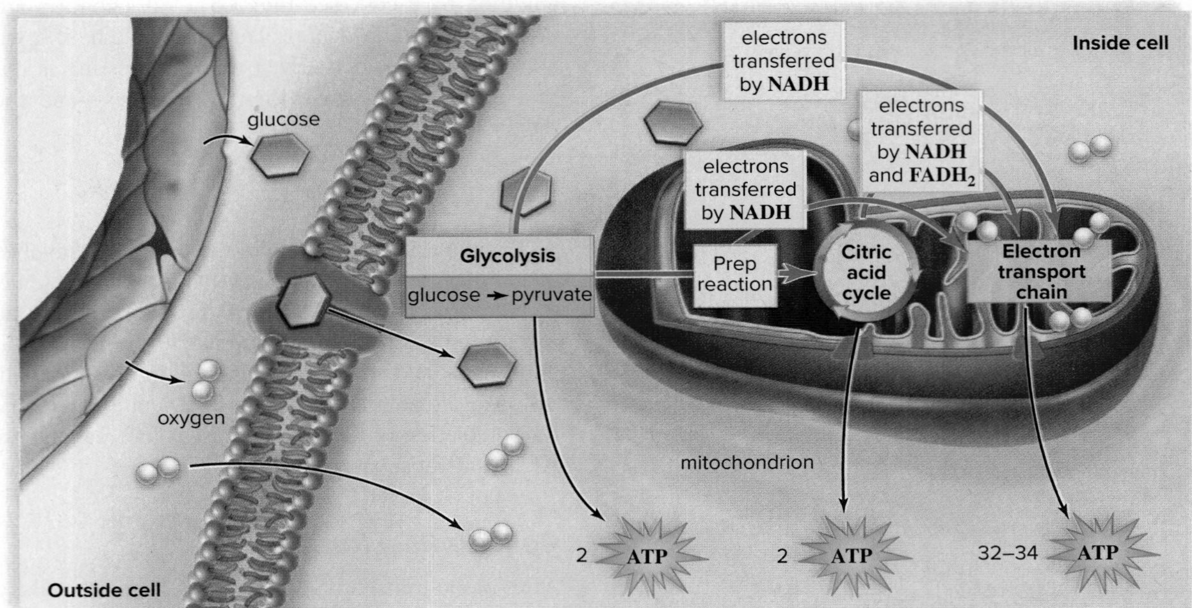

Figure 3.22 Production of ATP.
Glucose enters a cell from the bloodstream by facilitated transport. The three main pathways of cellular respiration (glycolysis, citric acid cycle, and electron transport chain) all produce ATP, but most is produced by the electron transport chain. NADH carries electrons to the electron transport chain from glycolysis and the citric acid cycle. ATP exits a mitochondrion by facilitated transport.

and NADH results. The breaking of bonds releases enough energy for a net yield of two ATP molecules.

Preparatory Reaction Pyruvate is a pivotal molecule in cellular respiration. When oxygen is available, the molecule enters the preparatory (prep) reaction, named because it prepares the outputs of glycolysis (pyruvate molecules) for use in the citric acid cycle mitochondria so they may be completely broken down. A small amount of NADH is produced per glucose. As we will discuss later in this section, fermentation occurs when oxygen is not available.

Citric Acid Cycle Each of the pyruvate molecules, after a brief modification, enters the citric acid cycle as acetyl CoA. The **citric acid cycle,** also called the *Krebs cycle,* is a cyclical series of enzymatic reactions that occurs in the matrix of mitochondria.

The purpose of this pathway is to complete the breakdown of glucose by breaking the remaining C—C bonds. As the reactions progress, carbon dioxide is released, a small amount of ATP (two per glucose) is produced, and the remaining hydrogen and electrons are carried away by NADH and a similar molecule called $FADH_2$.

The cellular respiration pathways have the ability to use organic molecules other than carbohydrates as an energy source. Both fats and proteins may be converted to compounds that enter the citric acid cycle. More information on these processes is provided in the Health feature "The Metabolic Fate of Pizza."

Electron Transport Chain NADH molecules from glycolysis and the citric acid cycle deliver electrons to the **electron transport chain.** The members of the electron transport chain are carrier proteins grouped into complexes. These complexes are embedded in the cristae of a mitochondrion. Each carrier of the electron transport chain accepts two electrons and passes them on to the next carrier. The hydrogens carried by NADH molecules will be used later.

High-energy electrons enter the chain, and as they are passed from carrier to carrier, the electrons lose energy. Low-energy electrons emerge from the chain. Oxygen serves as the final acceptor of the electrons at the end of the chain. After oxygen receives the electrons, it combines with hydrogens and becomes water.

The presence of oxygen makes the electron transport chain **aerobic.** Oxygen does not combine with any substrates during cellular respiration. Breathing is necessary to our existence, and the sole purpose of oxygen is to receive electrons at the end of the electron transport chain.

The energy, released as electrons that pass from carrier to carrier, is used for ATP production. It took many years for investigators to determine exactly how this occurs, and the details are beyond the scope of this text. Suffice it to say that the inner mitochondrial membrane contains an ATP–synthase complex that combines ADP + Ⓟ to produce ATP. The ATP–synthase complex produces about 32 ATP per glucose molecule. Overall, the reactions of cellular respiration produce 36 to 38 ATP molecules.

BIOLOGY TODAY ▶ **Health**

The Metabolic Fate of Pizza

Obviously, our diets do not consist solely of carbohydrates. Because fats and proteins are also organic nutrients, it makes sense that our bodies can utilize the energy found in the bonds of these molecules. In fact, the metabolic pathways we have discussed in this chapter are more than capable of accessing the energy of fats and proteins. For example, let's trace the fate of a pepperoni pizza, which contains carbohydrates (crust), fats (cheese), and protein (pepperoni).

We already know that the glucose in the carbohydrate crust is broken down during cellular respiration. When the cheese in the pizza (a fat) is used as an energy source, it breaks down into glycerol and three fatty acids. As Figure 3A indicates, glycerol can be converted to pyruvate and enter glycolysis. The fatty acids are converted to an intermediate that enters the citric acid cycle. An 18-carbon fatty acid results in nine acetyl CoA molecules. Calculation shows that respiration of these can produce a total of 108 ATP molecules. This is why fats are an efficient form of stored energy—the three long fatty acid chains per fat molecule can produce considerable ATP when needed.

Proteins are less frequently used as an energy source, but are available if necessary. The carbon skeleton of amino acids can enter glycolysis, be converted to acetyl groups, or enter the citric acid cycle at another point. The carbon skeleton is produced in the liver when the amino group is removed from the amino acid, a process called deamination. The amino group becomes ammonia (NH_3), which enters the urea cycle and becomes part of urea, the primary excretory product of humans.

In Section 9.6, we will take a more detailed look at the nutritional needs of humans, and will include discussions on how vitamins and minerals interact with metabolic pathways, as well as the dietary guidelines for proteins, fats, and carbohydrates.

Questions to Consider

1. How might a meal of a cheeseburger and fries be processed by the cellular respiration pathways?
2. Even though Figure 3A does not indicate the need for water, it is an important component of our diet. Where would water interact with these pathways?

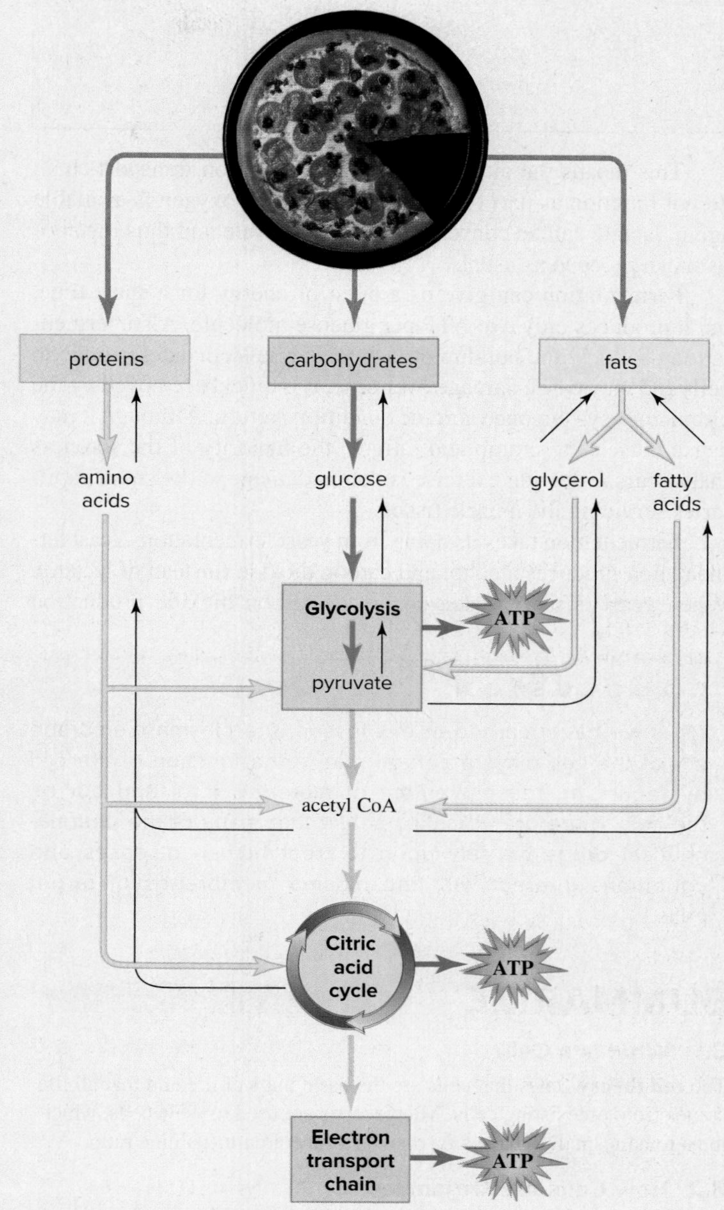

Figure 3A The use of fats and proteins for energy. Carbohydrates, fats, and proteins can be used as energy sources, and their monomers (carbohydrates and proteins) or subunits (fats) enter degradative pathways at specific points.
(photo): C Squared Studios/Photodisc/Getty Images

Fermentation

Fermentation is an anaerobic process, meaning it does not require oxygen. When oxygen is not available to cells, the electron transport chain soon becomes inoperative. This is because oxygen is not present to accept electrons. In this case, most cells have a safety valve so that some ATP can still be produced. Glycolysis operates as long as it is supplied with "free" NAD^+ that is available to pick up hydrogens and electrons. Normally, NADH takes electrons to the electron transport chain and, thereby, is recycled to become NAD^+. However, if the system is not working due to a lack of oxygen, NADH passes its hydrogens and electrons to pyruvate molecules, as shown in the following reaction:

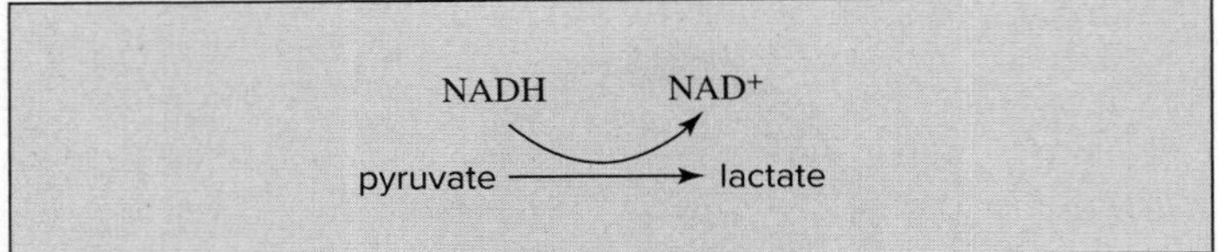

This means the citric acid cycle and electron transport chain do not function as part of fermentation. When oxygen is available again, lactate can be converted back to pyruvate and thus metabolism can proceed as usual.

Fermentation can give us a burst of energy for a short time, but it produces only two ATP per glucose molecule. Also, fermentation results in the buildup of lactate. While lactic acid is toxic to cells and may cause damage over time, it is quickly removed by the circulatory system once aerobic conditions return. Although it may cause muscles to cramp and fatigue, the majority of the soreness that occurs following exercise is due to damage to the small capillaries servicing the muscle tissue.

Fermentation takes its name from yeast fermentation. Yeast fermentation produces alcohol and carbon dioxide (instead of lactate). When yeast is used to leaven bread, carbon dioxide production makes the bread rise. When yeast is used to produce alcoholic beverages, it is the alcohol that humans make use of.

CHECK YOUR PROGRESS 3.6

1. Summarize the roles of enzymes in chemical reactions.
2. Describe the basic steps required to break down glucose by cellular respiration.
3. Explain why the ATP cycle resembles that of a rechargeable battery.
4. Explain the differences between cellular respiration and fermentation.

CONNECTING THE CONCEPTS

For additional information on the processing of nutrients for energy, refer to the following discussions:

Sections 2.3 to **2.5** provide a more detailed look at carbohydrates and other energy nutrients.

Section 9.3 explores how the small intestine processes nutrients for absorption.

Section 9.6 describes the importance of carbohydrates, fats, and proteins in the diet.

CONCLUSION

As we have learned in this lesson, the plasma membrane of the cell plays a central role in the function of the cell by regulating the movement of materials into, and out of, the cell. Therefore, it makes sense that many of the pharmaceutical drugs we rely upon to treat human diseases and conditions interact with the plasma membranes of target cells.

In some cases, drugs that have been designed to treat a condition, such as opioids and the sensation of pain, may be abused, and result in addiction and secondary health issues. By better understanding the structure of the plasma membrane, and more importantly the proteins embedded in it, it may be possible to design medications that have the same benefits in the treatment of disease, but reduce the chance of addictive behaviors.

SUMMARIZE

3.1 What Is a Cell?

The **cell theory** states that cells are the basic units of life and that all life comes from preexisting cells. Microscopes are used to view cells, which must remain small to have a favorable surface-area-to-volume ratio.

3.2 How Cells Are Organized

The human cell is a **eukaryotic cell** with a **nucleus** that contains the genetic material. **Prokaryotic cells,** such as bacteria, are smaller than eukaryotic cells and lack a nucleus.

The cell is surrounded by a **plasma membrane,** a **selectively permeable** barrier that limits the movement of materials into and out of the cell. Between the plasma membrane and the nucleus is the **cytoplasm.** In eukaryotic cells, the cytoplasm contains various **organelles,** each with specific functions.

3.3 The Plasma Membrane and How Substances Cross It

The **fluid-mosaic model** describes the structure of the plasma membrane. The plasma membrane contains

- A phospholipid bilayer that selectively regulates the passage of molecules and ions into and out of the cell.

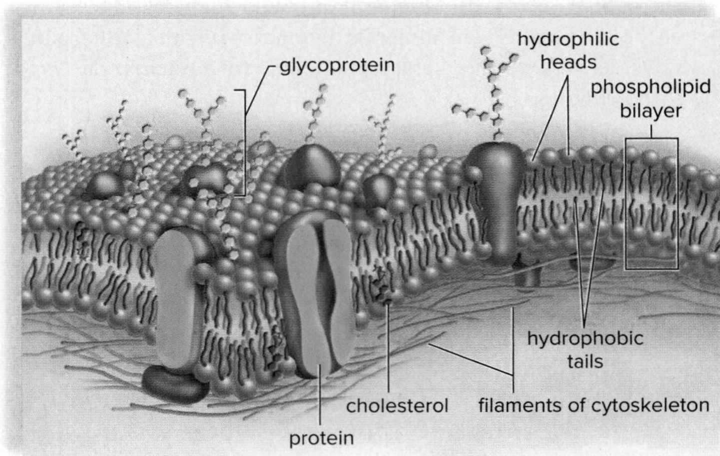

- Embedded proteins, which allow certain substances to cross the plasma membrane.

Passage of molecules into or out of cells can be passive or active.

- Passive mechanisms do not require energy. Examples are **diffusion, osmosis,** and **facilitated transport. Tonicity** and **osmotic pressure** control the process of osmosis.

- Active mechanisms require an input of energy. Examples are **active transport** (sodium–potassium pump), endocytosis (phagocytosis and pinocytosis), receptor-mediated endocytosis, and exocytosis.

3.4 The Nucleus and Endomembrane System

- The nucleus houses DNA, which contains **genes** that specify the order of amino acids in proteins. **Chromatin** is a combination of DNA molecules and proteins that make up **chromosomes.**
- The nucleus is surrounded by a **nuclear envelope** that contains **nuclear pores** for communication and the movement of materials.
- The **nucleolus** produces ribosomal RNA (rRNA).
- Protein synthesis occurs in **ribosomes,** small organelles composed of proteins and rRNA.

The Endomembrane System

The **endomembrane system** consists of the nuclear envelope, **endoplasmic reticulum (ER),** Golgi apparatus, lysosomes, and **vesicles.**

- The rough ER has ribosomes, where protein synthesis occurs.
- Smooth ER has no ribosomes and has various functions, including lipid synthesis.
- The **Golgi apparatus** processes and packages proteins and lipids into vesicles for secretion or movement into other parts of the cell.
- **Lysosomes** are specialized vesicles produced by the Golgi apparatus. They fuse with incoming vesicles to digest enclosed material, and they autodigest old cell parts.

3.5 The Cytoskeleton, Cell Movement, and Cell Junctions

- The **cytoskeleton** consists of **microtubules, actin filaments,** and **intermediate filaments** that give cells their shape; and it allows organelles to move about the cell. Microtubules are organized by **centrosomes. Cilia** and **flagella,** which contain microtubules, allow a cell to move.
- Cell junctions connect cells to form tissues and to facilitate communication between cells.
- The **extracellular matrix (ECM)** is located outside the plasma membrane. It may provide structure and regulate the movement of materials into the cell.

3.6 Metabolism and the Energy Reactions

Metabolic Pathways

- **Metabolism** represents all the chemical reactions that occur in a cell. A metabolic pathway is a series of reactions, each of which has its own enzyme. The materials entering these reactions are called **reactants,** and the materials leaving the pathway are called **products.**

Enzymes

- **Enzymes** bind their **substrates** in the **active site.**
- Enzymes accelerate chemical reactions by lowering the **energy of activation (E_a)** needed to start the reaction.
- **Coenzymes,** such as **NAD^+ (nicotinamide adenine dinucleotide),** are nonprotein molecules that assist enzymes.

Mitochondria and Cellular Respiration

- **Mitochondria** are involved in **cellular respiration,** which uses oxygen and releases carbon dioxide.
- During cellular respiration, mitochondria convert the energy of glucose into the energy of ATP molecules.

Cellular Respiration and Metabolism

- Cellular respiration includes three pathways: glycolysis, the citric acid cycle, and the electron transport chain.
- **Glycolysis** occurs in the cytoplasm and is **anaerobic.** It produces two pyruvate molecules and small amounts of ATP and NADH.
- The pyruvate molecules are modified by the preparatory reactions in the mitochondria before entering the citric acid cycle.
- The **citric acid cycle** occurs in the matrix of the mitochondria. Its role is to break C—C bonds and generate ATP, NADH, and $FADH_2$.
- The **electron transport chain** is located along the cristae of the mitochondria. It is an **aerobic** pathway that uses the electrons in the NADH and $FADH_2$ molecules to generate the majority of the ATP in the cell.
- If oxygen is not available in cells, the electron transport chain is inoperative, and **fermentation** (which does not require oxygen) occurs. Fermentation recycles NAD^+ molecules so the cell can produce a small amount of ATP by glycolysis.

ENGAGE

BioNOW

Want to know how this science is relevant to your life? Check out the BioNOW videos below:

- Cell Size

McGraw Hill

- Saltwater Filter

McGraw Hill

- Energy Part I: Energy Transfers

McGraw Hill

- Energy Part III: Cellular Respiration

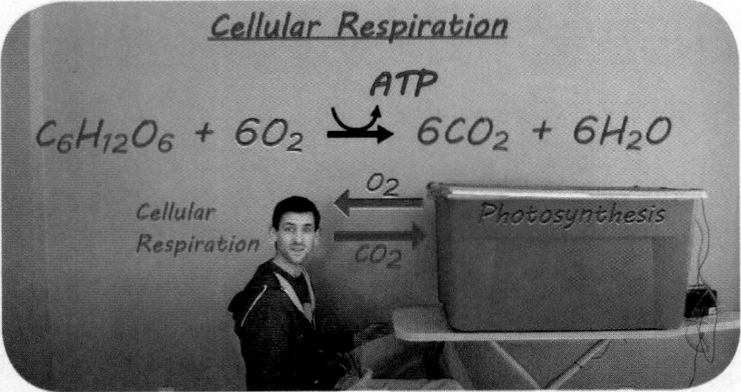

McGraw Hill

1. **Cell Size:** Why would a larger surface-area-to-volume ratio increase metabolic efficiency?
2. **Saltwater Filter:** Explain how the potato uses the principles of diffusion to measure the salt concentration in the branch samples.
3. **Energy Transfers:** Explain how both laws of thermodynamics apply to the experiments in this video.
4. **Cellular Respiration:** What cellular processes are producing the CO_2 being measured in this experiment?

THINKING CRITICALLY

1. What might occur if the cells of the body contain malfunctioning mitochondria?
2. What would happen to homeostasis if enzymes were no longer produced in the body?
3. Knowing what you know about the function of a lysosome, what might occur if the cells' lysosomes are overproductive instead of malfunctioning?

MAKING IT RELEVANT

1. Based on what you have learned, how do your cells interact with opioids?
2. Do you think prescription-based opioids should be prescribed to patients suffering from chronic pain or other ailments? What limitations would you impose?
3. Is it possible that individuals who lack or have altered transmembrane receptors will not become addicted to opioids?

Find answers to all of the chapter questions at connect.mheducation.com

mihtiander/Getty Images

CHAPTER 4

Tissues, Organ Systems, and Homeostasis

Your Body Under Water

No matter where we are or what our activities, the systems of our bodies work to maintain an established set of internal operating conditions, or *homeostasis*. Let's say you are visiting the tropics to explore the biodiversity of coral reefs. As you begin your dive, your respiratory system adjusts its activity to provide oxygen to power your muscles and brain, while simultaneously removing carbon dioxide waste material. Powering your muscles takes energy, so your endocrine system must adjust for the level of glucose in your blood to meet demand. Simultaneously, your urinary system works to maintain salt balances in your blood and prepare waste material for removal.

As you enjoy the complexity of the reef, your nervous system not only processes visual images, it also monitors the internal conditions of your body: its temperature, the pressure of the water on your body, and the level of carbon dioxide in your blood. If you are cold, your nervous system instructs the muscles to shiver to generate heat. If excited or you exert yourself, the nervous system increases your respiratory rate. And while all of this is happening, your nervous system keeps reminding you of the position of your arms and legs so you can swim more effectively.

Our ability to perform tasks, such as scuba diving, are the result of a close integration of our body systems. These interactions are often complex and usually occur without our conscious thought. From a genetic to a cellular to a physiological level, the same tissue and organ systems that make exploring a coral reef possible let us control our bodies during our daily activities.

In this chapter, we will first explore the tissues of the body, and then discuss organ systems and the concept of homeostasis.

As you read through the chapter, think about the following questions:

1. Why is the maintenance of a constant temperature and oxygen concentration important?
2. What types of tissues make up each of the human body's major organ systems?
3. How do feedback mechanisms help maintain homeostasis?

CHAPTER OUTLINE

BEFORE YOU BEGIN

Before beginning this chapter, take a few moments to review the following discussions:

Section 1.1 How do tissues and organs fit into the levels of biological organization?

Section 3.2 How are eukaryotic cells structured?

Section 3.5 How are cells linked together to form tissues?

4.1 Types of Tissues

LEARNING OUTCOMES

Upon completion of this section, you should be able to

1. Understand where tissues relate in the biological levels of organization.
2. Describe the four major classes of tissues and provide a general function for each.

Recall from our discussion on the levels of biological organization (see Fig. 1.2) that cells are composed of molecules; tissues are a group of similar cells; organs contain several different types of tissues; and multiple organs are found in an organ system. In this chapter, we will explore the tissue, organ, and organ system levels of organization.

A **tissue** is composed of specialized cells of the same type that perform a common function in the body. The tissues of the human body can be categorized into four major types:

- *Connective tissue* binds and supports body parts.
- *Muscular tissue* moves the body and its parts.
- *Nervous tissue* receives sensory information and conducts nerve impulses.
- *Epithelial tissue* covers body surfaces and lines body cavities.

BIOLOGY IN YOUR LIFE

How are cancers named?

Cancers are classified according to the type of tissue from which they arise. Sarcomas are cancers arising in muscular or connective tissue (especially bone or cartilage). Leukemias are cancers of the blood. Lymphomas are cancers of lymphoid tissue. Carcinomas, the most common type, are cancers of epithelial tissue. The chance of developing cancer in a particular tissue is related to the rate of cell division. Both epithelial cells and blood cells reproduce at a high rate. Thus, carcinomas and leukemias are common types of cancer.

CHECK YOUR PROGRESS 4.1

1. Explain the relationship among cells, tissues, and organs in the biological levels of organization.
2. Distinguish between muscular tissue and nervous tissue.
3. Distinguish between connective tissue and epithelial tissue.

CONNECTING THE CONCEPTS

For more information on the roles of each of these tissues in the body, refer to the following discussions:

Section 6.1 explores how blood functions as a connective tissue.

Section 9.3 examines how the epithelial tissues of the digestive system absorb nutrients.

Section 13.2 examines how muscular tissue provides for movement.

4.2 Connective Tissue Connects and Supports

LEARNING OUTCOMES

Upon completion of this section, you should be able to

1. Describe the primary types of connective tissue and provide a function for each.
2. Compare the structure and function of bone and cartilage.
3. Differentiate between blood and lymph.

Connective tissue is diverse in structure and function, but all types of connective tissue have three similar components: specialized cells, ground substance, and protein fibers (Fig. 4.1). The ground substance is a noncellular material that separates the cells. It varies in consistency from solid (bone), to semifluid (cartilage), to fluid (blood).

The fibers are of three possible types. White **collagen fibers** contain collagen, a protein that gives them flexibility and strength. **Reticular fibers** are very thin collagen fibers, highly branched proteins that form delicate supporting networks. Yellow **elastic fibers** contain elastin, a protein that is not as strong as collagen but is more elastic. Elastic fibers return to their original shape and may stretch to over 100 times their relaxed size without damage. Inherited connective tissue disorders arise when people inherit genes that lead to malformed fibers. For example, in Marfan syndrome, there are mutations in the fibrillin gene *(FBN1)*. Fibrillin is a protein component of elastic fibers, and these mutations cause a decrease in the elasticity of the connective tissues that are normally rich in elastic fibers, such as the aorta, a major blood vessel that carries blood from the heart to the tissues of the body. Because of this mutation, the aorta cannot expand in response to increased blood pressure, and therefore may rupture, resulting in death.

Figure 4.2 summarizes the classification of each of the major types of connective tissue that we will discuss in this section.

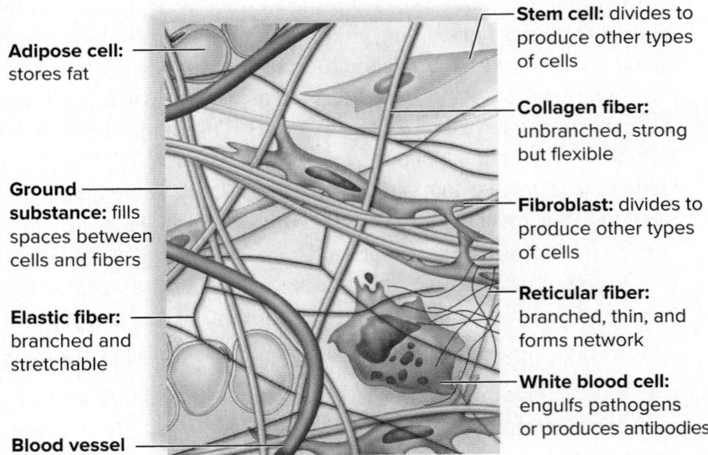

Figure 4.1 Components of connective tissues.
All connective tissues have three components: specialized cells, ground substance, and protein fibers. Loose fibrous connective tissue is shown here.

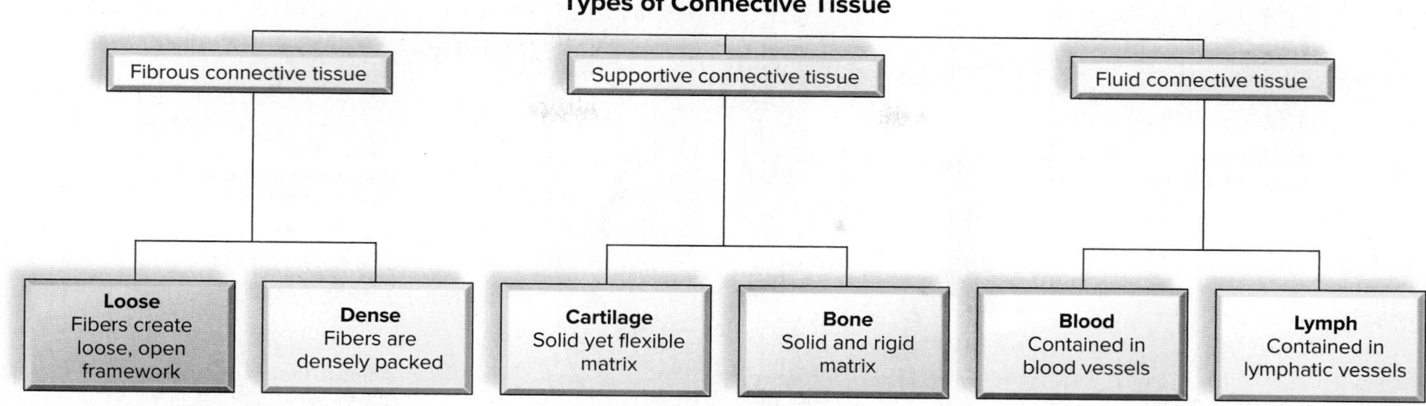

Figure 4.2 Types of connective tissue.
Connective tissue is divided into three general categories—fibrous, supportive, and fluid.

Fibrous Connective Tissue

Fibrous tissue exists in two forms: loose fibrous tissue and dense fibrous tissue. Both loose fibrous and dense fibrous connective tissues have cells called **fibroblasts** located some distance from one another and separated by a jellylike ground substance containing white collagen fibers and yellow elastic fibers (Fig. 4.3). **Matrix** includes ground substance and fibers.

Loose fibrous connective tissue, which includes areolar and reticular connective tissue, supports epithelium and many internal organs. Its presence in lungs, arteries, and the urinary bladder allows these organs to expand. It forms a protective covering enclosing many internal organs, such as muscles, blood vessels, and nerves.

Adipose tissue is a special type of loose connective tissue in which the cells enlarge and store fat. Adipose tissue has little extracellular matrix. Its cells, which are called **adipocytes,** are crowded, and each is filled with liquid fat. The body uses this stored fat for energy, insulation, and organ protection. Adipose tissue is primarily found beneath the skin, around the kidneys, and on the surface of the heart. Adipose tissue also releases a hormone that regulates appetite-control centers in the brain (see Section 16.6).

BIOLOGY IN YOUR LIFE

Does dieting get rid of fat cells?

Unfortunately, dieting can shrink the size of fat cells (adipocytes), but their number stays the same. This means it is easier to regain the lost weight if diet and exercise are not maintained. The surgical removal of these cells, a process called liposuction, is the only way to remove fat cells from the body.

Dense fibrous connective tissue contains many collagen fibers packed together. This type of tissue has more specific functions than does loose connective tissue. For example, dense fibrous connective tissue is found in **tendons,** which connect muscles to bones, and in **ligaments,** which connect bones to other bones at joints.

Supportive Connective Tissue

Cartilage and bone are the two main supportive connective tissues. Each provides structure, shape, protection, and leverage for movement. Generally, cartilage is more flexible than bone because it lacks mineralization of the matrix. The supportive connective tissues are covered in more detail in Section 12.1.

Cartilage

In **cartilage,** the cells lie in small chambers called *lacunae* (*sing.,* lacuna), separated by a solid, yet flexible, matrix. This matrix is formed by cells called *chondroblasts* and *chondrocytes.* Because this tissue lacks a direct blood supply, it often heals slowly. The three types of cartilage are distinguished by the type of fiber found in the matrix.

Hyaline cartilage (Fig. 4.3), the most common type of cartilage, contains only fine collagen fibers. The matrix has a glassy, translucent appearance. Hyaline cartilage is found in the nose and at the ends of the long bones and the ribs, and it forms rings in the walls of respiratory passages. The fetal skeleton also is made of this type of cartilage. Later, the cartilaginous fetal skeleton is replaced by bone.

Elastic cartilage contains a greater number of elastic fibers. For this reason, it is more flexible and is found, for example, in the framework of the outer ear.

Fibrocartilage has a matrix containing strong collagen fibers. Fibrocartilage is found in structures that withstand tension and pressure, such as the disks between the vertebrae in the backbone and the cushions in the knee joint.

Bone

Bone is the most rigid connective tissue. It consists of an extremely hard matrix of inorganic salts, notably calcium salts. These salts are deposited around protein fibers, especially collagen fibers. The inorganic salts give bone rigidity. The protein fibers provide elasticity and strength, much as steel rods do in reinforced concrete. Cells called *osteoblasts* and *osteoclasts* are responsible for forming the matrix in bone tissue.

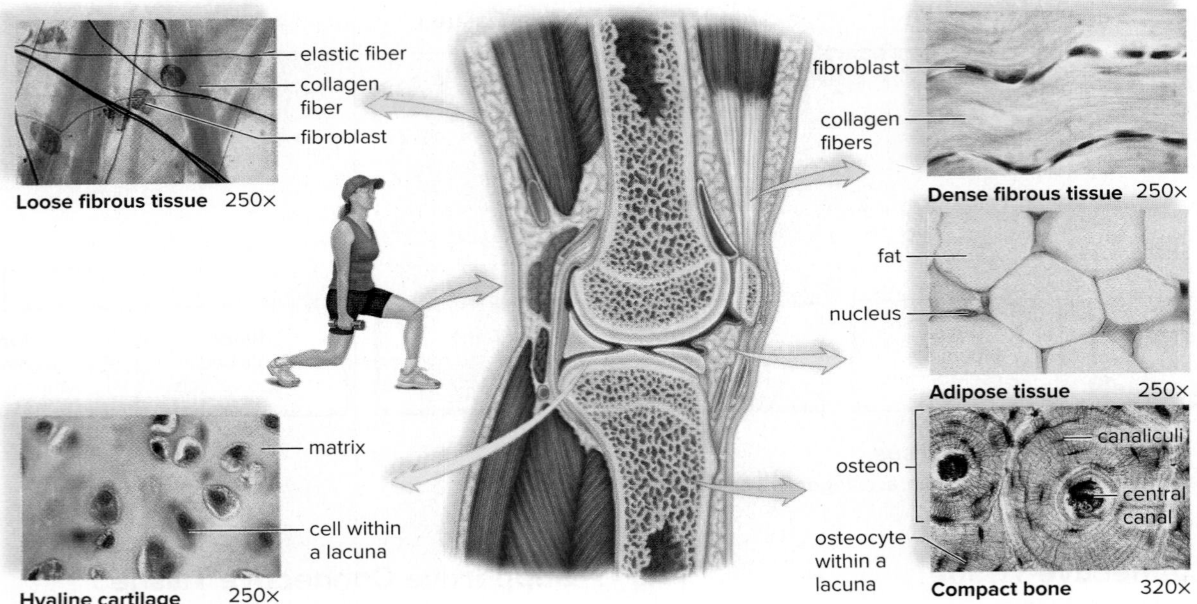

Figure 4.3 Connective tissues in the knee.
Most types of connective tissue may be found in the knee.
(photos, all): Ed Reschke

Compact bone makes up the shaft of a long bone (Fig. 4.3). It consists of cylindrical structural units called *osteons* (see Section 12.1). The central canal of each osteon is surrounded by rings of hard matrix. Bone cells, called *osteocytes,* are located in lacunae between the rings of matrix. In the central canal, nerve fibers carry nerve impulses, and blood vessels carry nutrients that allow bone to renew itself.

The ends of the long bones are composed of spongy bone covered by compact bone. Spongy bone also surrounds the bone marrow cavity. This, in turn, is covered by compact bone, forming a "sandwich" structure. **Spongy bone** appears as an open, bony latticework with numerous bony bars and plates, separated by irregular spaces. Although lighter than compact bone, spongy bone is still designed for strength. Just as braces are used for support in buildings, the solid portions of spongy bone follow lines of stress.

Fluid Connective Tissue

The human body has two different types of fluid connective tissue: blood and lymph.

Blood

Blood is a fluid connective tissue. It consists of formed elements (Fig. 4.4) and plasma, and is located in blood vessels. Blood transports nutrients and oxygen to the interstitial fluid that surrounds the body's cells, and it removes carbon dioxide and other wastes. Blood helps distribute heat and plays a role in fluid, ion, and pH balance. A number of the systems of the body help keep blood composition and chemistry within normal limits. The structure and function of blood are covered in more detail in Section 6.1.

Each formed element of blood has a specific function. The **red blood cells (erythrocytes)** are small, biconcave, disk-shaped cells that lose their nuclei as they mature. The presence of the red pigment hemoglobin makes the cells red, which in turn makes the blood red. Hemoglobin is composed of four units, and each unit is composed of the protein *globin* and a complex, iron-containing structure called *heme.* The iron forms a loose association with oxygen; therefore, red blood cells transport oxygen.

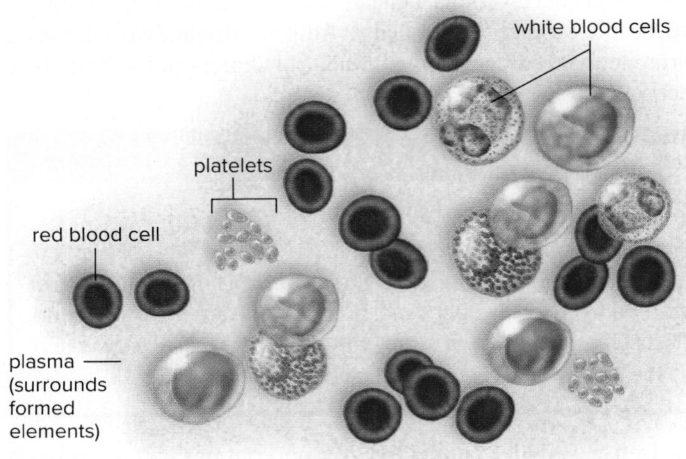

Figure 4.4 The formed elements of blood.
Red blood cells, which lack a nucleus, transport oxygen. Each type of white blood cell has a particular way to fight infections. Platelets, fragments of a particular cell, help seal injured blood vessels.

White blood cells (leukocytes) may be distinguished from red blood cells because they have a nucleus. Without staining, leukocytes would be translucent. There are many different types of white blood cells, but all are involved in protecting the body from infection. Many white blood cells are phagocytic cells, because they engulf infectious agents, such as bacteria. Others are more specific and either produce antibodies (molecules that combine with foreign substances to inactivate them) or directly attack specific invading agents or infected cells in the body.

Platelets (thrombocytes) are fragments of giant cells present only in the bone marrow. When a blood vessel is damaged, platelets form a plug that seals the vessel, and injured tissues release molecules that help the clotting process.

Lymph

Lymph is also a fluid connective tissue. It is a clear (sometimes faintly yellow) fluid derived from the fluids surrounding the tissues. It contains white blood cells. Lymphatic vessels absorb excess interstitial fluid and various dissolved solutes in the tissues. They transport lymph to particular vessels of the cardiovascular system. Lymphatic vessels absorb fat molecules from the small intestine. Lymph nodes, composed of fibrous connective tissue, occur along the length of lymphatic vessels. Lymph is cleansed as it passes through lymph nodes, in particular, because white blood cells congregate there. Lymph nodes enlarge when you have an infection.

CHECK YOUR PROGRESS 4.2

1. Describe the three general categories of connective tissue, and provide some examples of each type.
2. Explain the difference in the composition of the matrix in each of the three classes of connective tissue.
3. Describe how each of the two fluid connective tissues is important to homeostasis.

CONNECTING THE CONCEPTS

The tissue types discussed in this section are examined in greater detail later in the book. For more information, refer to the following discussions:

Section 6.1 details the types of formed elements found in blood.

Section 7.1 explains the role of the lymphatic system in moving lymph through the body.

Section 12.1 provides a more detailed examination of cartilage and bone.

4.3 Muscular Tissue Moves the Body

LEARNING OUTCOME

Upon completion of this section, you should be able to

1. Distinguish among the three types of muscles with regard to location and function in the body.

Muscular tissue is specialized to contract. It is composed of cells called *muscle fibers* that contain actin and myosin filaments. The interaction of these filaments accounts for movement. These interactions, and the structure of the muscles of the body, are covered in greater detail in Chapter 13. The three types of vertebrate muscular tissue are skeletal, smooth, and cardiac.

Skeletal muscle (Fig. 4.5*a*) is attached by tendons to the bones of the skeleton. When it contracts, body parts move. Contraction of skeletal muscle is under voluntary control and occurs faster than in the other muscle types. Skeletal muscle fibers are cylindrical and long—some run the length of the muscle. They arise during development when several cells fuse, resulting in one fiber with multiple nuclei. The nuclei are located at the periphery of the cell, just inside the plasma membrane. The fibers have alternating light and dark bands that give them a **striated,** or striped, appearance under a microscope. These bands are due to the placement of actin filaments and myosin filaments in the cell and are involved in the process of contraction (see Section 13.2).

Smooth muscle is so named because the cells lack striations (Fig. 4.5*b*). Each spindle-shaped cell has a single nucleus. These cells form layers in which the thick middle portion of one cell is opposite the thin ends of adjacent cells. Consequently, the nuclei form an irregular pattern in the tissue. Smooth muscle is involuntary, meaning it is not under conscious control. Smooth muscle is found in the walls of viscera (intestine, bladder, and other internal organs) and blood vessels. For this reason, it is sometimes referred to as *visceral muscle.* Smooth muscle contracts more slowly than skeletal muscle but can remain contracted for a longer time. When the smooth muscle of the bladder contracts, urine is sent into a tube called the urethra, which takes it to the outside. When the smooth muscle of the blood vessels contracts, the blood vessels constrict, helping raise blood pressure.

Cardiac muscle (Fig. 4.5*c*) is found only in the walls of the heart. Its contraction pumps blood and accounts for the heartbeat. Cardiac muscle combines features of both smooth and skeletal muscle. Like skeletal muscle, it has striations, but the contraction of the heart is involuntary for the most part. Cardiac muscle cells also differ from skeletal muscle cells in that they usually have a single, centrally placed nucleus. The cells are branched and seemingly fused together. While the heart appears to be a single, large muscle, it is in fact composed of numerous separate cardiac muscle cells that are bound end to end by *intercalated discs* (see Fig. 5.3).

CHECK YOUR PROGRESS 4.3

1. Explain the differences in the structure and function of skeletal, smooth, and cardiac muscle.
2. Describe where each type of muscle fiber is found in the body.
3. Explain why smooth muscle and cardiac muscle are involuntary, and summarize what advantage this provides homeostasis.

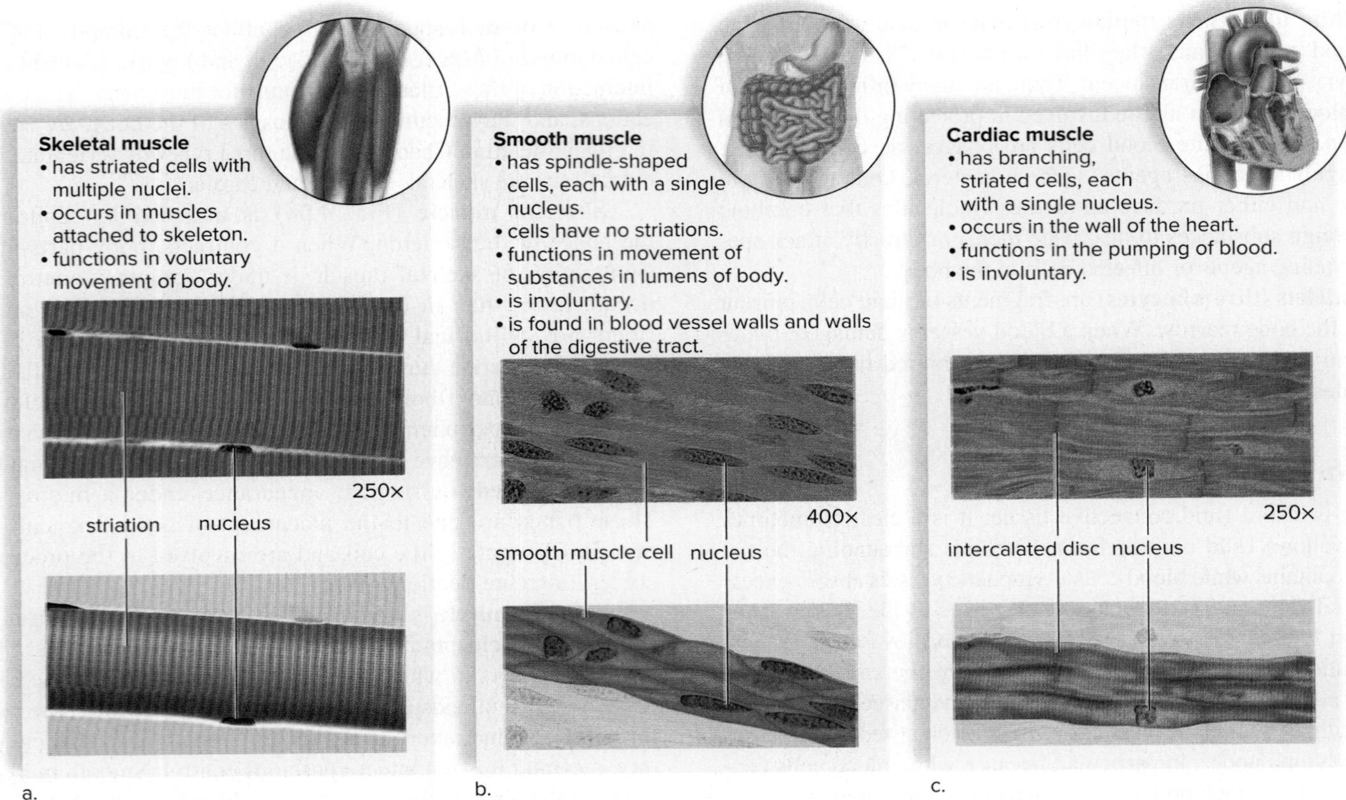

Skeletal muscle
• has striated cells with multiple nuclei.
• occurs in muscles attached to skeleton.
• functions in voluntary movement of body.
250×
striation
nucleus
a.
Smooth muscle
• has spindle-shaped cells, each with a single nucleus.
• cells have no striations.
• functions in movement of substances in lumens of body.
• is involuntary.
• is found in blood vessel walls and walls of the digestive tract.
400×
smooth muscle cell
nucleus
b.
Cardiac muscle
• has branching, striated cells, each with a single nucleus.
• occurs in the wall of the heart.
• functions in the pumping of blood.
• is involuntary.
250×
intercalated disc
nucleus
c.

Figure 4.5 The three types of muscular tissue.
a. Skeletal muscle is voluntary and striated. **b.** Smooth muscle is involuntary and nonstriated. **c.** Cardiac muscle is involuntary and striated.
(photos) (skeletal and cardiac muscle): Ed Reschke; (smooth muscle): Dennis Strete/McGraw Hill

CONNECTING THE CONCEPTS

Muscular tissue plays an important role in our physiology. For more information on each of the three types of muscles, refer to the following discussions:

Section 5.3 provides a more detailed look at how the heartbeat is generated.

Figure 9.2 illustrates how smooth muscle lines the digestive tract.

Section 13.2 examines the structure and function of skeletal muscle.

4.4 Nervous Tissue Communicates

LEARNING OUTCOMES

Upon completion of this section, you should be able to

1. Distinguish between neurons and neuroglia.
2. Describe the structure of a neuron.

Nervous tissue is the central component of the nervous system (see Section 14.1). It consists of two different types of cells: neurons and neuroglia. Nervous tissue serves three primary functions in the body: sensory input, integration of information, and motor output.

Neurons

A **neuron** is a specialized cell that has three parts: dendrites, a cell body, and an axon (Fig. 4.6). A *dendrite* is an extension that receives signals from sensory receptors or other neurons. The *cell body* contains most of the cell's cytoplasm and the nucleus. An *axon* is an extension that conducts nerve impulses. The axons of some neurons are covered by *myelin,* a white, fatty substance. The term *fiber* is used several different ways when discussing human anatomy. Here, it refers to an axon, along with its myelin, if present. Outside the brain and spinal cord, fibers bound by connective tissue form nerves. **Nerves** conduct signals from sensory receptors to the spinal cord and the brain, where integration, or processing, occurs. However, the phenomenon called sensation occurs only in the brain. Nerves also conduct signals from the spinal cord and brain to muscles, glands, and other organs. This triggers a characteristic response from each tissue. For example, muscles contract, and glands secrete. In this way, a coordinated response to the original sensory input is achieved.

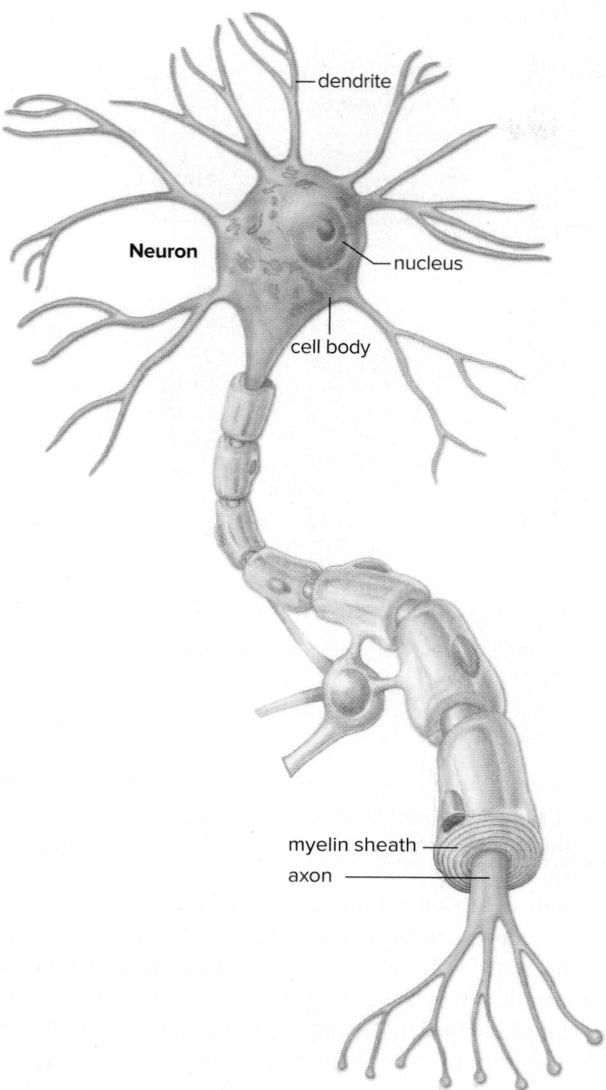

a. Structure of a neuron

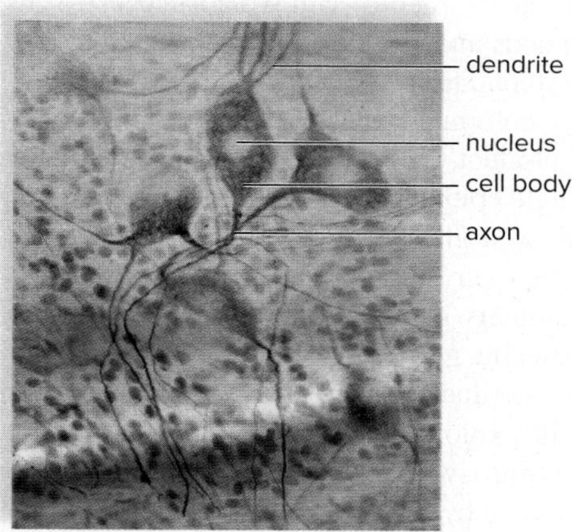

b. Micrograph of a neuron 400×

Figure 4.6 **Structure of a neuron.**
a. Neurons conduct nerve impulses in the body. They consist of dendrites, axons (with or without myelin), and a cell body. **b.** Micrograph of a neuron.
(b): Xia Yuan/Getty Images

BIOLOGY IN YOUR LIFE

What is MS?

Multiple sclerosis, or MS, is a disease that occurs when the immune system of the body mistakenly targets the myelin covering of neurons. This causes the signals traveling along the neurons to become scrambled, which may lead to a wide variety of symptoms. Anyone may develop MS, but scientists believe that those at highest risk have a combination of genetic susceptibility and exposure to yet-unidentified environmental factors.

Neuroglia

In addition to neurons, nervous tissue contains neuroglia. **Neuroglia** are cells that outnumber neurons nine to one and take up more than half the volume of the brain. Although the primary function of neuroglia is to support and nourish neurons, research is being conducted to determine how much they directly contribute to brain function. Neuroglia do not have long extensions (axons or dendrites). However, researchers are gathering evidence that neuroglia communicate among themselves and with neurons, even without these extensions. Examples of neuroglia in the brain are microglia, astrocytes, and oligodendrocytes. We will explore the function of the neuroglia more in Section 14.1.

CHECK YOUR PROGRESS 4.4

1. Describe the structure and function of a neuron.
2. Explain the general function of the neuroglia.

CONNECTING THE CONCEPTS

Nervous tissue plays an important role in transmitting the signals needed to maintain homeostasis. For more information on how neurons work, refer to the following discussions:

Section 14.1 provides a more detailed examination of how neurons function.

Section 15.1 discusses how neurons are involved in sensation.

4.5 Epithelial Tissue Protects

LEARNING OUTCOMES

Upon completion of this section, you should be able to

1. State the role of epithelial cells in the body.
2. Distinguish between the different forms of epithelial tissue with regard to location and function.

Epithelial tissue, also called *epithelium* (*pl.,* epithelia), consists of tightly packed cells that form a continuous layer. Epithelial tissue covers surfaces and lines body cavities. Usually, it has a protective function. It can also be modified to carry out secretion, absorption, excretion, and filtration.

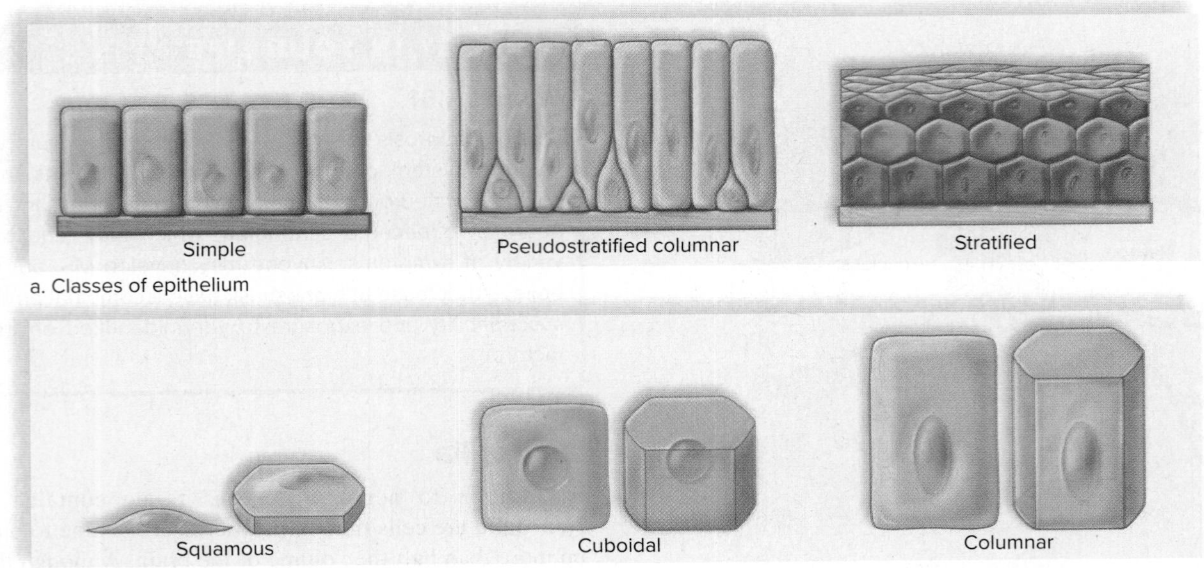

Figure 4.7 **Epithelial cells.**
a. Epithelial cells may be arranged in a simple or stratified (layered) configuration. Pseudostratified epithelium appears stratified but is actually a single layer. **b.** Shapes of epithelial cells.

All epithelial cells are exposed on one side. On the other side, they are connected to a **basement membrane.** The basement membrane should not be confused with the plasma membrane (in the cell) or the membranes that line the cavities of the body. Instead, the basement membrane is a thin layer of various types of carbohydrates and proteins that anchors the epithelium to underlying connective tissue.

Epithelial tissue is named based on the number of cell layers (simple or stratified) and the shape of the cells (Fig. 4.7).

Simple Epithelia

Simple epithelia have only a single layer of cells (Fig. 4.8*a, b, c*) and are classified according to cell shape. Simple **squamous epithelium,** composed of flattened cells, is found lining the air sacs of lungs and walls of blood vessels (Fig. 4.8*a*). Its shape and arrangement permit exchanges of substances in these locations. Oxygen–carbon dioxide exchange occurs in the lungs, and nutrient-waste exchange occurs across blood vessels in the tissues.

Simple **cuboidal epithelium** (Fig. 4.8*b*) consists of a single layer of cube-shaped cells. This type of epithelium is frequently found in glands, such as the salivary glands, the thyroid, and the pancreas. Simple cuboidal epithelium also covers the ovaries and lines kidney tubules, the portions of the kidney in which urine is formed. When cuboidal cells are involved in absorption, they have *microvilli* (minute cellular extensions of the plasma membrane). These increase the surface area of the cells. When cuboidal cells function in active transport, they contain many mitochondria.

Simple **columnar epithelium** (Fig. 4.8*c*) has cells resembling rectangular pillars or columns, with nuclei usually located near the bottom of each cell. This epithelium lines the digestive tract, where microvilli expand the surface area and aid in absorbing the products of digestion. Ciliated columnar epithelium is found lining the uterine tubes, where it propels the egg toward the uterus.

Pseudostratified columnar epithelium (Fig. 4.8*d*) is named because it appears to be layered. However, it does not have true layers, because each cell touches the basement membrane. Its appearance of having several layers is largely due to the irregular placement of the nuclei. The lining of the windpipe, or trachea, is pseudostratified ciliated columnar epithelium. A secreted covering of mucus traps foreign particles. The upward motion of the cilia carries the mucus to the back of the throat, where it may either be swallowed or expectorated (spit out). Smoking can cause a change in the secretion of mucus and inhibit ciliary action, resulting in a chronic inflammatory condition called *bronchitis.*

In some cases, columnar and pseudostratified columnar epithelium secrete a product. In this case, it is said to be glandular. A **gland** can be a single epithelial cell, as in the case of a mucus-secreting goblet cell, or a gland can contain many cells. Glands with ducts that secrete their product onto the outer surface (e.g., sweat glands and mammary glands) or into a cavity (e.g., salivary glands) are called **exocrine glands.**

Glands that have no ducts are appropriately known as endocrine glands. We will explore the function of endocrine glands (e.g., pituitary and thyroid), which secrete hormones into the interstitial fluid to be absorbed by the bloodstream, in Section 16.1.

Stratified Epithelia

Stratified epithelia have layers of cells piled one on top of the other (Fig. 4.8*e*). Only the bottom layer touches the basement membrane. The nose, mouth, esophagus, anal canal, outer portion of the

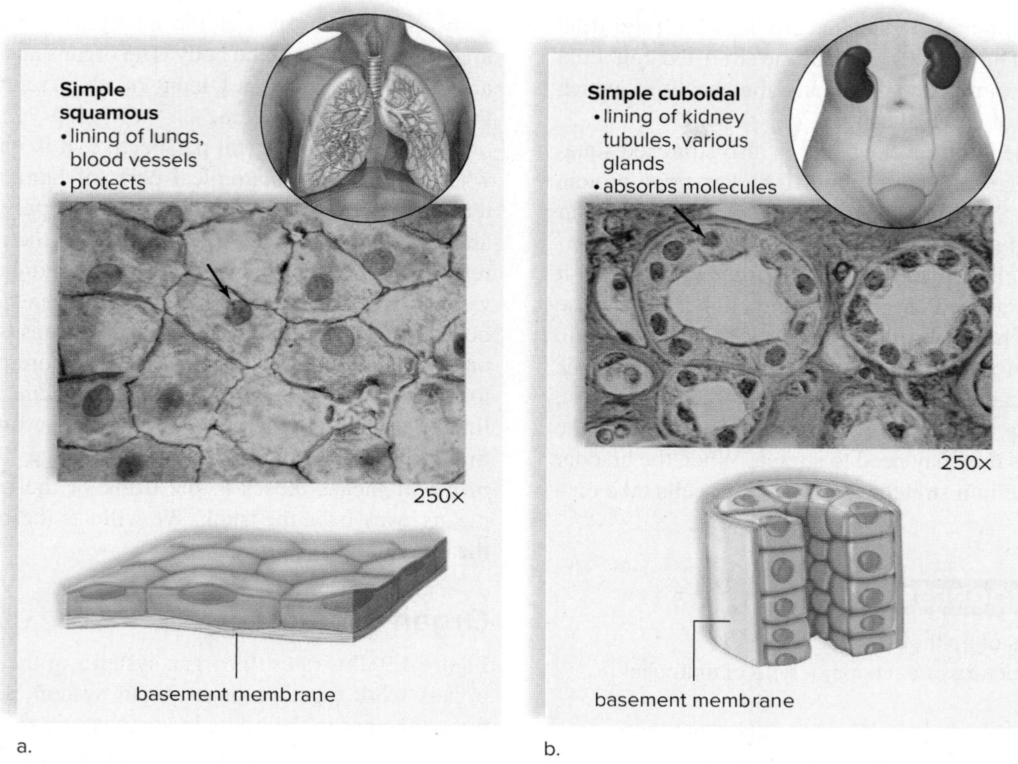

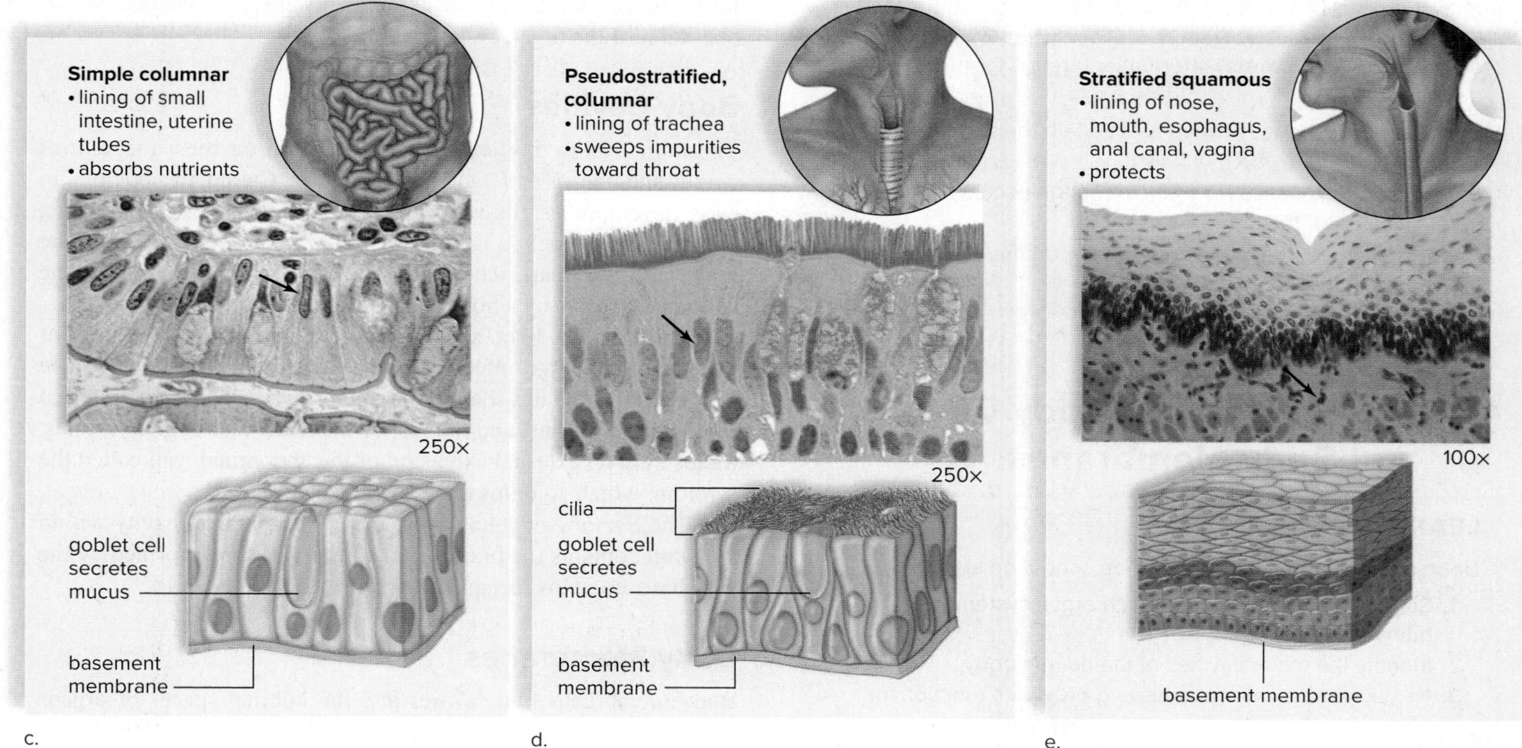

Figure 4.8 **The basic types of epithelial cells.**
Basic epithelial tissues found in humans are shown, along with locations of the tissue and the primary function of the tissue at these locations.
(all photos): Ed Reschke

cervix (adjacent to the vagina), and vagina are lined with stratified squamous epithelium. During a *Pap smear,* the stratified epithelial cells of the cervix are examined to detect any abnormalities, which may indicate the onset of cervical cancer.

As we will see, the outer layer of skin is also stratified squamous epithelium, but the cells are reinforced by keratin, a protein that provides strength. Stratified cuboidal and stratified columnar epithelia also are found in the body.

Transitional epithelium was originally so named because it was thought to be an intermediate form of epithelial cell. Now the term is used to imply changeability, because the tissue changes in response to tension. It forms the lining of the urinary bladder, the ureters (the tubes that carry urine from the kidneys to the bladder), and part of the urethra (the single tube that carries urine to the outside). All are organs that may need to stretch. When the bladder is distended, this epithelium stretches and the outer cells take on a squamous appearance.

CHECK YOUR PROGRESS 4.5

1. List the functions of epithelial tissue.
2. Describe the structure of each major type of epithelial tissue.
3. Summarize how the structure of some epithelial tissue relates to its function. Give some specific examples.

CONNECTING THE CONCEPTS

Epithelial tissue is involved in the operation of most organs of the body. For more information, refer to the following discussions:

Section 9.3 describes how specialized epithelial cells in the stomach secrete hydrochloric acid.

Section 10.6 examines how gas exchange occurs across the epithelial cells of the lungs.

Section 16.1 provides more information on the endocrine and exocrine glands of the body.

4.6 Organ Systems, Body Cavities, and Body Membranes

LEARNING OUTCOMES

Upon completion of this section, you should be able to

1. Summarize the function of each organ system in the human body.
2. Identify the major cavities of the human body.
3. Name the body membranes and provide a function for each.

In Section 4.1, we mentioned that a group of tissues performing a common function is called an **organ.** Organs with a similar function, in turn, form **organ systems.** Some of these organ systems, such as the respiratory system, occupy specific cavities of the body, and others, such as the muscular and circulatory systems, are found throughout the body. The organs and cavities of the body are lined with membranes, many of which secrete fluid to lubricate the organ or organ system.

From a physiological perspective, it is important to note that when referring to anatomical parts of humans, certain standard terms are used. Many of the same terms apply to other organisms, although there is some variation because the human terms always refer to a body that is in the upright, standing position. The term *ventral* or *anterior* refers to the front, and *dorsal* or *posterior* both mean toward the back. *Superior* means toward the head, and *inferior* means toward the feet. Other anatomical terms are relative to other body parts; something that is *medial* is closer to the midline of the body, whereas *lateral* means away from the midline. Similarly, when referring to an appendage like an arm or a leg, *proximal* means closer to the trunk of the body, whereas *distal* means away from the trunk. We will use these terms frequently in the upcoming chapters.

Organ Systems

Figure 4.9 illustrates the organ systems of the human body. Just as organs work together in an organ system, so do organ systems work together in the body. In some cases, organs may be involved in the function of more than one organ system, such as the pancreas's role in both the endocrine and digestive systems. In addition, the organs listed in Figure 4.9 represent the major structures in the body. Often, other structures and glands contribute to the operation of the organ system.

Body Cavities

The human body is divided into two main cavities: the *ventral cavity* and the *dorsal cavity* (Fig. 4.10). Called the coelom in early development, the *ventral cavity* later becomes the thoracic, abdominal, and pelvic cavities. The *thoracic cavity* contains the lungs and the heart. The thoracic cavity is separated from the abdominal cavity by a horizontal muscle called the diaphragm.

The stomach, liver, spleen, pancreas, gallbladder, and most of the small and large intestines are in the *abdominal cavity*. The *pelvic cavity* contains the rectum, the urinary bladder, the internal reproductive organs, and the rest of the small and large intestines. Males have an external extension of the abdominal wall called the scrotum, which contains the testes.

The *dorsal cavity* has two parts: (1) the cranial cavity within the skull contains the brain; (2) the vertebral canal, formed by the vertebrae, contains the spinal cord.

Body Membranes

Body membranes line cavities and the internal spaces of organs and tubes that open to the outside. These membranes are of four types: mucous, serous, and synovial membranes, and the meninges.

Mucous membranes line the tubes of the digestive, respiratory, urinary, and reproductive systems. They are composed of an epithelium overlying a loose fibrous connective tissue layer. The

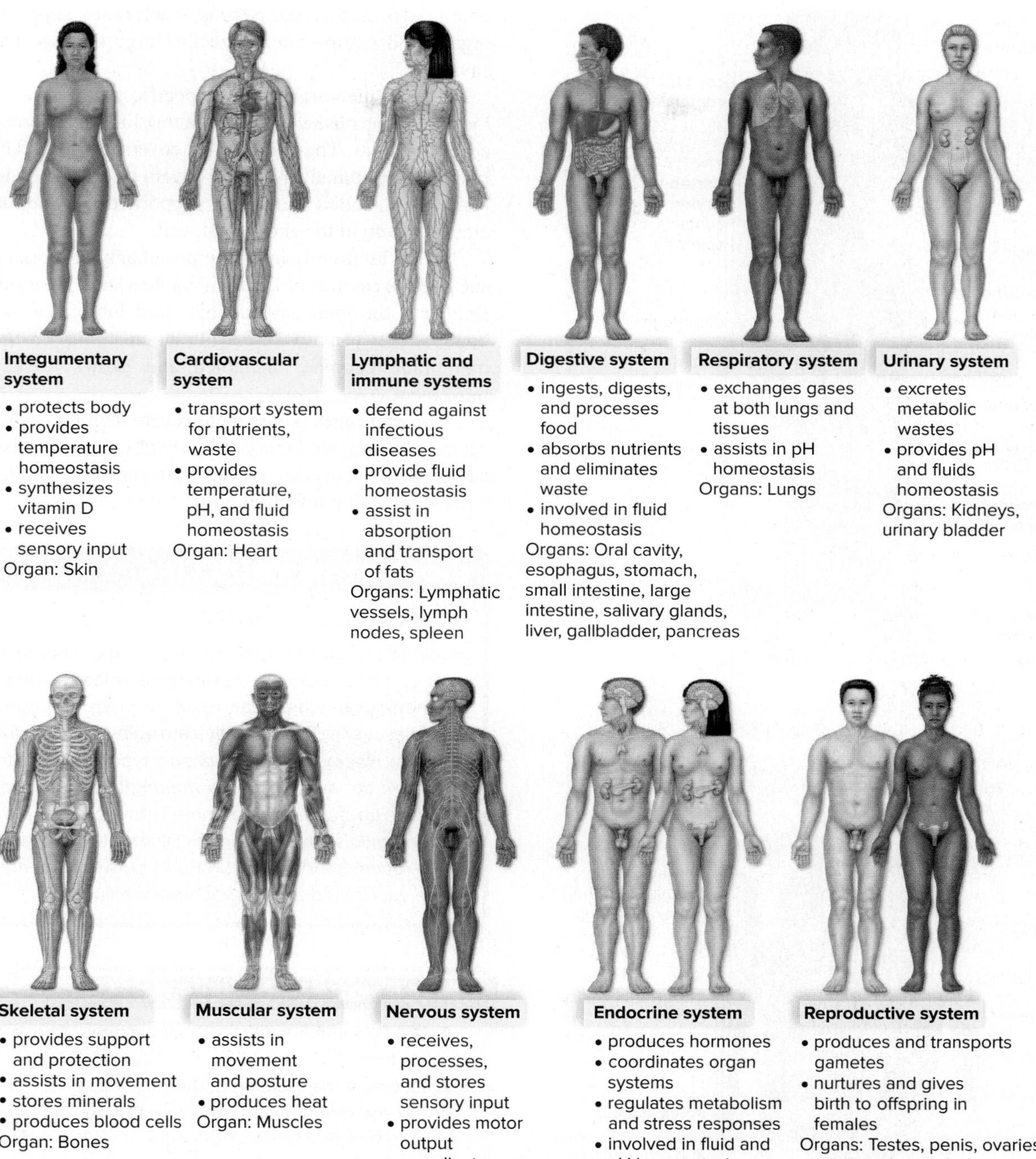

Integumentary system
• protects body
• provides temperature homeostasis
• synthesizes vitamin D
• receives sensory input
Organ: Skin
Cardiovascular system
• transport system for nutrients, waste
• provides temperature, pH, and fluid homeostasis
Organ: Heart
Lymphatic and immune systems
• defend against infectious diseases
• provide fluid homeostasis
• assist in absorption and transport of fats
Organs: Lymphatic vessels, lymph nodes, spleen
Digestive system
• ingests, digests, and processes food
• absorbs nutrients and eliminates waste
• involved in fluid homeostasis
Organs: Oral cavity, esophagus, stomach, small intestine, large intestine, salivary glands, liver, gallbladder, pancreas
Respiratory system
• exchanges gases at both lungs and tissues
• assists in pH homeostasis
Organs: Lungs
Urinary system
• excretes metabolic wastes
• provides pH and fluids homeostasis
Organs: Kidneys, urinary bladder
Skeletal system
• provides support and protection
• assists in movement
• stores minerals
• produces blood cells
Organ: Bones
Muscular system
• assists in movement and posture
• produces heat
Organ: Muscles
Nervous system
• receives, processes, and stores sensory input
• provides motor output
• coordinates organ systems
Organs: Brain, spinal cord
Endocrine system
• produces hormones
• coordinates organ systems
• regulates metabolism and stress responses
• involved in fluid and pH homeostasis
Organs: Testes, ovaries, adrenal glands, pancreas, thymus, thyroid, pineal gland
Reproductive system
• produces and transports gametes
• nurtures and gives birth to offspring in females
Organs: Testes, penis, ovaries, uterus, vagina

Figure 4.9 **Organ systems of the body.**
Many of the organs of the body may have functions that are associated with more than one organ system.

epithelium contains specialized cells that secrete mucus. This mucus ordinarily protects the body from invasion by bacteria and viruses. Hence, more mucus is secreted and expelled when a person has a cold and has to blow their nose. In addition, mucus usually protects the walls of the stomach and small intestine from digestive juices. This protection breaks down when a person develops an ulcer.

Serous membranes line the closed cavities of the body. They support the lungs, heart, and abdominal cavity and its internal organs (Fig. 4.10*b*). They secrete a watery fluid that keeps the

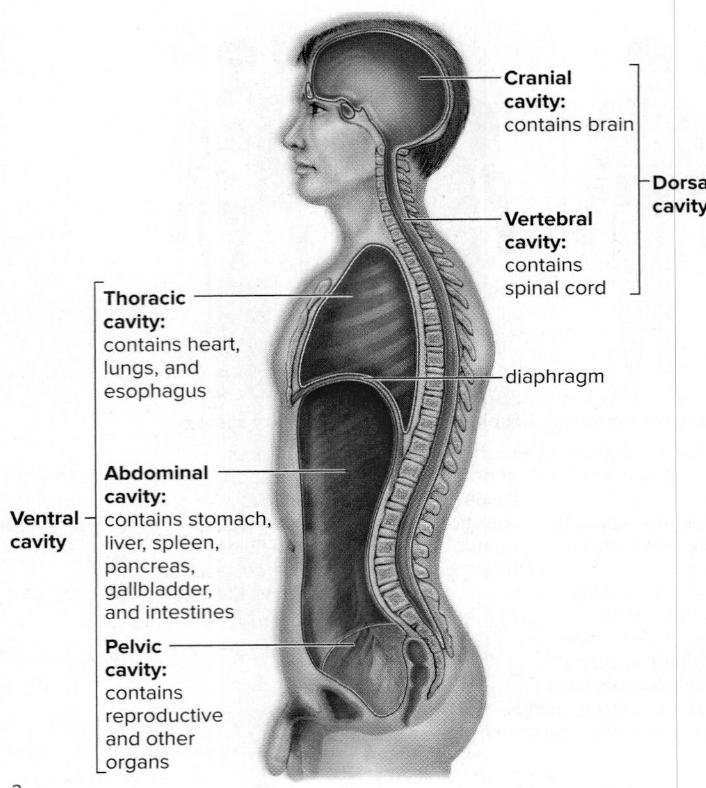

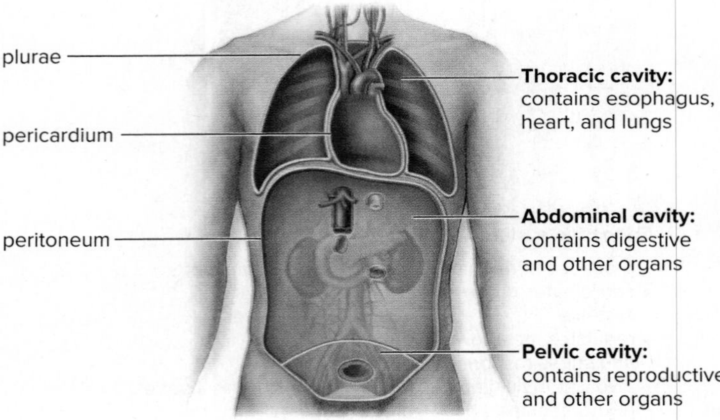

Figure 4.10 Body cavities of humans.
a. Side view. The posterior, or dorsal (toward the back), cavity contains the cranial cavity and the vertebral canal. The brain is in the cranial cavity, and the spinal cord is in the vertebral canal. In the anterior, or ventral (toward the front), cavity, the diaphragm separates the thoracic cavity from the abdominal cavity. The heart and lungs are in the thoracic cavity; the other internal organs are in either the abdominal cavity or the pelvic cavity. **b.** Frontal view of the thoracic cavity, showing serous membranes.

membranes lubricated. Serous membranes support the internal organs and compartmentalize the large thoracic and abdominal cavities.

Serous membranes have specific names according to their location. The *pleurae* (*sing.*, pleura) line the thoracic cavity and cover the lungs. The *pericardium* covers the heart. The *peritoneum* lines the abdominal cavity and covers its organs. A double layer of peritoneum, called *mesentery,* supports the abdominal organs and attaches them to the abdominal wall.

Synovial membranes composed only of loose connective tissue line the cavities of freely movable joints. They secrete *synovial fluid* into the joint cavity. This fluid lubricates the ends of the bones so they can move freely. In rheumatoid arthritis, the synovial membrane becomes inflamed and grows thicker, restricting movement.

The **meninges** (*sing.*, meninx) are membranes within the dorsal cavity. They are composed only of connective tissue and serve as a protective covering for the brain and spinal cord. Meningitis is a life-threatening infection of the meninges.

BIOLOGY IN YOUR LIFE

What causes meningitis?

Meningitis is caused by an infection of the meninges by either a virus or a bacterium. Viral meningitis is less severe than bacterial meningitis, which can result in brain damage and death. Bacterial meningitis is usually caused by one of three species of bacteria: *Haemophilus influenzae* type b (Hib), *Streptococcus pneumoniae,* and *Neisseria meningitidis.* Vaccines are available for Hib bacteria and some forms of *S. pneumoniae* and *N. meningitidis.* The Centers for Disease Control and Prevention (CDC) recommends that individuals between the ages of 11 and 18 be vaccinated against bacterial meningitis.

CHECK YOUR PROGRESS 4.6

1. Briefly summarize the overall function of each of the body systems.
2. Describe the location of the major body cavities.
3. List the four types of body membranes, and describe the structure and function of each.

CONNECTING THE CONCEPTS

Each of the organ systems in this section is covered in greater detail in later chapters of the text. For more information on body cavities and body membranes, refer to the following discussions:

Section 7.3 describes how mucous membranes assist in the immune response of the body.

Section 10.4 illustrates how the thoracic cavity is involved in breathing.

Section 12.4 explains how synovial joints (and their associated membranes) allow movement.

4.7 Integumentary System

LEARNING OUTCOMES

Upon completion of this section, you should be able to

1. Explain the function of human skin.
2. Describe the structure of the epidermis and dermis.
3. Identify the function of the accessory organs associated with the skin.

The **skin** is an organ comprised of all four tissue types: epithelial, connective, muscular, and nervous tissue. The **integumentary system** consists of the skin and several accessory organs (hair, nails, sweat glands, and sebaceous glands).

Because it covers our bodies, and is largely associated with our physical appearance, the skin is the most conspicuous organ system in the body. In an adult, the skin has a surface area of about 1.8 square meters (m^2) (over 19.5 square feet [ft^2]). It accounts for nearly 15% of the weight of an average human.

The skin has numerous functions. It protects underlying tissues from physical trauma, pathogen invasion, and water loss. It also helps regulate body temperature. Therefore, skin plays a significant role in homeostasis, the relative constancy of the internal environment. The skin even synthesizes certain chemicals that affect the rest of the body. Skin contains sensory receptors, such as touch and temperature receptors. Thus, it helps us be aware of our surroundings and to communicate with others.

Regions of the Skin

The skin has two regions: epidermis and dermis (Fig. 4.11). A **subcutaneous layer,** sometimes called the *hypodermis,* is found between the skin and any underlying structures, such as muscle or bone.

The Epidermis

The **epidermis** is made up of stratified squamous epithelium. New epidermal cells for the renewal of skin are derived from stem (basal) cells. The importance of these stem cells is observed when there is an injury to the skin. If an injury, such as a burn, is deep enough to destroy stem cells, then the skin can no longer replace itself. As soon as possible, the damaged tissue is removed and skin grafting begins. The skin needed for grafting is usually taken from other parts of the patient's body. This is called *autografting,* as opposed to allografting. In *allografting,* the graft is received from another person and is sometimes obtained from dead bodies (called cadavers). Autografting is preferred, because rejection rates are low. If the damaged area is extensive, it may be difficult to acquire enough skin for autografting. In that case, small amounts of epidermis are removed and cultured in the laboratory.

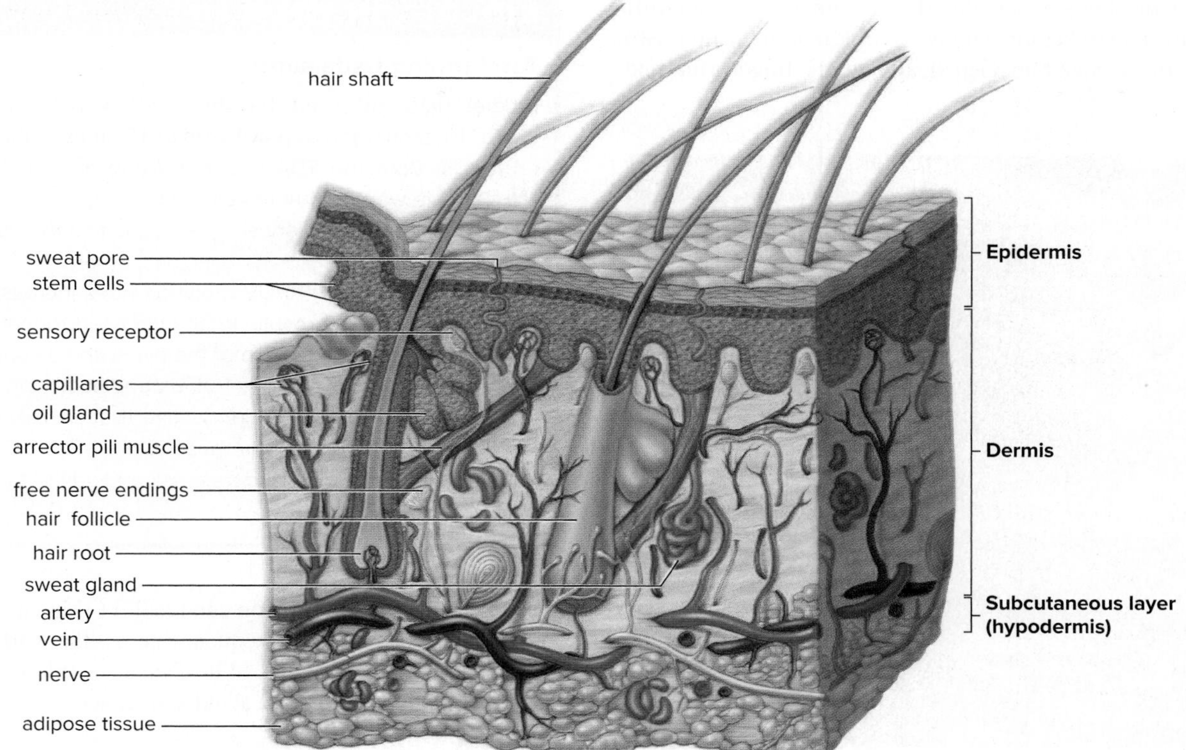

Figure 4.11 Anatomy of human skin.
Skin consists of two regions: epidermis and dermis. A subcutaneous layer (the hypodermis) lies below the dermis.

This produces thin sheets of skin that can be transplanted back to the patient.

BIOLOGY IN YOUR LIFE

How is artificial skin used to treat burn victims?

The first step of the procedure, after the removal of the burned tissue, is to cover the wound with artificial skin. This skin contains collagen, a connective tissue, and an adhesive-like carbohydrate that allows the artificial skin to bind to the underlying tissue. Initially, the artificial skin contains a plastic wrapping that simulates the epidermis and protects the tissue from water loss and infection. The next step is to remove a small sample of epidermal cells from an unburned area of skin on the patient's body. These are taken to a laboratory and placed in incubators to grow sheets of skin. Once ready, the plastic covering on the patient is replaced by the sheets of epidermal cells. Over time, the laboratory-grown artificial skin is integrated into the newly growing skin.

Newly generated skin cells become flattened and hardened as they push to the surface (Fig. 4.12). Hardening takes place because the cells produce *keratin,* a waterproof protein. These cells are also called *keratinocytes*. Outer skin cells are dead and keratinized, so the skin is waterproof. This prevents water loss and helps maintain water homeostasis. The skin's waterproofing also prevents water from entering the body when the skin is immersed. Dandruff occurs when the rate of keratinization in the skin of the scalp is two or three times the normal rate. Genetically unique fingerprints and footprints are formed by a thick layer of dead, keratinized cells arranged in spiral and concentric patterns.

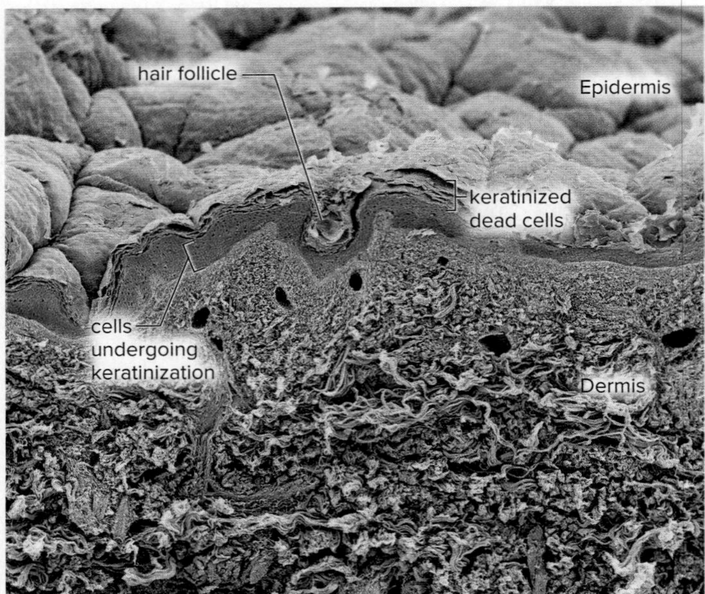

Figure 4.12 **Structure of human skin.**
This image shows the structure of the skin and the process of keratinization.
Eye of Science/Science Source

Two types of specialized cells are located deep in the epidermis. **Dendritic cells** (previously called Langerhans cells) are macrophages, white blood cells that phagocytize infectious agents and then travel to lymphatic organs. There they stimulate the immune system to react to the pathogen. **Melanocytes,** lying deep in the epidermis, produce *melanin*, the main pigment responsible for skin color. The number of melanocytes is about the same in all individuals, so variation in skin color is due to the amount of melanin produced and its distribution. When skin is exposed to the sun, melanocytes produce more melanin. This protects the skin from the damaging effects of the ultraviolet (UV) radiation in sunlight. The melanin is passed to other epidermal cells, and the result is tanning. In some people, this results in the formation of patches of melanin called freckles. Another pigment, called carotene, is present in epidermal cells and in the dermis. It gives the skin of some Asian populations its yellowish hue. The pinkish color of fair-skinned people is due to the pigment hemoglobin in the red blood cells in the blood vessels of the dermis.

Some ultraviolet radiation does serve a purpose, however. Certain cells in the epidermis convert a steroid related to cholesterol into vitamin D with the aid of UV radiation (see Section 9.6). Vitamin D leaves the skin and helps regulate both calcium and phosphorus metabolism in the body. Calcium and phosphorus have a variety of roles and are important in the proper development and mineralization of the bones.

BIOLOGY IN YOUR LIFE

Are tanning beds safe?

Studies have indicated that the levels of UV radiation being emitted in tanning beds may be up to 15 times higher than natural levels. Both the FDA and the World Health Organization (WHO) have warned that the use of tanning beds increases the risk of melanoma skin cancer by 59% and that the risk increases with each use.

Although exposure to UV radiation does increase vitamin D levels slightly, it also results in an increased formation of cataracts (clouding of the cornea of the eyes) and a suppressed immune system. This high level of UV radiation can reduce the amount of collagen in the connective tissues, resulting in premature aging of the skin. For these reasons, the FDA now classifies tanning beds as a moderate risk and advises users to take precautions to reduce risk.

Overexposure to UV radiation can result in skin cancer, a form of cancer that is increasing in frequency across the world. The Health feature "UV Radiation and Skin Cancer" explores some of the recommendations on how to avoid skin cancer.

The Dermis

The **dermis** is a region of dense fibrous connective tissue beneath the epidermis. Dermatology is a branch of medicine that specializes in diagnosing and treating skin disorders. The dermis contains

BIOLOGY TODAY ▶ **Health**

UV Radiation and Skin Cancer

The sun is the major source of energy for life on Earth. Without the sun, most organisms would quickly die out. But the sun's energy can also be damaging. In addition to visible light, the sun emits ultraviolet (UV) radiation, which has a shorter wavelength (and thus a higher energy) than visible light. Based on wavelength, UV radiation can be grouped into three types: UVA, UVB, and UVC, but only UVA and UVB reach the Earth's surface. Scientists have developed a UV index to determine how powerful the solar rays are in different U.S. cities. In general, the more southern the city, the higher the UV index and the greater the risk of skin cancer. Maps indicating the daily risk levels for various U.S. regions can be viewed at http://www.nws.noaa.gov/om/heat/uv.shtml.

Both UVA and UVB rays can damage skin cells. Tanning occurs when melanin granules increase in keratinized cells at the surface of the skin as a way to prevent further damage by UV rays. Too much exposure to UVB rays can directly damage skin cell DNA, leading to mutations that can cause skin cancer. UVB is also responsible for the pain and redness characteristic of a sunburn. In contrast, UVA rays do not cause sunburn, but penetrate more deeply into the skin, damaging collagen fibers and inducing premature aging of the skin, as well as certain types of skin cancer. UVA rays can also induce skin cancer by causing the production of highly reactive chemicals that can indirectly damage DNA.

Skin cancer is the most commonly diagnosed type of cancer in the United States, outnumbering cancers of the lung, breast, prostate, and colon combined. The most common type of skin cancer is basal cell carcinoma (Fig. 4A*a*), which is rarely fatal but can be disfiguring if allowed to grow. Squamous cell carcinoma (Fig. 4A*b*), the second most common type, is fatal in about 1% of cases. The most deadly form is melanoma (Fig. 4A*c*), which can occur at any stage of life. If detected early, over 95% of patients survive at least five years, but if the cancer cells have already spread throughout the body, only 10% to 20% can expect to live this long.

Melanoma affects pigmented cells and often has the appearance of an unusual mole (Fig. 4A*c*). Any moles that become malignant are removed surgically. If the cancer has spread, chemotherapy and a number of other treatments are also available. In March 2007, the USDA approved a vaccine to treat melanoma in dogs, which was the first time a vaccine was approved as a treatment for any cancer in animals or humans. Early clinical trials suggest that the vaccine may prevent a recurrence of melanoma following surgery. Advances have also been made in the field of immunotherapy, where the cells of a person's immune system (see Section 7.4) are directed to attack melanoma cells. For example, the FDA has approved a drug called ipilimumab, after it was shown to extend the lives of patients with advanced, late-stage melanoma.

According to the Skin Cancer Foundation, about 90% of nonmelanoma skin cancers, and 65% of melanomas, are associated with exposure to UV radiation from the sun. So how can we protect ourselves? First, try to minimize sun exposure between 10 A.M. and 4 P.M. (when the UV rays are most intense) by wearing protective clothing, hats, and sunglasses. Second, use sunscreen. Sunscreens generally do a better job of blocking UVB than UVA rays. In fact, the SPF, or sun protection factor printed on sunscreen labels, refers only to the degree of protection against UVB. Many sunscreens don't provide as much protection against UVA, and because UVA doesn't cause sunburn, people may have a false sense of security. Some sunscreens do a better job of blocking UVA—look for those that contain zinc oxide, titanium dioxide, avobenzone, or Mexoryl SX. Unfortunately, tanning salons use lamps that emit UVA rays that are two to three times more powerful than the UVA rays emitted by the sun. Because of the potential damage to deeper layers of skin, most medical experts recommend avoiding indoor tanning salons altogether.

Because UV light is potentially damaging, why haven't all humans developed the more protective dark skin that is common to humans living in tropical regions? It turns out that vitamin D is produced in the body only when UVB rays interact with a form of cholesterol found mainly in the skin. This "sunshine vitamin" serves several important functions in the body, including keeping bones strong, boosting the immune system, and reducing blood pressure. Certain foods also contain vitamin D, but it can be difficult to obtain sufficient amounts through diet alone. Therefore, in more temperate areas of the planet, lighter-skinned individuals have the advantage of being able to synthesize sufficient vitamin D.

So how much sun exposure is enough in temperate regions of the world? During the summer months, an average fair-skinned person will synthesize plenty of vitamin D after exposure to 10–15 minutes of midday sun. During winter months, however, those living north of Atlanta probably receive too few UV rays to stimulate vitamin D synthesis, and therefore they must fulfill their requirement through their diet.

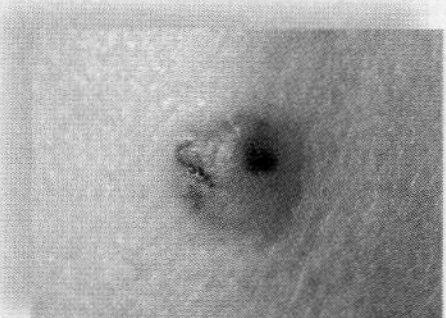

a. Basal cell carcinoma

b. Squamous cell carcinoma

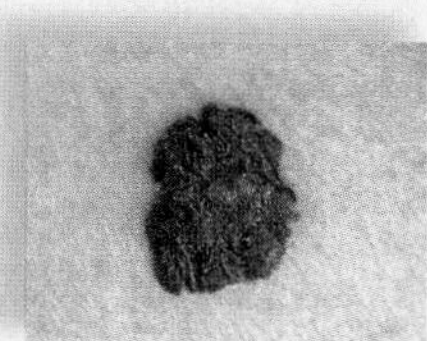

c. Melanoma

Figure 4A Types of skin cancer.
a. Basal cell carcinomas are the most common type of skin cancer. **b.** Squamous cell carcinomas arise from the epidermis, and usually occur in areas exposed to the sun. **c.** Malignant melanomas result from a proliferation of pigmented cells. Warning signs include a change in the shape, size, or color of a normal mole, as well as itching, tenderness, or pain.
(a, b): Dr. P. Marazzi/Science Source; (c): James Stevenson/Science Source

Questions to Consider

1. How would skin cancer negatively affect homeostasis?
2. If caught early, melanoma is rarely fatal. What are some factors that could delay detection of a melanoma?

collagen and elastic fibers. The collagen fibers are flexible but offer great resistance to overstretching. They prevent the skin from being torn. The elastic fibers maintain normal skin tension but also stretch to allow movement of underlying muscles and joints. The number of collagen and elastic fibers decreases with age and with exposure to the sun, causing the skin to become less supple and more prone to wrinkling. The dermis also contains blood vessels that nourish the skin. When blood rushes into these vessels, a person blushes. When blood is minimal in them, a person turns "blue." Blood vessels in the dermis play a role in temperature regulation. If body temperature starts to rise, the blood vessels in the skin dilate. As a result, more blood is brought to the surface of the skin for cooling. If the outer temperature cools, the blood vessels constrict, so less blood is brought to the skin's surface.

The sensory receptors—primarily in the dermis—are specialized for touch, pressure, pain, hot, and cold. These receptors supply the central nervous system with information about the external environment. The sensory receptors also account for the use of the skin as a means of communication between people. For example, the touch receptors play a major role in sexual arousal.

The Subcutaneous Layer

Technically speaking, the subcutaneous layer beneath the dermis is not a part of skin. This layer is composed of loose connective tissue and adipose tissue, which stores energy as fat. Adipose tissue helps thermally insulate the body from either gaining heat from the outside or losing heat from the inside. A well-developed subcutaneous layer gives the body a rounded appearance and provides protective padding against external assaults. Excessive development of the subcutaneous layer accompanies obesity. The subcutaneous layer is also a common site for injections, which is why the instrument used for the injection is called a hypodermic needle.

Accessory Organs of the Skin

Nails, hair, and glands are structures of epidermal origin, even though some parts of hair and glands are largely found in the dermis. **Nails** are a protective covering of the distal part of fingers and toes, collectively called *digits* (Fig. 4.13). Nails grow from epithelial cells at the base of the nail in the portion called the *nail root.* The *cuticle* is a fold of skin that hides the nail root. The whitish color of the half-moon-shaped base, or *lunula,* results from the thick layer of cells in this area. The cells of a nail become keratinized as they grow out over the underlying skin, called the *nail bed.*

Hair follicles are the part of the epidermis that wraps around the hair itself. The *hair root* is the portion of the hair that exists beneath the skin where the *hair shaft* extends beyond the skin (see Fig. 4.11). Contraction of the *arrector pili muscles* attached to hair follicles causes the hairs to "stand on end" and goosebumps to develop. Hair grows when stem cells at the base of the hair root divide. The cells become keratinized and die as they are pushed farther from the root. Hair color is largely due to the production of melanin by melanocytes present in the bulb. If the melanin contains iron and sulfur, hair is blond or red. Graying occurs when melanin cannot be produced, and white hair is due to air trapped in the hair shaft.

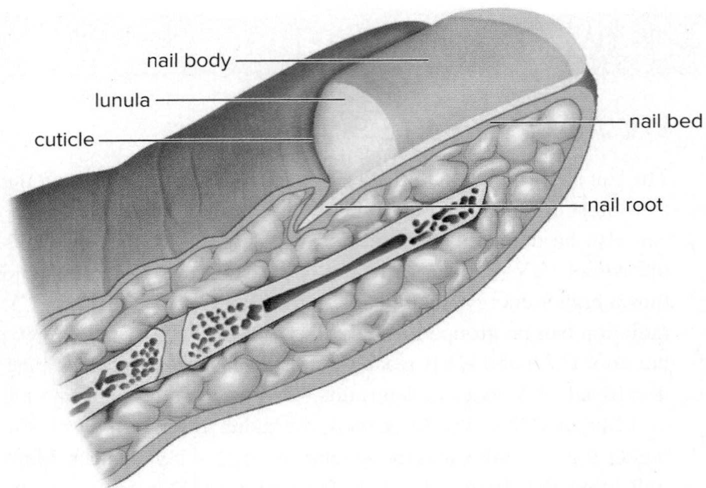

Figure 4.13 **Anatomy of a human nail.**
Cells produced by the nail root become keratinized, forming the nail body.

Each hair follicle has one or more **oil glands** (see Fig. 4.11), also called *sebaceous glands,* which secrete *sebum.* Sebum is an oily substance that lubricates the hair in the follicle and the skin. The oil secretions from sebaceous glands are acidic and retard the growth of bacteria. If the sebaceous glands fail to discharge (usually because they are blocked with keratinocytes), the secretions collect and form "whiteheads." Over time, the sebum in a whitehead oxidizes to form a "blackhead." Acne is an inflammation of the sebaceous glands, which most often occurs during adolescence due to hormonal changes.

Sweat glands (see Fig. 4.11) are numerous and present in all regions of the body. A sweat gland is a tubule that begins in the dermis and either opens into a hair follicle or, more often, opens onto the surface of the skin. Sweat glands play a role in modifying body temperature. When body temperature starts to rise, sweat glands become active. Sweat absorbs body heat as it evaporates. Once the body temperature lowers, sweat glands are no longer active.

CHECK YOUR PROGRESS 4.7

1. Briefly list the functions of the skin.
2. Compare structures and functions of the epidermis and dermis.
3. Explain how each accessory organ of the skin aids in homeostasis.

CONNECTING THE CONCEPTS

For more information on the role of the skin in human physiology, refer to the following discussions:

Section 9.6 provides more information on the relationship between vitamin D and bone calcium homeostasis.

Sections 20.1 and **20.2** explain how cells develop into cancer cells and present some of the different forms of cancer.

Section 23.5 explores the evolutionary reasons for variations in skin color.

4.8 Homeostasis

LEARNING OUTCOMES

Upon completion of this section, you should be able to

1. Define *homeostasis* and provide an example.
2. Distinguish between positive and negative feedback mechanisms.

Homeostasis represents the relative constancy of the internal environment of the body. The body systems help maintain homeostasis by adjusting their physiological processes. Even though external conditions may change dramatically, we have physiological mechanisms that respond to disturbances and limit the amount of internal change. Conditions usually stay within a narrow range of normalcy. For example, blood glucose, pH levels, and body temperature typically fluctuate during the day, but not usually within tolerable limits. If internal conditions change to any great degree, illness often results.

The Internal Environment

The internal environment has two parts: blood and **interstitial fluid.** Blood delivers oxygen and nutrients to the tissues and carries away carbon dioxide and wastes. Interstitial fluid, not blood, bathes the body's cells. Therefore, interstitial fluid is the medium through which substances are exchanged between cells and blood. Oxygen and nutrients pass through interstitial fluid on their way to tissue cells from the blood. Then, carbon dioxide and wastes are carried away from the tissue cells by the interstitial fluid and are brought back into the blood. The cooperation of body systems is required to keep these substances within the range of normalcy in blood and interstitial fluid.

The Body Systems and Homeostasis

The nervous and endocrine systems are particularly important in coordinating the activities of all the other organ systems as they function to maintain homeostasis (Fig. 4.14). The nervous system is able to bring about rapid responses to any changes in the internal

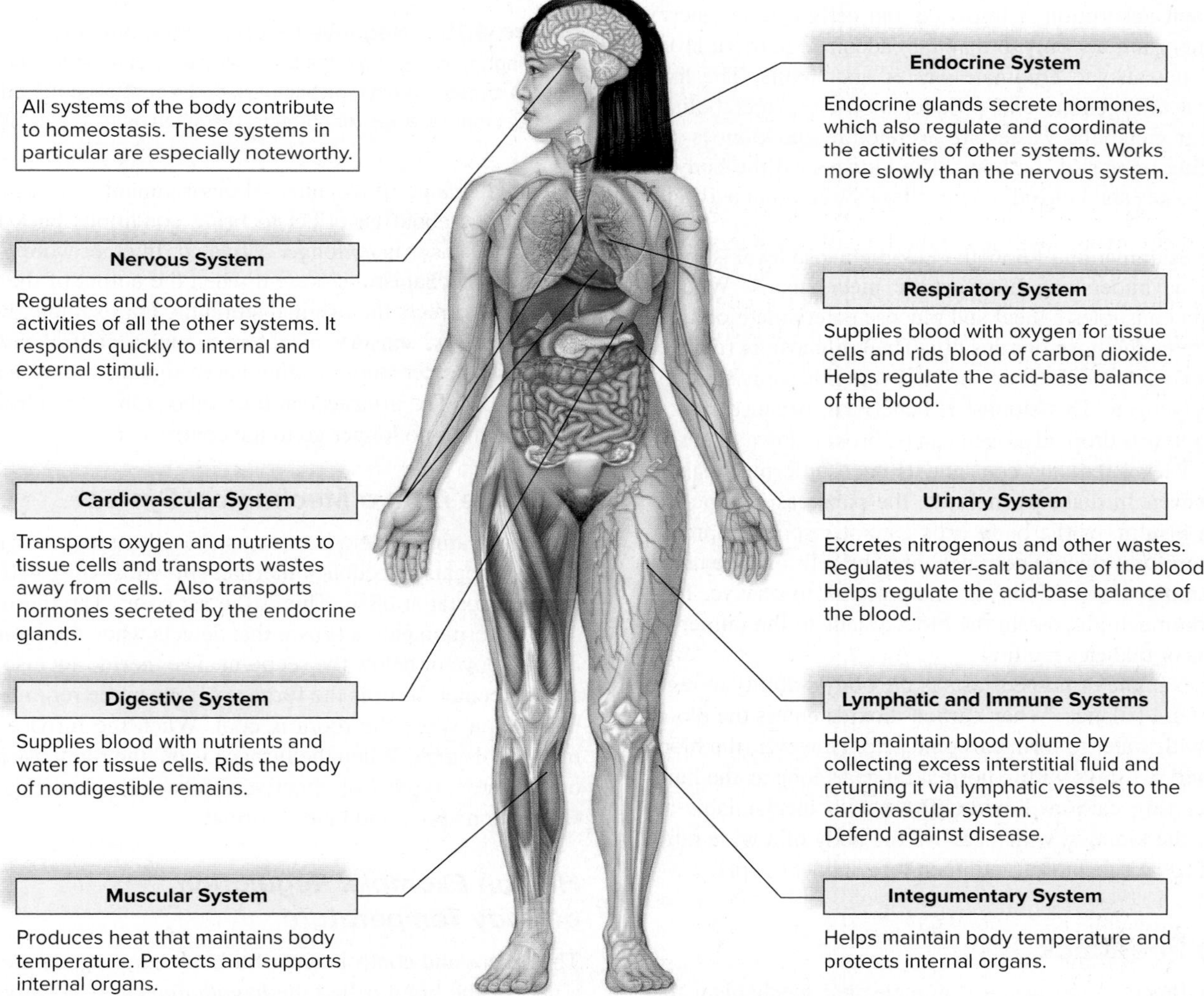

All systems of the body contribute to homeostasis. These systems in particular are especially noteworthy.
Endocrine System
Endocrine glands secrete hormones, which also regulate and coordinate the activities of other systems. Works more slowly than the nervous system.
Nervous System
Regulates and coordinates the activities of all the other systems. It responds quickly to internal and external stimuli.
Respiratory System
Supplies blood with oxygen for tissue cells and rids blood of carbon dioxide. Helps regulate the acid-base balance of the blood.
Cardiovascular System
Transports oxygen and nutrients to tissue cells and transports wastes away from cells. Also transports hormones secreted by the endocrine glands.
Urinary System
Excretes nitrogenous and other wastes. Regulates water-salt balance of the blood. Helps regulate the acid-base balance of the blood.
Digestive System
Supplies blood with nutrients and water for tissue cells. Rids the body of nondigestible remains.
Lymphatic and Immune Systems
Help maintain blood volume by collecting excess interstitial fluid and returning it via lymphatic vessels to the cardiovascular system.
Defend against disease.
Muscular System
Produces heat that maintains body temperature. Protects and supports internal organs.
Integumentary System
Helps maintain body temperature and protects internal organs.

Figure 4.14 Homeostasis by the organ systems of the human body.
All the organ systems contribute to homeostasis in many ways. Some of the main contributions of each system are shown in this illustration.

environment. The nervous system issues commands by electrochemical signals rapidly transmitted to effector organs, which can be muscles, such as skeletal muscles, or glands, such as sweat and salivary glands. The endocrine system brings about slower responses, but they generally have more lasting effects. Glands of the endocrine system, such as the pancreas and the thyroid, release hormones. *Hormones,* such as insulin from the pancreas, are chemical messengers that must travel through the blood and interstitial fluid to reach their targets.

The nervous and endocrine systems together direct numerous activities that maintain homeostasis, but all the organ systems must do their part to keep us alive and healthy. Picture what would happen if any component of the cardiovascular, respiratory, digestive, or urinary system failed (Fig. 4.14). If someone is having a heart attack, the heart is unable to pump the blood to supply cells with oxygen. Or think of a person who is choking. The trachea (windpipe) is blocked, so no air can reach the lungs for uptake by the blood; unless the obstruction is removed quickly, cells will begin to die as the blood's supply of oxygen is depleted. When the lining of the digestive tract is damaged, as in a severe bacterial infection, nutrient absorption is impaired and cells face an energy crisis. It is important not only to maintain adequate nutrient levels in the blood but also to eliminate wastes and toxins. The liver makes urea, a nitrogenous end product of protein metabolism. Urea and other metabolic wastes are excreted by the kidneys, the urine-producing organs of the body. The kidneys rid the body of nitrogenous wastes and help adjust the blood's water-salt and acid-base balances.

A closer examination of how the blood glucose level is maintained helps us understand homeostatic mechanisms. When a healthy person consumes a meal and glucose enters the blood, the pancreas secretes the hormone insulin. Then, glucose is removed from the blood as cells take it up. In the liver, glucose is stored in the form of glycogen. This storage is beneficial, because later, if blood glucose levels drop, glycogen can be broken down to ensure that the blood level remains constant. Homeostatic mechanisms can fail, however. In diabetes mellitus, the pancreas cannot produce enough insulin, or the body cells cannot respond appropriately to it. Therefore, glucose does not enter the cells and they must turn to other molecules, such as fats and proteins, to survive. This, along with too much glucose in the blood, leads to the numerous complications of diabetes mellitus.

Another example of homeostasis is the body's ability to regulate the acid-base balance. When carbon dioxide enters the blood, it combines with water to form carbonic acid. However, the blood is buffered, and pH stays within normal range as long as the lungs are busy excreting carbon dioxide. These two mechanisms are backed up by the kidneys, which can rid the body of a wide range of acidic and basic substances and, therefore, adjust the pH.

Negative Feedback

Negative feedback is the primary homeostatic mechanism that keeps a variable, such as blood glucose level, close to a particular value, or set point. A homeostatic mechanism has at least two components: a sensor and a control center (Fig. 4.15). The sensor detects a change in the internal environment. The control center then brings about an effect to bring conditions back to normal. Then, the sensor is no longer activated. In other words, a negative feedback mechanism is present when the output of the system resolves or corrects the original stimulus. For example, when blood pressure rises, sensory receptors signal a control center in the brain. The center stops sending nerve signals to muscles in the arterial walls. The arteries can then relax. Once the blood pressure drops, signals no longer go to the control center.

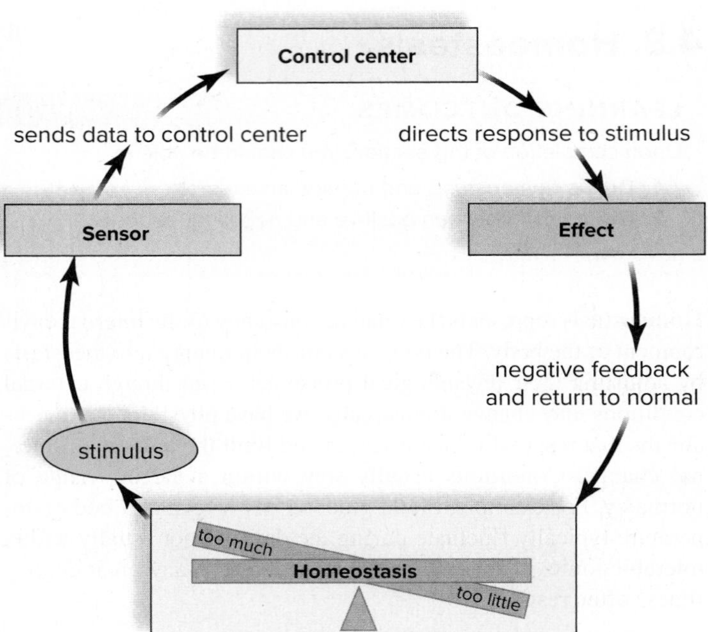

Figure 4.15 Negative feedback mechanisms.
This diagram shows how the basic elements of a feedback mechanism work. A sensor detects the stimulus, and a control center brings about an effect that resolves, or corrects, the stimulus.

Example from a Mechanical System

A home heating system is often used to illustrate how a more complicated negative feedback mechanism works (Fig. 4.16). You set the thermostat at 68°F. This is the *set point.* The thermostat contains a thermometer, a sensor that detects when the room temperature is above or below the set point. The thermostat also contains a control center. It turns the furnace off when the room is warm and turns it on when the room is cool. When the furnace is off, the room cools a bit. When the furnace is on, the room warms a bit. In other words, typical of negative feedback mechanisms, there is a fluctuation above and below normal.

Human Example: Regulation of Body Temperature

The sensor and control center for body temperature are located in a part of the brain called the *hypothalamus.* A negative feedback mechanism limits change in the same direction. Body temperature does not get warmer and warmer, because warmth brings about a change toward a lower body temperature. Likewise, body

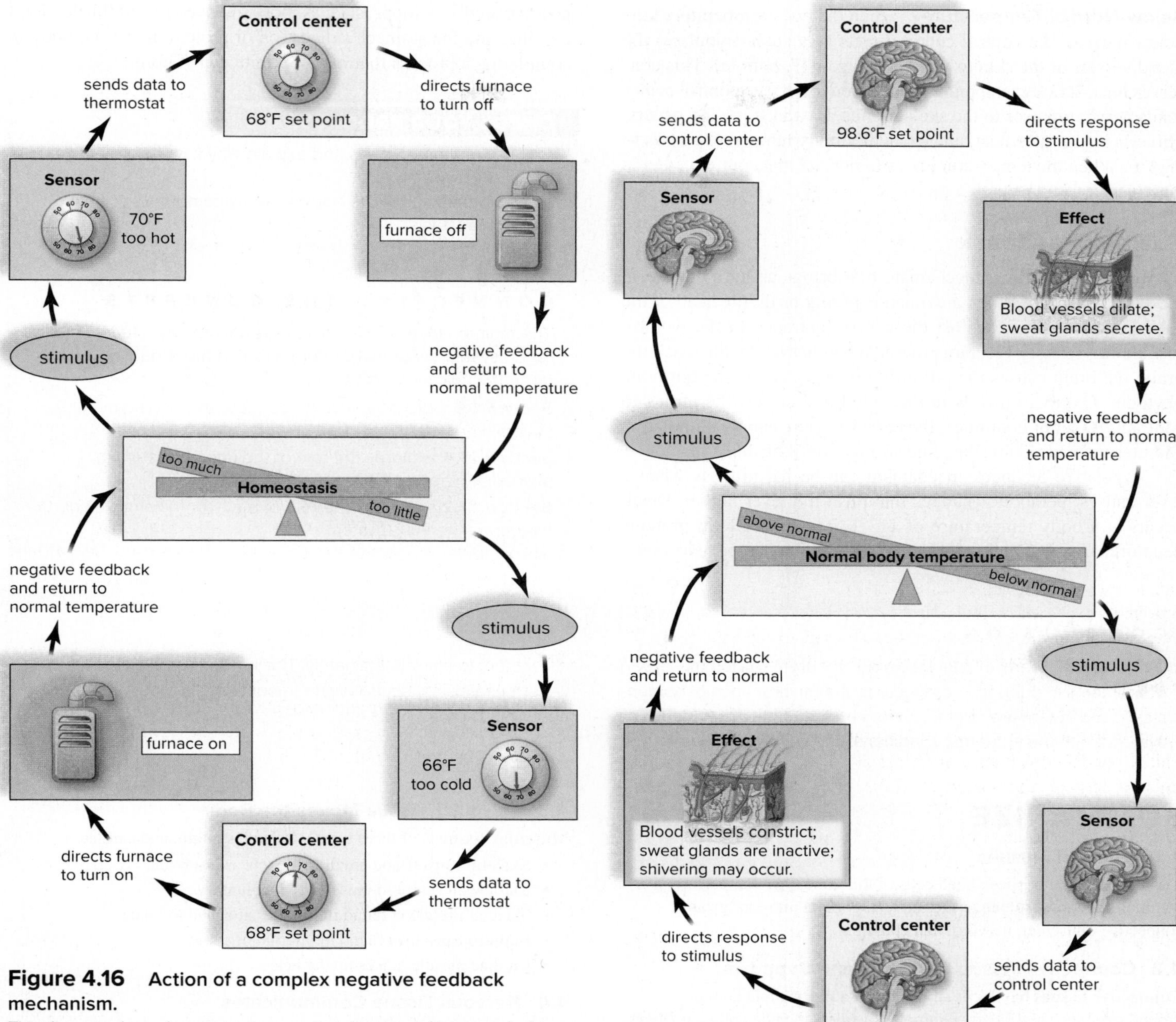

Figure 4.16 Action of a complex negative feedback mechanism.
This diagram shows how room temperature is returned to normal when the room becomes too hot (*top*) or too cold (*bottom*). The thermostat contains both the sensor and the control center. *Top:* The sensor detects that the room is too hot, and the control center turns the furnace off. The stimulus is resolved, or corrected, when the temperature returns to normal. *Bottom:* The sensor detects that the room is too cold, and the control center turns the furnace on. Once again, the stimulus is resolved, or corrected, when the temperature returns to normal.

Figure 4.17 Body temperature homeostasis.
Top: When body temperature rises above normal, the hypothalamus senses the change and causes blood vessels to dilate and sweat glands to secrete so that the temperature returns to normal. *Bottom:* When body temperature falls below normal, the hypothalamus senses the change and causes blood vessels to constrict. In addition, shivering may occur to bring the temperature back to normal. In this way, the original stimulus is resolved, or corrected.

temperature does not get continuously colder. A body temperature below normal brings about a change toward a warmer body temperature.

Above-Normal Temperature When the body temperature is above normal, the control center directs the blood vessels of the skin to dilate (Fig. 4.17, *top*). This allows more blood to flow near the surface of the body, where heat can be lost to the environment. In addition, the nervous system activates the sweat glands, and the evaporation of sweat helps lower body temperature. Gradually body temperature decreases to 98.6°F.

Below-Normal Temperature When the body temperature falls below normal, the control center directs (via nerve impulses) the blood vessels of the skin to constrict (Fig. 4.17, *bottom*). This conserves heat. If body temperature falls even lower, the control center sends nerve impulses to the skeletal muscles and shivering occurs. Shivering generates heat, and gradually body temperature rises to 98.6°F. When the temperature rises to normal, the control center is inactivated.

Positive Feedback

Positive feedback is a mechanism that brings about a change in the same direction. When a woman is giving birth, the head of the baby begins to press against the cervix (entrance to the womb), stimulating sensory receptors there. When nerve signals reach the brain, the brain causes the pituitary gland to secrete the hormone oxytocin. Oxytocin travels in the blood and causes the uterus to contract. As labor continues, the cervix is increasingly stimulated, and uterine contractions become stronger until birth occurs.

A positive feedback mechanism can be harmful, as when a fever causes metabolic changes that push the fever higher. Death occurs at a body temperature of 113°F, because cellular proteins denature at this temperature and metabolism stops. However, positive feedback loops, such as those involved in childbirth, blood clotting, and the stomach's digestion of protein, assist the body in completing a process that has a definite cutoff point.

CHECK YOUR PROGRESS 4.8

1. Define *homeostasis* and explain why it is important to body function.
2. Summarize how the body systems contribute to homeostasis.

CONNECTING THE CONCEPTS

The maintenance of homeostasis is an important function of all organ systems. For more information on the organ systems, refer to the following discussions:

Section 6.6 describes how the cardiovascular system helps maintain homeostasis.

Section 11.4 explores the role of the urinary system in maintaining homeostasis.

Section 14.2 describes the role of the hypothalamus as part of the central nervous system.

CONCLUSION

As we will learn in the following chapters, all of the organ systems in our body contribute to the maintenance of homeostasis, and in turn are reliant on this environment to provide these systems with the nutrients, conditions, and removal of wastes that allow them to operate efficiently. This is true regardless of whether we are exercising, scuba diving, mountain climbing, or just going about our daily routines.

SUMMARIZE

4.1 Types of Tissues

Tissues are made of specialized cells of the same type that perform a common function. Human tissues are categorized into four groups: connective, muscular, nervous, and epithelial.

4.2 Connective Tissue Connects and Supports

Connective tissues have cells separated by a **matrix** that contains ground substance and fibers. Examples of fibers include **collagen fibers, reticular fibers,** and **elastic fibers.** There are three general classes of connective tissue:

- Fibrous connective tissue contains cells called **fibroblasts.** An example of **loose connective tissue** is **adipose tissue,** which contains cells called **adipocytes. Dense fibrous connective tissue** is found in **tendons** and **ligaments.**
- Supportive connective tissue consists of **cartilage** and bone. The matrix for cartilage is solid yet flexible. The cells are found in chambers called lacunae. Examples are **hyaline cartilage, elastic cartilage,** and **fibrocartilage.** The matrix for bone is solid and rigid. Examples are **compact bone** and **spongy bone.**
- Fluid connective tissue is found in the **blood** and **lymph.** The cells of blood include **red blood cells (erythrocytes), white blood cells (leukocytes),** and **platelets (thrombocytes)** in a fluid called plasma.

4.3 Muscular Tissue Moves the Body

Muscular tissue is of three types: skeletal, smooth, and cardiac.

- **Skeletal muscle** and **cardiac muscle** are **striated.**
- Cardiac and smooth muscle are involuntary.
- Skeletal muscle is found in muscles attached to bones.
- **Smooth muscle** is found in internal organs.
- Cardiac muscle makes up the heart.

4.4 Nervous Tissue Communicates

- **Nervous tissue** is composed of **neurons** and several types of **neuroglia.**
- Each neuron has dendrites, a cell body, and an axon. Axons conduct nerve impulses.
- Neurons may be organized into **nerves,** which are surrounded by connective tissue.

4.5 Epithelial Tissue Protects

Epithelial tissue covers the body and lines its cavities.

- Types of simple epithelia are **squamous, cuboidal, columnar,** and **pseudostratified columnar.**
- Certain epithelial tissues may have cilia or microvilli.
- Stratified epithelia have many layers of cells, with only the bottom layer touching the **basement membrane.**
- Epithelia may be structured as a **gland,** which secretes a product either into ducts (exocrine glands) or into the blood (endocrine glands).

4.6 Organ Systems, Body Cavities, and Body Membranes

Organs make up **organ systems,** which are summarized by general function in Table 4.1. Some organs are found in particular body cavities. Body cavities are lined by membranes, such as the **mucous membranes, serous membranes, synovial membranes,** and **meninges.**

Table 4.1 Organ Systems

Transport	**Integumentary**
Cardiovascular (heart and blood vessels)	Skin and accessory organs
Lymphatic and immune (lymphatic vessels)	
Maintenance	**Motor**
Digestive (e.g., stomach, intestines)	Skeletal (bones and cartilage)
Respiratory (tubes and lungs)	Muscular (muscles)
Urinary (tubes and kidneys)	
Control	**Reproduction**
Nervous (brain, spinal cord, and nerves)	Reproductive (tubes and testes in males; tubes and ovaries in females)
Endocrine (glands)	

4.7 Integumentary System

Skin and its accessory organs constitute the **integumentary system.** The major components of skin and the integumentary system include:

- The **epidermis** contains stem cells, which produce new epithelial cells, and **Langerhans cells,** which provide protection against infectious agents. **Melanocytes** produce the coloration of the skin. Within the epidermis, **vitamin D** may be synthesized from cholesterol.
- The **dermis** contains epidermally derived glands and hair follicles, nerve endings, blood vessels, and sensory receptors.
- A **subcutaneous layer** (hypodermis) lies beneath the skin.
- Accessory organs of the skin include the **nails, hair follicles, oil glands,** and **sweat glands.**

4.8 Homeostasis

Homeostasis is the relative constancy of the internal environment, **interstitial fluid,** and blood. All organ systems contribute to homeostasis.

- The cardiovascular, respiratory, digestive, and urinary systems directly regulate the amount of gases, nutrients, and wastes in the blood, keeping interstitial fluid constant.
- The lymphatic system absorbs excess interstitial fluid and functions in immunity.
- The nervous system and endocrine system regulate the other systems.

Negative feedback mechanisms keep the environment relatively stable. When a sensor detects a change above or below a set point, a control center brings about an effect that reverses the change and returns conditions to normal. Examples include the following:

- Regulation of blood glucose level by insulin
- Regulation of room temperature by a thermostat and furnace
- Regulation of body temperature by the brain and sweat glands.

In contrast to negative feedback, a **positive feedback** mechanism brings about rapid change in the same direction as the stimulus and does not achieve relative stability. These mechanisms are useful under certain conditions, such as during birth.

ENGAGE

THINKING CRITICALLY

1. In what way(s) is blood like a tissue?
2. Which of these homeostatic mechanisms in the body are examples of positive feedback, and which are examples of negative feedback? Why?
   a. The adrenal glands produce epinephrine in response to a hormone produced by the pituitary gland in times of stress; the pituitary gland senses the epinephrine in the blood and stops producing the hormone.
   b. As the bladder fills with urine, pressure sensors send messages to the brain with increasing frequency, signaling that the bladder must be emptied. The more the bladder fills, the more messages are sent.
   c. When you drink an excess of water, specialized cells in your brain, as well as stretch receptors in your heart, detect the increase in blood volume. Both signals are transmitted to the kidneys, which increase the production of urine.
3. Explain how a failure of homeostasis leads to death.

MAKING IT RELEVANT

1. What organ systems of the body would have to evolve to allow humans to survive in harsh environments such as the moon or under water?
2. How might the design of a space suit to support life on Mars, or the moon, provide scientists with the information needed to let humans adapt to harsh environments on our planet?
3. When preparing for a spaceflight, astronauts often practice using their space suits in large swimming pools. Why do you think this is effective, and what are some of the problems with this approach with regard to body systems?

Find answers to all of the chapter questions at connect.mheducation.com

CHAPTER 5

Cardiovascular System: Heart and Blood Vessels

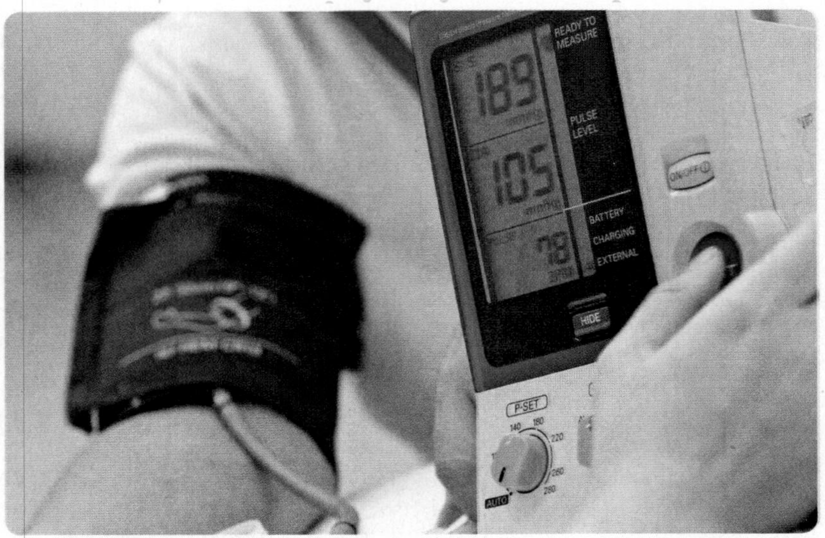

anucha maneechote/Shutterstock

CHAPTER OUTLINE

BEFORE YOU BEGIN

Before beginning this chapter, take a few moments to review the following discussions:

Section 3.3 How do substances cross plasma membranes?

Section 4.1 What are the four types of tissues?

Section 4.8 What is the role of the cardiovascular system in maintaining homeostasis?

Hypertension in Young Adults

High blood pressure, or hypertension, is a disease that affects over half of adults in the U.S. population. Most people consider hypertension to be a disease of middle age, because chances are you know an older friend or family member who is taking medication for this disease. However, recent studies suggest that almost one in five young adults may have high blood pressure, making it one of the major health risks facing this age group.

What then is hypertension? Hypertension is a disease of the cardiovascular system, which includes the heart, blood, and blood vessels. The disease is defined as blood pressure that has a value over 130/80. These numbers refer to the active and resting blood pressures within blood vessels. The first number refers to pressure while the heart is contracting, and the lower number is the resting pressure.

Long-term elevated blood pressure is correlated with an increase in heart disease, stroke, kidney disease, and vision problems. In fact, hypertension is one of the leading causes of death in the United States. But even if you don't have blood pressure readings that indicate hypertension, you may still be at risk. Systolic blood pressures between 120 and 129 are considered elevated, or prehypertensive, and indicate an increased risk of developing hypertension in the future.

In this chapter, you will explore the structure and function of the cardiovascular system, as well as the importance of blood pressure in maintaining homeostasis. We will also explore what is meant by blood pressure values of 189/105, and the factors that can contribute to an increased risk of developing hypertension.

As you read through the chapter, think about the following questions:

1. What is the difference between the diastolic and systolic values?
2. How is blood pressure normally regulated in the body?
3. What factors may cause an individual to develop hypertension?

5.1 Overview of the Cardiovascular System

LEARNING OUTCOMES

Upon completion of this section, you should be able to

1. Identify the two components of the cardiovascular system.
2. Summarize the functions of the cardiovascular system.
3. Explain the purpose of the lymphatic system in circulation.

The **cardiovascular system** consists of the heart, which pumps blood, and the blood vessels, through which the blood flows. The beating of the heart sends blood into the blood vessels. In humans, blood is always contained within blood vessels.

Circulation Allows for the Exchange of Materials

Even though the circulation of blood depends on the beating of the heart, the overall purpose of circulation is to service the cells of the body. Remember that cells are surrounded by interstitial fluid that is used to exchange substances between the blood and cells. Blood removes waste products from that fluid. Blood also provides the interstitial fluid with the oxygen and nutrients cells require to continue their existence.

The cardiovascular system works closely with all of the other organ systems. For example, at the lungs, blood drops off carbon dioxide and picks up oxygen for the respiratory system. However, gas exchange is not the only function of blood. Nutrients enter the bloodstream at the intestines and transport much-needed substances to the body's cells. The cardiovascular system also works closely with the liver, an important organ in metabolism, the detoxification of harmful substances, and homeostasis. The blood of the cardiovascular system is purified of its wastes at the kidneys, and water and salts are retained as needed. Thousands of miles of blood vessels, which form an intricate circuit reaching almost every cell of the body, move the blood and its contents through the body to and from all the body's organs.

Functions of the Cardiovascular System

The following are the general functions of the cardiovascular system:

- *Transport:* The cardiovascular system not only transports oxygen to the cells of the body but also removes carbon dioxide and other waste products of metabolism. It also transports nutrients from the digestive system and hormones from the endocrine system to the cells of the body. In addition, the cardiovascular system transports the cells of the immune system. These cells, and their associated antibodies and chemical signals, help protect the body from infection.
- *Homeostasis:* The cardiovascular system plays a central role in maintaining homeostasis for a variety of internal conditions, including temperature, pH balance, and water and electrolyte levels (Fig. 5.1).

The **lymphatic system** (see Section 7.1) assists the cardiovascular system. In addition to working with the immune system, the lymphatic vessels collect excess interstitial fluid and return it to the cardiovascular system. As exchanges occur between blood and the interstitial fluid, some fluid naturally collects in the tissues. This excess fluid enters lymphatic vessels, which start in the tissues and end at cardiovascular veins in the shoulders. As soon as fluid enters lymphatic vessels, it is called *lymph.* Lymph, you will recall, is a fluid connective tissue, as is blood (see Section 4.2).

CHECK YOUR PROGRESS 5.1

1. Describe the two parts of the cardiovascular system.
2. Summarize the functions of the cardiovascular system.
3. Explain how the lymphatic system interacts with the cardiovascular system.

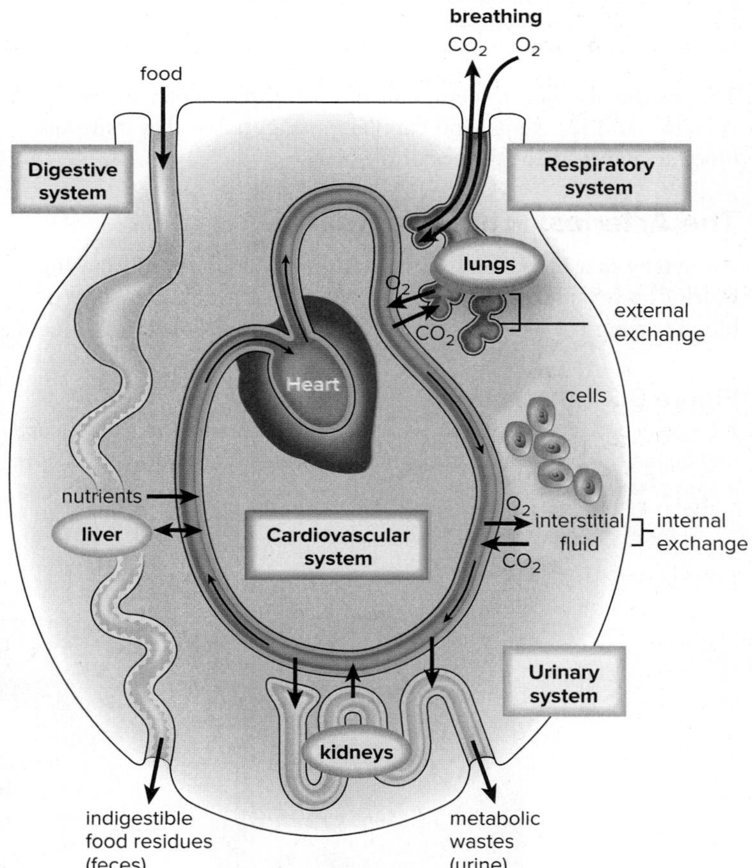

Figure 5.1 The cardiovascular system and homeostasis. The cardiovascular system plays an important role in homeostasis by transporting blood to the organ systems of the body, some of which are shown here.

CONNECTING THE CONCEPTS

As the primary transport system in the human body, the cardiovascular system interacts with all the major organ systems. In doing so, it plays an important role in the homeostasis of a variety of body functions. For more information on these interactions, refer to the following discussions:

Section 4.8 investigates the role of the cardiovascular system in homeostasis.

Section 7.2 takes a greater look at how the lymphatic system interacts with the cardiovascular system.

Section 9.3 examines how the cardiovascular system moves the nutrients that are absorbed by the small intestine.

Section 11.2 explores the interaction of the cardiovascular system with the urinary system.

5.2 The Types of Blood Vessels

LEARNING OUTCOMES

Upon completion of this section, you should be able to

1. Describe the structure and function of the three types of blood vessels.
2. Explain how blood flow is regulated in each of the three types of blood vessels.

The cardiovascular system consists of three types of blood vessels—arteries, veins, and capillaries (Fig. 5.2)—that transport blood to and from the tissues of the body.

The Arteries: From the Heart

An **artery** is a blood vessel that transports blood away from the heart. The structure of an artery is well suited for the transport of blood leaving the heart under pressure. The arterial wall has three layers (Fig. 5.2), the innermost of which is a thin layer of cells called *endothelium.* Endothelium is surrounded by a relatively thick middle layer of smooth muscle and elastic tissue. The artery's outer layer is connective tissue. The strong walls of an artery give it support when blood enters under pressure; the elastic tissue allows an artery to expand to absorb the pressure.

Arterioles are small arteries barely visible to the naked eye. Whereas the middle layer of arterioles has some elastic tissue, it is composed mostly of smooth muscle. These muscle fibers encircle the arteriole. When the fibers contract, the vessel constricts; when these muscle fibers relax, the vessel dilates. The constriction or dilation of arterioles controls blood pressure. When arterioles constrict, blood pressure rises. Dilation of arterioles causes blood pressure to fall.

The Capillaries: Sites of Exchange

Arterioles branch into **capillaries,** the smallest of the blood vessels. The structure of a capillary is adapted for the exchange of materials with the cells of the body. Each capillary is an extremely narrow, microscopic tube with a wall composed only of endothelium. Capillary endothelium is formed by a single layer of epithelial cells with a basement membrane. Although capillaries are small, their total surface area in humans is about 6,300 square meters (m^2). Capillary beds (networks of many capillaries) are present in all regions of the body, so no cell is far from a capillary and thus not far from gas exchange with blood. In the tissues, only certain capillaries are open at any given time. For example, after eating, the capillaries supplying the digestive system are open, whereas most serving the muscles are closed. Rings of muscle called *precapillary sphincters* control the blood flow through a capillary bed (Fig. 5.2). Constriction of the sphincters closes the capillary bed. When a capillary bed is closed, the blood moves to an area where gas exchange is needed, going directly from arteriole to venule through a pathway called an **arteriovenous shunt.**

Figure 5.2 **Structure of a capillary bed.**
A capillary bed is a maze of tiny vessels that lies between an arteriole and a venule. When precapillary sphincter muscles are relaxed, the capillary bed opens and blood flows through the capillaries. Otherwise, blood flows through a shunt directly from the arteriole to the venule.
(photo): Ed Reschke

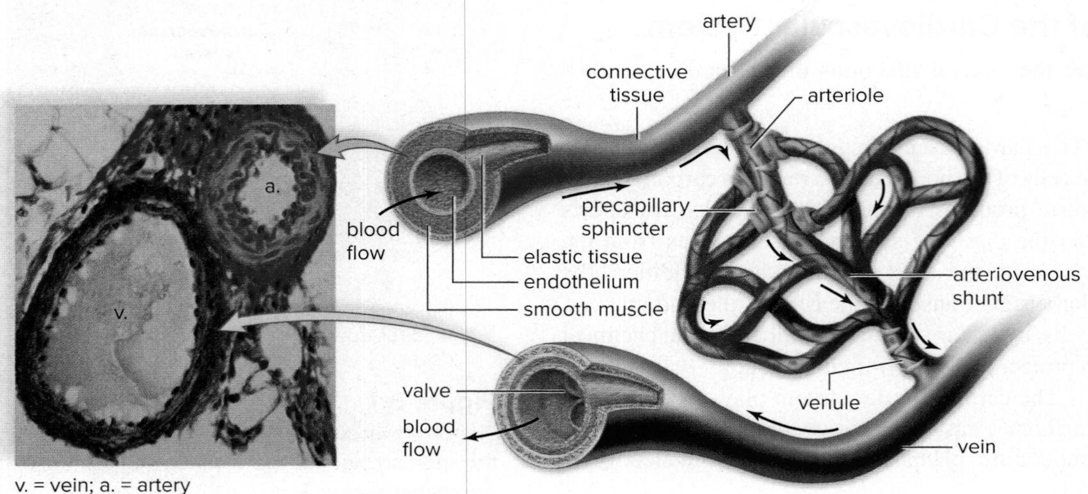

BIOLOGY IN YOUR LIFE

Why do my feet swell when I have been standing all day?

When you stand for long periods, gravity increases the pressure inside the capillaries of the lower limbs. This forces fluid from the capillaries into the interstitial spaces, causing the tissues to swell. When you lie down at night, your feet are level with your heart. Excess interstitial fluid that caused swelling now filters back into lymphatic vessels, which empty into shoulder veins, and fluid returns to the cardiovascular system. By morning, your feet have lost their excess water, and those shoes are loose again.

The Veins: To the Heart

Veins are blood vessels that return blood to the heart. **Venules** are small veins that drain blood from the capillaries and then join to form a vein. The walls of both veins and venules have the same three layers as arteries. However, there is less smooth muscle in the middle layer of a vein and less connective tissue in the outer layer. Therefore, the wall of a vein is thinner than that of an artery.

Because the blood leaving the capillaries is usually under low pressure (see Section 5.4), veins often have valves, which allow blood to flow only toward the heart when open and prevent backward flow of blood when closed. Valves are extensions of the inner-wall layer and are found in the veins that carry blood against the force of gravity, especially the veins of the lower extremities. The walls of veins are thinner, so they can expand to a greater extent. At any one time, about 70% of the blood is in the veins. In this way, the veins act as a blood reservoir. If blood is lost due to hemorrhaging, nervous stimulation causes the veins to constrict, providing more blood to the rest of the body.

CHECK YOUR PROGRESS 5.2

1. List and describe the different types of blood vessels.
2. Describe how each blood vessel contributes to the flow of blood in the body.
3. Explain why the structure of the veins is different from that of the arteries.

CONNECTING THE CONCEPTS

Blood vessels act as conduits for the movement of blood, and in doing so, blood vessels interact with all of the tissues and cells of the body. For more information on blood and blood vessels, refer to the following discussions:

Section 6.1 examines the composition of blood and the function of its various components.

Figure 10.11 illustrates the major arteries and veins involved in moving gases within the body.

Figure 11.7 demonstrates how the capillaries in the kidneys assist in the filtration of the blood.

5.3 The Heart Is a Double Pump

LEARNING OUTCOMES

Upon completion of this section, you should be able to

1. Identify the structures and chambers of the human heart.
2. Describe the flow of blood through the human heart.
3. Explain the internal and external controls of the heartbeat.

The **heart** is a cone-shaped, muscular organ located between the lungs, directly behind the sternum (breastbone). The heart is tilted so that the apex (the pointed end) is oriented to the left side of the body (Fig. 5.3). To approximate the size of your heart, make a fist; then clasp the fist with your opposite hand. The major portion of the heart is the interior wall of tissue called the **myocardium,** consisting largely of cardiac muscle tissue.

The muscle fibers of myocardium are branched. Each fiber is tightly joined to neighboring fibers by structures called *intercalated discs* (Fig. 5.3*b*). The intercalated discs also include cell junctions like gap junctions and desmosomes. Gap junctions aid in the simultaneous contractions of the cardiac fibers. Desmosomes include arrangements of protein fibers that tightly hold the membranes of adjacent cells together and prevent overstretching. The heart is surrounded by the **pericardium,** a thick, membranous sac that supports and protects the heart. The inside of the pericardium secretes *pericardial fluid* (a lubrication fluid), and the pericardium slides smoothly over the heart's surface as it pumps the blood.

Internally, a wall called the **septum** separates the heart into a right side and a left side (Fig. 5.4*a*). The heart has four chambers. The two upper, thin-walled **atria** (*sing.,* atrium) are called the right atrium and the left atrium. The two lower chambers are the thick-walled **ventricles,** called the right ventricle and the left ventricle (Fig. 5.4*a*).

Heart valves keep blood flowing in the right direction and prevent its backward movement. The valves that lie between the atria and the ventricles are called the **atrioventricular (AV) valves.** These valves are supported by strong, fibrous strings called *chordae tendineae,* which are attached to muscles that project from the ventricular walls. The chordae anchor the valves, preventing them from inverting when the heart contracts. The AV valve on the right side is called the *tricuspid valve,* because it has three flaps, or cusps. The AV valve on the left side is called the *mitral valve,* because it has a shape like a bishop's hat, or miter.

The remaining two valves are the **semilunar valves,** with flaps shaped like half-moons. These valves lie between the ventricles and their attached vessels. The semilunar valves are named for their attached vessels: The *pulmonary semilunar valve* lies between the right ventricle and the pulmonary trunk. The *aortic semilunar valve* lies between the left ventricle and the aorta.

Coronary Circulation: The Heart's Blood Supply

The myocardium receives oxygen and nutrients from the coronary arteries. Likewise, wastes are removed by the cardiac veins. The blood that flows through the heart contributes little to either nutrient supply or waste removal.

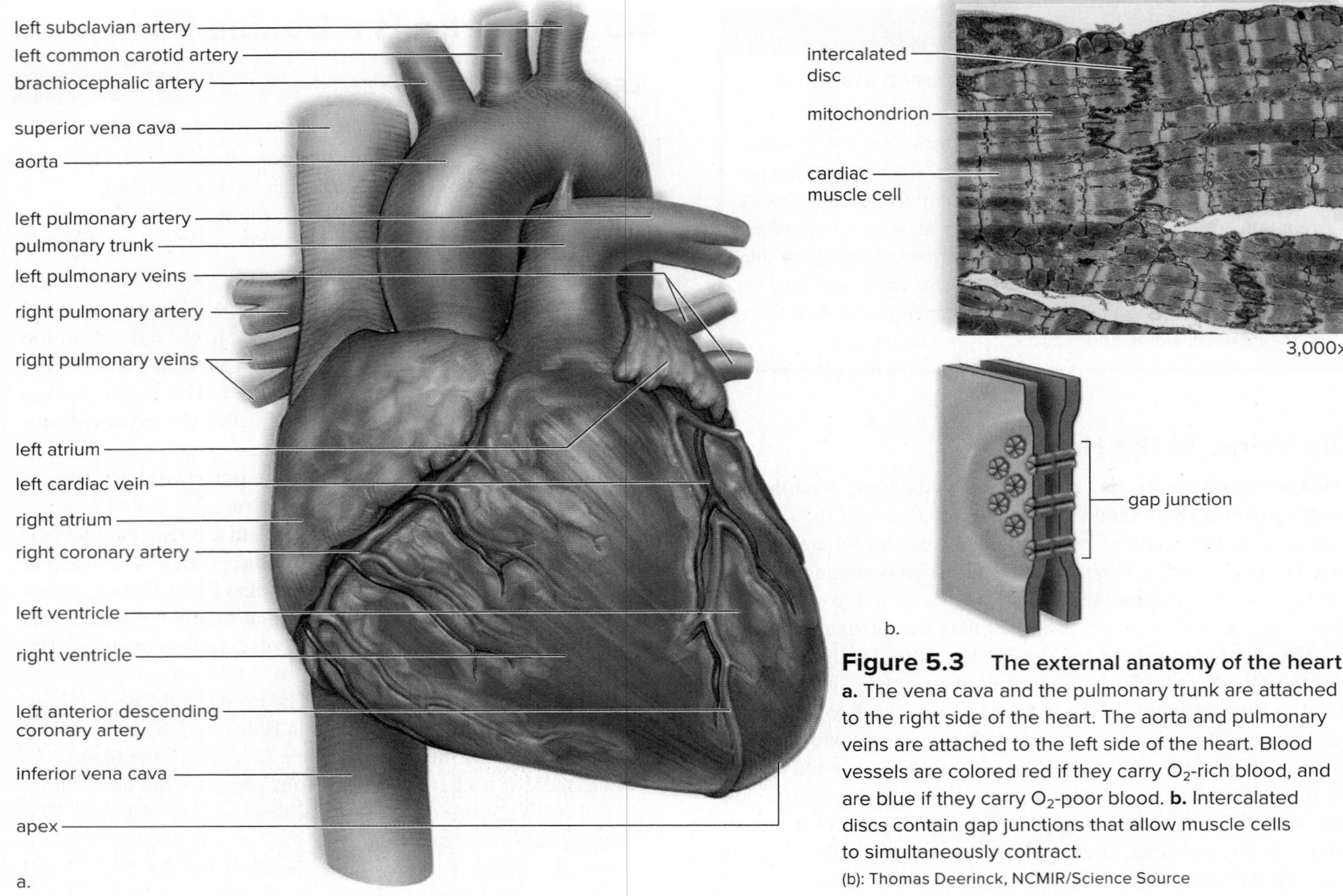

Figure 5.3 **The external anatomy of the heart.** **a.** The vena cava and the pulmonary trunk are attached to the right side of the heart. The aorta and pulmonary veins are attached to the left side of the heart. Blood vessels are colored red if they carry O_2-rich blood, and are blue if they carry O_2-poor blood. **b.** Intercalated discs contain gap junctions that allow muscle cells to simultaneously contract.

(b): Thomas Deerinck, NCMIR/Science Source

The myocardium receives oxygen and nutrients from the **coronary arteries.** These arteries are the first branches off the aorta (see Fig. 5.3*a*). They originate just above the aortic semilunar valve. They lie on the exterior surface of the heart, where they divide into diverse arterioles. The coronary capillary beds join to form venules, which converge to form the cardiac veins, which empty into the right atrium. Because they have a very small diameter, they can become easily clogged, a characteristic of *coronary artery disease*.

If these vessels become completely clogged, oxygen and nutrients such as glucose will not reach the muscles of the heart. This may result in a *myocardial infarction,* or heart attack. Coronary artery disease may be treated with medication, coronary bypass surgery, angioplasty, or stem cell therapies (see Section 5.7).

Passage of Blood Through the Heart

Recall that intercalated discs (see Fig. 5.3*b*) join fibers of cardiac muscle cells, allowing them to communicate with each other. By sending electrical signals between cells, both atria and then both

BIOLOGY IN YOUR LIFE

Heart attack or cardiac arrest?

While we often hear these terms used interchangeably, there is a medical difference.

A heart attack occurs when the muscles of the heart do not receive adequate oxygen, and thus fail to contract correctly. This is usually due to blockages in the coronary arteries that supply the heart muscles. Like other tissues, the heart muscle starts to die after a few minutes of not receiving oxygen, but unlike many other tissues in the body, heart muscle does not regenerate.

A cardiac arrest occurs when the electrical system of the heart, which controls the contractions of the heart, malfunctions. As a result, blood does not reach the brain, and a person often becomes unconscious.

While heart attacks may lead to cardiac arrest, it is possible that a cardiac arrest does necessarily cause a heart attack. However, in both cases, the individual may die if normal heart function is not restored.

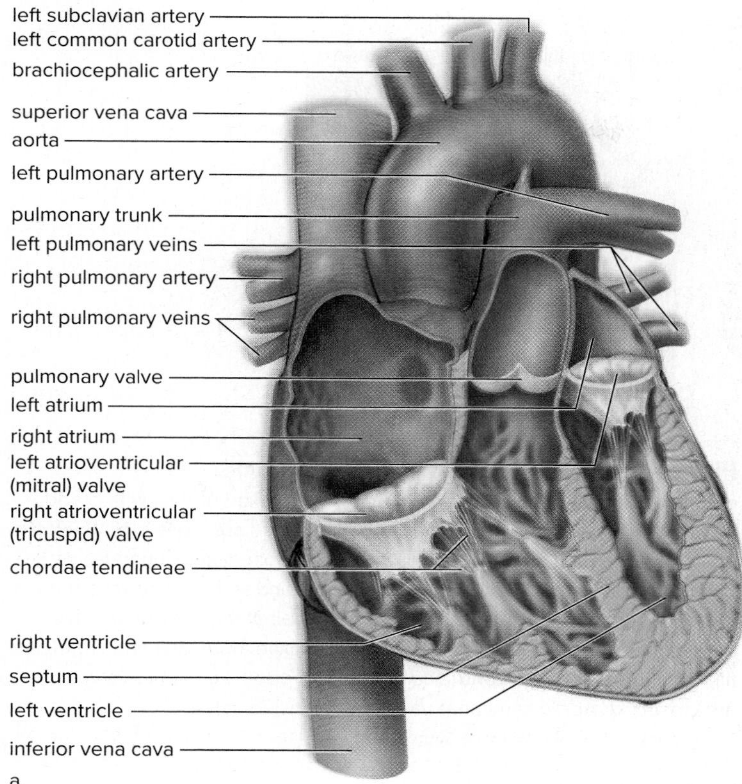

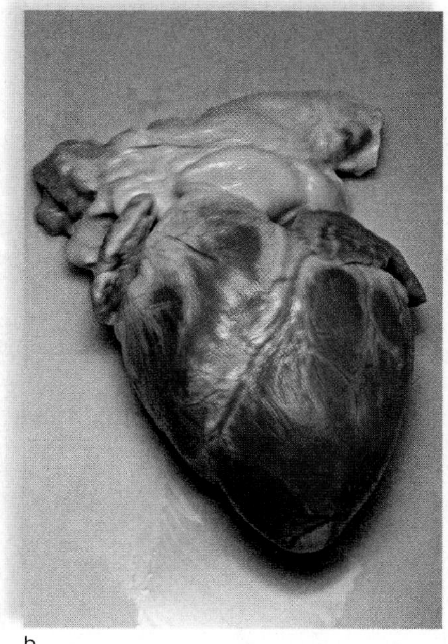

Figure 5.4 **The heart is a double pump.**
A cutaway diagram of the human heart. **a.** The heart is a double pump with four chambers. The two right and two left chambers are separated by a septum. The right side pumps the blood to the lungs, and the left side pumps blood to the rest of the body. **b.** Photo of a human heart.
(b): A. & F. Michler/Peter Arnold/Getty Images

ventricles contract simultaneously. We can trace the path of blood through the heart and body in the following manner.

- The inferior and superior **vena cava** (Fig. 5.4*a*) carry oxygen-poor blood from systemic veins to the right atrium.
- The right atrium contracts (simultaneously with the left atrium), sending blood through an atrioventricular valve (the tricuspid valve) to the right ventricle.
- The right ventricle contracts, pumping blood through the pulmonary semilunar valve into the pulmonary trunk. The pulmonary trunk, which carries oxygen-poor blood, divides into two **pulmonary arteries,** which go to the lungs.
- Pulmonary capillaries within the lungs allow gas exchange. Oxygen enters the blood; carbon dioxide waste is excreted from the blood.
- Four **pulmonary veins,** which carry oxygen-rich blood, enter the left atrium.
- The left atrium pumps blood through an atrioventricular valve (the mitral valve) to the left ventricle.
- The left ventricle contracts (at the same time as the right ventricle), sending blood through the aortic semilunar valve into the **aorta.**
- Arteries and arterioles supply tissue capillaries. Tissue capillaries drain into increasingly larger veins. Veins drain into the superior and inferior venae cavae, and the cycle starts again.

From this description, you can see that oxygen-poor blood never mixes with oxygen-rich blood and that blood must go through the lungs to pass from the right side to the left side of the heart. The heart is a double pump, because the right ventricle of the heart sends blood through the lungs, while the left ventricle sends blood throughout the body. Thus, the left ventricle has the harder job of pumping blood.

The atria have thin walls, and each pumps blood into the ventricle right below it. The ventricles are thicker, and they pump blood into arteries (pulmonary artery and aorta) that travel to other parts of the body. The thinner myocardium of the right ventricle pumps blood to the lungs nearby in the thoracic cavity. The left ventricle has a thicker wall with more cardiac muscle cells than the right ventricle, and this enables it to pump blood out of the heart with enough force to send it through the body.

The pumping of the heart sends blood under pressure out into the arteries. The left side of the heart pumps with greater force, so blood pressure is greatest in the aorta. Blood pressure then decreases as the total cross-sectional area of arteries and then arterioles increases (see Fig. 5.9). A different mechanism, aside from blood pressure, is used to move blood in the veins.

The Cardiac Cycle

Each heartbeat is called a **cardiac cycle** (Fig. 5.5). Recall that when the heart beats, the two atria contract at the same time. Almost immediately after, the two ventricles contract at the same time. Then, all chambers relax. **Systole,** the working phase, refers to the contraction of the chambers, and **diastole,** the resting phase, refers to the relaxation of the chambers (Fig. 5.5). The heart contracts, or beats, about 70 times a minute, on average, in a healthy adult, with each heartbeat lasting about 0.85 of a second, and a normal resting rate that varies from 60 to 80 beats per minute.

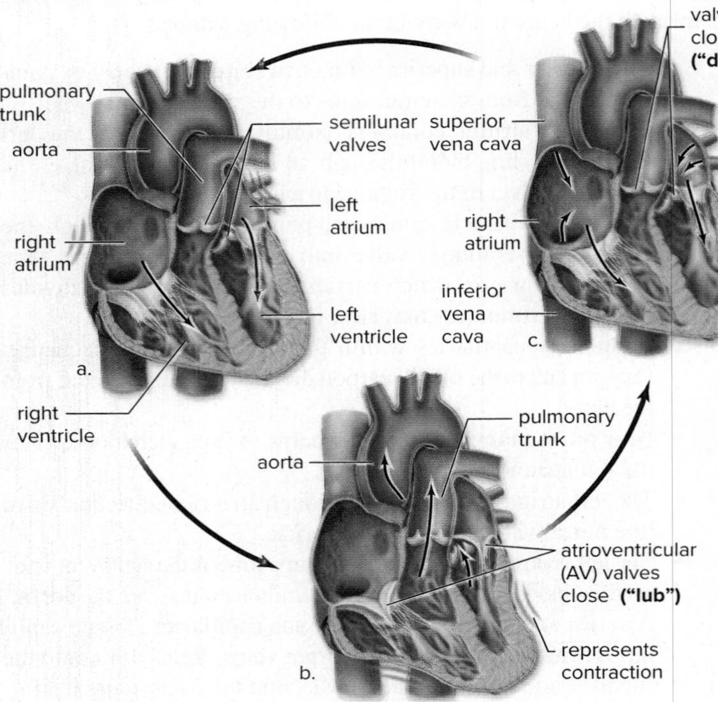

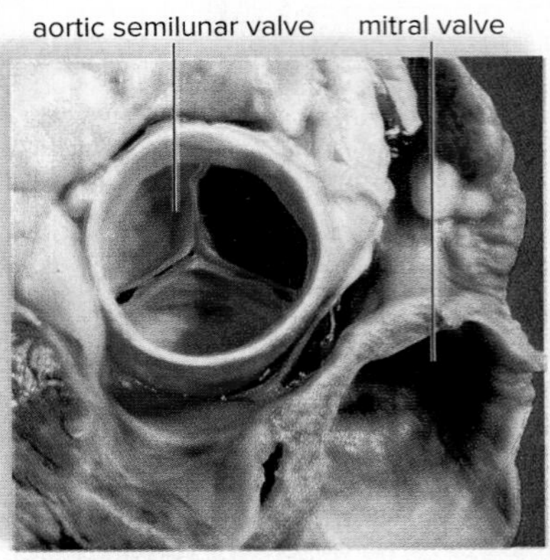

Figure 5.5 The stages of the cardiac cycle.
a. When the atria contract, the ventricles are relaxed and fill with blood. Atrioventricular valves are open; semilunar valves are closed. **b.** When the ventricles contract, atrioventricular valves are closed; semilunar valves are open. Blood is pumped into the pulmonary trunk and aorta; this corresponds to the "lub" sound. **c.** Backward flow of blood against the semilunar valves causes the "dub" sound. When the heart is relaxed, both atria and ventricles fill with blood. The atrioventricular valves are open; semilunar valves are closed. **d.** Aortic semilunar valve and bicuspid valve.
(d): Biophoto Associates/Science Source

There are two audible heartbeat sounds, referred to as "lub-dub." The first sound, "lub," occurs when increasing pressure of blood inside a ventricle forces the cusps of the AV valves to slam shut (Fig. 5.5*b*). In contrast, the pressure of blood inside a ventricle causes the semilunar valves (pulmonary and aortic) to open. The "dub" occurs when the ventricles relax, and blood in the arteries flows backward momentarily, causing the semilunar valves to close (Fig. 5.5*c*). A heart murmur, or a slight swishing sound after the "lub," is often due to leaky valves, which allow blood to pass back into the atria after the AV valves have closed. Faulty valves can be surgically corrected.

Internal Control of the Heartbeat

The heart contains an internal control system that regulates the heartbeat. The rhythmic contraction of the atria and ventricles is due to the internal (intrinsic) conduction system of the heart. Nodal tissue is a unique type of cardiac muscle that has both muscular and nervous characteristics. It is located in two regions of the heart. The **SA (sinoatrial) node** is located in the upper dorsal wall of the right atrium. The **AV (atrioventricular) node** is located in the base of the right atrium very near the septum (Fig. 5.6*a*). The SA node initiates the heartbeat and automatically sends out an excitation signal every 0.85 second. This causes the atria to contract. When the signal reaches the AV node, there is a slight delay, before the signal travels to the ventricles, that allows the atria to finish their contraction before the ventricles begin their contraction. The signal for the ventricles to contract travels from the AV node through the two branches of the *atrioventricular (AV) bundle* before reaching the numerous and smaller *Purkinje fibers*. The AV bundle, its branches, and the Purkinje fibers work efficiently because gap junctions (see Section 3.5) allow electrical current to flow from cell to cell (see Fig. 5.6). The SA node is also called

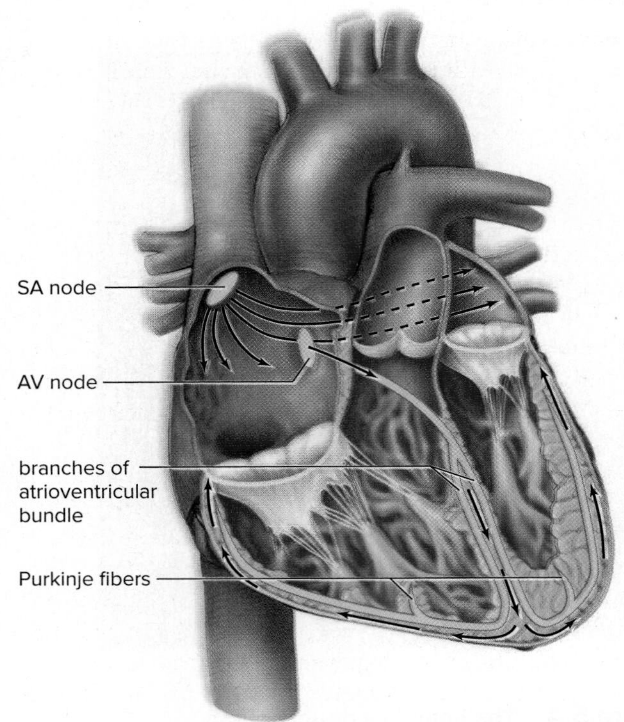

Figure 5.6 An electrical signal pathway through the heart.
The SA node sends out a signal (black arrows), which causes the atria to contract. When this signal reaches the AV node, it signals the ventricles to contract. The electrical signal passes down the two branches of the atrioventricular bundle to the Purkinje fibers. Thereafter, the ventricles contract.

the **pacemaker** because it regulates heartbeat. If the SA node fails to work properly, the heart still beats due to signals generated by the AV node. But the beat is slower (40 to 60 beats per minute). To correct this condition, it is possible to implant an artificial pacemaker, which automatically gives an electrical stimulus to the heart every 0.85 second.

External Control of the Heartbeat

The body has an external (extrinsic) way to regulate the heartbeat. A cardiac control center in the medulla oblongata, a portion of the brain that controls internal organs, can alter the beat of the heart by way of the parasympathetic and sympathetic portions of the nervous system (see Section 14.4). Basically activity, such as exercise or stress situations, increases SA and AV nodal activity, while restful situations, such as listening to music, decrease SA and AV nodal activity.

The hormones epinephrine and norepinephrine, released by the adrenal medulla, also stimulate the heart. During exercise, for example, the heart pumps faster and stronger due to sympathetic stimulation and the release of epinephrine and norepinephrine (for more information, see Sections 14.4 and 16.4).

An Electrocardiogram Is a Record of the Heartbeat

An **electrocardiogram (ECG)** is a recording of the electrical changes that occur in the myocardium during a cardiac cycle (Fig. 5.7). Body fluids contain ions that conduct electrical currents. Therefore, the electrical changes in the myocardium can be detected on the skin's surface. When an ECG is administered, electrodes placed on the skin are connected by wires to an instrument that detects the myocardium's electrical changes.

Figure 5.7*a* depicts the electrical signals during a normal cardiac cycle. When the SA node triggers an impulse, the atrial fibers produce an electrical change called the P wave. The P wave indicates the atria are about to contract. After that, the QRS complex signals that the ventricles are about to contract. The electrical changes that occur as the ventricular muscle fibers recover produce the T wave.

Various types of abnormalities can be detected by an ECG. One of these, called *ventricular fibrillation,* is caused by uncoordinated, irregular electrical activity in the ventricles. Compare Figure 5.7*a* with Figure 5.7*b* and note the irregular line illustrated in Figure 5.7*b*. Ventricular fibrillation is of special interest because it can be caused by an injury, a heart attack, or a drug overdose. It is the most common cause of sudden cardiac death in a seemingly healthy person over age 35. Once the ventricles are fibrillating, coordinated pumping of the heart ceases and body tissues quickly become oxygen starved. Normal electrical conduction must be reestablished as quickly as possible or the person will die. A strong electrical current is applied to the chest for a short time in a process called *defibrillation.* In response, all heart cells discharge their electricity at once. Then, the SA node may be able to reestablish a coordinated beat.

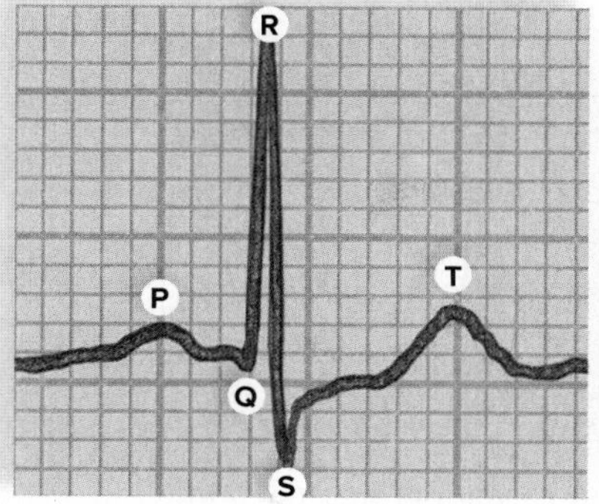

a. Normal ECG

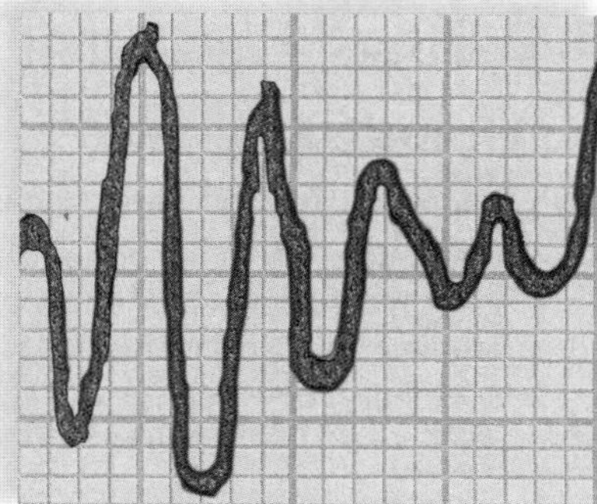

b. Ventricular fibrillation

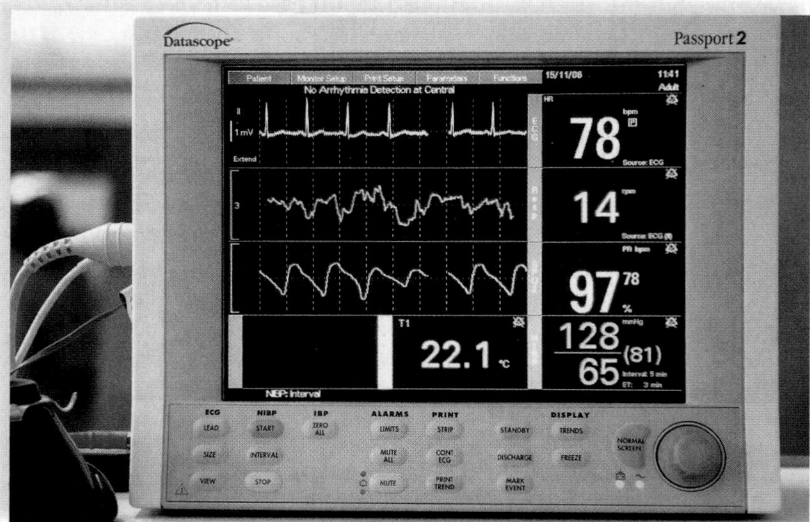

c. Recording of an ECG

Figure 5.7 An electrocardiogram.
a. A normal ECG indicates that the heart is functioning properly. The P wave occurs just prior to atrial contraction; the QRS complex occurs just prior to ventricular contraction; and the T wave occurs when the ventricles are recovering from contraction. **b.** Ventricular fibrillation produces an irregular ECG due to irregular stimulation of the ventricles. **c.** The recording of an ECG.
(a, b): Ed Reschke; (c): MedicImage/Alamy Stock Photo

CHECK YOUR PROGRESS 5.3

1. Describe the flow of blood through the heart.
2. Explain what causes the "lub" and the "dub" sounds of a heartbeat.
3. Summarize the internal and external controls of the heartbeat.

CONNECTING THE CONCEPTS

For more information on the heart as a muscle and to gain a greater understanding of how the heart develops and ages, refer to the following discussions:

Figure 13.1 compares the structure of cardiac muscle to that of other muscular tissues.

Figure 18.7 illustrates the fetal circulation pathway.

Section 18.5 explores some of the changes to the cardiovascular system as we age.

5.4 Blood Pressure

LEARNING OUTCOMES

Upon completion of this section, you should be able to

1. Understand how the pulse relates to heart rate.
2. Explain how blood flow and pressure differ in veins, arteries, and capillaries.
3. Distinguish between systolic and diastolic pressure.

When the left ventricle contracts, blood is sent out into the aorta under pressure. A progressive decrease in pressure occurs as blood moves through the arteries, arterioles, capillaries, venules, and finally the veins. Blood pressure is highest in the aorta. By contrast, pressure is lowest in the superior and inferior venae cavae, which enter the right atrium (see Fig. 5.4*a*).

Pulse Equals Heart Rate

The surge of blood entering the arteries causes their elastic walls to stretch, but then they almost immediately recoil. This rhythmic expansion and recoil of an arterial wall can be felt as a **pulse** in any artery that runs close to the body's surface. It is customary to feel the pulse by placing several fingers on either the radial artery (near the outer border of the palm side of the wrist) or the carotid artery (located on either side of the trachea in the neck).

Normally, the pulse rate indicates the heart rate, because the arterial walls pulse whenever the left ventricle contracts. As mentioned in Section 5.3, the pulse rate is usually 70 beats per minute in a healthy adult, but can vary between 60 and 80 beats per minute.

Blood Flow Is Regulated

The beating of the heart is necessary to homeostasis, because it creates the pressure that propels blood in the arteries and the arterioles. Arterioles lead to the capillaries where exchange with interstitial fluid takes place, thus supplying cells with nutrients and removing waste material.

Blood Pressure Moves Blood in Arteries

Blood pressure is the pressure of blood against the wall of a blood vessel. A *sphygmomanometer* (blood pressure instrument) can be used to measure blood pressure, usually in the brachial artery of the arm (Fig. 5.8). The highest arterial pressure, called the **systolic pressure,** is reached during ejection of blood from the heart. The lowest arterial pressure, called the **diastolic pressure,** occurs while the heart ventricles are relaxing.

Blood pressure is measured in millimeters mercury (mm Hg). Normal resting blood pressure for a young adult should be slightly lower than 120 mm Hg over 80 mm Hg, or 120/80, but these values can vary somewhat and still be within the range of normal

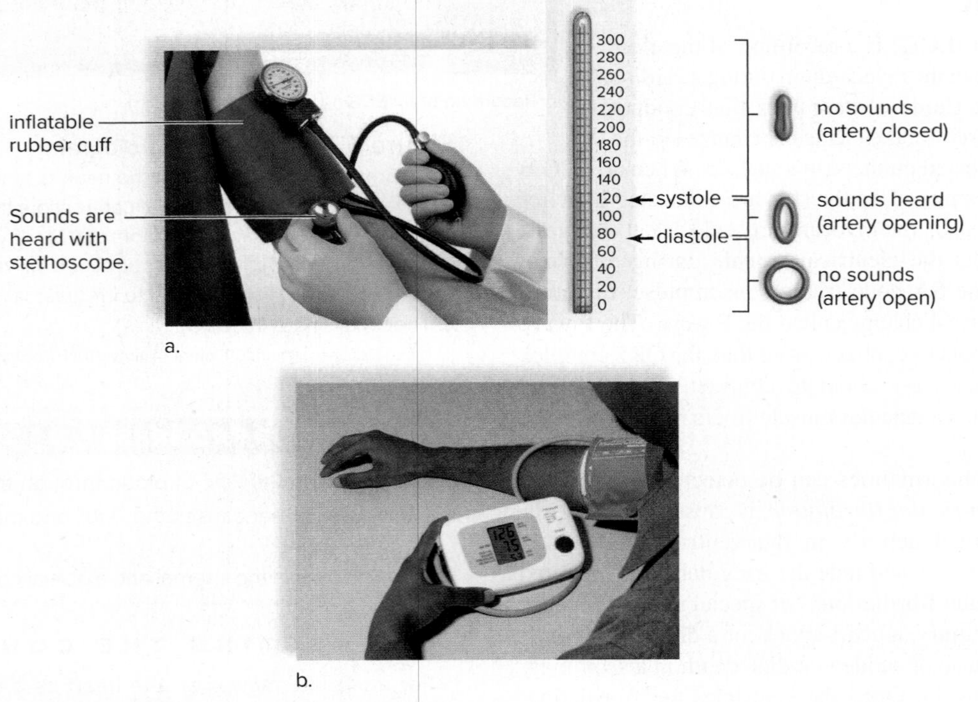

Figure 5.8 **Sphygmomanometers measure blood pressure.**
a. The sphygmomanometer cuff is first inflated until the artery is completely closed by its pressure. Next, the pressure is gradually reduced. The clinician listens with a stethoscope for the first sound, indicating that blood is moving past the cuff in an artery. This is systolic blood pressure. The pressure in the cuff is further reduced until no sound is heard, indicating that blood is flowing freely through the artery. This is diastolic pressure. **b.** Electronic sphygmomanometers can be purchased for home use.
(left): Jeffrey Coolidge/Stockbyte/Getty Images; (right): Alliance Images/Alamy Stock Photo

Table 5.1 Values for Adult Blood Pressure

	Systolic Pressure (mm Hg)		Diastolic Pressure (mm Hg)
Normal	below 120	and	below 80
Elevated	120–129	and	below 80
Stage 1 hypertension	130–139	or	80–89
Stage 2 hypertension	140 or higher	or	90 or higher
Hypertension crisis	180 or higher	and/or	120 or higher

Source: American Heart Association, www.heart.org.

blood pressure (Table 5.1). The number 120 represents the systolic pressure, and 80 represents the diastolic pressure. High blood pressure is called *hypertension,* and low blood pressure is called *hypotension.*

Both systolic and diastolic blood pressure decrease with distance from the left ventricle, because the total cross-sectional area of the blood vessels increases (Fig. 5.9)—there are more arterioles than arteries. The decrease in blood pressure causes the blood velocity to gradually decrease as it flows toward the capillaries.

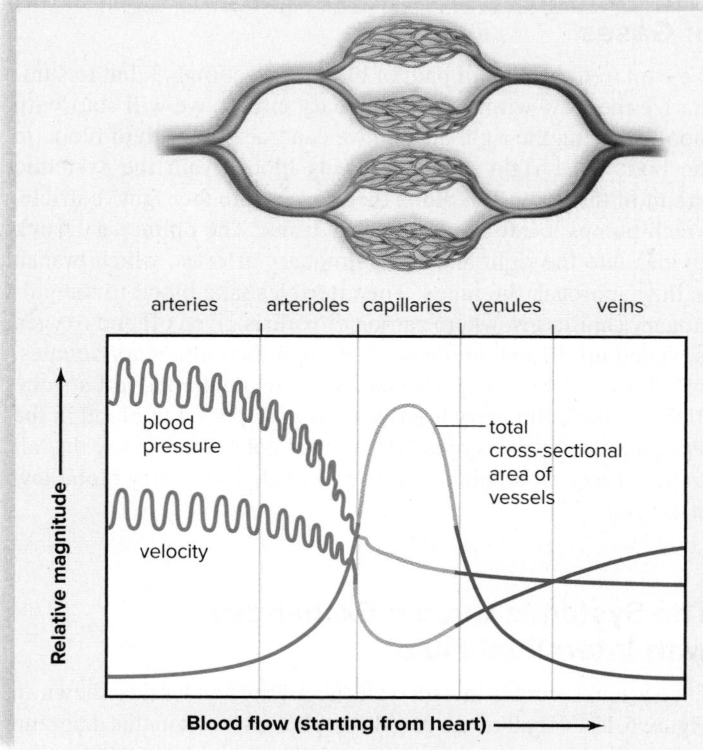

Figure 5.9 Blood velocity and pressure in the blood vessels. This diagram shows the velocity (speed) and relative blood pressure as the blood flows from the heart (*on left*) to the veins (*on right*). The cross-sectional line indicates the total area of the blood vessels. Notice how, as the area increases in the capillaries, there is a marked decrease in blood velocity and pressure.

Blood Flow Is Slow in the Capillaries

There are many more capillaries than arterioles, and blood moves slowly through the capillaries (Fig. 5.9). This is important because the slow progress allows time for the exchange of substances between the blood in the capillaries and the surrounding tissues. Any needed changes in flow rate are adjusted by the opening and closing of the precapillary sphincters.

Blood Flow in Veins Returns Blood to Heart

By studying Figure 5.9, it can be seen that the velocity of blood flow increases from capillaries to veins. As an analogy, imagine a single narrow street emptying its cars into a fast, multilane highway. Likewise, as capillaries empty into veins, blood can travel faster. However, it's also apparent from Figure 5.9 that blood pressure is minimal in venules and veins. Blood pressure thus plays only a small role in returning venous blood to the heart, called *venous return*. This is dependent on three additional factors:

- The *skeletal muscle pump,* dependent on skeletal muscle contraction
- The *respiratory pump,* dependent on breathing
- Valves in veins

The skeletal muscle pump functions every time a muscle contracts. When skeletal muscles contract, they compress the weak walls of the veins. This causes the blood to move past a valve (Fig. 5.10). Once past the valve, blood cannot flow backward. The importance of the skeletal muscle pump in moving blood in

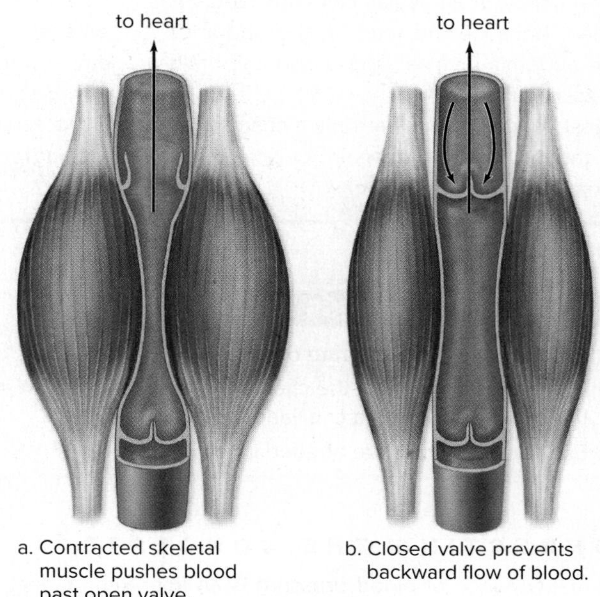

Figure 5.10 The skeletal muscle pump.
a. Pressure on the walls of a vein, exerted by skeletal muscles, increases blood pressure within the vein and forces a valve open. **b.** When external pressure is no longer applied to the vein, blood pressure decreases, and back pressure forces the valve closed. Closure of the valves prevents the blood from flowing backward. Therefore, veins return blood to the heart.

the veins can sometimes be observed when a person stands upright, without moving, for an extended period of time. A person may faint due to this, because the lack of muscle contraction causes blood to collect in the limbs, and poor venous return deprives the brain of needed oxygen. In this case, fainting is beneficial because the resulting horizontal position aids in getting blood to the head.

The respiratory pump works much like an eyedropper. When the dropper's suction bulb is released, the bulb expands. Fluid travels from higher pressure in the bottom of the glass tube, moving up the tube toward the lower pressure at the top. When we inhale, the chest expands, and this reduces pressure in the thoracic cavity. Blood will flow from higher pressure (in the abdominal cavity) to lower pressure (in the thoracic cavity). When we exhale, the pressure reverses, but again the valves in the veins prevent backward flow.

BIOLOGY IN YOUR LIFE

What are varicose veins?

Veins are thin-walled tubes divided into many separate chambers by vein valves. Excessive stretching occurs if veins are overfilled with blood. For example, if a person stands in one place for a long time, leg veins can't drain properly and blood pools in them. As the vein expands, vein valves become distended and fail to function. These two mechanisms cause the veins to bulge and be visible on the skin's surface. Hemorrhoids are varicose veins in the rectum. Obesity, a sedentary lifestyle, female gender, genetic predisposition, and aging are risk factors for varicose veins.

Pregnancy, in particular, can cause leg veins to become distended, because the fetus in the abdomen compresses the large abdominal veins. Leg veins can't drain properly and the valves malfunction.

Most varicose veins are only a cosmetic problem. Occasionally, though, they cause pain, muscle cramps, or itching and become a medical problem.

CHECK YOUR PROGRESS 5.4

1. Explain what the pulse rate of a person indicates.
2. Compare and contrast the characteristics of blood flow in the veins, arteries, and capillaries.
3. Explain why valves are needed in the veins.

CONNECTING THE CONCEPTS

The maintenance of blood pressure is an important aspect of homeostasis. Blood pressure is influenced by a variety of factors, including diet and internal controls. For examples, refer to the following discussions:

Section 9.6 explores how lipids and minerals—namely, sodium—in the diet influence blood pressure.

Section 11.4 explains how the water-salt balance and an enzyme called renin influence blood pressure.

5.5 Two Cardiovascular Pathways

LEARNING OUTCOMES

Upon completion of this section, you should be able to

1. Compare blood flow in the pulmonary and systemic circuits.
2. Identify the major arteries and veins of both the pulmonary and the systemic circuits.
3. Compare the oxygen content of the blood in the arteries and veins of the pulmonary and systemic circuits.
4. Explain the location and purpose of the hepatic portal system.

The blood flows in two circuits: the **pulmonary circuit,** which circulates blood through the lungs, and the **systemic circuit,** which serves the needs of body tissues (Fig. 5.11). While it is common to discuss these circuits relative to the movement of oxygen and carbon dioxide, it is important to note that these circuits also deliver a variety of nutrients, hormones, and other factors. For this reason, both circuits are important in the maintenance of homeostasis in the body.

The Pulmonary Circuit: Exchange of Gases

We explored the overall path of blood in Section 5.3, but to summarize the flow within the pulmonary circuit, we will start with blood entering the right atrium, we can trace the path of blood in the body. The right atrium collects blood from the systemic circuit of the body. The blood then passes into the right ventricle, which pumps it into the pulmonary trunk. The pulmonary trunk divides into the right and left pulmonary arteries, which branch as they approach the lungs. The arterioles take blood to the pulmonary capillaries, where carbon dioxide is given off and oxygen is picked up. Blood then passes through the pulmonary venules, which lead to the four pulmonary veins that enter the left atrium. Blood in the pulmonary arteries is oxygen-poor, but blood in the pulmonary veins is oxygen-rich, so it is not correct to say that all arteries carry blood high in oxygen and all veins carry blood low in oxygen.

The Systemic Circuit: Exchanges with Interstitial Fluid

The systemic circuit includes all the arteries and veins shown in Figure 5.12. Not all of the blood vessels are shown in this diagram. In fact, the heart pumps blood through the estimated 60,000 miles of blood vessels in the body to deliver nutrients and oxygen and remove wastes from all body cells.

The largest artery in the systemic circuit, the **aorta,** receives blood from the heart; the largest veins, the superior and inferior venae cavae (*sing.,* **vena cava**), return blood to the heart. The superior vena cava collects blood from the head, the chest, and the

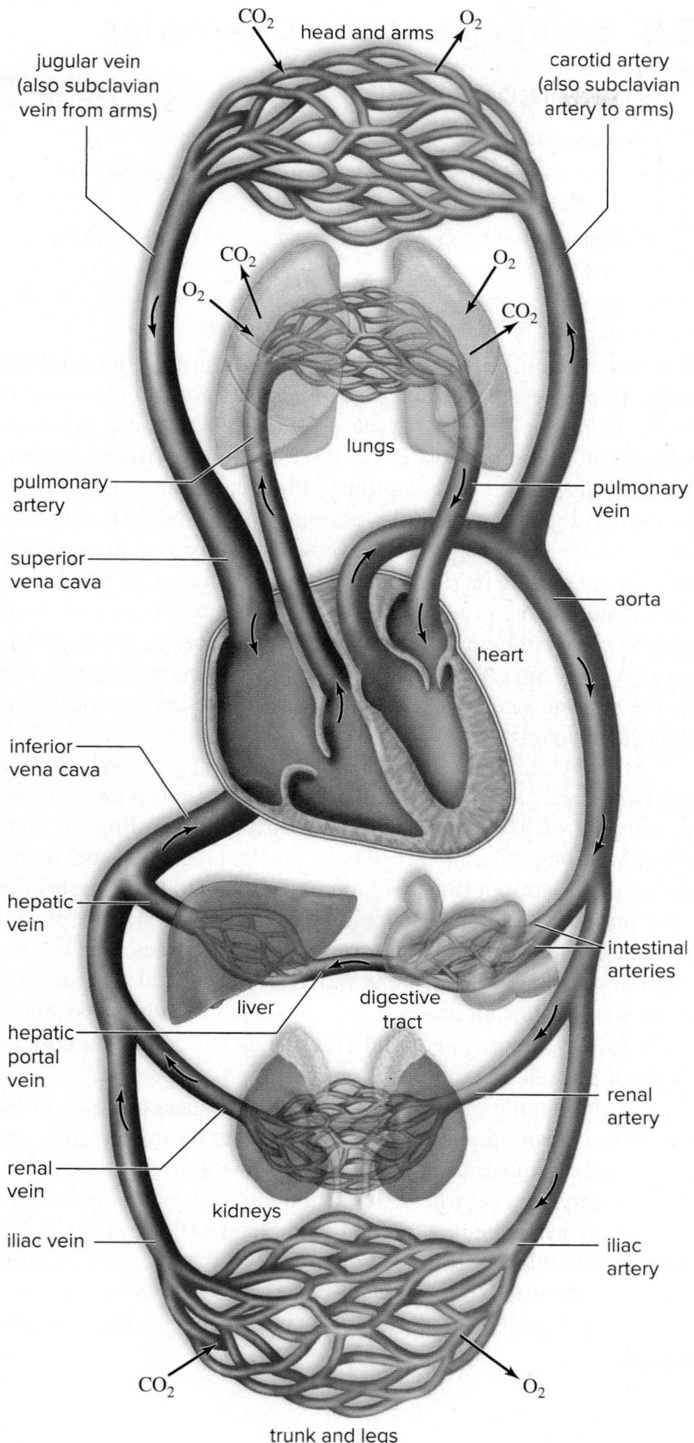

Figure 5.11 **Overview of the cardiovascular system.**
The blue-colored vessels carry blood rich in carbon dioxide, and the red-colored vessels carry blood rich in oxygen; the arrows indicate the flow of blood. Compare this diagram, useful for learning to trace the path of blood, with Figure 5.12 to realize that arteries and veins go to all parts of the body. Also, there are capillaries in all parts of the body.

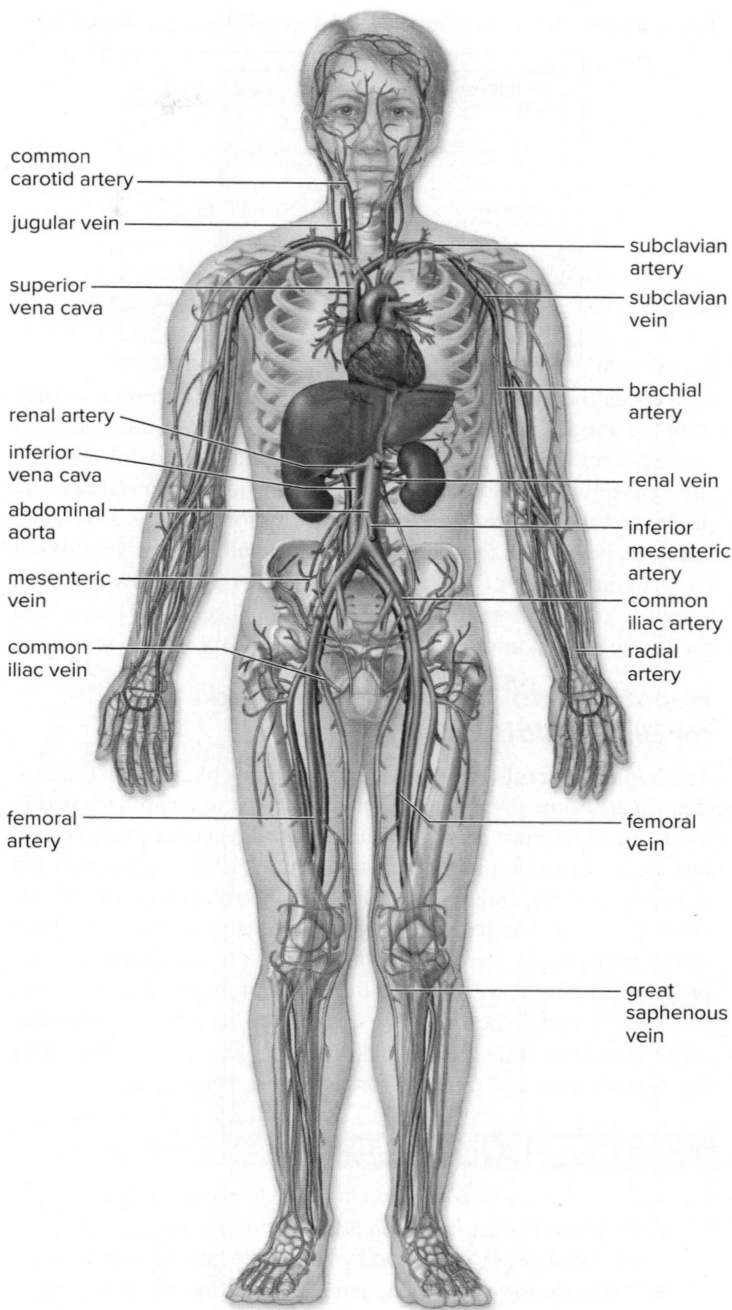

Figure 5.12 **The major arteries and veins of the systemic circuit.**
This illustration offers a realistic representation of major blood vessels (arteries and veins) of the systemic circuit.

arms, and the inferior vena cava collects blood from the lower body regions. Both enter the right atrium.

Tracing the Path of Blood

It's easy to trace the path of blood in the systemic circuit by beginning with the left ventricle, which pumps blood into the aorta. Branches from the aorta go to the organs and major body regions.

For example, this is the path of blood to and from the lower legs:

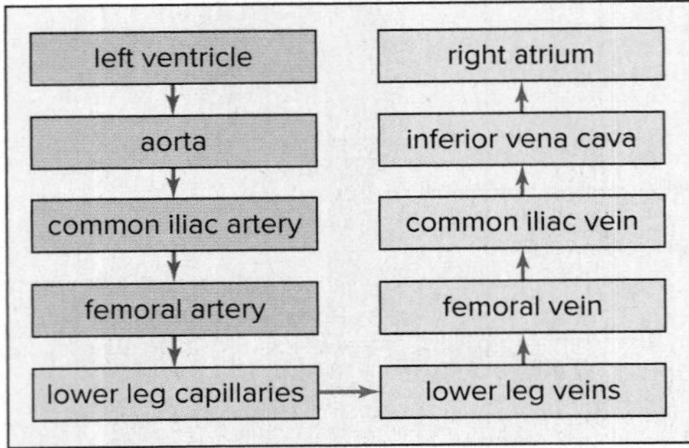

When tracing blood to a specific organ, it is common to start with the aorta, then the artery branching from the aorta. Then, list the region of the body where the capillaries are found, followed by the vein returning blood to the vena cava. In many instances, the artery and the vein that serve the same region are given the same name, as is the case for the femoral artery and femoral vein. What happens in between the artery and the vein? Arterioles from the artery branch into capillaries, where exchange takes place, and then venules join into the vein that enters a vena cava.

Hepatic Portal System: Specialized for Blood Filtration

The **hepatic portal vein** (see Fig. 5.11) drains blood from the capillary beds of the digestive tract and carries it to a capillary bed in the liver. The term *portal* indicates that it lies between two capillary beds. The blood in the hepatic portal vein is oxygen-poor but is rich in glucose, amino acids, and other nutrients absorbed by the small intestine. The liver stores glucose as glycogen, and it either stores amino acids or uses them immediately to manufacture blood proteins. The liver also purifies the blood of toxins and pathogens that have entered the body by way of the intestinal capillaries. After blood has filtered slowly through the liver, it is collected by the **hepatic vein** and returned to the inferior vena cava.

CHECK YOUR PROGRESS 5.5

1. Describe the flow of blood in the pulmonary circuit.
2. Describe the path of blood from the heart to the digestive tract and back to the heart by way of the hepatic portal vein.
3. Compare the relative oxygen content of the blood flowing in the pulmonary artery with that in the pulmonary vein.

CONNECTING THE CONCEPTS

During fetal development, minor changes in the flow of blood occur due to a bypassing of the lungs. For more on this and additional information on the hepatic portal system and pulmonary circuits, refer to the following discussions:

Figure 9.8 illustrates how the hepatic portal vein takes nutrients to the liver.

Figure 10.11 diagrams the transport of oxygen and carbon dioxide in the pulmonary and systemic circuits.

Figure 18.7 shows how the systemic circuit interacts with the placenta during development.

5.6 Exchange at the Capillaries

LEARNING OUTCOMES

Upon completion of this section, you should be able to

1. Describe the processes that move materials across the walls of a capillary.
2. Explain what happens to the excess fluid that leaves the capillaries.

Two forces control the movement of fluid through the capillary wall: blood pressure, which tends to cause fluids in the blood to move from capillary to tissue spaces, and osmotic pressure, which tends to cause water to move in the opposite direction. At the arterial end of a capillary, blood pressure (30 mm Hg) is higher than the osmotic pressure of blood (21 mm Hg) (Fig. 5.13). Osmotic pressure is created by the presence of solutes dissolved in plasma, the liquid fraction of the blood. Dissolved plasma proteins are of particular importance in maintaining the osmotic pressure. Most plasma proteins are manufactured by the liver. Blood pressure is higher than osmotic pressure at the arterial end of a capillary, so water exits a capillary at the arterial end.

Midway along the capillary, where blood pressure is lower, the two forces essentially cancel each other, and there is no net movement of fluid. Solutes now diffuse according to their concentration gradient: Oxygen and nutrients (glucose and amino acids) diffuse out of the capillary; carbon dioxide and wastes diffuse into the capillary. Red blood cells and almost all plasma proteins remain in the capillaries. The substances that leave a capillary contribute to interstitial fluid, the fluid between the body's cells. Plasma proteins are too large to readily pass out of the capillary. Thus, interstitial fluid tends to contain all components of plasma, except much lower amounts of protein.

At the venule end of a capillary, blood pressure has fallen even more. Osmotic pressure is greater than blood pressure, and fluid tends to move back. Almost the same amount of fluid that left the capillary returns to it, although some excess interstitial fluid is always collected by the lymphatic capillaries (Fig. 5.14). Interstitial fluid within lymphatic vessels is called **lymph.** Lymph is returned to the systemic venous blood when the major lymphatic vessels enter the subclavian veins in the shoulder region.

CHECK YOUR PROGRESS 5.6

1. Explain what happens to the excess fluid created during capillary exchange.
2. Describe the exchange of materials across the walls of a capillary.
3. Summarize what occurs when blood and osmotic pressure change at the venous end of a capillary.

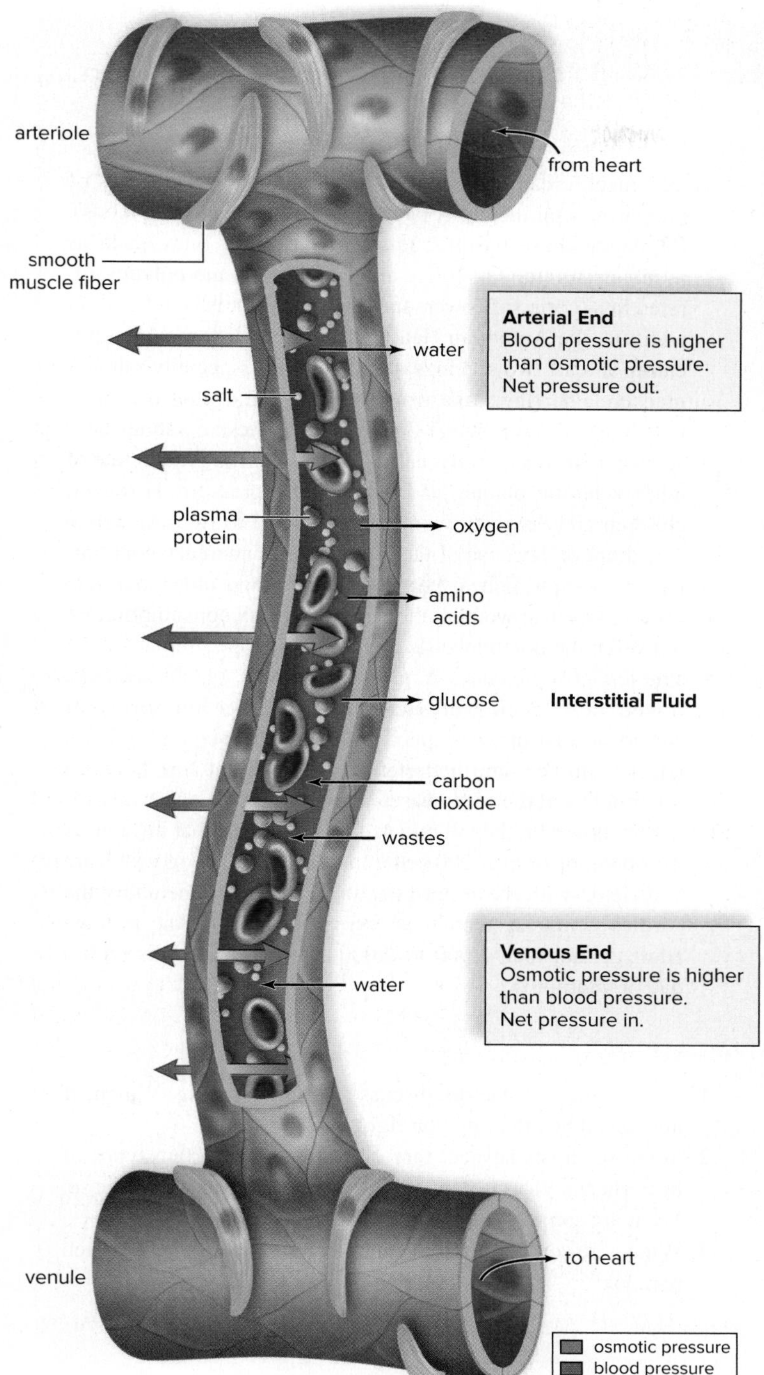

Figure 5.13 **The movement of fluid in a capillary bed.** The figure shows the process of capillary exchange and the forces that aid the process. At the arterial end of a capillary, the blood pressure is higher than the osmotic pressure. Fluids tend to leave the bloodstream and enter the interstitial fluid. In the midsection of the diagram, solutes, including oxygen (O_2) and carbon dioxide (CO_2), diffuse from high to low concentration. Carbon dioxide and wastes diffuse into the capillary, while nutrients and oxygen enter the tissues. At the venous end of a capillary, the osmotic pressure is higher than the blood pressure. Interstitial fluid tends to reenter the bloodstream. The red blood cells and plasma proteins are too large to exit a capillary.

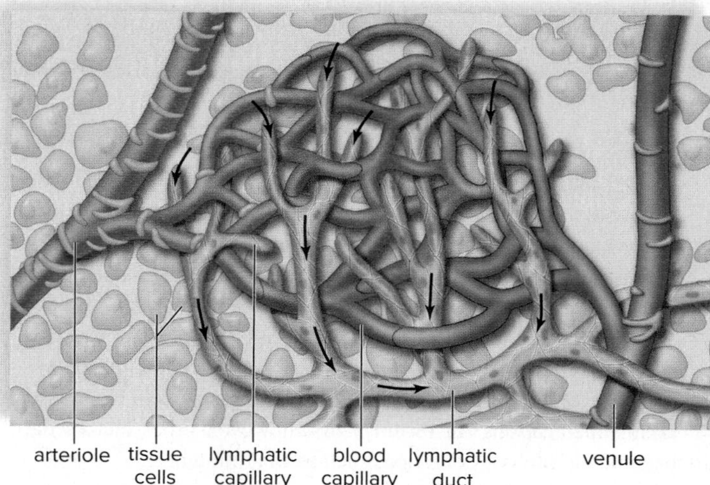

Figure 5.14 **Movement of fluid into lymphatic vessels.** Lymphatic capillary beds lie alongside blood capillary beds. When lymphatic capillaries take up excess interstitial fluid, it becomes lymph. Lymph returns to the cardiovascular system through cardiovascular veins in the chest. Precapillary sphincters can shut down a capillary bed, and blood then flows through a shunt.

CONNECTING THE CONCEPTS

The movement of materials into and out of the capillaries plays an important role in the function of a number of other body systems. For examples of the importance of capillaries, refer to the following discussions:

Section 7.2 provides additional information on the role of the lymphatic system.

Section 10.6 explains how gas exchange occurs across the walls of the capillaries in the lungs.

Section 11.3 explores how the urinary system establishes gradients to move waste materials out of the capillaries for excretion.

5.7 Cardiovascular Disorders

LEARNING OUTCOMES

Upon completion of this section, you should be able to

1. Explain the underlying causes of cardiovascular disease in humans.
2. Summarize how advances in medicine can treat cardiovascular disorders.

Cardiovascular disease (CVD) is the leading cause of early death in Western countries. In the United States, CVD is responsible for more than 33% of all deaths. Modern research efforts have resulted in improved diagnosis, treatment, and prevention. This section examines some of the major forms of cardiovascular disease and also explores the range of advances that have been made in preventing

BIOLOGY TODAY ▶ Health

Recent Findings in Preventing Heart Disease

For decades in the United States, several factors have been associated with an increased risk of cardiovascular disease (CVD), especially atherosclerosis. Some of these cannot be avoided, such as increasing age, male gender, family history of heart disease, and belonging to certain races, including African American, Mexican American, and Native American. Other risk factors—smoking, obesity, high cholesterol, hypertension, diabetes, physical inactivity—can be avoided or at least affected by changing one's behavior or taking medications. In recent years, however, other factors have been taken into consideration, such as the following:

- *Alcohol*. Alcohol abuse can destroy just about every organ in the body, the heart included. Based on several large research studies, however, the AHA notes that people who consume one or two drinks per day have a 30–50% reduced risk of CVD compared to nondrinkers. However, the maximum protective effect is achieved with only one or two drinks per day—consuming more than that increases the risk of many alcohol-related problems. The American Heart Association does *not* recommend nondrinkers start using alcohol, or that drinkers increase their consumption, based on these findings.
- *Resveratrol*. The "red wine effect," or "French paradox," refers to the observation that levels of CVD in France are relatively low, despite the consumption of a high-fat diet. One possible explanation is that wine is frequently consumed with meals. In addition to its alcohol content, red wine contains especially high levels of antioxidants, including resveratrol. Resveratrol is mainly produced in the skin of grapes, so it is also found in grape juice. Resveratrol supplements are also available at health food stores. The benefits of resveratrol alone are questionable, however, and most controlled studies to date have demonstrated no beneficial effects. The lower incidence of CVD in the French may be due to multiple factors, including lifestyle and genetic differences.
- *Omega-3 fatty acids*. The influence that diet has on blood cholesterol levels has been well studied. It is generally beneficial to minimize our intake of foods high in saturated fat (red meat, cream, and butter) and trans fats (most kinds of margarine, commercially baked goods, and deep-fried foods). Replacing these harmful fats with healthier ones, such as monounsaturated fats (olive and canola oils) and polyunsaturated fats (corn, safflower, and soybean oils), is beneficial. In addition, the American Heart Association now recommends eating at least two servings of fish a week, especially salmon, mackerel, herring, lake trout, sardines, and albacore tuna, which are high in omega-3 fatty acids. These essential fatty acids can decrease triglyceride levels, slow the growth rate of atherosclerotic plaque, and lower blood pressure. However, children and pregnant women are advised to limit their fish consumption because of the high levels of mercury contamination in some fishes. For middle-aged and older men and postmenopausal women, the benefits of fish consumption far outweigh the potential risks.
- *Vitamin D deficiency*. A growing number of studies have linked deficiencies in vitamin D and certain forms of cardiovascular disease, specifically an increased rate of heart attacks, strokes, and hypertension. The direct link between vitamin D and the cardiovascular system is still under investigation; however, the vitamin acts as a hormone that influences the operation of over 200 genes in the body, many of which are associated with the overall health of the body, including the cardiovascular system. It is recommended that the average adult get between 1,000 to 2,000 International Units (IU) a day of vitamin D.

Questions to Consider

1. Review the risk factors discussed in this reading. Which, if any, could be affecting you right now?
2. Some scientists suspect that infections with certain types of bacteria and viruses may contribute to cardiovascular disease. What are some specific ways infections might do this?
3. What are other possible explanations for the "French paradox"?

and correcting CVD. The Health feature "Recent Findings in Preventing Heart Disease" outlines some of the factors that may increase your chances for developing CVD.

Disorders of the Blood Vessels

Hypertension and atherosclerosis often lead to stroke or heart attack, due to an artery blocked by a blood clot or clogged by plaque. Treatment involves removing the blood clot or prying open the affected artery. Another possible outcome is a burst blood vessel, or aneurysm. An aneurysm can be prevented by replacing a blood vessel that is about to rupture with an artificial one.

Hypertension

Hypertension occurs when blood moves through the arteries at a higher pressure than normal. Also known as high blood pressure, hypertension is sometimes called a silent killer. It may not be detected until it has caused a heart attack, stroke, or even kidney failure. Hypertension is now defined as when the systolic blood pressure is 130 or greater or the diastolic blood pressure is 80 or greater (see Table 5.1). Though systolic and diastolic pressures are both important, physicians often focus on diastolic pressure when medical treatment is being considered because this represents the resting pressure of the cardiovascular system.

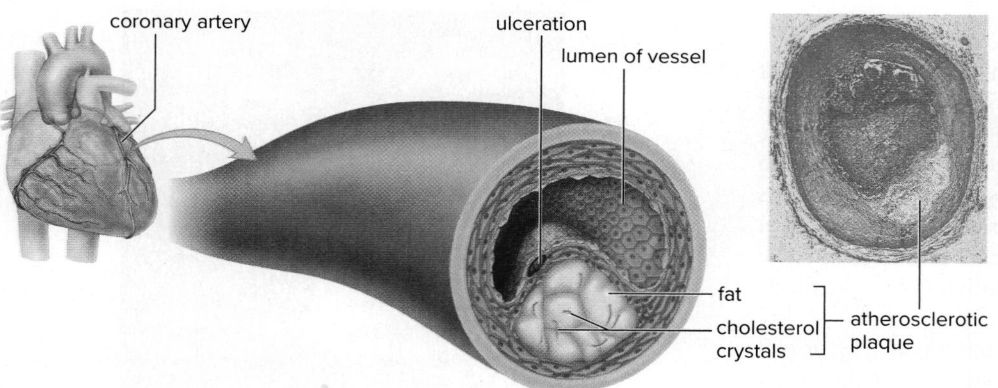

Figure 5.15 Coronary arteries and plaque.
Atherosclerotic plaque is an irregular accumulation of cholesterol and fat. When fat is present in a coronary artery, a heart attack is more likely to occur because of restricted blood flow.
(photo): Biophoto Associates/Science Source

The best safeguard against developing hypertension is regular blood pressure checks and a lifestyle that lowers the risk of CVD. If hypertension is present, prescription drugs can help lower blood pressure. Diuretics cause the kidneys to excrete more urine, ridding the body of excess fluid. In addition, hormones (the body's chemical messengers) that raise blood pressure can be inactivated. Drugs called beta blockers and ACE (angiotensin-converting enzyme) inhibitors help control hypertension caused by hormones.

Hypertension is often seen in individuals who have **atherosclerosis.** Atherosclerosis is caused by the formation of lesions, or *atherosclerotic plaques,* on the inside of blood vessels. The **plaques** narrow blood vessel diameter, choking off blood and oxygen supply to the tissues. In most instances, atherosclerosis begins in early adulthood and develops progressively through middle age, but symptoms may not appear until an individual is 50 or older. To prevent the onset and development of atherosclerosis, the American Heart Association and other organizations recommend a diet low in saturated fat and cholesterol but rich in omega-3 polyunsaturated fatty acids.

Atherosclerotic plaques (Fig. 5.15) can cause a clot to form on the irregular, roughened arterial wall. As long as the clot remains stationary, it is called a thrombus. If the thrombus dislodges and moves along with the blood, it is called an embolus. A **thromboembolism** consists of a clot first carried in the bloodstream that then becomes completely stationary when it lodges in a small blood vessel. If a thromboembolism is not treated, life-threatening complications can result.

BIOLOGY IN YOUR LIFE

What are statins?

Statins are a class of drug that reduces blood cholesterol level by reducing the amount of cholesterol produced by the liver. In doing so, they reduce the risk of cardiovascular disease associated with elevated cholesterol levels. While there have been reports that statins may cause health problems, such as liver disease, diabetes, and muscle damage, the FDA has not found any evidence that these drugs elevate these risk factors in most people. As with any medication, you should always consult with your physician before starting a new treatment.

Research has suggested several possible causes for atherosclerosis aside from hypertension. Chief among these are smoking and a diet rich in lipids and cholesterol. Research also indicates that a low-level bacterial or viral infection that spreads to the blood may cause an injury that starts the process of atherosclerosis. Surprisingly, such an infection may originate with gum diseases or be due to *Helicobacter pylori* (see Section 1.3). People who have high levels of C-reactive protein, which occurs in the blood following a cold or an injury, are more likely to have a heart attack.

Stroke, Heart Attack, and Aneurysm

Stroke, heart attack, and aneurysm are associated with hypertension and atherosclerosis. A cerebrovascular accident (CVA), also called a **stroke,** often results when a small cranial arteriole bursts or is blocked by an embolus. Lack of oxygen causes a portion of the brain to die, and paralysis or death can result. A person is sometimes forewarned of a stroke by a feeling of numbness in the hands or the face, difficulty in speaking, or temporary blindness in one eye.

A myocardial infarction (MI), also called a **heart attack,** occurs when a portion of the heart muscle dies due to lack of oxygen. If a coronary artery becomes partially blocked, the individual may then experience **angina pectoris.** Characteristic symptoms of angina pectoris include a feeling of pressure, squeezing, or pain in the chest. Pressure and pain can extend to the left arm, neck, jaw, shoulder, or back. Nausea and vomiting, anxiety, dizziness, and shortness of breath may accompany the chest discomfort. Nitroglycerin or related drugs dilate blood vessels and help relieve the pain. When a coronary artery is completely blocked, perhaps because of a thromboembolism, a heart attack occurs.

An **aneurysm** is a ballooning of a blood vessel, most often the abdominal artery or the arteries leading to the brain. Atherosclerosis and hypertension can weaken the wall of an artery to the point that an aneurysm develops. If a major vessel, such as the aorta, bursts, death is likely. It is possible to replace a damaged or diseased portion of a vessel, such as an artery, with a plastic tube. Cardiovascular function is preserved because exchange with tissue cells can still take place at the capillaries. Research is under way to use blood vessels made in the laboratory by injecting a patient's cells inside an inert mold or generating them using stem cells.

Dissolving Blood Clots

Medical treatment for a thromboembolism includes the use of tissue plasminogen activator (t-PA), a biotechnology drug that converts plasminogen, a protein in blood, into plasmin, an enzyme that dissolves blood clots. Tissue plasminogen activator is also being used for stroke patients, but with less success. Some patients experience life-threatening bleeding in the brain. A better treatment might be new biotechnology drugs that act on the plasma membrane to prevent brain cells from releasing and/or receiving toxic chemicals caused by the stroke.

While it is known that aspirin lowers the probability of clot formation, recent studies have begun to question the effectiveness of daily low doses of aspirin in preventing heart attacks, especially in certain age groups. The decision to start or stop using low-dose aspirin should be made under the advice of a physician.

Treating Clogged Arteries

In the past, cardiovascular disease required open-heart surgery and, therefore, a long recuperation time and a long scar that could occasionally ache. Now, bypass surgery (Fig. 5.16*a*) can be assisted by using robotic technology. A video camera and instruments are inserted through small cuts, while the surgeon sits at a console and manipulates interchangeable grippers, cutters, and other tools attached to movable arms above the operating table. Looking through two eyepieces, the surgeon gets a three-dimensional view of the operating field. Robotic surgery is also used in valve repairs and other heart procedures.

A *coronary bypass operation* is one way to treat an artery clogged with plaque. A surgeon takes a blood vessel—usually a vein from the leg—and stitches one end to the aorta and the other end to a coronary artery located past the point of obstruction. Figure 5.16*b* shows a triple bypass in which three blood vessel segments have been used to allow blood to flow freely from the aorta to cardiac muscle by way of the coronary artery. Since 1997, gene therapy has been used instead of a coronary bypass to grow new blood vessels that will carry blood to cardiac muscle. The surgeon needs only to make a small incision and inject many copies of the gene that codes for vascular endothelial growth factor (VEGF) between the ribs directly into the area of the heart that most needs improved blood flow. The VEGF encourages new blood vessels to sprout out of an artery. If collateral blood vessels do form, they transport blood past clogged arteries, making bypass surgery unnecessary. About 60% of patients who undergo the procedure show signs of vessel growth within 2 to 4 weeks.

Another alternative to bypass surgery is **angioplasty.** In the past, angioplasty involved inserting a plastic tube into an artery of an arm or a leg and then guiding it through a major blood vessel toward the heart. When the tube reached the region of plaque in an artery, a balloon attached to the end of the tube was inflated, forcing the vessel open. The procedure now uses the same procedure to deliver a stent to the blocked vessel (Fig. 5.16*c*). A stent is a small metal mesh cylinder that holds a coronary artery open after a blockage has been cleared. When the balloon inside the stent

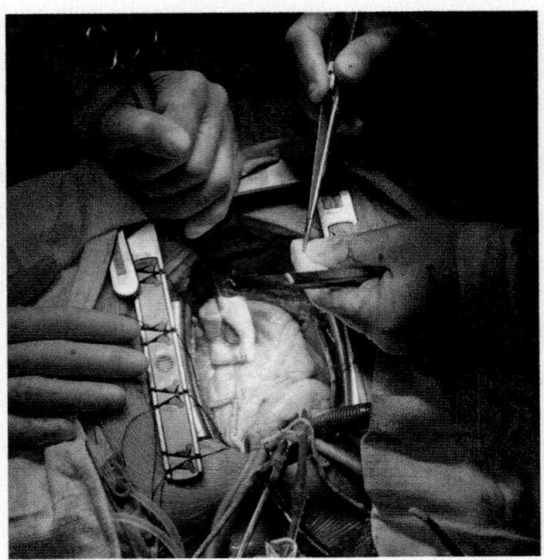

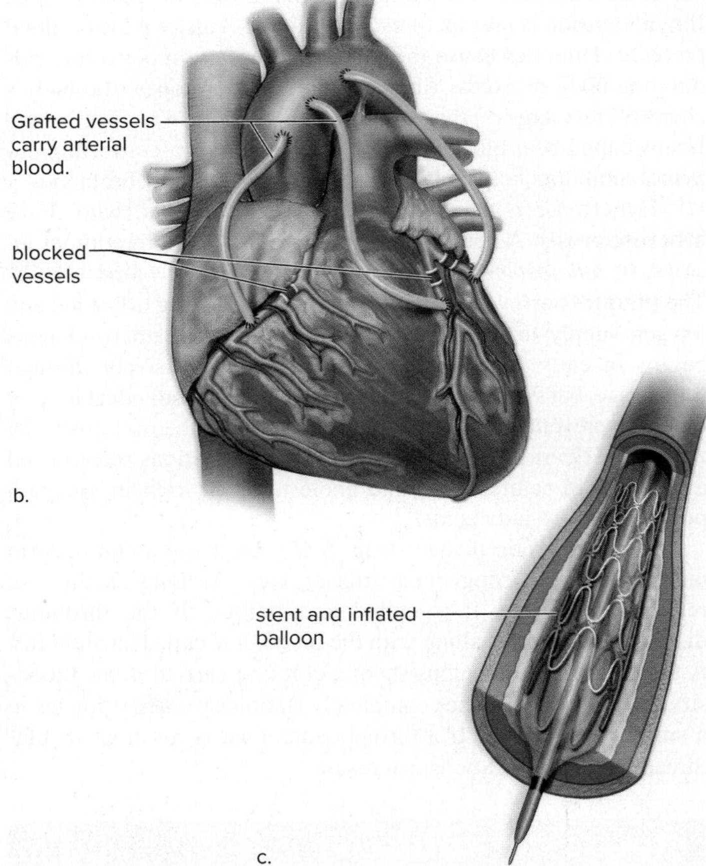

Figure 5.16 Treatments for atherosclerotic plaque in coronary arteries.
a. Improvements in surgery techniques can assist in coronary bypass operations. **b.** In this procedure, blood vessels (leg veins or arteries placed in the chest) are stitched to coronary arteries, bypassing the obstruction. **c.** In a stent procedure, a balloon-tipped catheter guides the stent (a cylinder of expandable metal mesh) to the obstructed area. When the balloon is inflated, the stent expands and opens the artery.
(a): aaM Photography, Ltd./Vetta/miralex/Getty Images

is inflated, the stent expands, locking itself in place. Some patients go home the same day or, at most, after an overnight stay. The stent is more successful when it is coated with a drug that seeps into the artery lining and discourages cell growth. Uncoated stents can close back up in a few months, but the drug used in the coated ones successfully discourages closure. Blood clotting might occur after stent placement, so recipients have to take anticlotting medications.

Heart Failure

When a person has *heart failure,* the heart no longer pumps as it should. Heart failure is a growing problem, because people who used to die from heart attacks now survive but are left with damaged hearts. Often the heart is oversized not because the cardiac wall is stronger but because it is sagging and swollen. One idea is to wrap the heart in a fabric sheath to prevent it from getting too big. This might allow better pumping, similar to the way a weightlifter's belt restricts and reinforces stomach muscles. But a failing heart can have other problems, such as an abnormal heart rhythm. To counter that condition, it's possible to place an implantable cardioverter-defibrillator (ICD) just beneath the skin of the chest. This device can sense both an abnormally slow and an abnormally fast heartbeat. If the former, the ICD generates the missing beat, as a pacemaker does. If the latter, it sends the heart a sharp jolt of electricity to slow it down. If the heart rhythm becomes erratic, the ICD sends an even stronger shock—as a defibrillator does.

Heart Transplants

Although heart transplants are now generally successful, many more people are waiting for new hearts than there are organs available. Today, only about 2,300 heart transplants are done annually, though many thousands of people could use them. Genetically altered pigs may one day be used as a source of hearts because of the shortage of human hearts. Also, bone marrow stem cells have been injected into the heart. Once in the heart, these cells have been able to form new cardiac muscle tissue to replace tissue damaged by a heart attack.

Today, a left ventricular assist device (LVAD), implanted in the abdomen, is an alternative to a heart transplant. A tube passes blood from the left ventricle to the device, which pumps it on to the aorta. A cable passes from the device through the skin to an external battery, which the patient must tote around. Another option is the Jarvik 2000, which is a pump inserted inside the left ventricle. The Jarvik is powered by an external battery no larger than a C battery.

Even fewer patients have received a device called a total artificial heart (TAH), such as that shown in Figure 5.17. An internal battery and a controller regulate the pumping speed, and an external battery powers the device by passing electricity through the skin via external and internal coils. A rotating centrifugal pump moves silicon hydraulic fluid between left and right sacs to force blood out of the heart into the pulmonary trunk and the aorta.

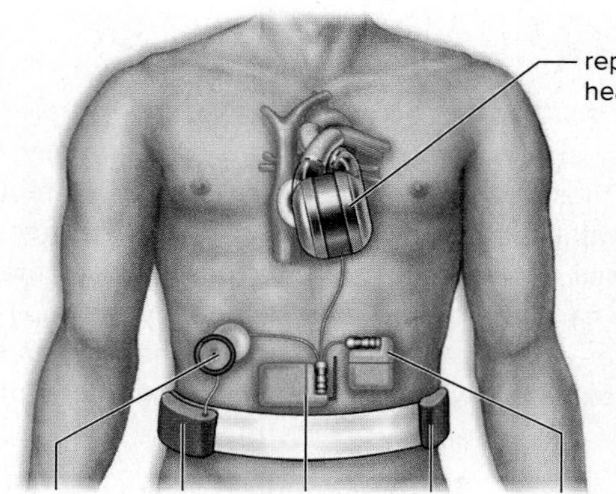

Figure 5.17 An artificial heart.
The SynCardia temporary total artificial heart moves blood in the same manner as a natural heart. The controller is implanted into the patient's abdomen. The heart is powered by an internal rechargeable battery, with an external battery as a backup system.
(photo): Courtesy of SynCardia Systems, Inc.

Initially, recipients were near death, and most survived for only a few days. However, medical advances have increased the survival time to months for many recipients, making the TAH a temporary treatment for people who are experiencing heart failure. To date, over 1,300 TAHs have been implanted into patients.

CHECK YOUR PROGRESS 5.7

1. List the cardiovascular disorders common in humans.
2. Summarize the treatments available for cardiovascular disorders.
3. Discuss why CVD is the leading source of death in Western countries.

CONNECTING THE CONCEPTS

Many cardiovascular disorders are caused by incorrect diets or sedentary lifestyles. Others are the result of genetic abnormalities. For more on the relationships between diet and cardiovascular disease and how scientists identify genes associated with cardiovascular disease, refer to the following discussions:

Section 9.6 explores how each class of nutrient relates to a healthy lifestyle.

Table 9.5 lists methods of lowering saturated fats and cholesterol in the diet.

Sections 22.3 and **22.4** explain how biotechnology and genomics are identifying new genes associated with disease.

CONCLUSION

In this chapter, we discussed the importance of the cardiovascular system in the body and its central role in maintaining homeostasis. To conduct these activities, the cardiovascular system must deliver blood within a relatively narrow range of pressures. Elevated blood pressure, or hypertension, not only reduces the effectiveness of the cardiovascular system, especially the capillaries, but can cause damage to organs such as the liver and kidneys. We also explored what a blood pressure value of 189/105 mm Hg really means. The larger number (189) is the maximum pressure as the individual's heart is beating, whereas the smaller number (105) is the resting pressure. Ideally, blood pressure should be less than 120/80 mm Hg, so these values indicate the patient is in a hypertension crisis. However, the good news is that, for young adults, prehypertension is typically due to lifestyle choices, namely diet and physical activity, which can be altered to promote better health.

SUMMARIZE

5.1 Overview of the Cardiovascular System

The **cardiovascular system** consists of the heart and blood vessels. The heart pumps blood, and blood vessels take blood to and from capillaries, where exchanges of nutrients for wastes occur with tissue cells. Blood is refreshed at the lungs, where gas exchange occurs; at the digestive tract, where nutrients enter the blood; and at the kidney, where wastes are removed from blood. The **lymphatic system** removes excess fluid from around the tissue and returns it to the cardiovascular system.

5.2 The Types of Blood Vessels

Arteries: **Arteries** and **arterioles** move blood away from the heart. Arteries have the thickest walls, which allow them to withstand blood pressure.

Capillaries: Exchange of substances occurs in the capillaries. Precapillary sphincters and **arteriovenous shunts** help control the flow of blood within the capillaries.

Veins: **Veins** and **venules** move blood toward the heart. Veins have relatively weak walls, with valves that keep the blood flowing in one direction.

5.3 The Heart Is a Double Pump

The **heart** is the pump of the circulatory system and consists of a right and left side separated by a **septum.** Each side has an **atrium** and a **ventricle.** Valves, such as the **atrioventricular (AV) valves** and **semilunar valves,** keep the blood moving in the correct direction. The tissue of the heart, the **myocardium,** is contained within a sac called the **pericardium.** At the cellular level, the tissues interact using gap junctions and **desmosomes.** The heart supplies itself with blood using the **coronary arteries.**

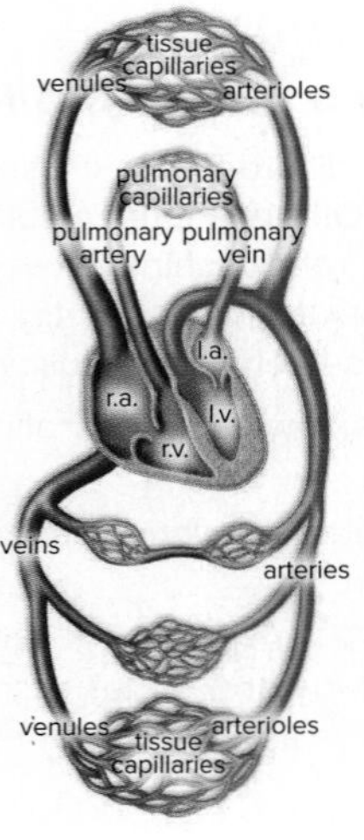

Passage of Blood Through the Heart

- The right atrium receives O_2-poor blood from the **vena cava,** and the right ventricle pumps it into the pulmonary circuit via the **pulmonary arteries.**
- The left atrium receives O_2-rich blood from the lungs **(pulmonary veins),** and the left ventricle pumps it into the **aorta** of the systemic circuit.

The Cardiac Cycle

During the **cardiac cycle,** the **SA (sinoatrial) node (pacemaker)** initiates the heartbeat by causing the atria to contract. The **AV (atrioventricular) node** conveys the stimulus to the ventricles, causing them to contract (**systole**). The heart sounds, "lub-dub," are due to the closing of the atrioventricular valves, followed by the closing of the semilunar valves. The muscles of the heart relax **(diastole)** between contractions. An **electrocardiogram (ECG)** may be used to measure the activity of the heart.

5.4 Blood Pressure

The **pulse** indicates the heartbeat rate. **Blood pressure** caused by the beating of the heart accounts for the flow of blood in the arteries. The **systolic pressure** is the maximum pressure in the arteries, while the **diastolic pressure** is the minimum. The reduced velocity of blood flow in capillaries facilitates exchange of nutrients and wastes in the tissues. Blood flow in veins is caused by skeletal muscle contraction (skeletal muscle pump), the presence of valves, and respiratory movements (respiratory pump).

5.5 Two Cardiovascular Pathways

The cardiovascular system is divided into the pulmonary circuit and the systemic circuit.

The Pulmonary Circuit: Exchange of Gases

In the **pulmonary circuit,** blood travels to and from the lungs.

The Systemic Circuit: Exchanges with Interstitial Fluid

In the **systemic circuit,** the aorta divides into blood vessels that serve the body's organs and cells. The vena cava returns O_2-poor blood to the heart. The hepatic portal system moves blood between the capillary beds of the digestive system and liver. This system consists of the **hepatic portal vein** and the **hepatic vein.**

5.6 Exchange at the Capillaries

The following diagram illustrates capillary exchange in the tissues of the body—not including the gas-exchanging surfaces of the lungs.

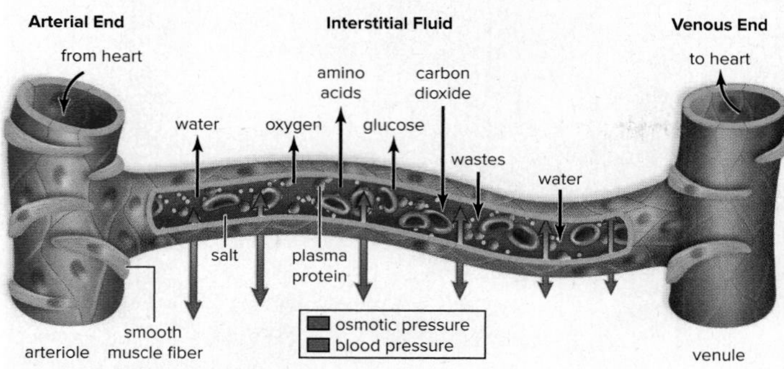

- At the arterial end of a cardiovascular capillary, blood pressure is greater than osmotic pressure; therefore, fluid leaves the capillary.
- In the midsection, oxygen and nutrients diffuse out of the capillary, and carbon dioxide and other wastes diffuse into the capillary.
- At the venous end, osmotic pressure created by the presence of proteins exceeds blood pressure, causing most of the fluid to reenter the capillary. Some fluid remains as interstitial (tissue) fluid.

Excess fluid not picked up at the venous end of the cardiovascular capillary enters the lymphatic capillaries.

- **Lymph** is interstitial fluid within lymphatic vessels.
- The lymphatic system is a one-way system. Its fluid is returned to blood by way of a cardiovascular vein.

5.7 Cardiovascular Disorders

Cardiovascular disease is the leading cause of death in Western countries.

- **Hypertension** and **atherosclerosis** can lead to **stroke, heart attack, angina pectoris** (chest pain), or an **aneurysm.** Atherosclerotic **plaques** increase the risk of these conditions. If these plaques dislodge in the circulatory system, a **thromboembolism** may result.
- Following a heart-healthy diet, getting regular exercise, maintaining a proper weight, and not smoking reduce cardiovascular disease risk.

ENGAGE

THINKING CRITICALLY

1. You have to stand in front of the class to give a report. You are nervous, and your heart is pounding. What is the specific mechanism behind this reaction? What would your ECG look like?
2. The cardiovascular system is an elegant example of the concept that structure supports function. Each type of blood vessel has a specific job. Each vessel's physical characteristics enable it to do that job. The muscle walls of the right and left ventricles vary in thickness, depending on where they pump the blood. When organ structure is damaged or changed (as arteries are in atherosclerosis), the organ's ability to perform its function may be compromised. Homeostatic conditions, such as blood pressure, may be affected as well. Dietary and lifestyle choices can either prevent damage or harm the cardiovascular system.
   a. What do you think the long-term effects of hypertension are on the heart? What about other organ systems?
   b. Why do you think a combination of hypertension and atherosclerosis is a particularly dangerous combination?
3. Examine the following abnormal ECG patterns. Compared with the normal tracing in Figure 5.7*a,* what is your best guess as to the type of problem each patient may have?

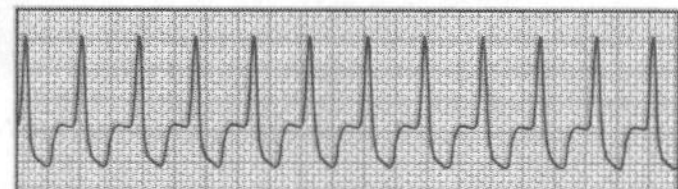
a.

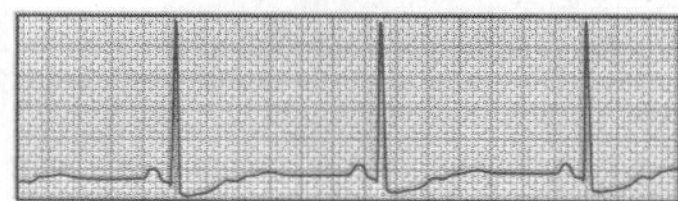
b.

MAKING IT RELEVANT

1. From what you have learned in this chapter, why do you think hypertension is often referred to as the "silent killer"?
2. Chances are, a member of your family has experienced blood pressure problems. Besides genetics, what other factors do you have in common with that person that may increase your chances of developing hypertension?
3. How can you alter your diet to reduce the chances of developing hypertension?

Find answers to all of the chapter questions at connect.mheducation.com

CHAPTER

6

Cardiovascular System: Blood

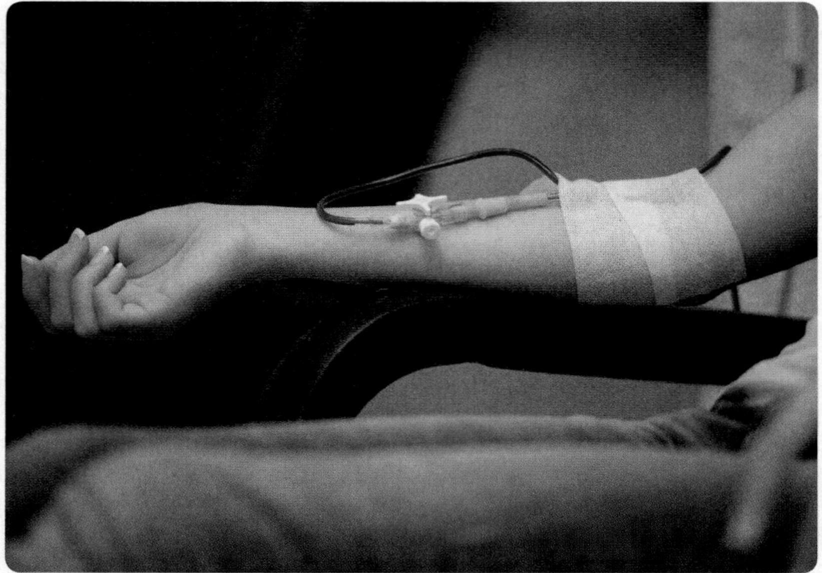
Wavebreakmediamicro/Wavebreakmedia/123RF

CHAPTER OUTLINE

BEFORE YOU BEGIN

Before beginning this chapter, take a few moments to review the following discussions:

Section 4.2 Why is blood considered to be a connective tissue?

Section 4.8 How does the circulatory system contribute to homeostasis?

Section 5.6 How does the blood exchange nutrients and wastes with the tissues of the body?

Synthetic Blood

Every 2 seconds, someone in the United States needs a transfusion of blood. The need may have been caused by an injury, a surgical procedure, or even a disease that requires regular transfusions. To answer these needs, blood donors provide over 36,000 units of blood every day, or 15 million units of blood every year.

Historically, the need for blood transfusions has been met by blood donors. Unfortunately, supply does not always meet demand. Natural disasters may place a strain on supplies, especially considering that blood can be stored for only about 42 days, which makes stockpiling difficult. Furthermore, some people are not able to receive blood from donors due to religious beliefs or medical conditions.

To meet the demand for transfusions, scientists have been developing synthetic, or artificial, blood. The use of an oxygen-carrying blood substitute, called oxygen therapeutics, has the goal of providing a patient's tissues with enough oxygen. In some cases, the blood substitute is completely synthetic, and contains chemicals that mimic the oxygen-carrying hemoglobin found in red blood cells. In other cases, scientists are applying biotechnology to manufacture replacement red blood cells. While several biotech companies are currently conducting clinical trials using synthetic blood, most medical professionals believe we are still several years from being able to produce a synthetic blood supply to meet the needs of society.

In this chapter, we will explore the structure and function of the cardiovascular system in the human body and explore why this organ system is so essential to life.

As you read through the chapter, think about the following questions:

1. What are the roles of red blood cells in the body?
2. Besides red blood cells, what other elements need to be present in synthetic blood?

6.1 Blood: An Overview

LEARNING OUTCOMES

Upon completion of this section, you should be able to

1. List the functions of blood in the human body.
2. List the formed elements of the blood and provide the function of each.
3. Describe the composition of plasma.

The human heart is an amazing muscular pump. With each beat, it pumps approximately 75 milliliters (ml) of blood. On average, the heart beats 70 times per minute. Thus, the heart pumps roughly 5,250 ml per minute (75 ml/beat × 70 beats/minute), which means that the heart circulates the body's entire blood supply once each minute! If needed (when exercising, for example), the heart can cycle blood throughout the body even faster.

We learned about the structure of the heart and blood vessels in Chapter 5. In this chapter, we will learn about the functions and composition of blood.

Functions of Blood

The functions of blood fall into three general categories: transport, defense, and regulation.

Transport

Blood is the primary transport medium. Blood acquires oxygen in the lungs and distributes it to tissue cells. Similarly, blood picks up nutrients from the digestive tract for delivery to the tissues. In its return trip to the lungs, blood transports carbon dioxide. Every time a person exhales, the carbon dioxide waste is eliminated. Blood also transports other wastes, such as excess nitrogen from the breakdown of proteins, to the kidneys for elimination. Blood exchanges nutrients and wastes with tissues by capillary exchange (see Fig. 5.13). In doing so, it maintains homeostasis by keeping the composition of interstitial fluid within normal limits.

In addition to the transport of nutrients and wastes, various organs and tissues secrete hormones into the blood. Blood transports these to other organs and tissues, where they serve as signals that influence cellular metabolism. Blood is well suited for its role in transporting substances. Proteins in the blood help transfer hormones to the tissues. Special proteins called lipoproteins (also known as HDL and LDL) carry lipids, or fats, throughout the body. Most important, hemoglobin (found in red blood cells) is specialized to combine with oxygen and deliver it to cells. Hemoglobin also assists in transferring waste carbon dioxide back to the lungs.

Defense

Blood defends the body against pathogen invasion and blood loss. Certain blood cells are capable of engulfing and destroying pathogens by a process called *phagocytosis* (see Section 3.3).

Other white blood cells produce and secrete antibodies into the blood. An **antibody** is a protein that combines with and disables specific pathogens. Disabled pathogens can then be destroyed by the phagocytic white blood cells.

When an injury occurs, blood clots and defends against blood loss. Blood clotting involves platelets (described in Section 6.4) and proteins. For example, prothrombin and fibrinogen are two inactive blood proteins. They circulate constantly, ready to be activated to form a clot if needed. Without blood clotting, we could bleed to death even from a small cut.

Regulation

Blood plays an important role in regulating the body's homeostasis. It helps regulate body temperature by picking up heat, mostly from active muscles, and transporting it about the body. If the body becomes too warm, blood is transported to dilated blood vessels in the skin. Heat disperses to the environment, and the body cools to a normal temperature.

The liquid portion of blood, the plasma, contains dissolved salts and proteins. These solutes create blood's *osmotic pressure,* which keeps the liquid content of the blood high (see Section 3.3 for a review of osmosis). In this way, blood plays a role in helping maintain its own water-salt balance.

Blood contains a number of chemical buffers that help regulate the body's acid-base balance and keep it at a relatively constant pH of 7.4.

Composition of Blood

Recall from Section 4.2 that blood is a form of liquid connective tissue. The cells and cell fragments present in blood are collectively called the **formed elements.** These cells and cell fragments are suspended in a liquid called **plasma.**

The Formed Elements

The formed elements are red blood cells, white blood cells, and platelets. They are produced in red bone marrow, which can be found in most bones of children but only in certain bones of adults. Red bone marrow contains *stem cells,* the parent cells that divide and give rise to all the types of blood cells (Fig. 6.1). Stem cells are the focus of a tremendous amount of research in the medical community. Researchers have been able to induce stem cells into becoming a variety of specialized cell types. These cells have already demonstrated the potential to treat a variety of human diseases (see Section 22.4 for a discussion of stem cell research).

BIOLOGY IN YOUR LIFE

Are stem cells present only in embryos?

Actually, this is a common misconception brought on by a media focus on embryonic stem (ES) cells. In reality, any actively dividing tissue requires a form of stem cell to act as the original source of cells. The difference is that many ES cells are totipotent—meaning they retain the ability to form almost any type of cell—whereas most adult stem cells are pluripotent. Pluripotent cells have undergone an additional stage of specialization and, therefore, can produce only a limited variety of new cell types.

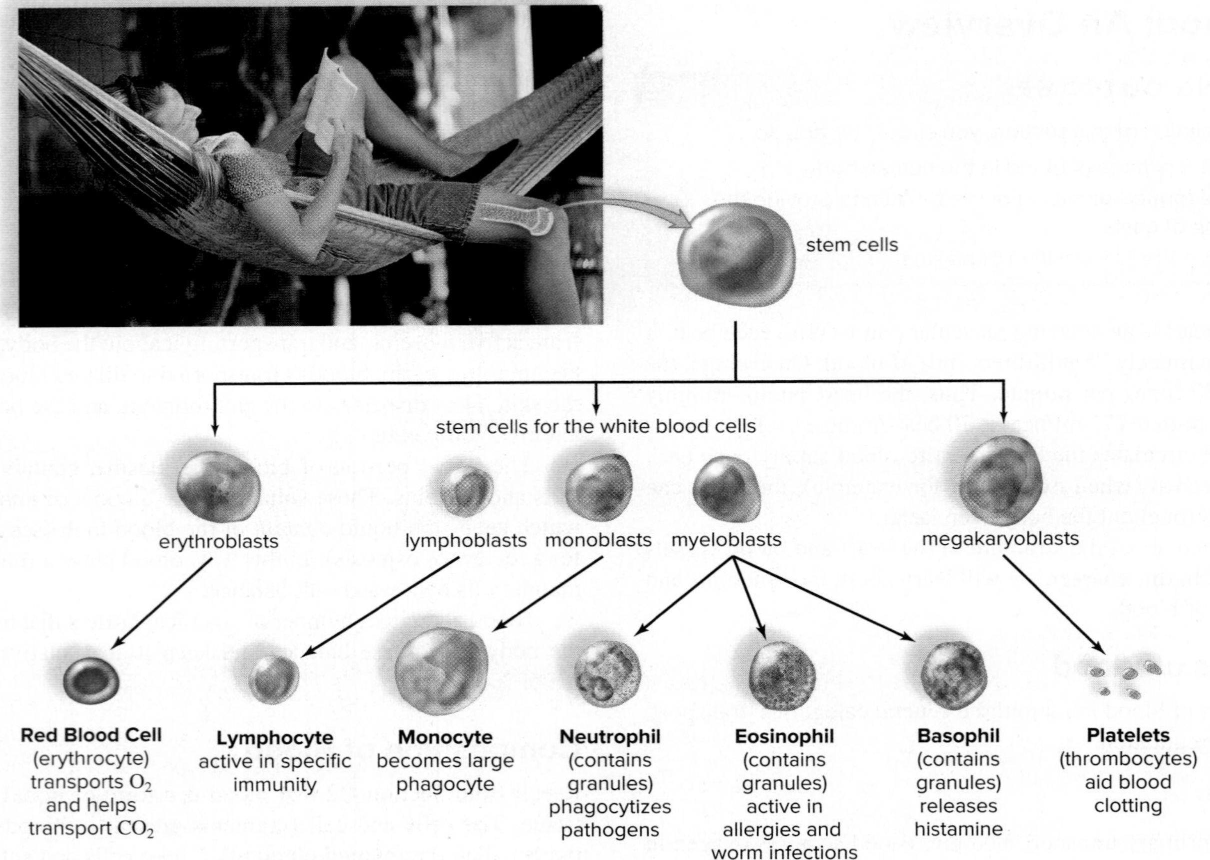

Figure 6.1 Origin of blood cells.
Stem cells in the red bone marrow produce all the many different types of blood cells.
(photo): Doug Menuez/Photodisc/Getty Images

Plasma

Plasma is the liquid medium for carrying various substances in the blood. It also distributes the heat generated as a by-product of metabolism, particularly muscle contraction. About 91% of plasma is water (Fig. 6.2). The remaining 9% of plasma consists of various salts, ions, and organic molecules. These salts are dissolved in the plasma and, along with plasma proteins, help maintain the osmotic pressure of blood. Salts also function as buffers that help maintain blood pH. Small organic molecules such as glucose and amino acids are nutrients for cells; urea is a nitrogenous waste product on its way to the kidneys for excretion.

The most abundant organic molecules in blood are called the **plasma proteins.** The liver produces the majority of the plasma proteins. The plasma proteins have many functions that help maintain homeostasis. They act as a buffer to help keep blood pH around 7.4. Plasma proteins are too large to pass through capillary walls; thus, they remain in the blood, establishing an osmotic gradient between blood and interstitial fluid. This **osmotic pressure** prevents excessive loss of plasma from the capillaries into the interstitial fluid.

Three major types of plasma proteins are the **albumins, globulins,** and **fibrinogen.** Albumins, the most abundant plasma

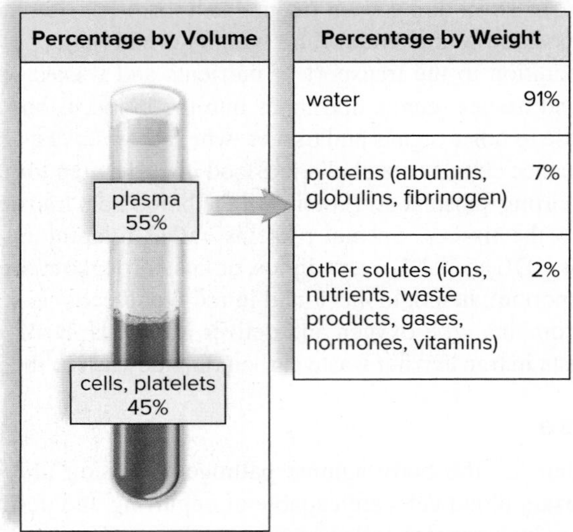

Figure 6.2 The composition of blood plasma.
Blood that has been separated into its components is primarily plasma. Plasma is the portion of blood that contains water and proteins. Solutes such as nutrients, vitamins, and hormones are transported in plasma.

proteins, contribute most to plasma's osmotic pressure. They also combine with and help transport other organic molecules. The globulins are of three types, called alpha, beta, and gamma globulins. Alpha and beta globulins also combine with and help transport substances in the blood, such as hormones, cholesterol, and iron. Gamma globulins, also known as antibodies, are produced by white blood cells called lymphocytes, not by the liver. Gamma globulins are important in fighting disease-causing pathogens (see Section 6.3). Fibrinogen is an inactive plasma protein that, once activated, participates in the formation of a blood clot (see Section 6.4).

CHECK YOUR PROGRESS 6.1

1. Summarize the components of blood.
2. Summarize the functions of blood.
3. List the types of plasma proteins and explain why each is important.

CONNECTING THE CONCEPTS

For more information on the topics presented in this section, refer to the following discussions:

Section 2.5 contains a Health feature "Good and Bad Cholesterol," which explains the differences between HDLs and LDLs in the blood.

Section 4.2 examines why blood is classified as a connective tissue.

Section 7.4 explores how white blood cells are involved in the immune response.

6.2 Red Blood Cells and the Transport of Gases

LEARNING OUTCOMES

Upon completion of this section, you should be able to

1. Explain the role of hemoglobin in gas transport.
2. Explain the transport of oxygen and carbon dioxide by red blood cells.
3. Summarize the role of erythropoietin in red blood cell production.

Red blood cells (RBCs), also known as **erythrocytes,** are small, usually between 6 and 8 micrometers (μm), biconcave disks (Fig. 6.3*a*). The presence of hemoglobin in these cells, and their unique internal structure, makes them an unusual cell type in the body. They are also very abundant; there are 4 to 6 million red blood cells per microliter (μl) of whole blood.

How Red Blood Cells Carry Oxygen

Red blood cells are highly specialized for oxygen (O_2) transport. RBCs contain **hemoglobin (Hb),** a pigment with a high affinity (attraction) for oxygen. It is also responsible for the red coloration of RBCs and the blood. The *globin* portion of hemoglobin is a protein that contains four highly folded polypeptide chains. The *heme* part of hemoglobin is an iron-containing group in the center of each polypeptide chain (Fig. 6.3*b*). The iron combines reversibly with oxygen. This means that heme accepts O_2 in the lungs and then lets go of it in the tissues. By contrast, carbon monoxide (CO) combines with the iron of heme and then will not easily let go.

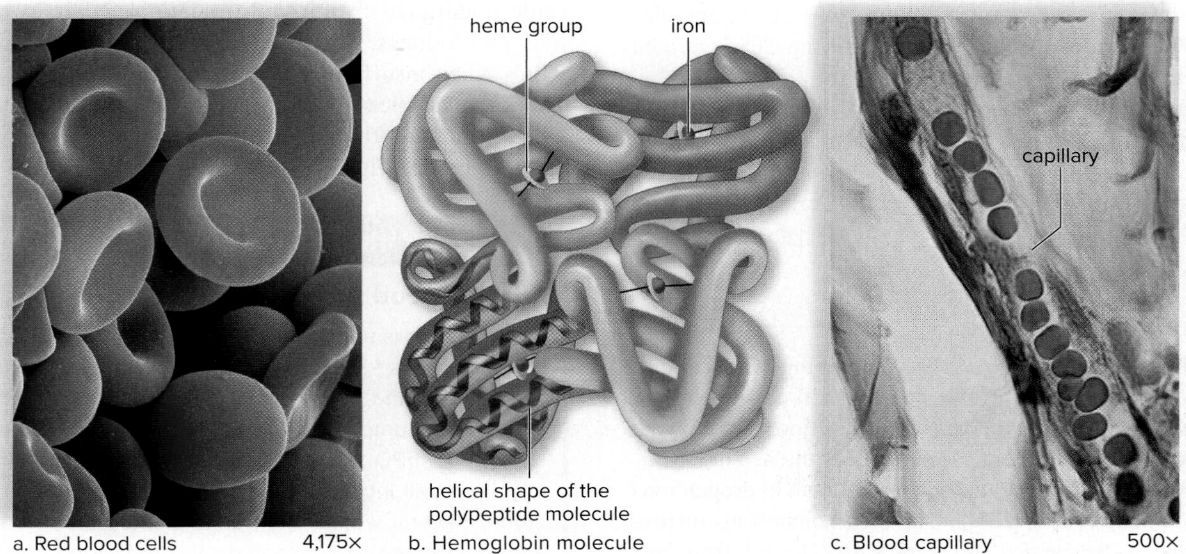

Figure 6.3 **Red blood cells and the structure of hemoglobin.**
a. Red blood cells are biconcave disks containing many molecules of hemoglobin. **b.** Hemoglobin contains two types of polypeptide chains (green, purple), forming the molecule's globin portion. An iron-containing heme group is in the center of each chain. Oxygen combines loosely with iron when hemoglobin is oxygenated. **c.** Red blood cells move single-file through the capillaries.
(a): Power and Syred/Science Photo Library/Getty Images; (c): Ed Reschke/Stone/Getty Images

BIOLOGY IN YOUR LIFE

Why is carbon monoxide dangerous?

Carbon monoxide (chemical formula CO) is a colorless, odorless gas that can also bind to hemoglobin. Each year, hundreds of people die accidentally from CO poisoning, caused by a malfunction of a fuel-burning appliance or by improper venting of CO fumes. When CO is present, it takes the place of oxygen (O_2) in hemoglobin. As a result, cells are starved of oxygen. Tragically, treatment may be delayed because the symptoms of poisoning—headache, body ache, nausea, dizziness, and drowsiness—can be mistaken for the "flu." Government guidelines recommend that *any* equipment producing CO be checked regularly to ensure proper ventilation. Finally, like smoke detectors, CO detectors should be installed and used properly.

Each hemoglobin molecule can transport four molecules of O_2, and each RBC contains about 280 million hemoglobin molecules. This means that each red blood cell can carry over a billion molecules of oxygen.

When oxygen binds to heme in the lungs, hemoglobin assumes a slightly different shape and is called **oxyhemoglobin.** In the tissues, heme gives up this oxygen, and hemoglobin resumes its former shape, called **deoxyhemoglobin.** The released oxygen diffuses out of the blood into the interstitial fluid and then into cells.

Carbon Dioxide Transport

After blood picks up carbon dioxide (CO_2) in the tissues, about 7% is dissolved in plasma. If the percentage of plasma CO_2 were higher than 7%, plasma would be carbonated and bubble like a soda. Instead, hemoglobin transports about 23% of CO_2, combining it with the globin protein. Hemoglobin-carrying CO_2 is termed **carbaminohemoglobin.**

The remaining CO_2 (about 70%) is transported as the bicarbonate ion (HCO_3^-) in the plasma. Consider the following equation:

$$\underset{\text{carbon dioxide}}{CO_2} + \underset{\text{water}}{H_2O} \rightleftharpoons \underset{\text{carbonic acid}}{H_2CO_3} \rightleftharpoons \underset{\text{hydrogen ion}}{H^+} + \underset{\text{bicarbonate ion}}{HCO_3^-}$$

Carbon dioxide moves into RBCs, combining with cellular water to form carbonic acid (arrows pointing left to right in the preceding equation illustrate this part of the reaction). An enzyme inside RBCs, called *carbonic anhydrase,* speeds the reaction. Carbonic acid quickly separates, or dissociates, to form hydrogen ions (H^+) and bicarbonate ions (HCO_3^-). The bicarbonate ions diffuse out of the RBCs to be carried in the plasma. The H^+ from this equation binds to globin, the protein portion of hemoglobin. Thus, hemoglobin assists plasma proteins and salts in keeping the blood pH constant. When blood reaches the lungs, the reaction is reversed (arrows pointing right to left). Hydrogen ions and bicarbonate ions reunite to re-form carbonic acid. The *carbonic anhydrase* enzyme also speeds this reverse reaction. Carbon dioxide diffuses out of the blood and into the airways of the lungs, to be exhaled from the body (see Fig. 10.11).

Red Blood Cells Are Produced in the Bone Marrow

The RBC stem cells in the bone marrow divide and produce new cells, which differentiate into mature RBCs (see Fig. 6.1). The structure of an RBC is well suited to its function in the body. As red blood cells mature, they acquire hemoglobin and lose their nucleus and other internal organelles. The lack of internal organelles means that RBCs are incapable of conducting many of the functions of other eukaryotic cells in the body. For example, because they lack mitochondria, RBCs are not able to carry out cellular respiration; instead they rely on the processes of glycolysis and fermentation. In addition, the cytoskeleton of RBCs contains proteins that provide their unique shape, thus allowing them to move through narrow capillary beds. Their shape also gives them a greater surface area for the diffusion of gases into and out of the cell. Also, due to their lack of a nucleus, RBCs are unable to replenish important proteins and repair cellular damage. Therefore, red blood cells live only about 120 days. When they age, red blood cells are phagocytized by white blood cells (macrophages) in the liver and spleen.

About 2 million RBCs are destroyed per second, and therefore an equal number must be produced to keep the red blood cell count in balance. When red blood cells are broken down, hemoglobin is released. The globin portion of hemoglobin is broken down into its component amino acids, which are recycled by the body. The majority of the iron is recovered and returned to the bone marrow for reuse, although a small amount is lost and must be replaced in the diet. The rest of the heme portion of the molecule undergoes chemical degradation and is excreted by the liver and kidneys. The body has a way to boost the number of RBCs when insufficient oxygen is being delivered to the cells: The kidneys release a hormone called **erythropoietin (EPO),** which stimulates the stem cells in bone marrow to produce more red blood cells (Fig. 6.4).

BIOLOGY IN YOUR LIFE

What is blood doping?

Blood doping is any method of increasing the normal supply of red blood cells for the purpose of delivering oxygen more efficiently, reducing fatigue, and giving an athlete a competitive edge. To accomplish blood doping, athletes can inject themselves with EPO some months before the competition. These injections will increase the number of red blood cells in their blood. Several weeks later, units of their blood are removed and centrifuged to concentrate the red blood cells. The concentrated cells are reinfused shortly before the athletic event. Blood doping is a dangerous, illegal practice and can cause death due to the fact that the blood may become too thick with cells for the heart to pump it effectively.

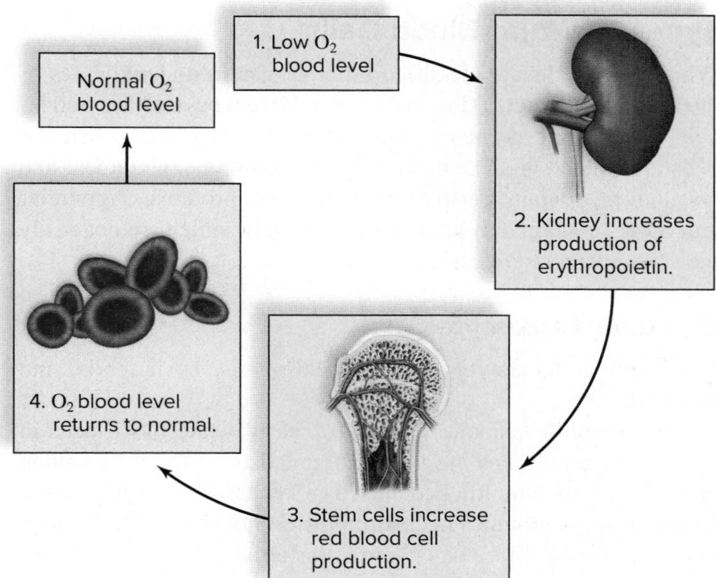

Figure 6.4 **Erythropoietin production by the kidneys.** The kidneys release increased amounts of erythropoietin whenever the oxygen capacity of the blood is reduced. Erythropoietin stimulates the red bone marrow to speed up its production of red blood cells, which carry oxygen.

Disorders Involving Red Blood Cells

The breakdown of hemoglobin by the liver and spleen produces a waste product called bilirubin. Normally, the liver secretes bilirubin into the digestive tract, where it exits the body in the feces. However, if the liver is unable to perform this task, then bilirubin will accumulate in the skin and tissues, producing a condition called *jaundice.* In jaundice, the skin and whites of the eyes turn yellow. Likewise, when the skin is bruised, the chemical breakdown of heme causes the skin to change color from red/purple to blue to green to yellow.

When there is an insufficient number of red blood cells or the cells do not have enough hemoglobin, the individual has **anemia** and often experiences a tired, run-down feeling. Iron, vitamin B_{12}, and the B vitamin folic acid are necessary for the production of red blood cells (see Section 9.6). *Iron-deficiency anemia* is the most common form. It results from an inadequate intake of dietary iron, which causes insufficient hemoglobin synthesis. A lack of vitamin B_{12} causes *pernicious anemia,* in which stem cell activity is reduced due to inadequate DNA production. As a consequence, fewer red blood cells are produced. *Folic-acid-deficiency anemia* also leads to a reduced number of RBCs, particularly during pregnancy. Pregnant women should consult with their health-care provider about the need to increase their intake of folic acid, because a deficiency can lead to birth defects in the newborn.

Hemolysis is the rupturing of red blood cells. In hemolytic anemia, the rate of red blood cell destruction increases. **Sickle-cell disease** is a hereditary condition in which the individual has sickle-shaped red blood cells (Fig. 6.5), which tend to rupture as they pass through the narrow capillaries. The problem arises because a mutation causes the protein in two of the four chains making up hemoglobin to be abnormal. The life expectancy of sickle-shaped red blood cells is about 90 days instead of 120 days.

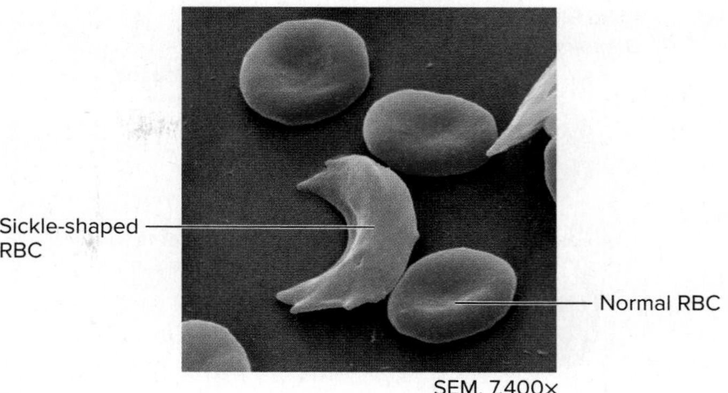

Figure 6.5 **Red blood cells and sickle-cell disease.** Sickle-cell disease causes red blood cells (RBCs) to form incorrectly due to a mutation in the globin gene.
Eye of Science/Science Source

CHECK YOUR PROGRESS 6.2

1. Explain how RBCs transport oxygen and carbon dioxide by outlining the chemical processes involved.
2. Summarize how the structure of an RBC makes it well suited for gas transport.
3. Describe the role of EPO in RBC production.

CONNECTING THE CONCEPTS

For additional information on the topics presented in this section, refer to the following discussions:

Section 10.6 details the process of gas exchange in the lungs.

Section 11.4 explains how the kidneys help maintain red blood cell homeostasis.

Section 21.2 describes the patterns of inheritance associated with sickle-cell disease.

6.3 White Blood Cells and Defense Against Disease

LEARNING OUTCOMES

Upon completion of this section, you should be able to

1. Explain the function of white blood cells in the body.
2. Distinguish between granular and agranular leukocytes.
3. Describe some of the disorders associated with white blood cells.

White blood cells (leukocytes) differ from red blood cells in that they are usually larger, have a nucleus, lack hemoglobin, and are translucent unless stained. White blood cells are not as numerous as red blood cells; there are only 5,000–11,000 per microliter (μl) of blood. White blood cells are derived from stem cells in the red

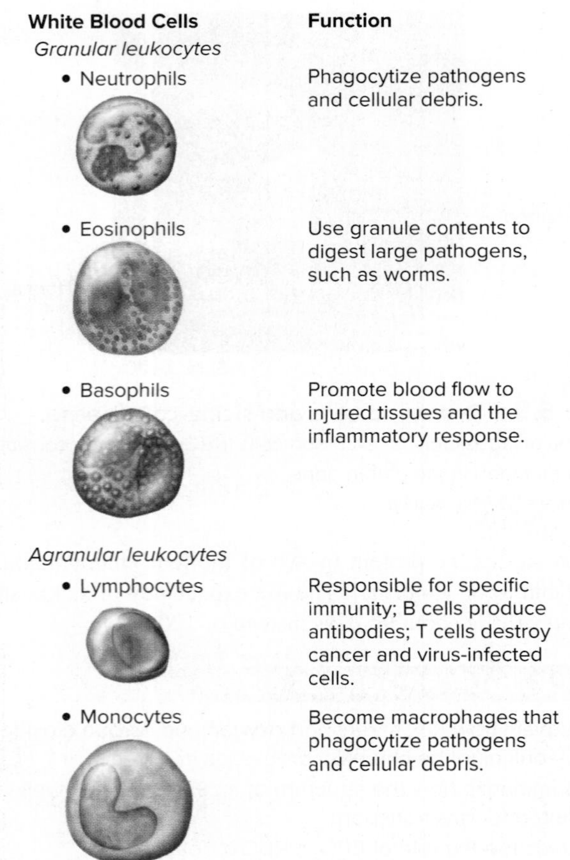

White Blood Cells
Function
Granular leukocytes
• Neutrophils
Phagocytize pathogens and cellular debris.
• Eosinophils
Use granule contents to digest large pathogens, such as worms.
• Basophils
Promote blood flow to injured tissues and the inflammatory response.
Agranular leukocytes
• Lymphocytes
Responsible for specific immunity; B cells produce antibodies; T cells destroy cancer and virus-infected cells.
• Monocytes
Become macrophages that phagocytize pathogens and cellular debris.

Figure 6.6 **Five types of white blood cells.** Neutrophils, eosinophils, and basophils are granular leukocytes. Lymphocytes and monocytes have few, if any, granules (agranular).

bone marrow, where most types mature. Several types of white blood cells exist (Fig. 6.6). In a person with normally functioning bone marrow, the numbers of white blood cells can double within hours, if needed.

White blood cells fight infection. Thus, they are an important part of the immune system. The immune system (see Section 7.2) consists of a variety of cells, tissues, and organs that defend the body against pathogens, cancer cells, and foreign proteins.

White blood cells fight infection in various ways. Certain types are excellent at phagocytosis, wherein a projection from the cell surrounds a pathogen and engulfs it. A vesicle containing the pathogen is formed inside the cell. Lysosomes attach and empty their digestive enzymes into the vesicle, and the enzymes break down the pathogen.

Other white blood cells produce antibodies, proteins that combine with antigens. An *antigen* is a cell or other substance foreign to the individual that invokes an immune response. The antibody–antigen pair is then marked for destruction, again by phagocytosis. We will examine the antigens and antibodies involved in blood typing and coagulation in Section 6.5. Many white blood cells live only a few days; often, they die while fighting pathogens. Others live for months or even years.

Types of White Blood Cells

White blood cells are classified as either **granular leukocytes** or **agranular leukocytes** (Fig. 6.6). Granular leukocytes have noticeable cytoplasmic granules, which can be easily seen when the cells are stained and examined with a microscope. Granules, like lysosomes, contain various enzymes and proteins. Agranular leukocytes contain only sparse, fine granules, which are not easily viewed under a microscope.

Granular Leukocytes

The granular leukocytes include neutrophils, eosinophils, and basophils.

Neutrophils account for 50–70% of all white blood cells in adults. Therefore, they are the most abundant of the white blood cells. They have a multilobed nucleus. Compared to other granular leukocytes, the granules of neutrophils do not stain well. Neutrophils are usually first responders to bacterial infection, and their intense phagocytic activity is essential to overcoming an invasion by a pathogen.

Neutrophils, and other types of white blood cells such as the macrophages, have the ability to squeeze through pores in the capillary wall; therefore, they are also found in interstitial fluid and lymph (Fig. 6.7).

Eosinophils have a bilobed nucleus and large, abundant granules that become red when stained. They help protect the body against large parasites (the parasitic worms) and the phagocytosis of the allergens and proteins associated with the inflammatory response.

Basophils are the rarest of white blood cells, but they play an important role in the immune response. They have a U-shaped or lobed nucleus. Their granules are dark-blue when stained. In the connective tissues, basophils and similar cells called **mast cells** release *histamine* associated with allergic reactions. Histamine dilates blood vessels but constricts the air passageways that lead to the lungs, which is what happens when someone has difficulty breathing during an asthma attack (see Section 7.5).

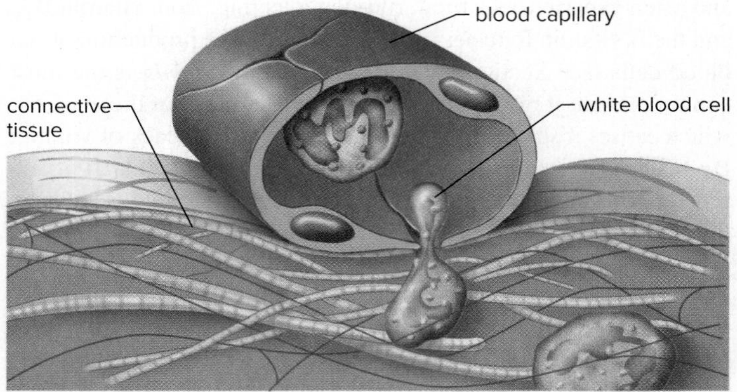

Figure 6.7 **Movement of white blood cells into the tissue.** White blood cells can squeeze between the cells of a capillary wall and enter body tissues.

Agranular Leukocytes

The agranular leukocytes include the lymphocytes and the monocytes. Lymphocytes and monocytes do not have granules, but they do have nonlobular nuclei. They are sometimes called mononuclear leukocytes.

Lymphocytes account for 25–35% of all white blood cells. Therefore, they are the second most abundant type of white blood cell. Lymphocytes are responsible for specific immunity to particular pathogens and toxins (poisonous substances). The lymphocytes are of two types: B cells and T cells. Mature B cells called plasma cells produce antibodies, the proteins that combine with target pathogens and mark them for destruction. Some T cells (cytotoxic T cells) directly destroy pathogens. The AIDS virus attacks one of several types of T cells. In this way, the virus causes immune deficiency, an inability to defend the body against pathogens. B lymphocytes and T lymphocytes are discussed more fully in Section 7.3.

Monocytes are the largest of the white blood cells. After taking up residence in the tissues, they differentiate into even larger macrophages. Like the neutrophils, macrophages are active phagocytes, destroying pathogens, old cells, and cellular debris. The macrophages also stimulate other white blood cells, including lymphocytes, to defend the body.

Disorders Involving White Blood Cells

Some immune deficiencies can be inherited. For example, children have *severe combined immunodeficiency (SCID)* when the stem cells of white blood cells lack an enzyme called adenosine deaminase. Without this enzyme, B and T lymphocytes do not develop and the body cannot fight infections. Injections of the missing enzyme can be given twice weekly, but a bone marrow transplant from a compatible donor is the best way to cure the disease. Treatment of SCID has largely turned to gene therapy to supply the missing enzyme to the cells of the individual (see Section 22.4).

As introduced in the chapter opener, cancer is due to uncontrolled cell growth. **Leukemia,** which means "white blood," refers to a group of cancers that involve uncontrolled white blood cell proliferation. Most of these white blood cells are abnormal or immature. Therefore, they are incapable of performing their normal defense functions. Each type of leukemia is named for the type of cell dividing out of control. We will take a closer look at cancer in Chapter 20.

An Epstein–Barr virus (EBV) infection of lymphocytes is the cause of *infectious mononucleosis,* so named because the lymphocytes are mononuclear. EBV, a member of the herpes virus family, is one of the most common human viruses. Symptoms of infectious mononucleosis are fever, sore throat, and swollen lymph glands. Although symptoms usually disappear in 1 or 2 months without medication, EBV remains dormant and hidden in a few cells in the throat and blood for the rest of a person's life. Stress can reactivate the virus, meaning that a person's saliva can pass on the infection to someone else, as with intimate kissing.

CHECK YOUR PROGRESS 6.3

1. Explain why there are different types of white blood cells.
2. Describe the structure and function of each major class of white blood cell.
3. Explain the relationship between leukemia and white blood cells.

CONNECTING THE CONCEPTS

White blood cells play an important role in the defense against disease. For more information on these cells, refer to the following discussions:

Section 7.2 describes the role of monocytes in the innate immune response.

Section 7.4 details how lymphocytes are involved in the adaptive defenses.

Section 8.2 explores how the HIV virus infects white blood cells, resulting in the disease called AIDS.

6.4 Platelets and Blood Clotting

LEARNING OUTCOMES

Upon completion of this section, you should be able to

1. Explain how blood clotting relates to homeostasis.
2. List the steps in the formation of a blood clot.
3. Describe disorders associated with blood clotting.

Platelets (thrombocytes) result from the fragmentation of large cells, called **megakaryocytes,** in the red bone marrow. Platelets are produced at a rate of 200 billion a day, and the blood contains between 130,000 to 400,000 platelets per microliter (μl). These formed elements are involved in the process of blood **clotting,** or **coagulation.** Also involved are the plasma proteins **prothrombin** and **fibrinogen,** manufactured in the liver and deposited in the blood. Vitamin K is necessary for the production of prothrombin.

Blood Clotting

The blood-clotting process helps the body maintain homeostasis in the cardiovascular system by ensuring that the plasma and formed elements remain within the blood vessels. Thirteen different clotting factors, calcium ions (Ca^{2+}), and a variety of enzymes participate in the formation of a blood clot.

When a blood vessel in the body is damaged, platelets clump at the site of the puncture and partially seal the leak (Fig. 6.8). Platelets and the injured tissues release a clotting factor called prothrombin activator, which converts prothrombin in the plasma to **thrombin.** This reaction requires calcium ions (Ca^{2+}). Thrombin, in turn, acts as an enzyme that severs two short amino acid chains from a fibrinogen molecule, one of the proteins in plasma. These activated fragments then join end to end, forming long threads of **fibrin.**

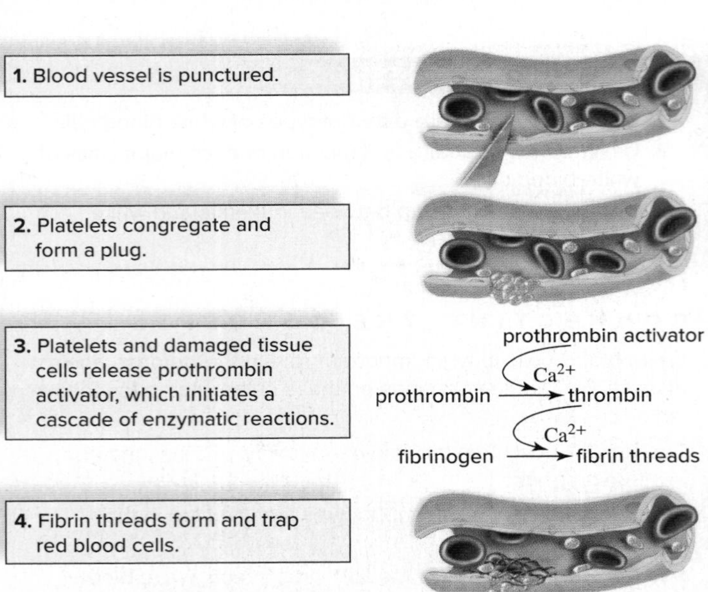
1. Blood vessel is punctured.
2. Platelets congregate and form a plug.
3. Platelets and damaged tissue cells release prothrombin activator, which initiates a cascade of enzymatic reactions.
prothrombin activator
Ca^{2+}
prothrombin
thrombin
Ca^{2+}
fibrinogen
fibrin threads
4. Fibrin threads form and trap red blood cells.
a. Blood-clotting process

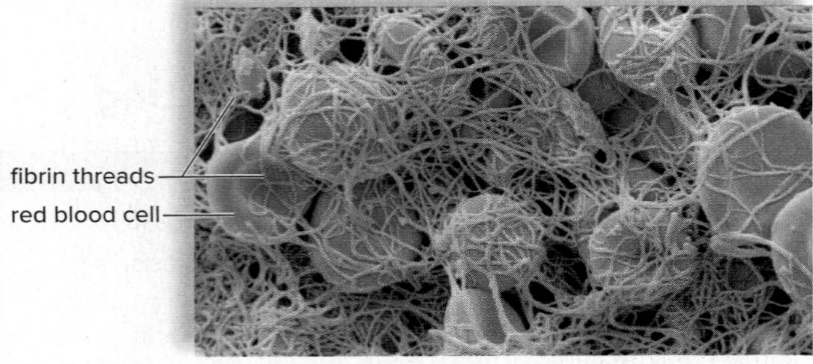
fibrin threads
red blood cell
b. Blood clot
5,000×

Figure 6.8 The steps in the formation of a blood clot. **a.** Platelets and damaged tissue cells release prothrombin activator, which acts on prothrombin in the presence of calcium ions (Ca^{2+}) to produce thrombin. Thrombin acts on fibrinogen in the presence of Ca^{2+} to form fibrin threads. **b.** A scanning electron micrograph of a blood clot shows red blood cells caught in the fibrin threads.

(b): Steve Gschmeissner/Science Photo Library/Getty Images

Fibrin threads wind around the platelet plug in the damaged area of the blood vessel and provide the framework for the clot. Red blood cells trapped within the fibrin threads make the clot appear red. A fibrin clot is temporary. Once blood vessel repair starts, an enzyme called *plasmin* destroys the fibrin network so tissue cells can grow.

After the blood clots, a yellowish fluid called *serum* escapes from the clot. It contains all the components of plasma except fibrinogen and prothrombin.

The Health feature "Aspirin and Heart Disease" explains how low doses of aspirin interact with the clotting pathways.

Disorders Related to Blood Clotting

An insufficient number of platelets is called **thrombocytopenia.** Thrombocytopenia is due to either low platelet production in bone marrow or an increased breakdown of platelets outside the marrow. A number of conditions, including leukemia, can lead to thrombocytopenia. It can also be drug-induced. Symptoms include bruising, rash, and nosebleeds or bleeding in the mouth. Gastrointestinal bleeding and bleeding in the brain are possible complications.

If the lining of a blood vessel becomes roughened, a clot can form spontaneously inside an unbroken blood vessel. Most often, roughening occurs because an atherosclerotic plaque has formed (see Section 5.7). Rarely, the vessel lining is damaged during the placement of an intravenous tube. The spontaneous clot is called a *thrombus* (*pl.,* thrombi) if it remains stationary inside the blood vessel. Sitting for long periods, as when traveling, can also cause thrombus formation. If the clot dislodges and travels in the blood, it is called an *embolus*. If the embolus blocks a blood vessel, it forms a **thromboembolism.** If left untreated, blood flow to the tissues can stop completely, resulting in a heart attack or stroke (see Section 5.7).

Hemophilia is an inherited clotting disorder that causes a deficiency in a clotting factor. There are many forms of the disorder. Hemophilia A, caused by a deficiency of clotting factor VIII, is more likely to occur in boys than in girls. Hemophilia A is caused by an abnormal copy of the factor VIII production gene, found on the X chromosome. In males, this form of hemophilia occurs when a male has an abnormal allele on the single X chromosome. Females need only one normal gene between their two X chromosomes to make the normal amounts of clotting factor VIII (see Section 21.5).

In hemophilia, the slightest bump can cause bleeding into the joints. Cartilage degeneration in the joints and absorption of underlying bone can follow. The most frequent cause of death is bleeding into the brain, with accompanying neurological damage. Regular injections of factor VIII can successfully treat the disease.

In addition to hemophilia A, there are several other forms of clotting disorders. Hemophilia B, also called *Christmas disease* after the first person to be diagnosed with it (Stephen Christmas in 1952), is caused by a deficiency in clotting factor IX. von Willebrand disease is caused by a deficiency in the gluelike protein that holds the platelets together at the site of a damaged blood vessel. All these disorders can be partially treated with injections of the missing proteins.

CHECK YOUR PROGRESS 6.4

1. List the components of blood involved in forming a blood clot.
2. Describe the stages of blood clotting.
3. Summarize a few of the blood-clotting disorders.

CONNECTING THE CONCEPTS

For more information on the disorders discussed in this section, refer to the following discussions:

Section 5.7 describes how blood clots relate to disorders of the cardiovascular system.

Section 21.5 explores the inheritance of hemophilia in the royal families of Europe.

BIOLOGY TODAY ▶ Health

Aspirin and Heart Disease

Aspirin (Fig. 6A), acetylsalicylic acid, has long been recognized as a treatment for pain. However, low-dose use of aspirin is now known to reduce the chances of some forms of heart disease, including strokes and heart attacks. It does this by interfering with the normal cascade of events in the blood-clotting pathway, as shown in Figure 6.8*a*.

When platelets (thrombocytes) are located in the blood, they exist as individual cell fragments. However, following an injury, the damaged cells release chemicals that cause the platelets to become "sticky" and clump together into larger groups called aggregates.

The conversion of platelets to the stickier version is due to a chemical called thromboxane. Thromboxane is released by a platelet in response to an injury or a wound in the area. As platelets aggregate, they release more thromboxane. This is an example of a positive feedback mechanism (see Section 4.8), and it allows for a rapid response to an injury, thus reducing the loss of blood.

A problem occurs when platelets start to stick together in the absence of a wound. These unintended clots can form blockages in the heart and brain, causing heart attacks and strokes. Aspirin inhibits the activity of thromboxane, effectively making the platelets less likely to stick together. Several studies have indicated that the use of aspirin by individuals with heart disease, such as atherosclerosis, reduces the chances of a heart attack or stroke.

It is important to note that the actual dosage of aspirin that produces this effect has not been conclusively determined by the medical community, although most agree that doses around 75–80 milligrams (mg) per day are sufficient. There is no evidence that higher doses produce an increased effect, and higher doses can cause side effects such as ulcers and abdominal bleeding. While it is known that aspirin lowers the probability of clot formation, recent studies have begun to question the effectiveness of daily low doses of aspirin in preventing heart attacks, especially in certain age groups. The decision to start or stop using low-dose aspirin should be made under the advice of a physician.

Questions to Consider

1. If you were a medical researcher, what other areas of the blood-clotting pathway would you target for inhibition to decrease the risks of stroke?
2. Under what medical conditions do you think aspirin should not be used? Why?

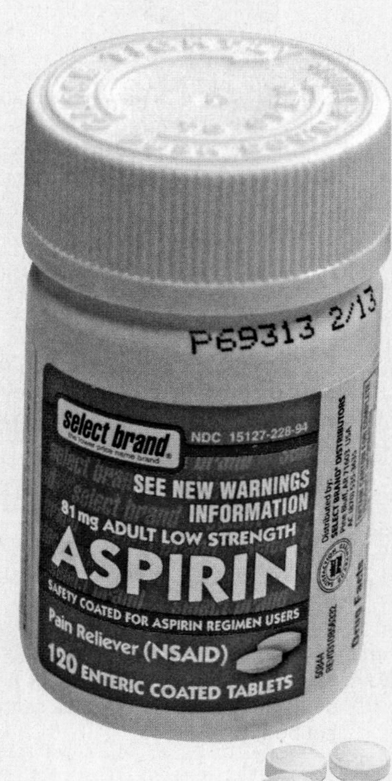

Figure 6A Aspirin and heart disease. Low doses of aspirin may prevent some forms of heart disease. Mark Dierker/McGraw Hill

6.5 Human Blood Types

LEARNING OUTCOMES

Upon completion of this section, you should be able to

1. Explain what determines blood types in humans.
2. Predict the compatibility of blood types for a given transfusion.
3. Summarize the role of Rh factor in hemolytic disease of the newborn.

The term *blood type* refers to variations in the surface proteins found on the surface of red blood cells (RBCs). These proteins play an important role in **blood transfusions,** or the transfer of blood from one individual to another. For transfusions to be done safely, blood must be typed, so that **agglutination** (clumping of red blood cells) does not occur when blood from different people is mixed. Blood typing usually involves determining the ABO blood group and whether the individual is Rh-negative (Rh^-) or Rh-positive (Rh^+).

ABO Blood Groups

Only certain types of blood transfusions are safe because the plasma membranes of red blood cells carry a type of glycoproteins that identifies the blood type. These glycoproteins may act as antigens to individuals with other blood types. As we will learn in Section 7.2, an antigen is any substance that is foreign to a person's body that invokes an immune response. ABO blood typing is based on the presence or absence of two possible glycoprotein antigens, called type A antigen and type B antigen. Whether these antigens are present or not depends on the inheritance of the individual.

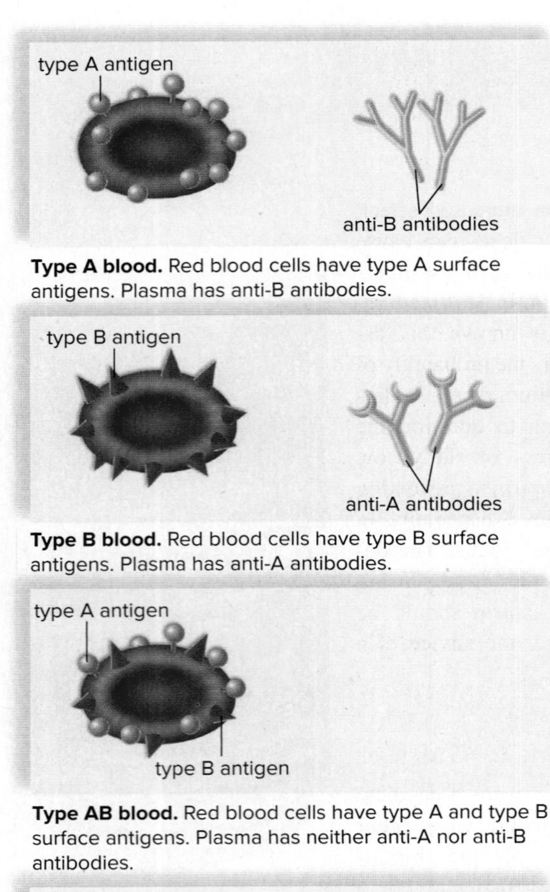

Type A blood. Red blood cells have type A surface antigens. Plasma has anti-B antibodies.

Type B blood. Red blood cells have type B surface antigens. Plasma has anti-A antibodies.

Type AB blood. Red blood cells have type A and type B surface antigens. Plasma has neither anti-A nor anti-B antibodies.

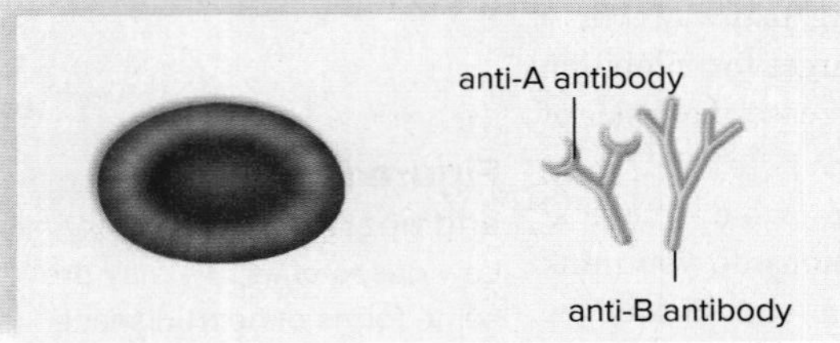

Type O blood. Red blood cells have neither type A nor type B surface antigens. Plasma has both anti-A and anti-B antibodies.

Figure 6.9 **The ABO blood type system.**
In the ABO system, blood type depends on the presence or absence of antigens A and B on the surface of red blood cells. In these drawings, A and B antigens are represented by different shapes on the red blood cells. The possible anti-A and anti-B antibodies in the plasma are shown for each blood type. An anti-B antibody cannot bind to an A antigen, and vice versa.

In Figure 6.9, type A antigen and type B antigen are given different shapes and colors. Study the figure to see the type(s) of antigens found on the red blood cell plasma membrane. As you might expect, type A blood has the A antigen (blue spheres) and type B blood has the B antigen (violet triangles). If you guessed that type AB blood has both A and B antigens, you're correct. Finally, notice that type O blood has neither antigen on its red blood cells.

Types A and B blood have antibodies (the yellow, Y-shaped molecules in Fig. 6.9) that correspond to the antigens they do not have on their own cells. Thus, an individual with type A blood has anti-B antibodies in the plasma, and a person with type B blood has anti-A antibodies in the plasma. Further, a person with type O blood has both antibodies in the plasma, and someone with type AB blood lacks both antibodies (Fig. 6.9). Anti-A and/or anti-B antibodies are not present at birth, but they appear over the course of several months.

Notice in Figure 6.9 that each antibody has a binding site that will combine with its corresponding antigen in a tight lock-and-key fit. The anti-B antibodies have a triangular binding site on the top of each Y-shaped molecule. This binding site fits snugly with the purple, triangular B antigen. Similarly, the anti-A antibodies have a spherical binding site shaped to form a perfect fit with the A antigen.

BIOLOGY IN YOUR LIFE

How does blood type relate to the risk of getting COVID-19?

The disease COVID-19 is caused by the SARS-CoV-2 virus. This virus primarily attacks the cells lining the respiratory system, although it does have other targets within the body. Researchers have been exploring the connection between the virus and human blood types.

Studies have indicated that individuals with type A blood have a greater chance of getting COVID-19 because the virus prefers respiratory cells that contain the glycoprotein associated with the type A antigen blood type. However, having type A blood does not increase the severity of the disease or mortality rates.

Blood Compatibility

Blood compatibility is very important when transfusions are done. The antibodies in the plasma must not combine with the antigens on the surface of the red blood cells or else agglutination occurs. With agglutination, anti-A antibodies have combined with type A antigens, and anti-B antibodies have combined with type B antigens. Therefore, agglutination is expected if the donor has type A blood and the recipient has type B blood (Fig. 6.10). The same situation occurs if the donor has type B blood and the recipient has type A blood.

Type O blood is sometimes called the *universal donor,* because the red blood cells of type O blood lack A and B antigens. When type O blood is donated to a recipient with any other blood type, agglutination should not occur. Likewise, type AB blood is sometimes called *universal recipient* blood, because the plasma lacks A and B antibodies. Agglutination should not occur when a person with type AB blood receives a transfusion from a donor with any other type of blood.

In practice, however, there are other possible blood groups, aside from ABO blood groups. Before blood can be safely transfused from one person to another, it is necessary to physically combine donor blood with recipient blood and observe whether agglutination occurs. This procedure, called blood-type crossmatching, takes only a few minutes. It is done before every

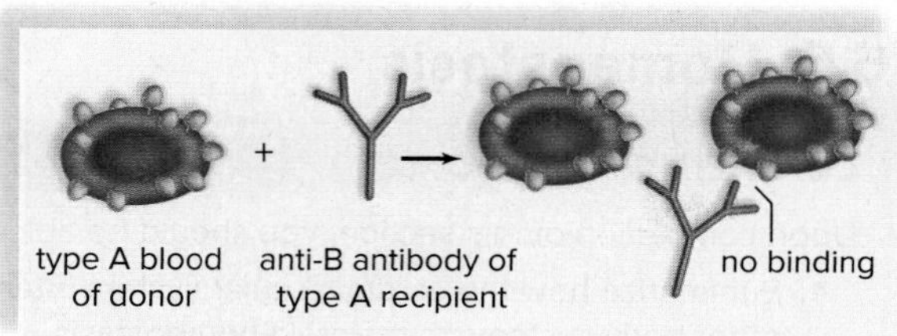

a. No agglutination

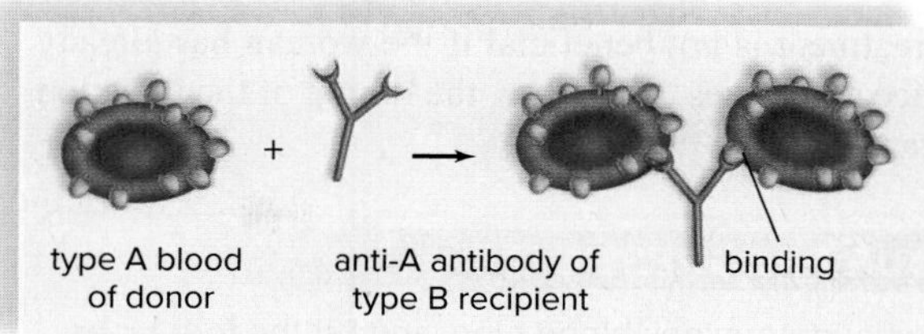

b. Agglutination

Figure 6.10 **Blood compatibility and agglutination.**
No agglutination occurs in (**a**) because anti-B antibodies cannot combine with the A antigen. Agglutination occurs in (**b**) when anti-A antibodies in the recipient combine with A antigens on donor red blood cells.

blood transfusion is performed. Type O blood donation without crossmatching is performed only in an emergency, when blood loss is severe and the patient's survival is at stake.

BIOLOGY IN YOUR LIFE

Is ABO blood typing accurate?

Usually, the answer is yes. However, there are some genetic disorders that may complicate traditional ABO blood typing. For example, individuals with Bombay syndrome lack the enzyme to correctly attach A and B antigens to the surface of the red blood cells. These individuals may carry the genes to produce the A and B antigens on the surface of the red blood cells, but because these are not attached, they may appear to have type O blood.

Rh Blood Groups

The designation of blood type usually also includes whether the person has or does not have an antigen, called the Rh factor, on the red blood cell. Individuals who are Rh-negative normally do not have antibodies to the Rh factor, but they make them when exposed to the Rh factor.

If a mother is Rh-negative and the father is Rh-positive, a child can be Rh-positive. During childbirth, Rh-positive antigens can leak across the placenta into the mother's bloodstream. The presence of these Rh-positive antigens causes the mother to produce anti-Rh antibodies (Fig. 6.11).

In a subsequent pregnancy with another baby who is Rh-positive, the anti-Rh antibodies can cross the placenta and destroy the unborn child's red blood cells. This is called *hemolytic disease of the newborn,* because hemolysis starts in the womb and continues after the baby is born. Due to red blood cell destruction, the baby will be severely anemic. Excess hemoglobin breakdown products in the blood can lead to brain damage and intellectual disability, or even death.

The Rh problem is prevented by giving women who are Rh-negative an Rh immunoglobulin injection no later than 72 hours after giving birth to a child who is Rh-positive. This injection contains anti-Rh antibodies that attack any of the baby's red blood cells in the mother's blood before these cells can stimulate her immune system to produce her own antibodies. Called RhoGAM, this treatment does not harm the newborn's red blood cells;

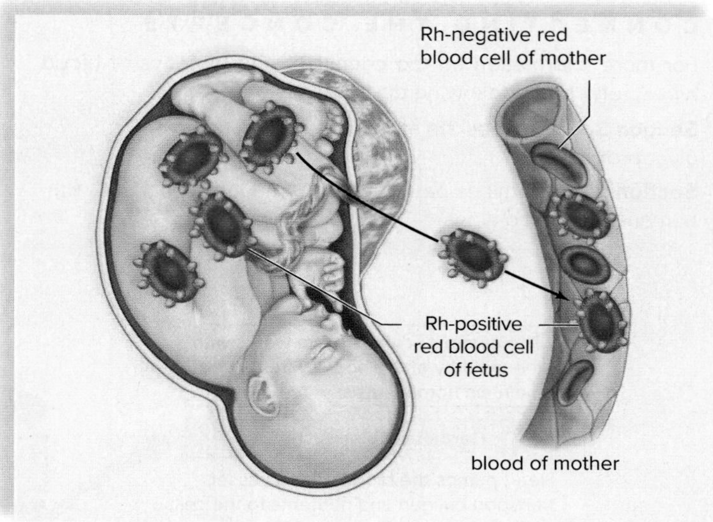

a. Fetal Rh-positive red blood cells leak across placenta into mother's bloodstream.

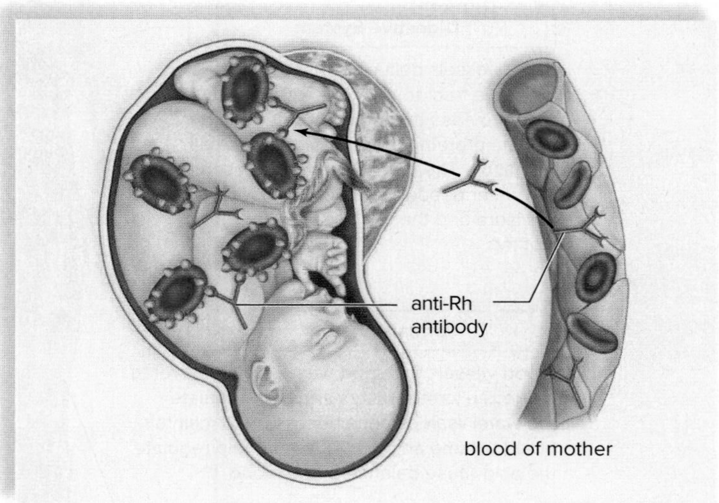

b. Mother forms anti-Rh antibodies that cross the placenta and attack fetal Rh-positive red blood cells.

Figure 6.11 **Rh factor disease (hemolytic disease of the newborn).**
a. Due to a pregnancy in which the child is Rh-positive, a mother who is Rh-negative can begin to produce antibodies against Rh-positive red blood cells. **b.** In pregnancy, these antibodies can cross the placenta and cause hemolysis of the Rh-positive child's red blood cells.

however, the treatment is not beneficial if the woman has already begun to produce antibodies. Therefore, the timing of the injection is most important.

CHECK YOUR PROGRESS 6.5

1. Explain what determines blood type, and list the four types of blood.
2. Explain whom a donor with type A blood is able to donate blood to.
3. Explain what causes hemolytic disease of the newborn.

CONNECTING THE CONCEPTS

For more information on the chemistry and genetics of blood types, refer to the following discussions:

Section 3.3 describes the structure and function of glycoproteins.

Section 21.4 examines patterns of inheritance associated with human ABO blood types.

6.6 Homeostasis

LEARNING OUTCOME

Upon completion of this section, you should be able to

1. Summarize how the cardiovascular system interacts with other body systems to maintain homeostasis.

Figure 6.12 summarizes how the organ systems of the body interact with the cardiovascular system to maintain homeostasis. You previously learned that the body's internal environment contains not only blood but also interstitial fluid. Interstitial fluid originates from blood plasma but contains very little plasma protein. Interstitial fluid is absorbed by lymphatic capillaries, after which it is referred to as lymph. The lymph courses through lymphatic vessels, eventually returning to the venous system. Thus, the cardiovascular and lymphatic systems are intimately linked.

Homeostasis is possible only if the cardiovascular system delivers oxygen from the lungs, as well as nutrients from the digestive system, to the interstitial fluid surrounding cells. Simultaneously,

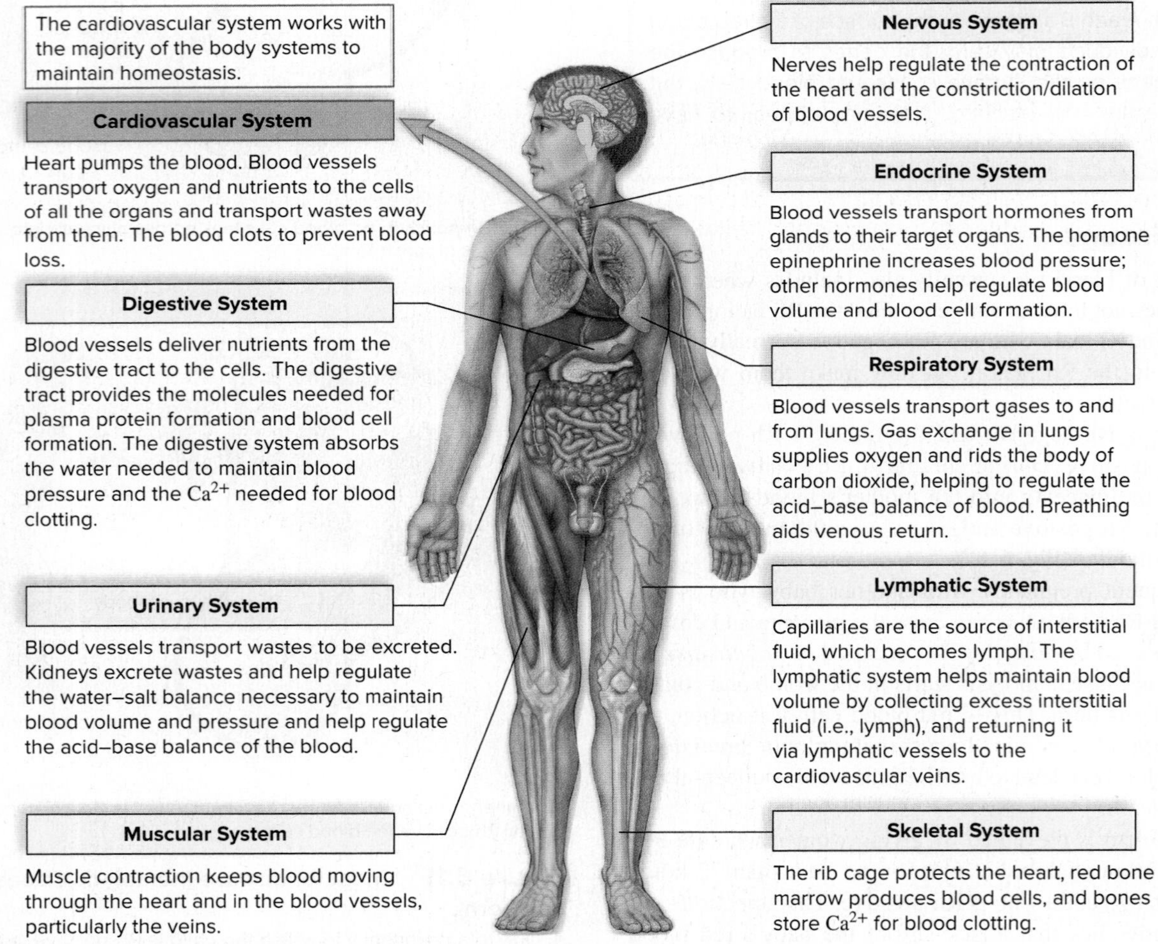

The cardiovascular system works with the majority of the body systems to maintain homeostasis.
Cardiovascular System
Heart pumps the blood. Blood vessels transport oxygen and nutrients to the cells of all the organs and transport wastes away from them. The blood clots to prevent blood loss.
Digestive System
Blood vessels deliver nutrients from the digestive tract to the cells. The digestive tract provides the molecules needed for plasma protein formation and blood cell formation. The digestive system absorbs the water needed to maintain blood pressure and the Ca^{2+} needed for blood clotting.
Urinary System
Blood vessels transport wastes to be excreted. Kidneys excrete wastes and help regulate the water–salt balance necessary to maintain blood volume and pressure and help regulate the acid–base balance of the blood.
Muscular System
Muscle contraction keeps blood moving through the heart and in the blood vessels, particularly the veins.
Nervous System
Nerves help regulate the contraction of the heart and the constriction/dilation of blood vessels.
Endocrine System
Blood vessels transport hormones from glands to their target organs. The hormone epinephrine increases blood pressure; other hormones help regulate blood volume and blood cell formation.
Respiratory System
Blood vessels transport gases to and from lungs. Gas exchange in lungs supplies oxygen and rids the body of carbon dioxide, helping to regulate the acid–base balance of blood. Breathing aids venous return.
Lymphatic System
Capillaries are the source of interstitial fluid, which becomes lymph. The lymphatic system helps maintain blood volume by collecting excess interstitial fluid (i.e., lymph), and returning it via lymphatic vessels to the cardiovascular veins.
Skeletal System
The rib cage protects the heart, red bone marrow produces blood cells, and bones store Ca^{2+} for blood clotting.

Figure 6.12 How body systems cooperate to ensure homeostasis.
Each of these systems makes critical contributions to the functioning of the cardiovascular system and, therefore, to homeostasis. See if you can suggest contributions by each system before looking at the information given.

the cardiovascular system also removes metabolic wastes, delivering waste to excretory organs.

The three components of the muscular system make essential contributions to blood movement. Cardiac muscle contractions circulate blood throughout the body. Contraction or relaxation of the smooth muscle in blood vessel walls changes vessel diameter and helps maintain the correct blood pressure. Further, skeletal muscle contraction compresses both cardiovascular and lymphatic vessels. Lymph returns to cardiovascular veins, and blood in the cardiovascular veins drains back to the heart. The circulation of interstitial fluid and blood is then complete.

The skeletal and endocrine systems are vital to cardiovascular homeostasis. Red bone marrow produces blood cells. Without the needed blood cells, the person becomes anemic and lacks an immune response. In addition, bones contribute calcium ions (Ca^{2+}) to the process of blood clotting. Without blood clotting, bleeding from an injury (even something as simple as skinning a knee) can be fatal. Both blood cell production and bone calcium release are regulated by hormones. Once again, the endocrine system cooperates with the cardiovascular system.

Finally, we must not forget that the urinary system has functions besides producing and excreting urine. The kidneys help regulate the acid-base and water-salt balances of the blood and interstitial fluid. Erythropoietin, a hormone produced by the kidneys, stimulates red blood cell production. The urinary system joins the muscular, skeletal, and endocrine systems to maintain the internal environment.

CHECK YOUR PROGRESS 6.6

1. Explain how the functions of the cardiovascular system contribute to homeostasis.
2. Summarize how each system listed in Figure 6.12 interacts with the cardiovascular system.

CONNECTING THE CONCEPTS

For more information on how the cardiovascular system interacts with other body systems, refer to the following discussions:

Section 7.2 examines the interaction of the cardiovascular system and lymphatic system.

Section 11.3 explores how the urinary system removes wastes from the blood.

CONCLUSION

In this chapter, we explored the function of human blood, the components of blood, and the concept of human blood groups. The importance of blood in maintaining homeostasis, due to its central role in the transport of almost all of the materials in the body, means that a loss of blood can quickly have a negative impact on the health of an individual. Historically, organizations, such as the Red Cross, have had a difficult time meeting demand during emergencies. The development of synthetic blood is seen by many as a means of increasing the amount of blood available and helping ensure there is an ample blood supply in times of crisis.

SUMMARIZE

6.1 Blood: An Overview

Blood

- Transports hormones, oxygen, and nutrients to cells.
- Transports carbon dioxide and other wastes from cells.
- Fights infections by transporting **antibodies** and cells of the immune system.
- Maintains blood pressure and regulates body temperature.
- Keeps the pH of body fluids within normal limits.

These functions help maintain homeostasis.

Blood has two main components: **plasma** and **formed elements** (red blood cells, white blood cells, and platelets).

Plasma

Plasma is a fluid connective tissue, 91% of which is water. Plasma transports essential molecules to and from the cells. **Plasma proteins** (albumins, globulins, and fibrinogen) are mostly produced by the liver. These proteins maintain **osmotic pressure** and help regulate pH. **Albumins** transport other molecules, **globulins** function in immunity, and prothrombin and **fibrinogen** enable blood clotting.

6.2 Red Blood Cells and the Transport of Gases

Red blood cells (erythrocytes) lack a nucleus and other organelles. They contain **hemoglobin (Hb),** which combines with oxygen and transports it to the tissues. Hemoglobin assists in carbon dioxide transport as well.

Red blood cell (RBC) production is controlled by the blood oxygen concentration. When oxygen concentration decreases, the kidneys increase production of the hormone **erythropoietin (EPO).** In response, more red blood cells are produced by the bone marrow.

Diseases involving RBCs include **anemia** (not enough hemoglobin to transport oxygen), **hemolysis** (rupturing of RBCs), and **sickle-cell disease** (malformed RBCs).

6.3 White Blood Cells and Defense Against Disease

White blood cells (leukocytes) are larger than red blood cells. They have a nucleus and are translucent unless stained. White blood cells are either **granular leukocytes** or **agranular leukocytes.** White blood cells are an important part of the immune system, which protects the body from infection. They often use phagocytosis to ingest foreign compounds or cells.

- The granular leukocytes are eosinophils, basophils (and mast cells), and neutrophils. Neutrophils are abundant, respond first to infections, and phagocytize pathogens.
- The agranular leukocytes include monocytes and lymphocytes. **Monocytes** are the largest white blood cells. They can become macrophages that phagocytize pathogens and cellular debris. **Lymphocytes** (B cells and T cells) are responsible for specific immunity.

Diseases associated with white blood cells include *severe combined immunodeficiency* (*SCID;* inability to fight infections), **leukemia** (white blood cell cancer), and infectious mononucleosis (produced by infection with the EBV virus).

6.4 Platelets and Blood Clotting

Platelets (thrombocytes) result from fragmentation of **megakaryocytes** in the red bone marrow and function in blood clotting.

Blood Clotting

Platelets and the plasma proteins, **prothrombin** (and **thrombin**) and **fibrinogen,** function in blood clotting **(coagulation),** an enzymatic process. **Fibrin** threads that trap red blood cells result from the enzymatic reaction.

Diseases associated with improper blood clotting include **thrombocytopenia** (insufficient number of platelets), a **thromboembolism** (movement of the blood clot into the heart, lungs, or brain), and **hemophilia** (loss of a specific clotting factor).

6.5 Human Blood Types

Blood typing usually involves determining the ABO blood group and whether the person is Rh^- or Rh^+. Determining blood type is necessary for transfusions, so that **agglutination** (clumping) of red blood cells does not occur.

ABO Blood Groups

ABO blood typing determines the presence or absence of type A antigen and type B antigen on the surface of red blood cells.

- *Type A blood:* Type A surface antigens; plasma has anti-B antibodies
- *Type B blood:* Type B surface antigens; plasma has anti-A antibodies
- *Type AB blood:* Both type A and type B surface antigens; plasma has neither anti-A nor anti-B antibodies (universal recipient)
- *Type O blood:* Neither type A nor type B surface antigens; plasma has both anti-A and anti-B antibodies (universal donor)
- *Agglutination:* Agglutination occurs if the corresponding antigen and antibody are mixed (i.e., if the donor has type A blood and the recipient has type B blood)

Rh Blood Groups

The Rh antigen must also be considered when transfusing blood. It is very important during pregnancy, because a mother who is Rh-negative may form antibodies to the Rh antigen while carrying or after the birth of a child who is Rh-positive. These antibodies can cross the placenta to destroy the red blood cells of a child who is Rh-positive.

6.6 Homeostasis

Homeostasis depends on the cardiovascular system, because it serves the needs of the cells. Other body systems are also critical to cardiovascular system function:

- The digestive system supplies nutrients.
- The respiratory system supplies oxygen and removes carbon dioxide from the blood.
- The nervous and endocrine systems help maintain blood pressure. Endocrine hormones regulate red blood cell formation and calcium balance.
- The lymphatic system returns interstitial fluid to the veins.
- Skeletal muscle contraction (skeletal system) and breathing movements (respiratory system) propel blood in the veins.

ENGAGE

THINKING CRITICALLY

1. Carbon monoxide (CO) is a deadly, odorless, colorless gas. Hemoglobin in red blood cells binds much more closely to CO than it does to oxygen. Hemoglobin's ability to transport oxygen is severely compromised in the presence of CO.
   a. A malfunctioning furnace is one potential cause for CO poisoning. What are some other situations in which you could be exposed to carbon monoxide? What safeguards should be in place when around these situations?
   b. If cells are deprived of oxygen, what is the effect on the production of cellular energy? Be specific.
2. There are three specific nutrients mentioned in this chapter that are necessary for the body to form red blood cells.
   a. Name the three nutrients.
   b. What are good food sources for these nutrients?
3. What type of organic molecule is hemoglobin? What nutrient is required to form hemoglobin?
4. The hormone erythropoietin is produced by the kidneys whenever more red blood cells are necessary. List several reasons the body needs more red blood cells.
5. Athletes who abuse erythropoietin have many more red blood cells than usual. After examining Figure 6.3 and imagining many more red blood cells than usual in this capillary, explain why an athlete might die from having too many red blood cells.
6. Researchers are now developing artificial blood for transfusions. Some forms of artificial blood are being used in clinical trials. Which characteristics of normal blood must artificial blood have to be useful, and which would probably be too difficult to reproduce?

MAKING IT RELEVANT

1. In addition to being used for transfusions, what other benefits do you think artificial blood may have in the delivery of drugs and the prevention of disease?
2. How might artificial blood be engineered to prevent accidental poisoning from carbon monoxide?
3. Human blood groups have been used as the basis for paternity tests for decades. How will that change once artificial blood becomes more widely used?

Find answers to all of the chapter questions at connect.mheducation.com

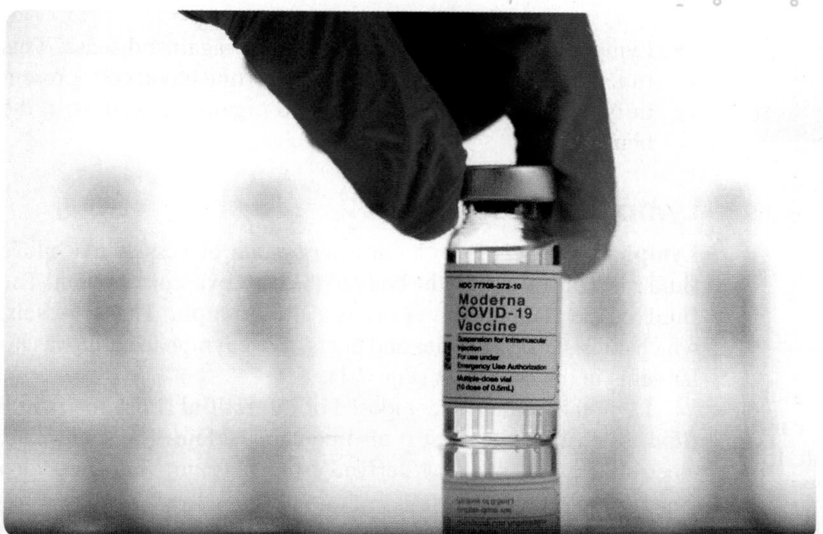

Oz Digital/Alamy Stock Photo

CHAPTER 7

The Lymphatic and Immune Systems

The COVID-19 Vaccine

For decades, scientists have warned us that a unique virus could emerge with the ability to jump from its animal hosts to humans and cause sickness across the globe, in a fashion not seen since the influenza pandemic of 1918. In late 2019, warnings began to emerge from the area of Wuhan, China, that a new form of coronavirus, called SARS-CoV-2, had arisen in the local population and was causing a unique form of respiratory disease. This disease, which eventually would be called COVID-19, quickly became a global pandemic, infecting hundreds of millions of people, disrupting society, and exacting a terrible death toll.

For most people, infection with the SARS-CoV-2 virus produces mild symptoms, such as a fever, cough, or loss of smell and taste. Some individuals are asymptomatic, and do not experience any symptoms, and thus may not know they have been infected. However, many groups, including people who are older or immunocompromised, are highly susceptible to the virus. As we have begun to understand the nature of this virus, the scientific community recognized that the only way to combat its effect was to develop a vaccine.

In order to create the vaccine, researchers had to identify the parts of the virus that cause our immune system to react as if it has been infected, and then build up antibodies to the actual virus. Later, if an individual is exposed to the virus, these antibodies are used by the body to provide immunity. In this chapter, we will explore how our immune system protects us, not only from viruses such as SARS-CoV-2, but from a wide variety of pathogens.

As you read through the chapter, think about the following questions:

1. How does your body respond to its first exposure to a new pathogen?
2. How do vaccines provide immunity?

CHAPTER OUTLINE

BEFORE YOU BEGIN

Before beginning this chapter, take a few moments to review the following discussions:

Section 2.6 How is a protein's structure related to its function?

Section 3.2 What are some differences between prokaryotic and eukaryotic cells?

Section 6.3 What is the role of white blood cells in defense against pathogens?

7.1 The Lymphatic System

LEARNING OUTCOMES

Upon completion of this section, you should be able to

1. Describe the structure and function of the lymphatic system.
2. Explain the origins and components of lymph.
3. Explain how the lymphatic system interacts with the circulatory system.

The **lymphatic system** consists of lymphatic vessels and lymphatic organs. This system, closely associated with the cardiovascular system, has three main functions that contribute to homeostasis:

- Lymphatic capillaries absorb excess interstitial fluid and return it to the bloodstream.
- Lymphatic capillaries absorb fats from the digestive tract and transport them to the bloodstream.
- Lymphoid organs help defend the body against disease. This function is mainly carried out by the white blood cells present in lymphatic vessels and lymphoid organs, as well as in the blood.

Lymphatic Vessels

Lymphatic vessels form a one-way system of vessels that move fluid from the tissues of the body to the cardiovascular system. The fluid inside lymphatic vessels is called **lymph.** These vessels, which consist of capillaries and ducts, move lymph to cardiovascular veins in the shoulders (Fig. 7.1).

Lymph is primarily composed of **interstitial fluid.** Interstitial fluid is mostly water, but it also contains solutes (i.e., nutrients, electrolytes, and oxygen) derived from plasma. This fluid also contains cellular products (i.e., hormones, enzymes, and wastes) secreted by cells. Lymph is usually a colorless liquid, but after a meal it may appear creamy due to its lipid content.

Lymphatic capillaries are usually found in close proximity to the capillaries of the cardiovascular system. The lymphatic

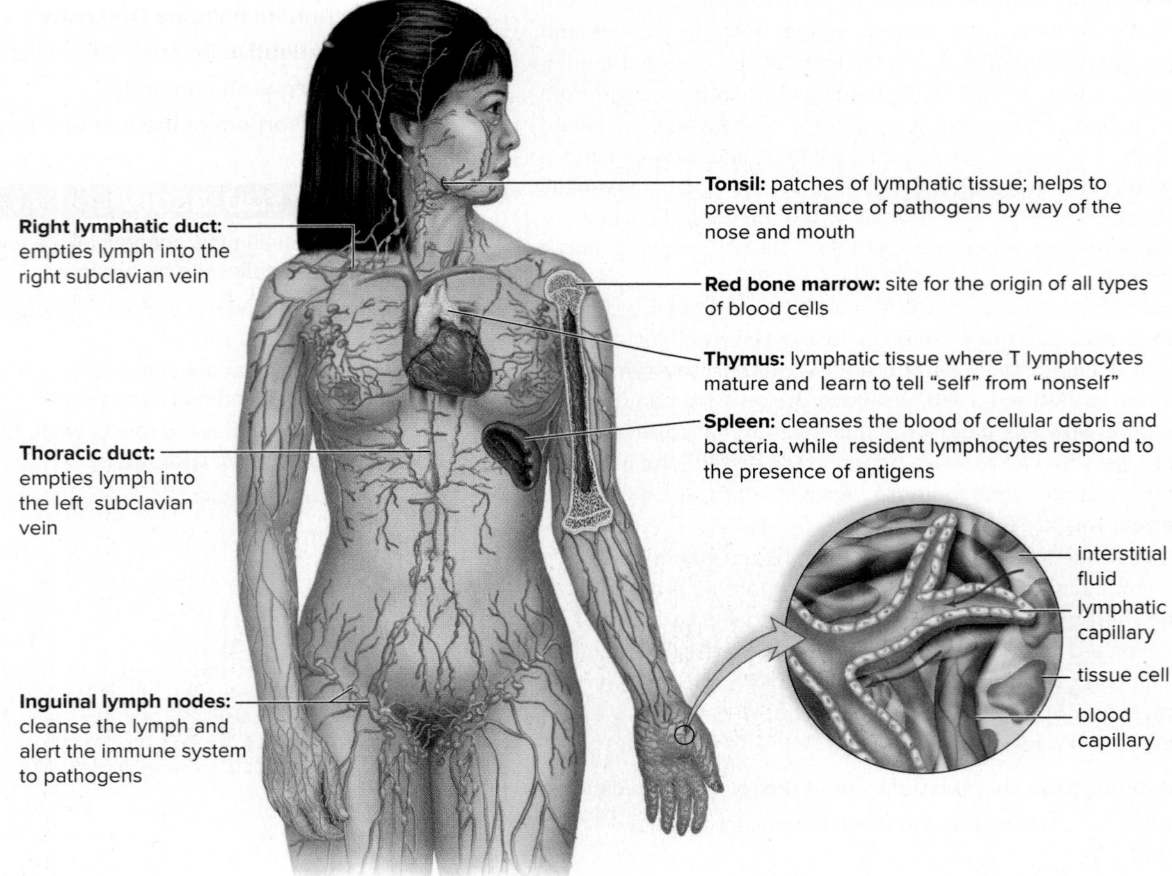
Tonsil: patches of lymphatic tissue; helps to prevent entrance of pathogens by way of the nose and mouth
Right lymphatic duct: empties lymph into the right subclavian vein
Red bone marrow: site for the origin of all types of blood cells
Thymus: lymphatic tissue where T lymphocytes mature and learn to tell "self" from "nonself"
Spleen: cleanses the blood of cellular debris and bacteria, while resident lymphocytes respond to the presence of antigens
Thoracic duct: empties lymph into the left subclavian vein
interstitial fluid
lymphatic capillary
tissue cell
blood capillary
Inguinal lymph nodes: cleanse the lymph and alert the immune system to pathogens

Figure 7.1 Organs and vessels of the lymphatic system.
Lymphatic vessels drain excess fluid from the tissues and return it to the cardiovascular system. The enlargement shows that lymphatic vessels, like cardiovascular veins, have valves to prevent backward flow. The lymph nodes, spleen, thymus, and red bone marrow are the main lymphatic organs that assist immunity.

capillaries join to form lymphatic vessels that merge before entering either the thoracic duct or the right lymphatic duct (Fig. 7.1). The larger thoracic duct returns lymph collected from the body below the thorax, the left arm, and the left side of the head and neck into the left subclavian vein. The right lymphatic duct returns lymph from the right arm and right side of the head and neck into the right subclavian vein.

The construction of the larger lymphatic vessels is similar to that of cardiovascular veins, including the presence of valves. The movement of lymph within lymphatic capillaries is largely dependent on skeletal muscle contraction. Lymph forced through lymphatic vessels as a result of muscular compression is prevented from flowing backward by one-way valves.

Lymphatic Organs

The **lymphatic organs** are divided into two categories. The primary lymphatic organs include the red bone marrow and the thymus, whereas the lymph nodes and spleen represent the secondary lymphatic organs. Figure 7.2 shows the tissue structure of the primary and secondary lymphatic organs.

The Primary Lymphatic Organs

Red bone marrow (Fig 7.2*a*) produces all types of blood cells. In a child, most bones have red bone marrow; in an adult, marrow is found only in the sternum, the vertebrae, the ribs, part of the pelvic girdle, and the upper ends of the humerus and femur. In addition to the red blood cells, bone marrow produces the five types of white blood cells: neutrophils, eosinophils, basophils, lymphocytes, and monocytes. Lymphocytes are either **B cells (B lymphocytes)** or **T cells (T lymphocytes).** B cells mature in the bone marrow, but T cells mature in the thymus. Any B cell that reacts with cells of the body is destroyed in the bone marrow and does not enter the circulation. This ensures that the B cells do not harm normal cells of the body.

The soft, bilobed **thymus** (Fig. 7.2*b*) is located in the thoracic cavity between the trachea and the sternum, superior to the heart. The thymus will begin shrinking in size before puberty and is noticeably smaller in an adult than in a child.

The thymus has two functions: First, it produces hormones, such as thymosin, that aid in the maturation of T lymphocytes. In addition, it acts as the maturation site for T lymphocytes, which migrate from the bone marrow through the bloodstream to the thymus. Only about 5% of these cells ever leave the thymus. These T lymphocytes have survived a critical test, because if any of these cells show the ability to react with the individual's cells, they are destroyed in the thymus. If they have the potential to attack a pathogen, they can leave the thymus. The thymus is absolutely critical to immunity, because without mature, properly functioning T cells, the body's response to specific pathogens is compromised.

The Secondary Lymphatic Organs

The secondary lymphatic organs are the spleen, the lymph nodes, and the tonsils. Many other organs, such as the appendix, contain clusters of lymphatic tissue called lymphatic nodules that help protect against pathogens. The mucosa of some organ systems, such as the gastrointestinal tract and respiratory system, also contain some lymphatic tissue.

The **spleen** (Fig. 7.2*c*) filters blood. It is the largest lymphatic organ and is located in the upper left region of the abdominal cavity posterior to the stomach. Connective tissue divides the spleen into regions known as white pulp and red pulp. The red pulp, which surrounds venous sinuses (cavities), is involved in filtering the

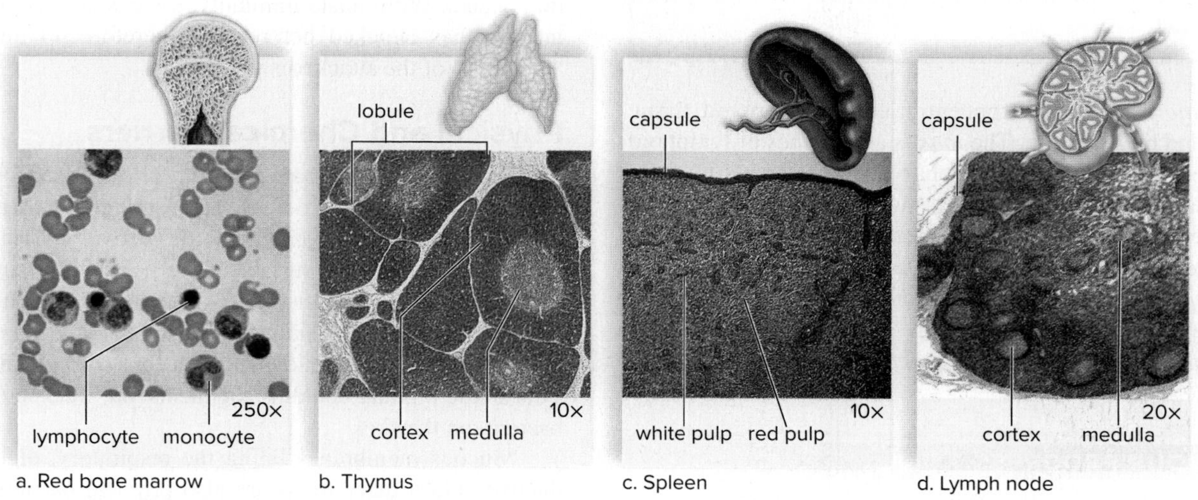

Figure 7.2 Tissue structure of the lymphatic organs.
Red bone marrow (**a**) and the thymus (**b**) are the primary lymphatic organs. Blood cells, including lymphocytes, are produced in red bone marrow. B cells mature in the bone marrow, but T cells mature in the thymus. The spleen (**c**) and the lymph nodes (**d**) are secondary lymphatic organs. Lymph is cleansed in lymph nodes, and blood is cleansed in the spleen.

(a and b): Ed Reschke/Stone/Getty Images; (c): Ed Reschke; (d): Alvin Telser/McGraw Hill

blood. Blood entering the spleen must pass through the sinuses before exiting. Here, macrophages, which are like powerful vacuum cleaners, engulf pathogens and debris, such as worn-out red blood cells.

The spleen's outer capsule is relatively thin, and an infection or a blow can cause the spleen to burst. Although the spleen's functions are replaced by other organs, a person without a spleen is often more susceptible to infections and may have to receive antibiotic therapy indefinitely.

Lymph nodes (Fig. 7.2*d*), which occur along lymphatic vessels, filter lymph. Connective tissue forms a capsule and divides a lymph node into compartments. Each compartment contains a sinus that increases in size toward the center of the node. As lymph courses through the sinuses, it is exposed to macrophages, which engulf pathogens and debris. Lymphocytes, also present in sinuses, fight infections and attack cancer cells.

Lymph nodes are named for their location. For example, inguinal nodes are in the groin, and axillary nodes are in the armpits. Physicians often feel for the presence of swollen, tender lymph nodes in the neck as evidence that the body is fighting an infection. This is a noninvasive, preliminary way to help make such a diagnosis.

BIOLOGY IN YOUR LIFE

What does a swollen lymph node mean?

Lymph nodes swell when they are fighting an infection. When the body is invaded by a bacterium or virus, individual nodes can swell from 0.5 to 2 inches in diameter. Cuts, burns, bites, rashes, and any break in the skin can cause an infection and thus the swelling of your lymph nodes. Swollen nodes near the groin mean infection on a leg or the lower abdomen; in your armpits, they mean infection on the arms or chest; and on the front of your neck, they mean an infection in the ears, nose, or throat. Some diseases, such as chickenpox, can cause all your nodes to swell.

Lymphatic nodules are concentrations of lymphoid tissue not surrounded by a capsule. The *tonsils* are patches of lymphoid tissue located in a ring about the pharynx. The tonsils perform the same functions as lymph nodes; however, because of their location, they are the first to encounter pathogens and antigens that enter the body by way of the nose and mouth.

Peyer's patches are located in the intestinal wall and in tissues within the appendix, a small extension of the large intestine, and encounter pathogens that enter the body by way of the digestive tract.

CHECK YOUR PROGRESS 7.1

1. Describe how the lymphatic system assists in fluid homeostasis for the body.
2. List the primary and secondary lymphatic organs.
3. Explain the link between the lymphatic and circulatory systems.

CONNECTING THE CONCEPTS

As noted, the lymphatic system plays a role in the movement of fats and the return of excess fluid to the circulatory system. For more information on these functions, refer to the following discussions:

Section 5.1 examines how the lymphatic system interacts with the circulatory system.

Section 9.3 explores how the lymphatic system is involved in the processing of fat in the diet.

Figure 9.6 diagrams the location of the lymphatic vessels in the small intestine.

7.2 Innate Immune Defenses

LEARNING OUTCOMES

Upon completion of this section, you should be able to

1. List examples of the body's innate defenses.
2. Summarize the events in the inflammatory response.
3. Explain the role of the complement system.

We are constantly exposed to microbes such as viruses, bacteria, and fungi in our environment. **Immunity** is the capability of killing or removing foreign substances, pathogens, and cancer cells from the body. There are two different aspects of immunity. Mechanisms of innate, or nonspecific, immunity are fully functional without previous exposure to these invaders, whereas adaptive immunity (see Section 7.3) is initiated and amplified by exposure.

As summarized in Figure 7.3, innate immune defenses include physical and chemical barriers; the inflammatory response (including the phagocytes and natural killer cells); and protective proteins, such as complement and interferons.

Innate defenses occur immediately or very shortly after infection occurs. With innate immunity, there is no recognition that an intruder has attacked before, and therefore no immunological "memory" of the attacker is present.

Physical and Chemical Barriers

The body has built-in barriers, both physical and chemical, that serve as the first line of defense against infection by pathogens.

The intact skin is generally an effective physical barrier that prevents infection. The surface of the skin is constantly being lost to exfoliation (see Section 4.7). The keratin of the skin prevents the entry of microbes. The skin also has the benefit of a chemical barrier in the form of secretions of sebaceous (oil) glands of the skin. This acidic mixture contains chemicals that weaken or kill certain bacteria on the skin.

Mucous membranes lining the respiratory, digestive, reproductive, and urinary tracts are also physical barriers to entry by pathogens. For example, the ciliated cells that line the upper respiratory tract sweep mucus and trapped particles up into the throat, where they can be coughed or spit out or swallowed.

Perspiration, saliva, and tears contain an antibacterial enzyme called **lysozyme.** Saliva also helps wash microbes off the teeth and

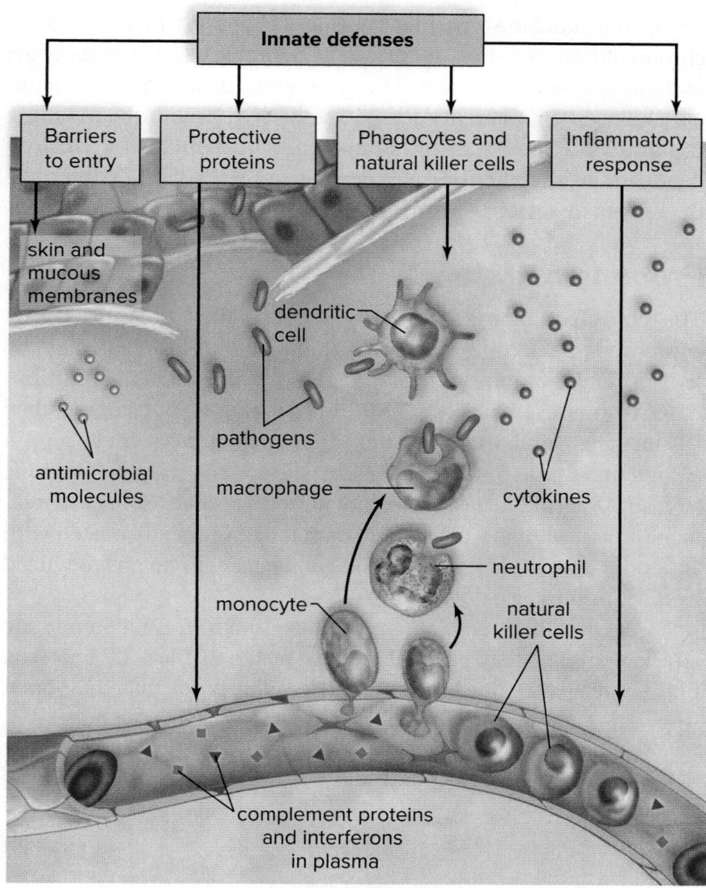

Figure 7.3 Overview of innate immune defenses. Most innate defenses act rapidly to detect and respond to pathogens that the body has not experienced in the past.

tongue, and tears wash the eyes. Similarly, as urine is voided from the body, it flushes bacteria from the urinary tract.

The acidic pH of the stomach inhibits growth or kills many types of bacteria. At one time, it was thought that no bacterium could survive the acidity of the stomach. But now we know that ulcers are caused by the bacterium *Helicobacter pylori* (see Section 1.3). Similarly, the acidity of the vagina and its thick walls discourage the presence of pathogens.

Finally, a significant chemical barrier to infection is created by the normal flora, microbes that usually reside in the mouth, large intestine, and other areas. By using available nutrients and releasing their own waste, these resident bacteria prevent potential pathogens from taking up residence. For this reason, chronic use of antibiotics can make a person susceptible to pathogenic infection by killing off the normal flora.

Inflammatory Response

The **inflammatory response** exemplifies the second line of defense against invasion by a pathogen. Inflammation employs mainly neutrophils and macrophages to surround and kill (engulf by phagocytosis) pathogens trying to get a foothold inside the body. Protective proteins are also involved. Inflammation is usually recognized by its four hallmark symptoms: redness, heat, swelling, and pain (Fig. 7.4).

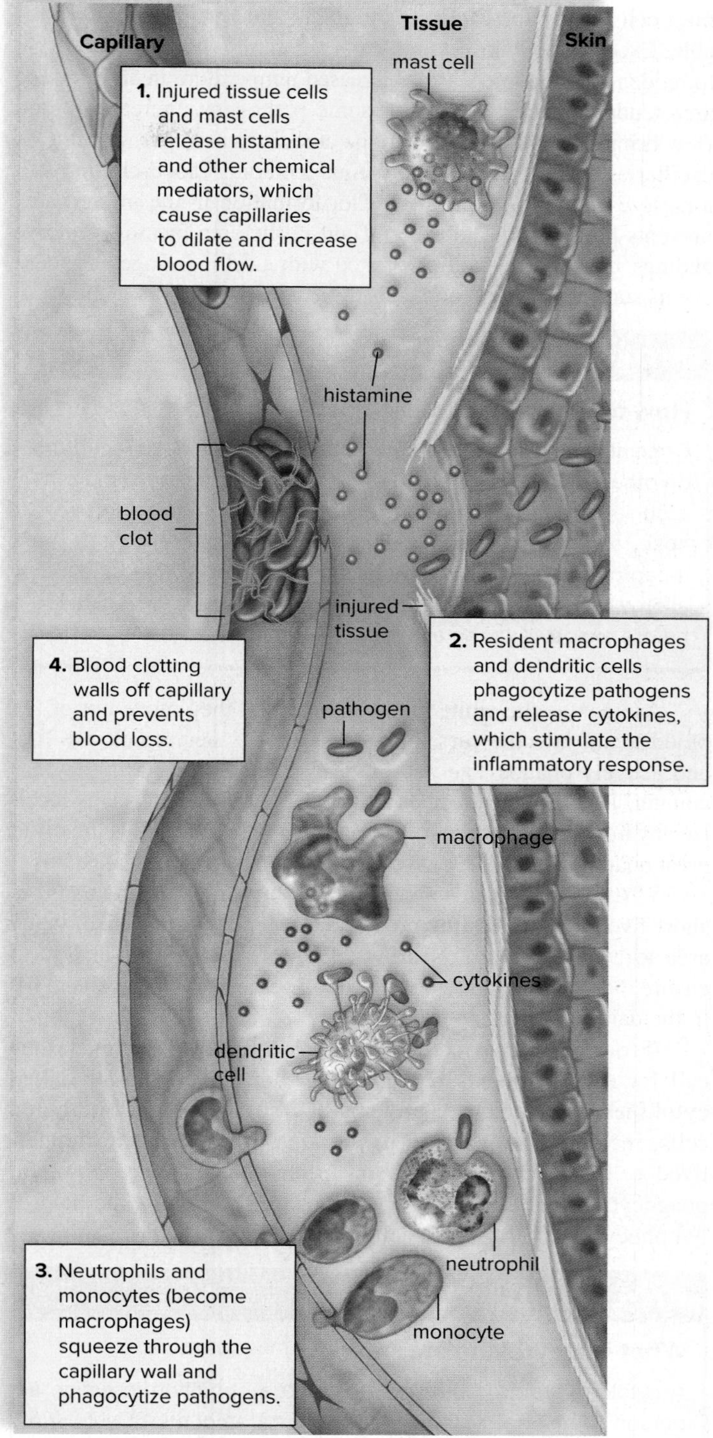

Figure 7.4 Steps of the inflammatory response. The stages of the inflammatory response are a defense mechanism against pathogens entering the tissues from damage or wounds.

The four signs of the inflammatory response are due to capillary changes in the damaged area, and all protect the body. Chemical mediators, such as **histamine,** released by damaged tissue cells and mast cells, cause the capillaries to dilate and become more permeable. Excess blood flow due to enlarged capillaries causes the skin to redden and become warm. Increased temperature in an inflamed area tends to inhibit growth of some pathogens. Increased blood flow brings white blood cells to the area. Increased permeability of capillaries allows fluids and proteins, including blood-clotting factors, to escape into the tissues. Clot formation in the injured area prevents blood loss. The excess fluid in the area presses on nerve endings, causing the pain associated with swelling. Together, these events summon white blood cells to the area.

BIOLOGY IN YOUR LIFE

How do antihistamines work?

Once histamine is released from mast cells, it binds to receptors on other body cells. There, the histamine causes the symptoms associated with infections and allergies: sneezing, itching, runny nose, and watery eyes. Antihistamines work by blocking the receptors on the cells so that histamine can no longer bind. For allergy relief, antihistamines are most effective when taken before exposure to the allergen.

As soon as the white blood cells arrive, they move out of the bloodstream into the surrounding tissue. The neutrophils are first and actively phagocytize debris, dead cells, and bacteria they encounter. The many neutrophils attracted to the area can usually localize any infection and keep it from spreading. If neutrophils die off in great quantities, they become a yellow-white substance called pus.

When an injury is not serious, the inflammatory response is short-lived and the healing process will quickly return the affected area to a normal state. Nearby cells secrete chemical factors to ensure the growth (and repair) of blood vessels and new cells to fill in the damaged area.

If, on the other hand, the neutrophils are overwhelmed, they call for reinforcements by secreting chemical mediators called **cytokines.** Cytokines are proteins that attract more white blood cells, including monocytes, to the area. Monocytes are longer-lived cells, which become **macrophages,** even more powerful phagocytes than neutrophils. Macrophages can enlist the help of lymphocytes to carry out specific defense mechanisms.

BIOLOGY IN YOUR LIFE

What is a cytokine storm?

A cytokine storm is used to describe a condition in which a person's immune system releases large amounts of cytokine signals (usually interleukins) in a short period of time. This causes a rapid escalation of the inflammation response. In the lungs, this results in an accumulation of fluids and mucus, and can contribute to respiratory distress.

Although the term is most often used to describe the severe symptoms associated with COVID-19, it can also occur in a number of other virus-related diseases, such as influenza, and some bacterial diseases.

Inflammation is the body's natural response to irritation or injury and serves an important role. Once the healing process has begun, inflammation rapidly subsides. However, in some cases, chronic inflammation lasts for weeks, months, or even years if the irritation or infection cannot be overcome. Inflammatory chemicals may cause collateral damage to the body, in addition to killing the invaders. Should an inflammation persist, anti-inflammatory medications, such as aspirin, ibuprofen, or cortisone can minimize the effects of various chemical mediators.

Protective Proteins

The **complement system,** often simply called complement, is composed of a number of blood plasma proteins designated by the letter *C* and a number. These proteins "complement" certain immune responses, which accounts for their name. For example, they are involved in and amplify the inflammatory response—certain complement proteins can bind to mast cells and trigger histamine release. Others can attract phagocytes to the scene. Some complement proteins bind to the surface of pathogens already coated with antibodies, which ensures that the pathogens will be phagocytized by a neutrophil or macrophage.

Certain other complement proteins join to form a membrane attack complex that produces holes in the surface of bacteria. Fluids then enter the bacterial cells to the point that they burst (Fig. 7.5).

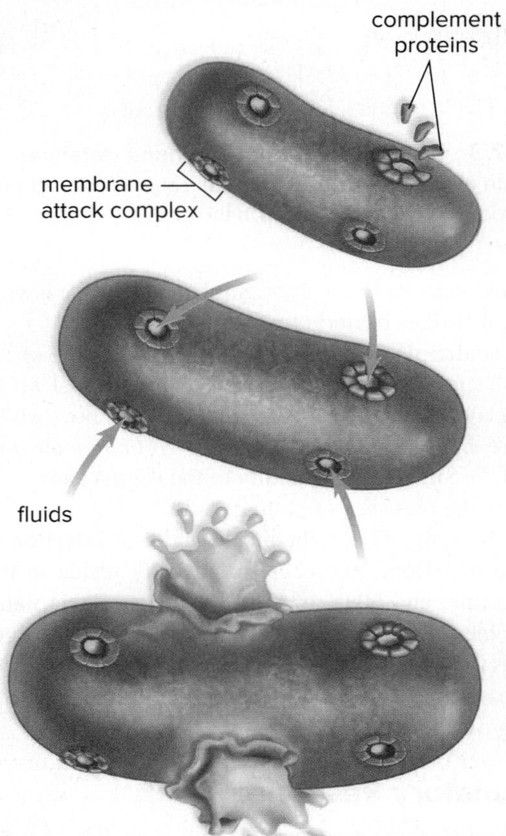

Figure 7.5 **Action of the complement system.**
When the immune response activates complement proteins in the blood plasma, they form a membrane attack complex that makes holes in bacterial cell walls and plasma membranes, allowing fluids to enter and causing the cell to burst.

Interferons are proteins produced by virus-infected cells as a warning to noninfected cells in the area. Interferons bind to receptors of noninfected cells, causing them to prepare for possible attack by producing substances that interfere with viral replication. Interferons are used to treat certain viral infections, such as hepatitis C.

CHECK YOUR PROGRESS 7.2

1. List some examples of the body's innate defenses.
2. Describe the blood cells associated with innate defenses, and detail how they function.
3. Discuss the role of complement proteins in immunity.

CONNECTING THE CONCEPTS

For more information on the topics presented in this section, refer to the following discussions:

Section 4.7 examines how the skin forms a physical barrier to the exterior environment.

Section 6.3 provides additional details on white blood cells.

Section 8.4 discusses the problems with the overuse of antibiotics.

7.3 Adaptive Immune Defenses

LEARNING OUTCOMES

Upon completion of this section, you should be able to

1. Explain the role of an antigen in the adaptive defenses.
2. Summarize the process of antibody-mediated immunity and list the cells involved in the process.
3. Summarize the process of cell-mediated immunity and list the cells involved in the process.

When innate (nonspecific) defenses have failed to prevent an infection, adaptive defenses come into play. Adaptive defenses overcome an infection by doing away with the particular disease-causing agent that has entered the body, and then establishing a mechanism for the immune system to "remember" the action in case the body is exposed to the same pathogen again. Adaptive defenses also provide some protection against cancer.

How Adaptive Defenses Work

Adaptive defenses respond to large molecules, normally protein structures called **antigens** that the immune system recognizes as foreign to the body. Fragments of bacteria, viruses, molds, and parasitic worms can all be antigenic. Further, abnormal plasma membrane proteins produced by cancer cells may also be antigens. We do not ordinarily develop an immune response to the cells of our body, so it is said that the immune system is able to distinguish self (our cells) from nonself (pathogens).

Adaptive defenses primarily depend on the action of lymphocytes, which differentiate as either B cells (B lymphocytes) or T cells (T lymphocytes). B cells and T cells are capable of recognizing antigens because they have specific antigen receptors. These antigen receptors are plasma membrane proteins whose shape allows them to combine with particular antigens. Each lymphocyte has only one type of receptor. It is often said that the receptor and the antigen fit together like a lock and key. We encounter millions of different antigens during our lifetime, so we need a diversity of B cells and T cells to protect us against them. Remarkably, this diversification occurs during the maturation process. Millions of specific B cells and/or T cells are formed, increasing the likelihood that at least one will recognize any possible antigen. Both B cells and T cells then have the ability to differentiate into a special form of lymphocyte that provides the immune system with a physiological memory.

There are two pathways that occur during adaptive immunity. In **cell-mediated immunity,** T cells target for destruction any cells presenting a specific antigen. In **antibody-mediated immunity** (also called humoral immunity), B cells produce antibodies that target free antigens in the fluids of the body. The stages and interaction of these two pathways are shown in Figure 7.6.

B Cells and Antibody-Mediated Immunity

The protein receptor on a B cell is called a *B-cell receptor (BCR).* The clonal selection model (Fig. 7.7) states that an antigen selects, then binds to, the BCR of only one type of B cell. Then, this B cell produces multiple copies of itself. The resulting group of identical cells is called a clone. As we will see, an antigen can bind to a T-cell receptor (TCR), and this T cell will clone.

Characteristics of B Cells

- Responsible for antibody-mediated immunity against pathogens.
- Produced and mature in bone marrow.
- Directly recognize antigen and then undergo clonal selection.
- Clonal expansion produces antibody-secreting plasma cells, as well as memory B cells.

B Cells Become Plasma Cells and Memory B Cells Note in Figure 7.7 that each B cell has a specific BCR represented by shape. Only the B cell with a BCR that has a shape that fits the antigen (green circle) undergoes clonal expansion. During clonal expansion, cytokines secreted by helper T (T_H) cells (discussed later in this section) stimulate B cells to clone. Most of the cloned B cells become **plasma cells,** which circulate in the blood and lymph. Plasma cells are larger than regular B cells because they have extensive rough endoplasmic reticulum. This is for the mass production and secretion of antibodies to a specific antigen. Antibodies identical to the BCR of the activated B cell are secreted from the plasma B cell. Some cloned B cells become **memory B cells,** from which long-term immunity is possible. If the same antigen enters the system again, memory B cells quickly divide and transform into plasma cells. The correct type of antibody can be produced quickly by these plasma cells.

Once the threat of an infection has passed, the development of new plasma cells ceases, and those present undergo apoptosis. **Apoptosis** is the process of programmed cell death. It involves a cascade of specific cellular events leading to the death and

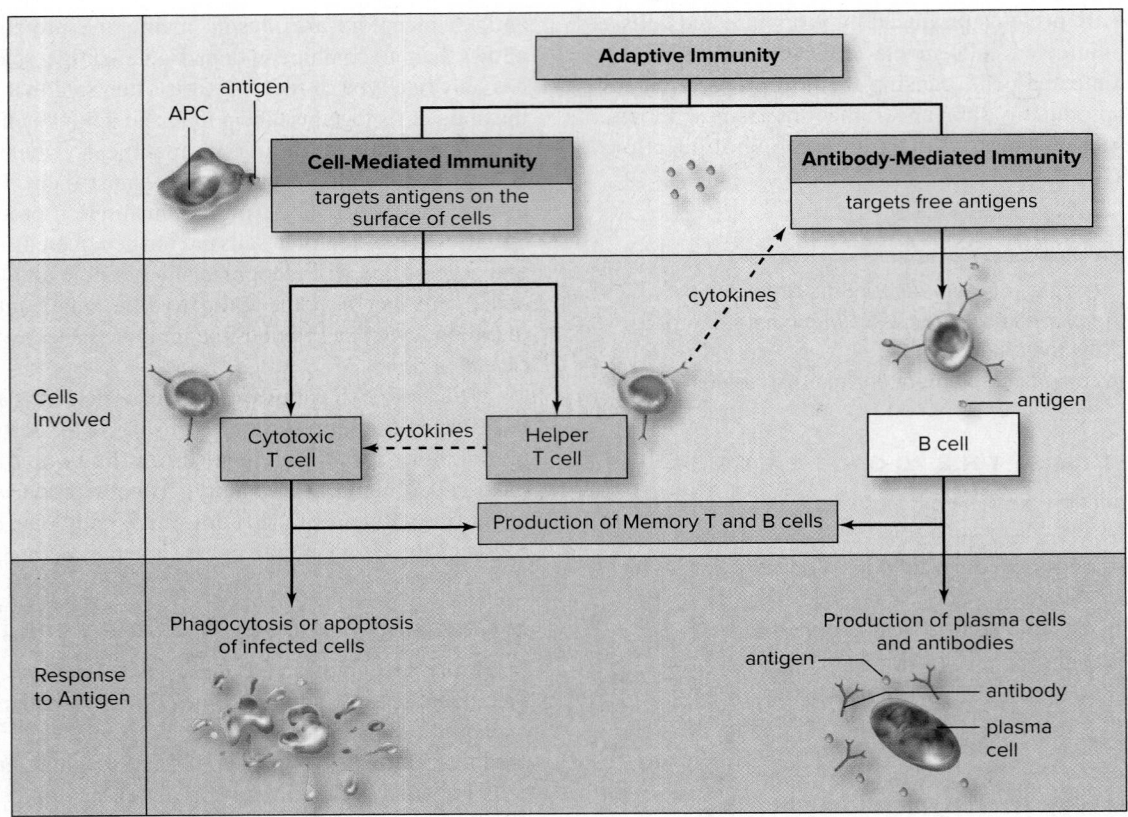

Figure 7.6 **Overview of adaptive immune defenses.**
The adaptive responses involve two branches. The cell-mediated immunity branch targets cells presenting a specific antigen. The antibody-mediated immunity branch produces antibodies located outside of the cells, such as the interstitial fluid.

destruction of the cell and removal of the cell remnants from the body as a waste product.

Defense by B cells is called humoral immunity, or antibody-mediated immunity, because activated B cells become plasma cells that produce antibodies. Collectively, plasma cells probably produce as many as 2 million different antibodies. Humans only have about 19,000 genes, so there cannot be a separate gene for each type of antibody. It has been found that scattered DNA segments can be shuffled and combined in various ways to produce the DNA sequence coding for the BCR unique to each type of B cell.

Structure of an Antibody The basic unit that composes antibody molecules is a Y-shaped protein molecule with two arms. Each arm has a "heavy" (long) polypeptide chain and a "light" (short) polypeptide chain (Fig. 7.8). These chains have constant regions, located at the trunk of the Y, where the sequence of amino acids is fixed. The class of antibody of each molecule is determined by the structure of the antibody's constant region. The variable regions form an antigen-binding site. Their shape is specific to a particular antigen. The antigen combines with the antibody at the antigen-binding site in a lock-and-key manner. Antibodies may consist of single Y-shaped molecules, called *monomers,* or may be paired together in a molecule termed a *dimer.* Some very large antibodies are *pentamers*—clusters of five Y-shaped molecules linked together.

Antigens can be part of a pathogen, such as a virus or a toxin produced by bacteria. Antibodies sometimes react with viruses and toxins by coating them completely, thus neutralizing their ability to cause a disease, a process called *neutralization.* Often, the reaction produces a clump of antigens combined with antibodies, termed an *immune complex.* The antibodies in an immune complex are like a beacon that attracts white blood cells.

Classes of Antibodies There are five classes of antibodies, listed in Table 7.1. IgG antibodies are the major type in blood, and smaller amounts are found in lymph and interstitial fluid. IgG antibodies bind to pathogens and their toxins. IgG antibodies can cross the placenta from a mother to her fetus, so the newborn has temporary, partial immune protection. IgM antibodies are pentamers; they are the first antibodies produced by a newborn's body. IgM antibodies are the first to appear in blood after an infection begins and the first to disappear before the infection is over. They are good activators of the complement system. IgA antibodies are monomers or dimers containing two Y-shaped structures. They are the main type of antibody found in body secretions: saliva, tears, mucus, and breast milk. IgA molecules bind to pathogens and prevent them from reaching the bloodstream. The main function of IgD

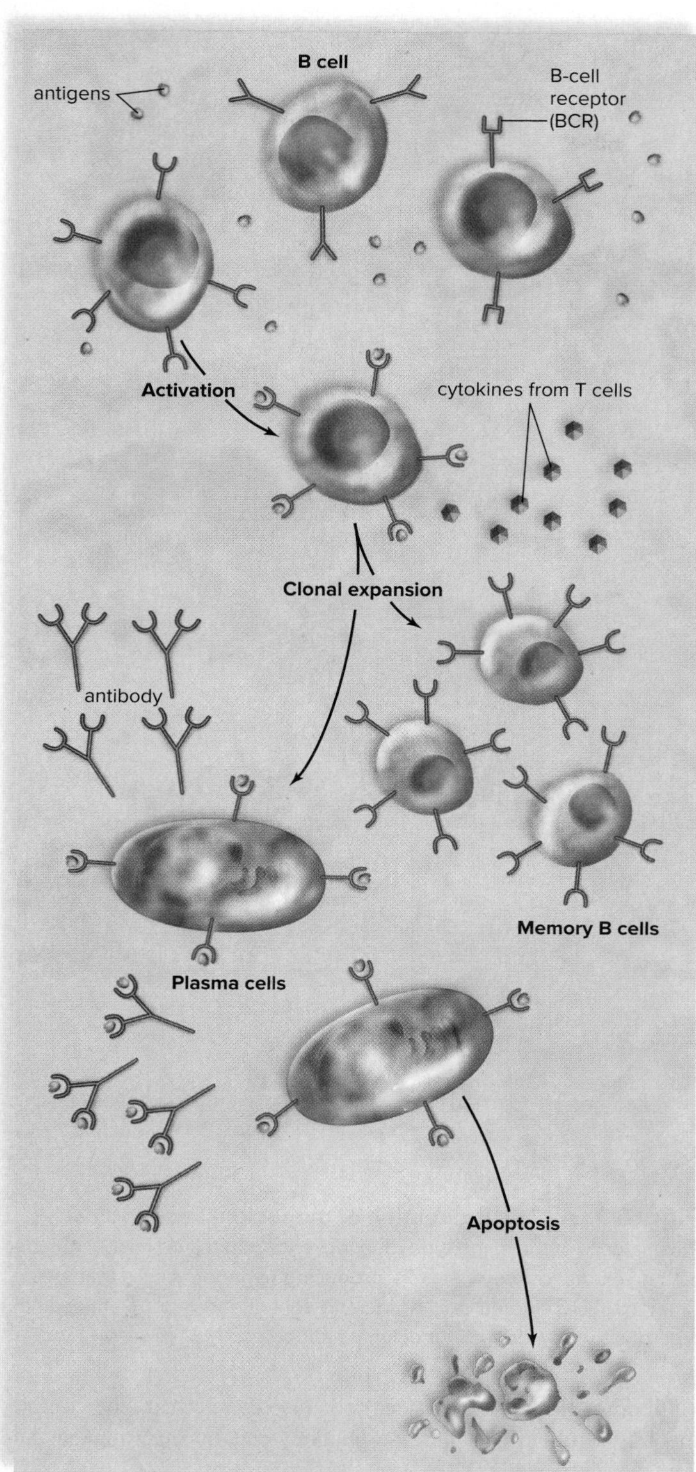

Figure 7.7 B-cell clonal selection.
Each B cell has a B-cell receptor (BCR) designated by shape that will combine with a specific antigen. Activation of a B cell occurs when its BCR combines with an antigen (colored green). In the presence of cytokines, the B cell undergoes clonal expansion, producing many plasma cells and memory B cells. These plasma cells secrete antibodies specific to the antigen, and memory B cells immediately recognize the antigen in the future. After the infection passes, plasma cells undergo apoptosis, also called programmed cell death.

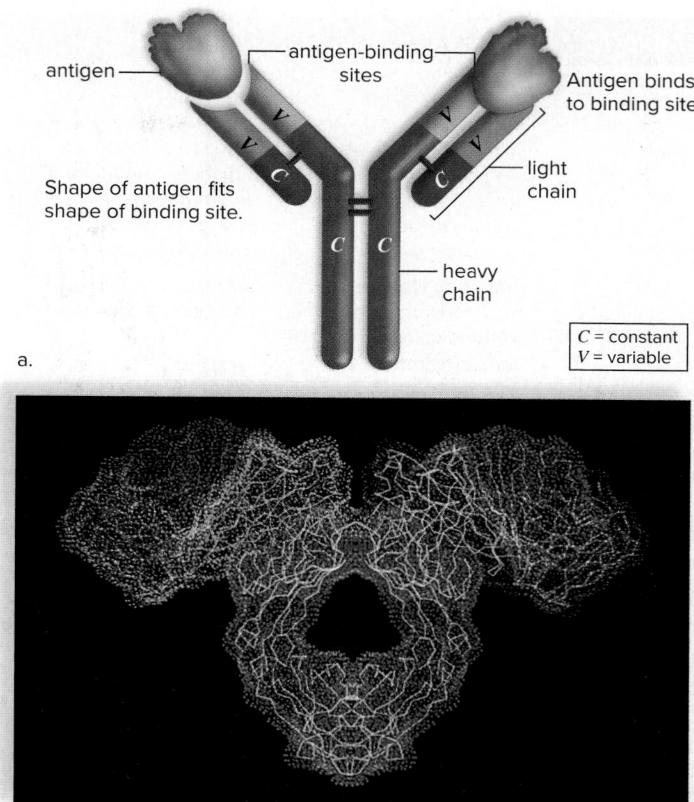

Figure 7.8 The structure of an antibody.
a. An antibody contains two heavy (long) polypeptide chains and two light (short) chains arranged so there are two variable regions where a particular antigen is capable of binding with an antibody. **b.** Computer model of an antibody molecule. The antigen combines with the two side branches.
(b): Dr. Arthur J. Olson

molecules seems to be to serve as antigen receptors on immature B cells. IgE antibodies are responsible for prevention of parasitic worm infections, but they can also cause immediate allergic responses.

Monoclonal Antibodies Every plasma cell derived from the same B cell secretes antibodies against a specific antigen. These are **monoclonal antibodies,** because all of them are the same type and because they are produced by plasma cells derived from the same B cell. One method of producing monoclonal antibodies in vitro (outside the body) is depicted in Figure 7.9. B lymphocytes are removed from an animal, normally a lab mouse, and are exposed to a particular antigen. The resulting plasma cells are fused with myeloma cells (malignant plasma cells that live and divide indefinitely; they are immortal cells). The fused cells are called hybridomas—*hybrid-* because they result from the fusion of two different cells, and *-oma* because one of the cells is a cancer cell.

Monoclonal antibodies may be used for quick and certain diagnosis of various conditions. For example, the hormone human chorionic gonadotropin (HCG) is present in the urine of a pregnant

Table 7.1 Classes of Antibodies

Class	Presence	Function
IgG	Main antibody type in circulation; crosses the placenta from mother to fetus	Binds to pathogens, activates complement, and enhances phagocytosis by white blood cells
IgM	Antibody type found in circulation; largest antibody; first antibody formed by a newborn; first antibody formed with any new infection	Activates complement and clumps cells
IgA	Main antibody type in secretions such as saliva and breast milk	Prevents pathogens from attaching to epithelial cells in digestive and respiratory tracts
IgD	Antibody type found on surface of immature B cells	Signifies readiness of B cell
IgE	Antibody type found as antigen receptors on mast cells in tissues	Responsible for immediate allergic response and protection against certain parasitic worms

woman. A monoclonal antibody can be used to detect this hormone. Monoclonal antibodies are also used to identify infections such as H1N1 flu, HIV, and RSV, a respiratory virus infection common in young children.

BIOLOGY IN YOUR LIFE

Can monoclonal antibodies be used to treat COVID-19?

When the consequences of COVID-19 first became evident in 2020, there were few methods of preventing individuals in high-risk groups from developing severe respiratory illnesses. However, the use of monoclonal antibodies, originally developed against the SARS virus, proved to be successful in reducing the SARS-CoV-2 viral load of some patients and helped keep patients who were high risk from hospitalization.

It is important to note that monoclonal antibody treatments are not the same as vaccinations; they are designed to give the body time to fight the virus while the adaptive immune defenses prepare the body's own antibodies.

Because they can be used to distinguish between cancerous and normal tissue cells, they are also used to carry radioisotopes or toxic drugs to tumors, which can then be selectively destroyed. Trastuzumab (Herceptin) is a monoclonal antibody used in the treatment of breast cancer. It binds to a protein receptor on breast cancer cells and prevents the cancer cells from dividing as quickly.

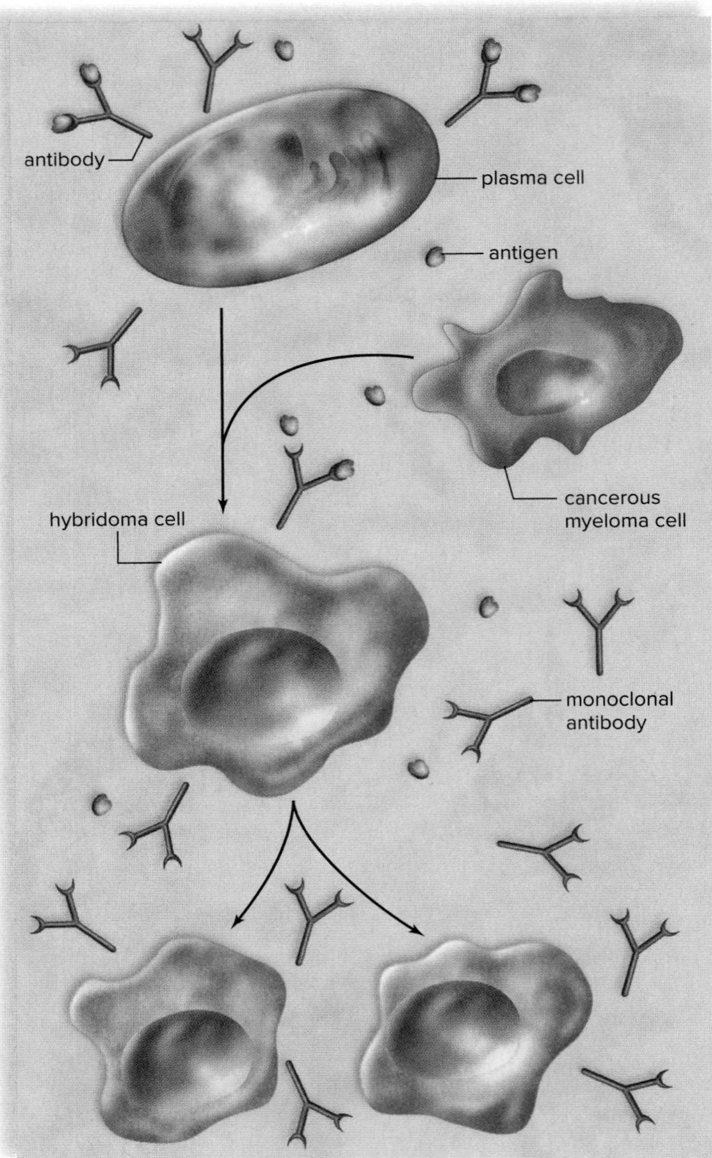

Figure 7.9 The production of monoclonal antibodies. Plasma cells of the same type (derived from immunized mice) are fused with myeloma (cancerous) cells, producing hybridoma cells that are "immortal." Hybridoma cells divide and continue to produce the same type of antibody, called monoclonal antibodies.

Antibodies that bind to cancer cells also can activate the complement system and can increase phagocytosis by macrophages and neutrophils.

T Cells and Cell-Mediated Immunity

Cell-mediated immunity is named for the action of T cells that directly attack diseased cells and cancer cells. Other T cells, however, release cytokines that stimulate both nonspecific and specific defenses.

How T Cells Recognize an Antigen When a T cell leaves the thymus, it has a unique **T-cell receptor (TCR),** just as B cells have. Unlike B cells, however, T cells are unable to recognize an antigen without help. The antigen must be displayed to them by an **antigen-presenting cell (APC),** such as a macrophage. After phagocytizing a pathogen, such as a bacterium, APCs travel to a lymph node or the spleen, where T cells also congregate. In the meantime, the APC has broken the pathogen apart in a lysosome. A piece of the pathogen is then displayed in the groove of a **major histocompatibility complex (MHC)** protein on the cell's surface. The two classes of MHC proteins are called MHC I and MHC II.

Human MHC II proteins are called **human leukocyte antigens (HLAs).** These proteins are found on all of our body cells. There are three general groups of HLAs (HLA-A, HLA-B, and HLA-DR), each with a number of protein variations. Each person has a unique combination of HLAs. One exception is the HLAs of identical twins. Because identical twins arise from division of a single zygote, their HLA proteins are identical. MHC antigens are "self" proteins because they mark the cell as belonging to a particular individual. The importance of self proteins in plasma membranes was first recognized when it was discovered that they contribute to the specificity of tissues and make it difficult to transplant tissue from one human to another. Comparison studies of the three classes of HLAs must always be carried out before a transplant is attempted. The greater the number of these proteins that match, the more likely the transplant will be successful.

When an antigen-presenting cell links a foreign antigen to the self protein on its plasma membrane, it carries out an important safeguard for the rest of the body. The T cell to be activated can compare the antigen and self protein side by side. The activated T cell, and all the daughter cells it will form, can recognize foreign from self. These T cells go on to destroy cells carrying foreign antigens, while leaving normal body cells unharmed.

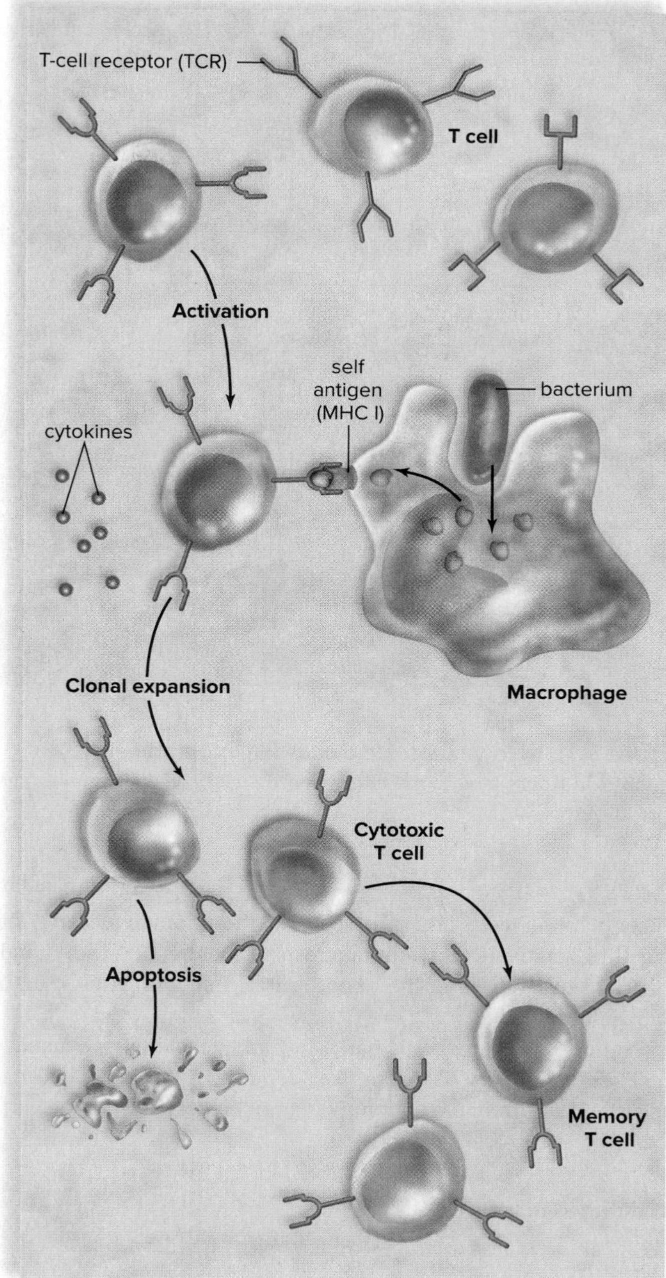

Figure 7.10 **The clonal selection model for T cells.** Activation of a T cell occurs when its T-cell receptor (TCR) can combine with an antigen presented by a macrophage. In this example, cytotoxic T cells are produced. When the immune response is finished, they undergo apoptosis. A small number of memory T cells remain.

Clonal Expansion In Figure 7.10, the T cells have specific TCRs, represented by their different shapes. A macrophage is presenting an antigen to a T cell that has the specific TCR that will combine with this particular antigen, represented by a green circle. The T cell is activated and undergoes clonal expansion. Many copies of the activated T cell are produced during clonal expansion. These activated cells become cytotoxic T cells and helper T cells, whose functions in the immune response we will explore next.

As the illness disappears, the immune reaction wanes. Activated T cells become susceptible to apoptosis. As mentioned previously, apoptosis contributes to homeostasis by regulating the number of cells present in an organ, or in this case, in the immune system. When apoptosis does not occur as it should, the potential exists for an autoimmune response (see Section 7.5) or for T-cell cancers (lymphomas and leukemias).

Cytotoxic T cells have storage vacuoles containing perforins and storage vacuoles containing enzymes called granzymes. After a cytotoxic T cell binds to a virus-infected cell or tumor cell, it releases perforin molecules, which punch holes in the plasma membrane, forming a pore. Cytotoxic T cells then deliver granzymes into the pore. These cause the cell to undergo apoptosis. Once cytotoxic T cells have released the perforins and granzymes, they move on to the next target cell. Cytotoxic T cells are responsible for cell-mediated immunity (Fig. 7.11).

Helper T cells regulate immunity by secreting cytokines, the chemicals that enhance the response of all types of immune cells. B cells cannot be activated without T-cell help (see Fig. 7.7). The human immunodeficiency virus (HIV), which causes AIDS,

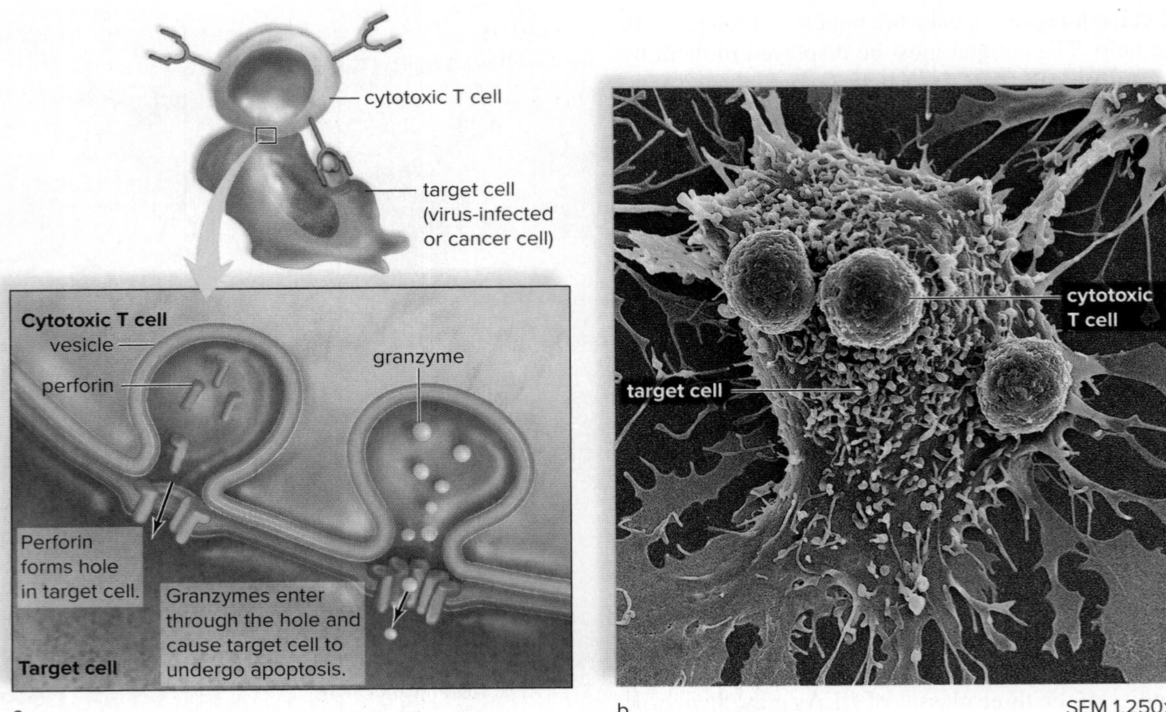

Figure 7.11 How cytotoxic T cells kill infected cells.
a. Cytotoxic T cells bind to the target cell, punch holes in its membrane, and inject chemicals that cause the cell to die. **b.** A micrograph of a cytotoxic T cell in action.
(b): Steve Gschmeissner/Science Source

infects helper T cells and other cells of the immune system. The virus thus inactivates the immune response and makes individuals with HIV susceptible to the opportunistic infections that eventually result in death.

Notice in Figure 7.10 that a few of the clonally expanded T cells are **memory T cells.** They remain in the body and can jump-start an immune reaction to an antigen previously present in the body.

Characteristics of T Cells

- Cell-mediated immunity against virus-infected cells and cancer cells.
- Produced in bone marrow, mature in thymus.
- Cytotoxic T cells destroy nonself antigen-bearing cells.
- Helper T cells secrete cytokines that control the immune response.

CHECK YOUR PROGRESS 7.3

1. Detail how innate defense differs from adaptive defense.
2. Distinguish between the cells involved in targeting an antigen present within a cell of the body versus an antigen free in the interstitial fluid.
3. Explain how memory lymphocytes are formed and state their function.

CONNECTING THE CONCEPTS

For more information on the topics presented in this section, refer to the following discussions:

Section 6.3 summarizes the formation and specialization of lymphocytes.

Section 8.2 provides additional information on HIV and the AIDS epidemic.

Section 20.4 examines how immunotherapy using cytotoxic T cells can be used to treat cancer.

7.4 Acquired Immunity

LEARNING OUTCOMES

Upon completion of this section, you should be able to

1. Distinguish between active and passive immunity.
2. Recognize the importance of cytokines in immunity.

Immunity occurs naturally through infection or is brought about artificially by medical intervention. The two types of acquired immunity are active and passive. In the process of **active immunity,** the individual alone produces antibodies against an antigen. In **passive immunity,** the individual is given prepared antibodies via an injection.

Active Immunity

Active immunity sometimes develops naturally after a person is infected with a pathogen. However, active immunity is often induced when a person is well to prevent future infection. Artificial exposure to an antigen through immunization can prevent future disease.

Immunization involves the use of **vaccines,** substances that contain an antigen to which the immune system responds. Traditionally, vaccines are the pathogens themselves, or their products, that have been treated to be no longer virulent (no longer able to cause disease). Today, it is possible to genetically engineer bacteria to mass-produce a protein from pathogens, and this protein can be used as a vaccine. This method is used to produce the vaccine for the viral-induced disease hepatitis B, and a vaccine for malaria made by the same method is currently going through FDA approval procedures.

The United States is committed to immunizing all children against common types of childhood disease. A full list of recommended childhood vaccinations is available from the Centers for Disease Control and Prevention (CDC) website at www.cdc.gov/vaccines. Information on recommended adult vaccinations is provided in the Health feature "Adult Vaccinations."

After a vaccine is given, it is possible to follow an immune response by determining the amount of antibody present in a sample of plasma—this is called the *antibody titer.* After the first exposure to a vaccine, a primary response occurs. For the first several days no antibodies are present. Then, the titer rises slowly, levels off, and gradually declines as the antibodies bind to the antigen or simply break down (Fig. 7.12). After a second exposure to the vaccine, a secondary response is expected. The titer rises rapidly to a level much greater than before. It then slowly declines. The second exposure is called a "booster," because it boosts the antibody titer to a high level. The secondary response also responds much faster than the primary response, as you can see by the slope of the response line in Figure 7.12. The high antibody titer now is expected to help prevent disease symptoms, even if the individual is exposed to the disease-causing antigen.

Active immunity depends on the presence of memory B cells and memory T cells capable of responding to lower doses of antigen. Active immunity is usually long-lasting, although for certain vaccines a booster may be required after many years.

Passive Immunity

Passive immunity occurs when an individual is given prepared antibodies or immune cells to combat a disease. These antibodies are not produced by the individual's plasma cells, so passive immunity is temporary. For example, newborn infants are passively immune to some diseases because IgG antibodies have crossed the placenta from the mother's blood (Fig. 7.13*a*). These antibodies soon disappear, and within a few months infants become more susceptible to infections. Breast-feeding prolongs the natural passive immunity an infant receives from the mother, because IgG and IgA antibodies are present in the mother's milk (Fig. 7.13*b*).

Even though passive immunity does not last, it is sometimes used to prevent illness in a patient who has been unexpectedly exposed to an infectious disease. Usually, the patient receives a gamma globulin injection of serum that contains antibodies, in

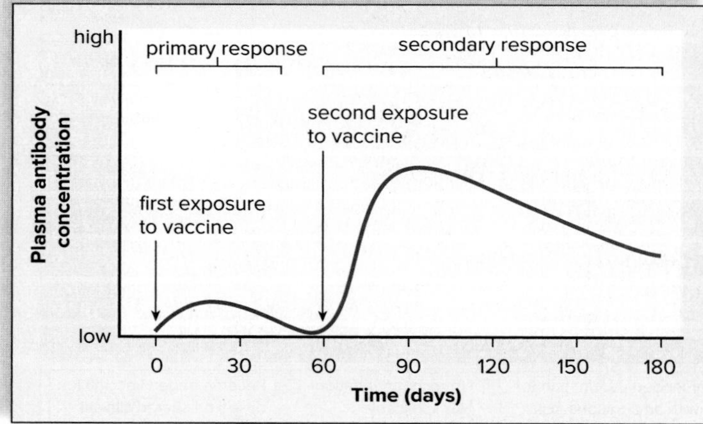

Figure 7.12 How immunizations cause active immunity. During immunization, the primary response, after the first exposure to a vaccine, is minimal, but the secondary response, which may occur after the second exposure, shows a dramatic rise in the amount of antibody present in plasma.

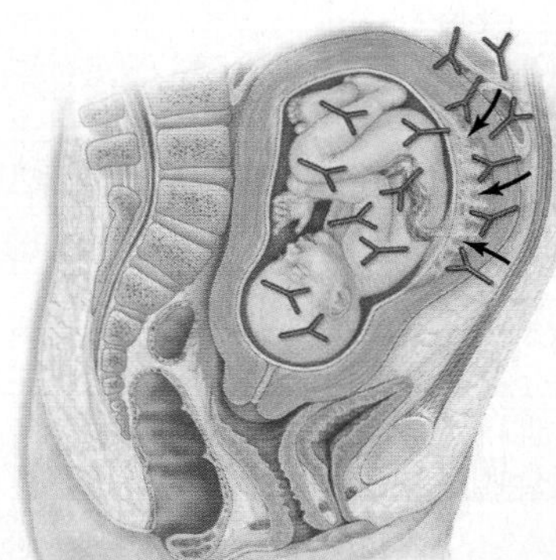

a. Antibodies (IgG) cross the placenta.

b. Antibodies (IgG, IgA) are secreted into breast milk.

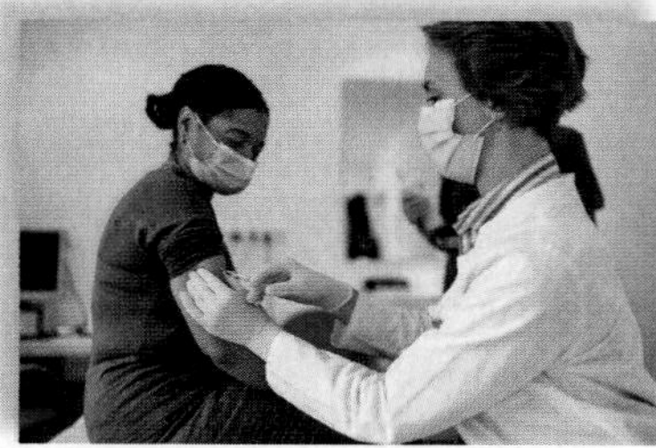

c. Antibodies can be injected by a physician.

Figure 7.13 Delivery mechanisms of passive immunity. During passive immunity, antibodies are received **(a)** by crossing the placenta, **(b)** in breast milk, or **(c)** by injection. The body is not producing the antibodies, so passive immunity is short-lived.

(b): JGI/Blend Images; (c): Luis Alvarez/DigitalVision/Getty Images

BIOLOGY TODAY ▶ Health

Adult Vaccinations

Many people mistakenly believe that individuals receive their full complement of vaccinations by the time they leave high school. In reality, being vaccinated is a lifelong activity. The Centers for Disease Control and Prevention (CDC) has identified a series of vaccinations that are recommended after the age of 18 (Table 7A). In many cases, vaccinations are recommended when an individual is determined to be at risk for a specific disease or condition. For example, while the vaccination for hepatitis B (HepB) may not be required, it is recommended for individuals who have had more than one sexual partner during a 6-month period, have been diagnosed with a sexually transmitted disease (STD; see Section 17.6), use injection drugs, or may have been exposed to blood or infected body fluid. In most cases, vaccinations are recommended as a protective measure even if you are not in an at-risk category.

As always, if you have questions regarding any of these diseases, or about your personal need for vaccinations, consult with your health-care provider. For more information on vaccination schedules from birth through adulthood, visit the CDC's website at www.cdc.gov/vaccines or the Immunization Action Coalition (www.immunize.org).

Questions to Consider

1. Why would some vaccines require multiple doses over an adult's lifetime?
2. Why would people over the age of 60 or 65 require different vaccinations?

Table 7A **Recommended Vaccination Schedule for Adults**

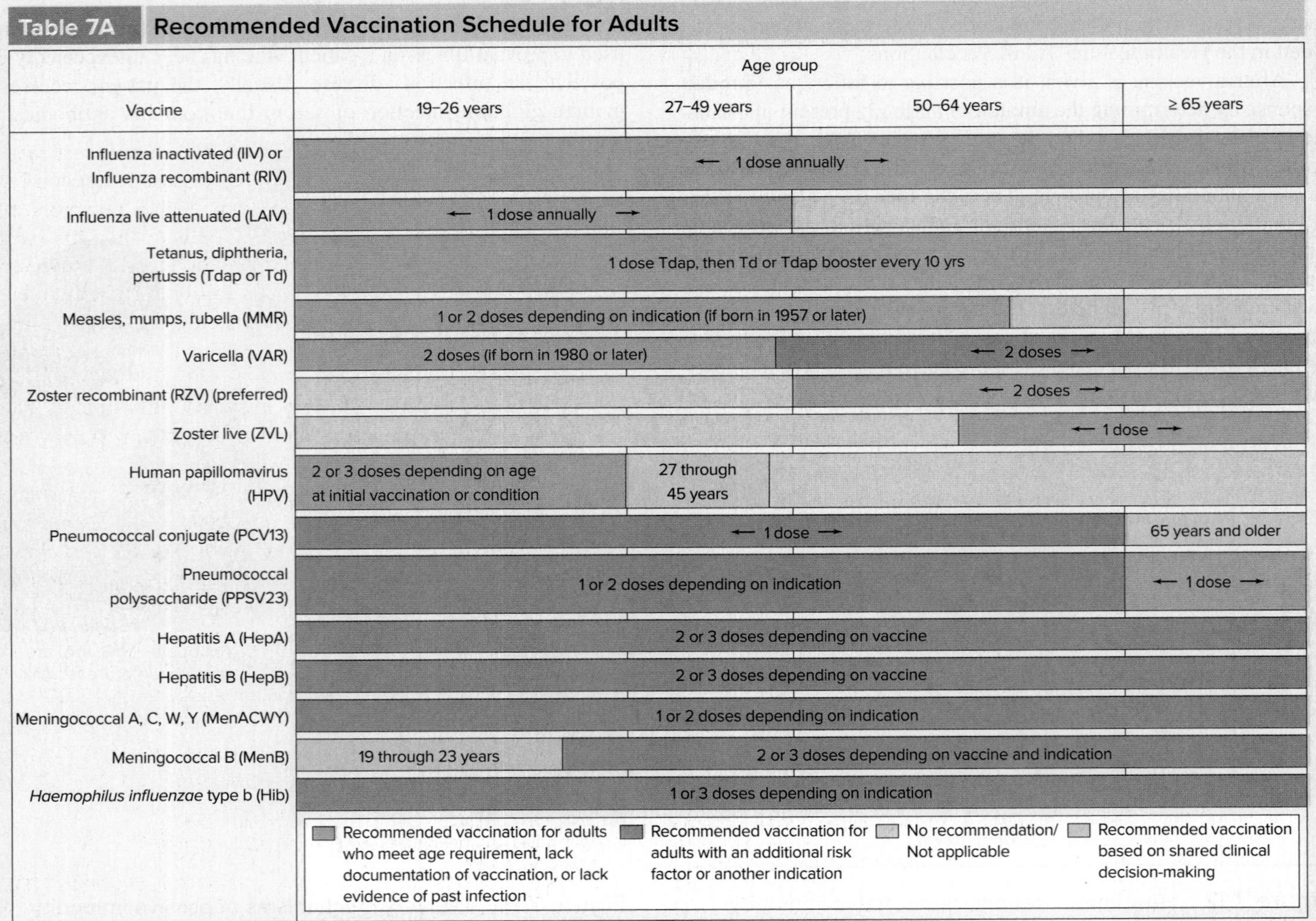

Vaccine	Age group			
	19–26 years	27–49 years	50–64 years	≥ 65 years
Influenza inactivated (IIV) or Influenza recombinant (RIV)	← 1 dose annually →			
Influenza live attenuated (LAIV)	← 1 dose annually →			
Tetanus, diphtheria, pertussis (Tdap or Td)	1 dose Tdap, then Td or Tdap booster every 10 yrs			
Measles, mumps, rubella (MMR)	1 or 2 doses depending on indication (if born in 1957 or later)			
Varicella (VAR)	2 doses (if born in 1980 or later)		← 2 doses →	
Zoster recombinant (RZV) (preferred)			← 2 doses →	
Zoster live (ZVL)			← 1 dose →	
Human papillomavirus (HPV)	2 or 3 doses depending on age at initial vaccination or condition	27 through 45 years		
Pneumococcal conjugate (PCV13)	← 1 dose →			65 years and older
Pneumococcal polysaccharide (PPSV23)	1 or 2 doses depending on indication			← 1 dose →
Hepatitis A (HepA)	2 or 3 doses depending on vaccine			
Hepatitis B (HepB)	2 or 3 doses depending on vaccine			
Meningococcal A, C, W, Y (MenACWY)	1 or 2 doses depending on indication			
Meningococcal B (MenB)	19 through 23 years	2 or 3 doses depending on vaccine and indication		
Haemophilus influenzae type b (Hib)	1 or 3 doses depending on indication			

Legend: Recommended vaccination for adults who meet age requirement, lack documentation of vaccination, or lack evidence of past infection; Recommended vaccination for adults with an additional risk factor or another indication; No recommendation/ Not applicable; Recommended vaccination based on shared clinical decision-making

* In medicine, an *indication* is a reason for conducting a test, procedure, or in this case, a vaccination.

some cases taken from individuals who have recovered from the illness (Fig. 7.13*c*). For example, a health-care worker who suffers an accidental needlestick may come into contact with the blood from a patient infected with hepatitis virus. Immediate treatment with a gamma globulin injection (along with simultaneous vaccination against the virus) typically can prevent the virus from causing infection.

Cytokines and Immunity

Cytokines are signaling molecules produced by T lymphocytes, macrophages, and other cells. Cytokines regulate white blood cell formation and/or function, so they are being investigated as a possible adjunct therapy (treatments used in conjunction with the primary treatment) for cancer and AIDS. Both interferon, produced by virus-infected cells, and **interleukins,** produced by various white blood cells, are cytokines that have been used as immunotherapeutic drugs. These are used particularly to enhance the ability of the individual's T cells to fight cancer.

Most cancer cells carry an altered protein on their cell surface, so they should be attacked and destroyed by cytotoxic T cells. Whenever cancer develops, it is possible that cytotoxic T cells have not been activated. In that case, cytokines might awaken the immune system and lead to the destruction of the cancer. In one technique, researchers withdrew T cells from the patient and presented cancer cell antigens to the isolated T cells. The cells were then activated by culturing them in the presence of an interleukin. The T cells were reinjected into the patient, who was given doses of interleukin to maintain the killer activity of the T cells.

Scientists actively engaged in interleukin research believe that interleukins soon will be used as adjuncts for vaccines. They are currently used as treatment adjuncts for chronic diseases such as psoriasis, rheumatoid arthritis, and irritable bowel syndrome and are sometimes used to treat chronic infectious diseases and to treat cancer. Interleukin antagonists also may prove helpful in preventing skin and organ rejection, autoimmune diseases such as lupus and Crohn's disease, and allergies.

CHECK YOUR PROGRESS 7.4

1. Define *acquired immunity* and give some examples.
2. Describe how passive immunity is developed.
3. Compare the two types of immune therapies that can assist passive immunity.

CONNECTING THE CONCEPT

For more information on the topics presented in this section, refer to the following discussion:

Section 20.4 examines how cytokines may be used to treat cancer.

7.5 Disorders of the Immune System

LEARNING OUTCOMES

Upon completion of this section, you should be able to

1. Explain the relationship between AIDS and opportunistic infections.
2. Summarize how the HIV virus is transmitted and the methods by which AIDS is treated.
3. Explain what causes an allergic reaction.
4. Identify the effects of autoimmune diseases on the body.

HIV and AIDS

Acquired immunodeficiency syndrome (AIDS) is caused by a virus known as the **human immunodeficiency virus (HIV).** There are two main types of HIV: HIV-1 and HIV-2. HIV-1 is the more widespread, virulent form of HIV. Of the two types of HIV, HIV-2 corresponds to a type of immunodeficiency virus found in the green monkey, which lives in western Africa. In addition, researchers have found a virus identical to HIV-1 in a subgroup of chimpanzees once common in west-central Africa. This suggests that HIV viruses were perhaps originally found only in nonhuman primates. The viruses could then have mutated to HIV after humans ate nonhuman primates for meat. With this in mind, we will take a closer look at the HIV life cycle, the structure of the HIV virus, and the global implications of this disease in Section 8.2.

HIV can infect cells with particular surface receptors. Most importantly, HIV infects and destroys cells of the immune system, particularly helper T cells and macrophages. As the number of helper T cells declines, the body's ability to fight an infection also declines (see Section 7.3). As a result, the person becomes ill with various diseases. AIDS is the advanced stage of HIV infection, in which a person develops one or more of a number of opportunistic infections. An **opportunistic infection** is one that has the *opportunity* to occur only because the immune system is severely weakened.

HIV occurs as several subtypes. HIV-1C is prominent in Africa, and HIV-1B causes most infections in the United States. The following description of the phases of HIV infection pertains to an HIV-1B infection. The helper T cells and macrophages infected by HIV are the *CD4 cells,* because they display a protein called CD4 on their surface. With the destruction of CD4 cells, the immune system is significantly impaired. This allows opportunistic infections, or those that otherwise would not normally cause harm to the body, to develop in the individual. The Health feature "Opportunistic Infections and HIV" explores this in more detail. The stages of an HIV infection are presented in Figure 7.14.

Transmission and Prevention of HIV

HIV is transmitted by sexual contact with a person with HIV, including vaginal or rectal intercourse and oral-genital contact. It can also be transmitted through needle sharing among people who use intravenous drugs. A less common mode of transmission (and

BIOLOGY TODAY ▶ Health

Opportunistic Infections and HIV

AIDS (acquired immunodeficiency syndrome) is caused by the destruction of the immune system, especially the helper T cells, following an HIV (human immunodeficiency virus) infection. Then, the individual succumbs to many unusual types of infections that would not cause disease in a person with a healthy immune system. Such infections are known as opportunistic infections (OIs).

HIV not only kills helper T cells by directly infecting them, it also causes many uninfected T cells to die by a variety of mechanisms, including apoptosis. In addition, many helper T cells are killed by the person's own immune system as it tries to overcome the HIV infection. After initial infection with HIV, it may take up to 10 years for an individual's helper T cells to become so depleted that the immune system can no longer organize a specific response to OIs. In a healthy individual, the number of helper T cells typically ranges from 800 to 1,000 cells per cubic millimeter (mm^3) of blood. The appearance of the following specific OIs can be associated with the helper T-cell count:

- Shingles—Painful infection with varicella-zoster (chicken pox) virus. Helper T-cell count of less than 500/mm^3.
- Candidiasis—Yeast infection of the mouth, throat, or vagina. Helper T-cell count of about 350/mm^3.
- *Pneumocystis* pneumonia—Fungal infection causing the lungs to fill with fluid and debris. Helper T-cell count of less than 200/mm^3.
- Kaposi sarcoma—Cancer of blood vessels due to human herpesvirus 8; gives rise to reddish-purple, coin-sized spots and lesions on the skin. Helper T-cell count of less than 200/mm^3.
- Toxoplasmic encephalitis—Protozoan infection characterized by severe headaches, fever, seizures, and coma. Helper T-cell count of less than 100/mm^3.
- *Mycobacterium avium* complex (MAC)—Bacterial infection resulting in persistent fever, night sweats, fatigue, weight loss, and anemia. Helper T-cell count of less than 75/mm^3.
- Cytomegalovirus—Viral infection that leads to blindness, inflammation of the brain, throat ulcerations. Helper T-cell count of less than 50/mm^3.

Due to the development of powerful drug therapies that slow the progression of AIDS, people infected with HIV in the United States are suffering a lower incidence of OIs than was common in the 1980s and 1990s.

Questions to Consider

1. People who don't have HIV also sometimes get OIs, such as shingles or candidiasis. How would you expect the outcome of, for example, a yeast infection to be different in a healthy person compared to a person infected with HIV?
2. Kaposi sarcoma occurs relatively rarely in people who are infected with human herpesvirus 8, but are HIV-negative. How might an HIV infection increase the odds of getting Kaposi sarcoma?

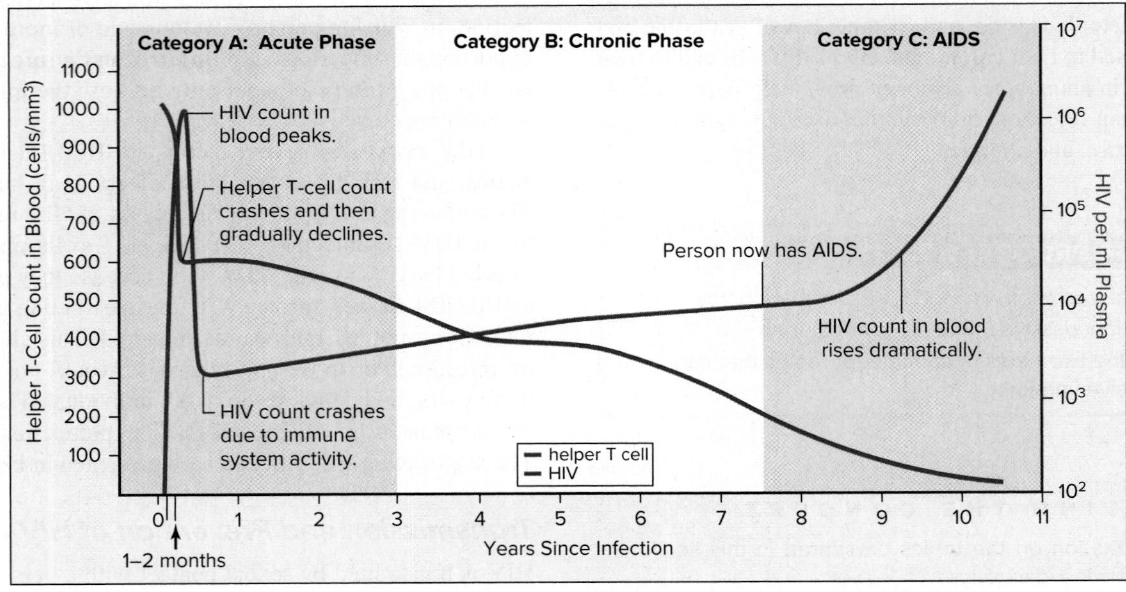

Figure 7.14 Stages of an HIV infection.
In category A, the individual may have no symptoms or very mild symptoms associated with the infection. By category B, opportunistic infections have begun to occur, such as candidiasis, shingles, and diarrhea. Category C is characterized by more severe opportunistic infections and is clinically described as AIDS.

now rare in countries where blood is screened for HIV) is through transfusions of infected blood or blood-clotting factors. Babies born to women with HIV may become infected before or during birth or through breast-feeding after birth. From a global perspective, heterosexual sex is the main mode of HIV transmission. In some nations, however, the most common transmitters of HIV are gay men, people who use IV drugs, and individuals who work in the sex industry. Differences in cultures, sexual practices, and belief systems around the world influence the type of HIV prevention strategies needed to fight the spread of the disease.

Blood, semen, vaginal fluid, and breast milk are the body fluids known to have the highest concentrations of HIV. HIV is not transmitted through contact in the workplace, schools, or social settings. Kissing, hugging, or shaking hands doesn't spread the virus. Likewise, you can't be infected by touching toilet seats, doorknobs, dishes, drinking glasses, food, or pets. The general message of HIV prevention across the globe is abstinence, sex with only one uninfected partner, or consistent use of a condom during sexual encounters.

HIV Treatment

At one time, an HIV infection almost invariably led to AIDS and an early death because there were no drugs for controlling the progression of HIV disease in people who were infected. But since late 1995, scientists have gained a much better understanding of the structure of HIV and its life cycle. Today, following a positive test for the presence of HIV in the body, individuals usually immediately undergo antiviral treatment.

There is no cure for AIDS yet, but a treatment called *highly active antiretroviral therapy (HAART)* is usually able to stop HIV replication to such an extent that the viral load becomes undetectable. HAART uses a combination of drugs that interfere with the life cycle of HIV.

- Entry inhibitors stop HIV from entering a cell. The virus is prevented from binding to a receptor in the plasma membrane.
- Reverse transcriptase inhibitors, such as zidovudine (AZT), interfere with the operation of the reverse transcriptase enzyme.
- Integrase inhibitors prevent HIV from inserting its genetic material into that of the host cells.
- Protease inhibitors prevent protease from cutting up newly created polypeptides.
- Assembly and budding inhibitors are in the experimental stage, and none are available as yet.

Ideally, a drug combination will make the virus less likely to replicate or successfully mutate. If reproduction can be suppressed, viral resistance to this therapy will be less likely to occur and the drugs won't lose their effectiveness. However, investigators have found that when HAART is discontinued, the virus rebounds.

Throughout the world, more than 21 million people are now receiving HIV treatment. Since 2002, there has been a 40-fold increase in the number of people with access to antiretroviral treatment, yet despite these global efforts approximately only 53% of those eligible globally were receiving treatment in 2017.

A pregnant woman with HIV who takes reverse transcriptase inhibitors during her pregnancy reduces the chances of HIV transmission to her newborn. If possible, drug therapy should be delayed until the tenth to twelfth week of pregnancy to minimize any adverse effects of AZT on fetal development. If treatment begins at this time and delivery is by cesarean section, the chance of transmission from mother to infant is very slim (about 1%).

While drug therapy may help control an HIV infection, it also creates some dangers. People with HIV may become lax in their efforts to avoid infection, because they know that drug therapy is available. Further, drug use leads to drug-resistant viruses. Even now, some HIV viruses are known to have become drug resistant when patients failed to adhere to their drug regimens.

Hypersensitivity Reactions

Sometimes the immune system responds in a manner that harms the body, as when individuals develop allergies, receive an incompatible blood type (see Section 6.5), suffer tissue rejection, or have an autoimmune disease.

Allergies

Allergies are hypersensitivities to substances, such as pollen, food, or animal hair, that ordinarily would do no harm to the body. The responses to these antigens, called **allergens,** usually include some degree of tissue damage.

An **immediate allergic response** can occur within seconds of contact with the antigen. The response is caused by IgE antibodies (see Table 7.1). IgE antibodies are attached to receptors on the plasma membrane of mast cells in the tissues and to basophils in the blood. When an allergen attaches to the IgE antibodies on these cells, the cells release histamine and other substances that bring about the allergic symptoms. When pollen is an allergen, histamine stimulates the mucous membranes of the nose and eyes to release fluid. This causes the runny nose and watery eyes typical of hay fever. In a person who has asthma, the airways leading to the lungs constrict, resulting in difficult breathing accompanied by wheezing. When food contains an allergen, an individual may experience nausea, vomiting, and diarrhea.

Anaphylactic shock is an immediate allergic response that occurs because the allergen has entered the bloodstream. Bee stings and penicillin shots are known to cause this reaction, because both inject the allergen into the blood. Anaphylactic shock is characterized by a sudden and life-threatening drop in blood pressure due to increased permeability of the capillaries by histamine. Injecting epinephrine (using an Epipen) can counteract this reaction until medical help is available.

People with allergies produce ten times more IgE than those without allergies. A new treatment using injections of monoclonal IgG antibodies for IgEs is being tested in individuals with severe food allergies. More routinely, injections of the allergen are given so that the body will build up high quantities of IgG antibodies. The hope is that IgG antibodies will combine with allergens received from the environment before they have a chance to reach the IgE antibodies located in the membranes of mast cells and basophils.

A **delayed allergic response** is initiated by memory T cells at the site of allergen contact in the body. The allergic response is regulated by the cytokines secreted by both T cells and macrophages. A classic example of a delayed allergic response is the skin test for tuberculosis (TB). When the test result is positive, the tissue where the antigen was injected becomes red and hardened. This shows that there was prior exposure to the bacterium that causes TB. Contact dermatitis, which occurs when a person is allergic to poison ivy, jewelry, cosmetics, and many other substances that touch the skin, is also an example of a delayed allergic response.

Other Immune Problems

Certain organs, such as the skin, the heart, and the kidneys, could be transplanted easily from one person to another if the body did not attempt to reject them. Rejection of transplanted tissue results because the recipient's immune system recognizes that the transplanted tissue is not "self." Cytotoxic T cells respond by attacking the cells of the transplanted tissue.

Organ rejection can be controlled by carefully selecting the organ to be transplanted and administering **immunosuppressive** drugs. It is best if the transplanted organ has the same type of MHC antigens as those of the recipient, because cytotoxic T cells recognize foreign MHC antigens. Two well-known immunosuppressive drugs, cyclosporine and tacrolimus, act by inhibiting the production of certain T-cell cytokines.

Xenotransplantation is the use of animal organs instead of human organs in human transplant patients. Scientists have chosen to use the pig because animal husbandry has long included the raising of pigs as a meat source and because pigs are prolific. Genetic engineering can make pig organs less antigenic. The ultimate goal is to make pig organs as widely accepted as type O blood.

An alternative to xenotransplantation exists because tissue engineering is making organs in the laboratory. Scientists have transplanted lab-grown urinary bladders into human patients. They hope that production of organs lacking HLA antigens will one day do away with the problem of rejection.

Immune system disorders occur when a patient has an immune deficiency or when the immune system attacks the body's own cells. When a person has an immune deficiency, the immune system is unable to protect the body against disease. Infrequently, a child may be born with an impaired immune system. For example, in **severe combined immunodeficiency disease (SCID),** both antibody- and cell-mediated immunity are lacking or inadequate. Without treatment, even common infections can be fatal. Bone marrow transplants and gene therapy (see Section 22.4) have been successful in patients with SCID. Acquired immune deficiencies can be caused by infections, chemical exposure, or radiation. Acquired immunodeficiency syndrome (AIDS) is a result of an infection with the human immunodeficiency virus (HIV). As a result of a weakened immune system, patients with AIDS show a greater susceptibility to infections and have a higher risk of cancer (see Section 8.2).

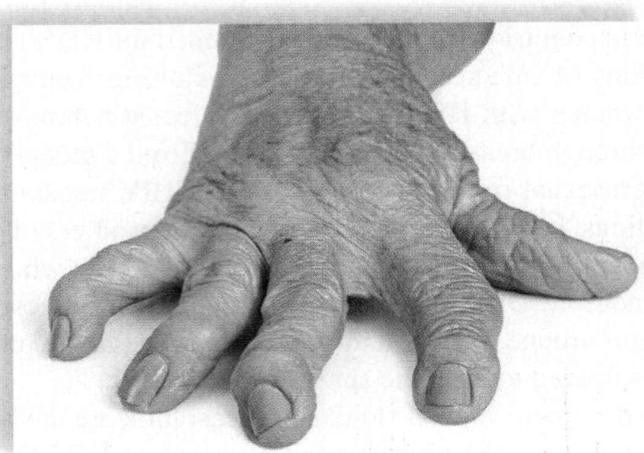

Figure 7.15 Rheumatoid arthritis.
Rheumatoid arthritis is due to recurring inflammation in skeletal joints. A variety of cells in the immune system, including T cells and B cells, participate in deterioration of the joints, which eventually become immobile.
lathuric/iStock/Getty Images

When cytotoxic T cells or antibodies mistakenly attack the body's own cells, the person has an **autoimmune disease.** The exact cause of autoimmune diseases is not known, although it appears to involve both genetic and environmental factors. People with certain HLA antigens are more susceptible. Women are more likely than men to develop an autoimmune disease.

Sometimes the autoimmune disease follows an infection. For example, in **rheumatic fever,** antibodies induced by a streptococcal (bacterial) infection of the throat also react with heart muscle. This causes an inflammatory response, with damage to the heart muscle and valves. **Rheumatoid arthritis** (Fig. 7.15) is an autoimmune disease in which the joints are chronically inflamed. It is thought that antigen-antibody complexes, complement, neutrophils, activated T cells, and macrophages are all involved in the destruction of cartilage in the joints. A person with **systemic lupus erythematosus (SLE),** commonly just called *lupus,* has various symptoms, including a facial rash, fever, and joint pain. In these patients, damage to the central nervous system, heart, and kidneys can be fatal. Patients with SLE produce high levels of anti-DNA antibodies. All human cells (except red blood cells) contain DNA, so the symptoms of lupus interfere with tissues throughout the body. **Myasthenia gravis** develops when antibodies attach to protein receptors on the surface of muscle cells. The result is severe muscle weakness, eventually resulting in death from respiratory failure.

In **multiple sclerosis (MS),** T cells attack the myelin sheath covering nerve fibers, causing CNS dysfunction, double vision, and muscular weakness. Some now believe that MS should be characterized as an immune-mediated disease, because a specific antigen has not been identified and the action of the T cells may be in response to inflammation or failures of the immune system. Treatments for all of these diseases usually involve drugs designed to decrease the immune response.

CHECK YOUR PROGRESS 7.5

1. Define the types of complications and disorders associated with the functioning of the immune system.
2. Detail how an antibody works during an allergic reaction.
3. Hypothesize why an autoimmune disorder sometimes develops after an infection.

CONNECTING THE CONCEPTS

For more information on the topics presented in this section, refer to the following discussions:

Section 8.2 examines how tuberculosis has become a worldwide epidemic.

Section 22.3 explores how gene therapy may be used to treat diseases such as SCID.

CONCLUSION

In this chapter, we explored the structure of both the lymphatic and immune systems and learned about how the immune system protects us against pathogens. Generally speaking, the immune system performs this task without us knowing it; we are usually not aware of an infection or illness until it overruns the defensive barriers of the immune system. However, even then the body has a way of protecting us against a repeat infection by use of memory and antibodies.

There are some diseases, such as AIDS and COVID-19, that can present significant problems for the immune system, either because the virus responsible for the disease attacks the cells of the immune system directly (as is the case with HIV/AIDS), or because it is a completely new form of virus that the body has not encountered in the past. SARS-CoV-2 and COVID-19 fall into this second category. As we will learn in the next chapter, this has created a global pandemic.

SUMMARIZE

7.1 The Lymphatic System

The lymphatic system consists of **lymphatic vessels** that return **lymph** to cardiovascular veins. Lymph is comprised primarily of interstitial fluid.

The primary **lymphatic organs** are:

- The **red bone marrow,** where all blood cells are made and the **B cells (B lymphocytes)** mature.
- The **thymus,** where **T cells (T lymphocytes)** mature.

The secondary lymphatic organs are:

- The **spleen, lymph nodes,** and other organs containing lymphoid tissue, such as the tonsils, Peyer's patches, and the appendix. Blood is cleansed of pathogens and debris in the spleen. Lymph is cleansed of pathogens and debris in the nodes.

7.2 Innate Immune Defenses

Immunity involves innate and adaptive defenses. The innate defenses include the following:

- Chemical barriers, such as **lysozyme** enzymes.
- Physical barriers to entry.
- The **inflammatory response,** which involves the action of phagocytic neutrophils and **macrophages.** Chemicals such as **histamine** and **cytokines** act as chemical signals.
- The **complement system** utilizes protective proteins and **interferons.**

7.3 Adaptive Immune Defenses

Adaptive defenses require B cells and T cells, also called B lymphocytes and T lymphocytes. The adaptive defenses respond to **antigens,** or foreign objects, in the body.

B Cells and Antibody-Mediated Immunity

- The clonal selection model explains how activated B cells undergo clonal selection with production of plasma cells and **memory B cells,** after their B-cell receptor (BCR) combines with a specific antigen.
- **Plasma cells** secrete antibodies and eventually undergo **apoptosis.** Plasma cells are responsible for **antibody-mediated immunity.**
- Most antibodies are Y-shaped molecules that have two binding sites for a specific antigen.
- Memory B cells remain in the body and produce antibodies if the same antigen enters the body at a later date.
- **Monoclonal antibodies,** produced by the same plasma cell, have various functions, from detecting infections to treating cancer.

T Cells and Cell-Mediated Immunity

- T cells possess a unique **T-cell receptor (TCR).** For a T cell to recognize an antigen, the antigen must be presented by an **antigen-presenting cell (APC),** such as a macrophage. Once digested within a lysosome, the antigen is presented on the **major histocompatibility complex (MHC)** of the cell. These MHC proteins belong to a class of molecules called **human leukocyte antigens (HLAs).**
- Activated T cells undergo clonal expansion until the illness has been stemmed. Then, most of the activated T cells undergo apoptosis. A few cells remain, however, as memory T cells.
- The two main types of T cells are cytotoxic T cells and helper T cells.
- **Cytotoxic T cells** kill on contact virus-infected cells or cancer cells, which bear nonself proteins. They are involved in the process of **cell-mediated immunity.**

- **Helper T cells** produce cytokines and stimulate other immune cells.
- Some activated T cells remain as **memory T cells** to combat future infections by the same pathogen.

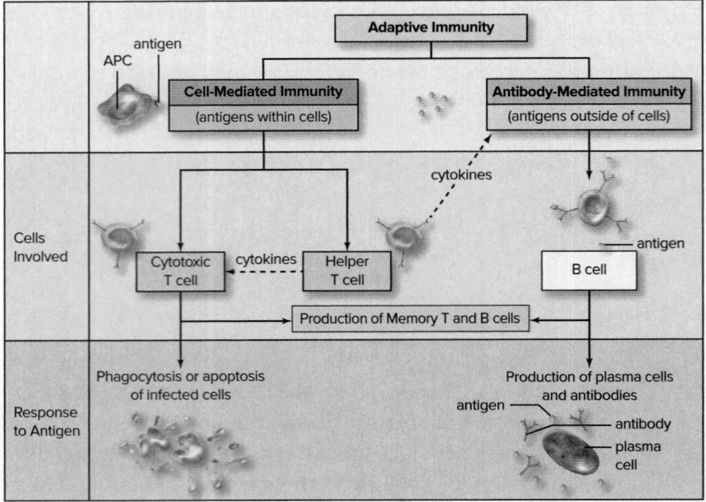

7.4 Acquired Immunity

- **Active immunity** can be induced by **immunization** using **vaccines** when a person is well and in no immediate danger of contracting an infectious disease. Active immunity depends on the presence of memory cells in the body.
- **Passive immunity** is needed when an individual is in immediate danger of succumbing to an infectious disease. Passive immunity is short-lived, because the antibodies are administered to—and not made by—the individual.
- **Cytokines,** including **interleukins,** are a form of passive immunity used to treat AIDS and to promote the body's ability to recover from cancer.

7.5 Disorders of the Immune System

- **Acquired immunodeficiency syndrome (AIDS)** is caused by the **human immunodeficiency virus (HIV).** HIV infects cells of the immune system, allowing for the development of **opportunistic infections.** Phases of an HIV infection are based on the number of CD4 T cells in the blood and the individual's health. The phases include an acute phase, a chronic phase, and AIDS. A number of treatments have been identified that slow down, but do not prevent, the development of AIDS in the body.
- **Allergies** occur when the immune system reacts vigorously to allergens, antigens that are not normally recognized as foreign. **Immediate allergic responses**, usually consisting of coldlike symptoms, are due to the activity of antibodies. One example is anaphylactic shock. **Delayed allergic responses**, such as contact dermatitis, are due to the activity of T cells.
- Tissue rejection occurs when the immune system recognizes a tissue as foreign. **Immunosuppressive** drugs may inhibit tissue rejection. Xenotransplantation is the use of animal tissue in place of human tissue.
- Immune deficiencies can be inherited or can be caused by infection, chemical exposure, or radiation. One example is **severe combined immunodeficiency disease (SCID),** in which adaptive responses are inoperative.
- **Autoimmune diseases** occur when the immune system reacts to tissues/organs of the individual as if they were foreign. Examples are **rheumatic fever, rheumatoid arthritis, systemic lupus erythematosus (SLE), myasthenia gravis,** and **multiple sclerosis (MS).**

ENGAGE

THINKING CRITICALLY

1. Why do you think certain allergens affect some people more than others? Why are some people asymptomatic to a particular antigen, whereas others are affected?
2. Why is it that Rh incompatibility can be a serious problem when an Rh-negative mother is carrying an Rh-positive fetus, but ABO incompatibility between mother and fetus is usually no problem? That is, a type A mother can usually safely carry a type B fetus. (*Hint:* The antibodies produced by an Rh-negative mother against the Rh antigen are usually IgG, whereas the antibodies produced against the A or B antigens are IgM.) Because the Rh antigen obviously serves no vital function (most humans lack it), why do you think it hasn't been completely eliminated during human evolution?
3. Someone bitten by a poisonous snake should be given some antivenom (antibodies) to prevent death. If the person is bitten by the same type of snake 3 years after the initial bite, will they have immunity to the venom, or should the person get another shot of antivenom? Justify your response with an explanation of the type of immunity someone gains from a shot of antibodies.

MAKING IT RELEVANT

1. The COVID-19 pandemic represents one of the biggest challenges to our health-care systems since the influenza pandemic of 1918. How might you personally contribute to reducing the spread of the SARS-CoV-2 virus, and reducing the impact of this pandemic?
2. Have you ever skipped getting a flu vaccine because you either got it the year before, or you thought it gave you the flu? Why do you now know this information is incorrect?
3. What dangers would an increase in people opposed to vaccinations, sometimes called anti-vaxxers, pose to the population?

Find answers to all of the chapter questions at connect.mheducation.com

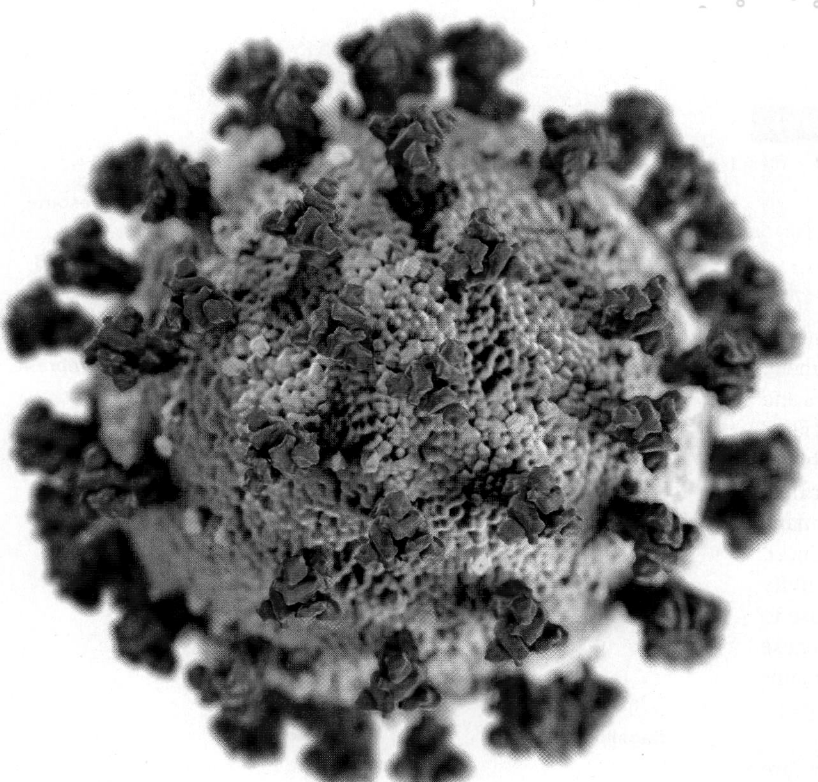

Alissa Eckert, MS; Dan Higgins, MAMS/CDC

CHAPTER 8

Biology of Infectious Diseases

The COVID-19 Pandemic

Starting in early 2020, schools and businesses were shut down, travel was suspended, and the borders of countries were closed, all because of a virus named SARS-CoV-2. The acronym stands for *s*evere *a*cute *r*espiratory *s*yndrome *co*rona*v*irus *2*. The virus causes a disease called COVID-19, whose name is a contraction of *co*rona*vi*rus *d*isease 20*19*.

COVID-19 is typically acquired by infected droplets (e.g., due to sneezing, coughing, talking) from someone who has the disease. Droplets enter through the nose, eyes, or mouth. As the virus replicates, the immune response is set into motion. What makes this virus so dangerous is that some people may carry the infection and be asymptomatic, while others can have heightened immune responses that require hospitalization.

SARS-CoV-2 belongs to a group of viruses called β-coronavirus, aptly named because the spike glycoproteins protrude from the viral surface and resemble a crown or corona. Coronaviruses are animal viruses, and it is likely the virus originated from bats. Understanding the structure and origins of a virus allows scientists to develop vaccines and treatments for current pandemics and any virus that may appear in the future.

Like many viruses, there are many misconceptions regarding the SARS-CoV-2 virus. However, in many ways SARS-CoV-2 is similar to any virus—it must invade specific cells of the body in order to hijack the cells' metabolic machinery to make more copies of itself. In this chapter, we will examine not only the interaction of viruses with living organisms, but also other members of the microbial world, such as bacteria and prions.

As you read through the chapter, think about the following questions:

1. How do viruses, such as SARS-CoV-2, infect the cells of the body?
2. Is Ebola considered an emerging disease?

CHAPTER OUTLINE

BEFORE YOU BEGIN

Before beginning this chapter, take a few moments to review the following discussions:

Section 1.1 What are the basic characteristics of living organisms?

Section 7.4 What is the role of a T cell in the immune response?

Section 7.5 How do immunizations protect an individual against disease?

8.1 Bacteria and Viruses

LEARNING OUTCOMES

Upon completion of this section, you should be able to

1. Define the term *pathogen*.
2. Identify the structures of a prokaryotic cell.
3. Describe the general structure of a virus.

The term *microbe* applies to microscopic organisms, such as bacteria, viruses, and protists, that are widely distributed in the environment. They may be found both on inanimate objects and on the surfaces and interiors of plants and animals. While the term often is associated with diseases, many activities of microbes are actually useful to humans. We eat foods produced by bacteria, and bacteria contribute to the production of yogurt, cheese, bread, beer, wine, and many pickled foods. Drugs available through biotechnology are produced by bacteria. Microbes help us in still another way. Without the activity of decomposers, the biosphere (including ourselves) would cease to exist. When a tree falls to the forest floor, it eventually rots because decomposers, including bacteria and fungi, break down the remains of dead organisms to inorganic nutrients. Plants need these inorganic nutrients to make the many molecules that become food for us.

Despite all these benefits, certain bacteria and viruses are known as **pathogens,** or disease-causing agents. In this chapter, we will focus on a few of the bacterial and viral pathogens responsible for human disease.

Recall from Chapter 7 that we are not defenseless against pathogens. Our body has multiple lines of defense against bacteria and viruses. For example:

- Barriers to entry, such as the skin and mucous membranes of body cavities, prevent pathogens from gaining entrance into the body.
- First responders, such as the phagocytic white blood cells, prevent an infection after an invasion has occurred due to a pathogen getting past a barrier and into the body.
- Acquired defenses overcome an infection by killing the disease-causing agent that has entered the body. Acquired defenses also protect us against cancer.

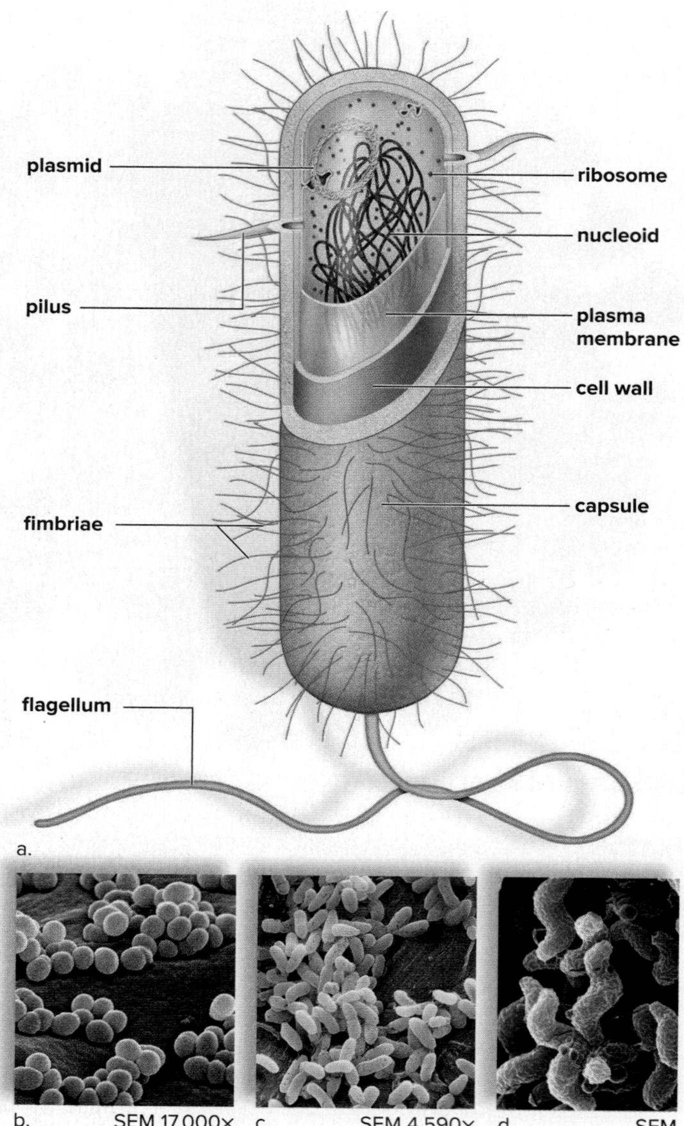

Figure 8.1 Typical shapes of bacteria.
a. The structure of a typical bacterial cell. **b.** Sphere-shaped *Staphylococcus aureus* causes toxic shock syndrome. **c.** Rod-shaped *Pseudomonas aeruginosa* causes urinary tract infections. **d.** Spirillum-shaped *Campylobacter jejuni* causes food poisoning.
(b): David M. Phillips/Science Source; (c): Steve Gschmeissner/Science Source; (d): De Wood, Chris Pooley/USDA

Bacteria

Bacteria are *prokaryotes,* single-celled organisms that do not have a nucleus or the membrane-bound organelles present in eukaryotic cells, such as human cells. Figure 8.1 illustrates the main features of bacterial anatomy and illustrates the three shapes common to bacteria: *coccus* (sphere-shaped), *bacillus* (rod-shaped), and *spirillum* (curved or spiral-shaped).

All bacterial cells have a *plasma membrane,* a lipid bilayer similar to the plasma membrane in plant and animal cells. Most bacterial cells are further protected by a **cell wall** that contains the unique molecule *peptidoglycan* (a disaccharide with an attached amino group). The "cillin" antibiotics, such as penicillin, interfere with the production of the cell wall. The cell wall of some bacteria is surrounded by a **capsule** that has a thick, gelatinous consistency. Capsules often allow bacteria to stick to surfaces, such as our teeth. The capsules also prevent the phagocytic white blood cells of our immune system from taking them up and destroying them.

Bacteria can be classified by differences in their cell walls, which are detected using a staining procedure devised more than 100 years ago by Hans Christian Gram, now called a *Gram stain.* Cell walls that have a thick layer of peptidoglycan outside the plasma membrane stain purple with the Gram stain procedure, and are called *Gram-positive bacteria.* If the peptidoglycan layer is either thin or lacking altogether, the cells stain pink and are considered *Gram-negative bacteria.* In addition to their plasma membrane, Gram-negative bacteria have an outer membrane that contains *lipopolysaccharide* molecules. When these Gram-negative cells are killed by your immune system, these molecules are released, stimulating inflammation and fever. Knowledge of the type of bacteria allows physicians to prescribe a more effective antibiotic treatment.

Motile bacteria usually have long, very thin appendages called **flagella** (*sing.,* flagellum). The flagella rotate 360°, which in turn causes the bacterium to move. Some bacteria have **fimbriae,** stiff fibers that allow the bacteria to adhere to surfaces such as host cells. Fimbriae allow a bacterium to cling to and gain access to the body. In contrast, a **pilus** is an elongated, hollow appendage used to transfer DNA from one cell to another. Genes that allow bacteria to be resistant to antibiotics can be passed between bacterial cells through a pilus by a process called *conjugation.*

Bacteria are independent cells capable of performing many diverse functions. Their DNA is packaged in a chromosome that occupies the center of the cell. Many bacteria also have small, circular pieces of DNA called **plasmids.** Genes that allow bacteria to be resistant to antibiotics are often located in a plasmid. Abuse of antibiotic therapy increases the number of resistant bacterial strains that are difficult to kill, even with antibiotics. We will explore how bacteria evolve resistance to antibiotics in Section 8.4.

BIOLOGY IN YOUR LIFE

Are antibacterial cleansers really effective?

Studies show that using antibacterial soap when washing your hands is no more effective in preventing the spread of bacteria than using pure soap and water. The main ingredient in most antibacterial soaps, triclosan, may actually cause some bacteria to become resistant to certain drugs, such as amoxicillin, which is used to kill bacteria. Furthermore, some states are banning antibacterial soaps because of concerns over chemicals entering the water supply, and because triclosan is considered a carcinogen.

Waterless hand sanitizers (which are alcohol-based) are recommended for use in conjunction with, not as a replacement for, regular hand washing. Proper hand washing and sanitizing, when done often and properly, can prevent the spread of colds, cases of flu, COVID-19, and certain diarrhea disorders.

Bacteria reproduce by a process called binary fission (Fig. 8.2). The single, circular chromosome attached to the plasma membrane is copied. Then, the chromosomes are separated as the cell enlarges. The newly formed plasma membrane and cell wall separate the cell into two cells. Bacteria can reproduce rapidly under favorable conditions, with some species doubling their numbers every 20 minutes.

Strep throat, tuberculosis, gangrene, gonorrhea, and syphilis are well-known bacterial diseases. Not only does growth of bacteria cause disease, but some bacteria release molecules called **toxins** that inhibit cellular metabolism. For example, it is important to have a tetanus shot, because the bacterium that causes this disease, *Clostridium tetani,* produces a toxin that prevents relaxation of muscles. In time, the body contorts, because all the muscles have contracted; if no medical treatment is available, suffocation can occur.

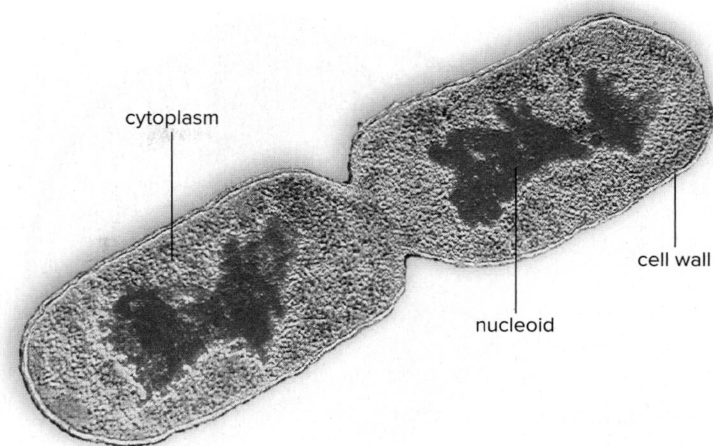

Figure 8.2 Binary fission.
Bacteria reproduce by binary fission, resulting in two cells that are identical to the original cell.
CNRI/Science Source

BIOLOGY IN YOUR LIFE

Does refrigeration kill bacteria?

The answer is no. The speed at which bacteria reproduce depends on a number of factors, including moisture in the environment and temperature. At the temperatures found in most refrigerators and freezers, bacterial growth is slowed, but the bacteria are not killed. Once the temperature returns to a favorable level, the bacteria resume normal cell division. The only way to kill most food-related bacteria is by using high temperatures, such as those employed in boiling or thorough cooking.

Viruses

Viruses are intracellular parasites, meaning they need to use a host cell to reproduce. Viruses are not made of cells (acellular) and they lack the metabolic machinery needed to acquire and use nutrients. For these reasons, historically, scientists have not classified viruses as living organisms. However, recent discoveries of giant viruses (tentatively called Megaviruses), which are almost the size of bacteria, are challenging the definitions of what is characterized as living (see Section 1.1). In this chapter, we will be exploring viruses associated with human disease. These viruses are considerably smaller than a bacterium, which is about one hundredth the size of a eukaryotic cell (Fig. 8.3).

A virus always has two parts: an outer *capsid* composed of protein units, and an inner core of nucleic acids (Fig. 8.4). These nucleic acids contain genetic information needed for viral reproduction. In contrast to cellular organisms, the viral genetic material need not be double-stranded DNA, or even DNA. Some viruses, such as HIV and influenza, have RNA as their genetic material. A virus may also contain various enzymes that help it reproduce.

This is why they are considered to be cellular parasites. Viruses are microscopic pirates, commandeering the metabolic machinery

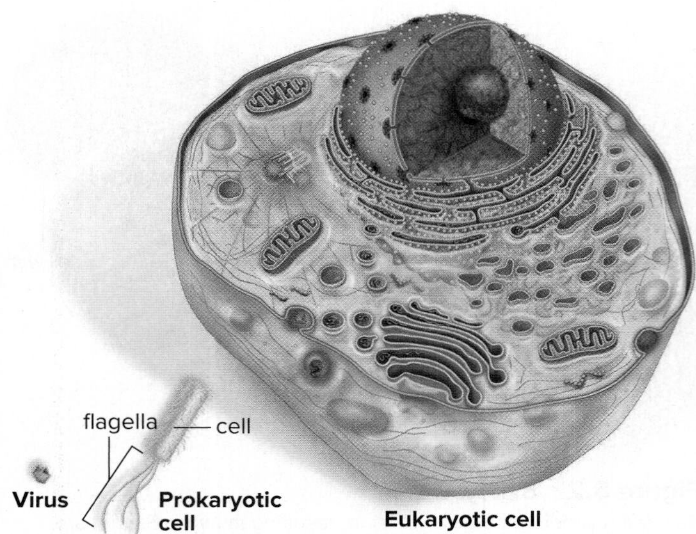

Figure 8.3 Comparative sizes of viruses, bacteria, and eukaryotic cells.
Viruses are tiny, acellular particles, whereas bacteria are small, independent cells. Eukaryotic cells are more complex and larger, because they contain a nucleus and many organelles.

of a host cell. Viruses gain entry into, and are specific to, a particular host cell because the spikes and proteins on the surface of the virus are specific for a receptor on the host cell's outer surface.

A general life cycle of a virus is shown in Figure 8.5*a*. This figure shows the life cycle of a type of a bacteriophage, a virus that infects bacteria. The stages of the life cycle include:

1. *Attachment.* The capsid of the virus combines with a receptor on the surface of the host cell.
2. *Penetration.* In the case of a bacteriophage, a viral enzyme digests away part of the cell wall, and the viral genetic material is injected into the bacterial cell. In other viruses, the entire virus enters the cell by endocytosis.
3. *Biosynthesis.* The machinery of the host cell carries out replication of the virus' genetic material and begins production of multiple copies of the capsid protein subunits.
4. *Maturation.* Also referred to as *assembly,* the viral genetic material and capsids combine to produce several new viruses.
5. *Release.* New viruses either leave the cell by exocytosis or by disrupting the cell membranes (and cell walls in bacteria), releasing the new viruses.

In some viruses, the infected cell does not immediately produce new viruses. Instead, after entering the cell, the virus becomes *latent,* meaning it is not actively reproducing. This is called the lysogenic cycle (Fig. 8.5*b*). Following attachment and penetration, *integration* occurs: Viral DNA becomes incorporated into the host cell. For bacteriophages, this is often referred to as *prophage.* This DNA is replicated along with the host DNA, and all subsequent cells, called lysogenic cells, carry a copy of the viral information. Certain environmental factors, such as ultraviolet radiation, can induce the prophage to enter the lytic stage of biosynthesis, followed by maturation and release.

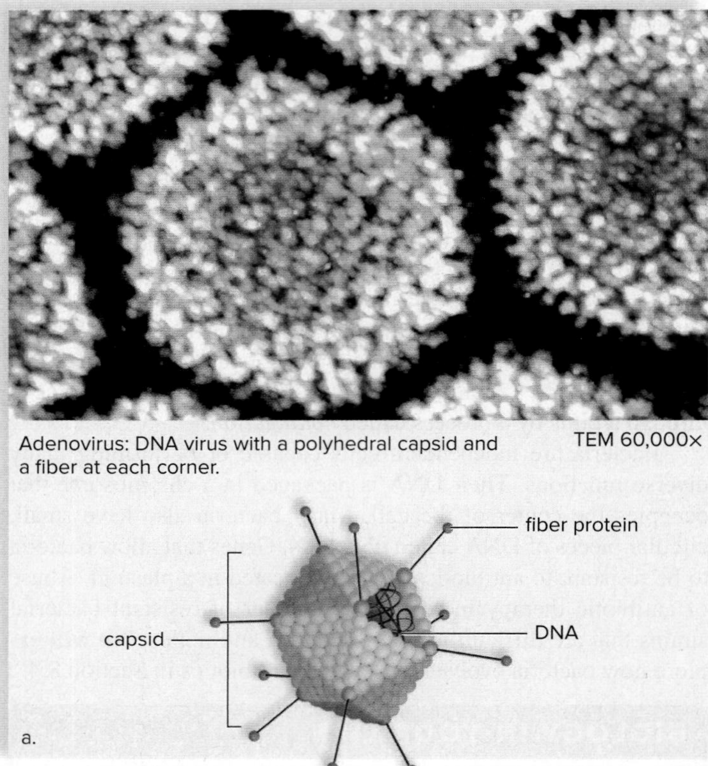

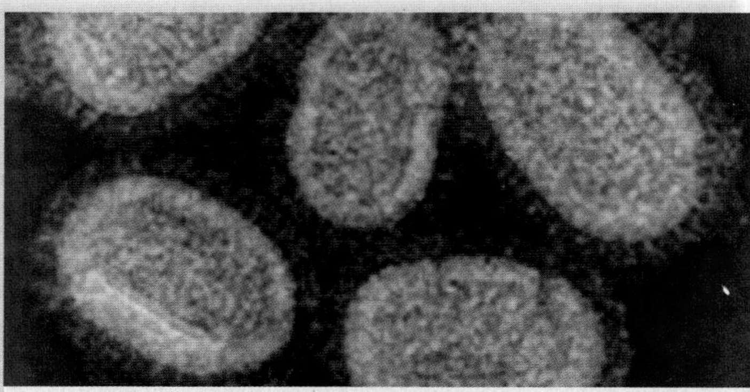
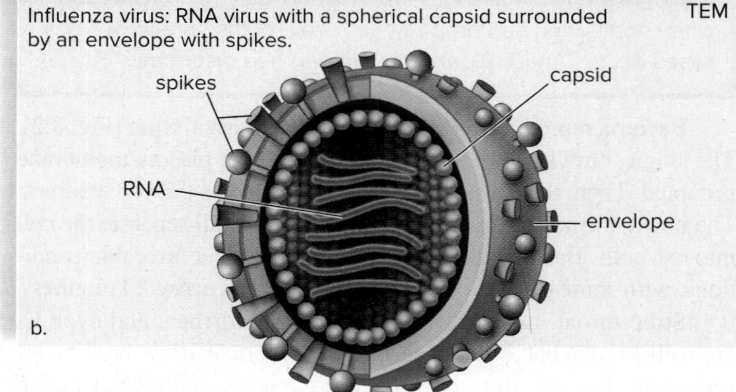

Figure 8.4 Typical virus structures.
All viruses have an outer capsid, composed of protein subunits, and a nucleic acid core, composed of either DNA or RNA, but not both. **a.** Adenoviruses cause colds, and (**b**) influenza viruses cause the flu.
(photos) (a): Biophoto Associates/Science Source; (b): Centers for Disease Control and Prevention/Cynthia Goldsmith

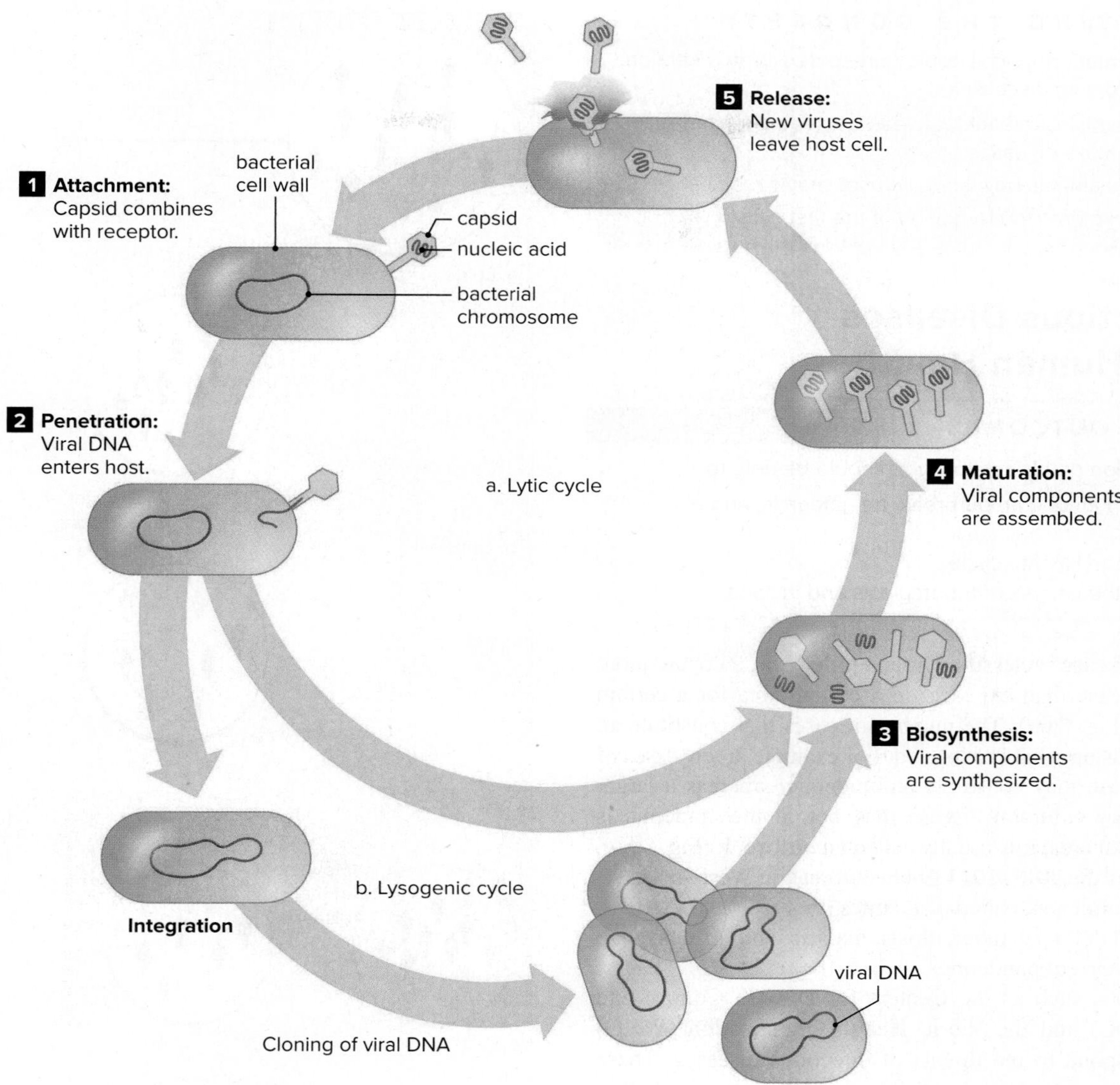

Figure 8.5 General life cycle of a virus.
a. In the lytic cycle, viral particles escape when the cell is lysed (broken open). **b.** In the lysogenic cycle, viral DNA is integrated into host DNA. At a future time, the lysogenic cycle can be followed by the last three steps of the lytic cycle.

Figure 8.5 represents a general life cycle. There are many variations in this cycle, depending on the type of virus. We will take a look at some of these in our discussions on the HIV virus (Section 8.2) and the SARS-CoV-2 virus (Section 8.3).

Prions

Prions, infectious particles made strictly of proteins, cause a group of degenerative diseases of the nervous system, also called wasting diseases. Originally thought to be viral diseases, Creutzfeldt–Jakob disease (CJD) in humans, scrapie in sheep, and bovine spongiform encephalopathy (BSE) in cattle (commonly called mad cow disease) are all caused by prions. These infections are apparently transmitted by ingestion of brain and nerve tissues from infected animals. These proteins are believed to normally play the role of a "housekeeper" in the brains of healthy individuals. However, in some people, a rogue form of the protein folds into a new shape, forming a prion, and in the process loses its original function. The rogue protein is able to refold other proteins into new shapes and thus cause disease. For example, prion activity may cause nervous tissue to be lost and generate calcified plaques in the brain. The incidence of prion diseases in humans is very low.

CHECK YOUR PROGRESS 8.1

1. Explain the differences among the structures of a bacterium, a eukaryotic cell, and a virus.
2. Detail the structures in bacteria that can be associated with the ability to cause disease.
3. Explain why viruses are considered intracellular parasites.

CONNECTING THE CONCEPTS

For more information on the topics presented in this section, refer to the following discussions:

Section 17.6 explains the link between bacteria and some sexually transmitted diseases.

Section 20.2 examines how some viruses may cause cancer.

Section 23.1 explores the evolution of the first cells.

8.2 Infectious Diseases and Human Health

LEARNING OUTCOMES

Upon completion of this section, you should be able to

1. Distinguish among an outbreak, an epidemic, and a pandemic.
2. Describe the HIV life cycle.
3. Describe the causes of tuberculosis and malaria.

An **infectious disease** is classified as an **epidemic** if there are more cases of the disease than expected in a certain area for a certain period of time (Fig. 8.6*a*). The number of cases that constitute an epidemic depends on what is expected. For example, a few cases of a very rare disease may constitute an epidemic, whereas a larger number of a very common disease may not. If the epidemic is confined to a local area, it is usually called an **outbreak** (Fig. 8.6*b*). One example was the 2013–2014 Ebola outbreak in West Africa.

Global epidemics are called pandemics (Fig. 8.6*c*). HIV/AIDS, SARS-CoV-2/COVID-19, tuberculosis, malaria, and influenza are all examples of current pandemics.

Organizations such as the Centers for Disease Control and Prevention (CDC) and the World Health Organization (WHO) monitor and respond to the threats of infectious diseases. These organizations are primarily responsible for determining whether an outbreak has reached epidemic or pandemic levels. We will take a closer look at some of these diseases in this section.

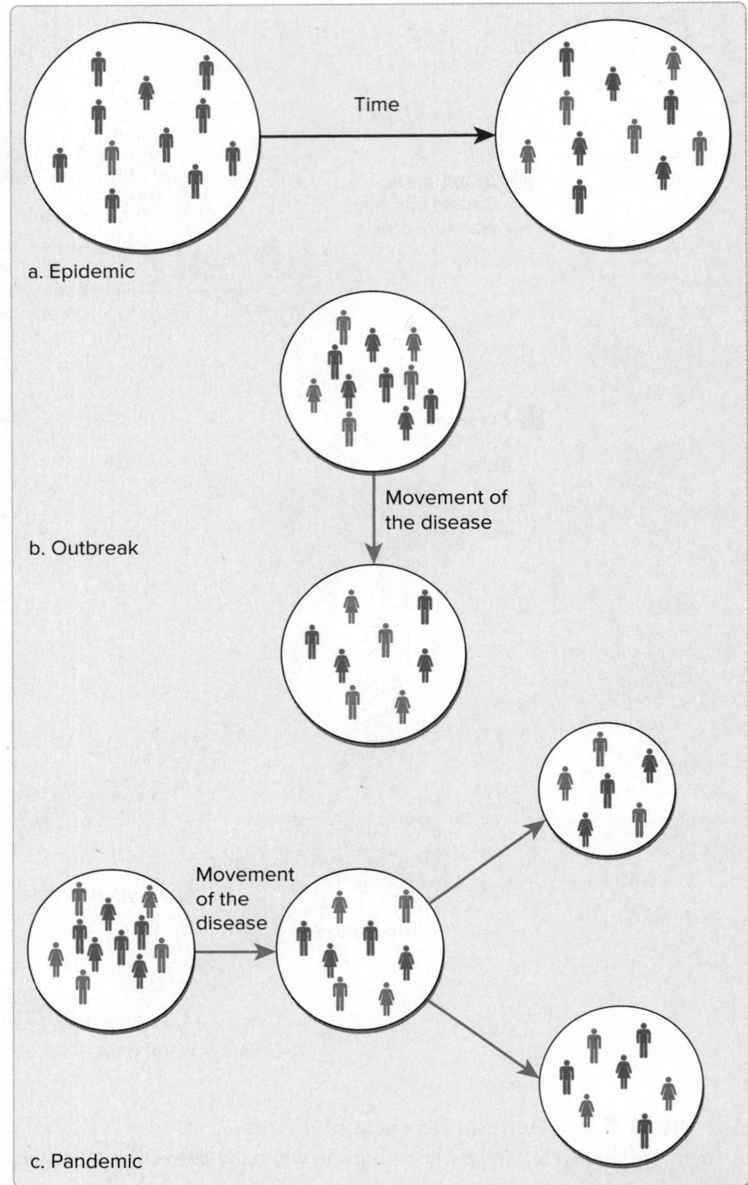

Figure 8.6 Outbreaks, Epidemics, and Pandemics.
a. In an epidemic, the number of individuals who are infected exceeds what was normal in previous years. **b.** In an outbreak, the disease moves between two populations. **c.** In a pandemic, the disease moves into many populations, often globally.

HIV/AIDS

Origin of and Prevalence of HIV

It is generally accepted that HIV originated in Africa and then spread to the United States and Europe by way of the Caribbean. However, the exact dates of the first human cases of HIV are still being investigated. Recent molecular analyses of the HIV virus suggest that the virus may have first infected humans sometime between 1884 and 1924. Direct evidence of HIV in humans has been obtained from tissue and blood samples taken in the 1950s and 1960s. HIV has been found in a preserved 1959 blood sample taken from a man who lived in an African country now called the Democratic Republic of the Congo. British scientists have been able to show that AIDS came to their country perhaps as early as 1959. They examined the preserved tissues of a Manchester seafarer who had died that year and concluded he had most likely died of AIDS. Similarly, it is thought that HIV entered the United States on numerous occasions as early as the 1950s. But the first documented case is a 15-year-old male who died in Missouri in 1969, with skin lesions now known to be characteristic of an AIDS-related cancer. Doctors froze some of his tissues because they could not identify the cause of death. Researchers also want to test the preserved tissue samples of a 49-year-old Haitian who died in New York in 1959 of the type of pneumonia now known to be AIDS-related.

Throughout the 1960s, it was customary in the United States to list leukemia as the cause of death in patients with immunodeficiencies. Most likely, some of these people actually died of AIDS. HIV is not extremely infectious, so it took several decades for the number of AIDS cases to increase to the point that AIDS became

Table 8.1 HIV Global Statistics, 2019

	People Living with HIV	New Infections	AIDS Deaths
Eastern and Southern Africa	20.7 million	730,000	300,000
Western and Southern Africa	4.9 million	240,000	140,000
Asia and the Pacific	5.8 million	300,000	160,000
Latin America	2.1 million	120,000	37,000
Caribbean	330,000	13,000	6,900
Western and Central Europe and North America	2.2 million	65,000	12,000
Eastern Europe and Central Asia	1.7 million	170,000	35,000
North Africa and the Middle East	240,000	20,000	8,000
Total	**38.0 million**	**1.7 million**	**690,000**

Source: UNAIDS website, www.unaids.org.

recognizable as a specific and separate disease. The name *AIDS* was coined in 1982, and HIV was found to be the cause of AIDS in 1983–1984.

Worldwide, estimates of HIV/AIDS infection rates and deaths are updated every 2 to 3 years. As of 2019, an estimated 38 million people were living with HIV infection (Table 8.1). There were 1.7 million new HIV infections in 2019, a 23% decline from 2010 annual statistics. Although the number of deaths due to HIV/AIDS is also declining annually, in 2019 the disease still claimed 690,000 lives, bringing the total number of deaths attributed to HIV/AIDS to over 32.7 million.

Although these numbers indicate that the global HIV/AIDS pandemic is still ongoing, there have been significant declines in both new infections and deaths (Fig. 8.7). For example, since 2010, new infections of HIV have dropped by 23%, mostly due to new international education programs. Furthermore, while the number of people living with HIV has increased slightly, the number of deaths has dropped by 39% since 2010 due to more widespread access to antiviral medications (see Section 7.5).

In our discussion of the immune system, we examined how HIV infects the body and impacts the cells that protect the body from pathogens (see Section 7.5). Here, we will explore the structure and life cycle of the HIV virus.

HIV Structure

HIV consists of two single strands of RNA (its nucleic acid genome); various proteins; and an envelope, which it acquires from its host cell (Fig. 8.8). The virus's genetic material is protected by a series of three protein coats: the nucleocapsid, capsid, and matrix. Within the matrix are the following three very important enzymes: reverse transcriptase, integrase, and protease:

- *Reverse transcriptase* catalyzes reverse transcription, the conversion of the viral RNA to viral DNA.
- *Integrase* catalyzes the integration of viral DNA into the DNA of the host cell.
- *Protease* catalyzes the breakdown of the newly synthesized viral polypeptides into functional viral proteins.

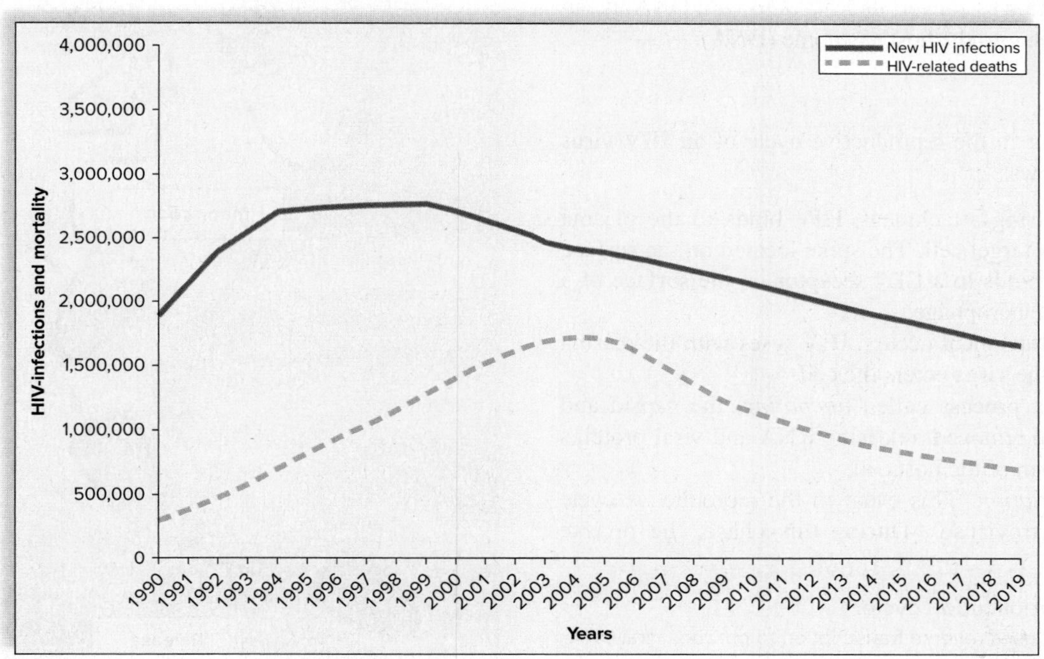

Figure 8.7 HIV/AIDS.
This graph shows the decline in both new infections and deaths related to HIV through 2019.
Source: World Health Organization.

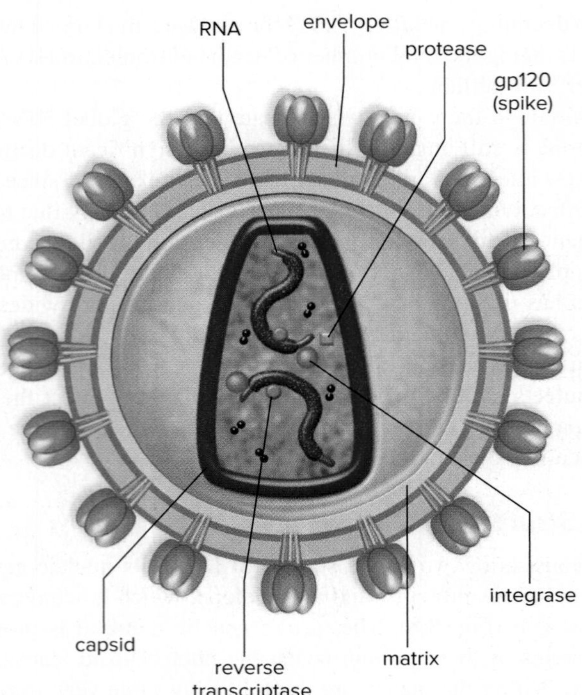

Figure 8.8 **The structure of the human immunodeficiency virus.**
HIV is composed of two strands of RNA, a capsid, and an envelope containing spike proteins.

Embedded in HIV's envelope are protein spikes referred to as *gp120s.* These spikes must be present for HIV to gain entry into its target immune cells. The genome for HIV consists of RNA instead of DNA, which classifies HIV as a retrovirus. A **retrovirus** must use reverse transcription to convert its RNA into viral DNA. It can then insert its genome into the host's genome (DNA).

HIV Life Cycle

The events that occur in the reproductive cycle of an HIV virus (Fig. 8.9) are as follows:

- *Attachment.* During attachment, HIV binds to the plasma membrane of its target cell. The spike located on the surface of HIV, gp120, binds to a CD4 receptor on the surface of a helper T cell or macrophage.
- *Fusion.* After attachment occurs, HIV fuses with the plasma membrane and the virus enters the cell.
- *Entry.* During a process called *uncoating,* the capsid and protein coats are removed, releasing RNA and viral proteins into the cytoplasm of the host cell.
- *Reverse transcription.* This event in the reproductive cycle is unique to retroviruses. During this phase, the reverse

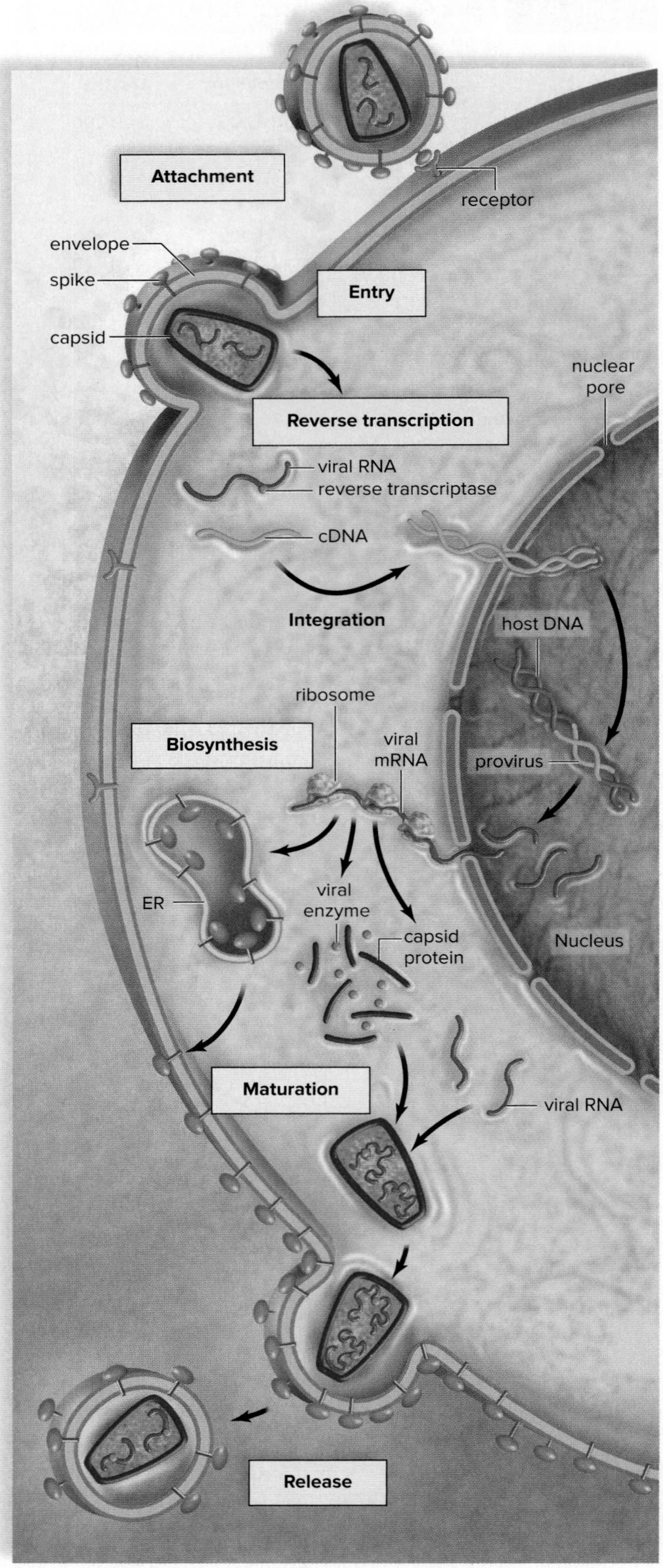

Figure 8.9 **HIV replication cycle.**
HIV is a retrovirus that uses reverse transcription to produce viral DNA. The viral DNA integrates into the cell's chromosomes, where it directs the production of viral RNA. The viral RNA is used in the synthesis of new viruses.

transcriptase enzyme catalyzes the conversion of HIV's single-stranded RNA first into single-stranded DNA (cDNA), and then into double-stranded viral DNA. Usually in cells, DNA is transcribed into RNA. Retroviruses can do the opposite only because they have a unique enzyme from which they take their name (*retro-* in Latin means "reverse").

- *Integration.* The newly synthesized viral DNA, along with the viral enzyme integrase, migrates into the nucleus of the host cell. Then, with the help of integrase, the host cell's DNA is spliced. Double-stranded viral DNA is then integrated into the host cell's DNA (chromosome). Once viral DNA has integrated into the host cell's DNA, HIV is referred to as a **provirus,** meaning it is now a part of the cell's genetic material. HIV is usually transmitted to another person by means of cells that contain proviruses. Also, proviruses serve as a latent reservoir for HIV during drug treatment. Even if drug therapy results in an undetectable viral load, investigators know there are still proviruses inside infected lymphocytes.
- *Biosynthesis and cleavage.* When the provirus is activated, perhaps by a new and different infection, the normal cell machinery directs the production of more viral RNA. Some of this RNA becomes the genetic material for new viral particles. The rest of the viral RNA brings about the synthesis of very long polypeptides. These polypeptides have to be cut up into smaller pieces. This cutting process, called cleavage, is catalyzed by the HIV protease enzyme.
- *Assembly.* Capsid proteins, viral enzymes, and RNA can now be assembled to form new viral particles.
- *Budding.* During budding, the virus acquires its envelope from the host cell's plasma membrane.

The life cycle of an HIV virus includes transmission to a new host. Body secretions, such as semen from a male who is infected, contain proviruses inside CD4 T cells. When this semen is discharged into the vagina, rectum, or mouth, infected CD4 T cells migrate through the organ's lining and enter the body. The receptive partner in anal-rectal intercourse appears to be most at risk, because the lining of the rectum is very thin, which provides the virus with more rapid access to immune system cells. CD4 macrophages present in tissues are believed to be the first infected when proviruses enter the body. When these macrophages move to the lymph nodes, HIV begins to infect CD4 T cells. HIV can hide out in local lymph nodes for some time, but eventually the lymph nodes degenerate. Large numbers of HIV particles can then enter the bloodstream. Now the viral load begins to increase; when it exceeds the CD4 T-cell count, the individual progresses to the final phase of an HIV infection.

There is no cure for AIDS, but a treatment called *highly active antiretroviral therapy (HAART)* is usually able to stop HIV replication to such an extent that the viral load becomes undetectable. HAART uses a combination of drugs that interfere with the life cycle of HIV. Entry inhibitors stop HIV from entering a cell. The virus is prevented from binding to a receptor in the plasma membrane. Reverse transcriptase inhibitors, such as zidovudine (AZT), interfere with the operation of the reverse transcriptase enzyme. Integrase inhibitors prevent HIV from inserting its genetic material into that of the host cells. Protease inhibitors prevent protease from cutting up newly created polypeptides. Assembly and budding inhibitors are in the experimental stage, and none are available as yet. Ideally, a drug combination will make the virus less likely to replicate or successfully mutate. If reproduction can be suppressed, viral resistance to this therapy will be less likely to occur and the drugs won't lose their effectiveness. However, investigators have found that when HAART is discontinued, the virus rebounds.

HIV Vaccine The consensus is that control of the AIDS pandemic will not occur until there is a vaccine that prevents HIV infection. Unfortunately, this would not be a cure. Instead, the vaccine would be a preventive measure that helps people who are not yet infected escape infection (preventive vaccine). Alternatively, a therapeutic vaccine could slow the progression of the disease. Scientists have studied more than 50 different preventive vaccines and over 30 therapeutic vaccines. A program called the HIV Vaccine Trials Network (HVTN) has been created to coordinate and analyze the data from all of the efforts currently underway to develop a vaccine. The Science feature "The Challenges of Developing an AIDS Vaccine" reviews the difficulties in developing an effective AIDS vaccine. This will help you understand why we do not have an AIDS vaccine yet and, indeed, why we may never have an ideal one.

Tuberculosis

In 1882, Robert Koch was the first to see the causative agent of tuberculosis (TB) with a microscope. At that time, TB caused around 14% of deaths in Europe. The disease was called *consumption,* because it seemed to consume the patients from the inside until they wasted away. In the 1940s, with the advent of effective antibiotics to fight TB, it was thought that the disease could be eliminated. However, control measures were not implemented consistently and tuberculosis cases began to rise in the 1980s. It is estimated that one-third of the world's population has been exposed to TB. In 2019, approximately 10 million people were infected with TB, and an estimated 1.4 million died. HIV infections are a contributing factor to the increase in TB cases. Tuberculosis is currently the number one cause of death in patients with AIDS.

Causative Agent and Transmission

Tuberculosis is caused by a species of rod-shaped bacterium called *Mycobacterium tuberculosis* (Fig. 8.10). In nature, it is a very slow-growing bacterium. The cells have a thick, waxy coating and can exist for weeks in a dehydrated state. The organism is spread by airborne droplets introduced into the air when an infected person coughs, sings, or sneezes. The bacteria can float in the air for several hours and still be infectious. The likelihood of infection increases with the length and frequency of exposure to an individual with active TB. This makes TB especially contagious on airplane flights longer than 8 hours. It also makes the caregivers for those with TB at risk.

Disease

The incubation period is 4 to 12 weeks, and the disease develops very slowly. Once the bacteria reach the lungs, they are consumed by macrophages. Other white blood cells rush to the infected area. Together they wall off the original infection site, producing

BIOLOGY TODAY ▶ **Science**

The Challenges of Developing an AIDS Vaccine

An ideal AIDS vaccine would be inexpensive and able to provide lifelong protection against all strains of HIV (Fig. 8A). Is such a vaccine possible? Effective vaccines have been developed against diseases such as hepatitis B, smallpox, polio, tetanus, influenza, and the measles. But what about AIDS? The top obstacles in the development of an AIDS vaccine include the following:

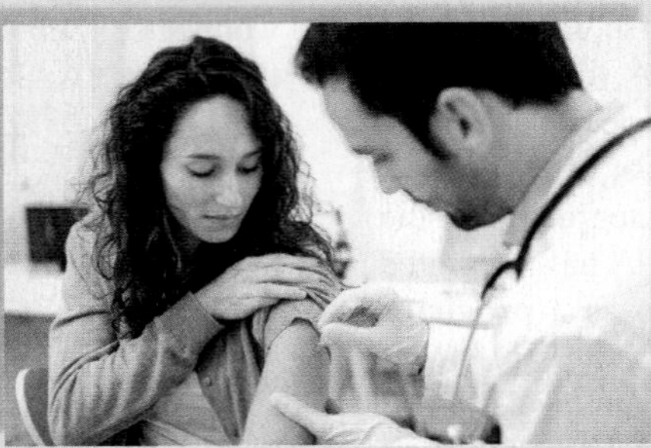

Figure 8A A preventive HIV vaccine is not yet available. Different strains of HIV and a high viral mutation rate are just two of the reasons it has been difficult to develop a vaccine against HIV.
Production Perig/Shutterstock

1. The ideal AIDS vaccine would prevent HIV entry into human cells and prevent the progression and transmission of the disease. However, no vaccine has ever proved to be 100% effective at blocking a virus from entry into cells. Instead, most vaccines prevent, modify, or weaken the disease caused by the infection.
2. Due to HIV's high rate of mutation, there are several genetically different types and subtypes of HIV. HIV strains may differ by 10% within one person and by 35% in people across the globe. Viruses that are genetically different may have different surface proteins, and HIV surface proteins are the focus of many AIDS vaccines. The question is, will scientists need a vaccine for each HIV subtype, or will one vaccine provide protection for all HIV variants?
3. If a vaccine produces only short-term protection, people would need to continue to get booster shots similar to shots given yearly for the flu.
4. There are concerns that an AIDS vaccine would make people more vulnerable to HIV infection. It is believed that in some diseases, such as yellow fever and Rift Valley fever, the antibodies produced after receiving the vaccine helped the virus infect more cells.
5. HIV can be transmitted as a free virus and in infected cells, so perhaps a vaccine would need to stimulate both cellular and antibody-mediated responses. This is complicated by the fact that HIV infects and destroys immune cells, particularly T cells. In addition, most successful vaccines stimulate only antibody production.
6. Most vaccines in use today against other diseases are prepared from live-attenuated (weakened) forms of the infectious virus. There are concerns that an AIDS vaccine made using weakened forms of the live virus will cause HIV disease (AIDS).
7. HIV inserts its genetic material into human cells, where it can hide from the immune system.

Although there are many difficulties in vaccine development, AIDS vaccine trials are underway. The process can take many years. After a vaccine has been tested in animals, it must pass through three phases of clinical trials before it is marketed or administered to the public. In Phases I and II, the vaccine is tested from 1 to 2 years in a small number of volunteers without HIV infection. The most effective vaccines move into Phase III. In Phase III, the vaccine is tested 3 to 4 years in thousands of people without HIV. A Phase III trial of the RV144 HIV vaccine was conducted from 2003 to 2009 in Thailand and involved over 16,000 volunteers. The vaccine was reported to reduce the rate of HIV infection by 32%. In February 2015, a second trial commenced in South Africa.

Although this is a much lower percentage than will be needed for a vaccine to be considered effective, most scientists have many reasons to be optimistic that an AIDS vaccine can and will be developed. The RV144 results, and other successes with vaccinating monkeys, suggest the research is beginning to yield results. But the most compelling reason for optimism is the human body's ability to suppress the infection. The immune system is able to successfully and effectively decrease the HIV viral load in the body, helping delay the onset of AIDS an average of 10 years in 60% of people who are HIV-infected in the United States. Studies have shown that a small number of people remain HIV-uninfected after repeated exposure to the virus, and a few individuals with HIV maintain a healthy immune system for over 15 years. These stories of the human body's ability to fight HIV infection keep scientists hopeful that there is a way to help the body fight HIV infection. Most scientists agree that—despite the obstacles and the setbacks—an AIDS vaccine is possible in our future.

Questions to Consider

1. Why might an HIV/AIDS vaccine give some people a false sense of security?
2. What cultural factors may be inhibiting the development of a vaccine?

small, hard nodules, or *tubercles,* in the lungs. It is these tubercles that give the disease its name. In most patients, the bacteria remain alive within the tubercles, but the disease does not progress. These patients are said to have latent TB. They do not feel sick, and they are not contagious. A person with latent TB will test positively on a tuberculosis skin test. Tubercles often calcify and can be seen on a chest X-ray (Fig. 8.11). The combination of skin testing and X-ray findings confirms the diagnosis of tuberculosis.

Active disease may occur if the immune system fails to control *Mycobacterium tuberculosis* in the lungs. A person with active disease is contagious. The tubercle liquefies and forms a cavity.

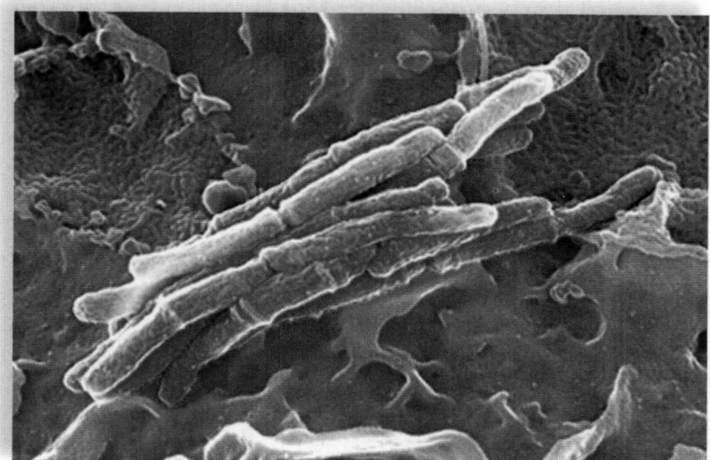

Figure 8.10 **The causative agent of tuberculosis.**
Tuberculosis is caused by *Mycobacterium tuberculosis,* shown here from a sputum sample.
SPL/Science Source

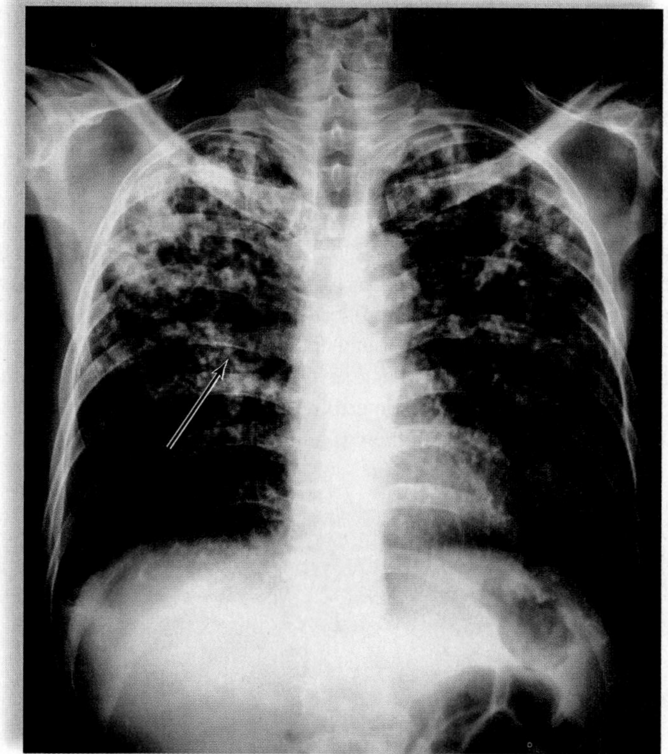

Figure 8.11 **An X-ray of a TB-infected lung.**
TB causes tubercles in the lungs. In the active state, these liquefy and cavities (colored red here) may be observed on an X-ray.
Stockdevil/Getty Images

The bacteria can then spread from these cavities throughout the body, especially to the kidneys, spine, and brain. It may be fatal. Symptoms of active TB include a bad cough, chest pain, and coughing up blood or sputum. As the disease progresses, symptoms include fatigue, loss of appetite, chills, fevers, and night sweats. The patient begins to lose weight and wastes away.

BIOLOGY IN YOUR LIFE

Does the TB skin test expose you to tuberculosis?

The TB skin test does not expose you to the bacterium *Mycobacterium tuberculosis*. Instead, in a lab, a small amount of purified protein derivative (called PPD) is obtained from strains of the bacterium. When PPD is injected under the skin, it acts as an antigen to the immune system. If you have previously been exposed to TB, the antibody-mediated response will invoke a reaction (swelling, hardness) against PPD. A medical professional familiar with your medical history then measures the degree of the reaction to assess your exposure. Because PPD is derived from the bacterium, it is not capable of causing the disease.

Treatment and Prevention

Due to the resurgence of antibiotic-resistant strains, multiple anti-TB drugs are given simultaneously for 12 to 24 months. The most common drugs are isoniazid (INH), rifampin (RIF), ethambutol, and pyrazinamide. Though it is unlikely that bacteria will develop resistance to multiple drugs at the same time, there are several drug-resistant forms of TB. Examples are multidrug-resistant TB (MDR TB), which is resistant to both isoniazid and rifampin, and extensively drug-resistant TB (XDR TB), a rare form of TB that is resistant to isoniazid and rifampin, plus one additional antibiotic. It takes at least 6 months to kill all the *Mycobacterium tuberculosis* in the body, so the length of drug treatment is long.

Public health officials try to prevent the spread of TB by identifying and treating all cases of active TB. Patients with active TB are isolated for at least 2 weeks at the beginning of drug treatment to prevent transmission. Thereafter, they are monitored for drug compliance and reappearance of symptoms. Anyone exposed to an active case of TB is treated.

Malaria

Malaria is called the world's invisible pandemic. Most people in the West do not even consider malaria a major health threat, yet in 2020 there were 220 million cases, with an estimated 409,000 deaths, mostly in sub-Saharan Africa. Key to the geographic distribution of malaria is transmission of the disease by a mosquito vector that depends on temperature and rainfall and thus survives well in tropical areas. A **vector** is a living organism—usually an insect or animal—that transfers the pathogen from one host to another.

Causative Agent and Transmission

The parasites that cause malaria belong to the genus *Plasmodium.* These are protists (see Fig. 1.6). There are four species that infect humans: *P. malariae, P. falciparum, P. vivax,* and *P. ovale. P. falciparum* causes more disease and death than the other species. The parasite is spread by the female *Anopheles gambiae* mosquito. Half of the life cycle occurs in the human, and the remainder happens in the mosquito. As the female mosquito feeds on human blood, she injects saliva containing an anticoagulant along with the parasite. The parasites travel to the liver, where they undergo asexual reproduction. The parasites are released from the liver to infect more liver cells and erythrocytes (red blood cells). Inside the erythrocyte, the *Plasmodium* enlarges and divides until it bursts the erythrocyte. This red blood cell stage is cyclic and repeats every 48 to 72 hours. Some parasites within the erythrocytes don't destroy their host cells. Instead, they develop into the sexual form of the parasite. When these are ingested by another mosquito during a blood meal, they develop into male and female gametes within the gut of the mosquito. The gametes fuse, undergo mitosis, and form the parasites that migrate to the salivary glands of the mosquito to continue the cycle.

Disease

People at significant risk for malaria include those who have little or no immunity to the parasite. Children, pregnant women, and travelers are most likely to contract the disease. Diagnosis of malaria depends on the presence of parasites in the blood. The incubation period from time of bite to onset of symptoms varies from 7 to 30 days. The symptoms of malaria range from very mild to fatal. Most people infected with malaria develop a flulike illness with chills and fevers interrupted by sweating. These symptoms exhibit a cyclical pattern every 48 to 72 hours corresponding to bursting of the red blood cells in the body. Milder cases of malaria are often confused with influenza or a cold; therefore, treatment is delayed. More severe cases cause severe anemia (due to the destruction of red blood cells), cerebral malaria, acute kidney failure, cardiovascular collapse, shock, and death.

Treatment and Prevention

Malaria is a curable disease if it is diagnosed and treated correctly and quickly. A person exhibiting malaria symptoms should be treated within 24 hours of onset. Common antimalarial drugs include quinine and artesunate. Treatment helps reduce symptoms and breaks the transmission pattern for the disease. Antimalarial drugs can also be used prophylactically, or before infection. They do not prevent the initial infection following the mosquito bite. Instead, they prevent the development of the parasites in the blood.

Health organizations are working on the prevention of infection through vector control. Strategies include eliminating the mosquito by removing its breeding sites and by insecticide fogging of large areas. Additional efforts are aimed at preventing humans from being bitten by the mosquito, using simple mosquito nets. The use of insecticide-treated mosquito nets for children has reduced the incidence of malaria.

Drug-resistant *Plasmodium* and insecticide-resistant *Anopheles* are becoming significant problems. *P. falciparum* and *P. vivax* have developed strains that are resistant to the antimalarial drugs. Efforts to develop a malaria vaccine are ongoing.

Influenza

The common name for influenza is the flu, and each year it affects 5–20% of Americans and causes an estimated 36,000 fatalities per year. Influenza is a viral infection that causes runny nose, cough, chills, fever, head and body aches, and nausea. You can catch influenza by inhaling virus-laden droplets that have been coughed or sneezed into the air by a person with influenza, or by contact with contaminated objects, such as door handles or bedding. The viruses then attach to and infect cells of the respiratory tract.

Influenza Viruses

The influenza virus has an H (hemagglutinin) spike and an N (neuraminidase) spike (Fig. 8.12*a*). Its H spike allows the virus to bind to its receptor, and its N spike attacks host plasma membranes in a way that allows mature viruses to exit the cell. Both H spikes and N spikes have variations in their shapes: 17 types of H and 10 types of N spikes are currently known. Furthermore, each type of spike can occur in different varieties called subtypes. Many of the influenza viruses are assigned specific codes based on the type of spike. For example, H5N1 virus gets its name from its variety of H5 spikes and its variety of N1 spikes. Our immune system can recognize only the particular variety of H spikes and N spikes it has been exposed to in the past by infection or immunization. When a new influenza virus arises, one for which there is little or no immunity in the human population, a flu pandemic (global outbreak) may occur.

Possible Bird Flu Pandemic of the Future

Currently, the H5N1 subtype of influenza virus is of great concern because of its potential to reach pandemic proportions. An H5N1 is common in wild birds, such as waterfowl, and can readily infect domestic poultry, such as chickens, which is why it is referred to as an avian influenza or a bird flu. An H5N1 virus has infected waterfowl for some time without causing serious illness. A more pathogenic version of H5N1 appeared about a decade ago in China and promptly started to cause widespread and severe illness in domestic chickens. Scientists are still trying to determine what made H5N1 become so lethal, first to chickens and then to humans.

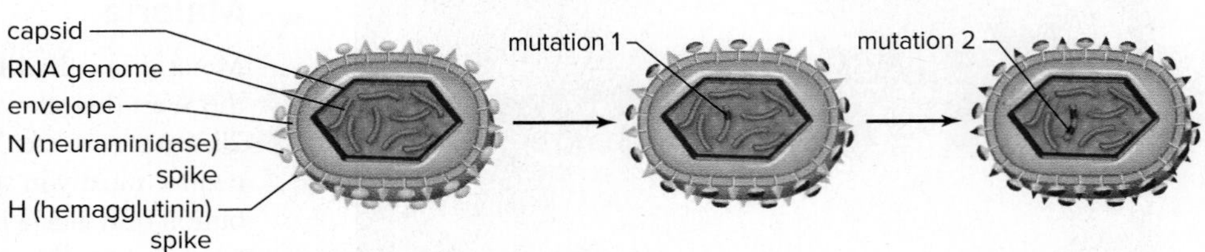

a. Viral genetic mutations occur in a bird host.

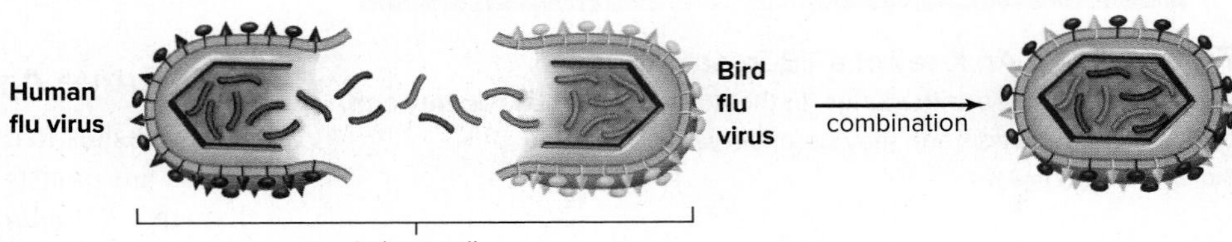

b. Combination of viral genes occurs in human host.

Figure 8.12 The bird flu virus.
a. Genetic mutations in bird flu viral spikes could allow the virus to infect the human upper respiratory tract. **b.** Alternatively, a combination of bird flu and human spikes could allow the virus to infect the human upper respiratory tract.

Why can bird flu H5N1 infect humans? Because the virus can attach to both a bird flu receptor and a human flu receptor. Close contact between domestic poultry and humans is necessary for this to happen. At this time, the virus has rarely been transmitted from one human to another, and only among people who have close contact with one another, such as members of the same household. The concern is that with additional mutations, the H5N1 virus could become capable of sustained human-to-human transmission, and then spread around the world.

How could H5N1 become better at spreading within the human population? Currently, bird flu H5N1 infects mostly the lungs. Most human flu viruses infect the upper respiratory tract, trachea, and bronchi and can be spread by coughing. If a spontaneous mutation in the H spike of H5N1 enabled it to attack the upper respiratory tract, it could be easily spread from human to human by coughing and sneezing. Another possibility is that a combining of spikes could occur in a person who was infected with both the bird flu and the human flu viruses (Fig. 8.12*b*). According to the CDC, over the past decade an increasing number of humans infected with an H5N1 virus have been reported in Asia, the Pacific, the Near East, Africa, and Europe. More than half of these people have died. The good news is that the FDA has approved an H5N1 vaccine for individuals between the ages of 18 and 64. Although additional mutations in the virus may reduce its overall effectiveness, the vaccine is believed to provide a good foundation of protection against this form of influenza.

CHECK YOUR PROGRESS 8.2

1. Describe the differences among an outbreak, an epidemic, and a pandemic, and give an example of each.
2. Summarize the HIV replication cycle, and list the types of cells this virus infects.
3. Explain the role of the mosquito in the malarial life cycle.
4. Explain how variation may occur in influenza viruses such as H5N1.

CONNECTING THE CONCEPTS

For more information on the topics presented in this section, refer to the following discussions:

Section 6.2 examines the role of erythrocytes in the body.

Section 8.1 describes the structure of a typical virus.

Section 10.3 explores the structure of the lungs.

8.3 Emerging Diseases and COVID-19

LEARNING OUTCOMES

Upon completion of this section, you should be able to

1. Define the term *emerging disease*.
2. List some examples of emerging diseases.

An infectious disease may be classified as an **emerging disease** if it is occurring for the first time in human populations, is rapidly increasing in its incidence (or frequency) in humans, or is entering into new geographic regions. As shown in Figure 8.13, examples of emerging diseases are avian influenza (H5N1) (see Section 8.2), swine flu (H1N1), Middle East respiratory syndrome (MERS), Zika virus, and SARS-CoV-2.

The National Institute of Allergy and Infectious Diseases (NIAID) maintains a list of pathogens considered to be, or have the potential to be, emerging diseases. In addition, NIAID maintains an ongoing record of reemerging diseases, or infectious diseases that have reappeared after a significant decline in incidence. *Streptococcus,* the bacterium that causes strep throat and other infections, is considered to be a reemerging pathogen due to increasing resistance to antibiotics. Finally, there are diseases that have been known throughout human history but had not been known to be caused by an infectious agent, or the pathogen had never been identified.

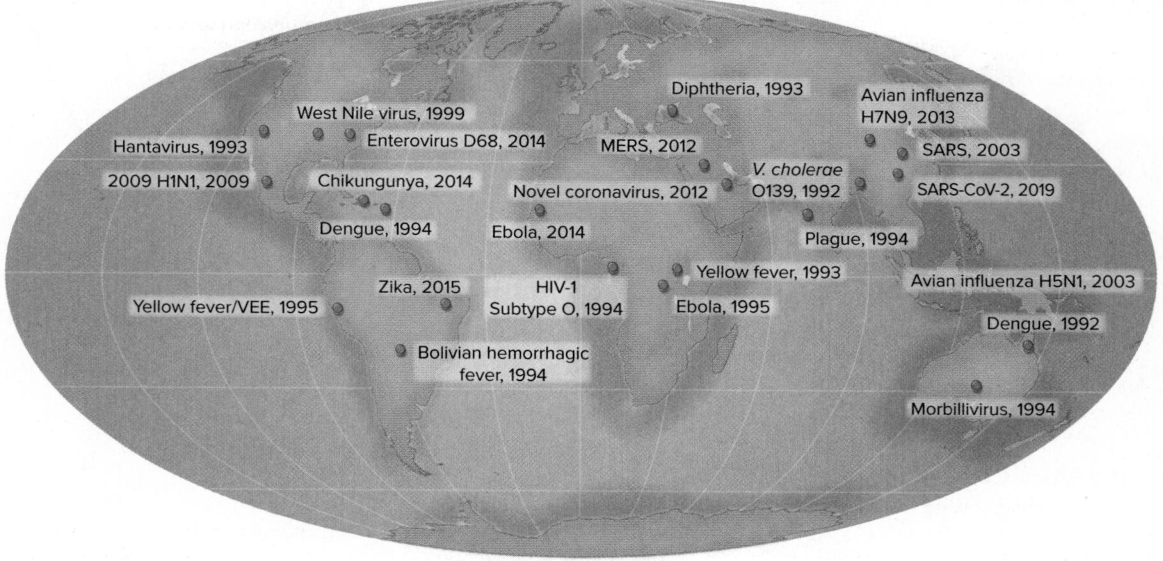

Figure 8.13 **Emerging diseases.**
The diseases here are known as emerging diseases because they are either new to humans, or have seen an increased prevalence in human populations.

BIOLOGY TODAY ▶ Science

The Biology of SARS-CoV-2

Coronaviruses are an example of a single-stranded animal RNA virus. They are considerably larger than most RNA viruses, and like many other single-stranded RNA viruses, such as Ebola virus and influenza, they have high mutation rates.

Coronaviruses have an exterior envelope made from the plasma membrane of the host cells. This membrane may be disrupted (or broken down) by the action of soaps and alcohol-based sanitizers. Embedded within this membrane is the "crown," a series of glycoproteins (Fig. 8B). These include:

- *S protein*. Spike proteins are responsible for the attachment of the virus to specific receptors on its host cell.
- *M protein*. Membrane proteins are involved in the assembly of the virus.
- *E protein*. Envelope proteins are also involved in the assembly of the virus, as well as the exit of the virus from its host cell.

Inside the coronavirus, the single-stranded RNA genetic material is surrounded by a helical protein structure, called a nucleocapsid (sometimes just referred to as a capsid). The genome of the SARS-CoV contains approximately 20 genes, 3 of which code for the S, M, and E proteins, plus 1, the N protein, for the nucleocapsid. In comparison, bacteria, on average, have less than 2,700 genes, and humans have around 19,000.

While the SARS-CoV-2 virus is a very new emerging virus, researchers have begun to piece together aspects of its life cycle based on their knowledge of other coronaviruses. This life cycle is shown in Figure 8C.

Because coronaviruses consist of single-stranded RNA, their genetic information can be translated directly into the four structural proteins (for a review of gene expression, see Section 22.3). With the exception of the N protein, the other structural proteins are sent to the rough ER and Golgi apparatus where they help assemble the new viruses and become part of the envelope surrounding the virus. The N protein is used to assemble the nucleocapsid, which surrounds the new RNA material produced by replication.

Recently, researchers have discovered another unique aspect of SARS-CoV-2. Unlike other viruses, which leave the Golgi apparatus in a vesicle for release from the cell, SARS-CoV-2 is packaged within a lysosome, a vesicle with a very low pH that is typically involved with the breakdown or digestion of organic molecules. The reason for this difference is still under investigation.

Questions to Consider

1. How might an understanding of the structure and life cycle of this virus help researchers investigate treatments and prevention methods, such as vaccines?
2. How is the life cycle of SARS-CoV-2 different from other viruses (see Section 8.1)?

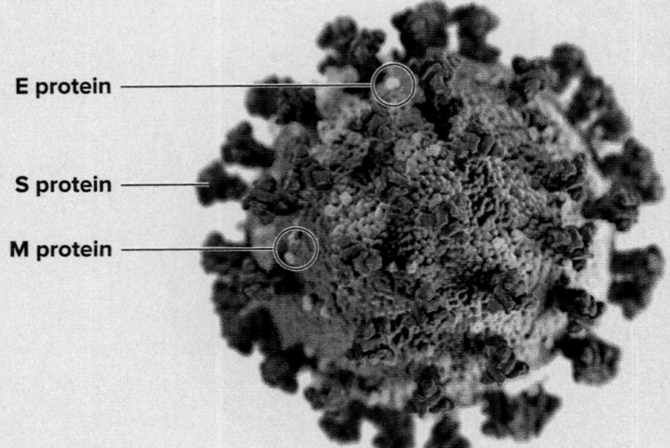

Figure 8B The SARS-CoV-2 virus.
The surface of a coronavirus showing the different forms of glycoproteins.
Alissa Eckert, MS; Dan Higgins, MAMS/CDC

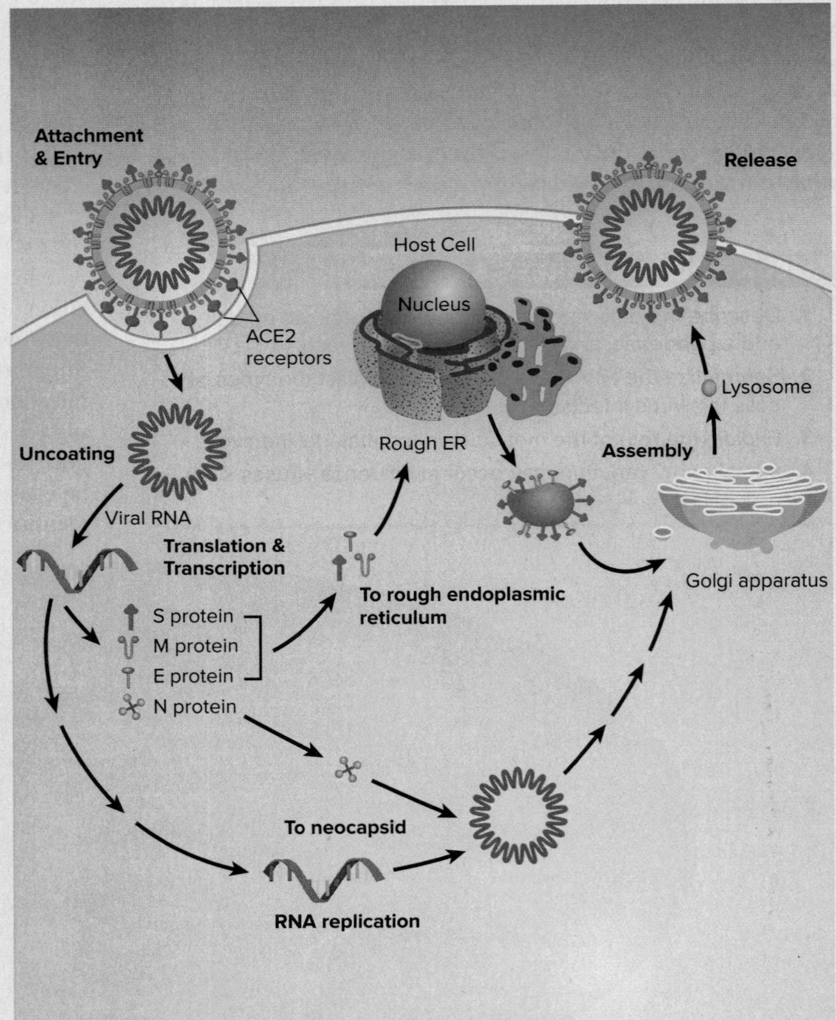

Figure 8C Life cycle of SARS-CoV-2.
The SARS-CoV-2 virus replicates its proteins and genetic material using the cellular machinery of its host cell.

Where do emerging diseases come from? Some of these diseases may result from new and/or increased exposure to animals or insect populations that act as vectors for disease. Changes in human behavior and use of technology can also result in new diseases.

NIAID, the WHO, and the CDC also monitor reemerging diseases. Reemerging diseases have been known in the past but were thought to have been controlled. Diseases in this category include known diseases that are spreading from their original geographic location and diseases that have suddenly increased in incidence. A change in geographic location could be due to global warming, allowing expansion of habitats for insect vectors. Reemerging diseases can also be due to human carelessness, as in the abuse of antibiotics or poorly implemented vaccination programs. This allows previously controlled diseases to resurge.

In this section, we will focus on the SARS-CoV-2 emerging virus and the COVID-19 pandemic.

COVID-19

SARS-CoV-2, the virus associated with the respiratory disease COVID-19 (see Section 10.7), is an example of a coronavirus. Coronaviruses are named for their distinctive, crownlike spikes emerging from the surface of the virus. They are a relatively common animal virus (zoonotic virus) that may infect a wide variety of animal species, such as bats, camels, birds, livestock, and humans. In some cases, coronaviruses are known to cause respiratory and intestinal diseases, especially in livestock (chickens, pigs, and cattle), and in the case of the SARS/MERS class of viruses, humans.

Coronavirus infections in humans were first recorded in the 1950s, and were typically associated with mild cases of the common cold. A more severe form of human coronavirus, SARS-CoV, appeared in China in 2002. Thought to have originated in bats or civet cats and then transmitted to humans, SARS-CoV spread to cause a global outbreak in early 2003. The outbreak totaled over 8,000 known cases and caused 774 deaths worldwide, with a fatality rate of just under 10%. No human cases of SARS-CoV have been reported since 2004.

Another form of human coronavirus, MERS-CoV, first appeared in Jordan in 2012. Most cases of MERS-CoV occurred in countries on the Arabian Peninsula and were linked to travel from infected areas. The virus is believed to have originated in bats, then it spread to camels, and finally, it was contracted by humans living or working near them. By the end of 2019, there were nearly 2,500 confirmed cases of MERS-CoV, resulting in 858 deaths—a fatality rate of 34.4%.

In late December 2019, a new coronavirus emerged in the Wuhan province of China. Originally called 2019-nCoV and Novel Coronavirus 2019, and later renamed SARS-CoV-2, this virus causes the respiratory disease COVID-19. This disease quickly became a global pandemic, infecting hundreds of millions of people and resulting in an ever-increasing death toll. In addition to the biological dangers of an infection with this coronavirus, the highly contagious characteristics of SARS-CoV-2 resulted in an almost complete global disruption of society by impacting travel, economies, and the social interactions of almost everyone on the planet.

The Scientific feature "The Biology of SARS-CoV-2" explores what we currently know about the structure and replication of the virus responsible for COVID-19.

CHECK YOUR PROGRESS 8.3

1. Distinguish between an emerging disease and a reemerging disease.
2. Explain how emerging diseases arise.
3. Explain what may be done to reduce the threat of emerging and reemerging diseases.

CONNECTING THE CONCEPTS

For more information on the topics in this section, refer to the following discussions:

Section 1.3 examines the research that identified *H. pylori* as a cause of ulcers.

Chapter 25 explores how increases in the human population are creating ecological consequences.

8.4 Antibiotic Resistance

LEARNING OUTCOMES

Upon completion of this section, you should be able to

1. Summarize how a pathogen becomes resistant to an antibiotic.
2. Explain the significance of antibiotic resistance.

Some well-known pathogens are becoming more difficult to fight due to the advent of **antibiotic resistance.** Just four years after penicillin was introduced in 1943, bacteria began developing resistance to it. The use of antibiotics does not cause humans to become resistant to the drugs. Instead, pathogens become resistant. Some organisms in a population are naturally resistant to the drug (Fig. 8.14). They have acquired this resistance through mutations or interactions with other organisms. The drug regimen kills the susceptible ones while leaving naturally resistant ones to multiply and repopulate the patient's body. The new population is then resistant to the drug.

Tuberculosis, malaria, gonorrhea, *Staphylococcus aureus,* and enterococci (or group D *Streptococcus*) are a few of the diseases and organisms connected to antibiotic resistance. Unfortunately, more and more organisms are becoming multidrug-resistant, leaving health-care facilities with few choices for treating infections.

What is being done about this problem? The CDC, U.S. Food and Drug Administration, and U.S. Department of Agriculture have formed a cooperative organization charged with monitoring antibiotic-resistant organisms. Pharmaceutical companies are actively developing new classes of antibiotics. However, new classes of drugs are expensive to develop and can take years to get approved. The best way to fight antibiotic resistance is to prevent it from happening by using antibiotics wisely, as the following outlines:

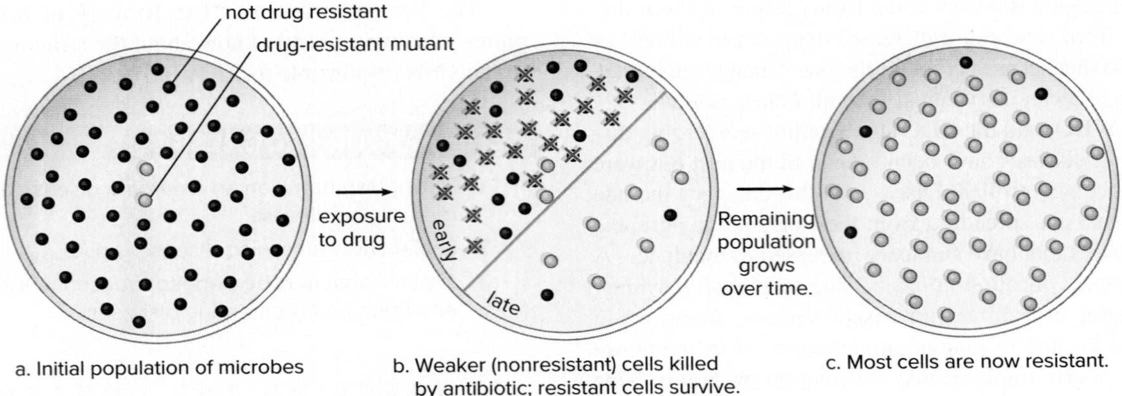

Figure 8.14 Development of antibiotic resistance.
a. In a microbe population, random mutation can result in cells with drug resistance. **b.** Drug use kills all nonresistant microbes, leaving only the stronger, resistant cells to survive. **c.** The new microbe population is now mostly resistant to the antibiotic.

- Take all of the antibiotics prescribed as directed. Do not skip doses or discontinue treatment when you feel better.
- Do not expect a doctor to prescribe antibiotics for all infections. For example, antibiotics are ineffective against viral infections, such as colds.
- Do not save unused antibiotics or take antibiotics prescribed for a different infection.

Antibiotic resistance is a serious health problem. Each year in the United States, at least 2.8 million people become infected with antibiotic-resistant bacteria, resulting in an estimated 35,000 deaths per year.

Multidrug-Resistant Organisms

The most severe threat from antibiotic resistance is the evolution of *multidrug-resistant organisms (MDROs).* These organisms are usually resistant to multiple different classes of antibiotics, making treatment difficult and in some cases impossible.

XDR Tuberculosis

XDR TB stands for extensively drug-resistant tuberculosis. It is resistant to almost all the drugs used to treat TB. This includes the first-line antibiotics (the older and cheaper ones), as well as the second-line antibiotics (the newer and more expensive drugs). Therefore, the treatment options are very limited. Fortunately, this is still relatively rare. There were only 63 cases in the United States between 1993 and 2011. MDR TB, multidrug-resistant TB, is more common. These organisms are resistant to the first-line antibiotics. Eastern Europe and Southeast Asia have the highest rates of MDR TB.

MRSA

Methicillin-resistant *Staphylococcus aureus,* or **MRSA,** is another antibiotic-resistant bacterium (Fig. 8.15). MRSA is resistant to methicillin and other common antibiotics, such as penicillin and amoxicillin. It causes "staph" infections, such as boils and infection of the hair follicles. In 1974, only 2% of staph infections were caused by MRSA, but by 2004 the number had risen to 63%. In response, the CDC conducted an aggressive campaign to educate health-care workers on MRSA prevention. The program was very successful, and between 2005 and 2008 the number of MRSA infections in hospitals declined by 28%.

MRSA is especially common in athletes who share equipment. It is also prevalent in nursing homes and hospitals where patients have already reduced immune responses. Patients infected with MRSA generally have longer hospital stays with poorer outcomes. Indeed, it can be fatal, and is passed from nonsymptomatic carriers to patients, usually through hand contact. Hand washing is critical for preventing transmission.

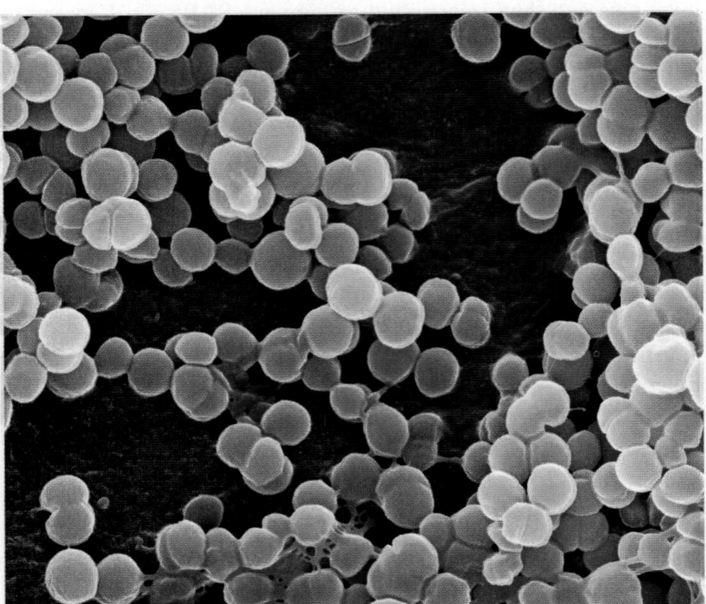

8,700×

Figure 8.15 Methicillin-resistant *Staphylococcus aureus*.
Paul Gunning/Science Photo Library/Getty Images

CHECK YOUR PROGRESS 8.4

1. Explain how bacteria become resistant to an antibiotic.
2. Describe the correct procedure for taking antibiotics.
3. Explain what is meant when an organism is classified as an MDRO and give an example.

CONNECTING THE CONCEPTS

For more information on the topics in this section, refer to the following discussion:

Section 23.2 examines how natural selection acts as the mechanism for evolutionary change.

CONCLUSION

In this chapter, we explored certain types of pathogenic viruses and bacteria that cause human disease. It is important to note that the majority of bacteria and viruses do not cause problems for humans. However, as we have learned from SARS-CoV-2 and COVID-19, and other viruses and bacteria described in this chapter, some have the potential to significantly impact human society.

SUMMARIZE

8.1 Bacteria and Viruses

Microbes perform valuable services, but they also cause disease. Disease-causing microbes are collectively called **pathogens.**

Bacteria

- **Bacteria** are prokaryotic cells that consist of a plasma membrane, a **cell wall** containing unique polysaccharides, and cytoplasm. Some bacteria have a gel-like **capsule** surrounding the cell wall. Some bacteria possess **fimbriae** to attach to surfaces, **flagella** for movement, and a **pilus** for the transfer of DNA between cells. Within the cell, **plasmids** sometimes contain genes that allow for resistance to antibiotics.
- Bacteria may cause disease by multiplying in hosts and by producing **toxins.**

Viruses and Prions

- **Viruses** are intracellular parasites consisting of a protein coat (called a capsid) and a nucleic acid core that take over the machinery of the host to reproduce.
- **Prions** are misfolded proteins that have the ability to infect cells. Creutzfeldt–Jakob disease (CJD) is a prion disease in humans.

8.2 Infectious Diseases and Human Health

Infectious diseases are classified as an **epidemic** if there is an above-average number of cases in a specific area. Local epidemics are often called **outbreaks,** and a global epidemic is referred to as a **pandemic.**

HIV/AIDS

- **Acquired immunodeficiency syndrome (AIDS)** is caused by the **human immunodeficiency virus (HIV).** HIV infects cells of the immune system, allowing for the development of **opportunistic infections.**
- Phases of an HIV infection are based on the number of CD4 T cells in the blood and the individual's health.
- The HIV virus is an example of a retrovirus. It contains RNA as its genetic material. The enzymes reverse transcriptase, integrase, and protease assist the virus in its replication within the host cell. When the genetic information from the HIV is integrated into the host cell's chromosomes, it is called a **provirus.**
- The HIV life cycle consists of a series of phases, including attachment, fusion, entry, reverse transcription, integration, biosynthesis and cleavage, assembly, and budding.

Tuberculosis

- Tuberculosis (TB) is caused by the *Mycobacterium tuberculosis* bacterium. The bacterium is spread through the air and infects the lungs, interfering with the respiratory system. The disease was historically referred to as consumption because the symptoms include weight loss.

Malaria

- Malaria is a disease of the circulatory system. It is caused by an infection of red blood cells by *Plasmodium* protists, which are carried by certain species of mosquitoes.

Influenza

- Commonly called the flu, influenza is caused by a virus that infects the cells of the respiratory tract.
- Influenza viruses are named based on the types of protein spikes on the surface of the cell. Bird flu, or H5N1, is an example.

8.3 Emerging Diseases and COVID-19

- Emerging diseases are those occurring for the first time in human populations, or rapidly increasing in their incidence (or frequency) in humans, or entering into new geographic regions. Reemerging diseases are those recurring after a period of decline.
- Examples of emerging diseases are SARS, MERS, Zika, and SARS-CoV-2.

8.4 Antibiotic Resistance

- **Antibiotic resistance** occurs when a bacterium becomes resistant to the chemicals being used to treat it.
- Examples are extensively drug-resistant tuberculosis **(XDR TB)** and methicillin-resistant *Staphylococcus aureus* **(MRSA).**

ENGAGE

THINKING CRITICALLY

1. The development of antibiotic resistance may be accelerated in individuals who stop taking the recommended doses of antibiotics before the end of their prescription. How would this cause an increase in the number of antibiotic-resistant bacteria in the body? (*Hint:* Use Figure 8.14 as an example.)
2. Antibiotics are not effective in the treatment of viral infections, such as HIV. By comparing the structure of a virus and a bacterium, what might be some ways an antibiotic chemical may target a type of bacteria, not a virus?
3. New antibiotics are often developed by examining how other species (plants, fungi, and other bacteria) resist bacterial infection. Explain how the conservation of biodiversity plays an important role in the development of new antibiotics.

MAKING IT RELEVANT

1. What has your experience with SARS-CoV-2 taught you about the importance of the need for global monitoring of emerging viruses?
2. Do you get an annual influenza vaccine? Why or why not?
3. The term *herd immunity* refers to many individuals in a population that are immune to an infection, usually by receiving a vaccine. Why would herd immunity be important to individuals who are vulnerable in a population?

Find answers to all of the chapter questions at connect.mheducation.com

CHAPTER 9

Digestive System and Nutrition

Gluten and Celiac Disease

On any trip to the grocery store, you may notice a wide abundance of foods labeled "gluten-free," and almost every restaurant has a gluten-free section on the menu. So what exactly is gluten?

Contrary to what most people believe, gluten is not a carbohydrate. Instead, it is a type of protein commonly found in wheat, rye, and barley. For most of us, gluten is processed by the digestive system in the same manner as any other protein, meaning it is broken down into amino acids and absorbed into the circulatory system.

However, in about 1 out of every 100 individuals, the body misidentifies gluten as a foreign pathogen. The result is celiac disease, a disorder of the lining of the small intestine. In celiac disease, an example of an autoimmune response, the body's reaction to gluten causes inflammation and loss of the intestinal linings. The damage to the intestines causes malnutrition and other health problems. Individuals with celiac disease therefore must eliminate gluten from their diet. Interestingly, a gluten-free diet does not seem to have health benefits for individuals who do not suffer from celiac disease.

In this chapter, you will learn about the function of the digestive system, as well as the basic principles of nutrients and nutrition.

As you read through the chapter, think about the following questions:

1. How are carbohydrates and proteins normally processed by the digestive system?
2. How would damage to the villi of the small intestine result in malnourishment?

CHAPTER OUTLINE

BEFORE YOU BEGIN

Before beginning this chapter, take a few moments to review the following discussions:

Sections 2.4 to **2.7** What are the roles of carbohydrates, lipids, proteins, and nucleic acids?

Section 3.3 What is the role of the facilitated and active transport mechanisms in moving nutrients across a plasma membrane?

Section 3.6 What are the roles of enzymes and coenzymes?

9.1 Overview of Digestion

LEARNING OUTCOMES

Upon completion of this section, you should be able to

1. State the function of each organ of the gastrointestinal tract.
2. List the accessory organs and name a function for each.
3. Describe the structure of the gastrointestinal tract wall.

The organs of the **digestive system** are located within a tube called the *gastrointestinal (GI) tract*. The organs associated with the GI tract are shown in Figure 9.1.

The purpose of the digestive system is to **hydrolyze,** or break down using water, the macromolecules (polymers) found in food to their subunit molecules (monomers). These molecules include the nutrient molecules carbohydrates, fats, and proteins we examined in Chapter 2. These are often found in the foods we eat as large polymers that generally are too large to cross the plasma membrane. Once broken down by the digestive system, the subunit molecules, mainly monosaccharides, amino acids, fatty acids, and glycerol, can cross plasma membranes using facilitated and active transport (see Section 3.3). Our food also contains water, salts, vitamins, and minerals that help the body function normally. These are absorbed by the digestive system and carried by the blood to our cells.

The expression "You are what you eat" recognizes that our diet is very important to our health. By learning about and developing good nutritional habits, we increase our likelihood of enjoying a longer, more active, and productive life. Unfortunately, poor diet and lack of physical activity now rival smoking as major causes of preventable death in the United States.

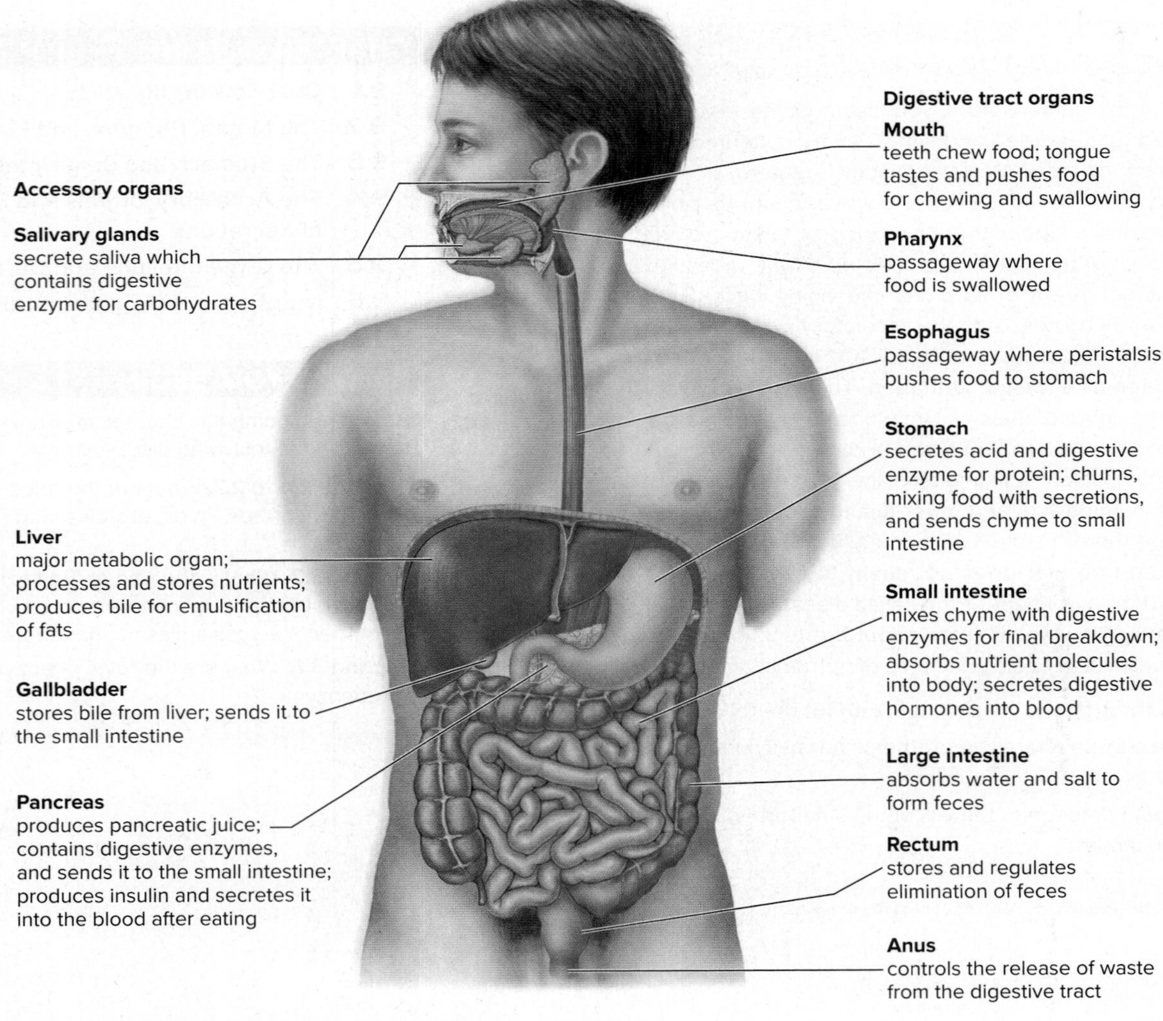
Accessory organs
Salivary glands
secrete saliva which contains digestive enzyme for carbohydrates
Liver
major metabolic organ; processes and stores nutrients; produces bile for emulsification of fats
Gallbladder
stores bile from liver; sends it to the small intestine
Pancreas
produces pancreatic juice; contains digestive enzymes, and sends it to the small intestine; produces insulin and secretes it into the blood after eating
Digestive tract organs
Mouth
teeth chew food; tongue tastes and pushes food for chewing and swallowing
Pharynx
passageway where food is swallowed
Esophagus
passageway where peristalsis pushes food to stomach
Stomach
secretes acid and digestive enzyme for protein; churns, mixing food with secretions, and sends chyme to small intestine
Small intestine
mixes chyme with digestive enzymes for final breakdown; absorbs nutrient molecules into body; secretes digestive hormones into blood
Large intestine
absorbs water and salt to form feces
Rectum
stores and regulates elimination of feces
Anus
controls the release of waste from the digestive tract

Figure 9.1 **Organs of the GI tract and accessory structures of digestion.**
Food is digested within the organs of the GI tract, from the mouth to the anus. Structures such as the liver, pancreas, and gallbladder are considered accessory structures.

Processes of Digestion

Digestion involves the following processes:

Ingestion occurs when we take in food through our mouth.

Digestion involves the breakdown of larger pieces of food into smaller pieces that can be acted on by the digestive enzymes. Digestion may be either mechanical or chemical.

- Mechanical digestion occurs primarily by chewing in the mouth and by wavelike contractions of the smooth muscles in the stomach.
- During chemical digestion, digestive enzymes hydrolyze our food's macromolecules into absorbable subunits. The digestive enzymes all have pH ranges at which they are most effective; the compartmentalization of the digestive tract helps establish these ideal pH ranges. Chemical digestion begins in the mouth, continues in the stomach, and is completed in the small intestine.

Movement of GI tract contents along the digestive tract is very important for the tract to fulfill its other functions. For example, food must be passed along from one organ to the next, normally by contractions of smooth muscle tissue called **peristalsis,** and the indigestible remains must be expelled.

Absorption occurs as subunit molecules produced by chemical digestion (i.e., nutrients) cross the wall of the GI tract and enter the cells lining the tract. From there, the nutrients enter the blood for delivery to the cells.

Elimination removes molecules that cannot be digested and need to be discharged from the body. The removal of indigestible wastes through the anus is termed *defecation.*

Wall of the Digestive Tract

We can compare the GI tract to a garden hose that has a beginning (mouth) and an end (anus). The **lumen** is the open area of a hollow organ or vessel, and in the GI tract is the central space that contains food being digested. The wall of the GI tract has four layers (Fig. 9.2). Each layer can be associated with a particular function and disorder.

The inner layer of the wall next to the lumen is called the **mucosa.** The mucosal layer contains cells that produce and secrete mucus used to protect all the layers of the tract from the digestive enzymes inside the lumen. Glands in the mucosa of the mouth, stomach, and small intestine also release digestive enzymes that act on specific classes of nutrients. Hydrochloric acid, an important component of digestion, is a compound produced by glands in the mucosa of the stomach.

Diverticulosis is a condition in which portions of the mucosa of any part of the GI tract—but primarily the large intestine—have pushed through the other layers and formed pouches. The pouches can be likened to an inner tube that pokes through weak places in a tire. When food collects in the pouches, they may become infected or inflamed. This condition is called *diverticulitis.*

The second layer in the GI wall is called the **submucosa.** The submucosal layer is a broad band of loose connective tissue that contains blood vessels, lymphatic vessels, and nerves. These are the vessels that will carry the nutrients absorbed by the mucosa. Lymph nodules, called Peyer's patches, are also in the submucosa of the small intestine. Like the tonsils, they help protect us from disease. The submucosa contains blood vessels, so it can be the site of an inflammatory response (see Section 7.2) that leads to *inflammatory bowel disease (IBD).* Chronic diarrhea, abdominal pain, fever, and weight loss are symptoms of IBD.

The third layer is termed the **muscularis** and contains two layers of smooth muscle. The inner, circular layer encircles the tract. The outer, longitudinal layer lies in the same direction as the tract. The contraction of these muscles, under nervous and hormonal control, accounts for peristalsis and subsequent movement of digested food from the esophagus to the anus. The muscularis can be associated with *irritable bowel syndrome (IBS),* in which contractions of the wall cause abdominal pain, constipation, and/or diarrhea. The underlying cause of IBS is not known, although some suggest that because this area is under nervous system control, stress may be an underlying cause.

The fourth and outermost layer of the tract is the **serosa,** which secretes a lubricating fluid. The serosa is a part of the peritoneum, the internal lining of the abdominal cavity.

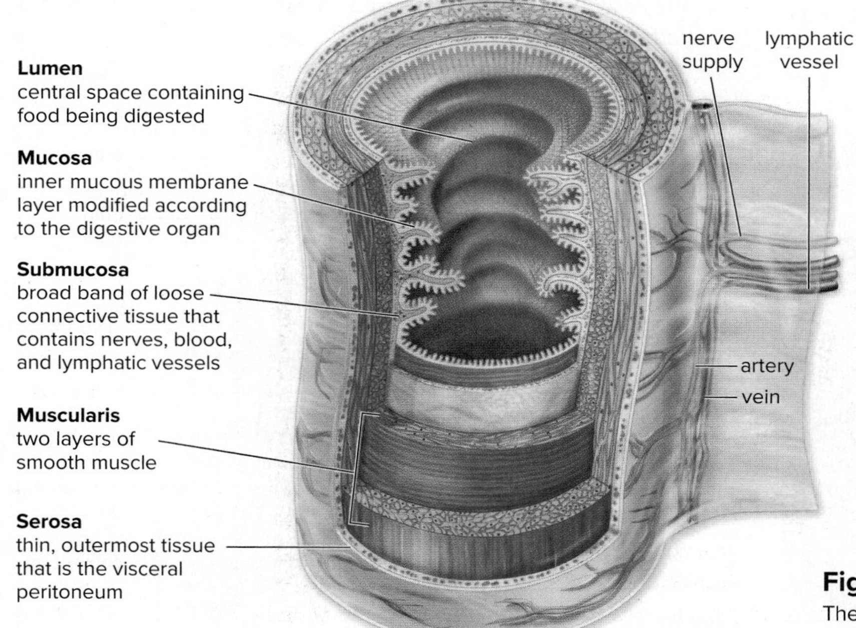
Lumen
central space containing food being digested
Mucosa
inner mucous membrane layer modified according to the digestive organ
Submucosa
broad band of loose connective tissue that contains nerves, blood, and lymphatic vessels
Muscularis
two layers of smooth muscle
Serosa
thin, outermost tissue that is the visceral peritoneum
nerve supply
lymphatic vessel
artery
vein

Figure 9.2 **The layers of the gastrointestinal tract wall.** The wall of the gastrointestinal tract contains four layers surrounding an internal space, or lumen.

CHECK YOUR PROGRESS 9.1

1. List the digestive organs and accessory structures of the digestive system.
2. Describe the processes that occur during the digestive process.
3. Identify the four layers of the GI tract from the lumen outward.

CONNECTING THE CONCEPTS

Several other organ systems interact directly with the digestive system. For more information on these interactions, refer to the following discussions:

Section 5.5 discusses the hepatic portal circulatory system, which moves blood from the intestines to the liver.

Section 7.1 examines the structure of the lymphatic system.

Section 14.4 explores how the nervous system controls the overall activity level of the gastrointestinal tract.

9.2 The Mouth, Pharynx, and Esophagus

LEARNING OUTCOMES

Upon completion of this section, you should be able to

1. Identify the structures of the mouth, pharynx, and esophagus and provide a function for each.
2. Explain the series of events involved in swallowing.
3. Summarize the diseases and conditions associated with the mouth, pharynx, and esophagus.

The mouth, pharynx, and esophagus are in the upper portion of the GI tract.

The Mouth

The **mouth** (also called the *oral cavity*) receives food and begins the process of mechanical and chemical digestion. The mouth is bounded externally by the lips and cheeks. The lips extend from the base of the nose to the start of the chin. The red portion of the lips is poorly keratinized, and this allows blood to show through.

The roof of the mouth separates the nasal cavities from the oral cavity. The roof has two parts: an anterior (toward the front) *hard palate* and a posterior (toward the back) *soft palate* (Fig. 9.3*a*). The hard palate contains several bones, but the soft palate is composed entirely of muscle. The soft palate ends in a finger-shaped projection called the *uvula.* The *tonsils* are also in the back of the mouth on either side of the tongue. Tonsils are lymphatic tissue that helps protect us from disease (see Section 7.1). In the *nasopharynx,* where the nasal cavity opens above the soft palate, there is a single pharyngeal tonsil, commonly called the *adenoids.*

Three pairs of **salivary glands** (see Fig. 9.1) secrete *saliva* by way of ducts to the mouth. One pair of salivary glands lies at the side of the face immediately below and in front of the ears. The ducts of these salivary glands open on the inner surface of the cheek just above the second upper molar. This pair of glands swells when a person has a viral disease called the *mumps.* The measles, mumps, and rubella (MMR) vaccination you likely had as a child prevents the mumps. Another pair of salivary glands lies beneath the tongue, and still another pair lies beneath the floor of the oral cavity. The ducts from these salivary glands open under the tongue. You can locate the openings if you use your tongue to feel for small flaps on the inside of your cheek and under your tongue. Saliva is a solution of mucus and water. Saliva also contains **salivary amylase,** an enzyme that begins the chemical digestion of starch, as well as a buffer called bicarbonate and an antimicrobial compound called lysozyme.

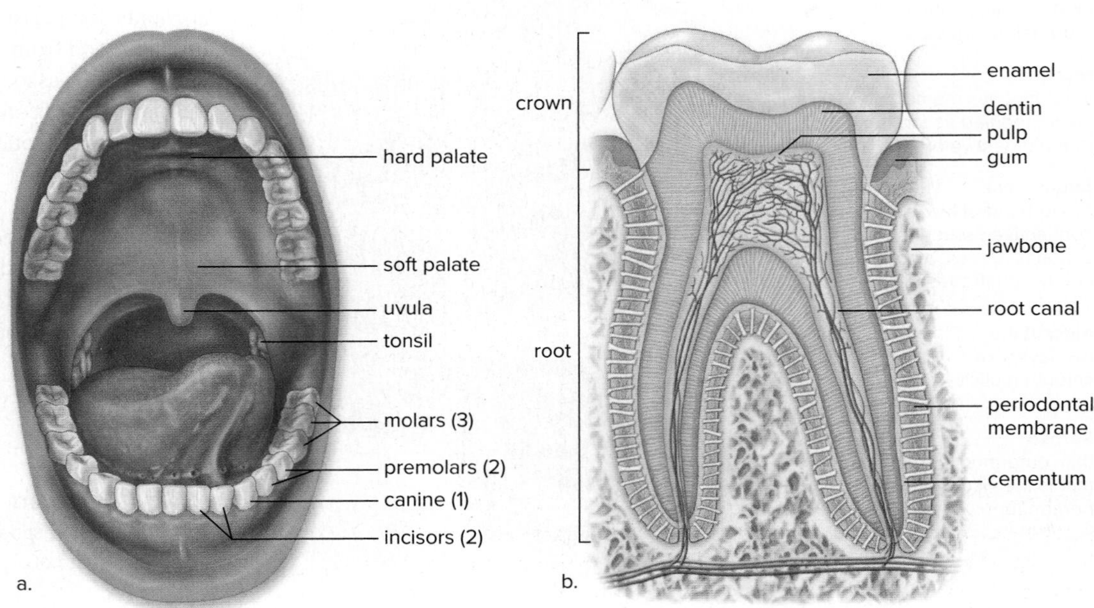

Figure 9.3 Structures of the mouth.
a. The chisel-shaped incisors bite; the pointed canines tear; the fairly flat premolars grind; and the flattened molars crush food.
b. Longitudinal section of a tooth. The crown is the portion that projects above the gum line and can be replaced by a dentist if damaged. When a "root canal" is done, the nerves are removed. When the periodontal membrane is inflamed, the teeth can loosen.

The Teeth and Tongue

Mechanical digestion occurs when our teeth chew food into pieces convenient for swallowing. During the first two years of life, the 20 smaller deciduous, or baby, teeth appear. These are eventually replaced by 32 adult teeth (see Fig. 9.3*a*). The "wisdom teeth," the third pair of molars, sometimes fail to erupt. If they push on the other teeth and/or cause pain, they can be removed by a dentist or an oral surgeon. Each tooth has two main divisions: a crown, the portion of the tooth above the gum line, and a root, the portion below the gum line (Fig. 9.3*b*). The crown has a layer of enamel, an extremely hard outer covering of calcium compounds; dentin, a thick layer of bonelike material; and an inner pulp, which contains the nerves and the blood vessels. Dentin and pulp also make up a portion of the root, which includes periodontal membranes to anchor the tooth into the jawbone.

Tooth decay, called **dental caries** or cavities, occurs when bacteria within the mouth metabolize sugar. Acids produced during this metabolism erode the teeth. Tooth decay can be painful when it is severe enough to reach the nerves of the inner pulp. Two measures can prevent tooth decay: eating a limited amount of sweets and daily brushing and flossing of teeth. Fluoride treatments, particularly in children, can make the enamel stronger and more resistant to decay. Gum disease, known to be linked to cardiovascular disease, is more apt to occur with aging. Inflammation of the gums, called **gingivitis,** can spread to the periodontal membrane, which lines the tooth socket. A person then has **periodontitis,** characterized by a loss of bone and loosening of the teeth. Extensive dental work may be required or teeth will be completely lost.

The tongue is covered by a mucous membrane, which contains the sensory receptors called taste buds (see Section 15.3). When taste buds are activated by the presence of food, nerve impulses travel by way of nerves to the brain. The tongue is composed of skeletal muscle, and it assists the teeth in carrying out mechanical digestion by moving food around in the mouth. In preparation for swallowing, the tongue forms chewed food into a mass called a **bolus,** which it pushes toward the pharynx.

The Pharynx and Esophagus

Both the mouth and the nasal passages lead to the **pharynx,** which is commonly called the *throat* (see Fig. 9.1). The pharynx opens into both the food passage (esophagus) and the air passage (trachea, or windpipe). These two tubes are parallel to each other, with the trachea in front of the esophagus.

Swallowing

Swallowing has a voluntary phase; however, once food or drink is pushed back far enough into the pharynx, swallowing becomes a reflex action performed involuntarily. During swallowing, food normally enters the **esophagus,** a muscular tube that moves food into the stomach, because other possible avenues are blocked. The soft palate moves back to close off the nasal passages, and the trachea moves up under the **epiglottis** to cover the glottis. The **glottis** is the opening to the larynx (voice box) and, therefore, the air passage. We do not breathe when we swallow. The up-and-down movement of the Adam's apple, the front part of the larynx, is easy to observe when a person swallows (Fig. 9.4*a*). Sometimes, the epiglottis does not cover the glottis fast enough or completely enough and food or liquid can end up in the trachea instead of the esophagus. When this occurs, the muscles around the lungs contract and force a cough that will bring the food back up the trachea and into the pharynx.

Peristalsis

Peristalsis moves the food through the esophagus. The peristaltic contractions continue in the stomach and intestines. The esophagus

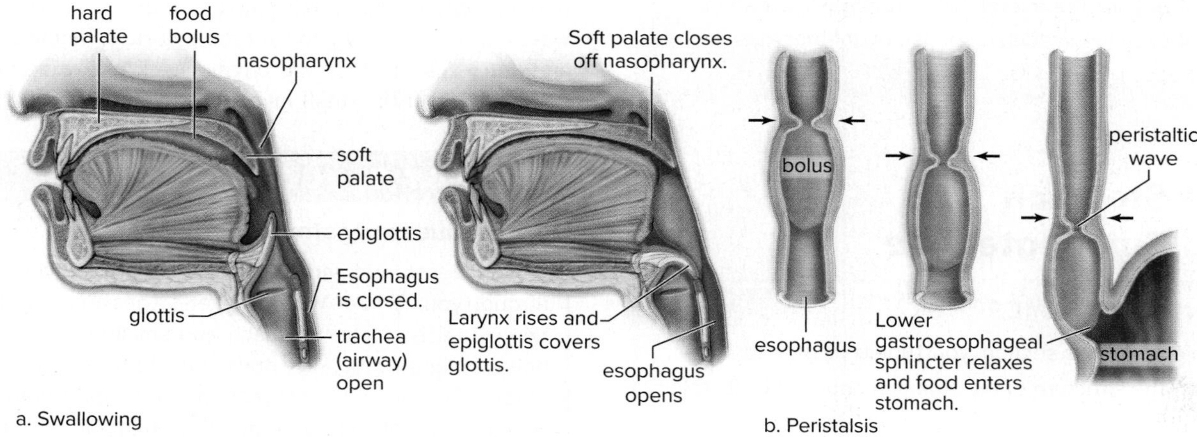

Figure 9.4 **The process of swallowing.**
a. When food is swallowed, the tongue pushes a bolus of food up against the soft palate (*left*). Then, the soft palate closes off the nasal cavities, and the epiglottis closes off the larynx, so the bolus of food enters the esophagus (*right*). **b.** Peristalsis moves food through the esophagus and through a sphincter into the stomach.

plays no role in the chemical digestion of food. Its sole purpose is to move the food bolus from the mouth to the stomach. A constriction called the *lower gastroesophageal sphincter* marks the entrance of the esophagus to the stomach. **Sphincters** are muscles that encircle tubes and act as valves. The tubes close when the sphincters contract, and they open when the sphincters relax. When food or saliva is swallowed, the sphincter relaxes for a moment to allow the food or saliva to enter the stomach (Fig. 9.4*b*). The sphincter then contracts, preventing the acidic stomach contents from backing up into the esophagus.

When the lower esophageal sphincter fails to open and allow food into the stomach, or when the sphincter is opened and food moves from the stomach back to the esophagus, **heartburn** occurs. As discussed in the Health feature "Heartburn (GERD)" in Section 9.3, this condition can lead to damage of the esophagus and lower esophageal sphincter. Vomiting occurs when strong contractions of the abdominal muscles and the **diaphragm** (the muscle separating the thoracic and abdominal cavities) force the contents of the stomach into the esophagus and oral cavity.

CHECK YOUR PROGRESS 9.2

1. Describe the role of the mouth, pharynx, and esophagus in digestion.
2. Detail how mechanical digestion and chemical digestion occur in the mouth.
3. Explain what ordinarily prevents food from entering the nose or trachea when you swallow.

CONNECTING THE CONCEPTS

For more information on the interaction of the oral cavity and pharynx with other body systems, refer to the following discussions:

Section 7.1 describes the function of lymphoid tissue, such as that found in the tonsils.

Section 10.4 defines the role of the diaphragm in breathing.

Section 14.4 explains a reflex response by the nervous system.

9.3 The Stomach and Small Intestine

LEARNING OUTCOMES

Upon completion of this section, you should be able to

1. Describe the structure of the stomach and explain its role in digestion.
2. Describe the structure of the small intestine and explain its role in digestion.
3. Explain how carbohydrates, lipids, and proteins are processed by the small intestine.

The stomach is responsible for the processing of food and the initiation of the process of digestion for proteins. The majority of nutrient processing occurs within the small intestine.

The Stomach

The **stomach** (Fig. 9.5) is a thick-walled, J-shaped organ that lies on the left side of the body beneath the diaphragm. The stomach is continuous with the esophagus above and the duodenum of the small intestine below. The gastroesophageal sphincter prevents the contents of the stomach from entering the esophagus. The Health feature "Heartburn (GERD)" explores what happens when stomach contents leak back into the esophagus.

The stomach stores food, initiates the digestion of protein, and controls the movement of food into the small intestine. Nutrients are not absorbed by the stomach. However, it does absorb alcohol, because alcohol is fat-soluble and can pass through membranes easily.

The stomach wall has the usual four layers (see Fig. 9.2), but two of them are modified for particular functions. The muscularis contains three layers of smooth muscle (Fig. 9.5*a*). In addition to the circular and longitudinal layers, the stomach contains a layer of smooth muscle that runs obliquely to the other two. The **oblique layer** also allows the stomach to stretch and to mechanically break down food into smaller fragments that are mixed with gastric juice.

The mucosa of the stomach has deep folds called **rugae.** These disappear as the stomach fills to an approximate capacity of one liter. The mucosa of the stomach has millions of gastric pits, which lead to **gastric glands** (Fig. 9.5*b, c*). The gastric glands produce gastric juice. Gastric juice contains an enzyme called **pepsin,** which digests protein, plus hydrochloric acid (HCl) and mucus. HCl causes the stomach to be very acidic with a pH of about 2. This acidity is beneficial because it kills most bacteria present in food. Although HCl does not digest food, it does break down the connective tissue of meat and activates pepsin.

Normally, the stomach empties in about 2 to 6 hours. When food leaves the stomach, it is a thick, soupy liquid of partially digested food called **chyme.** Chyme's entry into the small intestine is regulated, so that small amounts enter at intervals. Peristaltic waves move the chyme toward the pyloric sphincter, which closes and squeezes most of the chyme back, allowing only a small amount to enter the small intestine at one time (Fig. 9.5*d*).

BIOLOGY IN YOUR LIFE

What causes my stomach to growl?

As you digest food and liquids, you are also moving gas and air through your GI tract. When pockets of gas and air get squeezed by peristalsis in your stomach and small intestine, it makes a noise, or "growl." So, why does your stomach "growl" when it is empty? The process of digestion begins long before you eat. When your stomach is empty, the brain will tell the stomach muscles to begin peristalsis to aid in stimulating hunger. Those muscle contractions around an empty stomach vibrate and echo, causing the "growling" sound.

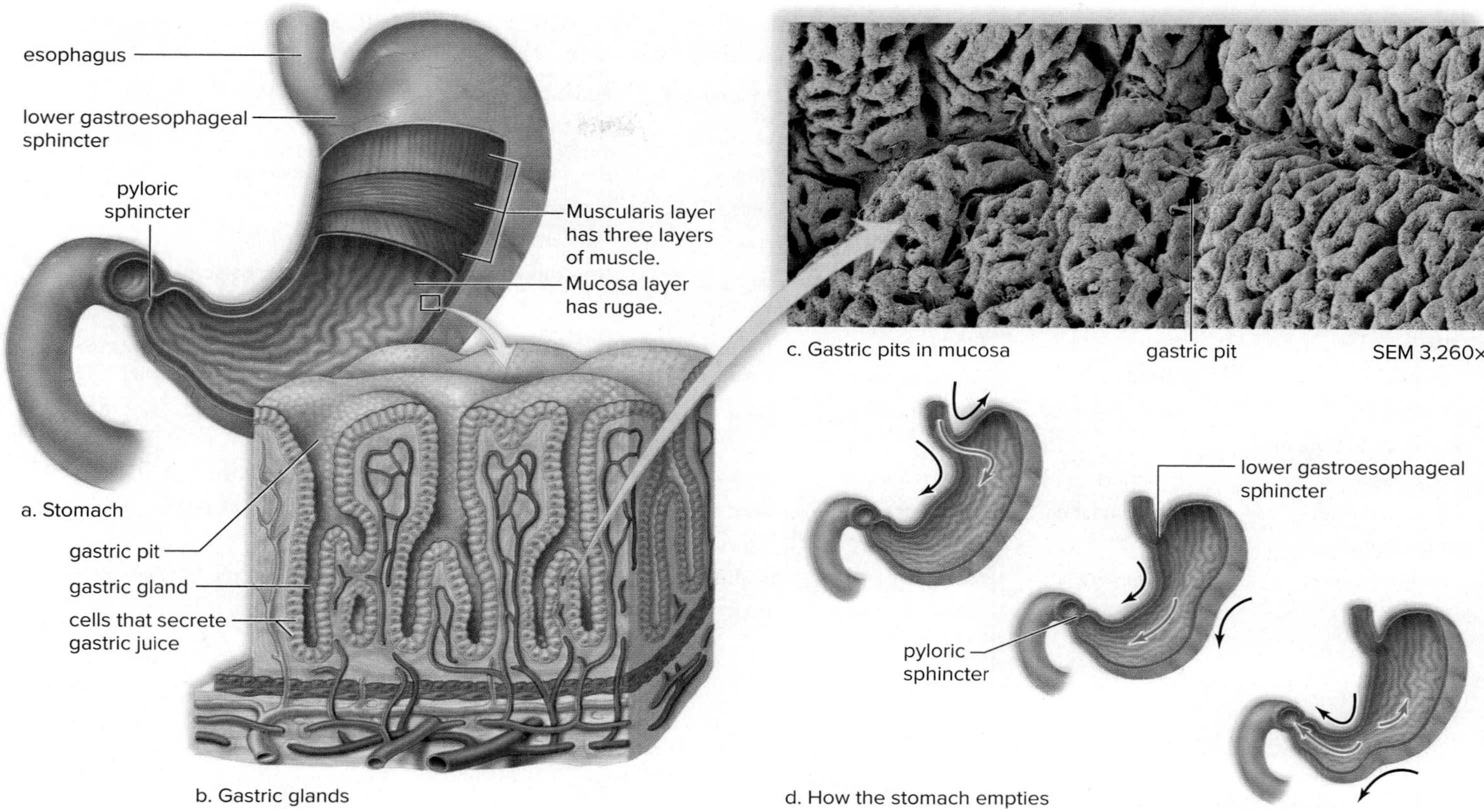

Figure 9.5 **Structure of the stomach.**
a. The three layers of the muscularis and the folds called rugae. **b, c.** Gastric glands present in the mucosa secrete mucus, HCl, and pepsin, an enzyme that digests protein. **d.** Contractions of the stomach control the secretion of chyme into the small intestine at the pyloric sphincter.
(c): Steve Gschmeissner/Brand X Pictures/SPL/Getty Images

The Small Intestine

The **small intestine** is named for its small diameter compared with that of the large intestine. The small intestine is very long, averaging about 6 m (18 ft) in length, compared with the large intestine, which is about 1.5 m (4.5 ft) in length. It consists of three regions: the *duodenum, jejunum,* and *ileum.*

The Small Intestine Is the Main Digestive Organ

The small intestine contains a wide range of enzymes to digest the carbohydrate, protein, and fat content of food (Table 9.1). Most of these enzymes are secreted by the pancreas and enter via a duct at the start of the small intestine, also called the duodenum. Another duct brings bile from the liver and gallbladder into the duodenum (see Fig. 9.8). Bile emulsifies fat. Emulsification is a form of mechanical digestion that causes fat droplets to disperse in water. After emulsification, the **lipase** enzyme, produced by the pancreas, hydrolyzes fats to form glycerol (monoglyceride) and fatty acids. Pancreatic **amylase** begins the digestion of carbohydrates. An intestinal enzyme completes the digestion of carbohydrates to glucose. Trypsin, a **protease** enzyme that originates in the pancreas, begins, and then intestinal enzymes finish the digestion of proteins to amino acids. The intestine has a slightly basic pH, because pancreatic juice contains sodium bicarbonate ($NaHCO_3$), which neutralizes chyme.

Nutrients Are Absorbed in the Small Intestine

The wall of the small intestine absorbs the sugar, amino acid, glycerol, and fatty acid molecules produced by the digestive process. The mucosa of the small intestine is modified for absorption. The mucosa of the small intestine contains fingerlike projections called **villi** (*sing.,* villus), which give the intestinal wall a soft, velvety appearance (Fig. 9.6). A villus has an outer layer of columnar epithelial cells, and each of these cells has thousands of microscopic extensions called **microvilli.** Collectively, in electron micrographs, microvilli give the villi a fuzzy border known as the brush border. The microvilli contain enzymes, called brush border enzymes, that complete the digestive process. The microvilli greatly increase the surface area of the villus for the absorption of nutrients. The surface area of the small intestine has been estimated to be approximately that of a tennis court.

Table 9.1 Major Digestive Enzymes

Enzyme	Produced by	Site of Action	Optional pH	Function
Carbohydrate Digestion				
Salivary amylase	Salivary glands	Mouth	Neutral	Begins the breakdown of starch to maltose
Pancreatic amylase	Pancreas	Small intestine	Basic	Breakdown of starch to maltose
Maltase	Small intestine	Small intestine	Basic	Breakdown of maltose to glucose
Lactase	Small intestine	Small intestine	Basic	Breakdown of lactose to glucose and galactose
Protein Digestion				
Pepsin	Gastric glands	Stomach	Acidic	Breakdown of proteins to peptides and amino acids
Trypsin	Pancreas	Small intestine	Basic	Breakdown of proteins to peptides and amino acids
Peptidases	Small intestine	Small intestine	Basic	Breakdown of peptides to amino acids
Nucleic Acid Digestion				
Nuclease	Pancreas	Small intestine	Basic	Breakdown of nucleic acids to nucleotides
Nucleosidases	Small intestine	Small intestine	Basic	Breakdown of nucleotides to phosphates, bases, and sugars
Fat Digestion				
Salivary lipase	Salivary glands	Mouth	Neutral	Begins the breakdown of triglycerides into fatty acids
Lipase	Pancreas	Small intestine	Basic	Breakdown of lipids to glycerol and fatty acids

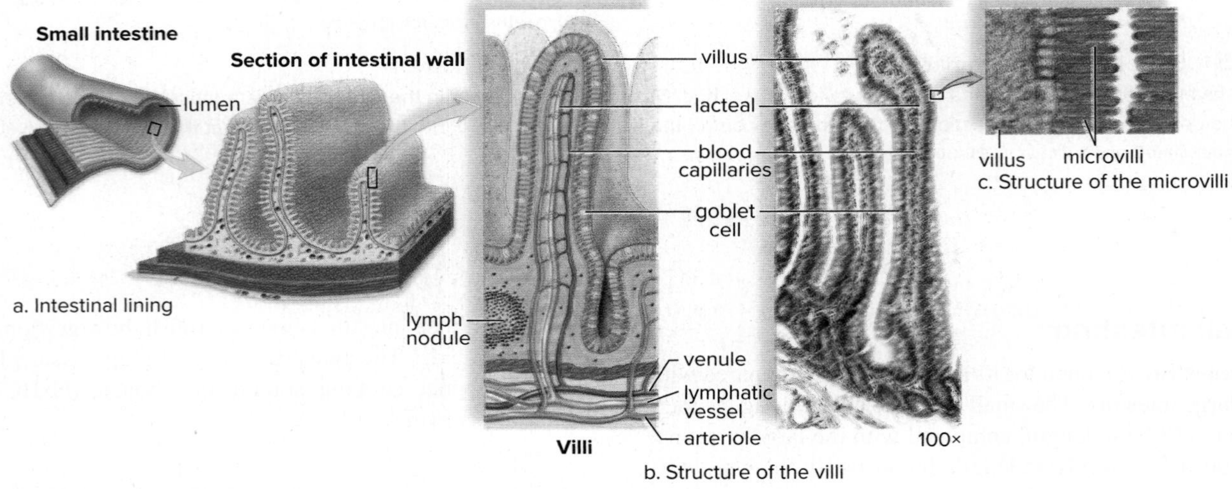

Figure 9.6 Absorption in the small intestine.
a. The wall of the small intestine has folds that bear fingerlike projections called villi. **b.** The products of digestion are absorbed by microvilli into the blood capillaries and the lacteals of the villi. **c.** A micrograph of the microvilli.
(photos) (b): Al Telser/McGraw Hill; (c): Steve Gschmeissner/Science Photo Library/Getty Images

Nutrients are absorbed into the vessels of a villus (Fig. 9.7). A villus contains blood capillaries and a small lymphatic capillary called a **lacteal.** As you know, the lymphatic system is an adjunct to the cardiovascular system. Lymphatic vessels carry a fluid called lymph to the cardiovascular veins. Sugars (monosaccharides) and amino acids enter the blood capillaries of a villus. Single molecules of glycerol, called monoglycerides, and fatty acids enter the epithelial cells of the villi. Lipoprotein droplets, called *chylomicrons,* are formed when monoglycerides and fatty acids are rejoined in the villi epithelia cells. Chylomicrons then enter a lacteal. After nutrients are absorbed, they are eventually carried to all the cells of the body by the bloodstream.

BIOLOGY TODAY ▶ **Health**

Heartburn (GERD)

In the absence of other symptoms, that burning sensation in your chest may have nothing to do with your heart. Instead, it is likely due to acid reflux. Almost everyone has had acid reflux and heartburn at some time. The burning sensation occurs in the area of the esophagus that lies behind the heart, and that is why it is termed heartburn, but its official name is Gastroesophageal Reflux Disease (GERD). Heartburn occurs because the contents of the stomach are more acidic than those of the esophagus, and the lining of the esophagus is thin. When the stomach contents pass upward into the esophagus (Fig. 9A), the acidity begins to erode the lining of the esophagus, producing the burning sensation associated with heartburn.

Some people experience heartburn after eating a large meal that overfills their stomach. Women sometimes get heartburn during pregnancy when the developing fetus pushes the internal organs upward. Pressure applied to the abdominal wall because of obesity also causes heartburn.

When heartburn or acid reflux becomes a chronic condition, the patient is diagnosed with gastroesophageal reflux disease (GERD). The term signifies that the stomach (*gastric* refers to the stomach) and the esophagus are involved in the disease. In GERD, patients' reflux is more frequent, remains in the esophagus longer, and often contains higher levels of acid than in a patient with typical heartburn or acid reflux. People diagnosed with GERD may also experience pain in their chest, feel like they are choking, and have trouble swallowing.

Patients with weak or abnormal esophageal contractions have difficulty pushing food into the stomach. These weak contractions can also prevent reflux from being pushed back into the stomach after it has entered the esophagus, thus producing GERD. When patients are lying down, the effects of abnormal esophageal contractions become more severe. This is because gravity is not helping to return reflux to the stomach. Some people with GERD may have weaker-than-normal lower gastroesophageal sphincters. Their sphincters don't fully close after food is pushed into the stomach. Surgery to tighten the sphincter may alleviate GERD.

Over-the-counter medications act as treatments for acid reflux because they have a basic pH, which neutralizes stomach acid. Other drugs, such as Nexium and Prilosec, reduce acid production. Overall, persons with acid reflux are advised to first try modifying their eating habits.

Diet and Exercise

It has been found that diet and weight control can help control acid reflux. Some tips to reduce acid reflux include:

- Eating several small meals a day instead of three large meals and avoiding foods that lead to stomach acidity, such as tomato sauces, citrus fruits, alcohol, and caffeinated beverages
- Reducing consumption of high-fat meals (fast food) and foods high in refined sugar (cakes and candy)
- Increasing the amount of complex carbohydrates (such as multigrain bread, brown rice, and pasta) in your diet
- Participating in light exercise (bike riding, walking, yoga) and light weightlifting to help control weight

Questions to Consider

1. From the perspective of pH, how do antacids help control heartburn and GERD?
2. Some medications work to control the production of acid. What cells do you think these medications are targeting?

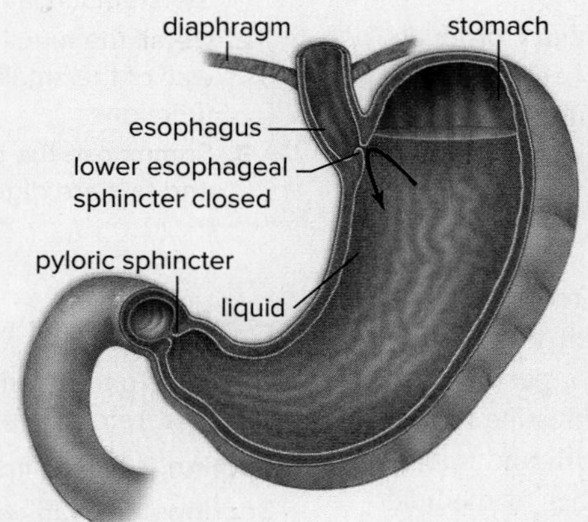

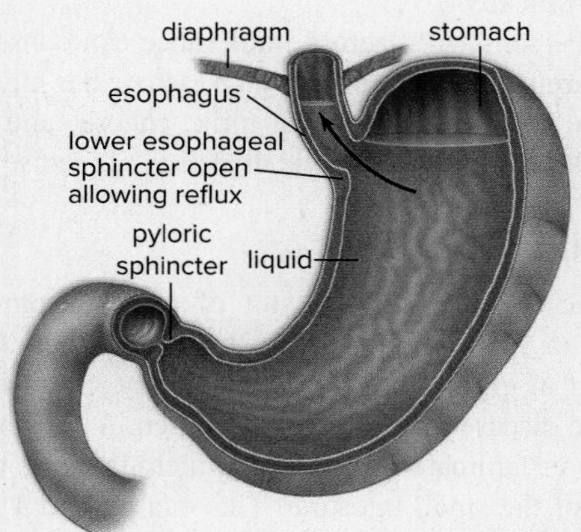

Figure 9A **Heartburn.** In a normal stomach (*left*), the esophageal sphincter is closed. In GERD (*right*), the lower esophageal sphincter does not close correctly, allowing the contents of the stomach to enter the esophagus.

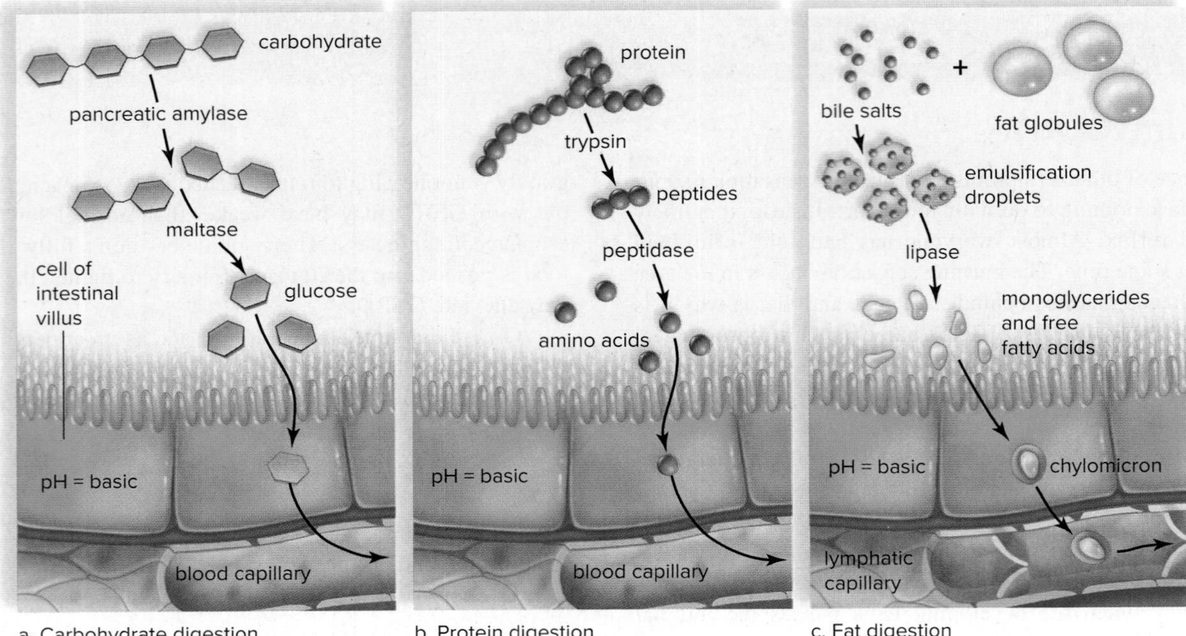

Figure 9.7 **Digestion and absorption of organic nutrients.**
a. Carbohydrate is digested to glucose, which is actively transported into the cells of intestinal villi. From there, glucose moves into the bloodstream. **b.** Proteins are digested to amino acids, which are actively transported into the cells of intestinal villi. From there, amino acids move into the bloodstream. **c.** Fats are emulsified by bile and digested to monoglycerides (glycerol) and fatty acids. These diffuse into cells, where they recombine and join with proteins. These lipoproteins, called chylomicrons, enter a lacteal.

Lactose Intolerance

Lactose is the primary sugar in milk. People who do not have the brush border enzyme lactase cannot digest lactose. The result is a condition called **lactose intolerance,** characterized by diarrhea, gas, bloating, and abdominal cramps after ingesting milk and other dairy products. Diarrhea occurs because the indigestible lactose causes fluid retention in the small intestine. Gas, bloating, and cramps occur when bacteria break down the lactose anaerobically.

Persons with lactose intolerance can consume dairy products that are lactose-free or in which lactose has already been digested. These include lactose-free milk, cheese, and yogurt. A dietary supplement that aids in the digestion of lactose is also available.

Celiac Disease

Celiac disease is the result of an autoimmune response (see Section 7.5) against a protein called gluten. Gluten is naturally found in grains such as wheat, barley, and rye. In a person with celiac disease, the presence of gluten in the small intestine results in an inflammatory response, which damages the villi and microvilli of the small intestine. This can lead to a number of medical conditions, including abdominal pain, diarrhea, and malnutrition.

There is a difference between celiac disease and gluten sensitivity. Individuals with gluten sensitivity have some of the same symptoms, but there is no damage to the intestines.

Individuals who have celiac disease are placed on a strict gluten-free diet. Many gluten-free foods can be found in grocery stores, but people who have not been diagnosed with celiac disease or gluten sensitivity will not benefit from a gluten-free diet.

CHECK YOUR PROGRESS 9.3

1. Describe the functions of the stomach and how the wall of the stomach is modified to perform these functions.
2. Detail the functions of the small intestine and how the wall of the small intestine is modified to perform these functions.
3. Summarize the differences in how carbohydrates, proteins, and fats are digested and absorbed by the small intestine.

CONNECTING THE CONCEPTS

To better understand the functions of the stomach and small intestine, refer to the following discussions:

Section 2.2 explains how to interpret pH values.

Sections 2.4, 2.5, and **2.6** provide additional details on the structure of carbohydrates, lipids, and proteins.

Section 4.5 describes the structure of the epithelial tissue that lines the small intestine.

9.4 The Accessory Organs and Regulation of Secretions

LEARNING OUTCOMES

Upon completion of this section, you should be able to

1. Explain the functions of the pancreas, liver, and gallbladder during digestion.
2. List the secretions of the pancreas, liver, and gallbladder.
3. Summarize how secretions of the accessory organs are regulated.

We first take a look at the roles of the pancreas, liver, and gallbladder in digestion before considering how the secretions of these organs and those of the GI tract are regulated.

The Accessory Organs

The **pancreas** is a fish-shaped, spongy, grayish-pink organ that stretches across the back of the abdomen behind the stomach. Most pancreatic cells produce pancreatic juice, which enters the duodenum via the pancreatic duct (Fig. 9.8*a*). Pancreatic juice contains sodium bicarbonate ($NaHCO_3$) and digestive enzymes for all types of nutrients. Sodium bicarbonate neutralizes acid chyme from the stomach. Pancreatic amylase digests starch, trypsin digests protein, and pancreatic lipase digests fat.

The pancreas is also an endocrine gland (see Section 16.1) that secretes the hormone insulin into the blood. A **hormone** is a protein or steroid produced by a cell that affects the function of a different (target) cell. When the blood glucose level rises rapidly, the pancreas produces an overload of insulin to bring the level under control and back to homeostasis. Type 1 diabetes occurs when the pancreas does not manufacture sufficient amounts of insulin. This condition is normally diagnosed in childhood. Type 2 diabetes occurs when the pancreas does not make enough insulin or when the body's cells have become insulin-resistant. Type 2 diabetes normally occurs in adulthood with risk factors such as obesity, inactivity, and a family history of the disease (see Section 16.5).

The largest gland in the body, the **liver,** lies mainly in the upper right section of the abdominal cavity, under the diaphragm (see Fig. 9.1). The liver is a major metabolic gland with approximately 100,000 lobules that serve as its structural and functional units (Fig. 9.8*b*). The hepatic portal vein (Fig. 9.8*b*) brings blood to the liver from the GI tract capillary bed. Capillaries of the lobules filter this blood. In a sense, the liver acts as a sewage treatment plant when it removes poisonous substances from the blood and detoxifies them (Table 9.2).

The liver is also a storage organ. It removes iron and the vitamins A, D, E, K, and B_{12} from blood and stores them. The liver is also involved in blood glucose homeostasis. In the presence of insulin, the liver stores glucose as glycogen. When blood glucose becomes low, the liver releases glucose by breaking down glycogen. If need be, the liver converts glycerol (from fats) and amino acids to glucose molecules. As amino acids are converted to glucose, the liver combines their amino groups with carbon dioxide to form **urea,** the usual nitrogenous waste product in humans. Plasma proteins needed in the blood (see Section 6.1) are also made by the liver.

The liver helps regulate blood cholesterol levels as well. Some cholesterol is converted to bile salts by the liver. **Bile** is a solution of bile salts, water, cholesterol, and bicarbonate. It has a

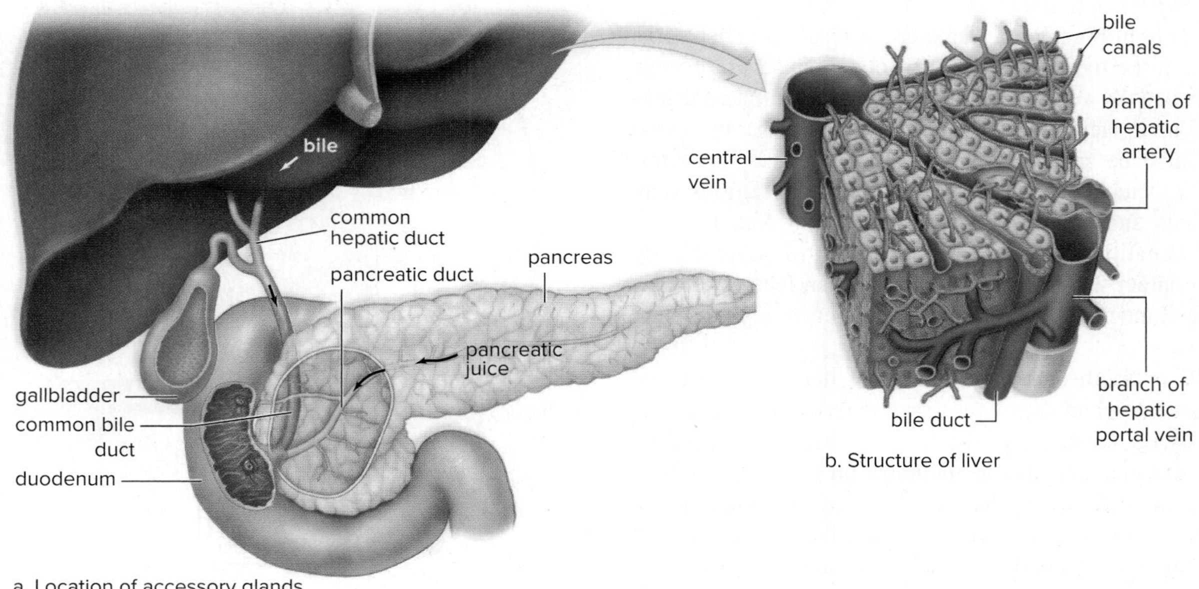

Figure 9.8 **Accessory organs of the digestive system.**
a. The location of the liver, gallbladder, and pancreas in relation to the small intestine. **b.** The liver contains over 100,000 lobules. Each lobule contains many cells that perform the various functions of the liver (see Table 9.2).

Table 9.2	Functions of the Liver

1. Destroys old red blood cells; excretes bilirubin, a breakdown product of hemoglobin in bile, a liver product
2. Detoxifies blood by removing and metabolizing poisonous substances
3. Stores iron (Fe^{2+}), the water-soluble vitamin B_{12}, and the fat-soluble vitamins A, D, E, and K
4. Makes plasma proteins, such as albumins and fibrinogen, from amino acids
5. Stores glucose as glycogen after a meal; breaks down glycogen to glucose to maintain the glucose concentration of blood between eating periods
6. Produces urea after breaking down amino acids
7. Helps regulate blood cholesterol level, converting some to bile salts

yellowish-green color, because it also contains bilirubin, a pigment protein formed during the breakdown of hemoglobin, which is a process also performed by the liver. Bile is stored in the **gallbladder,** a pear-shaped organ just below the liver, until it is sent via the bile ducts to the duodenum. **Gallstones** form when liquid stored in the gallbladder hardens into pieces of stonelike material. In the small intestine, bile salts emulsify fat. When fat is emulsified, it breaks up into droplets. The droplets provide a large surface area that can be acted upon by digestive enzymes.

Liver Disorders

Hepatitis and cirrhosis are two serious diseases that affect the entire liver and hinder its ability to repair itself. Therefore, they are life-threatening diseases. When a person has a liver ailment, bile pigments may leak into the blood, causing **jaundice.** Jaundice is a yellowish tint to the whites of the eyes and to the skin of persons who are light-pigmented. Jaundice can result from **hepatitis,** inflammation of the liver. Viral hepatitis occurs in several forms. Hepatitis A is usually acquired from sewage-contaminated drinking water and food. Hepatitis B, which is usually spread by sexual contact, can also be spread by blood transfusions or contaminated needles. The hepatitis B virus is more contagious than the AIDS virus and is spread in the same way. Vaccines are available for hepatitis A and hepatitis B. Hepatitis C is usually acquired by contact with infected blood and can lead to chronic hepatitis, liver cancer, and death. There is not currently a vaccine for hepatitis C.

Cirrhosis is another chronic disease of the liver. First, the organ becomes fatty, and then liver tissue is replaced by inactive, fibrous scar tissue. Cirrhosis of the liver is often seen in people with alcohol use disorder, due to malnutrition and the excessive amounts of alcohol (a toxin) the liver is forced to break down. Physicians have also observed cirrhosis of the liver in people with obesity, who are overweight due to a diet high in fatty foods.

The liver has amazing regenerative powers and can recover if the rate of regeneration exceeds the rate of damage. During liver failure, however, there may not be enough time to let the liver heal itself; liver transplantation is usually the preferred treatment. The liver is a vital organ, and its failure leads to death.

Regulation of Digestive Secretions

The secretions of digestive juices are controlled by the nervous system and by digestive hormones. When you look at or smell food, the parasympathetic nervous system automatically stimulates gastric secretion. Also, when a person has eaten a meal particularly rich in protein, the stomach produces the hormone gastrin. Gastrin enters the bloodstream, and soon the secretory activity of gastric glands increases.

Cells of the duodenal wall produce two other hormones of particular interest—secretin and cholecystokinin (CCK). Secretin release is stimulated by acid, especially the HCl present in chyme. Partially digested proteins and fat stimulate the release of CCK. Soon after these hormones enter the bloodstream, the pancreas increases its output of pancreatic juice. Pancreatic juice buffers the acidic chyme entering the intestine from the stomach and helps digest food. CCK also causes the liver to increase its production of bile and causes the gallbladder to contract and release stored bile. The bile then aids the digestion of fats that stimulated the release of CCK. Figure 9.9 summarizes the actions of gastrin, secretin, and CCK.

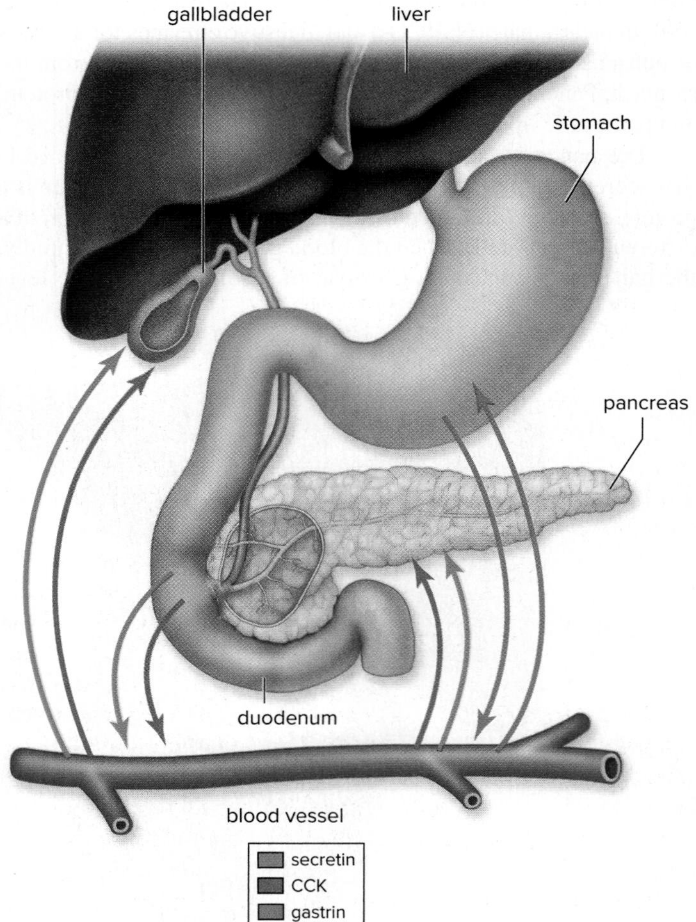

Figure 9.9 Hormonal control and regulation of digestion. Gastrin (blue) from the lower stomach feeds back to stimulate the upper part of the stomach to produce digestive juice. Secretin (green) and CCK (purple) from the duodenal wall stimulate the pancreas to secrete digestive juice and the gallbladder to release bile.

CHECK YOUR PROGRESS 9.4

1. Name and describe the functions of three main accessory organs that assist with the digestive process.
2. Discuss what could occur if each of the accessory organs of digestion did not function properly.
3. Detail why the regulation of digestive secretions is important to the overall process of digestion. Describe what could occur without regulation.

CONNECTING THE CONCEPTS

For more information on the accessory organs, refer to the following discussions:

Section 5.5 describes the movement of blood and nutrients from the intestines to the liver via the hepatic portal system.

Section 14.4 outlines how the nervous system interacts with the liver and pancreas to maintain homeostasis.

Section 16.5 explains the role of the pancreas in maintaining blood glucose homeostasis.

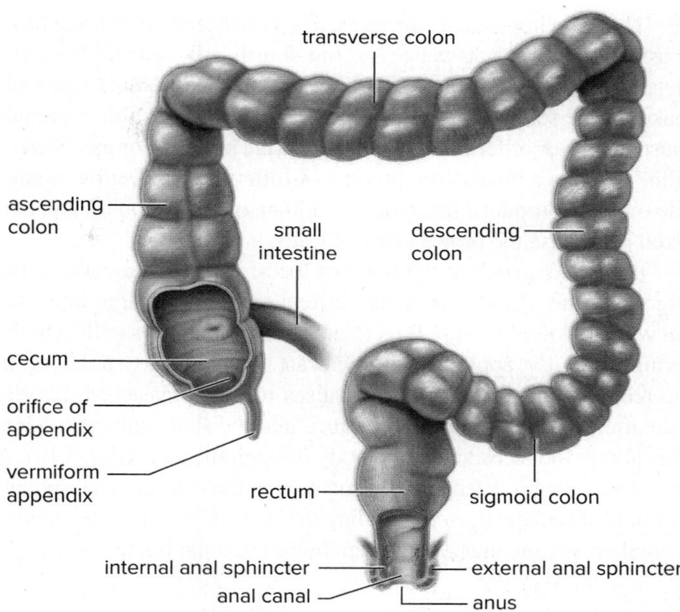

Figure 9.10 The regions of the large intestine. The regions of the large intestine are the cecum, colon, rectum, and anal canal.

9.5 The Large Intestine and Defecation

LEARNING OUTCOMES

Upon completion of this section, you should be able to

1. Describe the structure and function of the large intestine.
2. List the disorders of the large intestine and provide a cause for each.

The **large intestine** includes the cecum, the colon, the rectum, and the anal canal (Fig. 9.10). The large intestine is larger in diameter than the small intestine (6.5 cm compared with 2.5 cm), but it is shorter in length (see Fig. 9.1).

The **cecum** is the first portion of the large intestine, joining the end of the small intestine. The cecum usually has a small projection called the vermiform **appendix** (the term *vermiform* describes its "wormlike" appearance) (Fig. 9.10). In humans, the appendix is thought to aid in fighting infections. Scientists have recently proposed that the appendix may also contribute to the population of needed bacteria in the large intestine. An inflamed appendix *(appendicitis)* may be treated using antibiotics or removed surgically. Should the appendix burst, the result can be *peritonitis,* a life-threatening swelling and infection of the peritoneum.

The **colon** includes the ascending colon, which goes up the right side of the body to the level of the liver; the transverse colon, which crosses the abdominal cavity just below the liver and the stomach; the descending colon, which passes down the left side of the body; and the sigmoid colon, which enters the **rectum,** the last 20 cm of the large intestine. The rectum opens at the **anus,** where **defecation,** the expulsion of feces, occurs.

Functions of the Large Intestine

The large intestine does not produce any digestive enzymes, and because the majority of nutrients processing occurred in the small intestine, it does not play a major role in the absorption of any nutrients except for some vitamins. The primary function of the large intestine is to absorb water, an important process to prevent dehydration of the body and maintain homeostasis.

The large intestine can absorb vitamins produced by intestinal flora, the bacteria that inhabit the intestine, and aid in keeping us healthy. For many years it was believed that *Escherichia coli* were the major inhabitants of the colon, but culture methods now show that over 99% of the colon bacteria are other types of bacteria. The bacteria in the large intestine break down indigestible material and produce B-complex vitamins and most of the vitamin K needed by our bodies.

BIOLOGY IN YOUR LIFE

Why monitor for coliform bacteria in the water?

Water is considered unsafe for swimming when the coliform (nonpathogenic intestinal) bacterial count reaches a certain number. A high count indicates that a significant amount of feces has entered the water. The more feces present, the greater the possibility that disease-causing bacteria are also present. For most states, the fecal coliform count has to be under 200 fecal bacteria per every 100 milliliters (ml) of water to be considered safe for swimming. The national standard for safe drinking water is 0 fecal bacteria per 100 ml of water.

The large intestine forms feces. The consistency of normal feces is usually three-fourths water and one-fourth solid wastes. Bacteria, dietary fiber (indigestible remains), and other indigestible materials make up the solid wastes. Bacterial action on indigestible materials causes the odor of feces and accounts for the presence of gas. Stercobilin, which is a breakdown product of **bilirubin** (the yellow-orange bile pigment produced from the breakdown of hemoglobin), and oxidized iron cause the brown color of feces.

Defecation, ridding the body of feces, is also a function of the large intestine. Peristalsis occurs infrequently in the large intestine, but when it does, feces are forced into the rectum. Feces collect in the rectum until it is appropriate to defecate. At that time, stretching of the rectal wall initiates nerve impulses to the spinal cord. Shortly thereafter, the rectal muscles contract, and the anal sphincters relax. This allows the feces to exit the body through the anus (Fig. 9.10). A person can inhibit defecation by contracting the external anal sphincter made of skeletal muscle. Ridding the body of indigestible remains is another way the digestive system helps maintain homeostasis.

Disorders of the Colon and Rectum

The large intestine is subject to a number of disorders. Many of these can be prevented or minimized by a proper diet and hygiene.

Diarrhea

Diarrhea is characterized by bowel movements that are loose or watery. The major causes of diarrhea are infection of the lower intestinal tract and nervous stimulation. The intestinal wall becomes irritated, and peristalsis increases when an infection occurs. Water is not absorbed, and the diarrhea that results rids the body of the infectious organisms. In nervous diarrhea, the nervous system stimulates the intestinal wall and diarrhea results. Most people have several occurrences of diarrhea each year without suffering any health consequences. However, prolonged diarrhea can lead to dehydration because of water loss, which can lead to an imbalance of salts in the blood that can affect heart muscle contraction and potentially lead to death.

Constipation

When a person is constipated, the feces are dry and hard, making it difficult for them to be expelled. Diets that lack whole-grain foods, as well as ignoring the urge to defecate, are often the causes of **constipation.** When feces are not expelled regularly, additional water is absorbed from them. The material becomes drier, harder, and more difficult to eliminate. Adequate water and fiber intake can help the regularity of defecation. The frequent use of laxatives is discouraged, because it can result in dependence on their use for normal bowel movements. If, however, it is necessary to take a laxative, the most natural is a bulk laxative. Like fiber, it produces a soft mass of cellulose in the colon. Lubricants such as mineral oil make the colon slippery; saline laxatives such as milk of magnesia act osmotically by preventing water from being absorbed. Some laxatives are irritants that increase peristalsis.

Chronic constipation is associated with the development of **hemorrhoids,** enlarged and inflamed blood vessels at the anus. Other contributing factors for hemorrhoid development include pregnancy, aging, and anal intercourse.

Diverticulosis

As mentioned previously (see Section 9.1), diverticulosis is the occurrence of little pouches of mucosa where food can collect. The pouches form when the mucosa pushes through weak spots in the muscularis. A frequent site is the last part of the descending colon.

Irritable Bowel Syndrome

Also mentioned previously (see Section 9.1), irritable bowel syndrome (IBS), or spastic colon, is a condition in which the muscularis contracts powerfully but without its normal coordination. The symptoms are abdominal cramps; gas; constipation; and urgent, explosive stools (feces discharge).

Inflammatory Bowel Disease

Inflammatory bowel disease (IBD) is a collective term for a number of inflammatory disorders. Ulcerative colitis and Crohn's disease are the most common of these. Ulcerative colitis affects the large intestine and rectum and results in diarrhea, rectal bleeding, abdominal cramps, and urgency in defecation. Crohn's disease is normally isolated to the small intestine but can affect any area of the digestive tract, including the colon and rectum. It is characterized by the breakdown of the lining of the affected area, resulting in ulcers. Ulcers are painful and cause bleeding because they erode the submucosal layer, where there are nerves and blood vessels. This also results in the inability to absorb nutrients at the affected sites. Symptoms of Crohn's disease include diarrhea, weight loss, abdominal cramping, anemia, bleeding, and malnutrition.

BIOLOGY IN YOUR LIFE

What is a fecal transplant?

The balance of bacteria, or microbiota, in the large intestine is important not only for the health of the digestive tract but for the entire individual. A bacteria called *Clostridioides difficile,* commonly referred to as *C. diff.,* can cause an imbalance in the normal microbiota, resulting in inflammation (colitis) and severe diarrhea. While antibiotics can eliminate *C. diff.,* they usually also negatively affect the normal microbiota, making the individual susceptible to another round of infection.

In a fecal material transplant, bacteria from a healthy individual are delivered to the colon using an enema, endoscopy, or oral pills to reestablish a healthy community of microbiota.

Fecal transplants may also be used to treat other diseases of the large intestine, such as Crohn's disease and ulcerative colitis.

Polyps and Cancer

The colon is subject to the development of **polyps,** small growths arising from the epithelial lining. Polyps, whether benign or cancerous, can be removed surgically. If colon cancer is detected while still confined to a polyp, the expected outcome is a complete cure. The American Cancer Society estimates that over 104,000 new cases of colon and rectal (colorectal) cancer will be diagnosed annually in the United States. Some investigators believe that dietary fat increases the likelihood of colon cancer, because dietary fat causes an increase in bile secretion. It could be that intestinal bacteria convert bile salts to substances that promote the development of cancer. Fiber in the diet seems to inhibit the development of colon cancer, and regular elimination reduces the time during which the colon wall is exposed to any cancer-promoting agents in feces.

One diagnostic tool for all of these disorders is an endoscopic exam called a *colonoscopy*. In a colonoscopy, a flexible tube containing a camera is inserted into the GI tract, usually from the anus. The doctor may then examine the length of the colon, as well as take tissue samples (biopsies) for additional tests.

CHECK YOUR PROGRESS 9.5

1. Describe the parts of the large intestine and provide the function for each.
2. Explain the role of the large intestine in the digestive tract.
3. Describe how constipation and diarrhea are related to the large intestine.

CONNECTING THE CONCEPTS

For more information on the large intestine, refer to the following discussions:

Section 2.4 describes the role of fiber as a complex carbohydrate.

Section 7.3 examines how the bacteria in the large intestine act as an innate defense against disease.

Section 20.2 outlines some of the more common causes of cancer.

9.6 Nutrition and Weight Control

LEARNING OUTCOMES

Upon completion of this section, you should be able to

1. Calculate a BMI value and interpret its relationship to your overall health.
2. Identify the role of each class of nutrient in the human body.

Obesity, or being significantly overweight, has become one of the greatest health problems in the United States. According to the Centers for Disease Control and Prevention (CDC), almost 42% of adults, and 18.5% of children, are classified as obese. These statistics are of great concern, because excess body fat is associated with a higher risk for premature death, type 2 diabetes, hypertension, cardiovascular disease, stroke, gallbladder disease, respiratory dysfunction, osteoarthritis, and certain types of cancer.

Overall, physicians recommend that achieving or maintaining a healthy weight requires not only eating a variety of healthy foods but also exercising. In other words, to reverse a trend toward obesity, eat fewer calories by making wiser food choices and be more active.

Defining Obesity

Today, obesity is often defined as having a **body mass index (BMI)** of 30 or greater. The body mass index uses a person's height and weight (Fig. 9.11) to calculate a general approximation of the percent body fat. BMI can also be calculated by dividing weight in pounds (lb) by height in inches (in.) squared and multiplying by a conversion factor of 703. Using the metric system, the weight in kilograms (kg) is divided by the height in meters (m) squared:

Table 9.3 BMI Values

Classification	BMI Values
Healthy	18.5–24.9
Overweight	25.0–29.9
Obese	30.0–39.9
Extremely (morbid) obese	40.0 and higher

$$\text{BMI} = \frac{\textit{weight}\ (\text{lb})}{\textit{height}^2\ (\text{in.}^2)} \times 703$$

$$\text{BMI} = \frac{\textit{weight}\ (\text{kg})}{\textit{height}^2\ (\text{m}^2)}$$

Most people find it is easier to use a table (Table 9.3), figure (Fig. 9.11), or one of the many online calculators.

Your BMI gives you an idea of how much of your weight is due to adipose tissue, commonly known as fat. In general, the taller you are, the more you could weigh without it being due to fat. Using BMI in this way works for most people, especially if they tend to be sedentary. But your BMI number should be used only as a general guide. It does not take into account fitness, bone structure, or gender. For example, a weightlifter's BMI might fall in the obese range, not because of the amount of body fat but because of increased bone and muscle weight.

Classes of Nutrients

A **nutrient** can be defined as a required component of food that performs a physiological function in the body. Nutrients provide us with energy, promote growth and development, and regulate cellular metabolism.

Carbohydrates

Carbohydrates are either simple or complex (see Section 2.4). Glucose is a simple sugar preferred by the body as an energy source. Complex carbohydrates, consisting of multiple sugar units, are digested to glucose. Although body cells can use fatty acids as an energy source, brain cells require glucose.

Any product made from refined grains, such as white bread, cake, and cookies, should be minimized in the diet. During refinement, **fiber** is removed from the grains, along with vitamins and minerals, in order for the final product to be mainly starch. In contrast, sources of complex carbohydrates, such as beans, peas, nuts, fruits, and whole-grain products, are recommended as good sources of vitamins, minerals, and fiber (Fig. 9.12). Insoluble fiber adds bulk to fecal material and stimulates movements of the large intestine, preventing constipation. Soluble fiber combines with bile salts and cholesterol in the small intestine and prevents them from being absorbed.

Can Carbohydrates Be Harmful? Nutritionists now recognize that the high intake of refined carbohydrates and fructose

Body Mass Index Table																	
	Normal						Overweight					Obese					
BMI	**19**	**20**	**21**	**22**	**23**	**24**	**25**	**26**	**27**	**28**	**29**	**30**	**31**	**32**	**33**	**34**	**35**
Height (inches)														**Body Weight (pounds)**			
58	91	96	100	105	110	115	119	124	129	134	138	143	148	153	158	162	167
59	94	99	104	109	114	119	124	128	133	138	143	148	153	158	163	168	173
60	97	102	107	112	118	123	128	133	138	143	148	153	158	163	168	174	179
61	100	106	111	116	122	127	132	137	143	148	153	158	164	169	174	180	185
62	104	109	115	120	126	131	136	142	147	153	158	164	169	175	180	186	191
63	107	113	118	124	130	135	141	146	152	158	163	169	175	180	186	191	197
64	110	116	122	128	134	140	145	151	157	163	169	174	180	186	192	197	204
65	114	120	126	132	138	144	150	156	162	168	174	180	186	192	198	204	210
66	118	124	130	136	142	148	155	161	167	173	179	186	192	198	204	210	216
67	121	127	134	140	146	153	159	166	172	178	185	191	198	204	211	217	223
68	125	131	138	144	151	158	164	171	177	184	190	197	203	210	216	223	230
69	128	135	142	149	155	162	169	176	182	189	196	203	209	216	223	230	236
70	132	139	146	153	160	167	174	181	188	195	202	209	216	222	229	236	243
71	136	143	150	157	165	172	179	186	193	200	208	215	222	229	236	243	250
72	140	147	154	162	169	177	184	191	199	206	213	221	228	235	242	250	258
73	144	151	159	166	174	182	189	197	204	212	219	227	235	242	250	257	265
74	148	155	163	171	179	186	194	202	210	218	225	233	241	249	256	264	272
75	152	160	168	176	184	192	200	208	216	224	232	240	248	256	264	272	279
76	156	164	172	180	189	197	205	213	221	230	238	246	254	263	271	279	287

Figure 9.11 The body mass index chart.
Match your weight with your height, and then determine your body mass index (BMI). The limits for each category are presented in Table 9.3.
Source: Adapted from "Clinical Guidelines on the Identification, Evaluation, and Treatment of Overweight and Obesity in Adults: The Evidence Report."

sweeteners processed from cornstarch is contributing to the increase in obesity in the United States. In addition, these foods are said to have a high **glycemic index (GI),** because they quickly increase blood glucose. When the blood glucose level rises rapidly, the pancreas produces an overload of insulin to bring the level under control. Investigators tell us that a chronically high insulin level may lead to insulin resistance, type 2 diabetes, and increased fat deposition. Deposition of fat is associated with coronary heart disease, liver ailments, and several types of cancer.

Figure 9.12 Foods rich in fiber.
Plants provide a good source of fiber in the diet. They also are a good source of vitamins and minerals when they are not processed (refined).
Cole Group/Getty Images

Table 9.4 gives suggestions on how to reduce your intake of dietary sugars.

Carbohydrates are the preferred energy source for the body. The complex carbohydrates in whole grains, beans, nuts, and fruits contain fiber in addition to simple carbohydrates. Complex carbohydrate foods are often a good source of vitamins and minerals.

Proteins

Dietary proteins are digested to amino acids (see Section 2.6), which cells use to synthesize hundreds of cellular proteins. Of the 20 different amino acids, 8 are *essential amino acids* that must be present in the diet because the body cannot make them, and 2 others are ones the body makes insufficiently. Eggs, milk products,

Body Mass Index Table

Obese				Extreme Obesity														
36	**37**	**38**	**39**	**40**	**41**	**42**	**43**	**44**	**45**	**46**	**47**	**48**	**49**	**50**	**51**	**52**	**53**	**54**
172	177	181	186	191	196	201	205	210	215	220	224	229	234	239	244	248	253	258
178	183	188	193	198	203	208	212	217	222	227	232	237	242	247	252	257	262	267
184	189	194	199	204	209	215	220	225	230	235	240	245	250	255	261	266	271	276
190	195	201	206	211	217	222	227	232	238	243	248	254	259	264	269	275	280	285
196	202	207	213	218	224	229	235	240	246	251	256	262	267	273	278	284	289	295
203	208	214	220	225	231	237	242	248	254	259	265	270	278	282	287	293	299	304
209	215	221	227	232	238	244	250	256	262	267	273	279	285	291	296	302	308	314
216	222	228	234	240	246	252	258	264	270	276	282	288	294	300	306	312	318	324
223	229	235	241	247	253	260	266	272	278	284	291	297	303	309	315	322	328	334
230	236	242	249	255	261	268	274	280	287	293	299	306	312	319	325	331	338	344
236	243	249	256	262	269	276	282	289	295	302	308	315	322	328	335	341	348	354
243	250	257	263	270	277	284	291	297	304	311	318	324	331	338	345	351	358	365
250	257	264	271	278	285	292	299	306	313	320	327	334	341	348	355	362	369	376
257	265	272	279	286	293	301	308	315	322	329	338	343	351	358	365	372	379	386
265	272	279	287	294	302	309	316	324	331	338	346	353	361	368	375	383	390	397
272	280	288	295	302	310	318	325	333	340	348	355	363	371	378	386	393	401	408
280	287	295	303	311	319	326	334	342	350	358	365	373	381	389	396	404	412	420
287	295	303	311	319	327	335	343	351	359	367	375	383	391	399	407	415	423	431
295	304	312	320	328	336	344	353	361	369	377	385	394	402	410	418	426	435	443

Table 9.4 Reducing High-Glycemic-Index Carbohydrates

To Reduce Dietary Sugar
• Eat fewer sweets, such as candy, soft drinks, ice cream, and pastries.
• Eat fresh or frozen fruits or fruits canned without heavy syrup. Avoid artificial fruit juices.
• Use less sugar—white, brown, or raw—and less honey and syrups.
• Avoid sweetened breakfast cereals.
• Eat less jelly, jam, and preserves.
• When cooking, use spices, such as cinnamon, instead of sugar to flavor foods.
• Do not put sugar in tea or coffee.
• Avoid processed foods made from refined carbohydrates, such as white bread, rice, and pasta, and limit potato intake.

meat, poultry, and most other foods derived from animals contain all 8 essential amino acids and are "complete," or "high-quality," protein sources. Legumes (beans and peas) (Fig. 9.13), other types of vegetables, seeds and nuts, and grains also supply us with amino acids. However, each of these alone is an incomplete protein source, because each is deficient in at least 1 of the essential amino acids. Absence of 1 essential amino acid prevents use of the other 19 amino acids. Therefore, vegetarians are counseled to combine two or more incomplete types of plant products to acquire all the

Figure 9.13 Foods rich in proteins and complex carbohydrates. Beans are a good source of complex carbohydrates and protein. But beans don't supply all the essential amino acids. To ensure a complete source of protein in the diet, beans should be eaten in combination with a grain, such as rice.
Birgit Reitz-Hofmann/Getty Images

BIOLOGY TODAY ▶ Health

Protein and Vegetarians

There are an estimated 23 million vegetarians in the United States. Although definitions vary, most abstain from eating red meat, poultry, and fish. About a third of vegetarians are vegans, who avoid all animal products, while less stringent vegetarians may include eggs and/or dairy products as a part of their regular diet. Although vegetarianism is an important part of certain Eastern religions, most American vegetarians cite ethical or health reasons. Ethical concerns may include the treatment of animals raised as food, and/or the effects of animal agriculture on the environment. On the health side, most nutritional research seems to support the benefits of a low-fat, well-balanced vegetarian diet in reducing the incidence of cardiovascular disease, obesity, diabetes, and certain cancers, especially colon and prostate cancer.

Certain health risks are associated with vegetarian diets. Highly restricted vegetarian diets are probably not appropriate for pregnant or lactating women, or for very young children. Vegans, especially, have to be careful to obtain enough iron, vitamin D, vitamin B_{12}, and certain fatty acids. However, most American vegetarians would likely agree that the most common question they are asked about their dietary habits is, "Where do you get your protein?" Many people believe that humans require meat in their diet in order to obtain sufficient protein. Adding to the confusion, in 1971, Frances Moore Lappé published *Diet for a Small Planet,* which advocated vegetarianism as a more ecologically sustainable diet. That book also introduced the concept of protein complementation, the idea that foods with insufficient levels of one or more essential amino acids needed to be ingested at the same time as foods higher in those amino acids. This idea has influenced American nutritionists for several decades, but in a later edition of her famous book, Lappé noted that with the exception of a few extreme diets, "if people are getting enough calories, they are virtually certain of getting enough protein."

A position paper published in 2003 by the American Dietetic Association and Dietitians of Canada echoed these ideas, stating that "plant protein can meet requirements when a variety of plant foods is consumed and energy needs are met," as well as "complementary proteins do not need to be consumed at the same meal." Because proteins in plant food such as cereals may be harder to digest than animal proteins, vegetarians may need to include a higher percentage of protein in their diet. Beans, nuts, and legumes are particularly good protein sources, and according to the U.S. Food and Drug Administration, soybeans (Fig. 9B) contain complete protein, meaning that like animal protein, soy protein contains sufficient amounts of all essential amino acids for human nutrition. Soy may have other benefits. In October 1999, the FDA gave food manufacturers permission to put labels on products high in soy protein, indicating that they may help lower heart disease risk.

Figure 9B Soy products.
For most adults, protein needs can be met by eating vegetables, such as soybeans, that contain high-quality proteins.
Ricochet Creative Productions, LLC/McGraw Hill

Questions to Consider

1. What are some of the challenges an individual faces when moving toward a meat-free diet?
2. In general, proteins are not stored by the body in the way that carbohydrates or fats can be stored. Considering this idea, why do you think the idea of complementary proteins became so well established?

essential amino acids. Tofu, soy milk, and other foods made from processed soybeans are complete protein sources. A balanced vegetarian diet is possible with a little knowledge and planning (see the Health feature "Protein and Vegetarians").

A daily supply of essential amino acids is needed because they are not stored in the body, unlike the other amino acids, which can be stored as proteins and metabolized for cells' needs. However, it does not take very much protein to meet the daily requirement. Two servings of meat a day (one serving is equal in size to a deck of cards) is usually plenty.

Can Proteins Be Harmful? The liver removes the nitrogen-containing compound from an amino acid. By converting this portion to urea, the liver enables potentially toxic nitrogen to be removed from our bodies. However, large amounts of water are needed to properly excrete urea. Therefore, dehydration may occur if protein consumption is excessive. High-protein diets, especially those rich in animal proteins, can also increase calcium loss in urine. Excretion of calcium may lead to kidney stones and bone loss.

Certain types of meat, especially red meat, are known to be high in saturated fats; other sources of protein, such as chicken,

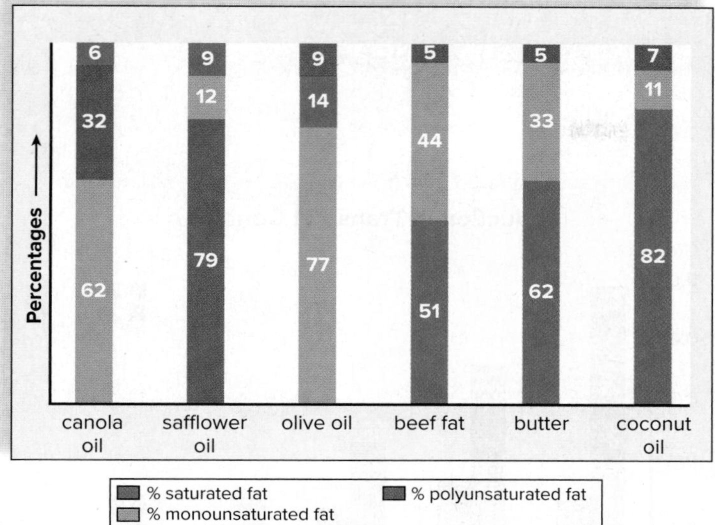

Figure 9.14 **Saturated and unsaturated fatty acids.** This graph shows the percentages of saturated and unsaturated fatty acids in select fats and oils.

fish, and eggs, are more likely to be low in saturated fats. As you recall from Section 5.7, excessive dietary saturated fat is a risk factor for cardiovascular disease.

> Sufficient proteins are needed to supply the essential amino acids. Meat and dairy sources of protein may supply unwanted saturated fat, but vegetable sources do not.

Lipids

Fats, oils, and cholesterol are lipids (see Section 2.5). Saturated fats, which are solids at room temperature, usually have an animal origin. Two well-known exceptions are palm oil and coconut oil, which contain mostly saturated fats and come from the plants mentioned (Fig. 9.14). Butter and fats associated with meats (like the fat on steak and bacon) contain saturated fats.

Oils contain unsaturated fatty acids, which do not promote cardiovascular disease. Corn oil and safflower oil are high in polyunsaturated fatty acids. Polyunsaturated oils are the only type of fat that contains linoleic acid and linolenic acid, two fatty acids the body cannot make. These fatty acids must be supplied by diet, so they are called *essential fatty acids.*

Olive oil and canola oil contain a larger percentage of monounsaturated fatty acids than other types of cooking oils. Omega-3 fatty acids—with a double bond in the third position—are believed to preserve brain function and protect against heart disease. Flaxseed contains abundant omega-3 fatty acids. Cold-water fish like salmon, sardines, and trout are also an excellent source.

Can Lipids Be Harmful? The risk for cardiovascular disease is increased by a diet high in saturated fats and cholesterol. Saturated fats contribute to the formation of lesions associated with atherosclerosis inside the blood vessels. These lesions, called *atherosclerotic plaques,* limit the flow of blood through these vessels (see Section 5.7). Cholesterol is carried in the blood by the two transport proteins: high-density lipoprotein (HDL) and low-density lipoprotein (LDL). Cholesterol transported by HDL (the "good" lipoprotein) ends up in the liver, where the cholesterol is metabolized. Cholesterol carried by LDL (the "bad" lipoprotein) ends up being deposited in the tissues. Atherosclerotic plaques form when levels of HDL are low and/or when levels of LDL are high. Recommended levels of HDL and LDL can be reestablished by a diet low in saturated fats and cholesterol.

Trans fatty acids (trans fats) arise when unsaturated fatty acids are hydrogenated to produce a solid fat. The function of the plasma membrane receptors that clear cholesterol from the bloodstream may be reduced by trans fats, resulting in a higher blood cholesterol level. Trans fats are found in commercially packaged goods, such as cookies and crackers. Unfortunately, other snacks, such as microwave popcorn, may be sources as well. Be aware that any packaged goods containing *partially hydrogenated* vegetable oils or shortening contain trans fats. Some margarines used for home cooking or baking incorporate hydrogenated vegetable oil. Commercially fried foods, such as french fries from some fast-food chains, should be strictly limited in a healthy diet. Though tasty, these are often full of trans fats. The Health feature "The Rise and Fall of Artificial Trans Fatty Acids" explores trans fats in greater detail.

Table 9.5 gives suggestions on how to reduce dietary saturated fat and cholesterol. It is not a good idea to rely on commercially produced low-fat foods. In some products, the fat has been replaced by sugars; in some others, the fat has been replaced by protein.

Table 9.5 **Reducing Lipids in the Diet**

To Reduce Saturated Fats and Trans Fats in the Diet

- Choose poultry, fish, or dry beans and peas as a protein source.
- Remove skin from poultry, and trim fat from red meats before cooking; place on a rack, so that fat drains off.
- Broil, boil, or bake rather than fry.
- Limit your intake of butter, cream, trans fats, shortenings, and tropical oils (coconut and palm oils).
- Use herbs and spices to season vegetables instead of butter, margarine, or sauces. Use lemon juice instead of salad dressing.
- Drink skim milk instead of whole milk, and use skim milk in cooking and baking.

To Reduce Dietary Cholesterol

- Avoid cheese, egg yolks, liver, and certain shellfish (shrimp and lobster). Preferably, eat white fish and poultry.
- Substitute egg whites for egg yolks in both cooking and eating.
- Include soluble fiber in the diet. Oat bran, oatmeal, beans, corn, and fruits, such as apples, citrus fruits, and cranberries, are high in soluble fiber.

> Unsaturated fats such as those in oils do not lead to cardiovascular disease and are preferred. Fats and oils contain many more calories per gram than do carbohydrates and protein.

BIOLOGY TODAY ▶ **Health**

The Rise and Fall of Artificial Trans Fatty Acids

The chemical process for creating artificial trans fats was patented in the early 1900s. At the height of their use in the 1990s, nearly all processed foods, such as cookies, crackers, donuts, frozen breakfasts, and frozen pizzas, contained trans fats. In addition, they were used for frying fast food and cooking at home in the form of Crisco and other vegetable shortenings. It all ended in 2018 when trans fats were banned by the FDA. Both the rise of artificial trans fats and their subsequent fall from favor were the result of continuous scientific research.

Trans Fats in Food Products

Oils are relatively cheap to include in food products compared to solid fats like butter and lard. Unfortunately, they don't last long on the shelf before going rancid, nor do they provide the texture of solid fats. The scientific discovery of hydrogenation solved these problems by turning the unsaturated fatty acids in oils into trans fatty acids that have a long shelf life and are semisolid.

The use of artificial trans fats in food drastically increased as scientific research began establishing a link between diets high in saturated fat and heart disease. Artificial trans fats were thought to be a more healthy alternative and were even promoted for a period of time.

Trans Fat Research

As their use increased, so did the research into trans fats. In the 1980s and 1990s, several studies discovered that even small amounts of artificial trans fats increased the risk of heart disease. Because the link was apparent, scientists and health officials started to push for bans and give more information to the public.

Some parts of the food industry tried to push back and funded a scientific study with the hope of finding that trans fats were not harmful to a person's health. However, it showed similar results. Despite the industry objections, the FDA required food manufacturers to list trans fats on nutrition facts labels. This led to consumers wanting products without trans fats and caused industry scientists to create alternatives that lowered the amount of trans fats in new food products (Fig. 9C).

Trans Fat Ban

Bans on artificial trans fats began appearing in the early 2000s. For example, Denmark established a ban in 2003, New York City in 2006, and the state of California in 2011.

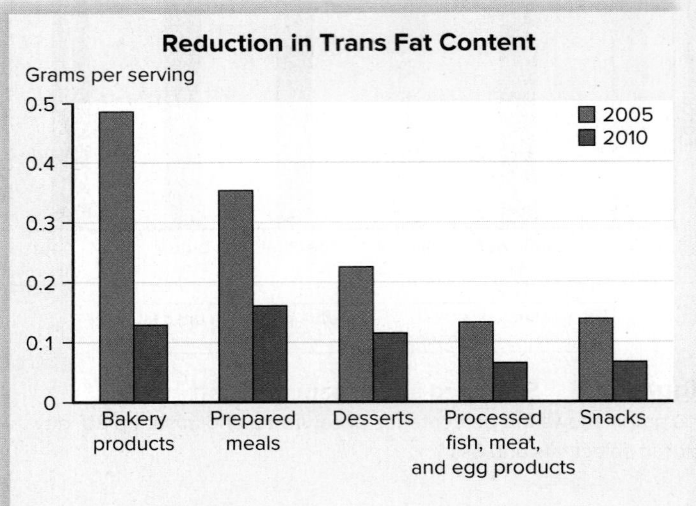

Figure 9C Reduction of artificial trans fats. The amount of trans fats used in food products significantly decreased between 2005 and 2010 after food manufacturers were required to list trans fats on food labels.
USDA, Economic Research Service calculations using Mintel Global New Products Database.

Having a full ban was important because food manufacturers could claim a food had 0 grams of trans fat as long as a serving had less than 0.5 gram of trans fat. Because even small amounts impact a person's health, consumers could unknowingly be increasing their risk of heart disease.

Nearly 115 years after the first trans fats were artificially created in a lab, they were banned from foods in the United States. The FDA established the ban in 2015 and companies had until 2018 to fully comply. It is estimated the elimination of artificial trans fats will prevent 50,000 heart attacks per year.

Questions to Consider

1. Concerns about trans fats began in the 1950s. Why did it take so many decades for studies to provide results of their effects on heart disease?
2. Why do you think some parts of the food industry were opposed to listing trans fats on nutrition labels?

Minerals

Minerals are divided into *major minerals* and *trace minerals.* Major minerals are needed at quantities greater than 100 milligrams (mg) per day. Trace minerals are needed at levels less than 100 mg per day. Table 9.6 lists selected minerals and gives their functions and food sources.

The major minerals are constituents of cells and body fluids and are structural components of tissues. The trace minerals are often part of larger molecules. For example, iron (Fe^{2+}) is present in hemoglobin, and iodine (I^-) is a part of hormones produced by the thyroid gland. Zinc (Zn^{2+}), copper (Cu^{2+}), and manganese (Mn^{2+}) are present in enzymes that catalyze a variety of reactions.

Table 9.6 Minerals

Mineral	Functions	Food Sources	Health Concerns: Deficiency	Health Concerns: Toxicity
Major (More than 100 mg/Day Needed)				
Calcium (Ca^{2+})	Strong bones and teeth, nerve conduction, muscle contraction, blood clotting	Dairy products, leafy green vegetables	Stunted growth in children, low bone density in adults	Kidney stones, interferes with iron and zinc absorption
Phosphorus (PO_4^{3-})	Bone and soft tissue growth; part of phospholipids, ATP, and nucleic acids	Meat, dairy products, sunflower seeds, food additives	Weakness, confusion, pain in bones and joints	Low blood and bone calcium levels
Potassium (K^+)	Nerve conduction, muscle contraction	Many fruits and vegetables, bran	Paralysis, irregular heartbeat, eventual death	Vomiting, heart attack, death
Sulfur (S^{2-})	Stabilizes protein shape, neutralizes toxic substances	Meat, dairy products, legumes	Not likely	In animals, depresses growth
Sodium (Na^+)	Nerve conduction, pH and water balance	Table salt	Lethargy, muscle cramps, loss of appetite	Edema, high blood pressure
Chloride (Cl^-)	Water balance	Table salt	Not likely	Vomiting, dehydration
Magnesium (Mg^{2+})	Part of various enzymes for nerve and muscle contraction, protein synthesis	Whole grains, leafy green vegetables	Muscle spasm, irregular heartbeat, convulsions, confusion, personality changes	Diarrhea
Trace (Less than 100 mg/Day Needed)				
Zinc (Zn^{2+})	Protein synthesis, wound healing, fetal development and growth, immune function	Meats, legumes, whole grains	Delayed wound healing, stunted growth, diarrhea, mental lethargy	Anemia, diarrhea, vomiting, renal failure, abnormal cholesterol levels
Iron (Fe^{2+})	Hemoglobin synthesis	Whole grains, meats, prune juice	Anemia, physical and mental sluggishness	Iron toxicity disease, organ failure, eventual death
Copper (Cu^{2+})	Hemoglobin synthesis	Meat, nuts, legumes	Anemia, stunted growth in children	Damage to internal organs if not excreted
Iodine (I^-)	Thyroid hormone synthesis	Iodized table salt, seafood	Thyroid deficiency	Depressed thyroid function, anxiety
Selenium (SeO_4^{3-})	Part of antioxidant enzyme	Seafood, meats, eggs	Vascular collapse, possible cancer development	Hair and fingernail loss, discolored skin
Manganese (Mn^{2+})	Part of enzymes	Nuts, legumes, green vegetables	Weakness and confusion	Confusion, coma, death

As research continues, more and more elements are added to the list of trace minerals considered essential. During the past three decades, for example, very small amounts of selenium, molybdenum, chromium, nickel, vanadium, silicon, and even arsenic have been found to be essential to good health. Table 9.6 also provides signs of deficiency and toxicity for the selected minerals.

Occasionally, individuals do not receive enough iron (especially women), calcium, magnesium, or zinc in their diets. Adult females need more iron in their diet than males (8–18 mg compared with 8–11 mg), because they lose hemoglobin each month during menstruation. Stress can bring on a magnesium deficiency, and due to its high-fiber content, a vegetarian diet may make zinc less available to the body. However, a varied and complete diet usually supplies enough of each type of mineral.

Calcium

Calcium (Ca^{2+}) is a major mineral needed for the construction of bones and teeth. It is also necessary for nerve conduction, muscle contraction, and blood clotting. Many people take calcium supplements to prevent or counteract **osteoporosis,** a degenerative bone disease that afflicts an estimated one-fourth of older men and one-half of older women in the United States. Osteoporosis develops because bone-eating cells called osteoclasts are more active than bone-forming cells called osteoblasts. The bones become porous, and they break easily because they lack sufficient calcium. Recommended calcium intakes vary by age, but in general 1,000 mg a day is recommended for men and women. After age 50 in women, and 70 in men, this increases to 1,200 mg a day. For many people, calcium supplements are needed to obtain these levels.

Women who are white, small-framed, and have a family history of osteoporosis are at greatest risk of developing the disease. Smoking and drinking more than nine cups of caffeinated drinks daily may also contribute. Vitamin D is an essential companion to calcium in preventing osteoporosis. Other vitamins may also be helpful; for example, magnesium has been found to suppress the cycle that leads to bone loss. In addition to adequate calcium and vitamin intake, exercise helps prevent osteoporosis. Medications are also available that slow bone loss while increasing skeletal mass.

Sodium

Sodium plays a major role in regulating the body's water balance, as does chloride (Cl^-). Sodium plays an important role in the movement of materials across the plasma membrane (see Section 3.3), as well as the conduction of a nerve impulse (see Section 14.1). The recommended amount of sodium intake per day is 1,500 mg, although the average American takes in more than 3,400 mg every day. This imbalance has caused concern, because sodium in the form of salt intensifies hypertension (high blood pressure). About one-third of the sodium we consume occurs naturally in foods. Another third is added during commercial processing, and we add the last third either during home cooking or at the table in the form of table salt.

Clearly, it is possible to cut down on the amount of sodium in the diet. Table 9.7 gives recommendations for doing so.

Table 9.7 Reducing Dietary Sodium

To Reduce Dietary Sodium
• Use spices instead of salt to flavor foods.
• Add little or no salt to foods at the table, and add only small amounts of salt when you cook.
• Eat unsalted crackers, pretzels, potato chips, nuts, and popcorn.
• Avoid hot dogs, ham, bacon, luncheon meats, smoked salmon, sardines, and anchovies.
• Avoid processed cheese and canned or dehydrated soups.
• Avoid brine-soaked foods, such as pickles and olives.
• Read nutrition labels to avoid high-salt products.

BIOLOGY IN YOUR LIFE

Where does most of the sodium in our diet come from?

Contrary to popular belief, the majority of the sodium in our diet does not come from the salt we put on our food when eating. Instead, most of our sodium (over three-quarters of it!) comes from processed foods and condiments. Sodium is used in these items both to preserve the food or condiment and to make it taste better. But sometimes the amount of sodium is phenomenal. A single teaspoon of soy sauce contains almost 1,000 mg of sodium, and a half-cup of prepared tomato sauce typically has over 400 mg of sodium. Websites such as nutritiondata.self.com can help us track our daily sodium intake.

Vitamins

Vitamins are organic compounds (other than carbohydrate, fat, and protein) that the body uses for metabolic purposes but is unable to produce in adequate quantity. Many vitamins are portions of coenzymes, enzyme helpers. For example, niacin is part of the coenzyme NAD, and riboflavin is part of another dehydrogenase, FAD (see Section 3.6). Coenzymes are needed in only small amounts, because each can be used over and over. Not all vitamins are coenzymes. Vitamin A, for example, is a precursor for the visual pigment that prevents night blindness. If vitamins are lacking in the diet, various symptoms develop. There are 13 vitamins, divided into those that are *fat soluble* (Table 9.8) and those that are *water soluble* (Table 9.9). The differences between fat-soluble and water-soluble vitamins have to do with how the compound gets absorbed into the body, how it is transported by the body, its interaction with body tissues, and how it is stored in the cells.

Antioxidants

Over the past several decades, numerous statistical studies have determined that a diet rich in fruits and vegetables can protect against cancer. Cellular metabolism generates free radicals, unstable molecules that carry an extra electron. The most common free radicals in cells are superoxide (O_2^-) and hydroxide (OH^-). To stabilize themselves, free radicals donate an electron to DNA, to proteins (including enzymes), or to lipids, which can be found in

Table 9.8 Fat-Soluble Vitamins

Vitamin	Functions	Food Sources	Health Concerns	
			Deficiency	Toxicity
Vitamin A	Antioxidant synthesized from beta-carotene; needed for healthy eyes, skin, hair, and mucous membranes and for proper bone growth	Deep yellow/orange and leafy, dark green vegetables; fruits; cheese; whole milk; butter; eggs	Night blindness, impaired growth of bones and teeth	Headache, dizziness, nausea, hair loss, abnormal development of fetus
Vitamin D	Group of steroids needed for development and maintenance of bones and teeth and for absorption of calcium	Milk fortified with vitamin D, fish liver oil; also made in the skin when exposed to sunlight	Rickets, decalcification and weakening of bones	Calcification of soft tissues, diarrhea, possible renal damage
Vitamin E	Antioxidant that prevents oxidation of vitamin A and polyunsaturated fatty acids	Leafy green vegetables, fruits, vegetable oils, nuts, whole-grain breads and cereals	Unknown	Diarrhea, nausea, headaches, fatigue, muscle weakness
Vitamin K	Needed for synthesis of substances active in clotting of blood	Leafy green vegetables, cabbage, cauliflower	Easy bruising and bleeding	Can interfere with anticoagulant medication

Table 9.9 Water-Soluble Vitamins

Vitamin	Functions	Food Sources	Health Concerns	
			Deficiency	**Toxicity**
Vitamin C	Antioxidant; needed for forming collagen; helps maintain capillaries, bones, and teeth	Citrus fruits, leafy green vegetables, tomatoes, potatoes, cabbage	Scurvy, delayed wound healing, infections	Gout, kidney stones, diarrhea, decreased copper
Thiamine (vitamin B_1)	Part of coenzyme needed for cellular respiration; also promotes activity of the nervous system	Whole-grain cereals, dried beans and peas, sunflower seeds, nuts	Beriberi, muscular weakness, enlarged heart	Can interfere with absorption of other vitamins
Riboflavin (vitamin B_2)	Part of coenzymes, such as FAD; aids cellular respiration, including oxidation of protein and fat	Nuts, dairy products, whole-grain cereals, poultry, leafy green vegetables	Dermatitis, blurred vision, growth failure	Unknown
Niacin (nicotinic acid)	Part of coenzyme NAD; needed for cellular respiration, including oxidation of protein and fat	Peanuts, poultry, whole-grain cereals, leafy green vegetables, beans	Pellagra, diarrhea, mental disorders	High blood sugar and uric acid, vasodilation, etc.
Folacin (folic acid)	Coenzyme needed for production of hemoglobin and formation of DNA	Dark, leafy green vegetables; nuts; beans; whole-grain cereals	Megaloblastic anemia, spina bifida	May mask B_{12} deficiency
Vitamin B_6	Coenzyme needed for synthesis of hormones and hemoglobin; CNS control	Whole-grain cereals, bananas, beans, poultry, nuts, leafy green vegetables	Rarely, convulsions, vomiting, seborrhea, muscular weakness	Insomnia, neuropathy
Pantothenic acid	Part of coenzyme A needed for oxidation of carbohydrates and fats; aids in the formation of hormones and certain neurotransmitters	Nuts, beans, dark green vegetables, poultry, fruits, milk	Rarely, loss of appetite, mental depression, numbness	Unknown
Vitamin B_{12}	Complex, cobalt-containing compound; part of the coenzyme needed for synthesis of nucleic acids and myelin	Dairy products, fish, poultry, eggs, fortified cereals	Pernicious anemia	Unknown
Biotin	Coenzyme needed for metabolism of amino acids and fatty acids	Generally in foods, especially eggs	Skin rash, nausea, fatigue	Unknown

FAD = flavin adenine dinucleotide; NAD = nicotinamide adenine dinucleotide

plasma membranes. Such donations often damage these cellular molecules and thereby may lead to disruptions of cellular functions, including even cancer.

Vitamins C, E, and A are believed to defend the body against free radicals and are therefore termed antioxidants. These vitamins are especially abundant in fruits and vegetables. Dietary guidelines suggest we increase our consumption of fruits and vegetables each day. To achieve this goal, think in terms of salad greens, raw or cooked vegetables, dried fruit, and fruit juice, in addition to apples and oranges and other fresh fruits.

Dietary supplements may provide a potential safeguard against cancer and cardiovascular disease. Nutritionists do not think people should take supplements instead of improving their intake of fruits and vegetables. There are many beneficial compounds in these foods that cannot be obtained from a vitamin pill. These compounds enhance one another's absorption or action and perform independent biological functions.

Vitamin D

Skin cells contain a precursor cholesterol molecule converted to vitamin D after UV exposure. Vitamin D leaves the skin and is modified first in the kidneys and then in the liver until finally it becomes calcitriol. Calcitriol promotes the absorption of calcium by the intestines. When taking a calcium supplement, it is a good idea to get one with added vitamin D. The lack of vitamin D leads to rickets in children. Rickets, characterized by bowing of the legs, is caused by defective mineralization of the skeleton. Most milk is fortified with vitamin D, which helps prevent the occurrence of rickets.

How to Plan Nutritious Meals

Many serious disorders in Americans are linked to a diet that results in excess body fat. Whereas genetics is a factor in being overweight, a person cannot become overweight without taking in more food energy (calories) than is needed. People need calories (energy) for their basal metabolism. Basal metabolism is the number of calories a person's body burns at rest to maintain normal body functions. A person also needs calories for exercise. The less exercise, the fewer calories needed beyond the basal metabolic rate. So the first step in planning a diet is to limit the number of calories to an amount the person will use each day. Let's say you do all the necessary calculations (beyond the scope of this book). You discover that, as a woman, the maximum number of calories you can take in each day is 2,000. If you're a man, you can afford 2,500 calories without gaining weight.

The new guidelines developed by the U.S. Department of Agriculture (USDA) are called MyPlate (Fig. 9.15). This graphical

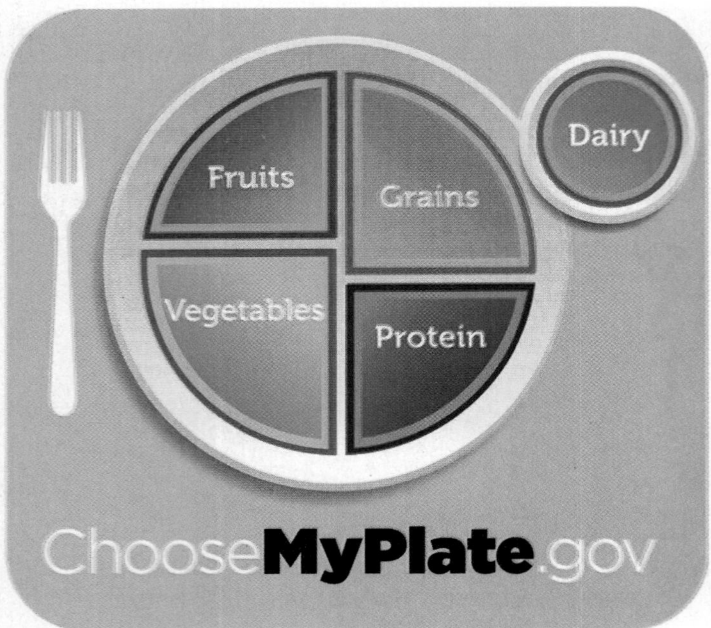

Figure 9.15 **The MyPlate dietary recommendations.** The U.S. Department of Agriculture (USDA) developed this visual representation of a food plate as a guide to better health. The size differences on the plate for each food group suggest what portion of your meal should consist of each category. The five different colors illustrate that each food category, in correct proportions, is needed each day for good health. See MyPlate.gov.
U.S. Department of Agriculture

representation replaced the older pyramids because most people found the plate graphic easier to interpret. It can be used to help you decide how those calories should be distributed among the foods to eat. MyPlate emphasizes the proportions of each food group that should be consumed daily.

In 2020, the U.S. Department of Health and Human Services and the U.S. Department of Agriculture released a new set of dietary guidelines that focuses more on healthy eating patterns than on strict amounts of nutrients. These guidelines are outlined in the Health feature "New Dietary Guidelines."

Eat a variety of foods. Foods from all food groups should be included in the diet.

- Eat more of these foods: fruits, vegetables, whole grains, and fat-free or low-fat milk products. Choose dark green vegetables, orange vegetables, and leafy vegetables. Dry beans and peas are good sources of fiber and a great protein source as well. Limit potatoes and corn. When eating grains, choose whole grains, such as brown rice, oatmeal, and whole-wheat bread. Choose fruit as a snack or a topping for foods, instead of sugar.
- Choose lean meats, such as poultry, and fish high in omega-3 fatty acids, such as salmon, trout, and herring, in moderate-sized portions. Include oils rich in monounsaturated and polyunsaturated fatty acids in the diet.

BIOLOGY TODAY ▶ **Health**

New Dietary Guidelines

Dietary guidelines are typically revised by the U.S. government every 5 years to reflect changes in nutrition science. The latest guidelines were released in 2020 by the Departments of Agriculture and Health and Human Services. The overall purposes of these guidelines were to:

- Promote health.
- Prevent chronic (long-term) disease.
- Assist people in reaching and maintaining a healthy weight.

The new guidelines focus less on prescribing quantitative levels for nutrients, and more on establishing healthy eating patterns. These patterns include the following foods:

- A variety of vegetables, including leafy vegetables, beans, red and yellow vegetables, and starches.
- Fruits.
- Grains. At least half of all grains should be whole grains.
- Fat-free or low-fat dairy products (including soy).
- Proteins in the form of seafood, lean meats, poultry, eggs, legumes, nuts, and soy products.
- Oils.

To establish these healthy eating patterns, specific recommendations were made to limit certain nutrients that are recognized as raising health concerns:

- Consume less than 10 percent of calories per day from added sugar.
- Consume less than 10 percent of calories per day from saturated fats.
- Consume less than 2,300 milligrams (mg) per day of sodium.
- Alcohol should be consumed only in moderation. A maximum of one drink per day for women and up to two drinks per day for men (and only by adults of legal drinking age).

For more information on these guidelines, including the science of how they were determined, visit https://www.dietaryguidelines.gov/resources/2020-2025-dietary-guidelines-online-materials.

Questions to Consider

1. Why do you think quantitative values were removed for many of the nutrients?
2. Reflect on your diet over the past 24 hours. How does your diet relate to these general guidelines?

- Eat less of foods high in saturated or trans fats, added sugars, cholesterol, salt, and alcohol.
- Be physically active every day. If you need to lose weight, decrease your calorie intake slowly while maintaining an adequate nutrient intake and increasing your physical activity.

Eating Disorders

Eating disorders are complex psychological disorders characterized by abnormal and unhealthy eating patterns. Although many people with eating disorders may be dissatisfied with their body image, this is but one underlying cause. Various social, cultural, emotional, and biological factors all contribute to the development of an eating disorder. Serious conditions such as obesity, anorexia nervosa, and bulimia nervosa can lead to malnutrition, disability, and death. Regardless of the eating disorder, early recognition and treatment are crucial.

Anorexia nervosa is a severe psychological disorder characterized by an irrational fear of getting fat. Individuals with anorexia nervosa refuse to eat enough food to maintain a healthy body weight. A self-imposed starvation diet is often accompanied by occasional binge eating, followed by purging and extreme physical activity to avoid weight gain. Binges usually include large amounts of high-calorie foods, and purging episodes involve self-induced vomiting and laxative abuse. About 90% of people with anorexia nervosa are young women; an estimated 1 in 200 teenage girls is affected.

A person with **bulimia nervosa** binge eats and then purges to avoid gaining weight. The cyclical binge-purge behavior can occur several times a day. People with bulimia nervosa can be difficult to identify, because their body weights are often normal and they tend to conceal their bingeing and purging practices. Women are more likely than men to develop bulimia; an estimated 4% of young women have this condition.

Other eating disorders include binge-eating disorder and muscle dysmorphia. Many people with obesity have **binge-eating disorder,** a condition characterized by episodes of overeating without purging. Stress, anxiety, anger, and depression can trigger food binges. People with **muscle dysmorphia** think their body is underdeveloped. Bodybuilding activities and a preoccupation with diet and body form accompany this condition. The person may spend hours in the gym every day, working out on muscle-strengthening equipment. Unlike anorexia nervosa and bulimia, muscle dysmorphia affects more men than women.

CHECK YOUR PROGRESS 9.6

1. Briefly describe and give an example of each class of nutrients.
2. Discuss why carbohydrates and fats might be the cause of the obesity epidemic today.
3. Explain the difference between a vitamin and mineral.

CONNECTING THE CONCEPTS

For more information on how the body utilizes nutrients, refer to the following discussions:

Section 12.1 explains how vitamin D acts as a hormone that influences bone growth.

Section 15.4 examines the role of vitamin A in vision.

Section 20.2 examines how a diet with adequate levels of vitamins A and C may help prevent cancer.

CONCLUSION

In this chapter, we not only explored the structure and function of the digestive system, but also the principles of human nutrition.

Celiac disease is a serious condition that affects roughly 1 out of every 100 individuals. Unlike gluten sensitivity, which has many of the same symptoms, celiac disease can cause severe damage to the villi and microvilli lining of the small intestine.

As we have seen in this chapter, the small intestine plays a central role in the processing of nutrients. Any condition that damages the villi and microvilli reduces the effectiveness of the small intestine and can result in weight loss, vitamin and mineral deficiencies, and even cancer of the intestines. Currently, the only treatment for celiac disease is a lifelong diet that strictly avoids exposure to the gluten protein.

SUMMARIZE

9.1 Overview of Digestion

- The purpose of the **digestive system** is to **hydrolyze** macromolecules to their smallest subunits. The organs of the digestive system are located within the GI tract.
- The processes of digestion require **ingestion, digestion, movement (peristalsis), absorption,** and **elimination.**
- All parts of the tract have four layers, called the **mucosa, submucosa, serosa,** and **muscularis.** These layers surround the **lumen,** or interior space of the GI tract.
- A disorder of the muscularis called **diverticulosis** can affect any organ of the GI tract, but primarily occurs in the large intestine.

9.2 The Mouth, Pharynx, and Esophagus

- In the **mouth** (oral cavity), teeth chew the food. The **salivary glands** produce saliva, which contains **salivary amylase** for digesting starch, and the tongue forms a **bolus** for swallowing.
- Both the mouth and the nose lead into the **pharynx.** The pharynx opens into both the esophagus (food passage) and the trachea (air passage). During swallowing, the opening into the nose is blocked by the soft palate, and the **epiglottis** covers the opening to the trachea **(glottis).** Food enters the esophagus, and peristalsis begins. The esophagus moves food to the stomach by peristalsis. **Sphincters** control the movement of the bolus.
- Disorders of the mouth include **dental caries** (cavities) of the teeth, and **gingivitis** and **periodontitis** of the gums.
- **Heartburn** occurs when the contents of the stomach enter the **esophagus.** During vomiting, the abdominal muscles and **diaphragm** propel the food through the esophagus and out the mouth.

9.3 The Stomach and Small Intestine

- The **stomach** expands and stores food and churns, mixing food with the acidic gastric juices. The stomach contains an **oblique layer** of smooth muscle, and folds called **rugae,** to assist in mixing the food.

Gastric glands produce gastric juice, which contains **pepsin,** an enzyme that digests protein. The material leaving the stomach is called **chyme.**

- The duodenum of the **small intestine** receives bile from the liver and pancreatic juice from the pancreas. Bile emulsifies fat and readies it for digestion by lipase.
- The pancreas produces enzymes that digest starch **(amylase),** protein (**proteases,** such as trypsin), and fat **(lipase).** The intestinal enzymes finish the process of chemical digestion.
- Brush border enzymes of the small intestine complete the digestive process. Small nutrient molecules are absorbed at the **villi** and **microvilli** in the walls of the small intestine. The nutrients enter the capillaries of the circulatory system and **lacteals** of the lymphatic system. People with **lactose intolerance** are missing the lactase enzyme in the small intestine.

9.4 The Accessory Organs and Regulation of Secretions

Three accessory organs of digestion send secretions to the duodenum via ducts. These organs are the pancreas, liver, and gallbladder.

- The **pancreas** produces pancreatic juice, which contains digestive enzymes for carbohydrate, protein, and fat. The pancreas also releases the **hormone** insulin, which regulates blood glucose levels.
- The **liver** produces **bile,** destroys old blood cells, detoxifies blood, stores iron, makes plasma proteins, stores glucose as glycogen, breaks down glycogen to glucose, produces **urea,** and helps regulate blood cholesterol levels.
- The **gallbladder** stores bile, produced by the liver. The secretions of digestive juices are controlled by the nervous system and by hormones.
- Gastrin produced by the lower part of the stomach stimulates the upper part of the stomach to secrete pepsin. Secretin and CCK produced by the duodenal wall stimulate the pancreas to secrete its juices and the gallbladder to release bile.
- Disorders of the liver include **jaundice, hepatitis,** and **cirrhosis. Gallstones** may affect the operation of the gallbladder.

9.5 The Large Intestine and Defecation

- The **large intestine** consists of the **cecum;** the **colon** (including the ascending, transverse, and descending colon); the **appendix;** and the **rectum,** which ends at the **anus.**
- The large intestine absorbs water, salts, and some vitamins; forms the feces; and carries out **defecation.** Fiber provides bulk to the feces. The color of the feces is the result of **bilirubin** (a waste product).
- Disorders of the large intestine include **diarrhea, constipation, hemorrhoids,** diverticulosis, irritable bowel syndrome, inflammatory bowel disease, **polyps,** and cancer.

9.6 Nutrition and Weight Control

The **nutrients** released by the digestive process should provide us with adequate energy, essential amino acids and fatty acids, and all necessary vitamins and minerals.

- The **body mass index (BMI)** may be used to determine the percent body fat. **Obesity** is associated with many illnesses, including type 2 diabetes and cardiovascular disease. The new MyPlate dietary guidelines provide a visual representation of dietary proportions to maintain good health.
- Carbohydrates are necessary in the diet, but simple sugars and refined starches cause a rapid release of insulin that can lead to type 2 diabetes. **Fiber** is undigested carbohydrate. The **glycemic index** may be used to predict which foods will release carbohydrates quickly into the blood.
- Proteins supply essential amino acids.
- Unsaturated fatty acids, particularly the omega-3 fatty acids, are protective against cardiovascular disease. Saturated fatty acids and trans fats contribute to heart disease. Essential fatty acids must be supplied by the diet.
- **Minerals** are also required by the body in certain amounts. **Osteoporosis** is an example of a disease caused by a mineral deficiency (calcium).
- **Vitamins** are organic compounds that act as metabolic assistants.
- Eating disorders include **anorexia nervosa, bulimia nervosa, binge-eating disorder,** and **muscle dysmorphia.**

ENGAGE

THINKING CRITICALLY

1. Trace *all* of the types and locations of enzymes that might be involved in digesting a molecule of a complex carbohydrate such as starch, all the way through to the utilization of a glucose molecule by a body cell.
2. Suppose you are taking large doses of creatine, an amino acid supplement that is advertised for its ability to enhance muscle growth. Because your muscles can grow only at a limited rate, what do you suppose happens to the excess creatine that is not used for synthesis of new muscle?
3. Predict and explain the expected digestive results per test tube for this experiment.

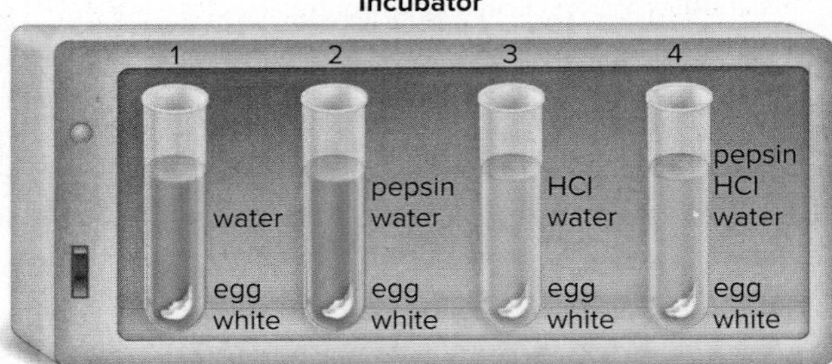

MAKING IT RELEVANT

1. What types of foods would you have to avoid if you had celiac disease? Can the nutrients, such as vitamins and minerals, in those foods be gained through other sources?
2. As we have learned, gluten is a protein, not a carbohydrate. Yet many manufacturers label foods such as fruits and vegetables as gluten-free. Can you provide examples of this from your own experiences? Why do you think this type of labeling is allowed?
3. Given what you now know about the immune system and nutrition, why would it be safe to say that most humans have some form of food allergy?

Find answers to all of the chapter questions at connect.mheducation.com

wavebreakmedia/Shutterstock

CHAPTER 10

Respiratory System

Ultrafine Particles and Asthma

Asthma is a disease in which the airways become constricted (narrowed) and inflamed (swollen), both of which can result in difficulty breathing. The symptoms often include wheezing and shortness of breath, a frequent cough (often at night), and a feeling of being very tired or weak, especially when exercising. Over 25 million children and adults in the United States have asthma, and the incidence seems to be increasing. Experts offer various explanations for this. One hypothesis is that we may be "too clean," in the sense that we are not exposed to enough common bacteria, viruses, and parasites as children. As a result, our immune systems may react to harmless material we inhale. There are many harmful forms of air pollution, but of increasing concern are tiny, "ultrafine" particles, those less than 0.1 micrometer (μm) across, which are produced at high levels by diesel engines. These particles can bypass the normal defenses of the upper respiratory tract and end up lodging deep in the lungs, with damaging effects.

Recently, there have been breakthroughs in asthma research. In addition to environmental factors, there appear to be a number of genes that increase susceptibility to asthma. For example, one set of genes on chromosome 5 has been linked to asthma and is associated with the body's inflammatory response. Inflammation can constrict the airways and increase fluid flow to the lungs. Variations in a gene on chromosome 17 have also been shown to increase susceptibility, especially in individuals who have been exposed to respiratory viruses. Although there is not currently a cure, the identification of these genes provides hope for those with asthma.

As you read through the chapter, think about the following questions:

1. How would narrowing and swelling of the airways affect the respiratory volumes?
2. How would asthma indirectly affect the other systems of the body?

CHAPTER OUTLINE

BEFORE YOU BEGIN

Before beginning this chapter, take a few moments to review the following discussions:

Section 2.2 What do the values of the pH scale indicate?

Section 4.8 What is the role of the respiratory system in maintaining homeostasis?

Section 6.2 How are red blood cells involved in transporting oxygen and carbon dioxide?

10.1 The Respiratory System

LEARNING OUTCOMES

Upon completion of this section, you should be able to

1. Summarize the role of the respiratory system in homeostasis.
2. Distinguish between inspiration and expiration.
3. Identify the structures of the human respiratory system.

The organs of the **respiratory system** ensure that oxygen enters the body and carbon dioxide leaves the body. The structures and organs of the respiratory system are shown in Figure 10.1.

During **inspiration,** or inhalation (breathing in), air is conducted from the atmosphere to the lungs by a series of cavities, tubes, and openings. During **expiration,** or exhalation (breathing out), air is conducted from the lungs to the atmosphere by way of the same structures.

Ventilation is another term for breathing that includes both inspiration and expiration. During ventilation, the respiratory system depends on the cardiovascular system to transport oxygen (O_2) from the lungs to the tissues and carbon dioxide (CO_2) from the tissues to the lungs.

Gas exchange is necessary because the cells of the body carry out cellular respiration to make energy in the form of ATP. During cellular respiration, cells use up O_2 and produce CO_2. The respiratory system therefore provides these cells with O_2 and removes CO_2.

The Respiratory System and Homeostasis

The respiratory system works with the cardiovascular system to participate in homeostasis in the following ways (Fig. 10.2):

- External respiration, the exchange of gases (oxygen and carbon dioxide) between air and the blood

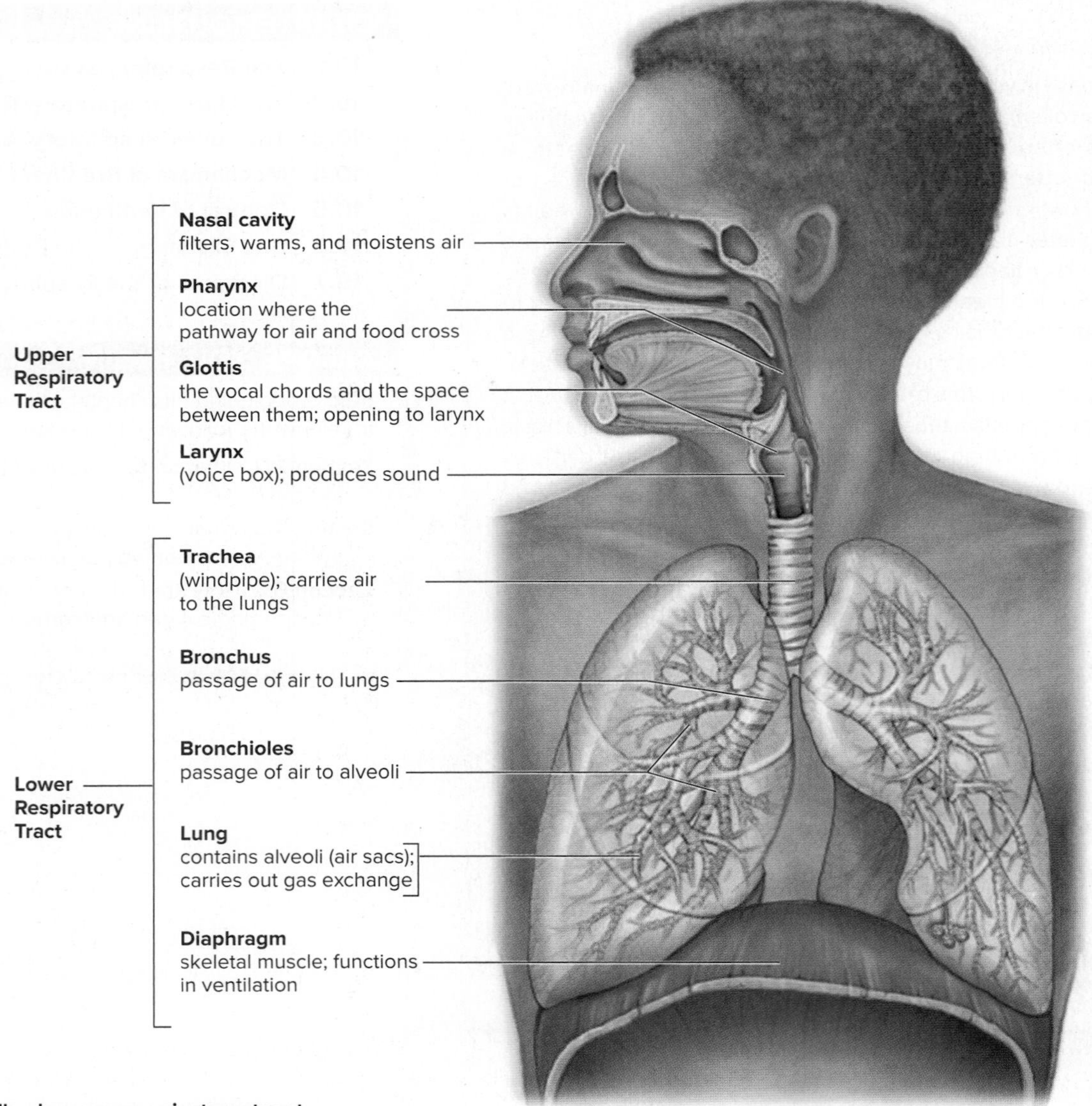
Upper Respiratory Tract
Nasal cavity
filters, warms, and moistens air
Pharynx
location where the pathway for air and food cross
Glottis
the vocal chords and the space between them; opening to larynx
Larynx
(voice box); produces sound
Lower Respiratory Tract
Trachea
(windpipe); carries air to the lungs
Bronchus
passage of air to lungs
Bronchioles
passage of air to alveoli
Lung
contains alveoli (air sacs); carries out gas exchange
Diaphragm
skeletal muscle; functions in ventilation

Figure 10.1 The human respiratory tract.
The respiratory tract extends from the nose to the lungs.

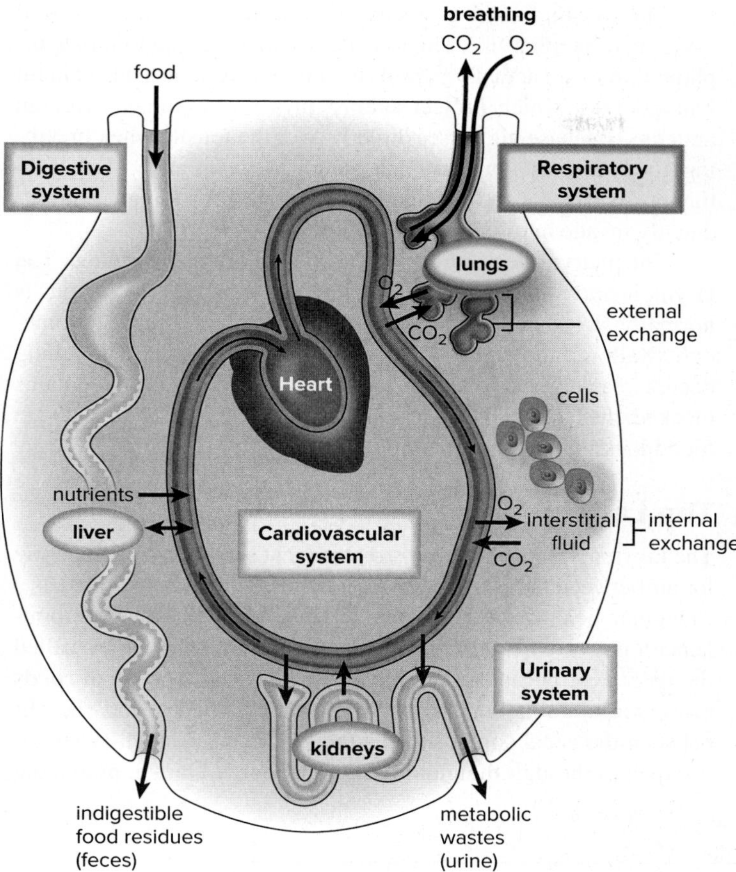

Figure 10.2 **The respiratory system and homeostasis.** The respiratory system works closely with the cardiovascular system in homeostasis by allowing for the exchange of gases with the external environment.

- Transport of gases to and from the lungs and the tissues
- Internal respiration, the exchange of gases between the blood and tissue fluid

CHECK YOUR PROGRESS 10.1

1. Trace the path of air from the nasal cavities to the lungs.
2. Explain how the flow of air differs during inspiration and expiration.
3. Describe the function(s) of the respiratory system.

CONNECTING THE CONCEPTS

The respiratory and circulatory systems cooperate extensively to maintain homeostasis in the body. For more on the interactions of these two systems, refer to the following discussions:

Section 5.5 outlines the circulatory pathways that move gases to and from the lungs.

Section 6.2 describes the role of red blood cells in the transport of gases.

10.2 The Upper Respiratory Tract

LEARNING OUTCOMES

Upon completion of this section, you should be able to

1. Summarize the role of the nose, pharynx, and larynx in respiration.
2. Identify the structures of the upper respiratory system and provide their function.
3. Explain how sound is produced by the larynx.

The nasal cavities, pharynx, and larynx are the structures of the upper respiratory tract (Fig. 10.3).

The Nose

The **nose** opens at the nares (nostrils), which lead to the **nasal cavities.** The nasal cavities are narrow canals separated from each other by a septum composed of bone and cartilage (Fig. 10.3).

Air entering the nasal cavities encounters large, stiff hairs that act as a screening mechanism. The hairs filter the air and trap small particles (dust, mold spores, pollen, etc.) so they don't enter air passages. The rest of the nasal cavities are lined by mucous membrane. The mucus secreted by this membrane helps trap dust and move it to the pharynx, where it can be swallowed or expectorated by coughing or spitting. Under the mucous layer is the submucosa. The submucosa contains a large number of capillaries that help warm and moisten the incoming air. When we breathe out on a cold day, the moisture in the outgoing air condenses, so we can see our breath. The abundance of capillaries in the submucosa also makes us susceptible to nosebleeds if the nose suffers an injury.

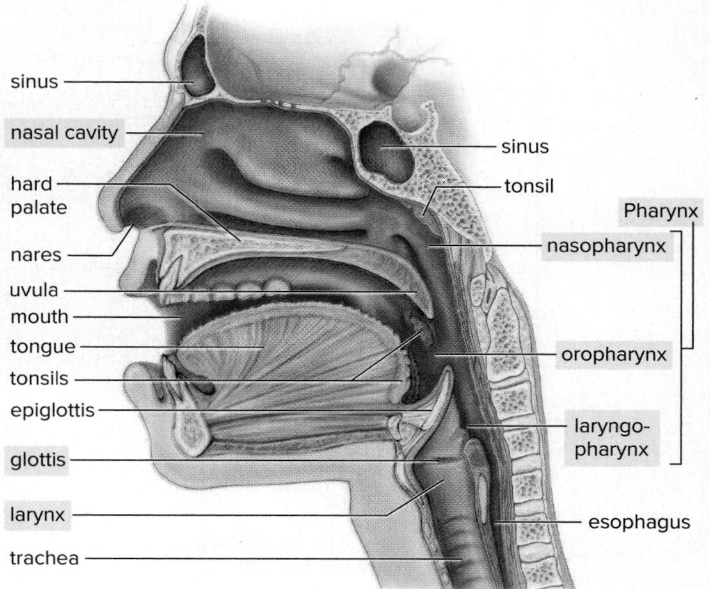

Figure 10.3 **The upper respiratory tract.** This drawing shows the path of air from the nasal cavities to the trachea, in the lower respiratory tract. The structures highlighted in blue are in the upper respiratory tract.

In the narrow upper recesses of the nasal cavities are ciliated cells that act as odor receptors. Nerves lead from these cells to the brain, where the impulses generated by the odor receptors are interpreted as smell (see Section 15.3).

The tear (lacrimal) glands drain into the nasal cavities by way of tear ducts. When you cry, your nose runs as tears drain from the eye surface into the nose. The nasal cavities also connect with the sinuses (cavities) of the skull. At times, fluid may accumulate in these sinuses, causing an increase in pressure, resulting in a sinus headache.

Air in the nasal cavities passes into the nasopharynx, the upper portion of the pharynx. Connected to the nasopharynx are tubes called **auditory tubes** (also called *eustachian tubes*) that connect to the middle ear. When air pressure inside the middle ears equalizes with the air pressure in the nasopharynx, the auditory tube openings may create a "popping" sensation. When in a plane taking off or landing, some people chew gum or yawn in an effort to move air from the ears and prevent the popping.

The Pharynx

The **pharynx,** commonly referred to as the throat, is a funnel-shaped passageway that connects the nasal and oral cavities to the larynx. The pharynx has three parts: the nasopharynx, where the nasal cavities open above the soft palate; the oropharynx, where the oral cavity opens; and the laryngopharynx, which opens into the larynx.

The **tonsils** form a protective ring at the junction of the oral cavity and the pharynx. The tonsils, which are composed of lymphoid tissue, are actually part of the immune system. They contain lymphocytes, which protect against invasion of inhaled foreign antigens. Because air passes directly over the tonsils when breathing, they serve as a primary defense for the respiratory system. In the tonsils, B cells and T cells respond to antigens that may subsequently invade internal tissues and fluids.

The pharynx serves as a passageway for both air and food. The larynx is normally open, allowing air to pass, but the esophagus is normally closed and opens only when a person swallows. If someone swallows and some of the food enters the larynx, coughing occurs in an effort to dislodge the food. If the passageway remains blocked, the Heimlich maneuver (Fig. 10.4) can be used to dislodge food blocking the airway.

The Larynx

The **larynx** is a cartilaginous structure that serves as a passageway for air between the pharynx and the trachea. It can be pictured as a triangular box whose apex, the Adam's apple (laryngeal prominence), is located at the front of the neck. The larynx is also called the *voice box,* because it houses the vocal cords. The **vocal cords** are mucosal folds supported by elastic ligaments, and the slit between the vocal cords is called the **glottis** (Fig. 10.5). When air is expelled through the glottis, the vocal cords vibrate, producing

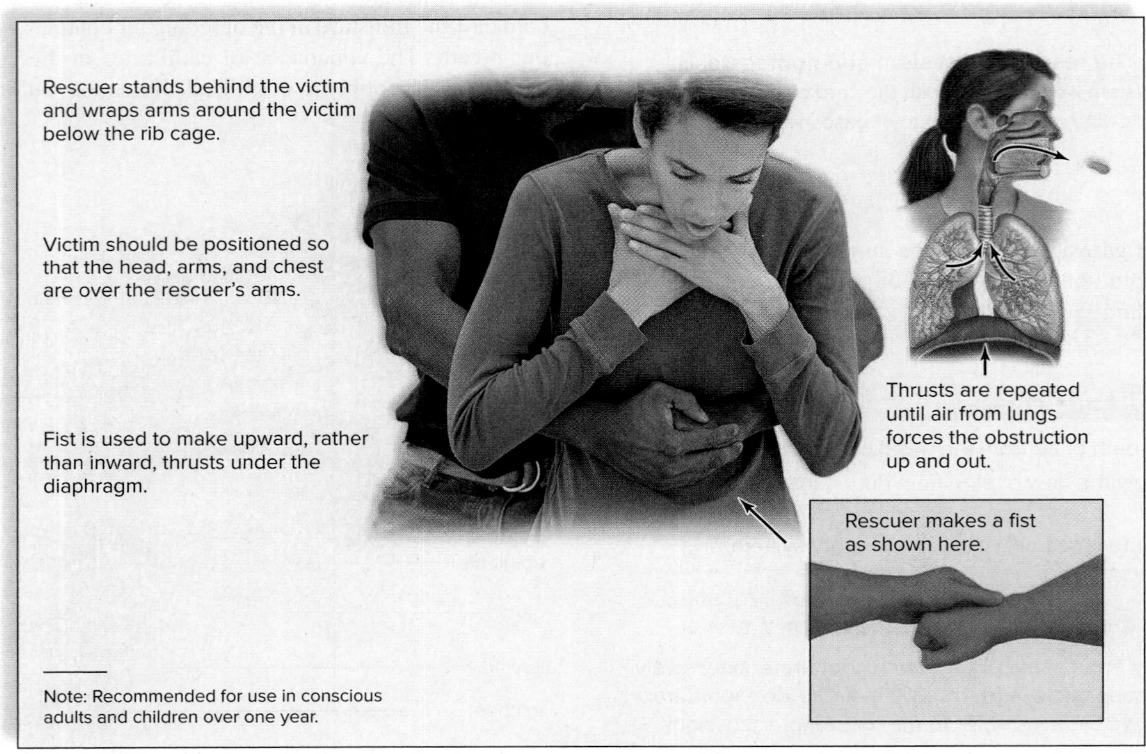

Figure 10.4 The Heimlich maneuver.
The Heimlich maneuver is used when someone's ability to breathe is prevented by an obstruction blocking the airway. The steps associated with the Heimlich maneuver are shown in the illustration.
(photo): Science Photo Library/Getty Images

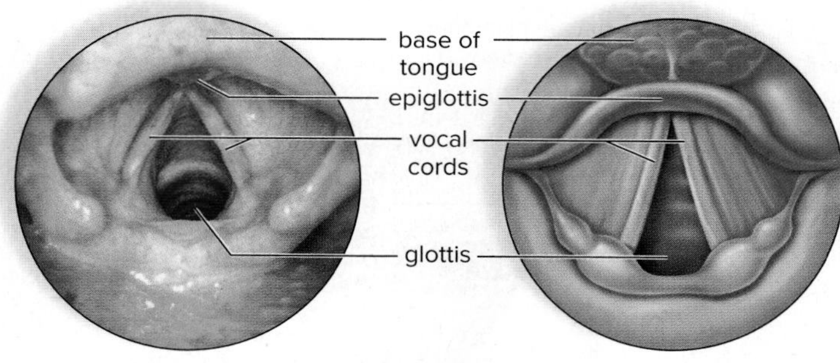

Figure 10.5 The vocal cords.
Viewed from above, the vocal cords can be seen to stretch across the glottis, the opening to the trachea. When air is expelled through the glottis, the vocal cords vibrate, producing sound. The glottis is narrow when we produce a high-pitched sound, and it widens as the pitch deepens.
(photo): CNRI/Science Photo Library/Getty Images

sound. At the time of puberty, the growth of the larynx and the vocal cords is much more rapid and accentuated in the male than in the female, causing the male to have a more prominent Adam's apple and a deeper voice. The voice "breaks" in the young male due to his inability to control the longer vocal cords.

The high or low pitch of the voice is regulated when speaking and singing by changing the tension on the vocal cords. The greater the tension, as when the glottis becomes narrower, the higher the pitch. When the glottis is wider, the pitch is lower (Fig. 10.5). The loudness or intensity of the voice depends on the amplitude of the vibrations—the degree to which the vocal cords vibrate.

Ordinarily, when food is swallowed, the larynx moves upward against the **epiglottis,** a flap of tissue that prevents food from passing into the larynx. You can detect the movement of the larynx by placing your hand gently on your larynx and swallowing.

CHECK YOUR PROGRESS 10.2

1. Describe the function of each of the structures of the upper respiratory tract.
2. Name and briefly describe the body systems that have connections with the pharynx.
3. Explain how sound is produced by the body.

CONNECTING THE CONCEPTS

Several organ systems interact in the region of the upper respiratory tract. For more information on these systems, refer to the following discussions:

Section 7.1 describes the organization of the lymphatic system and the role of lymphoid tissue.

Section 9.2 illustrates the connection between the upper digestive and upper respiratory systems.

Section 15.3 examines how the respiratory system contributes to the sense of smell.

10.3 The Lower Respiratory Tract

LEARNING OUTCOMES

Upon completion of this section, you should be able to

1. Summarize the role of the trachea, bronchial tree, and lungs in respiration.
2. Identify the structures of the lower respiratory tract and provide their function.
3. Explain how the alveoli increase the efficiency of the respiratory system.

Once the incoming air makes its way past the larynx, it enters the lower respiratory tract. The lower respiratory tract consists of the trachea, the bronchial tree, and the lungs.

The Trachea

The **trachea,** commonly called the windpipe, is a tube connecting the larynx to the primary bronchi. The trachea lies anterior to the esophagus. It is separated from the esophagus by a flexible, muscular wall. Its walls consist of connective tissue and smooth muscle reinforced by C-shaped cartilaginous rings. The rings prevent the trachea from collapsing. This allows the esophagus to expand when swallowing. The mucous membrane that lines the trachea has an outer layer of pseudostratified ciliated columnar epithelium (see Fig. 4.8) and goblet cells. The goblet cells produce mucus, which traps debris in the air as it passes through the trachea. The mucus is then swept toward the pharynx and away from the lungs by the cilia that project from the epithelium (Fig. 10.6).

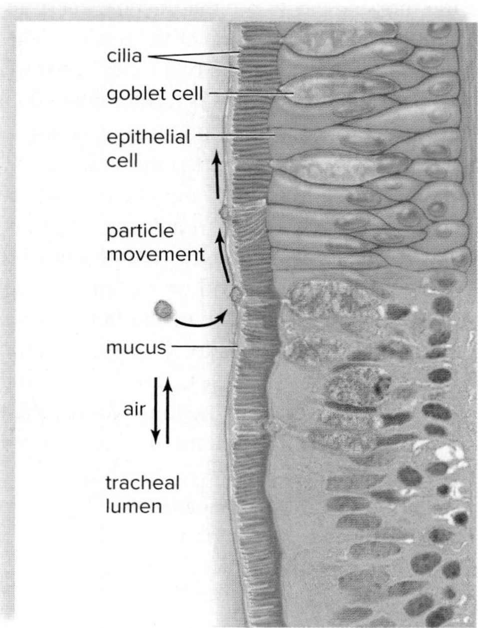

Figure 10.6 The cells lining the trachea.
The lining of the trachea consists of ciliated epithelium with mucus-producing goblet cells. The mucus traps particles, and the cilia help move the mucus toward the throat.
Ed Reschke

When you cough, the tracheal wall contracts, narrowing its diameter. Therefore, coughing causes air to move more rapidly through the trachea, helping expel mucus and foreign objects. Smoking is known to destroy the cilia; consequently, the soot in cigarette smoke collects in the lungs. People who smoke often develop heavy coughs as a result. Smoking is discussed more fully in the Health feature "Questions About Smoking, Tobacco, and Health" in Section 10.7.

If the trachea is blocked because of illness or the accidental swallowing of a foreign object, a breathing tube can be inserted by way of an incision made in the trachea. This tube acts as an artificial air intake and exhaust duct. The operation is called a *tracheostomy*.

The Bronchial Tree

The trachea divides into right and left primary **bronchi** (*sing.*, bronchus), which lead into the right and left lungs (see Fig. 10.1). The bronchi branch into a few secondary bronchi that also branch, until the branches become **bronchioles,** which are about 1 mm in diameter. The bronchi resemble the trachea in structure. As the bronchial tubes divide and subdivide, their walls become thinner and the small rings of cartilage are no longer present. During an asthma attack, the smooth muscle of the bronchioles contracts, causing bronchiolar constriction and characteristic wheezing. Each bronchiole leads to an elongated space enclosed by a multitude of air pockets, or sacs, called **alveoli** (*sing.*, alveolus) (Fig. 10.7).

The Lungs

The **lungs** are paired, cone-shaped organs in the thoracic cavity. In the center of the thoracic cavity are the trachea, heart, thymus, and esophagus. The lungs are on each side of the trachea. The right lung has three lobes, and the left lung has two lobes, allowing room for the heart, which points left. Each lobe is further divided into lobules, and each lobule has a bronchiole serving many alveoli.

The lungs follow the contours of the thoracic cavity, including the diaphragm, the muscle that separates the thoracic cavity from the abdominal cavity. Each lung is enclosed by pleurae (*sing.*, **pleura**), two layers of serous membrane that produce serous fluid. The parietal pleura adheres to the thoracic cavity wall, and the visceral pleura adheres to the surface of the lung. *Surface tension* is the tendency for water molecules to cling to one another due to hydrogen bonding between molecules. Surface tension holds the two pleural layers together, making the lungs follow the movement of the thorax when breathing occurs. If these layers become inflamed (a condition called *pleurisy*), breathing, sneezing, and coughing become quite painful, because the layers rub against each other. Causes of pleurisy include viral infections (such as the flu), tuberculosis, and pneumonia.

The Alveoli

The lungs have about 300 million alveoli, with a total cross-sectional area of 50–70 m^2. That's about the size of a tennis court. Each alveolar sac is surrounded by blood capillaries. The walls of the sac and the capillaries are largely simple squamous epithelium (see Fig. 4.8). Gas exchange occurs between air in the alveoli and blood in the capillaries. Oxygen diffuses across the alveolar wall and enters the bloodstream, and carbon dioxide diffuses from the blood across the alveolar wall to enter the alveoli (Fig. 10.7). The Science feature "Artificial Lungs" reviews how scientists are now able to generate artificial alveoli and lungs to aid in medical research.

The alveoli of human lungs are lined with a **surfactant,** a film of lipoprotein that lowers the surface tension of water and prevents the alveoli from closing. The lungs collapse in some newborn babies—especially premature infants—who lack this film. The condition, called *infant respiratory distress syndrome,* is now treatable by surfactant replacement therapy.

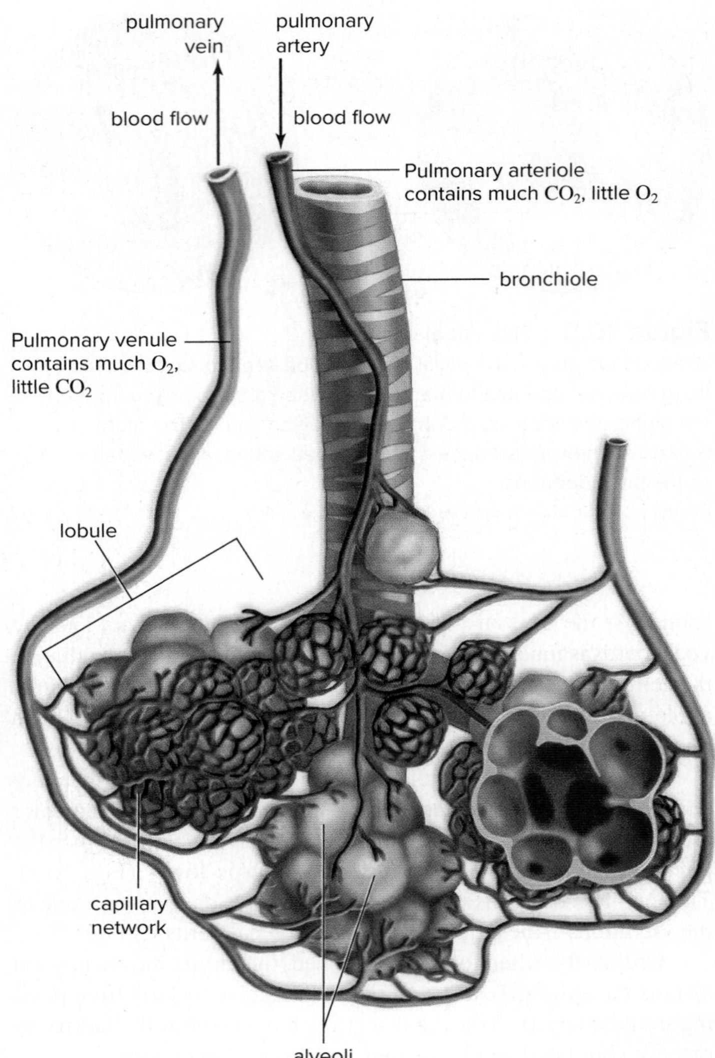

Figure 10.7 **Alveoli and pulmonary circulation.** The lungs consist of alveoli surrounded by an extensive capillary network. The pulmonary artery carries O_2-poor (CO_2-rich) blood (colored blue), and the pulmonary vein carries O_2-rich blood (colored red).

BIOLOGY TODAY ▶ Science

Artificial Lungs

Some organs, such as the kidneys, are relatively easy to transplant from one well-matched individual to another, with a high rate of success. Lungs are more difficult to transplant, however, with a 5-year survival rate of around 50%. However, the number of donor organs does not meet the demand, and thus medical device companies have been actively researching the development of artificial lungs (Fig. 10A).

One type of artificial lung, called extracorporeal membrane oxygenation (ECMO), is frequently used in premature infants whose lung functions have been compromised. During ECMO, the infant's blood is pumped from the body to a device that contains a series of membranes. These membranes exchange carbon dioxide and oxygen, thus mimicking the function of a natural lung. The device acts as both a heart and a lung, allowing the infant's cardiovascular system time to respond to medical treatment.

For adults, an artificial lung called the BioLung, manufactured by MC3Corp, can help provide lung functions while the individual is awaiting a transplant or is being treated for a serious lung infection. The BioLung is attached to the right ventricle of the heart. Blood leaving the ventricle passes over a series of microfibers that exchange carbon dioxide and oxygen. The oxygenated blood is then returned to the left atrium, thus bypassing the lungs. Unlike the ECMO device, the BioLung is small (about the size of a soda can) and is powered by the contractions of the heart.

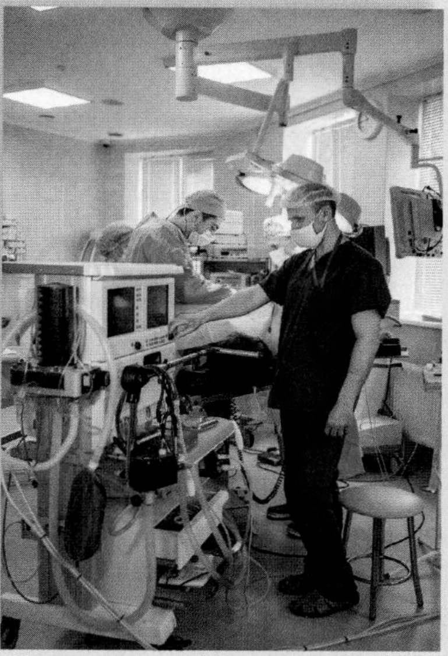

Figure 10A **An artificial lung.** Artificial lungs can prolong the life of an individual until a lung transplant is available.

Terelyuk/Shutterstock

Questions to Consider

1. Why do you think the use of artificial lungs is not considered a long-term solution for the treatment of lung disease?
2. Besides increased availability, what are other potential advantages of laboratory-grown lungs (or other tissues) compared to regular donor tissues?

CHECK YOUR PROGRESS 10.3

1. Briefly describe the functions of the organs of the lower respiratory system.
2. Trace the movement of gas in the organs of the lower respiratory system.
3. Explain why the alveoli have a high surface area.

CONNECTING THE CONCEPTS

For more information on the structures of the thoracic cavity, refer to the following discussions:

Section 2.2 explains the role of hydrogen bonds in the properties of water.

Section 7.1 describes the function of the thymus as an organ of the lymphatic system.

Section 9.2 summarizes the role of the esophagus in the digestive system.

10.4 Mechanism of Breathing

LEARNING OUTCOMES

Upon completion of this section, you should be able to

1. Contrast the processes of inspiration and expiration during ventilation.
2. Define the terms *tidal volume, vital capacity,* and *residual volume* in relation to ventilation.
3. Summarize the purpose of the inspiratory and expiratory reserve volumes.

Ventilation, or breathing, has two phases. The process of inspiration, also called inhalation, moves air into the lungs; the process of expiration, also called exhalation, moves air out of the lungs. To understand ventilation, the manner in which air enters and exits the lungs, it is necessary to remember the following facts:

- Normally, there is a continuous column of air from the pharynx to the alveoli of the lungs.
- The lungs lie within the sealed thoracic cavity (see Fig. 4.10). The rib cage, consisting of the ribs joined to the vertebral

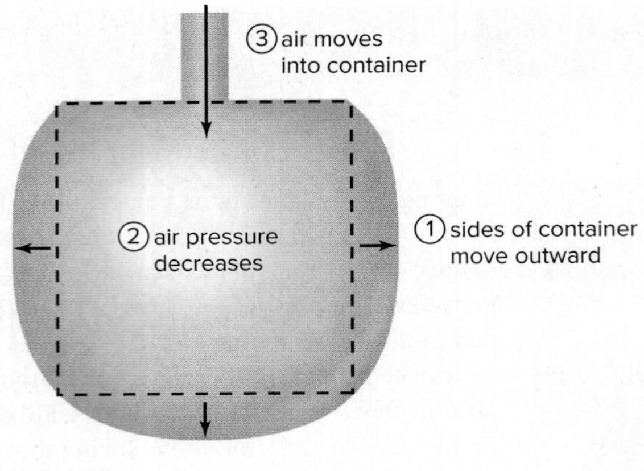

a. Inhalation

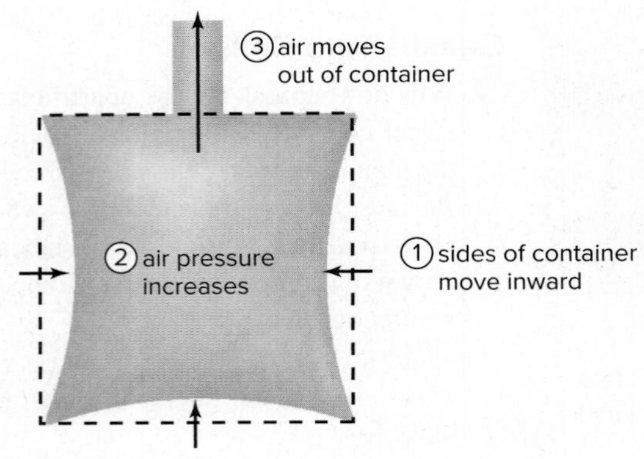

b. Exhalation

Figure 10.8 **The relationship between air pressure and volume.**
When the sides of the container move outward, the volume in the container increases and the air pressure decreases. When the sides of the container collapse, the volume decreases and air pressure increases.

column posteriorly and to the sternum anteriorly, forms the top and sides of the thoracic cavity. The intercostal muscles lie between the ribs. The diaphragm and connective tissue form the floor of the thoracic cavity.

- The lungs adhere to the thoracic wall by way of the pleura. The space between the two pleurae is minimal, and is filled with fluid.
- Ventilation is governed by **Boyle's Law,** which states that at a constant temperature the pressure of a given quantity of gas is inversely proportional to its volume. This relationship controls the processes of inhalation and exhalation (Fig. 10.8).

Inspiration

Inspiration is the active phase of ventilation, because this is the phase in which the diaphragm and the external intercostal muscles contract (Fig. 10.9*a*). In its relaxed state, the diaphragm is dome-shaped. During inspiration, it contracts and becomes a flattened sheet of muscle. Also, the external intercostal muscles contract, causing the rib cage to move upward and outward.

Following contraction of the diaphragm and the external intercostal muscles, the volume of the thoracic cavity is larger than it was before. As the thoracic volume increases, the lungs increase in volume as well, because the lung adheres to the wall of the thoracic cavity. As the lung volume increases, the air pressure in the alveoli decreases, creating a partial vacuum. In other words, alveolar pressure is now less than atmospheric pressure (air pressure outside the lungs). Air will naturally flow from outside the body into the respiratory passages and into the alveoli, because a continuous column of air reaches into the lungs. Figure 10.8*a* reviews how Boyle's Law applies to inspiration.

Air comes into the lungs because they have already opened up; air does not force the lungs open. The creation of a partial vacuum in the alveoli causes air to enter the lungs. Although inspiration is the active phase of breathing, the actual flow of air into the alveoli is passive.

Expiration

Usually expiration is the passive phase of breathing, and no effort is required to bring it about. During expiration, the diaphragm and external intercostal muscles relax. The rib cage returns to its resting position, moving down and inward (see Fig. 10.9*b*). The elastic properties of the thoracic wall and lung tissue help them recoil. In addition, the lungs recoil, because the surface tension of the fluid lining the alveoli tends to draw them closed. Returning to Boyle's Law (Fig. 10.8*b*), if the sides and bottom of the container relax, then the volume of the container decreases, and the air pressure inside increases. As a result, the air flows out.

What keeps the alveoli from collapsing as a part of expiration? Recall that the presence of surfactant lowers the surface tension within the alveoli. Also, as the lungs recoil, the pressure between the pleurae decreases, and this tends to make the alveoli stay open. The importance of the reduced pressure is demonstrated when, in an accident, the thoracic cavity is punctured (a "punctured lung"). Air now enters the space between the pleurae, causing the lung to collapse.

Maximizing Inspiration and Expiration

If you recall the last time you exercised vigorously—perhaps running in a race, or even just climbing all those stairs to your classroom—you probably remember that you were breathing a lot harder than normal during and immediately after that heavy exercise. Maximum inspiratory effort involves muscles of the back, chest, and neck. This increases the size of the thoracic cavity to larger than normal, thus allowing maximum expansion of the lungs.

Expiration can also be forced. The maximum inspiratory efforts of heavy exercise are accompanied by forced expiration. Forced expiration is also necessary to sing, blow air into a trumpet, or blow out birthday candles. Contraction of the internal intercostal muscles can force the rib cage to move downward and inward. Also, when the abdominal wall muscles contract, they push on the abdominal organs. In turn, the organs push upward against the diaphragm, and the increased pressure in the thoracic cavity helps expel air.

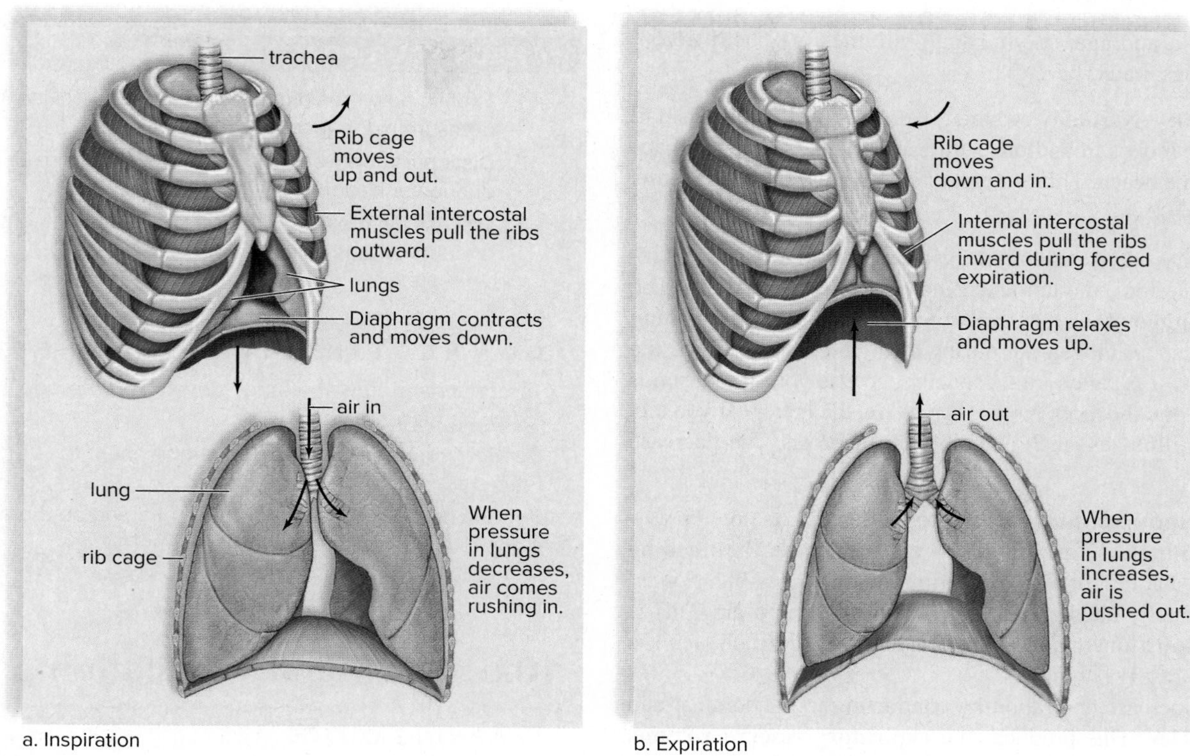

Figure 10.9 **The thoracic cavity during inspiration and expiration.**
a. During inspiration, the thoracic cavity and lungs expand, so air is drawn in. **b.** During expiration, the thoracic cavity and lungs resume their original positions and pressures. Now air is forced out.

Volumes of Air Exchanged During Ventilation

As ventilation occurs, air moves into the lungs from the nose or mouth during inspiration and then moves out of the lungs during expiration. A free flow of air to and from the lungs is vitally important. Therefore, a technique has been developed that allows physicians to determine if there is a medical problem that prevents the lungs from filling with air on inspiration and releasing it from the body on expiration. This technique is illustrated in Figure 10.10, which shows the measurements recorded by a spirometer when a person breathes as directed by a technician. The actual numbers mentioned in the following discussion about lung volumes are averages. These numbers are affected by

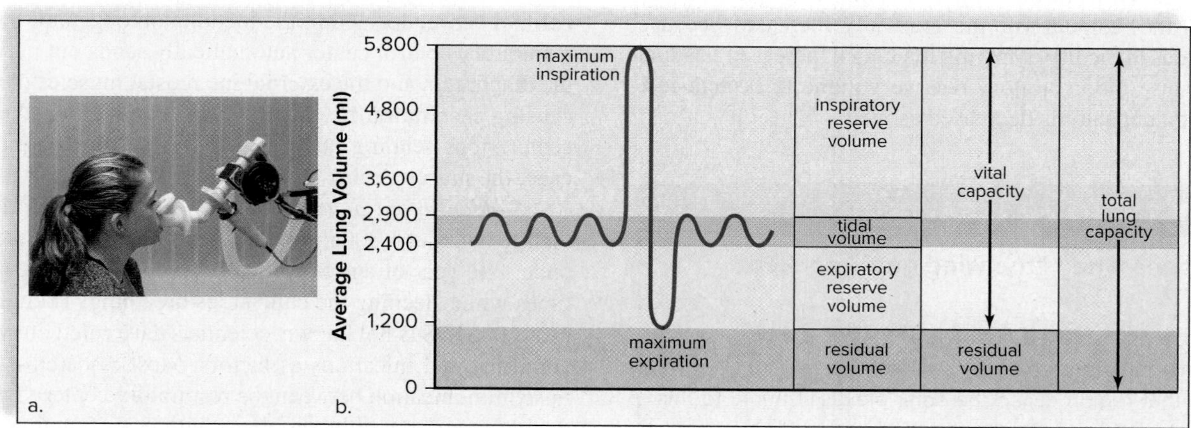

Figure 10.10 **Measuring the air capacity of the lungs.**
a. A spirometer is an instrument that measures the amount of air inhaled and exhaled with each breath. **b.** During inspiration, the volume of air increases, and during expiration, the volume of air decreases. Vital capacity (red) is measured by taking the deepest breath and then exhaling as much as possible.
(a): Goldsithney/Shutterstock

gender, height, and age, so your lung volumes may be different from the values stated here.

Tidal Volume Normally, when we are relaxed, only a small amount of air moves in and out with each breath, similar perhaps to the tide at the beach. This amount of air, called the **tidal volume,** is only about 500 ml.

Vital Capacity It is possible to increase the amount of air inhaled and, therefore, the amount exhaled by deep breathing. The maximum volume of air that can be moved in plus the maximum amount that can be moved out during a single breath is called the **vital capacity.** It is called vital capacity because your life depends on breathing, and the more air you can move, the better off you are. A number of illnesses, such as pulmonary fibrosis, can decrease vital capacity.

Inspiratory and Expiratory Reserve Volume As noted previously, we can increase inspiration by expanding the chest and by lowering the diaphragm to the maximum extent possible. Forced inspiration usually adds another 2,900 ml of inhaled air. This is called the **inspiratory reserve volume** and it is a definite increase over the tidal reserve volume.

We can increase expiration by contracting the abdominal and thoracic muscles. This produces the **expiratory reserve volume,** which is usually about 1,400 ml of air. You can see from Figure 10.9 that vital capacity is the sum of tidal, inspiratory reserve, and expiratory reserve volumes.

Residual Volume It is a curious fact that some of the inhaled air never reaches the lungs; instead, it fills the nasal cavities, trachea, bronchi, and bronchioles (see Fig. 10.1). These passages are not used for gas exchange; therefore, they are said to contain **dead air space.** To ensure that newly inhaled air reaches the lungs, it is better to breathe slowly and deeply.

Also, note in Figure 10.10 that even after a very deep exhalation, some air (about 1,000 ml) remains in the lungs. This is called the **residual volume.** The residual volume is the amount of air that can't be exhaled from the lungs. In some lung diseases (see Section 10.7), the residual volume gradually increases because the individual has difficulty emptying the lungs. Increased residual volume will cause the expiratory reserve volume to be reduced. As a result, vital capacity is decreased as well.

BIOLOGY IN YOUR LIFE

What happens when "the wind gets knocked out of you"?

The "wind may get knocked out of you" following a blow to the upper abdomen in the area of the stomach. There is a network of nerves in that region called the solar plexus. Trauma to this area can cause the diaphragm to experience a sudden, involuntary, and painful contraction called a spasm. It's not possible to breathe while the diaphragm experiences this spasm—hence, the feeling of being breathless. The pain and inability to breathe stop once the diaphragm relaxes.

CHECK YOUR PROGRESS 10.4

1. Explain how the volume of the thoracic cavity affects the pressure in the lungs.
2. Distinguish between the different volumes of air exchanged during ventilation.
3. Discuss what effect insufficient expiration might have on overall homeostasis.

CONNECTING THE CONCEPTS

To understand how the lungs develop as we age, refer to the following discussions:

Section 18.3 describes the development of the lungs in the fetus.

Section 18.5 examines the effects of aging on the ability of the lungs to exchange gases.

10.5 Control of Ventilation

LEARNING OUTCOMES

Upon completion of this section, you should be able to

1. Explain how the nervous system controls the process of breathing.
2. Explain the role of chemoreceptors and pH levels in regulating breathing rate.

Breathing is controlled by both nervous and chemical control mechanisms.

Nervous Control of Breathing

Normally, adults have a breathing rate of 12 to 20 ventilations per minute. The rhythm of ventilation is controlled by a **respiratory control center** located in the medulla oblongata of the brain. The respiratory control center automatically sends out nerve signals to the diaphragm and the external intercostal muscles of the rib cage, causing inspiration to occur (Fig. 10.11). When the respiratory center stops sending nerve signals to the diaphragm and the rib cage, the muscles relax and expiration occurs.

Sudden infant death syndrome (SIDS), or crib death, claims the life of about 1,300 infants a year in the United States. An infant under one year of age is put to bed seemingly healthy, and sometimes while sleeping the child stops breathing. Though the precise cause of SIDS is not known, scientists have ruled out vaccinations, vomiting, and infections as factors. Most research is focusing on miscommunication between the respiratory center of the brain and the lungs and, possibly, problems with heart function.

Although the respiratory center automatically controls the rate and depth of breathing, its activity can be influenced by nervous input. We can voluntarily change our breathing pattern to accommodate activities such as speaking, singing, eating, swimming underwater, and so forth. Following forced inspiration,

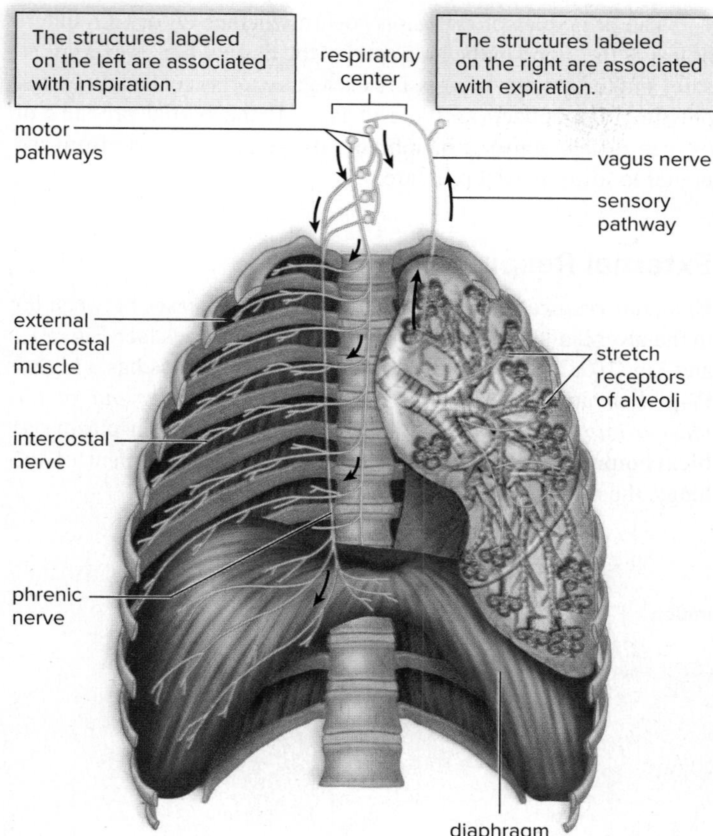

Figure 10.11 **The control of breathing by the respiratory center.**

The respiratory center automatically stimulates the external intercostal (rib) muscles and diaphragm to contract via the phrenic nerve. After forced inhalation, stretch receptors send inhibitory nerve impulses to the respiratory center via the vagus nerve. Usually, expiration automatically occurs due to lack of stimulation from the respiratory center to the diaphragm and intercostal muscles.

stretch receptors in the airway walls respond to increased pressure. These receptors initiate inhibitory nerve impulses. The impulses travel from the inflated lungs to the respiratory center. This temporarily stops the respiratory center from sending out nerve signals. In this manner, excessive stretching of the elastic tissue of the lungs is prevented.

Chemical Control of Breathing

The cells of our bodies produce carbon dioxide (CO_2) by the process of cellular respiration. The CO_2 enters the blood, where it combines with water, forming an acid that breaks down and gives off hydrogen ions (H^+). These hydrogen ions can change the pH of the blood. **Chemoreceptors** are sensory receptors in the body that are sensitive to the chemical composition of body fluids (see Section 15.1). Two sets of chemoreceptors sensitive to pH can cause breathing to speed up. A centrally placed set is located in the medulla oblongata of the brain stem, and a peripherally placed set is in the circulatory system. Carotid bodies, located in the carotid arteries, and aortic bodies, located in the aorta, are sensitive to blood pH. These chemoreceptors are not strongly affected by low oxygen (O_2) levels. Instead, they are stimulated when the carbon dioxide entering the blood is sufficient to change blood pH.

When the pH of the blood becomes more acidic (decreases), the respiratory center increases the rate and depth of breathing. With an increased breathing rate, more carbon dioxide is removed from the blood. The hydrogen ion concentration returns to normal, and the breathing rate returns to normal.

Most people are unable to hold their breath for more than 1 minute. When you hold your breath, metabolically produced carbon dioxide begins accumulating in the blood. As a result, H^+ accumulates and the blood becomes more acidic. The respiratory center, stimulated by the chemoreceptors, is able to override a person's voluntary inhibition of respiration. Breathing resumes, despite attempts to prevent it.

BIOLOGY IN YOUR LIFE

How long can you hold your breath?

Most individuals can hold their breath for 1 to 2 minutes. With practice, many are able to hold their breath for up to 3 minutes. Free divers, individuals who compete to see how long they can hold their breath while diving in water, can hold their breath for 5 minutes or more.

Researchers hope to more closely investigate divers' use of hyperventilation and lung "packing" to make free diving possible. Lung packing begins with very deep breathing. The diver then "packs," adding more air by additional breathing through the mouth. The use of hyperventilation or lung packing to prolong breath holding should never be tried by untrained individuals. People have drowned by attempting to do so.

CHECK YOUR PROGRESS 10.5

1. Explain why chemoreceptors are important for the regulation of ventilation.
2. Describe the importance of the respiratory control center in the brain.
3. Discuss why it's not possible to hold your breath for more than a few minutes.

CONNECTING THE CONCEPTS

For more on the structures that regulate breathing, refer to the following discussions:

Section 14.2 examines the location and function of the medulla oblongata.

Section 15.1 describes how chemoreceptors help maintain homeostasis.

10.6 Gas Exchange in the Body

LEARNING OUTCOMES

Upon completion of this section, you should be able to

1. Distinguish between external and internal respiration.
2. Summarize the chemical processes involved in external and internal respiration.
3. Identify the role of carbonic anhydrase and carbaminohemoglobin in respiration.

Gas exchange is critical to homeostasis. Oxygen needed to produce energy must be supplied to all the cells, and carbon dioxide must be removed from the body during gas exchange. As mentioned previously, respiration includes the exchange of gases not only in the lungs but also in the tissues (Fig. 10.12).

The principles of diffusion govern whether O_2 or CO_2 enters or leaves the blood in the lungs and in the tissues. Gases exert pressure, and the amount of pressure each gas exerts is called its partial pressure, symbolized as P_{O_2} and P_{CO_2}. If the partial pressure of oxygen differs across a membrane, oxygen will diffuse from the higher to lower partial pressure.

External Respiration

External respiration refers to the exchange of gases between air in the alveoli and blood in the pulmonary capillaries (see Fig. 10.7 and Fig. 10.12*a*). Blood in the pulmonary capillaries has a higher P_{CO_2} than atmospheric air. Therefore, *CO_2 diffuses out of the plasma into the lungs*. Most of the CO_2 is carried in plasma as **bicarbonate ions** (HCO_3^-). In the low-P_{CO_2} environment of the lungs, the reaction proceeds to the right.

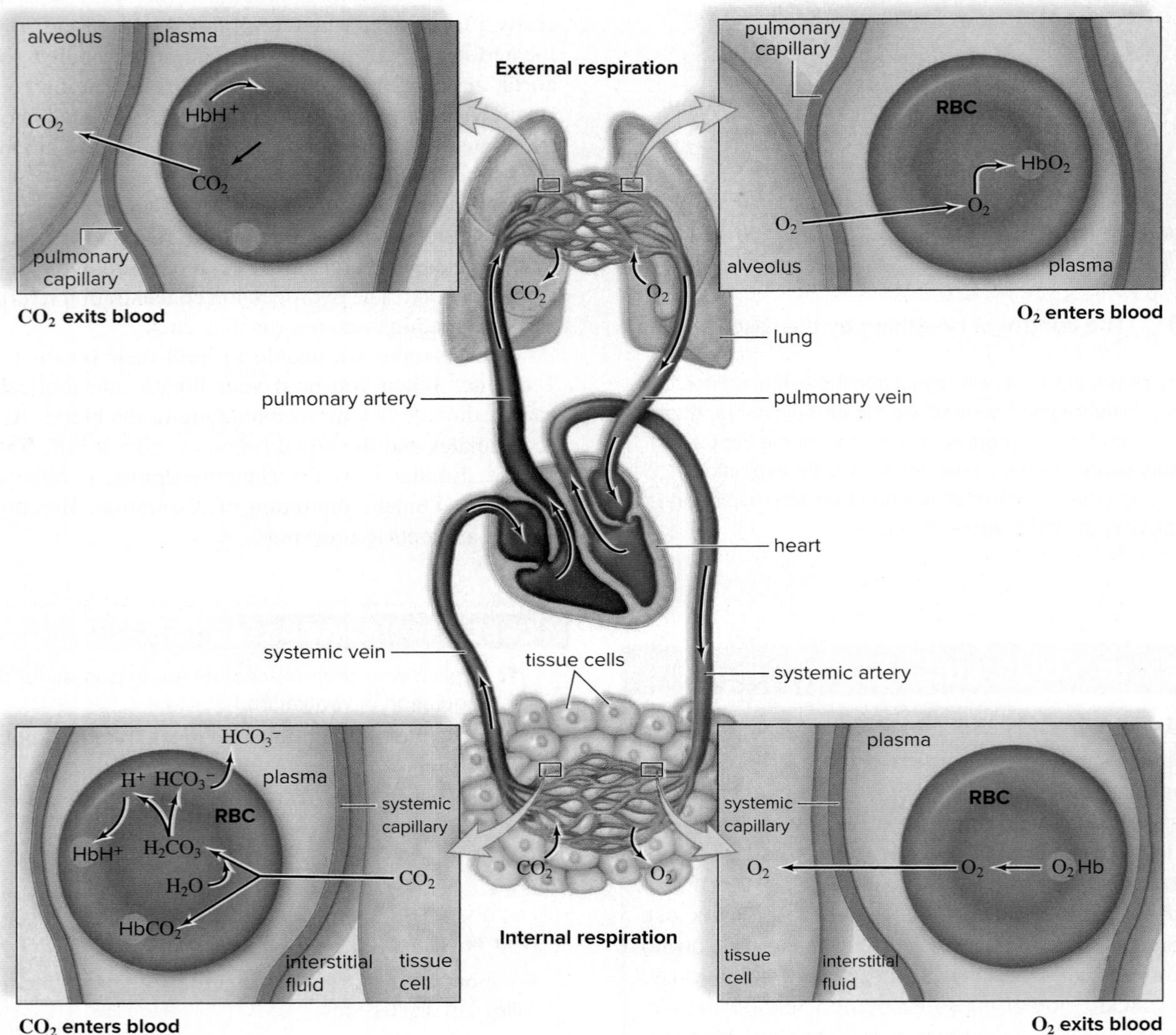

Figure 10.12 Movement of gases during external and internal respiration.
a. During external respiration in the lungs, HCO_3^- is converted to CO_2, which exits the blood. O_2 enters the blood and hemoglobin (Hb) carries O_2 to the tissues. **b.** During internal respiration in the tissues, O_2 exits the blood, and CO_2 enters the blood. Most of the CO_2 enters red blood cells, where it becomes the bicarbonate ion, carried in the plasma. Some hemoglobin combines with CO_2 and some combines with H^+.

$$H^+ + HCO_3^- \longrightarrow H_2CO_3 \xrightarrow{\text{carbonic anhydrase}} H_2O + CO_2$$

hydrogen ion — bicarbonate ion — carbonic acid — water — carbon dioxide

The enzyme **carbonic anhydrase** speeds the breakdown of carbonic acid (H_2CO_3) in red blood cells.

What happens if you hyperventilate (breathe at a high rate) and therefore push this reaction far to the right? The blood will have fewer hydrogen ions, and so alkalosis, a high blood pH, results. In that case, breathing is inhibited, and you experience various symptoms ranging from dizziness to continuous contractions of the skeletal muscles. You may have heard that you should inhale from and exhale into a paper bag after hyperventilating. Doing so increases the CO_2 in your blood, because you're inhaling the CO_2 you just exhaled into the bag. This restores a normal blood pH. What happens if you hypoventilate (breathe at a low rate) and this reaction does not occur? Hydrogen ions build up in the blood and acidosis occurs. Buffers may compensate for the low pH, and breathing most likely increases. Extreme changes in blood pH affect enzyme function, which may lead to coma and death.

The pressure pattern for O_2 during external respiration is the reverse of that for CO_2. Blood in the pulmonary capillaries is low in oxygen, and alveolar air contains a higher partial pressure of oxygen. Therefore, O_2 *diffuses into plasma and then into red blood cells in the lungs.* Hemoglobin takes up this oxygen and becomes **oxyhemoglobin** (HbO_2).

$$Hb + O_2 \longrightarrow HbO_2$$

deoxyhemoglobin — oxygen — oxyhemoglobin

Internal Respiration

Internal respiration refers to the exchange of gases between the blood in systemic capillaries and the tissue cells. In Figure 10.12*b*, internal respiration is shown at the bottom. Blood entering systemic capillaries is a bright red color because red blood cells contain oxyhemoglobin. The temperature in the tissues is higher and the pH is slightly lower (more acidic), so oxyhemoglobin naturally gives up oxygen. After oxyhemoglobin gives up O_2, it diffuses out of the blood into the tissues.

$$HbO_2 \longrightarrow Hb + O_2$$

oxyhemoglobin — deoxyhemoglobin — oxygen

Oxygen diffuses out of the blood into the tissues because the P_{O_2} of interstitial fluid is lower than that of blood. The lower P_{O_2} is due to cells continuously using up oxygen in cellular respiration (see Fig. 3.22). *Carbon dioxide diffuses into the blood from the tissues* because the P_{CO_2} of interstitial fluid is higher than that of blood. Carbon dioxide is produced during cellular respiration and collects in interstitial fluid.

After CO_2 diffuses into the blood, most of it enters the red blood cells, where a small amount is taken up by hemoglobin, forming **carbaminohemoglobin** ($HbCO_2$). In plasma, CO_2 combines with water, forming carbonic acid (H_2CO_3), which dissociates to hydrogen ions (H^+) and bicarbonate ions (HCO_3^-).

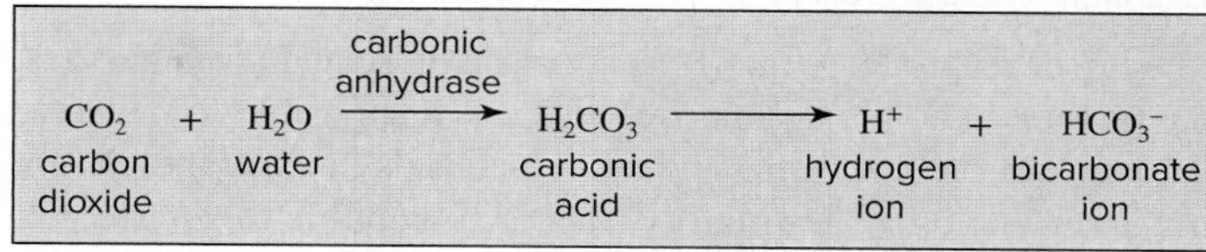

The enzyme carbonic anhydrase, mentioned previously, speeds the reaction in red blood cells. Bicarbonate ions (HCO_3^-) diffuse out of red blood cells and are carried in the plasma. The globin portion of hemoglobin combines with excess hydrogen ions produced by the overall reaction, and Hb becomes HHb, called *reduced hemoglobin.* In this way, the pH of blood remains fairly constant. Blood that leaves the systemic capillaries is a dark maroon color, because red blood cells contain reduced hemoglobin.

CHECK YOUR PROGRESS 10.6

1. Describe the differences between external respiration and internal respiration.
2. Describe how hemoglobin functions in the transport of both oxygen and carbon dioxide.
3. Detail the influence of P_{O_2} on both external and internal respiration.

CONNECTING THE CONCEPTS

For more on the mechanisms by which respiration maintains homeostasis, refer to the following discussions:

Section 2.2 explores the relationship between H^+ concentration and pH.

Section 6.1 examines how components of the blood plasma help buffer the pH of the blood.

Section 6.2 provides additional information on hemoglobin and red blood cells.

10.7 Disorders of the Respiratory System

LEARNING OUTCOMES

Upon completion of this section, you should be able to

1. Identify the symptoms and causes of selected upper respiratory tract infections.
2. Identify the symptoms and causes of selected lower respiratory tract disorders.
3. Summarize how smoking is related to cancer and emphysema.

The respiratory tract is constantly exposed to environmental air. The quality of this air and whether it contains infectious pathogens—such as bacteria, viruses, or harmful chemicals—influence the overall health of the respiratory system.

Upper Respiratory Tract Infections

The upper respiratory tract consists of the nose and nasal cavities, the pharynx, and the larynx. Because it is responsible for filtering out many of the pathogens and other materials that may be present in the air, the upper respiratory tract is susceptible to a variety of viral and bacterial infections. Upper respiratory infections can also spread from these areas to the middle ear or the sinuses.

Viral Infections

Most "colds" are relatively mild viral infections of the upper respiratory tract characterized by sneezing, a runny nose, and perhaps a mild fever. Many different viruses can cause colds, the most common being a group called the rhinoviruses (*rhin-* is Greek for "nose"). Most colds last from a few days to a week, when the immune response is able to eliminate the virus. Because colds are caused by viruses, antibiotics do not help, although decongestants and anti-inflammatory medications can ease the symptoms.

Sinusitis

Sinusitis develops when nasal congestion blocks the tiny openings leading to the sinuses (see Fig. 10.3). Symptoms include postnasal discharge and facial pain that worsens when the patient bends forward. Pain and tenderness usually occur over the lower forehead or over the cheeks (sometimes also producing toothaches). Successful treatment depends on restoring proper drainage of the sinuses. Even a hot shower and sleeping upright can be helpful. Nasal spray decongestants and oral antihistamines also alleviate the symptoms of sinusitis. Sprays may be preferred, because they treat the symptoms without the side effects, such as drowsiness, of oral medicine. However, nasal sprays can become habit-forming if used for long periods. Persistent sinusitis should be evaluated by a health-care professional.

Tonsillitis

Tonsillitis occurs when the tonsils become inflamed and enlarged. The tonsil in the posterior wall of the nasopharynx is often called the adenoid. If tonsillitis occurs frequently and enlargement makes breathing difficult, the tonsils can be removed surgically in a **tonsillectomy.** Fewer tonsillectomies are performed today than in the past, because we now know that the tonsils are lymphoid tissue that traps many of the pathogens that enter the pharynx. Therefore, they are a first line of defense against invasion of the body.

Laryngitis

Laryngitis is an infection of the larynx with accompanying hoarseness, leading to the inability to talk in an audible voice. Laryngitis usually disappears with treatment of an upper respiratory infection. Persistent hoarseness without the presence of an upper respiratory infection is one of the warning signs of cancer and should be looked into by a physician.

Lower Respiratory Tract Disorders

Lower respiratory tract disorders include infections, restrictive pulmonary disorders, obstructive pulmonary disorders, and lung cancer.

Lower Respiratory Infections

Acute bronchitis is an infection of the primary and secondary bronchi. Usually it is preceded by a viral upper respiratory infection that has led to a secondary bacterial infection. Most likely a nonproductive cough has become a deep cough that expectorates mucus and perhaps pus.

Pneumonia is a viral or bacterial infection of the lungs in which the bronchi and alveoli fill with thick fluid (Fig. 10.13). Most often it is preceded by influenza. High fever and chills with headache and chest pain are symptoms of pneumonia. Rather than being a generalized lung infection, pneumonia may be localized in specific lobules of the lungs. Obviously, the more lobules involved, the more serious the infection. Pneumonia can be caused by a bacterium that is usually held in check but has gained the upper hand due to stress and/or reduced immunity. Patients with AIDS are subject to a particularly rare form of pneumonia caused by a fungus named *Pneumocystis jiroveci* (formerly *Pneumocystis carinii*). Pneumonia of this type is almost never seen in individuals with a healthy immune system.

Pulmonary tuberculosis, commonly called **tuberculosis,** is a bacterial disease that in the past was called *consumption.* When the bacteria *(Mycobacterium tuberculosis)* invade the lung tissue, the cells build a protective capsule around the foreigners, isolating them from the rest of the body. This tiny capsule is called a tubercle. If the resistance of the body is high, the imprisoned organisms die, but if the resistance is low, the organisms eventually can be liberated. If a chest X-ray detects active tubercles, the individual is put on appropriate drug therapy to ensure the localization of the disease and the eventual destruction of any live bacteria. It is possible to tell if a person has ever been exposed to tuberculosis with a *tuberculin* test. This procedure uses a highly diluted bacterial extract injected into the patient's skin. If a tuberculin test is positive, an X-ray will be done to confirm an active disease. A person may have a positive test but no active disease.

BIOLOGY IN YOUR LIFE

How does SARS-CoV-2 infect the lungs?

The SARS-CoV-2 virus, which causes COVID-19, targets epithelial cells that line the interior surfaces of the lungs. On the surface of epithelial cells are receptors called ACE-2, which stands for angiotensin-converting enzyme 2. These receptors are involved in the regulation of a peptide hormone (angiotensin) that is involved in controlling blood pressure. In the lungs, this hormone helps the body regulate the amount of blood flowing into the alveoli, and thus the exchange of gases.

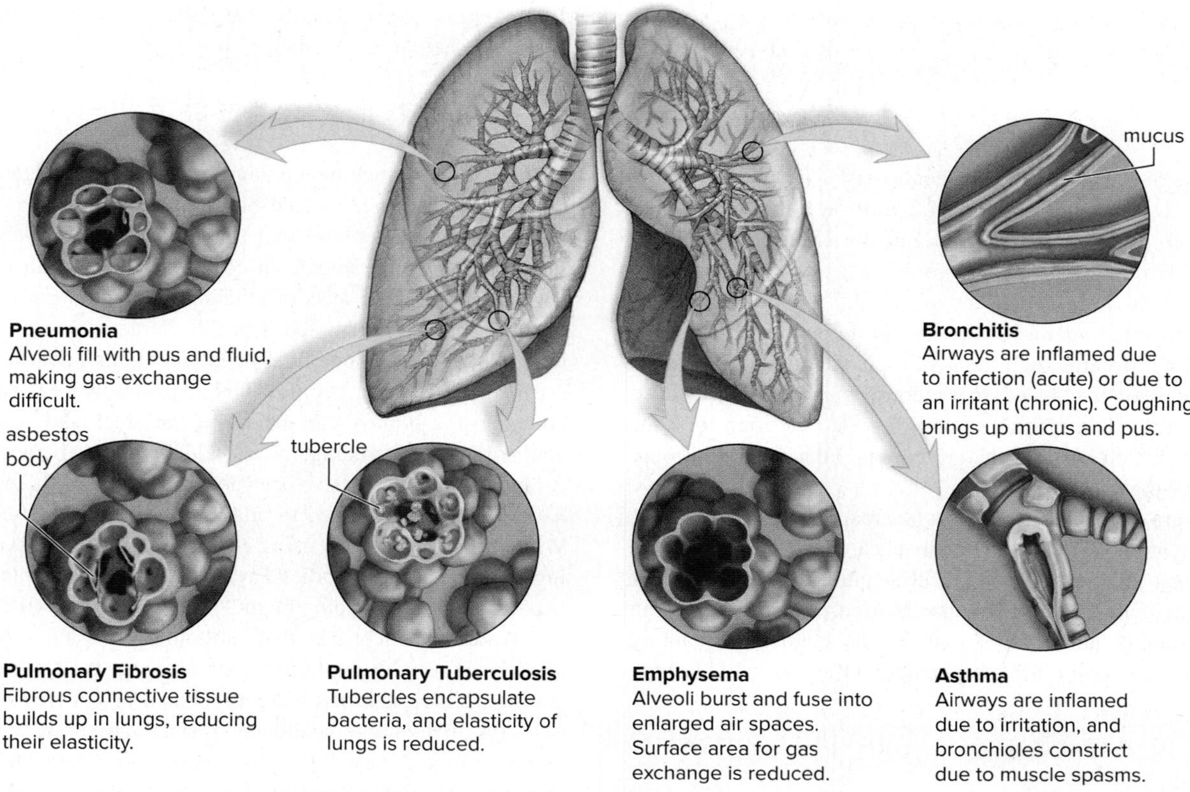
mucus
Pneumonia
Alveoli fill with pus and fluid, making gas exchange difficult.
Bronchitis
Airways are inflamed due to infection (acute) or due to an irritant (chronic). Coughing brings up mucus and pus.
asbestos body
tubercle
Pulmonary Fibrosis
Fibrous connective tissue builds up in lungs, reducing their elasticity.
Pulmonary Tuberculosis
Tubercles encapsulate bacteria, and elasticity of lungs is reduced.
Emphysema
Alveoli burst and fuse into enlarged air spaces. Surface area for gas exchange is reduced.
Asthma
Airways are inflamed due to irritation, and bronchioles constrict due to muscle spasms.

Figure 10.13 **Some diseases and disorders of the respiratory system.**
Exposure to infectious pathogens and/or polluted air, including tobacco smoke, causes the diseases and disorders shown here.

Restrictive Pulmonary Disorders

In restrictive pulmonary disorders, vital capacity is reduced, because the lungs have lost their elasticity. Inhaling particles such as silica (sand), coal dust, asbestos, and fiberglass can lead to **pulmonary fibrosis,** a condition in which fibrous connective tissue builds up in the lungs. The lungs cannot inflate properly and are always tending toward deflation. Breathing asbestos is also associated with the development of cancer. Asbestos was formerly used widely as a fireproofing and insulating agent, so unwarranted exposure has occurred. It has been projected that 2 million deaths caused by asbestos exposure—mostly in the workplace—will occur in the United States between 1990 and 2020.

BIOLOGY IN YOUR LIFE

What is cystic fibrosis?

Cystic fibrosis is a genetic disease in which chloride ion transporters in mucus-producing epithelial cells do not function correctly. Because of this, the mucous secretions are often very thick and easily clog small structures, such as the alveoli. Though cystic fibrosis is usually considered to be just a disease of the respiratory system, because this is where the symptoms usually first appear, it can also cause problems in organs such as the pancreas. Just a few decades ago, people with cystic fibrosis usually died before the age of 20. New advances in medicine and treatments now enable individuals to live into their thirties and forties.

Obstructive Pulmonary Disorders

In obstructive pulmonary disorders, air does not flow freely in the airways and the time it takes to inhale or exhale maximally is greatly increased. Several disorders, including chronic bronchitis, emphysema, and asthma, are collectively referred to as chronic obstructive pulmonary disease (COPD), because they tend to recur.

In **chronic bronchitis,** the airways are inflamed and filled with mucus. A cough that brings up mucus is common. The bronchi have undergone degenerative changes, including the loss of cilia and their normal cleansing action. Under these conditions, an infection is more likely to occur. Smoking is the most frequent cause of chronic bronchitis. Exposure to other pollutants can also cause chronic bronchitis.

Emphysema is a chronic and incurable disorder in which the alveoli are distended and their walls damaged. As a result, the surface area available for gas exchange is reduced. Emphysema, most often caused by smoking, is often preceded by chronic bronchitis. Air trapped in the lungs leads to alveolar damage and a noticeable ballooning of the chest. The elastic recoil of the lungs is reduced, so not only are the airways narrowed but the driving force behind expiration is also reduced. The individual is breathless and may have a cough. The surface area for gas exchange is reduced, so less

BIOLOGY TODAY ▶ **Health**

Are E-cigs Safe?

For at least 50 years, the many health risks of smoking have been clear. Despite this, about 34.2 million adult Americans smoke. Once a person starts smoking, the addictive power of nicotine is strong. But why do young people start smoking? Some may want to look mature or "cool," to be accepted by friends, or to rebel against authority. Some people who smoke believe the habit helps them control their weight; others admit they simply enjoy the "buzz" that nicotine can provide. Because of the unhealthy side effects of smoking, people often look for alternatives, which explains the growing popularity of electronic cigarettes (e-cigs).

E-cigs are often designed to look like real cigarettes (Fig. 10B), but instead of tobacco they contain a cartridge filled with an "e-liquid" that consists mainly of nicotine plus propylene glycol or vegetable glycerin. When the device is used, a battery heats the liquid, turning it into a vapor that can be inhaled (explaining the popular term *vaping* for this practice). Often, an LED light at the tip glows, mimicking a lit cigarette. There's no cigarette smell, though, because no tobacco is burning.

Figure 10B E-cigs.
While e-cigarettes have definite advantages over regular cigarettes, there are growing concerns over the health risks associated with their use, especially in young people.
Martina Paraninfi/Moment/Getty Images

Manufacturers claim that the vapor from an e-cig is much safer than cigarette smoke. In contrast, many health experts are concerned that the effects of inhaling pure nicotine vapor haven't yet been sufficiently studied. The U.S. Surgeon General has issued warnings about the potential negative health impacts of e-cigs, especially on young people. This is primarily because nicotine content of e-liquids can be quite variable, and a variety of contaminants—including metals, aldehydes, and trace levels of certain carcinogens—have been detected. Some of these chemicals have been directly linked to oral and respiratory system cancers. While some smokers say using e-cigarettes helped them quit smoking cigarettes, some studies have indicated that people who first become hooked on vaping might "graduate" to smoking.

Another concern is that, although companies claim they aren't marketing to children, the evidence suggests otherwise. Research has indicated that there has been a 78% increase in the use of e-cigs by high school students in just the past few years, and an alarming 48% increase in middle school use. The CDC estimates that 38% of high school students, and 13% of middle school students, have tried vaping.

So, is vaping safer than smoking? While it may have been initially considered a less dangerous alternative, evidence suggests there are considerable health risks associated with the use of e-cigarettes. According to the American Lung Association, the best way to prevent these health risks is to never start smoking, or if you are currently a smoker, cease all forms of smoking completely.

Questions to Consider

1. Compared to most drugs, nicotine is unusual, because at low doses it is mainly a stimulant, but at high doses it has more sedative effects. How might these properties contribute to nicotine's addictive potential?
2. Suppose you've never "vaped" before and someone offers you an e-cig at a party. Would you be tempted to try it? Why or why not?

oxygen reaches the heart and the brain. Even so, the heart works furiously to force more blood through the lungs, and an increased workload on the heart can result. Lack of oxygen to the brain can make the person feel depressed, sluggish, and irritable. Exercise, drug therapy, supplemental oxygen, and giving up smoking may relieve the symptoms and slow the progression of emphysema. Severe emphysema may be treated by lung transplantation or lung volume reduction surgery (LVRS). During LVRS, a third of the most diseased lung tissue is removed. The removal enables the remaining tissue to function better. The result is an increase in the patient's breathing ability and lung capacity.

Asthma is a disease of the bronchi and bronchioles that is marked by wheezing, breathlessness, and sometimes a cough and expectoration of mucus. The airways are unusually sensitive to specific irritants, which can include a wide range of allergens such as pollen, animal dander, dust, tobacco smoke, and industrial fumes. Even cold air can be an irritant. When exposed to the irritant, the smooth muscle in the bronchioles undergoes spasms. It now appears that chemical mediators given off by immune cells in the bronchioles cause the spasms. Most patients with asthma have some degree of bronchial inflammation that further reduces the diameter of the airways and contributes to the seriousness of an attack. Asthma is not

BIOLOGY TODAY ▶ Health

Questions About Smoking, Tobacco, and Health

Is cigarette smoking really addictive?

Yes. Nicotine is an addictive drug (just like heroin and cocaine). Small amounts make the smoker want to smoke more. Also, nicotine not only affects the mood and nature of the smoker but may also cause withdrawal symptoms if the smoker attempts to stop. The younger a person begins smoking, the more likely an addiction to nicotine will develop.

What are some of the short-term and long-term effects of smoking cigarettes?

Short-term effects include shortness of breath and nagging coughs, a diminished ability to smell and taste, and an increased risk of sexual impotence in men. People who smoke tend to tire easily during physical activity. Long-term effects include many types of cancer, premature aging of the skin, heart disease, aneurysms, bronchitis, emphysema, and stroke. Smoking contributes to the severity of pneumonia and asthma, also.

Does smoking cause cancer?

Yes. Tobacco use accounts for about one-third of cancer deaths in the United States. Smoking causes almost 90% of lung cancers. Smoking also causes cancers of the oral cavity, pharynx, larynx, and esophagus. It contributes to the development of cancers of the bladder, pancreas, cervix, kidney, and stomach. Smoking is also linked to the development of some leukemias.

Why do people who smoke have "smoker's cough"?

Cigarette smoke contains chemicals that irritate the air passages and lungs. When a person who smokes inhales these substances, the body tries to protect itself by producing mucus and coughing. The nicotine in smoke decreases the sweeping action of cilia, so some of the poisons in the smoke remain in the lungs.

If you smoke but do not inhale, is there any danger?

Yes. Wherever smoke touches living cells, it does harm. Even if people don't inhale, they are breathing the smoke as secondhand smoke and are still at risk for lung cancer. People who smoke pipes and cigars, who often do not inhale, are at an increased risk for lip, mouth, tongue, and several other cancers.

Does cigarette smoking affect the heart?

Yes. Smoking increases the risk of heart disease, the number one cause of death in the United States. Cigarette smoking is the biggest risk factor for sudden heart attacks. Of people who have a heart attack, people who smoke are more likely than people who do not smoke to die within an hour of the heart attack. Cigarette smoke at very low levels (much lower than the levels that cause lung disease) can cause damage to the heart.

How does smoking affect pregnant women and their babies?

Smoking during pregnancy is linked with a greater chance of miscarriage, premature delivery, stillbirth, infant death, low birth weight, and sudden infant death syndrome (SIDS). Up to 10% of infant deaths would be prevented if pregnant women did not smoke. When a pregnant woman smokes, the nicotine, carbon monoxide, and other dangerous chemicals in smoke enter her bloodstream and then pass into the baby's body. This prevents the baby from getting essential nutrients and oxygen for growth.

What are the dangers of environmental tobacco smoke?

Environmental tobacco smoke, also called secondhand smoke, increases the rate of heart disease by over 25% in nonsmokers and causes an estimated 46,000 deaths from heart disease each year. Children whose parents smoke are more likely to suffer from asthma, pneumonia or bronchitis, ear infections, coughing, wheezing, and increased mucus production in the first 2 years of life.

Are chewing tobacco and snuff safe alternatives to cigarette smoking?

No. The juice from smokeless tobacco is absorbed directly through the lining of the mouth. This creates sores and white patches that often lead to cancer of the mouth and damage to the teeth and gums. Smokeless tobacco users greatly increase their risk of other cancers, including those of the pharynx.

How can people stop smoking?

A number of organizations, including the American Cancer Society and the American Lung Association, offer suggestions for how to quit smoking. Both organizations also offer support groups to people interested in quitting. There is even advice about how people can help their friends quit smoking. Nicotine Anonymous offers a 12-step program for kicking a nicotine addiction, modeled after the 12-step Alcoholics Anonymous program. People recovering from smoking have reported that a support system is very important. Several smoking-cessation drugs have been approved by the FDA, and others are in development phases. One such drug, varenicline (Chantix), affects areas in the brain stimulated by nicotine. Varenicline may lessen withdrawal symptoms by mimicking the effects of nicotine. In addition, several over-the-counter products are available to replace nicotine. These include nicotine patches, gum, and lozenges. These products are designed to supply enough nicotine to alleviate the withdrawal symptoms people experience during attempts to stop smoking.

Questions to Consider

1. What can you do to reduce your exposure to secondhand smoke?
2. Why does cigarette smoke have a negative effect on organ systems that are not in direct contact with the actual smoke?

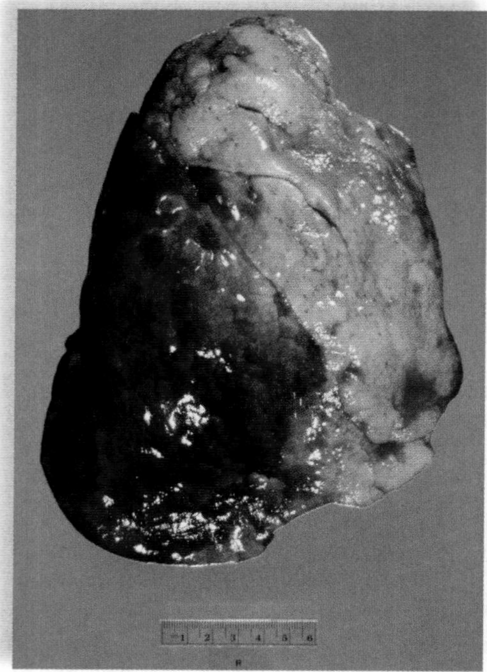
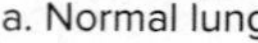

a. Normal lung

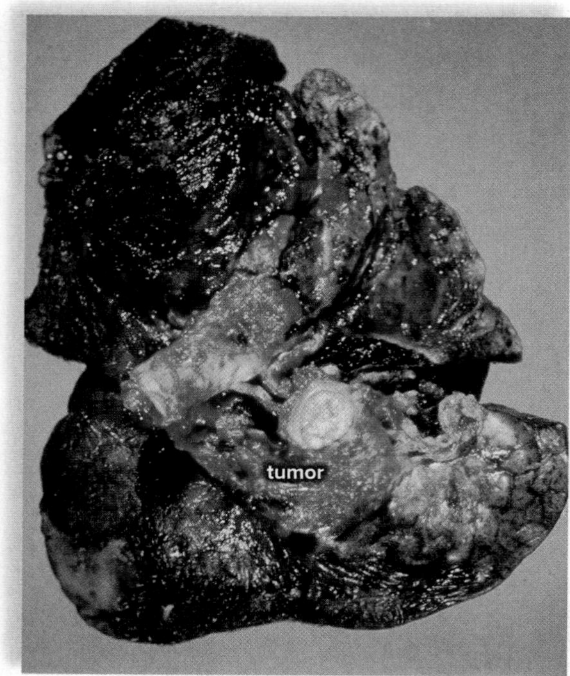

b. Lung cancer

Figure 10.14 **Effect of smoking on a human lung.**
a. Normal lung; note the healthy red color. **b.** Lung of a heavy smoker. Notice how black the lung is, except where cancerous tumors have formed.
(a): Southern Illinois University/Science Source; (b): Clinical Photography, Central Manchester University Hospitals NHS Foundation Trust, UK/Science Source

curable, but it is treatable. Special inhalers can control the inflammation and possibly prevent an attack, and other types of inhalers can stop the muscle spasms, should an attack occur.

Lung Cancer

Lung cancer is more prevalent in men than in women but has surpassed breast cancer as a cause of death in women. The increase in the incidence of lung cancer in women is directly related to increased numbers of women who smoke. Autopsies on people who smoke have revealed the progressive steps by which the most common form of lung cancer develops. The first event appears to be thickening and callusing of the cells lining the bronchi. Callusing occurs whenever cells are exposed to irritants. Cilia are then lost, making it impossible to prevent dust and dirt from settling in the lungs. Following this, cells with atypical nuclei appear in the callused lining. A tumor consisting of disordered cells with atypical nuclei is considered cancer in situ (at one location). A normal lung versus a lung with cancerous tumors is shown in Figure 10.14. A final step occurs when some of these cells break loose and penetrate other tissues, a process called metastasis. Now the cancer has spread. The original tumor may grow until a bronchus is blocked, cutting off the supply of air to that lung. The entire lung then collapses, the secretions trapped in the lung spaces become infected, and pneumonia or a lung abscess (localized area of pus) results. The only treatment that offers a possibility of cure is to remove a lobe or the whole lung before metastasis has had time to occur. This operation is called **pneumonectomy.** If the cancer has spread, chemotherapy and radiation are also required.

Research indicates that exposure to secondhand smoke can also cause lung cancer and other illnesses normally associated with smoking. If a person stops smoking and avoids secondhand smoke, and if the body tissues are not already cancerous, the lungs may return to normal over time.

CHECK YOUR PROGRESS 10.7

1. Name and describe the symptoms of some common respiratory infections and disorders of the upper respiratory tract and of the lower respiratory tract.
2. Detail how each of the common respiratory infections in the preceding question can be treated.
3. List the three respiratory disorders commonly associated with smoking tobacco.

CONNECTING THE CONCEPTS

For more on the diseases that influence the respiratory system, refer to the following discussions:

Section 8.2 provides a more detailed look at tuberculosis and influenza epidemics.

Section 8.4 explains the causes and consequences of antibiotic resistance.

Sections 20.1 and **20.2** examine the biology of cancer cells and the major causes of cancer.

CONCLUSION

Our respiratory system plays a critical role in maintaining homeostasis in the body. The exchange of oxygen and carbon dioxide not only allows our cells to carry out the process of cellular respiration, and thus provides us with the energy we need for our metabolic activities, this exchange also helps regulate the pH of our body, allowing enzymes to function at their optimal levels.

Diseases such as asthma, lung cancer, and cystic fibrosis interfere with the ability of the respiratory system to function correctly. Inflammation and destruction of the alveoli in the lungs reduce the surface area over which gas exchange may occur, and in the process, the ability of almost every other organ system to carry out its metabolic functions in the body.

SUMMARIZE

10.1 The Respiratory System

The **respiratory system** is responsible for the process of **ventilation** (breathing), which includes **inspiration** and **expiration.**

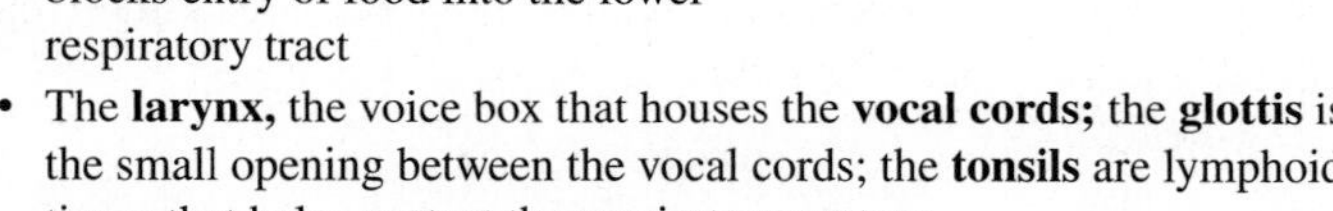

10.2 The Upper Respiratory Tract

Air from the **nose** enters the respiratory tract and then passes through

- The **nasal cavities,** which filter and warm the air
- The **pharynx,** the opening into parallel air and food passageways; the upper region of the pharynx, the nasopharynx, is connected to the middle ear by **auditory tubes** (eustachian tubes); the **epiglottis** blocks entry of food into the lower respiratory tract
- The **larynx,** the voice box that houses the **vocal cords;** the **glottis** is the small opening between the vocal cords; the **tonsils** are lymphoid tissue that helps protect the respiratory system

10.3 The Lower Respiratory Tract

- The **trachea** (windpipe) is lined with goblet cells and ciliated cells.
- The **bronchi** enter the **lungs** and branch into smaller **bronchioles.**
- The lungs consist of the **alveoli,** air sacs surrounded by a capillary network; alveoli are lined with a **surfactant** that prevents them from closing. Each lung is enclosed by a membrane called a **pleura.**

10.4 Mechanism of Breathing

Breathing involves inspiration and expiration of air. The movement of air in the lungs is due to the effects of **Boyle's Law,** which describes the relationship between pressure and volume for a gas.

- During inspiration, the diaphragm lowers, and the rib cage moves upward and outward; the lungs expand, and air rushes in.
- During expiration, the diaphragm relaxes and moves up. The rib cage moves down and in; pressure in the lungs increases; air is pushed out of the lungs.

Respiratory volumes can be measured by

- The **tidal volume,** the amount of air that normally enters and exits with each breath
- The **vital capacity,** the amount of air that moves in, plus the amount that moves out with maximum effort
- The **inspiratory reserve volume** and **expiratory reserve volume,** the difference between normal amounts and the maximum effort amounts of air moved
- The **residual volume,** the amount of air that stays in the lungs when we breathe, also called **dead air space**

10.5 Control of Ventilation

The **respiratory control center** in the brain automatically causes us to breathe 12 to 20 times a minute. Extra carbon dioxide in the blood can decrease the pH. If this happens, **chemoreceptors** alert the respiratory center, which increases the rate of breathing.

10.6 Gas Exchange in the Body

Both **external respiration** and **internal respiration** depend on diffusion. Hemoglobin activity is essential to the transport of gases and, therefore, to external and internal respiration.

External Respiration

- CO_2 diffuses out of plasma into lungs; **carbonic anhydrase** accelerates the breakdown of HCO_3^- ions in red blood cells.
- O_2 diffuses into the plasma and then into red blood cells in the capillaries. O_2 is carried by hemoglobin, forming **oxyhemoglobin.**

Internal Respiration

- O_2 diffuses out of the blood into the tissues.
- CO_2 diffuses into the blood from the tissues. CO_2 is carried in the plasma as **bicarbonate ions** (HCO_3^-); a small amount links with hemoglobin to form **carbaminohemoglobin.**

10.7 Disorders of the Respiratory System

A number of illnesses are associated with the respiratory tract.

Upper Respiratory Tract Infections

- Infections of the nasal cavities, sinuses, throat, tonsils, and larynx are all upper respiratory tract infections.
- These include **sinusitis, otitis media, laryngitis,** and **tonsillitis;** tonsils, which are lymphoid tissue, may be removed by a **tonsillectomy.**

Lower Respiratory Tract Disorders

- Lower respiratory infections include **acute bronchitis, pneumonia,** and pulmonary **tuberculosis.**
- Restrictive pulmonary disorders are exemplified by **pulmonary fibrosis.**
- Obstructive pulmonary disorders are exemplified by **chronic bronchitis, emphysema,** and **asthma.**
- Smoking can eventually lead to **lung cancer** and other disorders; sections of diseased lung may be removed by a **pneumonectomy.**

ENGAGE

THINKING CRITICALLY

1. Children may also have obstructive sleep apnea (OSA). Symptoms experienced by them during the day include breathing through the mouth and difficulty focusing, but they don't often experience the excessive sleepiness that some adults do during daytime hours. Children with OSA often have enlarged tonsils or adenoids, also. Removal of the tonsils and adenoids often alleviates this problem. Continuous positive airway pressure (CPAP) treatment might be necessary if the OSA continues after surgery. Why would enlarged tonsils or adenoids cause OSA?
2. Explain the expression "The food went down the wrong tube" by referring to structures along the path of air.
3. People who have smoked for a long time often develop a chronic cough.
   a. What purpose does smoker's cough serve?
   b. Why are nonsmokers less likely to develop a chronic cough?
4. Professional singers who need to hold a long note while singing must exert a great deal of control over their breathing. Which muscle (or muscles) needs conditioning for singers to acquire a better control over their breathing?
5. Why would someone who nearly drowned have a blue tint to their skin?

MAKING IT RELEVANT

1. How do you think exercise benefits individuals with asthma?
2. How might an understanding of the genetic basis of respiratory diseases, such as asthma and cystic fibrosis, help researchers develop personalized treatments?
3. Asthma can cause side effects such as anxiety, irritability, sleep problems, and restlessness, all of which are associated with the nervous system. Why do you think a respiratory disease would cause problems with the nervous system?

Find answers to all of the chapter questions at connect.mheducation.com

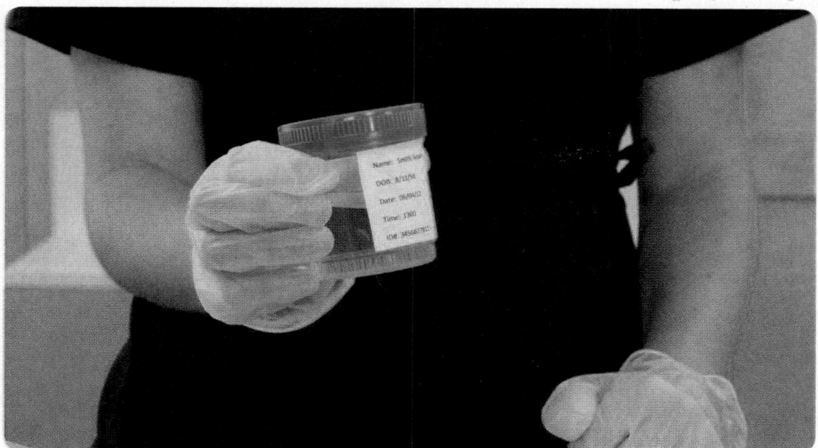
McGraw Hill

CHAPTER 11

Urinary System

Is Your Urine Sterile?

You may see television shows or read books that describe how people drank their own urine to prevent dehydration. While it is true that, because urine is 95% water, you can drink it, there is a common misconception that urine is sterile. This idea that your urine is sterile because it is produced within your body dates from studies in the 1950s. It was believed back then that any bacteria found during a urinalysis must be the result of either a urinary tract infection or some other disease of the urinary system.

Current research contradicts that idea, however. Based on studies of the natural bacterial populations of other body systems, such as the digestive system, researchers have determined that natural populations of microbiota, consisting of a number of different types of bacteria, normally inhabit the urinary system. Today's research focuses on determining what the normal environment is and what role these bacteria perform in the urinary tract. By determining this, it may be possible to develop better diagnostics on how to treat disorders and infections of the urinary system.

In this chapter, we will explore the role of the kidney as one of the major organs of homeostasis in the body.

As you read through the chapter, think about the following questions:

1. What is the role of the kidneys in the body?
2. If you were stranded on a desert island with plenty of food but only seawater to drink, how long do you think you could survive?
3. By what mechanisms is the human kidney able to regulate the salt concentration of urine it produces?

CHAPTER OUTLINE

BEFORE YOU BEGIN

Before beginning this chapter, take a few moments to review the following discussions:

Section 2.2 What determines whether a solution is acidic or basic?

Section 3.3 How does water move across a plasma membrane?

Section 4.8 How do feedback mechanisms contribute to the maintenance of homeostasis?

11.1 The Urinary System

LEARNING OUTCOMES

Upon completion of this section, you should be able to

1. Summarize the functions of the urinary system.
2. Identify the organs of the urinary system and state their function.

The **urinary system** is the organ system of the body that plays a major role in maintaining the salt, water, and pH homeostasis of the blood. Collectively, these organs carry out the process of **excretion,** or the removal of metabolic wastes from the body. These metabolic waste materials are the by-products of the normal activities of the cells and tissues. In comparison to excretion, defecation is a process of the digestive system (see Section 9.1) that eliminates undigested food and bacteria in the form of feces. Excretion in humans is performed by the formation and discharge of urine from the body.

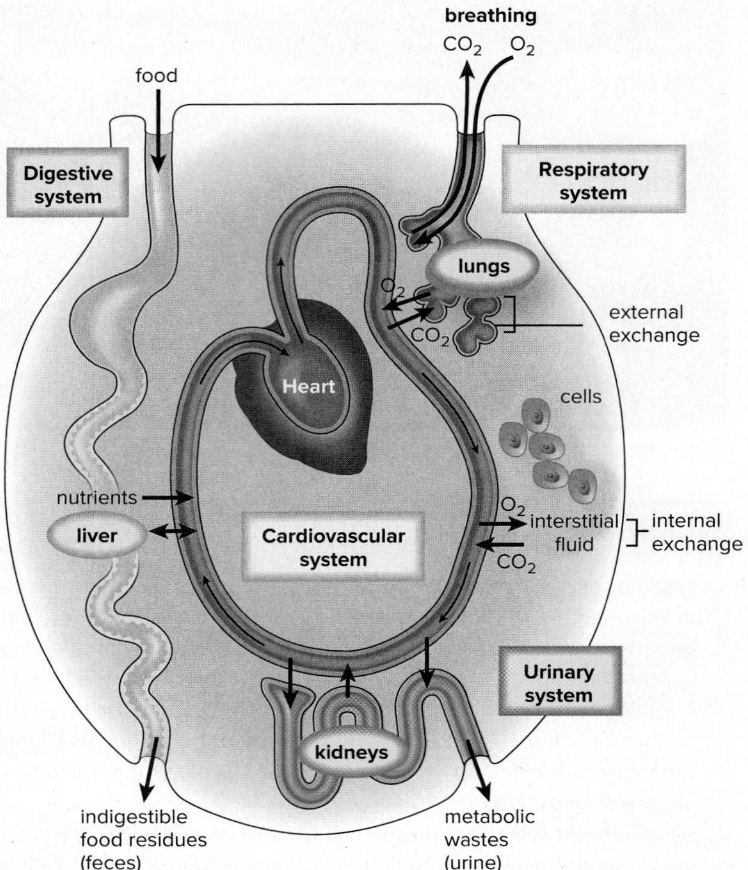

Figure 11.1 **The urinary system and homeostasis.** The urinary system assists homeostasis through the excretion of urea (produced by the liver) and other nitrogenous wastes, maintenance of water-salt balance, and maintenance of blood pH.

Functions of the Urinary System

As the urinary system carries out the process of excretion, it interacts with a number of other body systems to perform several important functions that contribute to homeostasis (Fig. 11.1). We will explore each of these functions in greater detail in Section 11.4.

Excretion of Metabolic Wastes

The metabolic waste of humans consists primarily of nitrogenous waste, such as urea, creatinine, ammonium, and uric acid. **Urea,** a waste product of amino acid metabolism, is the primary nitrogenous end product of metabolism in humans. In the liver, the breakdown of amino acids releases ammonia, a compound that is very toxic to cells. The liver rapidly combines ammonia with carbon dioxide to produce urea, which is much less harmful. Normally, urea levels in the blood are between 10 and 20 milligrams per deciliter (mg/dl). Elevated urea levels in the blood may cause **uremia,** a condition that causes a cardiac arrhythmia, vomiting, respiratory problems, and potentially death. Treatments for elevated urea levels are discussed in Section 11.5.

In addition to urea, the kidneys secrete creatinine and uric acid. **Creatinine** is a waste product that results from the breakdown of creatine phosphate, a high-energy phosphate reserve molecule in muscles. **Uric acid** is formed from the metabolic processing of nucleotides (such as adenine and thymine). Uric acid is rather insoluble. If too much uric acid is present in the blood, crystals form and precipitate out. Crystals of uric acid sometimes collect in the joints, producing a painful ailment called **gout.**

Maintenance of Water-Salt Balance

A principal function of the kidneys is to maintain the appropriate water-salt balance of the blood. As you know, salts, such as NaCl, have the ability to influence the rate and direction of osmosis (see Section 3.3). Therefore, the more salts in the blood, the greater the blood volume and the greater the blood pressure. By regulating the concentration of certain ions, namely sodium (Na^+) and potassium (K^+), in the blood, the kidneys regulate blood pressure. In addition, the kidneys also maintain the appropriate blood level of other ions such as bicarbonate (HCO_3^-) and calcium (Ca^{2+}).

Maintenance of Acid-Base Balance

The kidneys regulate the acid-base balance of the blood. For a person to remain healthy, the blood pH should be just about 7.4. The kidneys monitor and help control blood pH, mainly by excreting hydrogen ions (H^+) and reabsorbing the bicarbonate ions (HCO_3^-) as needed to keep blood pH at 7.4. Urine usually has a pH of 6 or lower, because our diet often contains acidic foods.

Secretion of Hormones

The kidneys assist the endocrine system in hormone secretion. The kidneys release *renin,* an enzyme that leads to aldosterone secretion. Aldosterone is a hormone produced by the adrenal glands, which lie atop the kidneys. As described in Section 11.4, *aldosterone* is involved in regulating the water-salt balance of the blood.

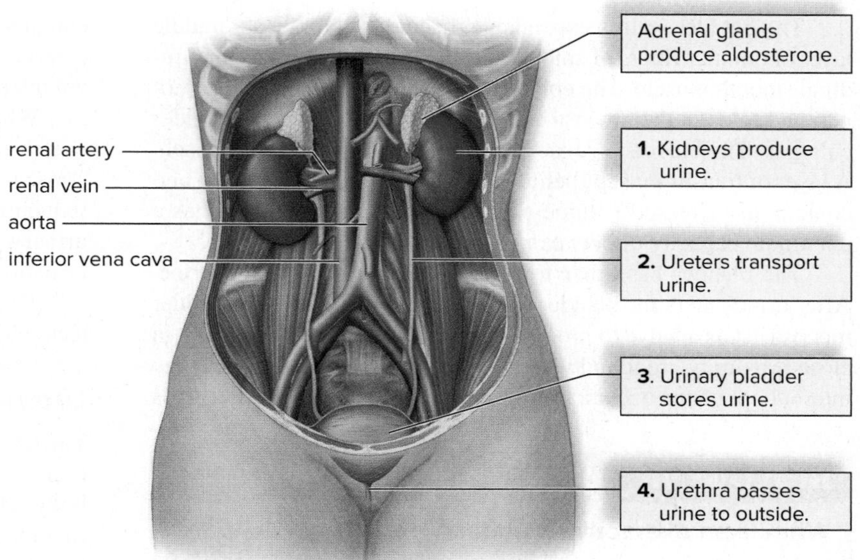

Figure 11.2 The urinary system.
The kidneys, ureters, urinary bladder, and urethra. The adrenal glands are part of the endocrine system.

The kidneys also release *erythropoietin (EPO),* a hormone that regulates the production of red blood cells.

Additional Functions of the Kidneys

The kidneys also reabsorb filtered nutrients and participate in the synthesis of vitamin D. Vitamin D is a hormone that promotes calcium ion (Ca^{2+}) absorption from the digestive tract.

Organs of the Urinary System

The urinary system consists of the kidneys, ureters, urinary bladder, and urethra (Fig. 11.2).

Kidneys

The **kidneys** are a pair of organs located one on each side of the vertebral column at the same level as the small of the lower back. They lie behind the peritoneum, the membrane that lines the abdominal cavity, where they receive some protection from the lower rib cage. Due to the shape of the liver, the right kidney is positioned slightly lower than the left. The kidneys are bean-shaped and reddish-brown in color. The fist-sized organs are covered by a tough capsule of fibrous connective tissue, called a renal capsule. Masses of adipose tissue adhere to each kidney. The concave side of a kidney has a depression where a **renal artery** enters and a **renal vein** and a ureter exit the kidney. The renal artery transports blood to be filtered to the kidneys, and the renal vein carries filtered blood away from the kidneys.

Ureters

The **ureters** conduct urine from the kidneys to the bladder. They are small, muscular tubes about 25 cm long and 5 mm in diameter. The wall of a ureter has three layers: an inner mucosa (mucous membrane), a smooth muscle layer, and an outer fibrous coat of connective tissue. Peristaltic contractions cause urine to enter the bladder even if a person is lying down. Urine enters the bladder in spurts at the rate of one to five spurts per minute.

Urinary Bladder

The **urinary bladder** stores urine until it is expelled from the body. The bladder has three openings: two for the ureters and one for the urethra, which drains the bladder (Fig. 11.3).

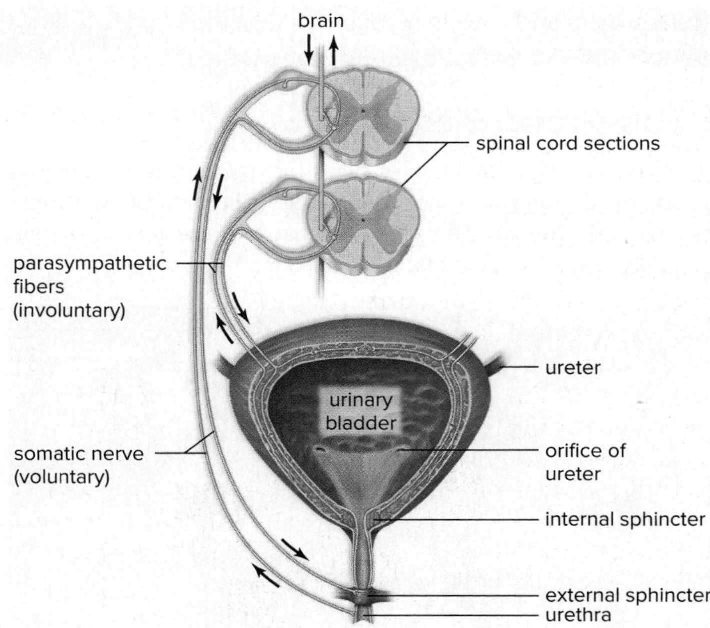

Figure 11.3 Sensory impulses trigger a desire to urinate.
As the bladder fills with urine, sensory impulses go to the spinal cord and then to the brain. The brain can override the urge to urinate. When urination occurs, motor nerve impulses cause the bladder to contract and the sphincters to relax.

The bladder wall is expandable, because it contains a middle layer of circular fibers of smooth muscle and two layers of longitudinal smooth muscle. The epithelium of the mucosa becomes thinner, and folds in the mucosa called rugae disappear as the bladder enlarges. The bladder's rugae are similar to those of the stomach. A layer of transitional epithelium enables the bladder to stretch and contain an increased volume of urine. The urinary bladder has a maximum capacity of between 700 and 800 ml.

The bladder has other features that allow it to retain urine. After urine enters the bladder from a ureter, small folds of bladder mucosa act as a valve to prevent backward flow. Two sphincters in close proximity are found where the urethra exits the bladder. The internal sphincter occurs around the opening to the urethra. It is composed of smooth muscle and is involuntarily controlled. An external sphincter is composed of skeletal muscle that can be voluntarily controlled.

When the urinary bladder fills to about 250 ml with urine, stretch receptors are activated by the enlargement of the bladder. These receptors send sensory nerve signals to the spinal cord. Subsequently, motor nerve impulses from the spinal cord cause the urinary bladder to contract and the sphincters to relax, so that urination, also called *micturition,* is possible (Fig. 11.3).

The Science feature "Lab-Grown Bladders" examines new technologies that enable the replacement of diseased bladders.

BIOLOGY IN YOUR LIFE

What is an overactive bladder?

In an overactive bladder, the muscles of the bladder contract, even if the bladder is not full. Muscle contraction causes strong feelings of urgency to go to the bathroom. Use of medications, such as tolterodine (Detrol LA) and oxybutynin (Ditropan XL), control the symptoms by blocking nerve signals to the bladder and calming the bladder's muscle contractions. An overactive bladder can also be treated without medication by urinating at set times of the day or by doing exercises to strengthen the muscles that control urination.

Urethra

The **urethra** is a small tube that extends from the urinary bladder to an external opening. Its function is to remove urine from the body. The urethra has a different length in females than in males. In females, the urethra is about 4 cm long. The short length of the female urethra makes bacterial invasion of the urinary tract easier. In males, the urethra averages 20 cm when the penis is flaccid (limp, nonerect). As the urethra leaves the male urinary bladder, it is encircled by the prostate gland. The prostate sometimes enlarges, restricting the flow of urine in the urethra. The Health feature "Urinary Difficulties Due to an Enlarged Prostate" in Section 11.5 discusses this problem in men.

In females, the reproductive and urinary systems are not connected. However, in males, the urethra carries urine during urination and sperm during ejaculation.

BIOLOGY TODAY ▶ Science

Lab-Grown Bladders

You're probably familiar with organ transplants done with organs harvested from people who have recently died or that even come from living donors. Did you know that some organs can now be grown in a lab and used for transplantation?

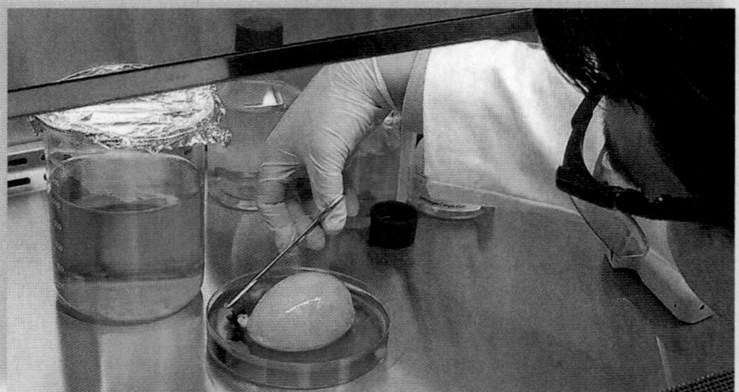

Figure 11A A lab-grown bladder is readied for transplantation.
There is less risk of rejection when a lab-grown bladder is transplanted.
Brian Walker/AP Images

Bladders grown in a lab have been successfully transplanted into a number of patients (Fig. 11A). In one study, patients contributed cells from their own diseased bladder. Those cells were cultured in a lab and encouraged to form a new bladder by being grown on a collagen form shaped like a bladder. Eventually, the new bladders were attached to each patient's diseased bladders. This alleviated the incontinence problems the patients had experienced. The risk of kidney damage was also decreased in these individuals by lowering the pressure inside their enlarged bladders. Because the cells for the new bladders had been taken from the patients, there was no risk of rejection.

Researchers hope this technique can be used to grow other types of tissues and organs for transplant. This could be a major solution to the limited number of organs available for transplant.

Questions to Consider

1. Why do you think it is possible to grow a bladder, but not a kidney, in the lab?
2. What do you think are some possible extensions of this technology in other parts of the body?

CHECK YOUR PROGRESS 11.1

1. List and briefly describe the functions of the organs of the urinary system.
2. Summarize the processes the kidneys perform to maintain homeostasis.
3. Predict what could occur to overall homeostasis if the kidneys could not excrete metabolic waste products from the body.

CONNECTING THE CONCEPTS

For more on the interaction of the urinary system with other body systems, refer to the following discussions:

Section 6.1 describes the composition of blood.

Section 13.3 describes how muscles use creatine phosphate as an energy molecule.

Section 16.4 examines the structure and function of the adrenal glands.

11.2 Kidney Structure

LEARNING OUTCOMES

Upon completion of this section, you should be able to

1. Identify the structures of a human kidney.
2. Identify the structures of a nephron and state the function of each.

A lengthwise section of a kidney shows that many branches of the renal artery and renal vein reach inside a kidney (Fig. 11.4). If the blood vessels are removed, it is easier to identify the three regions of a kidney:

- The **renal cortex** is an outer, granulated layer that dips down in between a radially striated inner layer called the renal medulla.
- The **renal medulla** consists of cone-shaped tissue masses called renal pyramids.
- The **renal pelvis** is a central space, or cavity, continuous with the ureter.

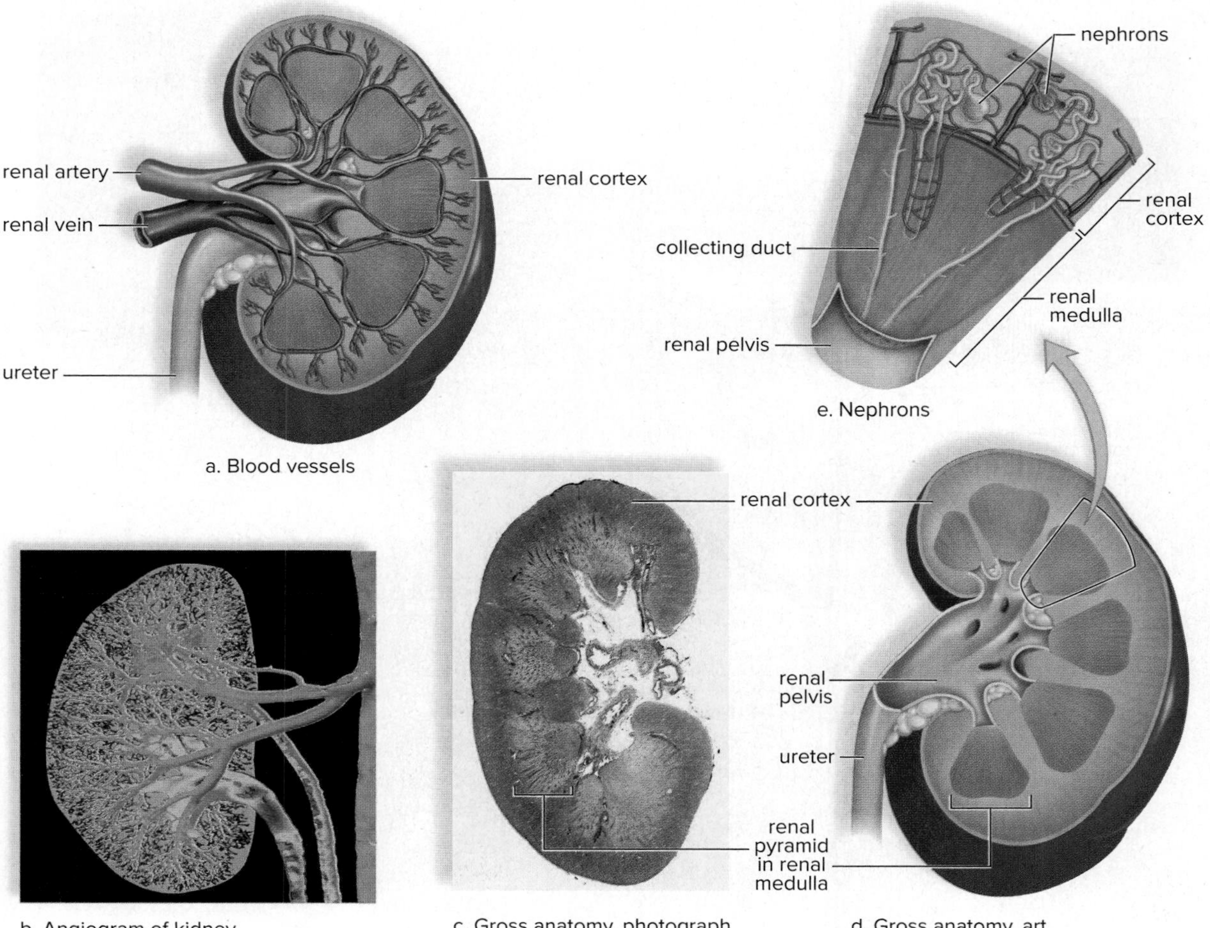

Figure 11.4 The anatomy of a human kidney.
a. A longitudinal section of the kidney showing the blood supply. The renal artery divides into smaller arteries, and these divide into arterioles. Venules join to form small veins, which join to form the renal vein. **b.** A procedure called an angiogram highlights blood vessels by injecting a contrast medium that is opaque to X-rays. **c.** The same section without the blood supply. **d.** A diagram of the renal cortex; the renal medulla; and the renal pelvis, which connects with the ureter. The renal medulla consists of the renal pyramids. **e.** An enlargement showing the placement of nephrons.
(photos) (b): James Cavallini/Science Source; (c): KAGE Mikrofotografie/Medical Images/DIOMEDIA

Microscopically, the kidney is composed of over 1 million **nephrons,** sometimes called renal, or kidney, tubules (Fig. 11.4*e*). The nephrons filter the blood and produce urine. Each nephron is positioned so that the urine flows into a collecting duct. Several nephrons enter the same collecting duct. The collecting ducts eventually enter the renal pelvis.

The Nephron

Each nephron has its own blood supply, including two capillary regions (Fig. 11.5). From the renal artery, an afferent arteriole transports blood to the **glomerulus,** a knot of capillaries inside the glomerular capsule. Blood leaving the glomerulus is carried away by the efferent arteriole. Blood pressure is higher in the glomerulus, because the efferent arteriole is narrower than the afferent arteriole. The efferent arteriole divides and forms the **peritubular capillary network,** which surrounds the rest of the nephron. Blood from the efferent arteriole travels through the peritubular capillary network. The blood then goes into a venule that carries blood into the renal vein.

Anatomy of a Nephron

Each nephron is made up of several parts (Fig. 11.5). Some functions are shared by all parts of the nephron. However, the specific structure of each part is especially suited to a particular function.

First, the closed end of the nephron is pushed in on itself to form a cuplike structure called the **glomerular capsule** (formally called the Bowman's capsule). The outer layer of the glomerular capsule is composed of squamous epithelial cells. The inner layer is made up of podocytes that have long, cytoplasmic extensions. The podocytes cling to the capillary walls of the glomerulus and leave pores that allow easy passage of small molecules from the glomerulus to the inside of the glomerular capsule. This process, called glomerular filtration, produces a filtrate of the blood.

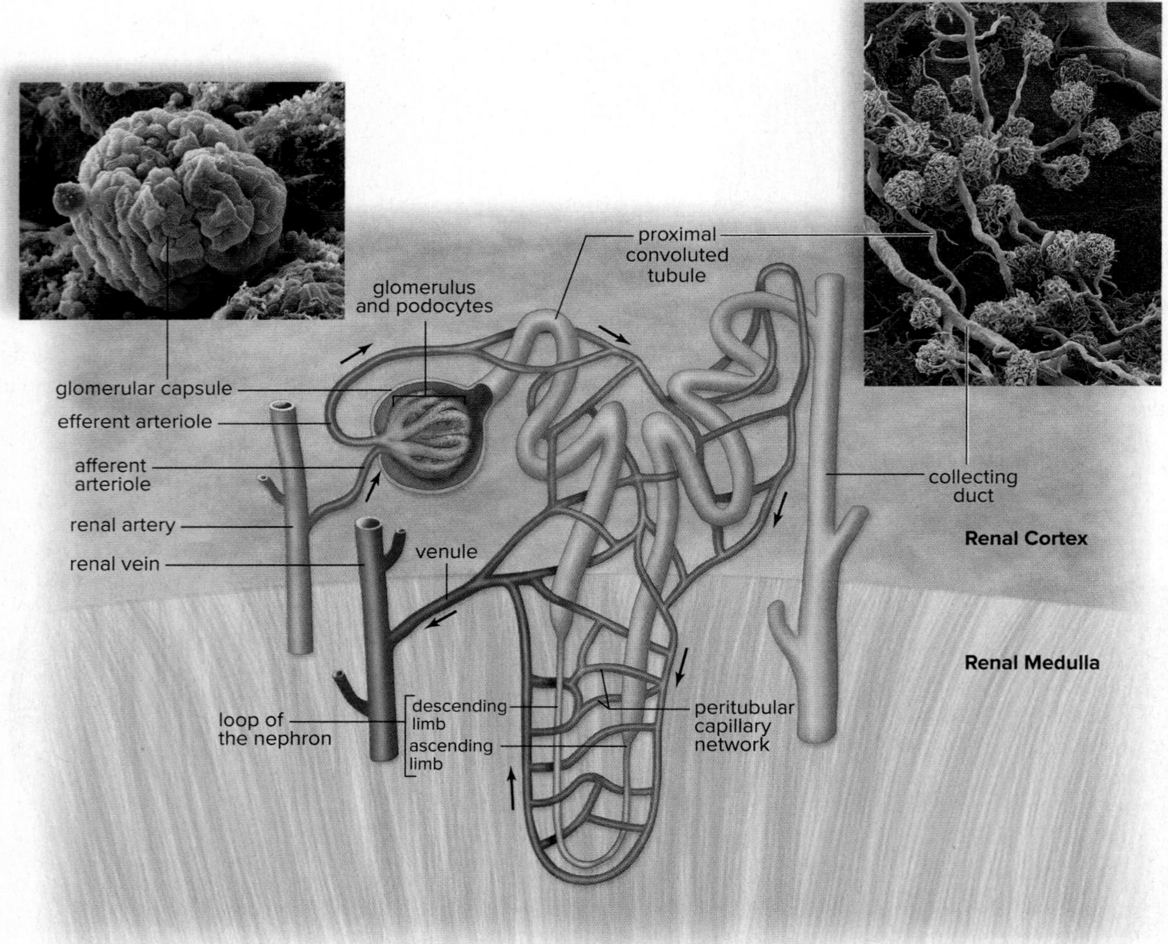

Figure 11.5 **The structure of a nephron.**
A nephron is made up of a glomerular capsule, the proximal convoluted tubule, the loop of the nephron, and the distal convoluted tubule. The collecting duct collects fluid from several nephrons. The photomicrographs show the microscopic anatomy of these structures. The arrows indicate the path of blood around the nephron.
(photos) (top left): Steve Gschmeissner/Science Photo Library/Science Source; (top right): Steve Gschmeissner/Science Photo Library/Getty Images

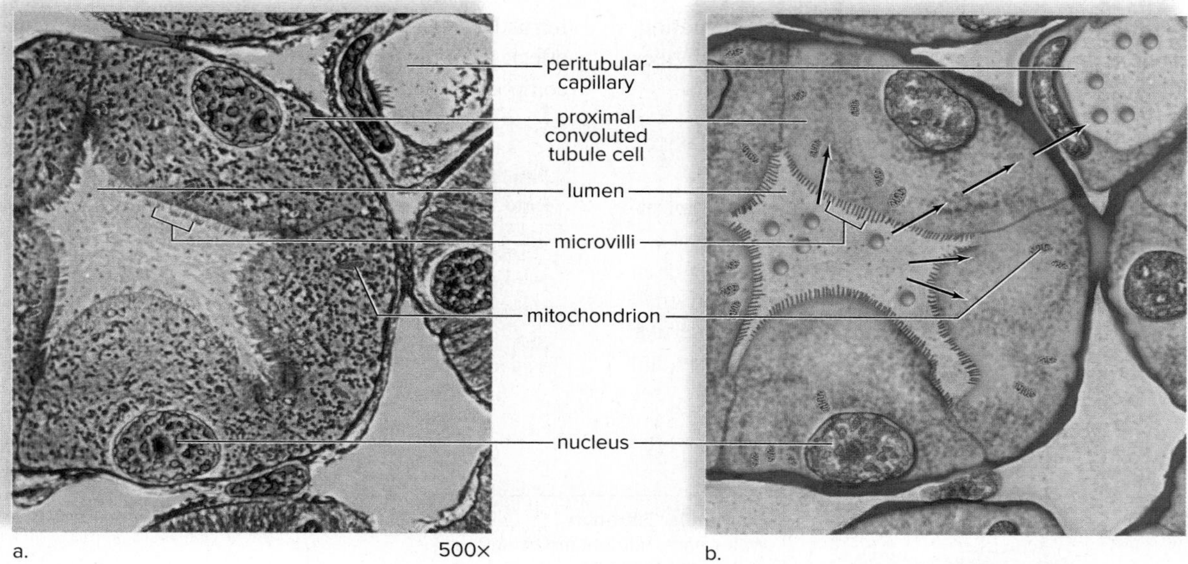

Figure 11.6 **The specialized cells of the proximal convoluted tubule.**
a. This photomicrograph shows that the cells lining the proximal convoluted tubule have a brushlike border composed of microvilli, which greatly increase the surface area exposed to the lumen. The peritubular capillary network surrounds the cells. **b.** Diagrammatic representation of (**a**) shows that each cell has many mitochondria, which supply the energy needed for active transport, the process that moves molecules (green) from the lumen of the tubule to the capillary, as indicated by the arrows.
(a): Joseph F. Gennaro Jr./Science Source

Next, there is a **proximal convoluted tubule.** The cuboidal epithelial cells lining this part of the nephron have numerous microvilli, about 1 micrometer (μm) in length, that are tightly packed and form a brush border (Fig. 11.6). A brush border greatly increases the surface area for the tubular reabsorption of filtrate components. Each cell also has many mitochondria, which can supply energy for active transport of molecules from the lumen to the peritubular capillary network.

Simple squamous epithelium appears as the tube narrows and makes a U-turn called the **loop of the nephron** (loop of Henle). Each loop consists of a descending limb and an ascending limb. The descending limb of the loop allows water to diffuse into tissue surrounding the nephron. The ascending limb actively transports salt from its lumen to interstitial tissue. As we will see, this activity facilitates the reabsorption of water by the nephron and collecting duct.

The cuboidal epithelial cells of the **distal convoluted tubule** have numerous mitochondria, but they lack microvilli. This means that the distal convoluted tubule is not specialized for reabsorption. Instead, its primary function is ion exchange. During ion exchange, cells reabsorb certain ions, returning them to the blood. Other ions are secreted from the blood into the tubule. The distal convoluted tubules of several nephrons enter one collecting duct. Many **collecting ducts** carry urine to the renal pelvis.

As shown in Figure 11.5, the glomerular capsule and the convoluted tubules always lie within the renal cortex. The loop of the nephron dips down into the renal medulla. A few nephrons have a very long loop of the nephron, which penetrates deep into the renal medulla. Collecting ducts are also located in the renal medulla, and together they give the renal pyramids their appearance.

CHECK YOUR PROGRESS 11.2

1. Name the three major areas of a kidney.
2. Describe the paths of blood and fluids in the nephron.
3. Explain the difference between the distal and proximal convoluted tubules.

CONNECTING THE CONCEPTS

For more information on the topics presented in this section, refer to the following discussions:

Section 4.5 illustrates the various forms of epithelial tissue and provides a function for each.

Section 5.2 summarizes the function of arterioles, capillaries, and venules in the circulatory system.

11.3 Urine Formation

LEARNING OUTCOMES

Upon completion of this section, you should be able to

1. Summarize the three processes involved in the formation of urine.
2. List the components of the glomerular filtrate.
3. Describe how tubular reabsorption processes nutrient and salt molecules.
4. Explain the substances removed from the blood by tubular secretion.

The formation of urine involves three stages: glomerular filtration, tubular reabsorption, and tubular secretion. Figure 11.7 provides an overview of these processes.

Glomerular Filtration

Glomerular filtration occurs when whole blood enters the glomerulus by way of the afferent arteriole. The afferent arteriole (Fig. 11.7, *inset*) has a larger diameter than the efferent arteriole, resulting in an increase in glomerular blood pressure. Because of this, water and small molecules move from the glomerulus to the inside of the glomerular capsule. This is a filtration process, because large molecules and formed elements are unable to pass through the capillary wall. In effect, then, blood in the glomerulus has two portions: the filterable components and the nonfilterable components.

Filterable Blood Components	Nonfilterable Blood Components
Water	Formed elements (blood cells and platelets)
Nitrogenous wastes	Plasma proteins
Nutrients	
Salts (ions)	

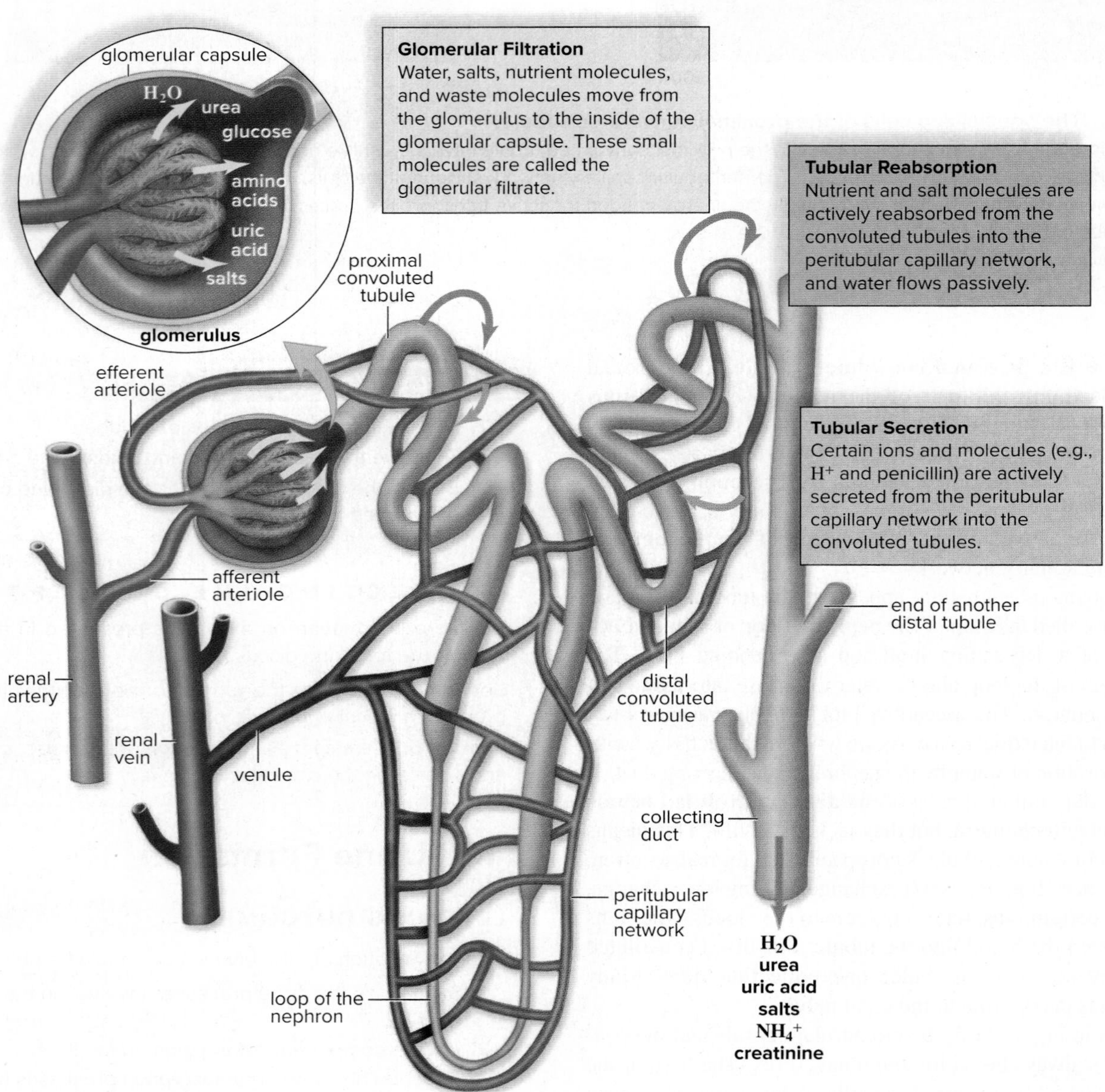
glomerular capsule
H_2O
urea
glucose
amino acids
uric acid
salts
glomerulus
Glomerular Filtration
Water, salts, nutrient molecules, and waste molecules move from the glomerulus to the inside of the glomerular capsule. These small molecules are called the glomerular filtrate.
proximal convoluted tubule
Tubular Reabsorption
Nutrient and salt molecules are actively reabsorbed from the convoluted tubules into the peritubular capillary network, and water flows passively.
efferent arteriole
Tubular Secretion
Certain ions and molecules (e.g., H^+ and penicillin) are actively secreted from the peritubular capillary network into the convoluted tubules.
afferent arteriole
end of another distal tubule
renal artery
renal vein
venule
distal convoluted tubule
collecting duct
peritubular capillary network
loop of the nephron
H_2O
urea
uric acid
salts
NH_4^+
creatinine

Figure 11.7 An overview of urine production.
The three main processes in urine formation are described in boxes and color-coded to arrows that show the movement of molecules into or out of the nephron at specific locations. In the end, urine is composed of the substances within the collecting duct (see brown arrow).

Table 11.1 Reabsorption from Nephrons

Substance	Amount Filtered (per Day)	Amount Excreted (per Day)	Reabsorption (%)
Water (l)	180	1.8	99.0
Sodium (g)	630	3.2	99.5
Glucose (g)	180	0.0	100.0
Urea (g)	54	30.0	44.0

l = liters; g = grams

The nonfilterable components leave the glomerulus by way of the efferent arteriole. The **glomerular filtrate** inside the glomerular capsule now contains the filterable blood components in approximately the same concentration as plasma.

As indicated in Table 11.1, nephrons in the kidneys filter 180 liters of water per day, along with a considerable amount of small molecules (such as glucose) and ions (such as sodium). If the composition of urine were the same as that of the glomerular filtrate, the body would continually lose water, salts, and nutrients. Therefore, we can conclude that the composition of the filtrate must be altered as this fluid passes through the remainder of the tubule.

Tubular Reabsorption

Tubular reabsorption occurs as molecules, especially ions, are passively and actively reabsorbed from the nephron into the blood of the peritubular capillary network. The osmolarity of the blood is maintained by the presence of plasma proteins and salt. Sodium ions (Na^+) are actively transported by one of two types of transport proteins. First, the movement of sodium may be coupled to the movement of larger solutes, such as amino acids or glucose. This is called a *symport,* because both solutes are being moved in the same direction. The second mechanism involves an *antiport* protein, which moves Na^+ ions into the cell while transporting H^+ ions out of the cell. This also regulates the pH balance of the blood, because the movement of H^+ ions outward reduces the acidity of the blood. As sodium ions are being moved, chloride ions (Cl^-) follow passively. The reabsorption of salt (NaCl) increases the osmolarity of the blood compared with the filtrate. Therefore, water moves passively from the tubule into the blood. About 65% of Na^+ is reabsorbed at the proximal convoluted tubule.

Nutrients such as glucose and amino acids return to the peritubular capillaries almost exclusively at the proximal convoluted tubule. This is a selective process, because only molecules recognized by carrier proteins are actively reabsorbed. Glucose is an example of a molecule that ordinarily is completely reabsorbed because there is a plentiful supply of carrier proteins for it. However, every substance has a maximum rate of transport. After all its carriers are in use, any excess in the filtrate will appear in the urine. In **diabetes mellitus,** because the liver and muscles fail to store glucose as glycogen, the blood glucose level is above normal and glucose appears in the urine. The presence of excess glucose in the filtrate raises its osmolarity. Therefore, less water is reabsorbed into the peritubular capillary network. The frequent urination and increased thirst experienced by people with untreated diabetes are due to less water being reabsorbed from the filtrate into the blood.

We have seen that the filtrate that enters the proximal convoluted tubule is divided into two portions: components reabsorbed from the tubule into blood, and components not reabsorbed that continue to pass through the nephron to be further processed into urine.

Reabsorbed Filtrate Components	Nonreabsorbed Filtrate Components
Most water	Some water
Nutrients	Much nitrogenous waste
Required salts (ions)	Excess salts (ions)

The substances not reabsorbed become the tubular fluid, which enters the loop of the nephron.

Tubular Secretion

Tubular secretion is the second way by which substances are removed from blood and added to the tubular fluid. Hydrogen ions (H^+), creatinine, and drugs such as penicillin are some of the substances moved by active transport from blood into the kidney tubule. In the end, urine contains substances that have undergone glomerular filtration but have not been reabsorbed, as well as substances that have undergone tubular secretion. Tubular secretion occurs along the length of the kidney tubule. The Health feature "Urinalysis" explains how the contents of the urine may be used as a diagnostic tool for assessing an individual's health.

CHECK YOUR PROGRESS 11.3

1. List the three major processes in urine formation, and state the location in the nephron where each occurs.
2. Summarize the functions of glomerular filtration, tubular reabsorption, and tubular secretion.
3. List the components of the blood that are reabsorbed, and those that are excreted during urine formation.

CONNECTING THE CONCEPTS

For more information on the topics presented in this section, refer to the following discussions:

Section 3.3 describes the processes of osmosis, active transport, and the movement of ions across a plasma membrane.

Section 6.1 lists the substances in the plasma component of blood.

BIOLOGY TODAY ▶ Health

Urinalysis

A routine urinalysis can detect abnormalities in urine color, concentration, and content. Significant information about the general state of one's health, particularly in the diagnosis of renal and metabolic diseases, is provided by this analysis also. A complete urinalysis consists of three phases of examination: physical, chemical, and microscopic.

Physical Examination

The physical examination describes urine color, clarity, and odor. The color of normal, fresh urine is usually pale yellow. However, the color may vary from almost colorless (dilute) to dark yellow (concentrated). Pink, red, or smoky brown urine is usually a sign of bleeding that may be due to a kidney, bladder, or urinary tract infection. Liver disorders can also produce dark brown urine. The clarity of normal urine may be clear or cloudy. However, a cloudy urine sample is also characteristic of abnormal levels of bacteria. Finally, urine odor is usually "nutty" or aromatic, but a foul-smelling odor is characteristic of a urinary tract infection. A sweet, fruity odor is characteristic of glucose in the urine or diabetes mellitus. Urine's odor is also affected by the consumption of garlic, curry, asparagus, and vitamin C.

Chemical Examination

The chemical examination is often done quickly with a dipstick, a thin strip of plastic impregnated with chemicals that change color upon reaction with certain substances present in urine (Fig. 11B). The color change on each segment of the dipstick is compared with a standardized color chart. Dipsticks can be used to determine urine's specific gravity; pH; and content of glucose, bilirubin, urobilinogen, ketone, protein, nitrite, blood, and white blood cells (WBCs) in the urine. Chemical analyses in a laboratory are then often used to confirm the results if there are concerns or questions.

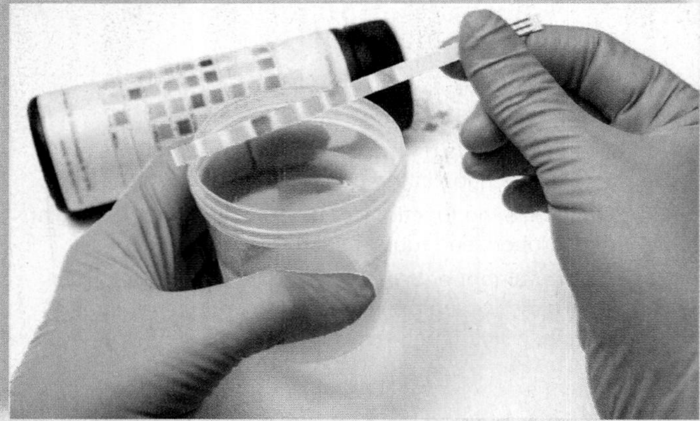

Figure 11B A urinalysis provides an indication of a person's overall health.
This patient's urine has been tested and the multiple-test stick is being compared to a reference chart. The dark brown pad shows that the patient has glucose in her urine. This indicates she has diabetes mellitus.
Alexander Raths/Shutterstock

- *Specific gravity* is an indicator of how well the kidneys are able to adjust tonicity in urine. Normal values for urine specific gravity range from 1.002 to 1.035. A high value (concentrated urine) may be a result of dehydration or diabetes mellitus.
- Normal *urine pH* can be as low as 4.5 and as high as 8.0. In patients with kidney stone disease, urine pH has a direct effect on the type of stones formed.
- *Glucose* is normally not present in urine. If present, diabetes mellitus is suspected.
- *Bilirubin* (a by-product of hemoglobin degradation) is not normally present in the urine. *Urobilinogen* (a by-product of bilirubin degradation) is normally present in very small amounts. High levels of bilirubin or urobilinogen may indicate liver disease.
- *Ketones* are not normally found in urine. Urine ketones are a by-product of fat metabolism. The presence of ketones in the urine may indicate diabetes mellitus or use of a low-carbohydrate diet, such as the Atkins diet.
- *Plasma proteins* should not be present in urine. A significant amount of urine protein (proteinuria) is usually a sign of kidney damage.
- Urine typically does not contain *nitrates* or *nitrites*. The presence of these nitrogen compounds is a sign of urinary tract infection.
- It is not abnormal for blood to show up in the urine when a woman is menstruating. Blood present in the urine at other times may indicate a bacterial infection or kidney damage.
- The chemical test for *WBCs* is normally negative. A high urine WBC count usually indicates a bacterial infection somewhere in the urinary tract.

Microscopic Examination

For the microscopic examination, the urine is centrifuged, and the sediment (solid material) is examined under a microscope. When renal disease is present, the urine often contains an abnormal amount of cellular material. Urinary casts are sediments formed by the abnormal coagulation of protein material in the distal convoluted tubule or the collecting duct. The presence of crystals in the urine is characteristic of kidney stones, kidney damage, or problems with metabolism.

Forensic Analysis

Urinalysis is also used by the federal government and some businesses to screen potential employees for the use of numerous illegal drugs. Drugs associated with date rape (such as flunitrazepam [Rohypnol], known as "roofies," and GHB, or gamma-hydroxybutyrate) can be detected in the urine of victims to determine if they were drugged.

Questions to Consider

1. What might be the difference between the levels of water-soluble and fat-soluble chemicals in the urine?
2. Why does diabetes result in high levels of glucose in the urine?

11.4 Kidneys and Homeostasis

LEARNING OUTCOMES

Upon completion of this section, you should be able to

1. Summarize how the kidney maintains the water-salt balance of the body.
2. State the purpose of ADH and aldosterone in homeostasis.
3. Explain how the kidneys assist in the maintenance of the pH levels of the blood.

The kidneys play a major role in homeostasis, from maintaining the water-salt balance in the body to regulating the pH of the blood. In doing so, the kidneys interact with every other organ system of the human body (Fig. 11.8).

Kidneys Excrete Waste Molecules

In Section 9.4, we compared the liver to a sewage treatment plant because it removes poisonous substances from the blood and prepares them for excretion. Similarly, the liver produces urea, the primary nitrogenous end product of humans, which is excreted by the kidneys. If the liver is a sewage treatment plant, the tubules of the kidney are like the trucks that take the sludge, prepared waste, away from the town (the body).

Metabolic waste removal is absolutely necessary for maintaining homeostasis. The blood must constantly be cleansed of the nitrogenous wastes, end products of metabolism. The liver produces urea, and muscles make creatinine. These wastes, as well as uric acid from the cells, are carried by the cardiovascular system to the kidneys. The urine-producing kidneys are responsible for the excretion of nitrogenous wastes. They are assisted to a limited degree by the sweat glands in the skin, which excrete perspiration,

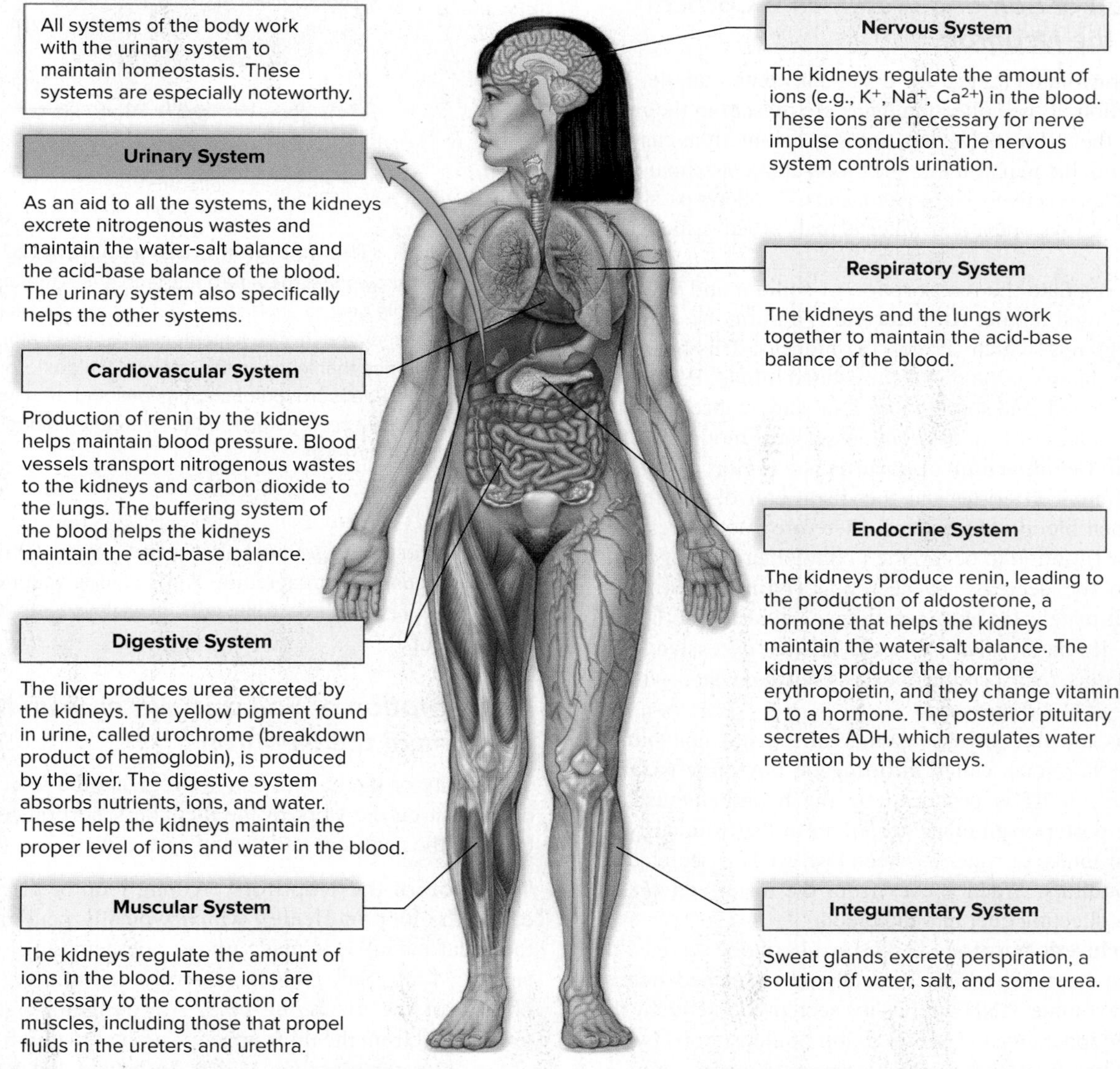

Figure 11.8 The urinary system and homeostasis.
The urinary system works primarily with these systems to bring about homeostasis.

a mixture of water, salt, and some urea. In times of kidney failure, urea is excreted by the sweat glands and forms a substance called uremic frost on the skin.

Water-Salt Balance

Most of the water in the filtrate is reabsorbed into the blood before urine leaves the body. The nephron is specialized for the reabsorption of water. The reabsorption of salt always precedes the reabsorption of water. In other words, water is returned to the blood by the process of osmosis. During the process of reabsorption, water passes through water channels, called **aquaporins,** within a plasma membrane protein.

Sodium ions (Na^+) are important in plasma. Usually, more than 99% of the Na^+ filtered at the glomerulus is returned to the blood. The kidneys also excrete or reabsorb other ions, such as potassium ions (K^+), bicarbonate ions (HCO_3^-), and magnesium ions (Mg^{2+}) as needed.

Reabsorption of Salt and Water from Cortical Portions of the Nephron

The proximal convoluted tubule, the distal convoluted tubule, and the cortical portion of the collecting ducts are present in the renal cortex. Most of the water (65%) that enters the glomerular capsule is reabsorbed from the nephron into the blood at the proximal convoluted tubule. Na^+ is actively reabsorbed, and Cl^- follows passively. Aquaporins are always open, and water is reabsorbed osmotically into the blood.

Hormones regulate the reabsorption of sodium and water in the distal convoluted tubule. **Aldosterone** is a hormone secreted by the adrenal glands, which sit atop the kidneys. This hormone promotes ion exchange at the distal convoluted tubule. Potassium ions (K^+) are excreted, and sodium ions (Na^+) are reabsorbed into the blood. The release of aldosterone is set into motion by the kidneys. The **juxtaglomerular apparatus** is a region of contact between the afferent arteriole and the distal convoluted tubule (Fig. 11.9). When blood volume (and, therefore, blood pressure) falls too low for filtration to occur, the juxtaglomerular apparatus can respond to the decrease by secreting **renin.** Renin is an enzyme that ultimately leads to secretion of aldosterone by the adrenal glands. Research scientists speculate that excessive renin secretion—and thus, reabsorption of excess salt and water—might contribute to high blood pressure.

Aquaporins are not always open in the distal convoluted tubule. Another hormone, called **antidiuretic hormone (ADH),** must be present. ADH is produced by the hypothalamus and secreted by the posterior pituitary according to the osmolarity of the blood. If our intake of water has been low, ADH is secreted by the posterior pituitary. Water moves from the distal convoluted tubule and the collecting duct into the blood.

Atrial natriuretic hormone (ANH) is a hormone secreted by the atria of the heart when cardiac cells are stretched due to increased blood volume. ANH inhibits the secretion of renin by the juxtaglomerular apparatus and the secretion of aldosterone by the adrenal glands. Its effect, therefore, is to promote the excretion of sodium ions (Na^+), called *natriuresis.* Normally, salt reabsorption creates an osmotic gradient that causes water to be reabsorbed. Thus, by causing salt excretion, ANH causes water excretion, too. If ANH is present, less water will be reabsorbed, even if ADH is also present.

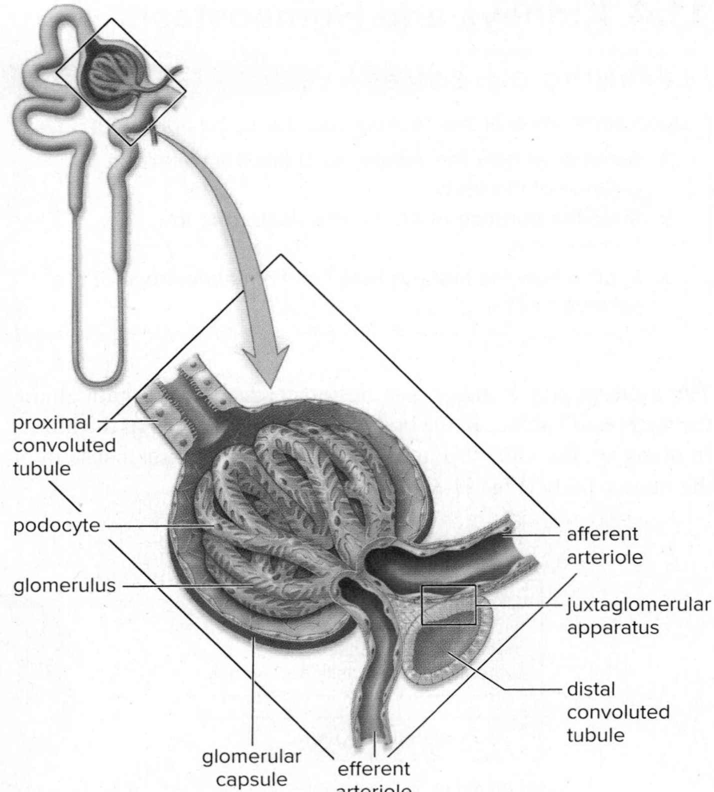

Figure 11.9 **The juxtaglomerular apparatus of the nephron.** This drawing shows that the afferent arteriole and the distal convoluted tubule usually lie next to each other. The juxtaglomerular apparatus occurs where they touch. The juxtaglomerular apparatus secretes renin, a substance that leads to the release of aldosterone by the adrenal cortex. Reabsorption of sodium ions and then water now occurs in the distal convoluted tubule. Thereafter, blood volume and blood pressure increase.

Reabsorption of Salt and Water from Medullary Portions of the Nephron

The ability of the human body to regulate the tonicity of urine is dependent on the work of the medullary portions of the nephron (loop of the nephron) and the collecting duct.

The Loop of the Nephron A long loop of the nephron (also called the loop of Henle), which typically penetrates deep into the renal medulla, is made up of a descending limb and an ascending limb. Salt (NaCl) passively diffuses out of the lower portion of the *ascending limb.* Any remaining salt is actively transported from the thick upper portion of the limb into the tissue of the outer medulla (Fig. 11.10). In the end, the concentration of salt is greater in the direction of the inner medulla. Surprisingly,

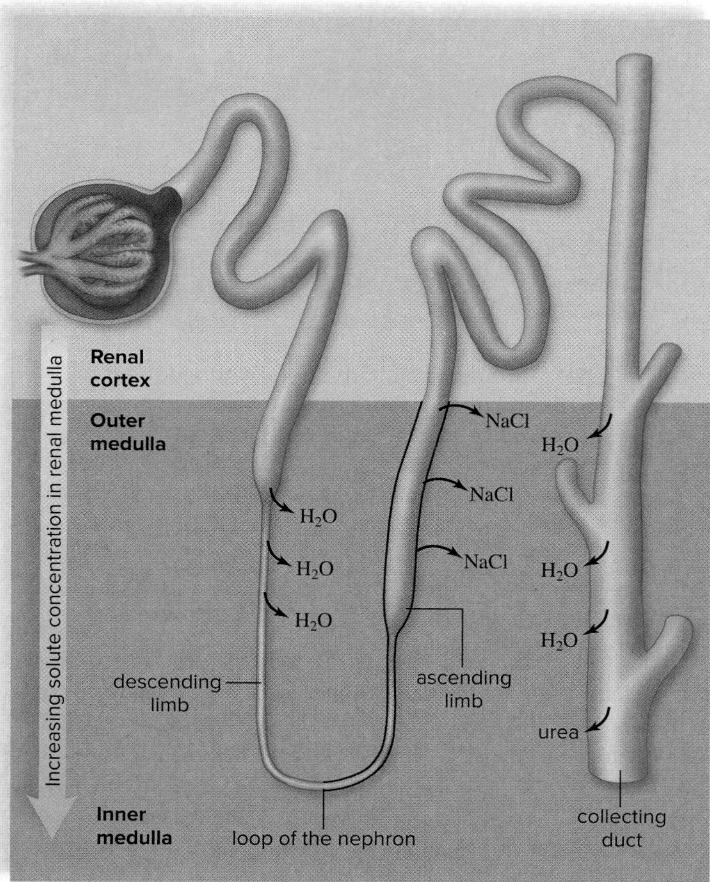

Figure 11.10 Movement of salt and water within a nephron. Salt (NaCl) diffuses and is actively transported out of the ascending limb of the loop of the nephron into the renal medulla. Also, urea is believed to leak from the collecting duct and to enter the tissues of the renal medulla. This creates a hypertonic environment, which draws water out of the descending limb and the collecting duct. This water is returned to the cardiovascular system. (The thick black outline of the ascending limb means it is impermeable to water.)

however, the inner medulla has an even higher concentration of solutes than expected. It is believed that urea leaks from the lower portion of the collecting duct, contributing to the high solute concentration of the inner medulla.

Water leaves the *descending limb* along its entire length via a countercurrent mechanism because of the osmotic gradient within the medulla. Although water is reabsorbed as soon as fluid enters the descending limb, the remaining fluid within the limb encounters an increasing osmotic concentration of solute. Therefore, water continues to be reabsorbed, even to the bottom of the descending limb. The ascending limb does not reabsorb water, primarily because it lacks aquaporins (as indicated by the dark line in Fig. 11.10). Its job is to help establish the solute concentration gradient. Water is returned to the cardiovascular system when it is reabsorbed.

The Collecting Duct Fluid within the collecting duct encounters the same osmotic gradient established by the ascending limb of the nephron. Therefore, water diffuses from the entire length of the collecting duct into the blood if aquaporins are open, as they are if ADH is present.

To understand the action of ADH, consider its name, *antidiuretic hormone. Diuresis* means "increased amount of urine," thus *antidiuresis* means "decreased amount of urine." When ADH is present, more water is reabsorbed (blood volume and pressure rise) and a decreased amount of urine results. ADH ultimately fine-tunes the tonicity of urine according to the needs of the body. For example, ADH is secreted at night when we are not drinking water, and this explains why the first urine of the day is more concentrated.

The Role of ANH

If blood does not have the usual water-salt balance, blood volume and blood pressure are affected. Without adequate blood pressure, exchange across capillary walls cannot take place, nor is glomerular filtration possible in the kidneys.

What happens if you have insufficient sodium ions (Na^+) in your blood and interstitial fluid? This can occur due to prolonged heavy sweating, as in athletes running a marathon. When blood Na^+ concentration falls too low, blood pressure falls and the renin–aldosterone sequence begins. The kidneys then increase Na^+ reabsorption, conserving as much as possible. Subsequently, the osmolarity of the blood and the blood pressure return to normal.

A marathon runner should not drink too much water too fast. Quickly ingesting a large amount of pure water can dilute the body's remaining Na^+ and disrupt water-salt balance. Although the sports drinks preferred by athletes contain both sodium and water, they may also be high in calories and are not recommended for routine exercise lasting less than 90 minutes.

By contrast, think about what happens if you eat a big tub of salty popcorn at the movies. When salt (NaCl) is absorbed from the digestive tract, the Na^+ content of the blood increases above normal. This results in increased blood volume. The atria of the heart are stretched by this increased blood volume, and the stretch triggers the release of ANH by the heart. ANH inhibits sodium and water reabsorption by the proximal convoluted tubule and collecting duct. Blood volume then decreases, because more sodium and water are excreted in the urine.

Diuretics

Diuretics are chemicals that increase the flow of urine. Drinking alcohol causes diuresis, because it inhibits the secretion of ADH. The dehydration that follows is believed to contribute to the symptoms of a hangover. Caffeine is a diuretic because it increases the glomerular filtration rate and decreases the tubular reabsorption of sodium ions (Na^+). Diuretic drugs developed to counteract high blood pressure also decrease the tubular reabsorption of Na^+. A decrease in water reabsorption and a decrease in blood volume and pressure follow.

Acid-Base Balance of Body Fluids

The pH scale, as discussed in Section 2.2, can be used to indicate the basicity (alkalinity) or the acidity of body fluids. A basic solution has a lower hydrogen ion concentration ($[H^+]$) than the neutral pH of 7.0. An acidic solution has a greater [H^+] than neutral pH. The normal pH for body fluids is between 7.35 and 7.45. This is the pH at which our proteins, such as cellular enzymes, function properly. If the blood pH rises above 7.45, a person is said to have **alkalosis,** and if the blood pH decreases below 7.35, a person is said to have **acidosis.** Alkalosis and acidosis are abnormal conditions that may need medical attention.

The foods we eat add basic or acidic substances to the blood, and so does metabolism. For example, cellular respiration adds carbon dioxide that combines with water to form carbonic acid, and fermentation adds lactic acid. The pH of body fluids stays at just about 7.4 via several mechanisms, primarily acid-base buffer systems, the respiratory center, and the kidneys.

Acid-Base Buffer Systems

The pH of the blood stays near 7.4 because the blood is buffered. A **buffer** is a chemical or a combination of chemicals that can take up excess hydrogen ions (H^+) or excess hydroxide ions (OH^-). One of the most important buffers in the blood is a combination of carbonic acid (H_2CO_3) and bicarbonate ions (HCO_3^-). When hydrogen ions (H^+) are added to blood, the following reaction occurs:

$$H^+ + HCO_3^- \longrightarrow H_2CO_3$$

When hydroxide ions (OH^-) are added to blood, this reaction occurs:

$$OH^- + H_2CO_3 \longrightarrow HCO_3^- + H_2O$$

These reactions temporarily prevent any significant change in blood pH. A blood buffer, however, can be overwhelmed unless a more permanent adjustment is made. The next adjustment to keep the pH of the blood constant occurs at pulmonary capillaries.

Respiratory Center

As discussed in Section 10.5, the respiratory center in the medulla oblongata increases the breathing rate if the hydrogen ion concentration of the blood rises. Increasing the breathing rate rids the body of hydrogen ions, because the following reaction takes place in pulmonary capillaries:

$$H^+ + HCO_3^- \rightleftharpoons H_2CO_3 \rightleftharpoons H_2O + CO_2$$

In other words, when carbon dioxide is exhaled, this reaction shifts to the right and the amount of hydrogen ions is reduced.

It is important to have the correct proportion of carbonic acid and bicarbonate ions in the blood. Breathing readjusts this proportion, so that this acid-base buffer system can continue to absorb H^+ and OH^- as needed.

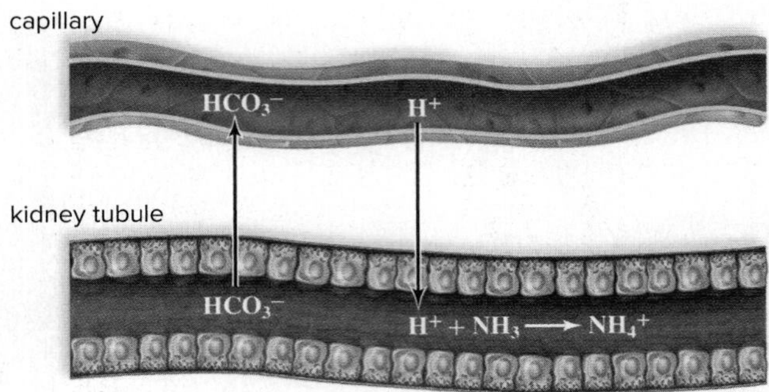

Figure 11.11 **Blood pH is maintained by the kidneys.** In the kidneys, bicarbonate ions (HCO_3^-) are reabsorbed and hydrogen ions (H^+) are excreted as needed to maintain the pH of the blood. Excess hydrogen ions are buffered, for example, by ammonia (NH_3), which becomes ammonium (NH_4^+). Ammonia is produced in tubule cells by the deamination of amino acids.

The Kidneys

As powerful as the acid-base buffer and the respiratory center mechanisms are, only the kidneys can rid the body of a wide range of acidic and basic substances and, otherwise, adjust the pH. The kidneys are slower acting than the other two mechanisms, but they have a more powerful effect on pH. For the sake of simplicity, we can think of the kidneys as reabsorbing bicarbonate ions and excreting hydrogen ions as needed to maintain the normal pH of the blood (Fig. 11.11).

If the blood is acidic, hydrogen ions are excreted and bicarbonate ions are reabsorbed. If the blood is basic, hydrogen ions are not excreted and bicarbonate ions are not reabsorbed. The urine is usually acidic, so it follows that an excess of hydrogen ions is usually excreted. Ammonia (NH_3) provides another means of buffering and removing the hydrogen ions in urine:

$$H^+ + NH_3 \longrightarrow NH_4^+$$

Ammonia (whose presence is obvious in the diaper pail or kitty litter box) is produced in tubule cells by the deamination of amino acids. Phosphate provides another means of buffering hydrogen ions in urine.

The importance of the kidneys' ultimate control over the pH of the blood cannot be overemphasized. As mentioned, the enzymes of cells cannot continue to function if the internal environment does not have near-normal pH.

The Kidneys Assist Other Systems

Aside from producing renin, the kidneys assist the endocrine system and the cardiovascular system by producing erythropoietin (EPO), a hormone secreted by the kidneys. When blood oxygen decreases, EPO increases red blood cell synthesis by stem cells in the bone marrow (see Section 6.2). When the concentration of red blood cells increases, blood oxygen increases also. During kidney failure, the kidneys may produce less EPO, resulting in fewer red blood cells and symptoms of fatigue. Drugs such as epoetin (Procrit) represent a form of EPO produced by genetic engineering and biotechnology (see Section 22.3). Like normal EPO, epoetin increases red blood cell synthesis and energy levels. This drug is often used to stimulate red bone marrow production in patients in renal failure or recovering from chemotherapy.

The kidneys assist the skeletal, nervous, and muscular systems by helping regulate the amount of calcium ions (Ca^{2+}) in the blood. The kidneys convert vitamin D to its active form needed for Ca^{2+} absorption by the digestive tract, and they regulate the excretion of electrolytes, including Ca^{2+}. The kidneys also regulate the sodium ion (Na^+) and potassium ion (K^+) content of the blood. These ions, needed for nerve conduction, are necessary to the contraction of the heart and other muscles in the body.

CHECK YOUR PROGRESS 11.4

1. Detail the differences between dilute and concentrated urine.
2. Describe the action of the three hormones used to influence urine production, and discuss how they work together.
3. Summarize how the action of the kidneys regulates body fluid pH, and clarify why this is important to homeostasis.

CONNECTING THE CONCEPTS

For additional information on water-salt balance and maintenance of the pH of the blood, refer to the following discussions:

Section 2.2 explains how buffers regulate pH levels.

Section 10.5 examines the role of the respiratory center in the medulla oblongata of the brain.

Section 16.4 explores the production of aldosterone by the adrenal glands.

11.5 Urinary System Disorders

LEARNING OUTCOMES

Upon completion of this section, you should be able to

1. List the major diseases of the urinary system and summarize their causes.
2. Describe how hemodialysis can help restore homeostasis of the blood in the event of kidney failure.

Many types of illnesses—especially diabetes, hypertension, and inherited conditions—cause progressive renal disease and renal failure. Infections are also contributory. If the infection is localized in the urethra, it is called **urethritis.** If the infection invades the urinary bladder, it is called **cystitis.** Finally, if the kidneys are affected, the infection is called **pyelonephritis.**

BIOLOGY IN YOUR LIFE

How does cranberry juice prevent or cure a urinary tract infection?

Research has supported the use of cranberry juice to prevent urinary tract infections. Cranberry juice contains chemicals that prevent bacteria that would cause infection (such as *E. coli*) from adhering to the surfaces of the urinary tract. However, most studies have indicated that cranberry juice is not an effective treatment for an already existing urinary tract infection, and that most juices and supplements contain a very low level of the protective chemicals.

Urinary tract infections, an enlarged prostate gland (see the Health feature "Urinary Difficulties Due to an Enlarged Prostate"), pH imbalances, or an intake of too much calcium can lead to kidney stones. Kidney stones are hard granules made of calcium, phosphate, uric acid, and protein. Kidney stones form in the renal pelvis and usually pass unnoticed in the urine flow. If they grow to several centimeters and block the renal pelvis or ureter, a reverse pressure builds up and destroys nephrons. When a large kidney stone passes, strong contractions in a ureter can be excruciatingly painful.

One of the first signs of nephron damage is albumin, white blood cells, or even red blood cells in the urine. As described in the Health feature "Urinalysis" (Section 11.3), a urinalysis can detect urine abnormalities rapidly. If damage is so extensive that more than two-thirds of the nephrons are inoperative, urea and other waste substances accumulate in the blood. This condition is called **uremia.** Although nitrogenous wastes can cause serious damage, the retention of water and salts is of even greater concern. The latter causes edema, fluid accumulation in the body tissues. Imbalance in the ionic composition of body fluids can lead to loss of consciousness and heart failure.

Hemodialysis

Patients with renal failure can undergo **hemodialysis,** using either an artificial kidney machine or continuous ambulatory peritoneal dialysis (CAPD). *Dialysis* is defined as the diffusion of dissolved molecules through a semipermeable natural or synthetic membrane that has pore sizes that allow only small molecules to pass through. In an artificial kidney machine (Fig. 11.12), the patient's blood is passed through a membranous tube that is in contact with a dialysis solution, or dialysate. Substances more concentrated in the blood diffuse into the dialysate, and substances more concentrated in the dialysate diffuse into the blood. The dialysate is continuously replaced to maintain favorable concentration gradients. In this way, the artificial kidney can be used either to extract substances from blood, including waste products or toxic chemicals and drugs, or to add substances to blood—for example, bicarbonate ions (HCO_3^-) if the blood is acidic. In the course of a 3- to 6-hour hemodialysis, 50–250 g of urea can be

BIOLOGY TODAY ▶ **Health**

Urinary Difficulties Due to an Enlarged Prostate

The prostate gland, part of the male reproductive system, surrounds the urethra at the point where the urethra leaves the urinary bladder (Fig. 11C). The prostate gland produces and adds a fluid to semen as semen passes through the urethra within the penis. At about age 50, the prostate gland often begins to enlarge, growing from the size of a walnut to that of a lime or even a lemon. This condition is called benign prostatic hyperplasia (BPH). As it enlarges, the prostate squeezes the urethra, causing urine to back up—first into the bladder, then into the ureters, and finally, perhaps, into the kidneys. While BPH is technically a disorder of the reproductive system, its symptoms are almost exclusively associated with urination and excretion, and therefore it is often discussed as a urinary system disorder.

Treatment Emphasis Is on Early Detection

The treatment for BPH can involve (1) invasive procedures to reduce the size of the prostate or (2) medications that shrink the prostate and/or improve urine flow. For the former, prostate tissue can be destroyed by applying microwaves to a specific portion of the gland. In some cases, a physician may decide to surgically remove that prostate tissue. This may be accomplished by abdominal surgery, which requires an incision of the abdomen, or access to the prostate via the urethra. This operation, called transurethral resection of the prostate (TURP), requires careful consideration, because one study found that the death rate during the 5 years following TURP is much higher than that following abdominal surgery.

Some drug treatments recognize that prostate enlargement is due to a prostate enzyme (5-alpha-reductase) that acts on the male sex hormone testosterone, converting it into a substance that promotes prostate growth. Growth is fine during puberty, but continued growth in an adult is undesirable. These drugs contain substances that interfere with the action of the enzyme that promotes growth. One of the ingredients is an extract from a plant called the saw palmetto. It is particularly effective during the early stages of prostate enlargement. While it is sold in tablet form as an over-the-counter nutrient supplement, it should not be taken unless the need for it is confirmed by a physician. The prescription drugs finasteride (Propecia) and dutasteride (Avodart) are more powerful inhibitors of the same growth enzyme, but patients complain of erectile dysfunction and loss of libido while on the drugs.

Another common treatment for BPH involves the use of alpha-blockers, such as tamsulosin (Flomax). Alpha-blockers target specific receptors (called α-adrenergic receptors) on the surface of smooth muscle tissue. Tamsulosin inhibits the interaction of the nervous system with the smooth muscle, causing it to relax and promote urine flow. Similarly, drugs such as tadalafil (Cialis) inhibit an enzyme called phosphodiesterase type 5 (PDE5) in smooth muscle tissue, causing it to relax. Like tamsulosin, the use of tadalafil causes the relaxation of the prostate, enhancing the flow of urine.

Many men are concerned that BPH may be associated with prostate cancer, but the two conditions are not necessarily related. BPH occurs in the inner zone of the prostate, whereas cancer tends to develop in the outer area. If prostate cancer is suspected, blood tests and a biopsy, in which a tiny sample of prostate tissue is surgically removed, will confirm the diagnosis.

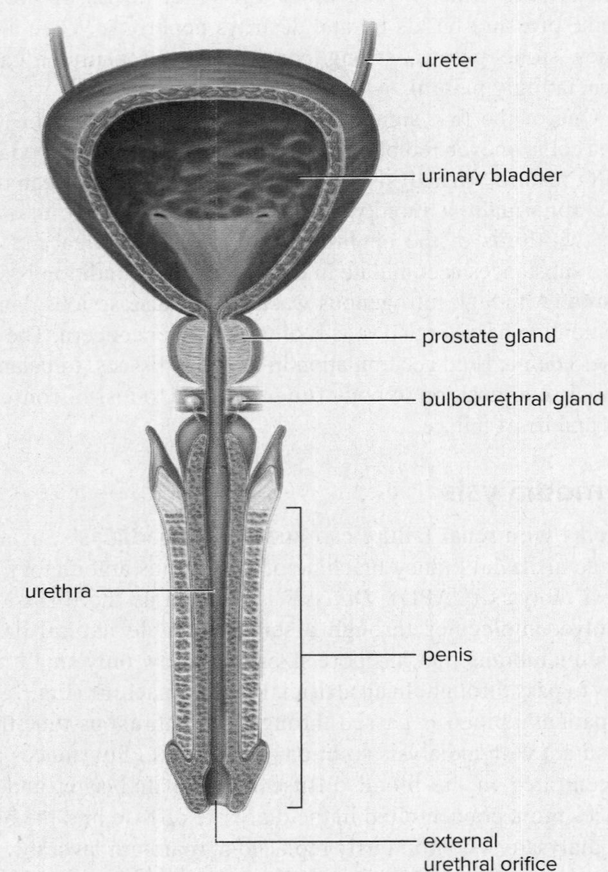

Figure 11C Location of the prostate gland.
Note the position of the prostate gland, which can enlarge to obstruct urine flow.

Enlarged Prostate and Cancer

Although prostate cancer is the second most common cancer in men, it is not a major killer. Typically, prostate cancer is so slow growing that the survival rate is about 98% if the condition is detected early.

Questions to Consider

1. What is the role of the prostate in the male reproductive system?
2. Given how alpha-blockers function, what other applications might they have in humans?

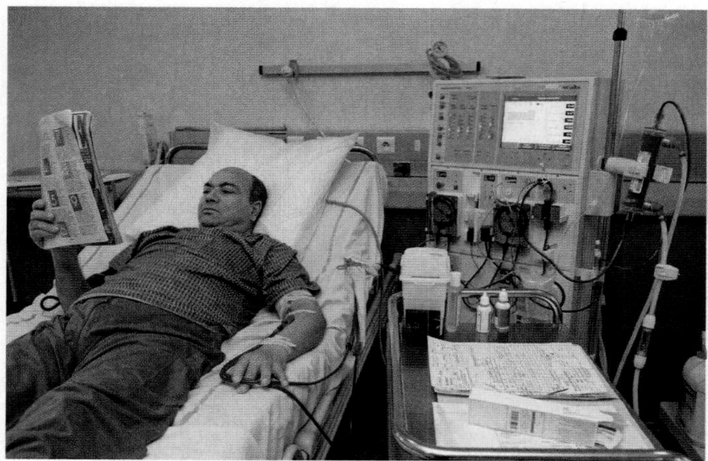

Figure 11.12 Hemodialysis using an artificial kidney machine.

As the patient's blood is pumped through dialysis tubing, it is exposed to a dialysate (dialysis solution). Wastes exit from blood into the solution because of a preestablished concentration gradient. In this way, not only is blood cleansed but its water-salt and acid-base balances can also be adjusted.

BSIP SA/Alamy Stock Photo

removed from a patient, which greatly exceeds the amount excreted by normal kidneys. Therefore, a patient needs to undergo treatment only about twice a week.

CAPD is so named because the peritoneum is the dialysis membrane. A fresh amount of dialysate is introduced directly into the abdominal cavity from a bag that is temporarily attached to a permanently implanted plastic tube. The dialysate flows into the peritoneal cavity by gravity. Waste and salt molecules pass from the blood vessels in the abdominal wall into the dialysate before the fluid is collected 4 to 8 hours later. The solution is drained into a bag from the abdominal cavity by gravity, and then it is discarded. One advantage of CAPD over an artificial kidney machine is that the individual can go about normal activities during CAPD.

Replacing a Kidney

Patients with renal failure sometimes undergo a kidney transplant operation, during which a functioning kidney from a donor is received. As with all organ transplants, there is the possibility of organ rejection. Receiving a kidney from a close relative has the highest chance of success. The current 1-year survival rate is 97% if the kidney is received from a relative and 90% if it is received from a nonrelative. In the future, transplantable kidneys may be created in a laboratory. Another option could be to use kidneys from specially bred pigs whose organs would not be antigenic to humans.

CHECK YOUR PROGRESS 11.5

1. List and detail a few common causes of renal disease.
2. Provide examples of diseases associated with the urinary tract and kidneys.
3. Explain why hemodialysis would need to be done frequently in a patient with renal failure.

CONNECTING THE CONCEPTS

For more information on organ transplants, refer to the following discussions:

Section 5.7 describes the options available for individuals experiencing heart failure.

Section 7.5 examines how the immune system potentially interferes with organ transplants.

Section 20.4 provides an overview of how bone marrow transplants can be used to treat cancer.

CONCLUSION

In this chapter, we explored the structure and function of the urinary system and its central role in homeostasis. We also examined the role of the kidneys in filtering the blood and the production of urine. This filtering does prevent the release of glucose and other valuable nutrients, which may support bacterial growth, into the urine. However, contrary to popular belief, the process does not guarantee the urine is sterile, because it may contain bacteria that are part of the normal biota of the human body.

SUMMARIZE

11.1 The Urinary System

The **urinary system** maintains the salt, water, and pH homeostasis of the body through **excretion** of waste materials.

Functions of the Urinary System

The functions of the urinary system include the following:

- Excreting nitrogenous wastes, including **urea, uric acid,** and **creatinine.** Elevated levels of urea result in **uremia,** while increased levels of uric acid cause **gout.**
- Maintaining the normal water-salt balance of the blood.
- Maintaining the acid-base balance of the blood.
- Assisting the endocrine system in hormone secretion by secreting erythropoietin (EPO) and releasing renin and aldosterone.

Organs of the Urinary System

- **Kidneys** produce urine. **Renal arteries** and **renal veins** transport blood to and from the kidneys.
- **Ureters** transport urine to the bladder.

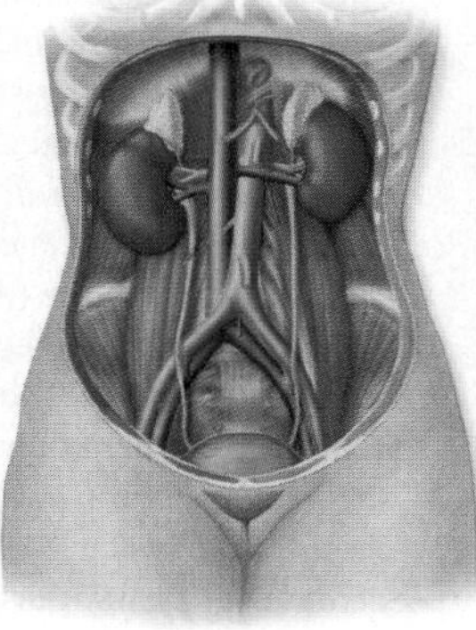

- The **urinary bladder** stores urine.
- The **urethra** releases urine to the outside.

11.2 Kidney Structure

- Macroscopic structures are the **renal cortex, renal medulla,** and **renal pelvis.**
- Microscopic structures are the **nephrons.**

The Nephron

- Each nephron has its own blood supply. The afferent arteriole divides to become the **glomerulus.** The efferent arteriole branches into the **peritubular capillary network.**
- Each region of the nephron is anatomically suited to its task in urine formation. The **glomerular capsule** begins the filtration of the blood. **Proximal convoluted tubules** are involved in the reabsorption of filtrates. The **loop of the nephron** facilitates the reabsorption of water, and the **distal convoluted tubule** is involved in ion exchange.
- The **collecting ducts** of the nephrons move urine to the renal pelvis, where it enters the ureters.

11.3 Urine Formation

Urine is composed primarily of nitrogenous waste products and salts in water. The steps in urine formation include the following:

Glomerular Filtration

Glomerular filtration separates the filterable and nonfilterable components of the blood. Water, salts, nutrients, and wastes move from the glomerulus to the inside of the glomerular capsule. The **glomerular filtrate** contains the filterable components.

Tubular Reabsorption

Tubular reabsorption reabsorbs ions and other molecules from the nephron into the blood. Nutrients and salt molecules are reabsorbed from the convoluted tubules into the peritubular capillary network; water follows. In **diabetes mellitus,** tubular reabsorption is unable to completely reabsorb the excess glucose, and some is excreted in the urine.

Tubular Secretion

Tubular secretion actively transports certain molecules from the peritubular capillary network into the convoluted tubules.

11.4 Kidneys and Homeostasis

- The kidneys maintain the water-salt balance of blood using transport channels called **aquaporins.**
- The kidneys also keep blood pH within normal limits.
- The urinary system works with the other systems of the body to maintain homeostasis.

Water-Salt Balance

- If blood volume falls, the **juxtaglomerular apparatus** releases **renin,** which in turn influences the production of aldosterone.
- In the renal cortex, most of the reabsorption of salts and water occurs in the proximal convoluted tubule. **Aldosterone** controls the reabsorption of sodium, and **antidiuretic hormone (ADH)** controls the reabsorption of water in the distal convoluted tubule. **Atrial natriuretic hormone (ANH)** acts contrary to aldosterone.
- In the renal medulla, the ascending limb of the loop of the nephron establishes a solute gradient that increases toward the inner medulla. The solute gradient draws water from the descending limb of the loop of the nephron and from the collecting duct. When ADH is present, more water is reabsorbed from the collecting duct and a decreased amount of urine results.
- **Diuretics** in the diet (e.g., caffeine) increase the flow of urine from the body.

Acid-Base Balance of Body Fluids

- The kidneys maintain the acid-base balance of the blood (blood pH). **Alkalosis** occurs when the blood pH is above 7.45, whereas **acidosis** represents a blood pH below 7.35.
- **Buffers** help maintain blood pH at about 7.4. Ammonia buffers H^+ in the urine.

11.5 Urinary System Disorders

- Various types of problems, including diabetes, kidney stones, and infections, can lead to renal failure, which necessitates either hemodialysis—by using a kidney machine or CAPD—or a kidney transplant.
- **Urethritis, cystitis,** and **pyelonephritis** are infections of the urethra, urinary bladder, and kidneys, respectively.
- During kidney failure, **hemodialysis** may be needed to perform the normal functions of the kidneys.

ENGAGE

THINKING CRITICALLY

1. High blood pressure often is accompanied by kidney damage. In some people, the kidney damage is subsequent to the high blood pressure, but in others the kidney damage is what caused the high blood pressure. How would a low-salt diet enable you to determine whether the high blood pressure or the kidney damage came first?
2. A form of diabetes that may be unfamiliar to most people is diabetes insipidus. When the word *diabetes* is used, everyone tends to think of the type related to insulin. That form of diabetes is diabetes mellitus, which can be type 1 or type 2. In diabetes insipidus, the kidneys are unable to perform their function of water and salt homeostasis due to a lack of ADH in the body. In both types of diabetes, kidney function is affected. Why would frequent urination be a symptom of both diabetes mellitus and diabetes insipidus?
3. Many men who have prostate cancer have some or all of the prostate removed. The surgeon tries very hard not to damage the sphincter muscles associated with the bladder. What problem might a man experience if the bladder's sphincter muscles are damaged during the surgery?
4. Recall the anatomical position of the kidneys and consider the ways they might be damaged in sports. Describe equipment designed specifically to protect the kidneys.

MAKING IT RELEVANT

1. Why might extended use of antibiotics for urinary tract infections produce problems for an individual over time?
2. How might an understanding of the bacteria that inhabit our urinary tracts help us in preventing diseases and disorders of this body system?
3. Given what you have learned in this chapter, why do you think physicians regularly order a urinalysis? What do these results tell them about the overall health of the individual?

Find answers to all of the chapter questions at connect.mheducation.com

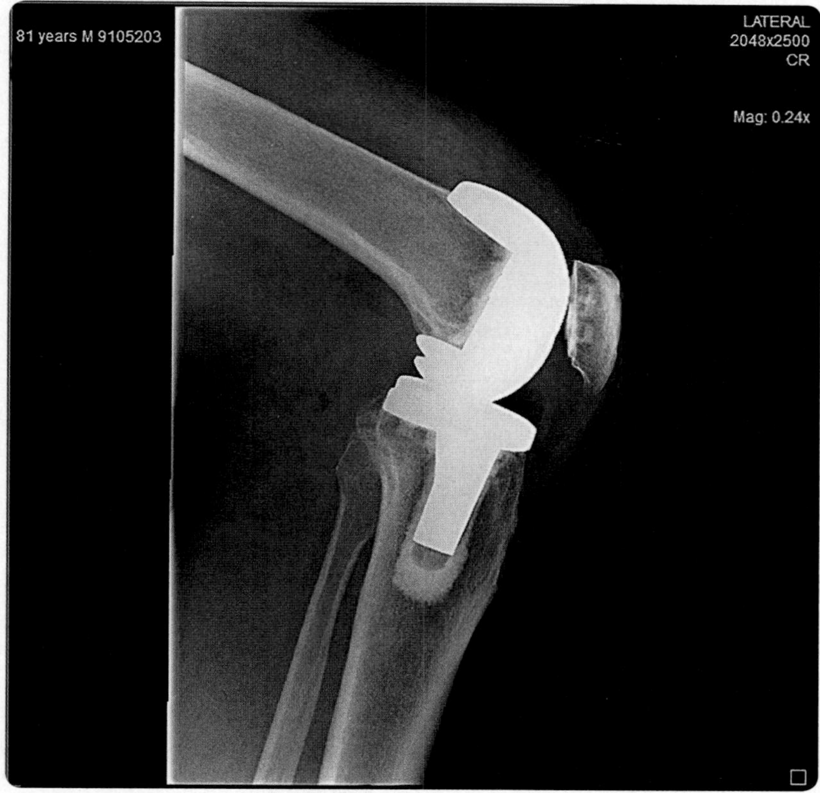

GSO Images/Photographer's Choice RF/Getty Images

CHAPTER 12

Skeletal System

Knee Replacement Surgery

Over time, our joints take a tremendous beating. Physical activity, such as running and sporting activities, while vital for our health, can place tremendous strain on knees, hips, and elbows. Also, as we age, the ability of our bodies to regenerate cartilage, the shock absorbers of the skeletal system, decreases. Furthermore, as we age, there is a general tendency to gain weight as our metabolism slows. For every 10 pounds of weight we gain, we place 30 pounds of additional stress on our knees. Over time, the result may be osteoarthritis, or a breakdown of the cartilage that lines these joints.

Although it sounds drastic, replacing old, arthritic joints with new, artificial ones is becoming increasingly routine. Almost 4 million Americans, and 1 in 20 individuals over the age of 50, have undergone either partial or total knee replacement surgery. During the procedure, a surgeon removes bone from the bottom of the femur and the top of the tibia and replaces each with caps made of metal or ceramic, held in place with bone cement. A plastic plate is installed to allow the femur and tibia to move smoothly against each other, and a smaller plate is attached to the kneecap (patella), so it can function properly.

In this chapter, we will explore the structure and function of the skeletal system and the joints that connect the bones of our body to allow for movement.

As you read through the chapter, think about the following questions:

1. What is the role of cartilage in the knee joint?
2. What specific portions of these long bones are being removed during knee replacement?

CHAPTER OUTLINE

BEFORE YOU BEGIN

Before beginning this chapter, take a few moments to review the following discussions:

Section 4.1 What is the role of connective tissue in the body?

Section 4.8 How does the skeletal system contribute to homeostasis?

Section 9.6 What are the roles of calcium and vitamin D in the body?

12.1 Overview of the Skeletal System

LEARNING OUTCOMES

Upon completion of this section, you should be able to

1. State the functions of the skeletal system.
2. Describe the structure of a long bone and list the types of tissues it contains.
3. List the three types of cartilage found in the body and provide a function for each.

The **skeletal system** provides attachment sites for the muscles, whose contraction makes the bones move so we can walk, play sports, send a text message, and perform all sorts of other daily activities. The skeletal system consists of two types of connective tissue: bone and the cartilage found at the **joints,** which is the point where two bones come together, and **ligaments,** formed of fibrous connective tissue, which join the bones. **Tendons** connect muscle to bones. In this chapter, we discuss the structure and function of the skeletal system. In Chapter 13, we will explore the muscular system in detail.

Functions of the Skeleton

The skeleton does more than merely provide a frame for the body. In addition, it has the following functions:

- *Support.* The bones of the legs support the entire body when we are standing, and bones of the pelvic girdle support the abdominal cavity.
- *Movement.* The skeletal system works with the muscular system to provide movement.
- *Protection.* The bones of the skull protect the brain; the rib cage protects the heart and lungs; and the vertebrae protect the spinal cord, which makes nervous connections to all the muscles of the limbs.
- *Production of blood cells.* The skeleton plays an important role in the formation of blood. In the fetus, all bones have red bone marrow to produce new blood cells. However, in adults, only certain bones produce blood cells.
- *Storage of minerals and fat.* All bones have a matrix that contains calcium phosphate, a source of calcium ions and phosphate ions in the blood. Fat is stored in yellow bone marrow.

BIOLOGY IN YOUR LIFE

Does everyone have the same number of bones?

A newborn has nearly 300 bones, some of which fuse together as the child grows. The adult human skeleton has approximately 206 bones, but the number varies between individuals. Some people have extra bones, called Wormian bones, which help fuse skull bones together. Others may have additional small bones in their ankles and feet.

Anatomy of a Long Bone

The bones of the body vary greatly in size and shape. To better understand the anatomy of a bone, we will use a long bone (Fig. 12.1), a type of bone common in the arms and legs. The shaft, or main portion of the bone, is called the *diaphysis.* The diaphysis

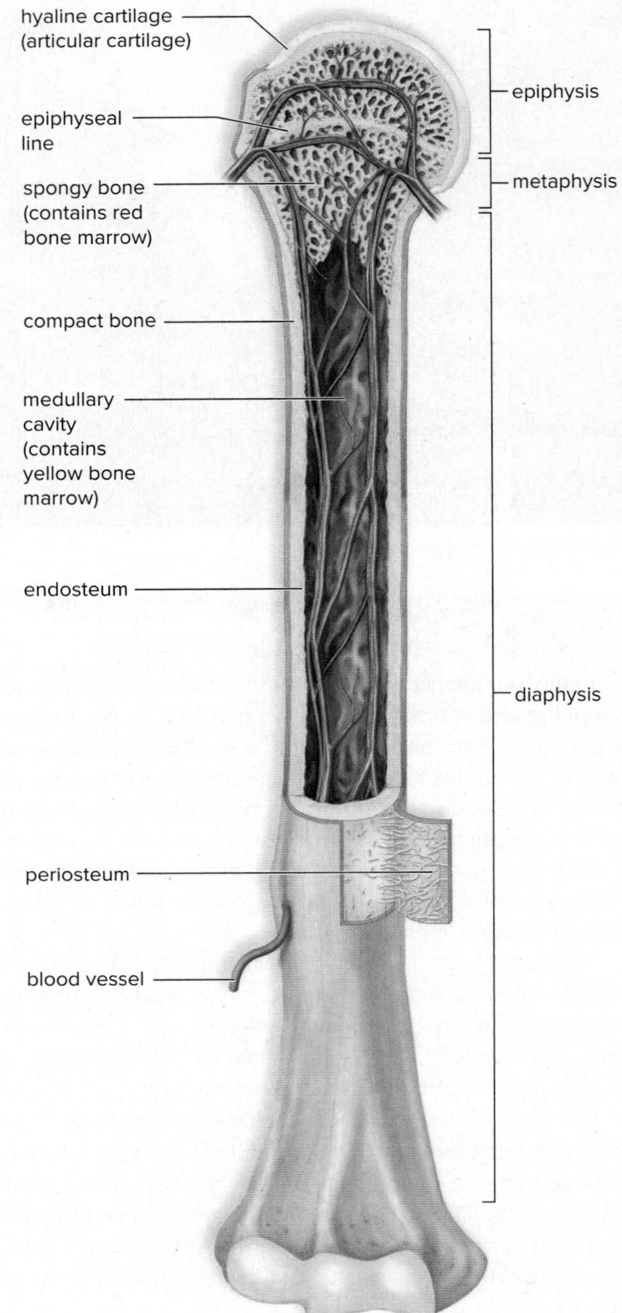

Figure 12.1 **The anatomy of a long bone.**
A long bone is formed of an outer layer of compact bone. The central shaft of a long bone contains yellow marrow, a form of stored fat. Periosteum, a fibrous membrane, encases the bone except at its ends, which are covered by hyaline cartilage.

has a large *medullary cavity,* whose walls are composed of compact bone. The medullary cavity is lined with a thin, vascular membrane (the *endosteum*) and is filled with yellow bone marrow, which stores fat.

The expanded region at the end of a long bone is called an *epiphysis* (*pl.,* epiphyses). The epiphyses are separated from the diaphyses by a small region of mature bone called the *metaphysis,* which contain the *epiphyseal plate,* a region of cartilage that allows for bone growth.

The epiphyses are composed largely of spongy bone that contains red bone marrow, where blood cells are made. The epiphyses are coated with a thin layer of hyaline cartilage, which is also called articular cartilage because it occurs at a joint.

Except for the articular cartilage on the bone's ends, a long bone is completely covered by a layer of fibrous connective tissue called the *periosteum.* This covering contains blood vessels, lymphatic vessels, and nerves. Note in Figure 12.1 how a blood vessel penetrates the periosteum and enters the bone. Branches of the blood vessel are found throughout the medullary cavity. Other branches can be found in hollow cylinders called central canals within the bone tissue. The periosteum is continuous with ligaments and tendons connected to a bone.

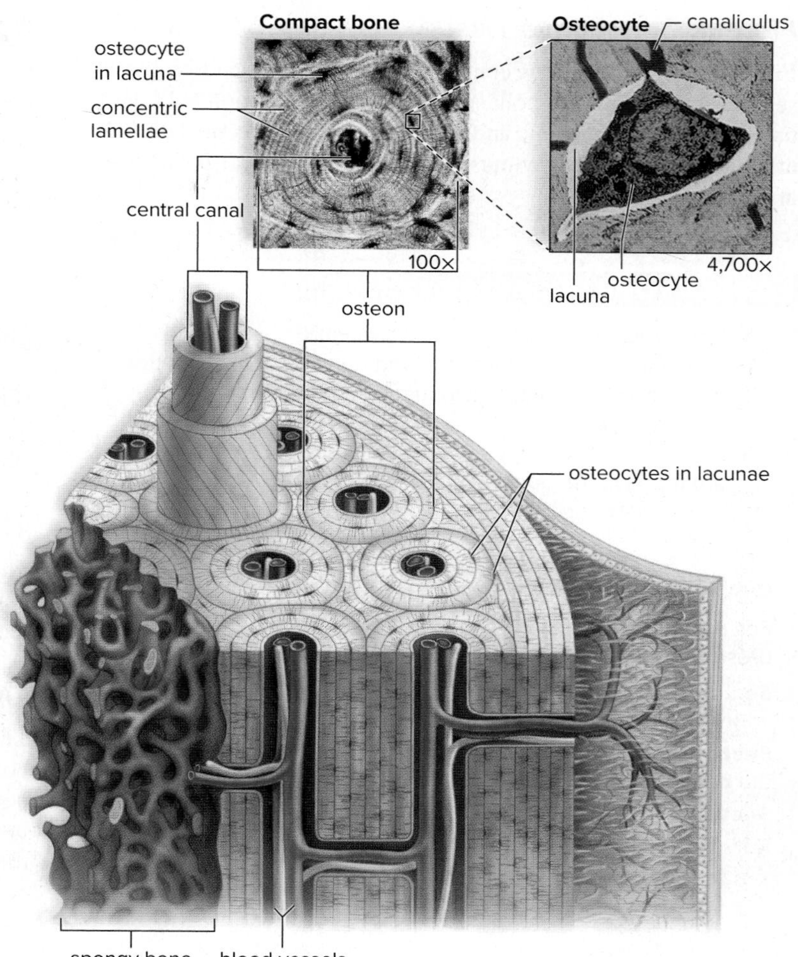

Figure 12.2 **Anatomy of compact bone.**
Compact bone is composed of cylinder-shaped structures called osteons, which contain osteocytes.
(photos) (compact bone): Ed Reschke; (osteocyte): Biophoto Associates/Science Source

Bone

Compact bone is highly organized and composed of tubular units called osteons (Fig. 12.2). In a cross-section of an osteon, bone cells called **osteocytes** lie in **lacunae** (*sing.,* lacuna), tiny chambers arranged in concentric circles around a central canal (Fig. 12.1). Matrix fills the space between the rows of lacunae. Tiny canals called *canaliculi* (*sing.,* canaliculus) run through the matrix. These canaliculi connect the lacunae with one another and with the central canal. The cells stay in contact by strands of cytoplasm that extend into the canaliculi. Osteocytes nearest the center of an osteon exchange nutrients and wastes with the blood vessels in the central canal. These cells then pass on nutrients and collect wastes from the other cells via gap junctions (see Fig. 3.17).

Compared with compact bone, **spongy bone** has an unorganized appearance (Fig. 12.2). It contains numerous thin plates, called *trabeculae,* separated by unequal spaces. Although this makes spongy bone lighter than compact bone, spongy bone is still designed for strength. Just as braces are used for support in buildings, the trabeculae follow lines of stress. The spaces of spongy bone are often filled with **red bone marrow,** a specialized tissue that produces all types of blood cells. The osteocytes of spongy bone are irregularly placed within the trabeculae. Canaliculi bring them nutrients from the red bone marrow.

Cartilage

Cartilage is not as strong as bone, but it is more flexible. Its matrix is gel-like and contains many collagenous and elastic fibers. The cells, called **chondrocytes,** lie within lacunae that are irregularly grouped. Cartilage has no nerves, making it well suited for padding joints where the stresses of movement are intense. Cartilage also has no blood vessels and relies on neighboring tissues for nutrient and waste exchange. This makes it slow to heal.

The three types of cartilage differ according to the type and arrangement of fibers in the matrix. *Hyaline cartilage* is firm and somewhat flexible. The matrix appears uniform and glassy, but actually it contains a generous supply of collagen fibers. Hyaline cartilage is found at the ends of long bones, in the nose, at the ends of the ribs, and in the larynx and trachea.

Fibrocartilage is stronger than hyaline cartilage because the matrix contains wide rows of thick, collagenous fibers. Fibrocartilage is able to withstand both tension and pressure and is found where support is of prime importance—in the discs between the vertebrae and in the cartilage of the knee.

Elastic cartilage is more flexible than hyaline cartilage, because the matrix contains mostly elastin fibers. This type of cartilage is found in the ear flaps and the epiglottis.

Fibrous Connective Tissue

Fibrous connective tissue contains rows of cells called fibroblasts separated by bundles of collagenous fibers (see Section 4.2). This tissue makes up ligaments and tendons. Ligaments connect bones at joints. Tendons connect muscle to bone at a joint (also called an articulation).

CHECK YOUR PROGRESS 12.1

1. List the functions of the skeletal system.
2. Summarize the structure of a long bone by describing the differences in structure and function of compact and spongy bone.
3. Describe the three types of cartilage and list where they are found in the body.

CONNECTING THE CONCEPTS

For a better understanding of the types of connective tissue presented in this section, refer to the following discussions:

Section 4.2 examines the general structure and function of the connective tissues of the body.

Section 6.1 provides an overview of the blood cells formed in the bone marrow.

Section 13.1 provides additional information on the function of tendons in the body.

12.2 Bones of the Axial Skeleton

LEARNING OUTCOMES

Upon completion of this section, you should be able to

1. Identify the bones of the skull, hyoid, vertebral column, and rib cage.
2. Identify the regions of the vertebral column.
3. Explain the function of the sinuses and intervertebral discs.

The 206 bones of the skeleton are classified according to whether they occur in the axial skeleton or the appendicular skeleton (Fig. 12.3). The **axial skeleton** lies in the midline of the body and consists of the skull, hyoid bone, vertebral column, and rib cage.

The Skull

The **skull** is formed by the cranium (braincase) and the facial bones. However, some cranial bones contribute to the structure of the face.

The Cranium

The cranium protects the brain. In adults, it is composed of eight bones fitted tightly together. In newborns, certain cranial bones are not completely formed. Instead, these bones are joined by membranous regions called **fontanels.** The fontanels usually close by the age of 16 months (see Section 12.5).

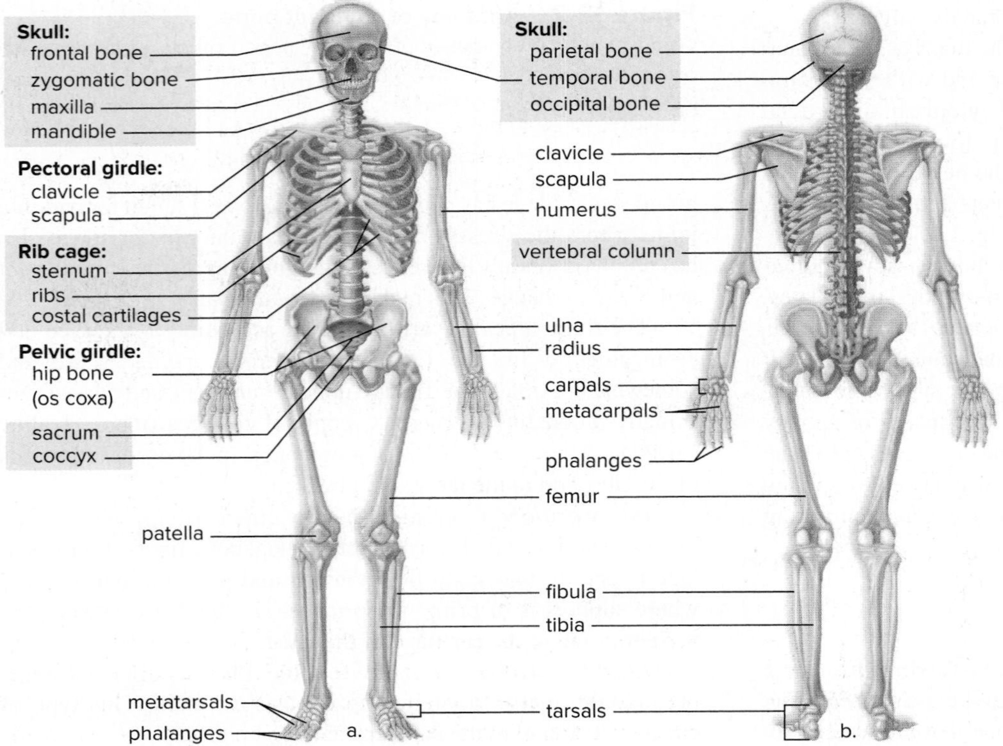

Figure 12.3 **The axial and appendicular skeletons.** Axial skeleton bones are colored blue. Bones of the appendicular skeleton are tan. **a.** Frontal view. **b.** Dorsal view.

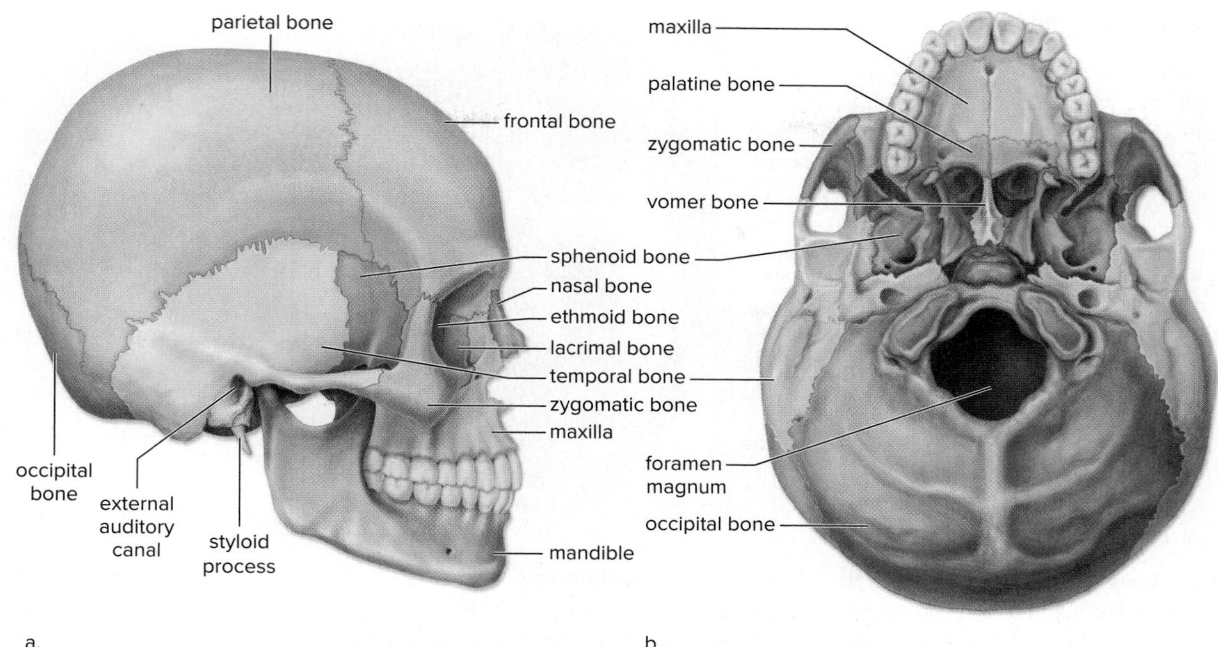

Figure 12.4 The bones of the skull.
a. Lateral view. **b.** Inferior view.

The major bones of the cranium have the same names as the lobes of the brain: frontal, parietal, occipital, and temporal. On the top of the cranium (Fig. 12.4*a*), the *frontal bone* forms the forehead, the *parietal bones* extend to the sides, and the *occipital bone* curves to form the base of the skull. Here, there is a large opening, the **foramen magnum** (Fig. 12.4*b*), through which the spinal cord passes. Below the much larger parietal bones, each *temporal bone* has an opening (external auditory canal) that leads to the middle ear.

The *sphenoid bone,* shaped like a bat with outstretched wings, extends across the floor of the cranium from one side to the other. The sphenoid is the keystone of the cranial bones, because all the other bones articulate with it. The sphenoid completes the sides of the skull and contributes to forming the orbits (eye sockets). The *ethmoid bone,* which lies in front of the sphenoid, also helps form the orbits and the nasal septum. The orbits are completed by various facial bones. The eye sockets are called orbits because we can rotate our eyes.

Some of the bones of the cranium contain the **sinuses,** air spaces lined by mucous membrane. The sinuses reduce the weight of the skull and give a resonant sound to the voice. Sinuses are named according to the bones in which they are located. The major sinuses are the frontal, sphenoid, ethmoid, and maxillary. A smaller set of sinuses, called the mastoid sinuses, drain into the middle ear. *Mastoiditis,* a condition that can lead to deafness, is an inflammation of these sinuses.

The Facial Bones

The most prominent of the facial bones are the mandible, the maxillae (*sing.,* maxilla), the zygomatic bones, and the nasal bones.

The mandible, or lower jaw, is the only movable portion of the skull, and it forms the chin (Fig. 12.4 and Fig. 12.5). The maxillae form the upper jaw and a portion of the eye socket. Further, the hard palate and the floor of the nose are formed by the maxillae (anterior) joined to the palatine bones (posterior). Tooth sockets are located on the mandible and on the maxillae. The grinding action of the mandible and maxillae allows us to chew our food.

The lips and cheeks have a core of skeletal muscle. The *zygomatic bones* form the cheekbone prominences, and the *nasal bones* form the bridge of the nose. Other bones (e.g., ethmoid and vomer) are a part of the nasal septum, which divides the interior of the nose into two nasal cavities. The lacrimal bone (see Fig. 12.4*a*) contains the opening for the nasolacrimal canal, which drains tears from the eyes to the nose.

Certain cranial bones contribute to the face. The temporal bone and the wings of the sphenoid bone account for the flattened areas we call the temples. The frontal bone forms the forehead and has supraorbital ridges, where the eyebrows are located. Glasses sit where the frontal bone joins the nasal bones.

The exterior portions of ears are formed only by cartilage and not by bone. The nose is a mixture of bones, cartilages, and connective tissues. The cartilages complete the tip of the nose, and fibrous connective tissue forms the flared sides of the nose.

The Hyoid Bone

The *hyoid bone* is not part of the skull but is mentioned here because it is a part of the axial skeleton. It is the only bone in the body that does not articulate with another bone (Fig. 12.5*c*). It is attached to the temporal bones by muscles and ligaments and to the

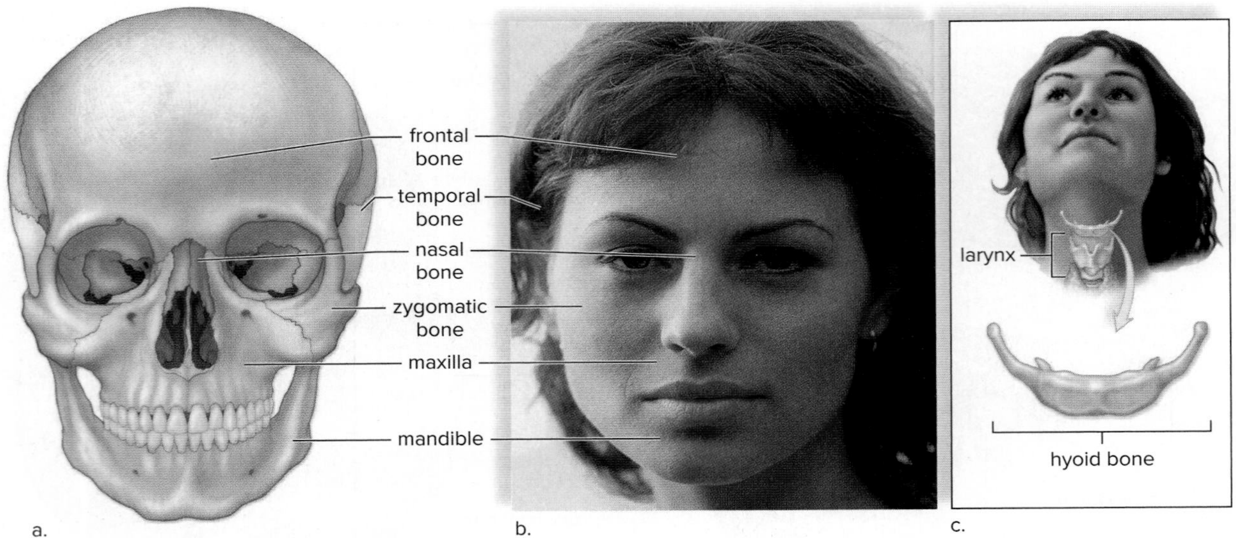

Figure 12.5 **The bones of the face and the location of the hyoid bone.**
a. The frontal bone forms the forehead and eyebrow ridges; the zygomatic bones form the cheekbones; and the maxillae have numerous functions. They assist in the formation of the eye sockets and the nasal cavity. They form the upper jaw and contain sockets for the upper teeth. The mandible is the lower jaw with sockets for the lower teeth. The mandible has a projection we call the chin. **b.** The maxillae, frontal, and nasal bones help form the external nose. **c.** The hyoid bone is located as shown.
(b, c): VCG/Corbis/Getty Images

larynx (see Fig. 10.1) by a membrane. The hyoid bone anchors the tongue and serves as the site for the attachment of muscles associated with swallowing. Due to its position, the hyoid bone does not fracture easily. In cases of a suspicious death, however, a fractured hyoid is a strong indication of manual strangulation.

The Vertebral Column

The **vertebral column** consists of 33 vertebrae (Fig. 12.6). These are named by their region and by number. Normally, the vertebral column has four curvatures that provide more resilience and strength for an upright posture than a straight column could provide. *Scoliosis* is an abnormal lateral (sideways) curvature of the spine. There are two other well-known abnormal curvatures. *Kyphosis* is an abnormal posterior curvature that often results in a "hunchback." An abnormal anterior curvature results in *lordosis,* or "swayback."

As the individual vertebrae are layered on top of one another, they form the vertebral column. The vertebral canal is in the center of the column, and the spinal cord passes through this canal. The *intervertebral foramina* (*sing.,* foramen, "a hole or opening") are found on each side of the column. Spinal nerves branch from the spinal cord and travel through the intervertebral foramina to locations throughout the body. Spinal nerves control skeletal muscle contraction, among other functions. If a vertebra is compressed, or slips out of position, the spinal cord and/or spinal nerves might be injured. The result can be paralysis or even death.

The *spinous processes* of the vertebrae can be felt as bony projections along the midline of the back. The *transverse processes* extend laterally. Both spinous and transverse processes serve as attachment sites for the muscles that move the vertebral column.

Types of Vertebrae

The various vertebrae are named according to their location in the vertebral column. The cervical vertebrae are located in the neck. The first cervical vertebra, called the *atlas,* holds up the head and allows it to tilt side to side. It is so named because Atlas, of Greek mythology, held up the world. The second cervical vertebra is called the *axis,* because it allows a degree of rotation. The thoracic vertebrae have long, thin spinous processes (Fig. 12.7*a*). The thoracic vertebrae articulate with one another and with the ribs at articular facets. Lumbar vertebrae have large bodies and thick processes. The five sacral vertebrae are fused together in the sacrum. The coccyx, or tailbone, is usually composed of four fused vertebrae.

Intervertebral Discs

Between the vertebrae are **intervertebral discs** composed of fibrocartilage that act as padding. The discs prevent the vertebrae from grinding against one another. They also absorb shock caused by movements such as running, jumping, and even walking. The presence of the discs allows the vertebrae to move as we bend forward, backward, and from side to side. Unfortunately, these discs become weakened with age and can herniate and rupture. Pain results if a disc presses against the spinal cord and/or spinal nerves. If that occurs, surgical removal of the disc may relieve the pain.

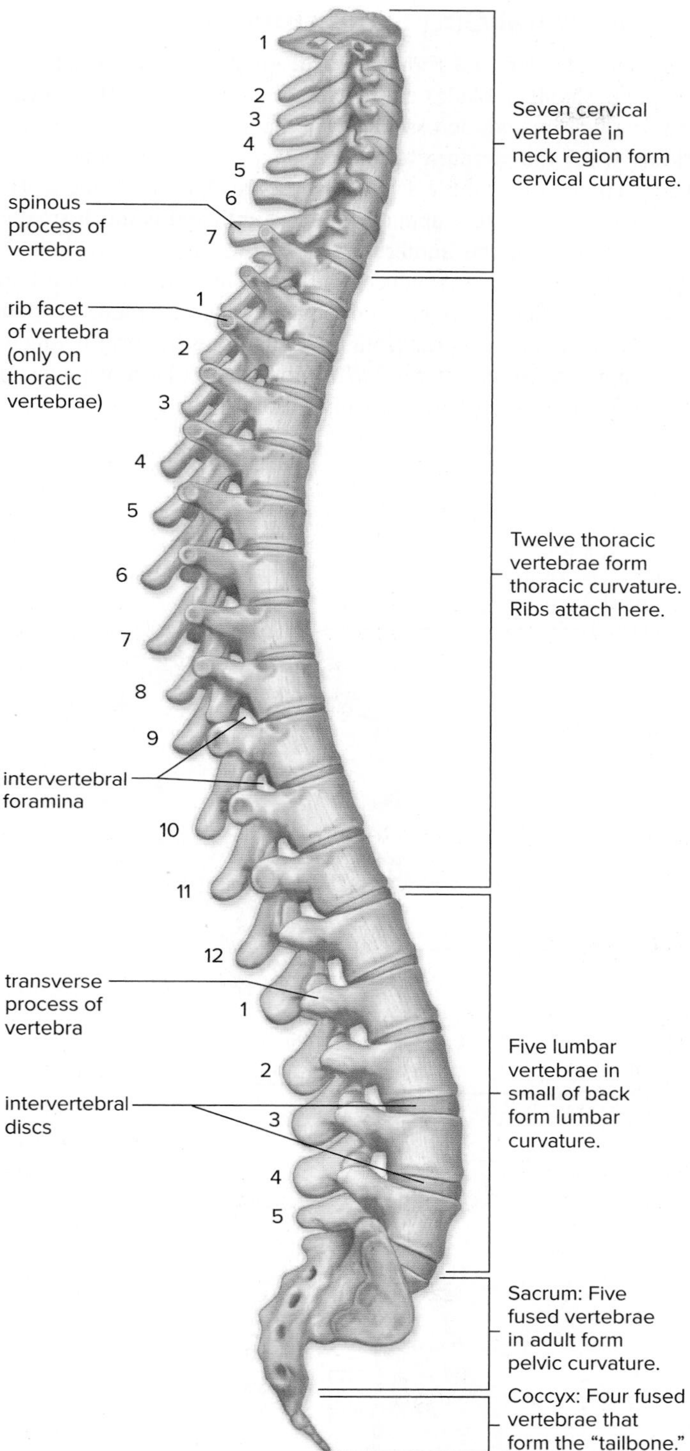

Figure 12.6 **The vertebral column.**
The vertebral column is made up of 33 vertebrae separated by intervertebral discs. The intervertebral discs make the column flexible. The vertebrae are named for their location in the vertebral column. For example, the thoracic vertebrae are located in the thorax. Humans have a coccyx, which is also called a tailbone.

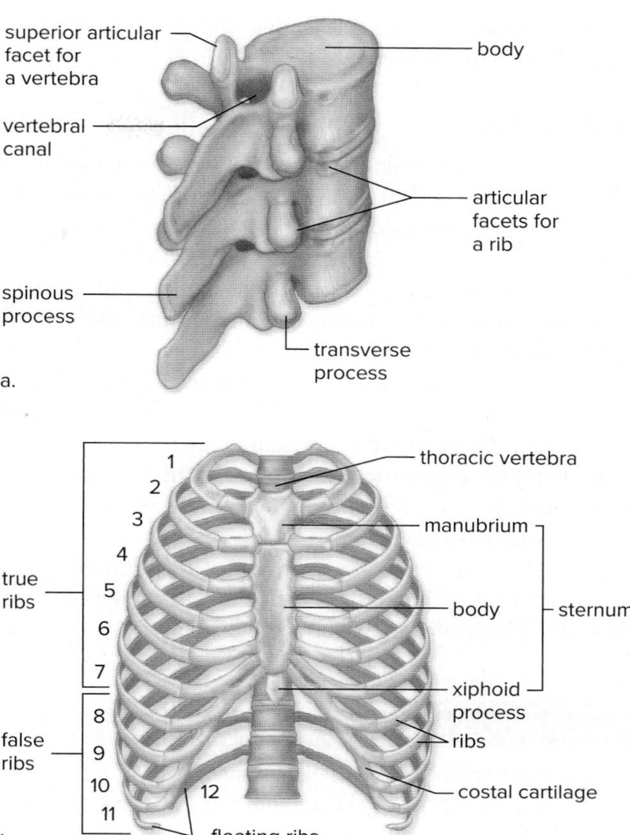

Figure 12.7 **The thoracic vertebrae, ribs, and sternum.**
a. Structure of a thoracic vertebra. **b.** The rib cage consists of the 12 thoracic vertebrae, the 12 pairs of ribs, the costal cartilages, and the sternum. The rib cage protects the lungs and the heart.

The Rib Cage

The rib cage, also called the thoracic cage, is composed of the thoracic vertebrae, the ribs and their associated cartilages, and the sternum (Fig. 12.7*b*). The rib cage is part of the axial skeleton.

The rib cage demonstrates how the skeleton is protective but also flexible. The rib cage protects the heart and lungs, yet it swings outward and upward upon inspiration and then downward and inward upon expiration (see Fig. 10.9).

The Ribs

A rib is a flattened bone that originates at the thoracic vertebrae and proceeds toward the anterior thoracic wall. There are 12 pairs of ribs. All 12 pairs connect directly to the thoracic vertebrae in the back. A rib articulates with the body and transverse process of its corresponding thoracic vertebra. Each rib curves outward and then forward and downward.

The upper seven pairs of ribs (ribs 1 through 7; Fig. 12.7*b*) connect directly to the sternum by means of a long strip of hyaline cartilage called costal cartilage. These are called "true ribs." Ribs 8 through 12 are called "false ribs" because their costal cartilage at the end of the ribs does not connect directly to the sternum.

Ribs 11 and 12 are also called "floating ribs" because they have no connection with the sternum.

The Sternum

The *sternum* lies in the midline of the body. Along with the ribs, it helps protect the heart and lungs. The sternum, or breastbone, is a flat bone that has the shape of a knife.

The sternum is composed of three bones. These bones are the *manubrium* (the handle), the *body* (the blade), and the *xiphoid process* (the point of the blade). The manubrium articulates with the clavicles of the appendicular skeleton. Costal cartilages from the first pair of ribs also join to the manubrium. The manubrium joins with the body of the sternum at an angle. This is an important anatomical landmark, because it occurs at the level of the second rib and therefore allows the ribs to be counted. Counting the ribs is sometimes done to determine where the apex of the heart is located—usually between the fifth and sixth ribs.

The xiphoid process is the third part of the sternum. The variably shaped xiphoid process serves as an attachment site for the diaphragm, which separates the thoracic cavity from the abdominal cavity.

CHECK YOUR PROGRESS 12.2

1. List the bones of the axial skeleton.
2. Identify the bones of the cranium and face, and describe how they contribute to facial features.
3. Describe the various types of vertebrae.

CONNECTING THE CONCEPTS

For more information on the interaction of the axial skeleton with other organ systems in the body, refer to the following discussions:

Section 10.4 examines how the rib cage is involved in respiration.

Section 14.2 details how the vertebral column and skull protect components of the central nervous system.

12.3 Bones of the Appendicular Skeleton

LEARNING OUTCOMES

Upon completion of this section, you should be able to

1. Identify the bones of the pelvic and pectoral girdles.
2. Identify the bones of the upper and lower limbs.

The **appendicular skeleton** consists of the bones within the pectoral and pelvic girdles and their attached limbs. A pectoral (shoulder) girdle and upper limb are specialized for flexibility. The pelvic (hip) girdle and lower limbs are specialized for strength.

The Pectoral Girdle and Upper Limb

The body has left and right **pectoral girdles.** Each consists of a scapula (shoulder blade) and a clavicle (collarbone) (Fig. 12.8). The *clavicle* extends across the top of the thorax. It articulates with (joins with) the sternum and the *scapula,* a visible bone in the back. The muscles of the arm and chest attach to the scapula. The *glenoid cavity* of the scapula articulates with and is much smaller than the head of the humerus. This allows the arm to move in almost any direction but reduces stability. This is the joint most apt to dislocate. Ligaments and tendons stabilize this joint. Tendons that extend to the humerus from four small muscles originating on the scapula form the *rotator cuff.* Vigorous circular movements of the arm can lead to rotator cuff injuries.

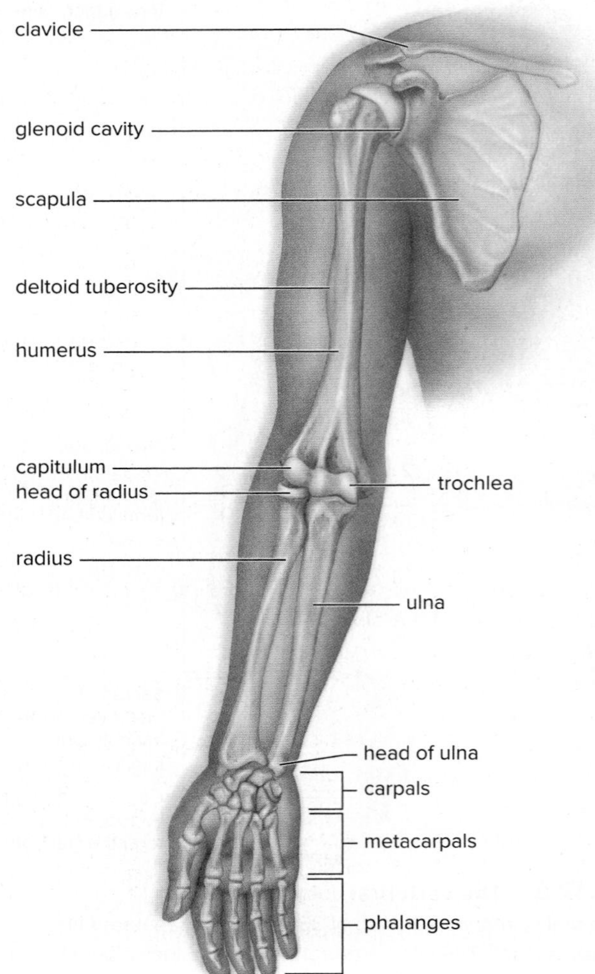

Figure 12.8 The bones of the pectoral girdle and upper limb. The pectoral girdle consists of the clavicle and the scapula. The humerus is the single bone of the arm. The forearm is formed by the radius and ulna. A hand contains carpals, metacarpals, and phalanges.

Pectoral girdle

- Scapula and clavicle

Upper limb

- Upper arm: humerus
- Forearm: radius and ulna
- Hand: carpals, metacarpals, and phalanges

The components of a pectoral girdle freely follow the movements of the upper limb, which consists of the humerus in the upper arm and the radius and ulna in the forearm. The *humerus* has a smoothly rounded head that fits into the glenoid cavity of the scapula, as mentioned. The shaft of the humerus has a tuberosity (protuberance) where the deltoid, a shoulder muscle, attaches. You can determine, even after death, whether the person did a lot of heavy lifting over their lifetime by the size of the deltoid tuberosity. The far end of the humerus has two protuberances that articulate respectively with the *radius* and the *ulna* at the elbow.

When the upper limb is held so that the palm is turned forward, the radius and ulna are about parallel to each other. When the upper limb is turned so that the palm is turned backward, the radius crosses in front of the ulna, a feature that contributes to the easy twisting motion of the forearm.

The hand has many bones, and this increases its flexibility. The wrist has eight *carpal* bones, which look like small pebbles. From these, five *metacarpal* bones fan out to form a framework for the palm. The metacarpal bone that leads to the thumb is opposable to the other digits. (The term *digits* refers to either fingers or toes.) An opposable thumb can touch each finger separately or cross the palm to grasp an object. The knuckles are the enlarged distal ends of the metacarpals. Beyond the metacarpals are the *phalanges,* the bones of the fingers and the thumb. The phalanges of the hand are long, slender, and lightweight.

BIOLOGY IN YOUR LIFE

Why are human toes shorter than fingers?

Though some scientists believe that toes are an example of a vestigial organ, there is growing evidence that short toes played an important role in our evolutionary history. According to some scientists, the shortness of our toes contributes to our ability to run long distances, a rare trait in the animal kingdom. Studies have shown that long toes require more energy to start and stop running. In most animals with toes, the fingers and toes are approximately the same length. As toe length shortens, the ability of the animal to run long distances increases. The shortness of our toes may have contributed to the success of our species in hunting large prey on the open plains of Africa.

The Pelvic Girdle and Lower Limb

Figure 12.9 shows how the lower limb is attached to the pelvic girdle. The **pelvic girdle** (hip girdle) consists of two heavy, large *hip bones,* also known as os coxa. The **pelvis** is a basin composed of the pelvic girdle, sacrum, and coccyx. The pelvis bears the weight of the body, protects the organs within the pelvic cavity, and serves as the place of attachment for the legs.

Each hip bone has three parts: the ilium, the ischium, and the pubis, which are fused in the adult (Fig. 12.9). The hip socket, called the *acetabulum,* is where these three bones meet. The *ilium* is the largest part of the hip bones. We sit on the *ischium,* which has a posterior spine for muscle attachment. The *pubis,* from which the term *pubic hair* is derived, is the anterior part of a hip bone. The two pubic bones are joined by a fibrocartilaginous joint called the *pubic symphysis.*

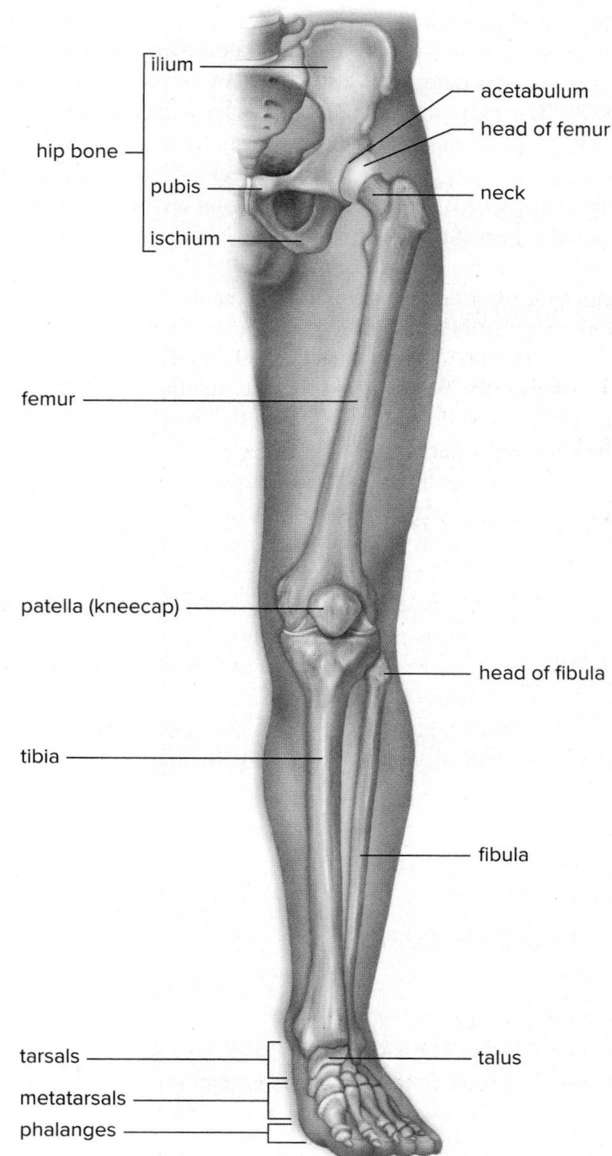

Figure 12.9 The bones of the pelvis and lower limb. The ilium, ischium, and pubis join at the acetabulum to form the hip bone. The pelvis is completed by the addition of the sacrum and coccyx. The femur, tibia, and fibula form the leg. Tarsals, metatarsals, and phalanges construct the foot.

BIOLOGY TODAY ▶ Science

Identifying Skeletal Remains

Regardless of how, when, and where human bones are found unexpectedly, many questions must be answered. How old was this person at the time of death? Are these the bones of a male or a female? What was their ethnicity? Are there any signs this person was murdered?

Clues about the identity and history of the deceased person are available throughout the skeleton (Fig. 12A). Age is approximated by *dentition,* or the structure of the teeth in the upper jaw (maxilla) and lower jaw (mandible). For example, infants between 0 and 4 months of age will have no teeth present; children approximately 6 to 10 years of age will have missing deciduous, or "baby," teeth; young adults acquire their last molars, or "wisdom teeth," around age 20. The age of older adults can be approximated by the number and location of missing or broken teeth. Studying areas of bone ossification also gives clues about the age of the deceased at the time of death. In older adults, signs of joint breakdown provide additional information about age. Hyaline cartilage becomes worn, yellowed, and brittle with age, and the hyaline cartilages covering bone ends wear down over time. The amount of yellowed, brittle, or missing cartilage helps scientists guess the person's age.

If skeletal remains include the individual's pelvic bones, these will provide the best method for determining an adult's gender. The pelvis is shallower and wider in the female than in the male. The long bones, particularly the humerus and femur, offer information about the gender as well. Long bones are thicker and denser in males, and points of muscle attachment are bigger and more prominent. The skull of a male has a square chin and more prominent ridges above the eye sockets, or orbits.

Determining the ethnic origin of skeletal remains can be difficult because so many people have a mixed racial heritage. Forensic anatomists rely on observed racial characteristics of the skull. In general, individuals of African or African American descent have a greater distance between the eyes, eye sockets that are roughly rectangular, and a jaw that is large and prominent. Skulls of Native Americans typically have round eye sockets, prominent cheek (zygomatic) bones, and a rounded palate. Skulls of whites usually have a U-shaped palate, and a suture line between the frontal bones is often visible. Additionally, the external ear canals in whites are long and straight, so that the auditory ossicles can be seen.

Once the identity of the individual has been determined, the skeletal remains can be returned to the family for proper burial.

Figure 12A **Forensic investigators uncover a skeleton.** A knowledge of bone structure and how bones age will help identify these remains.
Michael Donne/Science Source

Questions to Consider

1. Why do you think long bones are most often found by forensic investigators?
2. How does an examination of bone ossification provide an indication of age?

Pelvic girdle
- Hip bones (os coxa)

Lower limb
- Thigh: femur
- Leg: tibia and fibula
- Foot: tarsals, metatarsals, and phalanges

The male pelvis is different than the female pelvis. In the female, the iliac bones are more flared and the pelvic cavity is shallower, but the outlet is wider. These adaptations facilitate the birthing process during vaginal delivery.

The *femur* (thighbone) is the longest and strongest bone in the body. The head of the femur articulates with the hip bones at the acetabulum, and the short neck better positions the legs for walking. The femur has two large processes, which are places of attachment for thigh muscle and buttock muscles. At its distal end, the femur articulates with the *tibia* of the leg. This is the region of the knee and the *patella,* or kneecap. The patella is held in place by the quadriceps tendon, which continues as a ligament that attaches to the tibial tuberosity. The *fibula* is the more slender bone in the leg. The fibula has a head that articulates with the tibia.

Each foot has an ankle, an instep, and five toes. The many bones of the foot give it considerable flexibility, especially on rough surfaces. The ankle contains seven *tarsal* bones, one of which (the talus) can move freely where it joins the tibia and fibula. The calcaneus, or heel bone, is also considered part of the ankle. The talus and calcaneus support the weight of the body.

The instep has five elongated *metatarsal* bones. The distal ends of the metatarsals form the ball of the foot. If the ligaments that bind the metatarsals together become weakened, flat feet are apt to result. The bones of the toes are called *phalanges,* just like those of the fingers. In the foot, the phalanges are stout and extremely sturdy.

CHECK YOUR PROGRESS 12.3

1. List the bones of the pectoral girdle and the upper limb.
2. List the bones of the pelvic girdle and the lower limb.
3. Describe how you can tell the difference in gender from looking at the bones of the pelvic girdle.

CONNECTING THE CONCEPTS

For more information on the limbs of the body, refer to the following discussions:

Figure 5.12 diagrams the major blood vessels of the arms and legs.

Figure 13.5 illustrates the major muscles of the body.

Section 14.2 details the areas of the brain responsible for the movement of the arms and legs.

12.4 Articulations

LEARNING OUTCOMES

Upon completion of this section, you should be able to

1. List the three types of joints.
2. Describe the structure and operation of a synovial joint.
3. Summarize the types of movement made possible by a synovial joint.

Bones are joined at the joints, also called articulations, which are classified as fibrous, cartilaginous, or synovial. Many fibrous joints, such as the **sutures** between the cranial bones, are immovable. Cartilaginous joints may be connected by hyaline cartilage, as in the costal cartilages that join the ribs to the sternum. Other cartilaginous joints are formed by fibrocartilage, as in the intervertebral discs. Cartilaginous joints tend to be slightly movable. **Synovial joints** are freely movable (Fig. 12.10).

There are several general classes of synovial joints, two of which are shown in Figure 12.10. Figure 12.10*b* illustrates the general anatomy of a freely movable synovial joint. Ligaments connect bone to bone and support or strengthen the joint. A fibrous

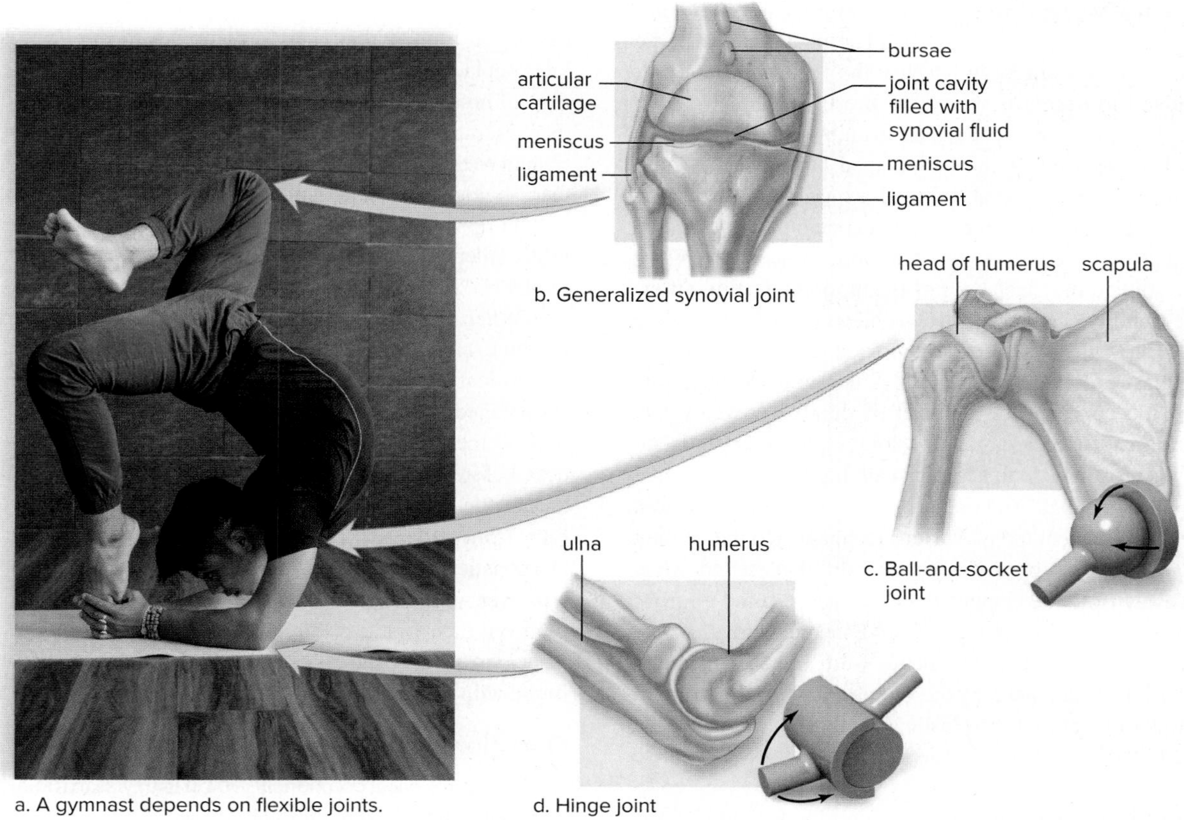

Figure 12.10 The structure of a synovial joint.

a. Synovial joints are movable and therefore flexible. **b.** The bones of joints are joined by ligaments that form a capsule. The capsule is lined with synovial membrane, which gives off synovial fluid as a lubricant. Bursae are fluid-filled sacs that reduce friction. Menisci (*sing.,* meniscus), formed of cartilage, stabilize a joint, and articular cartilage caps the bones. **c.** Ball-and-socket joints form the hip and shoulder. **d.** Hinge joints construct the knee and elbow.

(a): MangoStar_Studio/iStock/Getty Images

BIOLOGY TODAY ▶ Science

Osteoarthritis and the History of Joint Replacement Surgery

Osteoarthritis is a condition that affects nearly everyone, to a greater or lesser degree, as they age. The bones that unite to form joints, or articulations, are covered with a slippery cartilage. This articular cartilage wears down over time, as friction in the joint wears it away (Fig. 12B). By age 80, people typically have osteoarthritis in one or more joints. By contrast, rheumatoid arthritis is an autoimmune disorder (see Section 7.5) that causes inflammation within the joint. Unlike osteoarthritis, which typically affects older people, rheumatoid arthritis can affect a person of any age, even young children. Both forms of arthritis cause a loss of the joint's natural smoothness. This is what causes the pain and stiffness associated with arthritis. Arthritis is first treated with medications for joint inflammation and pain and with physical therapy to maintain and strengthen the joint. If these treatments fail, a total joint replacement is often performed. Successful replacement surgeries are now routine, thanks to the hard work and dedication of the British orthopedic surgeon Dr. John Charnley.

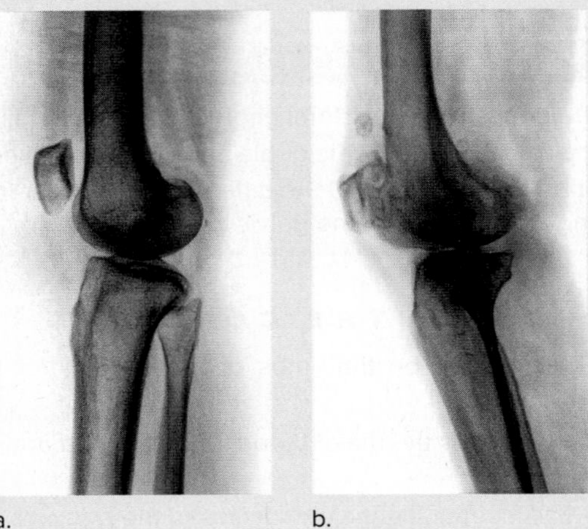

Figure 12B Osteoarthritis.
A comparison of a normal knee (**a**) and a knee with osteoarthritis (**b**).
(both): Puwadol Jaturawutthichai/Alamy Stock Photo

Early experimental surgeries by Charnley and others had been very disappointing. Fused joints were immobile, and fusion didn't always relieve the patient's pain. Postsurgical infection was common. The bones attached to the artificial joint eroded, and the supporting muscles wasted away because the joint wasn't useful. Charnley wanted to design a successful prosthetic hip, with the goal of replacing both parts of the diseased hip joint: the acetabulum, or "socket," as well as the ball-shaped head of the femur. Charnley soon determined that surgical experimentation alone wasn't enough. He studied bone repair, persuading a colleague to operate on Charnley's tibia, or shinbone, to see how repair occurred. He studied the mechanics of the hip joint, testing different types of synthetic materials. He achieved his first success using a hip socket lined with Teflon but soon discovered that the surrounding tissues became inflamed. After multiple attempts, his perfected hip consisted of a socket of durable polyethylene. Polyethylene is still used today as the joint's plastic component. The head of his prosthetic femur was a small, highly polished metal ball. Stainless steel, cobalt, and titanium, as well as chrome alloys, form the metal component today. Various techniques for cementing the polyethylene socket onto the pelvic bone had failed when bone pulled away from the cemented surface and refused to grow. Charnley's surgery used dental cement, slathered onto the bone surfaces. When the plastic components were attached, cement was squeezed into every pore of the bone, allowing the bone to regenerate and grow around the plastic. Finally, Charnley devised a specialized surgical tent and instrument tray to minimize infection.

Charnley's ideas were innovative and unorthodox, and he was reassigned to a former tuberculosis hospital, which he converted into a center for innovation in orthopedic surgery. His colleagues developed a prosthetic knee joint similar to the Charnley hip. In knee replacement surgery (see the chapter opener), the damaged ends of bones are removed and replaced with artificial components that resemble the original bone ends. Hip and knee replacements remain the most common joint replacement surgeries, but ankles, feet, shoulders, elbows, and fingers can also be replaced. Though many improvements on the procedure continue, the Charnley hip replacement remains the technique after which all others are modeled.

When a joint replacement is complete, the patient's hard work is vital to ensure the success of the procedure. Exercise and activity are critical to the recovery process. After surgery, the patient is encouraged to use the new joint as soon as possible. The extent of improvement and range of motion of the joint depend on its stiffness before the surgery, as well as the amount of patient effort during therapy following surgery. A complete recovery varies in time from patient to patient but typically takes several months. Older patients can expect their replacements to last about 10 years. However, younger patients may need a second replacement if they wear out their first prosthesis. Still, individuals who have joint replacement surgery can expect an improved quality of life and a bright future with greater independence and healthier, pain-free activity.

Questions to Consider

1. Compare each component of Charnley's artificial joint with that of a real synovial joint.
2. Explain why rheumatoid arthritis is actually a disorder of the immune system.

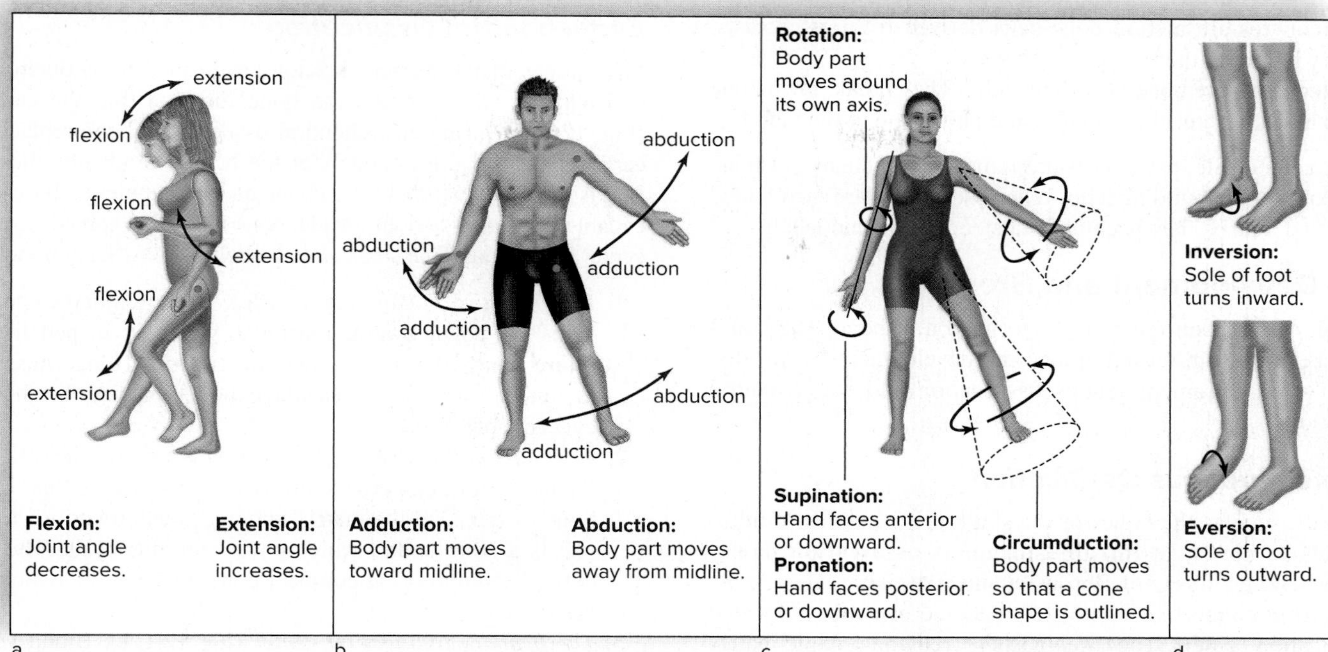

Figure 12.11 Synovial joints allow for a variety of movement.
a. Flexion and extension. **b.** Adduction and abduction. **c.** Rotation and circumduction. **d.** Inversion and eversion. Red dots indicate pivot points.

joint capsule formed by ligaments surrounds the bones at the joint. This capsule is not shown in Figure 12.10*b* so that the inner structure of the joint may be revealed. The joint capsule is lined with *synovial membrane,* which secretes a small amount of *synovial fluid* to lubricate the joint. Fluid-filled sacs called *bursae* (*sing.*, bursa) ease friction between bare areas of bone and overlapping muscles or between skin and tendons. The full joint contains *menisci* (*sing.*, meniscus), which are C-shaped pieces of fibrocartilage cartilage between the bones. These give added stability and act as shock absorbers.

The ball-and-socket joints at the hips and shoulders (Fig. 12.10*c*) allow movement in all planes, even rotational movement. The elbow and knee joints are synovial joints called hinge joints (Fig. 12.10*d*). Like a hinged door, they largely permit movement in one direction only. The Science feature "Osteoarthritis and the History of Joint Replacement Surgery" examines the history of how joint replacement therapy was developed.

Movements Permitted by Synovial Joints

Intact skeletal muscles are attached to bones by tendons that span joints. When a muscle contracts, one bone moves in relation to another bone. The more common types of movements are described in Figure 12.11.

CHECK YOUR PROGRESS 12.4

1. List the three major types of joints.
2. Describe the basic movements of cartilaginous and fibrous joints, and give an example of each in the body.
3. Describe the different movements of synovial joints, and give an example of each in the body.

CONNECTING THE CONCEPTS

For more information on ligaments and tendons, refer to the following discussion:

Section 4.2 describes the connective tissue found in the tendons and ligaments.

12.5 Bone Growth and Homeostasis

LEARNING OUTCOMES

Upon completion of this section, you should be able to

1. Summarize the process of ossification and list the types of cells involved.
2. Describe the process of bone remodeling.
3. Explain the steps in the repair of bone.

The importance of the skeleton to the human form is evident by its early appearance during development. The skeleton starts forming at about 6 weeks, when the embryo is only about 12 mm (0.5 in.) long. Most bones grow in length and width through adolescence, but some continue enlarging until about age 25. In a sense, bones can grow throughout a lifetime, because they are able to respond to stress by changing size, shape, and strength. This process is called remodeling. If a bone fractures, it can heal by bone repair.

Bones are living tissues, as shown by their ability to grow, remodel, and undergo repair. Several different types of cells are involved in bone growth, remodeling, and repair:

- **Osteoblasts** are bone-forming cells. They secrete the organic matrix of bone and promote the deposition of calcium salts into the matrix.

- **Osteocytes** are mature bone cells derived from osteoblasts. They maintain the structure of bone.
- **Osteoclasts** are bone-absorbing cells. They break down bone and assist in returning calcium and phosphate to the blood.

Throughout life, osteoclasts are removing the matrix of bone and osteoblasts are building it up. When osteoblasts are surrounded by calcified matrix, they become the osteocytes within lacunae.

Bone Development and Growth

The term **ossification** refers to the formation of bone. The bones of the skeleton form during embryonic development in two distinctive ways: intramembranous ossification and endochondral ossification.

Intramembranous Ossification

Flat bones, such as the bones of the skull, are examples of intramembranous bones. In **intramembranous ossification,** bones develop between sheets of fibrous connective tissue. Here, cells derived from connective tissue cells become osteoblasts located in ossification centers. The osteoblasts secrete the organic matrix of bone. This matrix consists of mucopolysaccharides and collagen fibrils. The osteoblasts promote ossification of the matrix by adding calcium salts.

Ossification results in the formation of soft sheets, or trabeculae, of spongy bone. Spongy bone remains inside a flat bone. A periosteum forms outside the spongy bone. Osteoblasts derived from the periosteum carry out further ossification. Trabeculae form and fuse to become compact bone. The compact bone forms a bone collar that surrounds the spongy bone on the inside.

Endochondral Ossification

Most bones of the human skeleton are formed by **endochondral ossification,** which means the bone forms within the cartilage (Fig. 12.12). During endochondral ossification, bone replaces the cartilaginous (hyaline) models of the bones. Gradually, the cartilage is replaced by the calcified bone matrix that makes these bones capable of bearing weight. Inside, bone formation spreads from the center to the ends. The steps of endochondral ossification include:

1. *The cartilage model* (Fig 12.12*a*). In the embryo, chondrocytes lay down hyaline cartilage, which is shaped like the future bones. Therefore, they are called cartilage models of the future bones. As the cartilage models calcify, the chondrocytes die off.
2. *The bone collar* (Fig 12.12*b*). Osteoblasts are derived from the newly formed periosteum. Osteoblasts secrete the organic bone matrix, and the matrix undergoes calcification. The result is a bone collar, which covers the diaphysis. The bone collar is composed of compact bone. In time, the bone collar thickens.
3. *The primary ossification center* (Fig 12.12*c*). Blood vessels bring osteoblasts to the interior, and they begin to lay down spongy bone. This region is called a primary ossification center, because it is the first center for bone formation.
4. *The medullary cavity and secondary ossification sites* (Fig. 12.12*d*). The spongy bone of the diaphysis is absorbed by osteoclasts, and the cavity created becomes the medullary cavity. Shortly after birth, secondary ossification centers form in the epiphyses. Spongy bone persists in the epiphyses, and it persists in the red bone marrow for quite some time. Cartilage

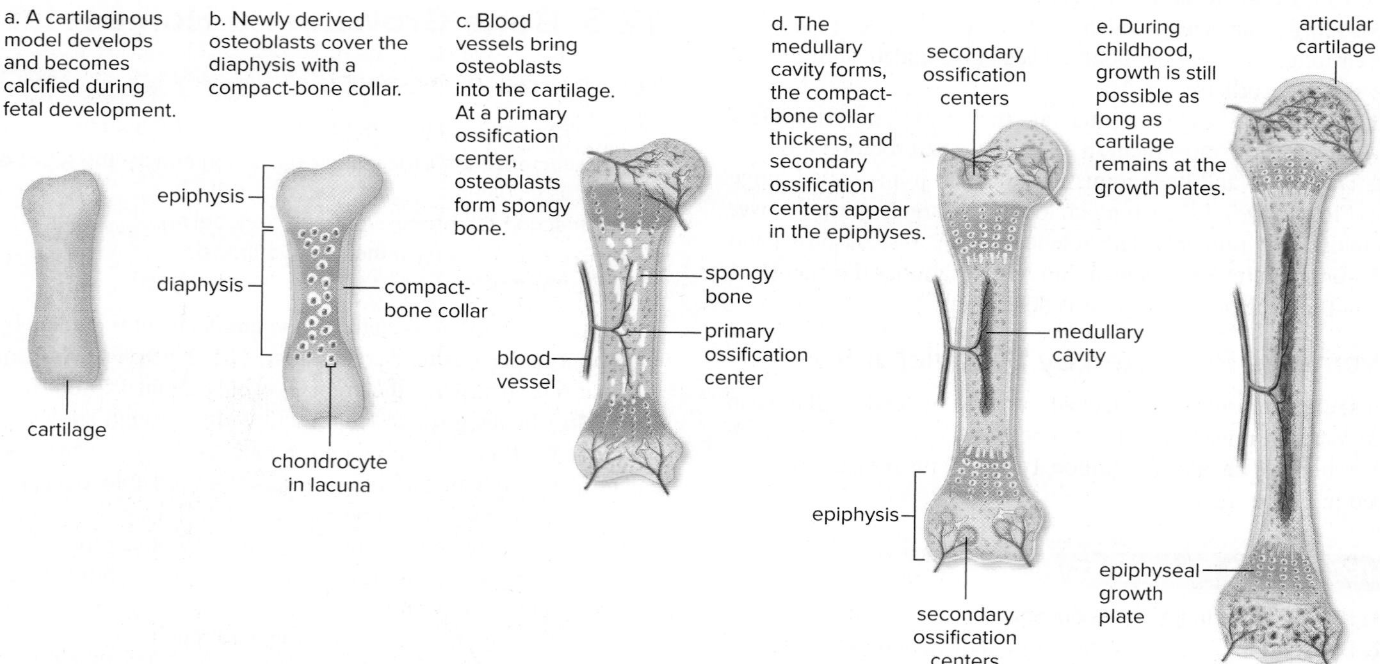

Figure 12.12 **Bone growth by endochondral ossification.**
In endochondral ossification, the bone begins as hyaline cartilage. Bone cells called osteoblasts colonize the cartilage, then ossify to turn cartilage into bone.

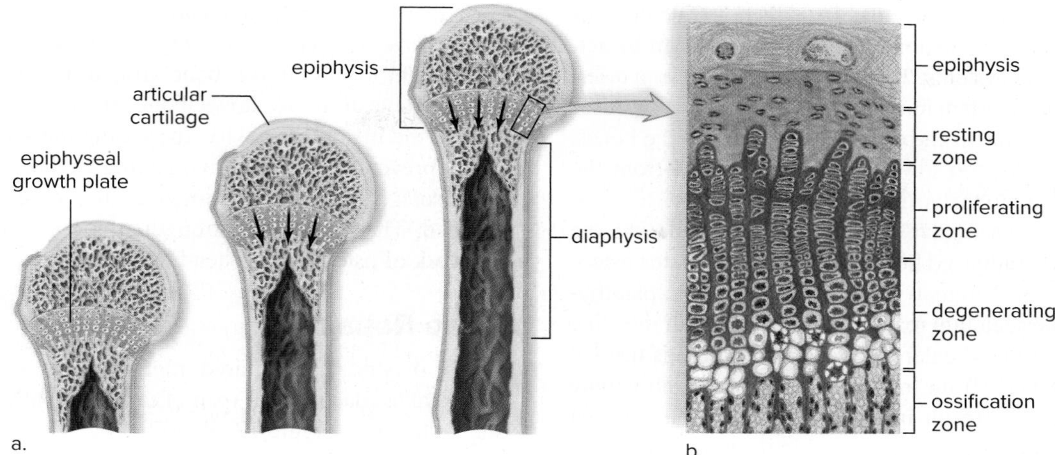

Figure 12.13 Increasing bone length.
a. Length of a bone increases when cartilage is replaced by bone at the growth plate. Arrows indicate the direction of ossification. **b.** Chondrocytes produce new cartilage in the proliferating zone, and cartilage becomes bone in the ossification zone closest to the diaphysis.

is present at two locations: the epiphyseal (growth) plate and articular cartilage, which covers the ends of long bones.

5. *The epiphyseal (growth) plate* (Fig 12.12*e*). A band of cartilage called the **epiphyseal plate** (also called a growth plate) remains between the primary ossification center and each secondary center (see Fig. 12.1). The limbs keep increasing in length as long as the epiphyseal plates are still present.

Figure 12.13 shows that the epiphyseal plate contains four layers. The layer nearest the epiphysis is the *resting zone*, where cartilage remains. The next layer is the *proliferating zone,* in which chondrocytes are producing new cartilage cells. In the third layer, the *degenerating zone,* the cartilage cells are dying off; and in the fourth layer, the *ossification zone,* bone is forming. Bone formation here causes the length of the bone to increase. The inside layer of articular cartilage also undergoes ossification in the manner described.

The diameter of a bone enlarges as a bone lengthens. Osteoblasts derived from the periosteum are active in new bone deposition as osteoclasts enlarge the medullary cavity from inside.

Final Size of the Bones When the epiphyseal plates close, bone lengthening can no longer occur. The epiphyseal plates in the arms and legs of women typically close at about age 16 to 18, and they do not close in men until about age 20. Portions of other types of bones may continue to grow until age 25.

Hormones, chemical messengers that are produced by one part of the body and act on a different part of the body, are secreted by the endocrine glands and distributed about the body by the bloodstream. Hormones control the activity of the epiphyseal plate, as is discussed next.

Hormones Affect Bone Growth

There are several hormones that play an important role in bone growth. One of these is vitamin D (see Section 9.6). While many would not consider vitamin D to be a hormone, it may be formed in the skin when exposed to sunlight, but it can also be consumed in the diet. Milk, in particular, is often fortified with vitamin D. In the kidneys, vitamin D is converted to a hormone that acts on the intestinal tract. The chief function of vitamin D is intestinal absorption of calcium. In the absence of vitamin D, children can develop rickets, a condition marked by bone deformities, including bowed long bones.

Growth hormone (GH) directly stimulates growth of the epiphyseal plate, as well as bone growth in general. However, growth hormone is somewhat ineffective if the metabolic activity of cells is not promoted. Thyroid hormone, in particular, promotes the metabolic activity of cells (see Section 16.6). Too little growth hormone in childhood results in *dwarfism.* Too much growth hormone during childhood (prior to epiphyseal fusion) can produce excessive growth and even *gigantism* (see Fig. 16.9). *Acromegaly* results from excess GH in adults following epiphyseal fusion. This condition produces excessive growth of bones in the hands and face (see Fig. 16.10).

Adolescents usually experience a dramatic increase in height, called the growth spurt, due to an increased level of sex hormones. These hormones apparently stimulate osteoblast activity. Rapid growth causes epiphyseal plates to become "paved over" by the faster-growing bone tissue within 1 or 2 years of the onset of puberty.

Bone Remodeling and Calcium Homeostasis

Bone is constantly being broken down by osteoclasts and re-formed by osteoblasts in the adult. As much as 18% of bone is recycled each year. This process of bone renewal, often called **bone remodeling,** normally keeps bones strong. In Paget's disease, new bone is generated at a faster-than-normal rate. This rapid remodeling produces bone that's softer and weaker than normal bone and can cause bone pain, deformities, and fractures.

Bone recycling allows the body to regulate the amount of calcium in the blood. To illustrate that the blood calcium level is critical, recall that calcium is required for blood to clot (see Section 6.4). Also, if the blood calcium concentration is too high, neurons and muscle cells no longer function. If calcium falls too low, nerve and muscle cells become so excited that convulsions occur. Calcium ions are also necessary for the regulation of cellular metabolism by acting in cellular messenger systems. Thus, the skeleton acts as a reservoir for storage of this important mineral—if the blood calcium rises above normal, at least some of the excess is deposited in the bones. If the blood calcium dips too low, calcium is removed from the bones to bring it back up to the normal level.

Two hormones in particular are involved in regulating the blood calcium level. Parathyroid hormone (PTH) stimulates osteoclasts to dissolve the calcium matrix of bone. In addition, parathyroid hormone promotes calcium reabsorption in the small intestine and kidney, increasing blood calcium levels. Vitamin D is needed for the absorption of Ca^{2+} from the digestive tract, which is why vitamin D deficiency can result in weak bones. It is easy to get enough of this vitamin, because your skin produces it when exposed to sunlight, and the milk you buy at the grocery store is fortified with vitamin D.

Calcitonin is a hormone that acts opposite to PTH. The female sex hormone estrogen can actually increase the number of osteoblasts; the reduction of estrogen in older women is often given as reason for the development of weak bones, called osteoporosis. Osteoporosis is discussed in the Health feature "Avoiding Osteoporosis." In the young adult, the activity of osteoclasts is matched by the activity of osteoblasts, and bone mass remains stable until about age 45 in women. After that age, bone mass starts to decrease.

Bone remodeling also accounts for why bones can respond to stress. If you engage in an activity that calls upon the use of a particular bone, the bone enlarges in diameter at the region most affected by the activity. During this process, osteoblasts in the periosteum form compact bone around the external bone surface and osteoclasts break down bone on the internal bone surface around the medullary cavity. Increasing the size of the medullary cavity prevents the bones from getting too heavy and thick. Today, exercises such as walking, jogging, and weightlifting are recommended. These exercises strengthen bone because they stimulate the work of osteoblasts instead of osteoclasts.

Bone Repair

Repair of a bone is required after it breaks or fractures. Fracture repair takes place over a span of several months in a series of four steps, shown in Figure 12.14:

1. *Hematoma.* After a fracture, blood escapes from ruptured blood vessels and forms a hematoma (mass of clotted blood) in the space between the broken bones. The hematoma forms within 6 to 8 hours.
2. *Fibrocartilaginous callus.* Tissue repair begins, and a fibrocartilaginous callus fills the space between the ends of the broken bone for about 3 weeks.
3. *Bony callus.* Osteoblasts produce trabeculae of spongy bone and convert the fibrocartilage callus to a bony callus that joins the broken bones together. The bony callus lasts about 3 to 4 months.
4. *Remodeling.* Osteoblasts build new compact bone at the periphery. Osteoclasts absorb the spongy bone, creating a new medullary cavity.

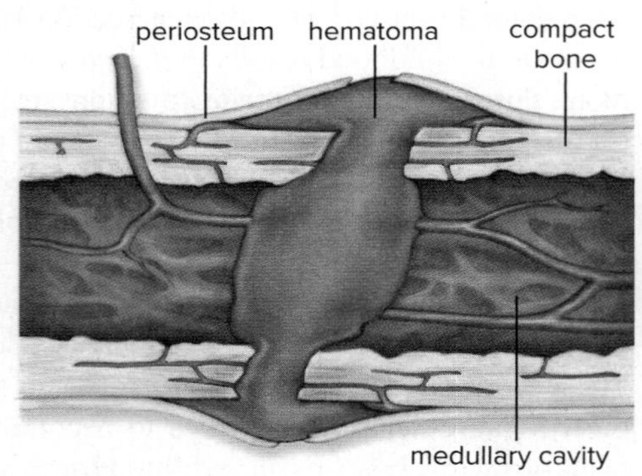

1. Hematoma

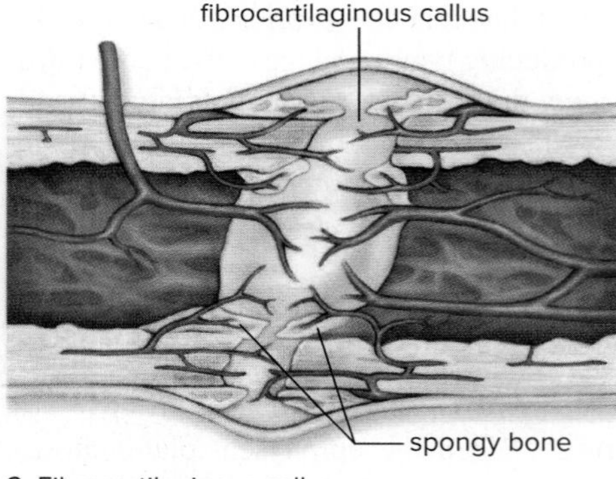

2. Fibrocartilaginous callus

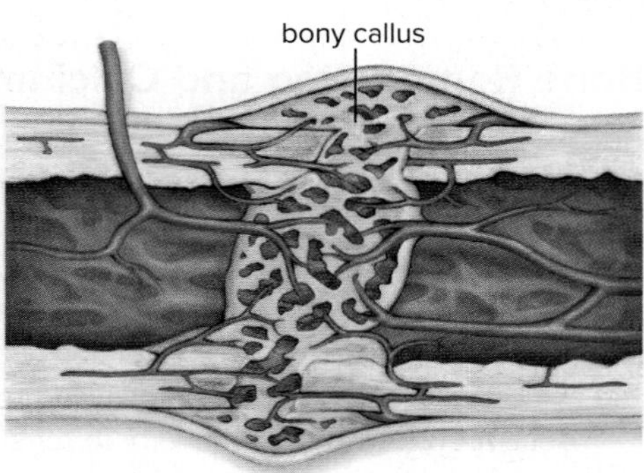

3. Bony callus

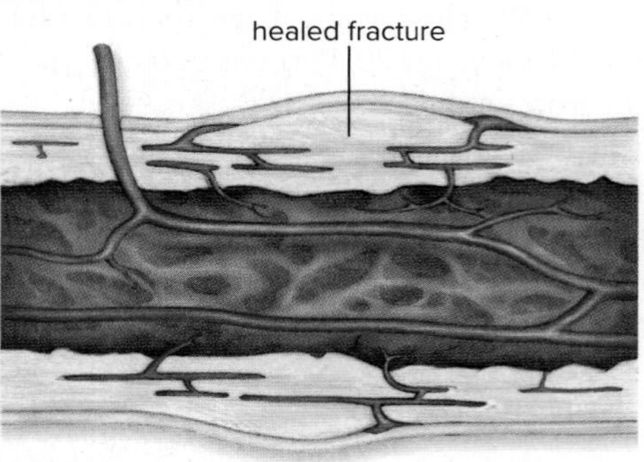

4. Remodeling

Figure 12.14 Bone repair following a fracture.
The stages in the repair of a fracture.

BIOLOGY TODAY ▶ Health

Avoiding Osteoporosis

Osteoporosis is a condition in which the bones are weakened due to a decrease in the bone mass that makes up the skeleton. The skeletal mass continues to increase until ages 20 to 30. After that, there is an equal rate of formation and breakdown of bone mass until ages 40 to 50. Then, reabsorption begins to exceed formation, and the total bone mass slowly decreases (Fig. 12C).

Over time, men are apt to lose 25% and women 35% of their bone mass. But we have to consider that men—unless they have taken asthma medications that decrease bone formation—tend to have denser bones than women anyway. Whereas a man's testosterone (male sex hormone) level generally declines slowly after the age of 45, estrogen (female sex hormone) levels in women begin to decline significantly at about age 45. Sex hormones play an important role in maintaining bone strength, so this difference means that women are more likely than men to have a higher incidence of fractures, involving especially the hip, vertebrae, long bones, and pelvis. Although osteoporosis may at times be the result of various disease processes, it is essentially a disease that occurs as we age.

How to Avoid Osteoporosis

Everyone can take measures to avoid having osteoporosis later in life. Adequate dietary calcium throughout life is an important protection against osteoporosis. The National Osteoporosis Foundation (www.nof.org) recommends that adults under the age of 50 take in 1,000 mg of calcium per day. After the age of 50, the daily intake should exceed 1,200 mg per day.

A small daily amount of vitamin D is also necessary for the body to use calcium correctly. Exposure to sunlight is required to allow skin to synthesize a precursor to vitamin D. If you reside on or north of a "line" drawn from Boston to Milwaukee, to Minneapolis, to Boise, chances are you're not getting enough vitamin D during the winter months. Therefore, you should take advantage of the vitamin D present in fortified foods such as low-fat milk and cereal. If you are under age 50, you should be receiving 400–800 IU of vitamin D per day. After age 50, this amount should increase to 800–1,000 IU of vitamin D daily.

People who are very inactive, such as those confined to bed, lose bone mass 25 times faster than people who are moderately active. On the other hand, moderate weight-bearing exercise, such as regular walking or jogging, is another good way to maintain bone strength (Fig. 12C).

Diagnosis and Treatment

Postmenopausal women with any of the following risk factors should have an evaluation of their bone density:

- White or Asian race
- Thin body type
- Family history of osteoporosis
- Early menopause (before age 45)
- Smoking
- A diet low in calcium or excessive alcohol consumption and caffeine intake
- Sedentary lifestyle

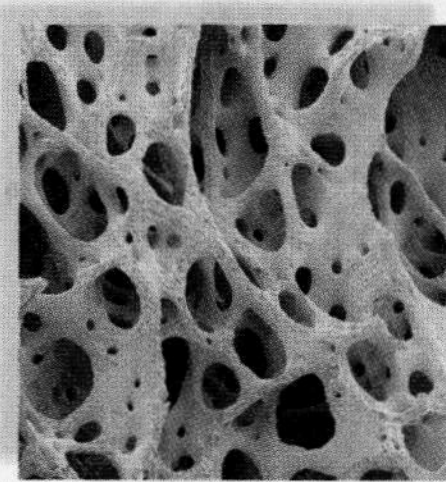

a. Normal bone

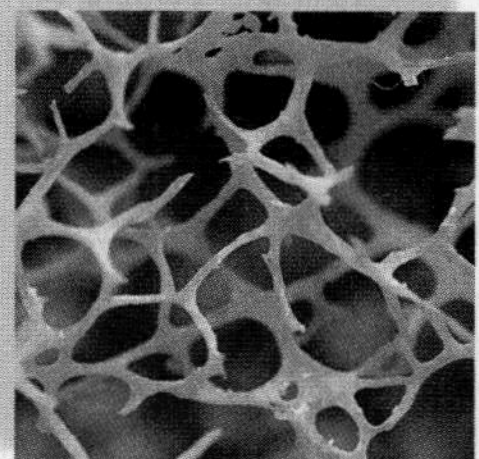

b. Osteoporosis

Figure 12C **Preventing osteoporosis.**
a. Normal bone. **b.** Bone from a person with osteoporosis.
(a): Susumu Nishinaga/Science Source; (b): Ed Reschke/Stone/Getty Images

Bone density is measured by a method called dual-energy X-ray absorptiometry (DEXA). This test measures bone density based on the absorption of photons generated by an X-ray tube. Blood and urine tests are used to detect the biochemical markers of bone loss. Over the past several years, it has become easier for physicians to screen older women and at-risk men for osteoporosis.

If the bones are thin, it is worthwhile to take all possible measures to gain bone density, because even a slight increase can significantly reduce fracture risk. Although estrogen therapy does reduce the incidence of hip fractures, long-term estrogen therapy is rarely recommended for osteoporosis. Estrogen is known to increase the risk of breast cancer, heart disease, stroke, and blood clots. Other medications are available, however. Calcitonin, a thyroid hormone, has been shown to increase bone density and strength while decreasing the rate of bone fractures. Also, the bisphosphonates are a family of nonhormonal drugs used to prevent and treat osteoporosis. To achieve optimal results with calcitonin or one of the bisphosphonates, patients should also receive adequate amounts of dietary calcium and vitamin D.

Questions to Consider

1. How may long-term digestive system problems promote the chances of developing osteoporosis?
2. Why are individuals at risk for osteoporosis encouraged to increase their exercise regimes, including load-bearing exercises?

In some ways, bone repair parallels the development of a bone except that the first step, hematoma, indicates that injury has occurred. Further, a fibrocartilaginous callus precedes the production of compact bone.

The naming of fractures tells you what type of break has occurred. A fracture is complete if the bone is broken clear through, and incomplete if the bone is not separated into two parts. A fracture is simple if it does not pierce the skin, and is compound if it does pierce the skin. Impacted means that the broken ends are wedged into each other. A spiral fracture occurs when the break is ragged due to twisting of a bone.

Blood Cells Are Produced in Bones

The bones of your skeleton contain two types of marrow: yellow and red. Fat is stored in yellow bone marrow, thus making it part of the body's energy reserves.

Red bone marrow is the site of blood cell production. The red blood cells are the carriers of oxygen in the blood. Oxygen is necessary for the production of ATP by aerobic cellular respiration. White blood cells also originate in the red bone marrow. The white cells are involved in defending your body against pathogens and cancerous cells; without them, you would soon succumb to disease and die.

CHECK YOUR PROGRESS 12.5

1. Describe how bone growth occurs during development.
2. Summarize the stages in the repair of bone.
3. Explain how the skeletal system is involved in calcium homeostasis.

CONNECTING THE CONCEPTS

For more on bone development and the hormones that influence bone growth, refer to the following discussions:

Section 9.6 provides additional information on inputs of vitamin D and calcium in the diet.

Section 16.2 examines the role of growth hormones in the body.

Section 16.3 describes the action of the hormones calcitonin and PTH.

CONCLUSION

In this chapter, we explored the structure and function of the skeletal system. As we learned, one of the main functions of this body system is to provide support and to interact with the muscular system to allow for movement. Joints, such as knees and hips, are locations where the bones of the body interact. Over time, these joints can experience wear and tear, creating discomfort and a loss of mobility. Replacement therapies, such as total knee replacement, have the ability to restore some, if not most, of the lost mobility, and provide for an increased quality of life as we age.

SUMMARIZE

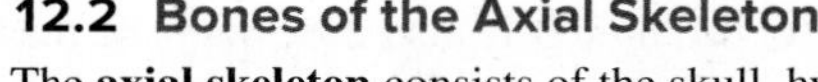

12.1 Overview of the Skeletal System

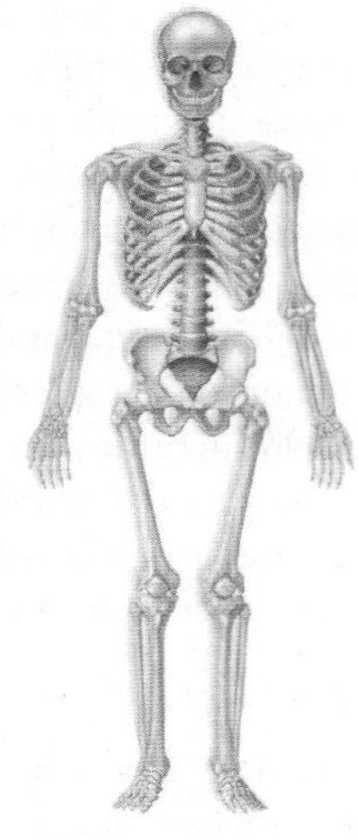

Functions of the **skeletal system:**

- It supports and protects the body.
- It produces blood cells.
- It stores mineral salts, particularly calcium phosphate. It also stores fat.
- Along with the muscles, it permits flexible body movement.

The bones of the skeleton are composed of bone tissues and cartilage. In a long bone,

- Cartilage covers the ends. **Periosteum** (fibrous connective tissue) covers the rest of the bone.
- **Spongy bone,** containing **red bone marrow,** is in the epiphyses.
- Yellow bone marrow is in the medullary cavity of the diaphysis.
- **Compact bone** makes up the wall of the diaphysis.
- Bone cells called **osteocytes** reside within the **lacunae** of compact bone.

Cartilage is a connective tissue that is more flexible than bone. Cartilage is formed by cells called **chondrocytes.**

Ligaments composed of **fibrous connective tissue** connect bones at **joints. Tendons** connect muscles to bone.

12.2 Bones of the Axial Skeleton

The **axial skeleton** consists of the skull, hyoid bone, vertebral column, and rib cage.

- The **skull** is formed by the cranium, which protects the brain, and the facial bones. Membranous regions called **fontanels** connect the bones at birth. **Sinuses** are air spaces that reduce the weight of the skull. The **foramen magnum** is the opening through which the spinal cord passes.
- The hyoid bone anchors the tongue and is the site of attachment of muscles involved with swallowing.
- The **vertebral column** is composed of vertebrae separated by shock-absorbing discs, which make the column flexible. **Intervertebral discs** separate and pad the vertebrae. The vertebral column supports the head and trunk, protects the spinal cord, and is a site for muscle attachment.
- The rib cage is composed of the thoracic vertebrae, ribs, costal cartilages, and sternum. It protects the heart and lungs.

12.3 Bones of the Appendicular Skeleton

The **appendicular skeleton** consists of the bones of the pectoral girdles, upper limbs, pelvic girdle, and lower limbs.

- The **pectoral girdles** and upper limbs are adapted for flexibility.
- The **pelvic girdle** and the lower limbs are adapted for supporting weight. The **pelvis** consists of the pelvic girdle, sacrum, and coccyx. The femur is the longest and strongest bone in the body.

12.4 Articulations

Bones are joined at joints, of which there are three types:

- Fibrous joints (such as the **sutures** of the cranium) are immovable.
- Cartilaginous joints (such as those between the ribs and sternum and the pubic symphysis) are slightly movable.
- **Synovial joints** (which have a synovial membrane) are freely movable.

12.5 Bone Growth and Homeostasis

Cells involved in growth, remodeling, and repair of bone are

- **Osteoblasts,** bone-forming cells
- **Osteocytes,** mature bone cells derived from osteoblasts
- **Osteoclasts,** which break down and absorb bone

Bone Development and Growth

- **Ossification** refers to the formation of bone.
- **Intramembranous ossification:** Bones develop between sheets of fibrous connective tissue. Examples are flat bones, such as bones of the skull.
- **Endochondral ossification:** Cartilaginous models of the bones are replaced by calcified bone matrix. Bone grows at a location called the **epiphyseal plate.**
- Bone growth is affected by vitamin D, growth hormone, and sex hormones.

Bone Remodeling and Its Role in Homeostasis

- **Bone remodeling** is the renewal of bone. Osteoclasts break down bone, while osteoblasts re-form bone. Some bone is recycled each year.
- Bone recycling allows the body to regulate blood calcium.
- Two hormones, parathyroid hormone and calcitonin, direct bone remodeling and control blood calcium.

Bone Repair

Repair of a fracture requires the following four steps:

- Hematoma formation
- Fibrocartilaginous callus
- Bony callus
- Remodeling

ENGAGE

THINKING CRITICALLY

1. Most authorities emphasize the importance of calcium consumption for the prevention of osteoporosis. However, surveys have shown that osteoporosis is rare in some countries, such as China, where calcium intake is lower than in the United States. These studies often point to the higher level of animal protein consumed in the United States as having a detrimental effect on bone mass. If this were true, what physiological mechanism might explain it? Can you think of any other differences between the lifestyles in China and the United States that also might explain the difference?
2. Individuals who spend the majority of their day indoors (e.g., residents in nursing homes) are more susceptible to fracture. Why?
3. Pediatricians are becoming increasingly concerned by the increased incidence of rickets in children eating a typical fast-food diet. What nutrients are missing from their diet?

MAKING IT RELEVANT

1. In many cases, before recommending knee replacement surgery, doctors suggest to their patients that they try to lose 10–15 pounds of weight. How might this contribute to prolonging the life of the knee joint?
2. Osteoporosis is also a concern of individuals who are highly active. How might these individuals alter their diet and exercise routines to reduce the risk of needing knee replacement surgery later in life?
3. The development of "replacement" surgeries is gaining momentum in medicine. In addition to joints, such as knees and hips, what other parts of the human body should researchers be looking to "replace"?

Find answers to all of the chapter questions at connect.mheducation.com

CHAPTER

13

Muscular System

Soeren Stache/Picture Alliance/Getty Images

CHAPTER OUTLINE

13.1 Overview of the Muscular System
13.2 Skeletal Muscle Fiber Contraction
13.3 Whole Muscle Contraction
13.4 Muscular Disorders
13.5 Homeostasis

BEFORE YOU BEGIN

Before beginning this chapter, take a few moments to review the following discussions:

Section 3.6 How do fermentation and cellular respiration produce ATP?

Figure 3.21 What are the stages of the ATP cycle?

Section 4.8 How do feedback mechanisms contribute to homeostasis?

World Record Marathon

Endurance running is one of the supreme tests of human physiology. At the 2018 Berlin Marathon, Eliud Kipchoge of Kenya set a new world record of 2 hours 1 minute and 39 seconds on the 26.2-mile course. To accomplish this, he set an average pace of 4 minutes and 38.4 seconds per mile. However, this was not his personal best. A year earlier, Kipchoge ran a similar (but unratified) marathon in 2 hours and 25 seconds.

To be a marathon runner, you have to train constantly, and be physically fit, but what does that mean with regard to muscles? As we will learn, muscles have a complex structure that is unique in that it permits them to interact with the skeletal system and contract, thus allowing for movement. They also need to generate the energy for contraction through a number of different pathways both aerobic and anaerobic. Training for a marathon means preparing the muscles for these tasks.

In this chapter, we will examine the anatomy and physiology of muscles. We will focus primarily on the skeletal muscles, those associated with the majority of movements we are familiar with, such as that used for walking or running marathons.

As you read through the chapter, think about the following questions:

1. How does the nervous system specifically control the skeletal system?
2. How do the sensory systems exert influence over the nervous system and therefore over the muscular and skeletal systems?
3. How does the muscular system contribute to homeostasis?

13.1 Overview of the Muscular System

LEARNING OUTCOMES

Upon completion of this section, you should be able to

1. List the three types of muscle tissue and provide a function for each.
2. Describe the general structure of a skeletal muscle.
3. Recognize how skeletal muscles are named.

The **muscular system** is involved with movement. This may be the movement of the entire organism (walking or running) or the movement of materials (blood, food) within the organism. The muscular system is made up of muscles. The structure of a muscle allows it to provide movement by contracting, or shortening.

Types of Muscles

Humans have three types of muscle tissue: smooth, cardiac, and skeletal (Fig. 13.1). The cells of these tissues are collectively called **myocytes.**

Smooth muscle fibers are shaped like narrow cylinders with pointed ends. Each has a single nucleus (uninucleated). The cells are usually arranged in parallel lines, forming sheets. Striations (alternating light and dark bands) are seen in cardiac and skeletal muscle but not in smooth muscle. Smooth muscle is located in the walls of hollow internal organs (see Section 9.1) and blood vessels (see Section 5.2) and causes these walls to contract. Contraction of smooth muscle is involuntary, occurring without conscious control. Although smooth muscle is slower to contract than skeletal muscle, it can sustain prolonged contractions and does not fatigue easily.

Cardiac muscle forms the heart wall (see Section 5.3). Its fibers are generally uninucleated, striated, and tubular. Branching allows the fibers to interlock at **intercalated discs.** The plasma membranes at intercalated discs contain gap junctions (see Section 3.5) that permit contractions to spread quickly throughout the heart wall. Cardiac fibers relax completely between contractions, which prevents fatigue. The contraction of cardiac muscle is rhythmic. It occurs without outside nervous stimulation and without conscious control. Thus, cardiac muscle contraction is involuntary.

Skeletal muscle fibers are tubular, multinucleated, and striated and make up the skeletal muscles attached to the skeletal system (see Section 12.1). Fibers run the length of the muscle and can be quite long. The myocytes of skeletal muscle are commonly called **muscle fibers.** Skeletal muscle is voluntary; we can decide to move a particular part of the body, such as the arms and legs.

Skeletal Muscles of the Body

Humans belong to a class of animals called the *vertebrates* (see Section 23.3). Vertebrate animals possess an internal vertebral column, a skeleton, and jointed appendages. Our skeletal muscles are attached to the skeleton, and their contraction causes the movement of bones at a joint.

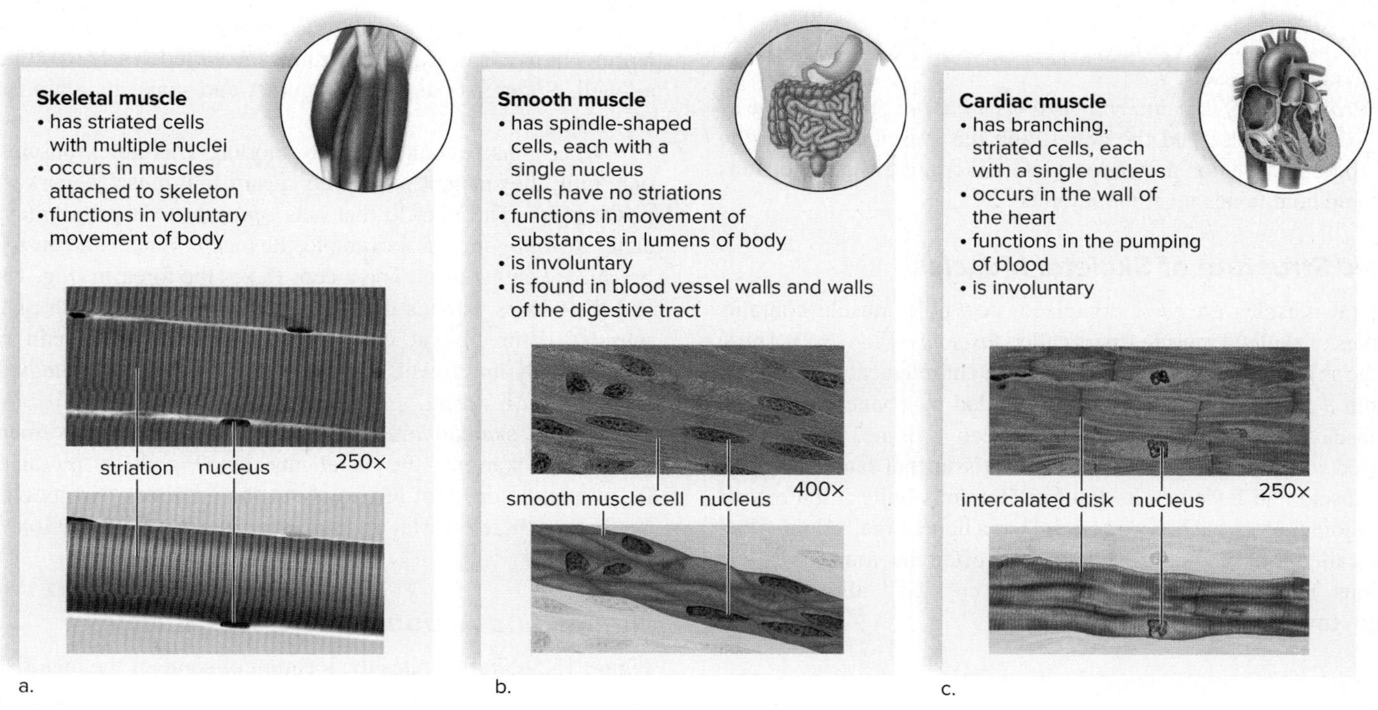

Skeletal muscle
• has striated cells with multiple nuclei
• occurs in muscles attached to skeleton
• functions in voluntary movement of body
striation
nucleus
250×
a.
Smooth muscle
• has spindle-shaped cells, each with a single nucleus
• cells have no striations
• functions in movement of substances in lumens of body
• is involuntary
• is found in blood vessel walls and walls of the digestive tract
smooth muscle cell
nucleus
400×
b.
Cardiac muscle
• has branching, striated cells, each with a single nucleus
• occurs in the wall of the heart
• functions in the pumping of blood
• is involuntary
intercalated disk
nucleus
250×
c.

Figure 13.1 **The three classes of muscles in humans.**
Human muscles are of three types: (**a**) skeletal, (**b**) smooth, and (**c**) cardiac. Each muscle type has different characteristics.
(photos) (a, c): Ed Reschke; (b): Dennis Strete/McGraw Hill

> **BIOLOGY IN YOUR LIFE**
>
> **How many muscles are there in the human body?**
>
> Most experts agree there are over 600 muscles in the human body. The exact number varies because some experts lump muscles together under one name and others differentiate them. Some state the number of muscles is as high as 800.
>
> The smallest muscle, the stapedius, is a 1.27-mm-long muscle in the middle ear. The longest muscle is the sartorius, which starts at the hip and extends to the knee. The biggest muscle (in terms of mass) is the gluteus maximus, the muscle that makes up the majority of the buttocks.

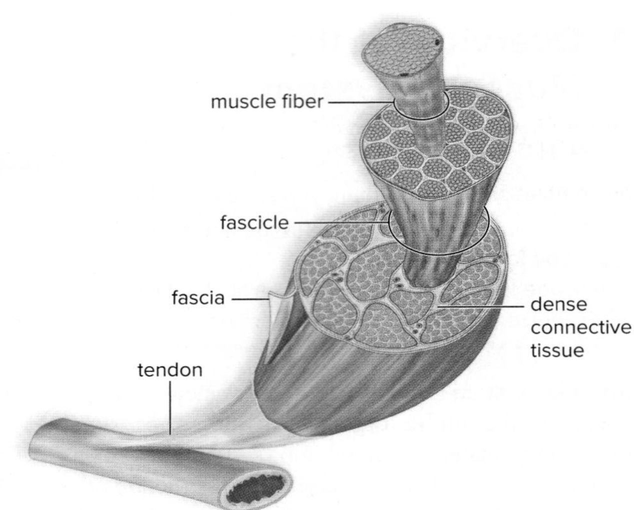

Figure 13.2 **Connecting muscle to bone.**
Connective tissue separates bundles of muscle fibers that make up a skeletal muscle. A layer of connective tissue covering the muscle contributes to the tendon, which attaches muscle to bone.

Functions of Skeletal Muscles

The skeletal muscles of the body have a wide variety of functions, including the following:

- *Support.* Skeletal muscle contraction opposes the force of gravity and allows us to remain upright.
- *Movements of bones and other body structures.* Muscle contraction accounts not only for the movement of arms and legs but also for movements of the eyes, facial expressions, and breathing.
- *Maintenance of a constant body temperature.* Skeletal muscle contraction causes ATP to break down, releasing heat, which helps maintain temperature homeostasis in the body (see Section 13.5).
- *Movement of fluids in the cardiovascular and lymphatic systems.* The pressure of skeletal muscle contraction keeps blood moving in cardiovascular veins and lymph moving in lymphatic vessels.
- *Protection of the internal organs and the stabilization of joints.* Muscles pad the bones, and the muscular wall in the abdominal region protects the internal organs. Muscle tendons help hold bones together at joints.

Basic Structure of Skeletal Muscles

Skeletal muscles are well organized. A whole muscle contains bundles of skeletal muscle fibers called *fascicles* (Fig. 13.2). These are the strands of muscle we see when we cut red meat and poultry. Within a fascicle, each fiber is surrounded by connective tissue; the fascicle is also surrounded by connective tissue. Muscles are covered with *fascia,* a type of connective tissue that extends beyond the muscle and becomes its **tendon.** Tendons quite often extend past a joint before anchoring a muscle to a bone. Small, fluid-filled sacs called **bursae** (*sing.,* bursa) can often be found between tendons and bones. The bursae act as cushions, allowing ease of movement.

Skeletal Muscles Work in Pairs

In general, each muscle is concerned with the movement of only one bone. To simplify the discussion, we will focus on the movement of a single bone and no others. The **origin** of a muscle is on a stationary bone, and the **insertion** of a muscle is on a bone that moves. When a muscle contracts, it pulls on the tendons at its insertion and the bone moves. For example, when the biceps brachii contracts, it raises the forearm.

Skeletal muscles usually function in groups. Consequently, to make a particular movement, your nervous system does not stimulate a single muscle. Rather, it stimulates an appropriate group of muscles. Even so, for any particular movement, one muscle does most of the work and is called the *agonist,* or *prime mover.* While a prime mover is working, other muscles called *synergists* function as well. Synergists assist the agonist and make its action more effective.

When muscles contract, they shorten. Therefore, muscles can only pull; they cannot push. This means that muscles work in opposite pairs. The muscle that acts opposite to a prime mover is called an *antagonist.* For example, the biceps brachii and the triceps brachii are antagonists. The biceps flexes the forearm (Fig. 13.3*a*), and the triceps extends the forearm (Fig. 13.3*b*). If both of these muscles contracted at once, the forearm would remain rigid. Smooth body movements depend on an antagonist relaxing when a prime mover is acting.

Not all skeletal muscles are involved in the movement of limbs. For example, the facial muscles (Fig. 13.4) produce the facial expressions that tell us about the emotions and mood of a person and therefore play an important role in our interactions with other people.

Names and Actions of Skeletal Muscles

Figure 13.5*a*, *b* illustrates the location of some of the major skeletal muscles and gives their actions. (Not all the muscles mentioned are featured in Figure 13.5, but most are.)

When learning the names of muscles, considering what the names mean will help you remember them. The names of the

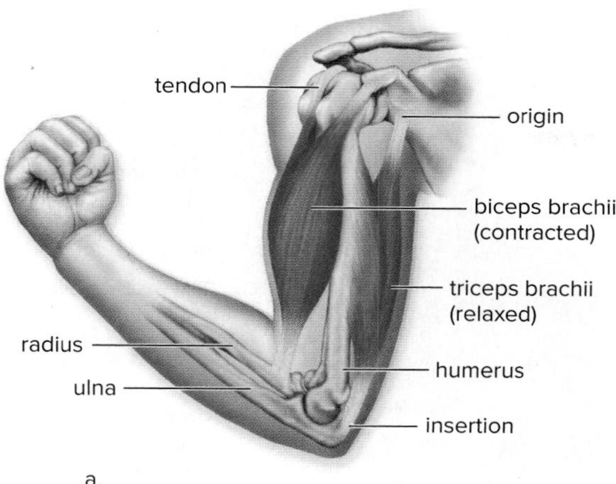

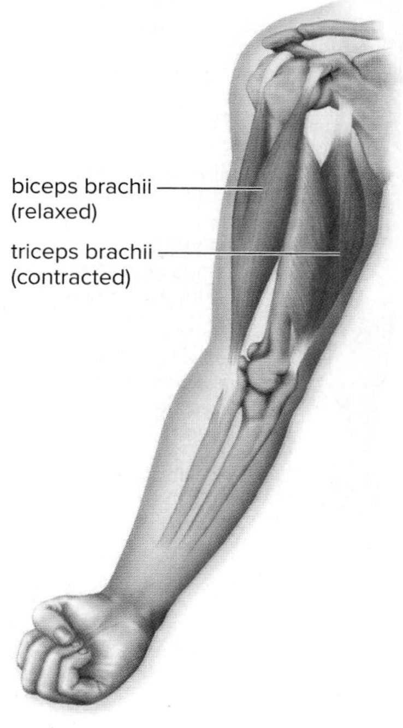

Figure 13.3 Skeletal muscles often work in pairs.
a. When the biceps brachii contracts, the forearm flexes. **b.** When the triceps brachii contracts, the forearm extends. Therefore, these two muscles are antagonistic. The origin of a skeletal muscle is on a bone that remains stationary, and the insertion of a muscle is on a bone that moves when the muscle contracts.

various skeletal muscles are often combinations of the following terms used to characterize muscles:

- *Size.* The *gluteus maximus* is the largest muscle that makes up the buttocks. The *gluteus minimus* is the smallest of the gluteal muscles. Other terms used to indicate size are *vastus* (huge), *longus* (long), and *brevis* (short).
- *Shape.* The *deltoid* is shaped like a triangle. (The Greek letter *delta* has this appearance: Δ.) The *trapezius* is shaped like a trapezoid. Other terms used to indicate shape are *latissimus* (wide) and *teres* (round).

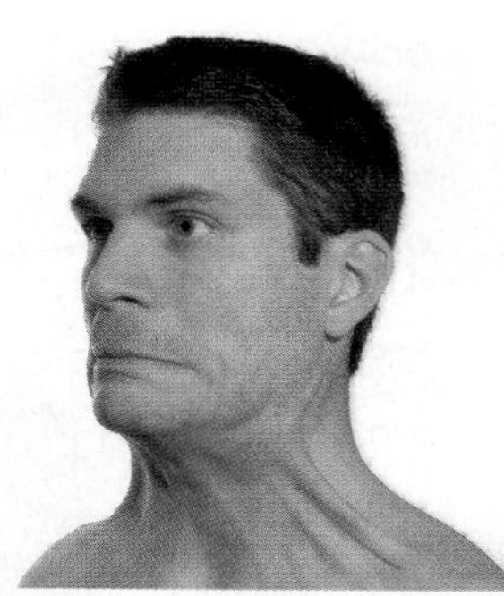

Figure 13.4 Facial expressions.
Our many facial expressions are due to muscle contractions.
(both photos): J.W. Ramsey/McGraw Hill

- *Location.* The *external oblique* muscles are located outside the *internal obliques.* The *frontalis* muscle overlies the frontal bone. Other terms used to indicate location are *pectoralis* (chest), *gluteus* (buttock), *brachii* (arm), and *sub* (beneath).
- *Direction of muscle fibers.* The *rectus abdominis* is a longitudinal muscle of the abdomen (*rectus* means "straight"). The *orbicularis oculi* is a circular muscle around the eye. Other terms used to indicate direction are *transverse* (across) and *oblique* (diagonal).
- *Attachment.* The *sternocleidomastoid* is attached to the sternum, clavicle, and mastoid process. The mastoid process is located on the temporal bone of the skull. The *brachioradialis* is attached to the brachium (arm) and the radius (forearm).
- *Number of attachments.* The *biceps brachii* has two attachments, or origins, and is located on the arm. The *quadriceps femoris* has four origins and is located on the femur.
- *Action.* The *extensor digitorum* extends the fingers, or digits. The *adductor longus* is a large muscle that adducts the thigh. Adduction is the movement of a body part toward the midline. Other terms used to indicate action are *flexor* (to flex or bend), *masseter* (to chew), and *levator* (to lift).

BIOLOGY IN YOUR LIFE

Which muscles are best to use for vaccines?

When giving intramuscular injections, health-care providers have to choose muscles that are sufficiently large and well developed to tolerate the injections. But they must also avoid muscles that contain large blood vessels or nerves, because an injection in these muscles could pierce a blood vessel or damage a nerve. Typically, they choose one of three preferred injection sites. The deltoid muscle on the upper arm is usually well developed in older children and adults. The vastus lateralis on the side of the thigh (part of the quadriceps group) is the best site for infants and young children. The gluteus medius is on the lower back, above the buttock. However, a clinician injecting into the gluteus medius must be careful to avoid the gluteus maximus (buttock) muscle. The body's largest nerve, the sciatic nerve, lies underneath and within the gluteus maximus.

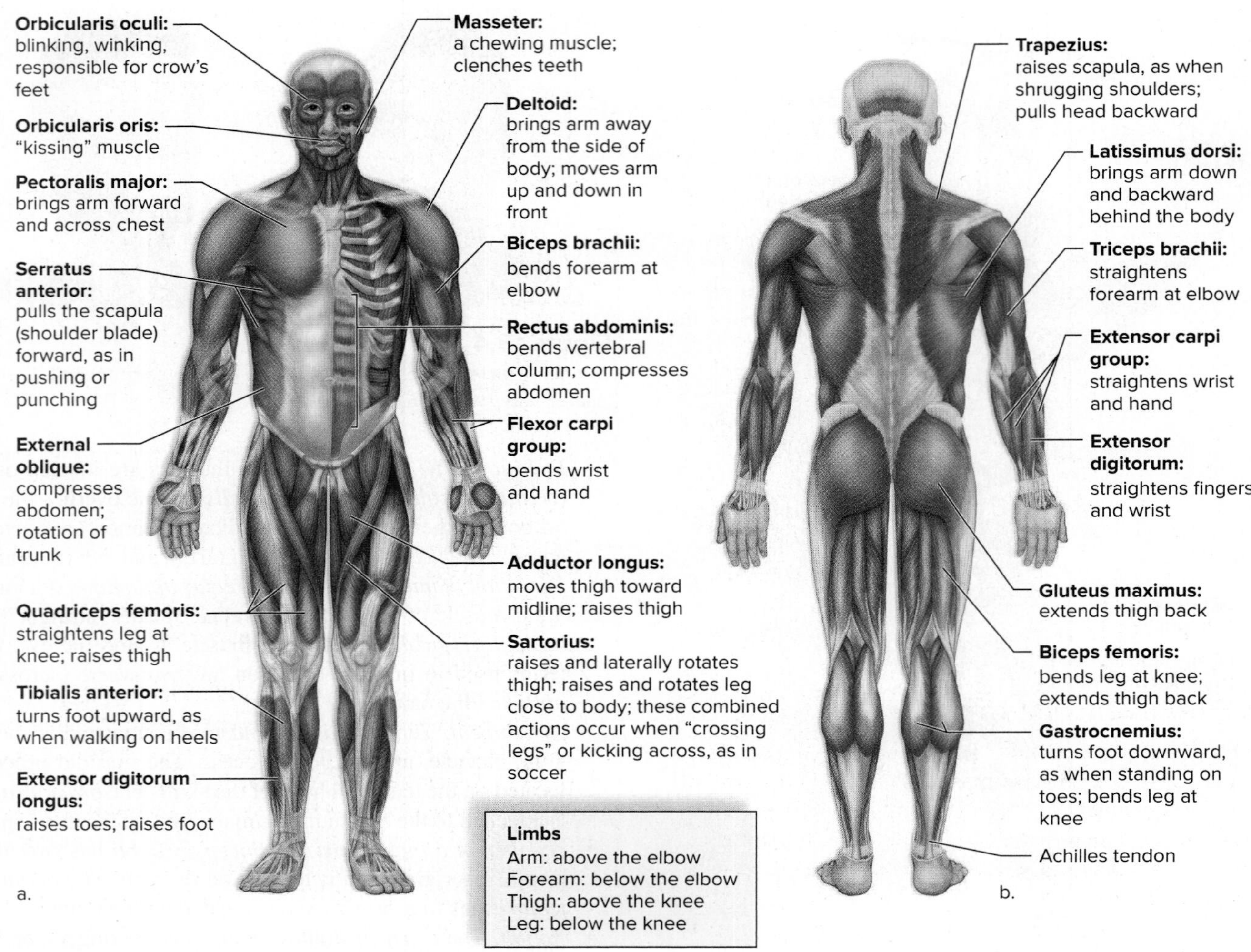

Orbicularis oculi: blinking, winking, responsible for crow's feet
Orbicularis oris: "kissing" muscle
Pectoralis major: brings arm forward and across chest
Serratus anterior: pulls the scapula (shoulder blade) forward, as in pushing or punching
External oblique: compresses abdomen; rotation of trunk
Quadriceps femoris: straightens leg at knee; raises thigh
Tibialis anterior: turns foot upward, as when walking on heels
Extensor digitorum longus: raises toes; raises foot
a.
Masseter: a chewing muscle; clenches teeth
Deltoid: brings arm away from the side of body; moves arm up and down in front
Biceps brachii: bends forearm at elbow
Rectus abdominis: bends vertebral column; compresses abdomen
Flexor carpi group: bends wrist and hand
Adductor longus: moves thigh toward midline; raises thigh
Sartorius: raises and laterally rotates thigh; raises and rotates leg close to body; these combined actions occur when "crossing legs" or kicking across, as in soccer
Limbs
Arm: above the elbow
Forearm: below the elbow
Thigh: above the knee
Leg: below the knee
Trapezius: raises scapula, as when shrugging shoulders; pulls head backward
Latissimus dorsi: brings arm down and backward behind the body
Triceps brachii: straightens forearm at elbow
Extensor carpi group: straightens wrist and hand
Extensor digitorum: straightens fingers and wrist
Gluteus maximus: extends thigh back
Biceps femoris: bends leg at knee; extends thigh back
Gastrocnemius: turns foot downward, as when standing on toes; bends leg at knee
Achilles tendon
b.

Figure 13.5 The major skeletal muscles of the human body.
a. Anterior view. **b.** Posterior view.

CHECK YOUR PROGRESS 13.1

1. State the three types of muscles in the human body and explain where each is found in the body.
2. Summarize the functions of skeletal muscles.
3. Explain how skeletal muscles work together to cause bones to move.

CONNECTING THE CONCEPTS

For more information on the three types of muscles, refer to the following discussions:

Section 4.3 describes the general structure of cardiac, smooth, and skeletal muscle.

Section 5.3 examines the function of cardiac muscle in the heart.

Section 9.1 illustrates how smooth muscle lines the wall of the digestive tract.

13.2 Skeletal Muscle Fiber Contraction

LEARNING OUTCOMES

Upon completion of this section, you should be able to

1. Identify the structures of a muscle fiber.
2. Explain how the sliding filament model is responsible for muscle contraction.
3. Summarize how activities within the neuromuscular junction control muscle fiber contraction.

In Section 13.1, we examined the structure of skeletal muscle. Skeletal muscle tissue has alternating light and dark bands, giving it a striated appearance. These bands are due to the arrangement of myofilaments in a muscle fiber.

Table 13.1 Anatomy of a Muscle Fiber

Name	Function
Sarcolemma	The plasma membrane of a muscle fiber that forms T tubules.
Sarcoplasm	The cytoplasm of a muscle fiber that contains the organelles, including myofibrils.
Myoglobin	A red pigment that stores oxygen for muscle contraction.
T tubule	An extension of the sarcolemma that extends into the muscle fiber and conveys impulses that cause Ca^{2+} to be released from the sarcoplasmic reticulum.
Sarcoplasmic reticulum	The smooth endoplasmic reticulum (ER) of a muscle fiber that stores Ca^{2+}.
Myofibril	A bundle of myofilaments that contracts.
Myofilament	Actin filaments and myosin filaments whose structure accounts for the muscle striations and functions in muscle contraction.

BIOLOGY IN YOUR LIFE

Why don't muscle cells use hemoglobin?

Hemoglobin is the primary transport pigment of oxygen in the bloodstream. However, as the temperature of the tissue rises and the pH becomes more acidic, hemoglobin loses its ability to bind the oxygen molecules. This is where myoglobin comes in. Like hemoglobin, myoglobin binds oxygen molecules. However, myoglobin has a higher affinity (attraction) for oxygen than hemoglobin. So when you exercise or use a muscle group, the increase in temperature causes the oxygen in the hemoglobin to be transferred to the myoglobin of the muscle cells. This allows for an efficient transfer of oxygen to those muscles that are actively contracting.

Muscle Fibers and How They Move

A muscle fiber is a cell containing the usual cellular components (see Section 3.2), but special names have been assigned to some of these components (Table 13.1). For example, the plasma membrane is called the **sarcolemma** (*sarco-* means "muscle"); the cytoplasm is the **sarcoplasm;** and the endoplasmic reticulum is the **sarcoplasmic reticulum.** A muscle fiber also has some unique anatomical characteristics. One feature is its T (for *transverse*) system. The sarcolemma forms **T (transverse) tubules,** which penetrate, or dip down, into the cells. The transverse tubules come into contact—but do not fuse—with expanded portions of the sarcoplasmic reticulum. The expanded portions of the sarcoplasmic reticulum are calcium storage sites. Calcium ions (Ca^{2+}), as we will see, are essential for muscle contraction. Glycogen, a complex carbohydrate (see Section 2.4), is the preferred energy source for muscle contraction.

The sarcolemma encases hundreds and sometimes even thousands of **myofibrils,** each about 1 μm in diameter. Myofibrils are the contractile portions of the muscle fibers. Any other organelles, such as mitochondria, are located in the sarcoplasm between the myofibrils. The sarcoplasm also contains glycogen, which provides stored energy for muscle contraction. In addition, sarcoplasm includes the red pigment myoglobin, which binds oxygen until it is needed for muscle contraction.

Myofibrils and Sarcomeres

Figure 13.6 illustrates the structure of a skeletal myocyte, also called a muscle fiber. Notice that the muscle fiber is roughly cylindrical in shape. Grouped inside this larger cylinder are smaller cylinders called **myofibrils** (Fig. 13.6*a*). Myofibrils run the entire length of the muscle fiber. Myofibrils are composed of even smaller cylinders called **myofilaments.** Thus, the muscle cell is a set of small cylinders (myofilaments) assembled into larger cylinders (myofibrils) clustered within the largest cylinder (the muscle fiber).

Under a light microscope, the skeletal muscle fibers have light and dark bands called striations (Fig. 13.6*b*). At the higher magnification provided by an electron microscope, one can see that the striations of skeletal muscle fibers are formed by the placement of myofilaments within myofibrils. There are two types of myofilaments. Thick myofilaments are made up of a protein called **myosin,** and thin myofilaments are composed of a second protein termed **actin.** Myofibrils are further divided vertically into **sarcomeres.** A sarcomere extends between two dark vertical lines called the Z lines. The I bands on either side of the Z line are light colored, because each contains only the thin actin myofilaments. The dark central A band within the sarcomere is composed of overlapping actin and myosin myofilaments. Centered within the A band is a vertical H band. In an uncontracted sarcomere, the H band lacks thin actin myofilaments and contains only thick myosin myofilaments.

The thick and thin filaments differ in the following ways:

- *Thick filaments.* A thick filament is composed of several hundred molecules of the protein myosin. Each myosin molecule is shaped like a golf club, with the straight portion of the molecule ending in a globular head. The heads occur on each side of a sarcomere but not in the middle (Fig. 13.6).
- *Thin filaments.* Primarily, a thin filament consists of two intertwining strands of the protein actin. Two other proteins, called tropomyosin and troponin, also play a role, as we will discuss later in this section.

The Sliding Filament Model

As we will see next, when muscles are stimulated, electrical signals travel across the sarcolemma and then down a T tubule. In turn, this signals calcium to be released from the sarcoplasmic reticulum.

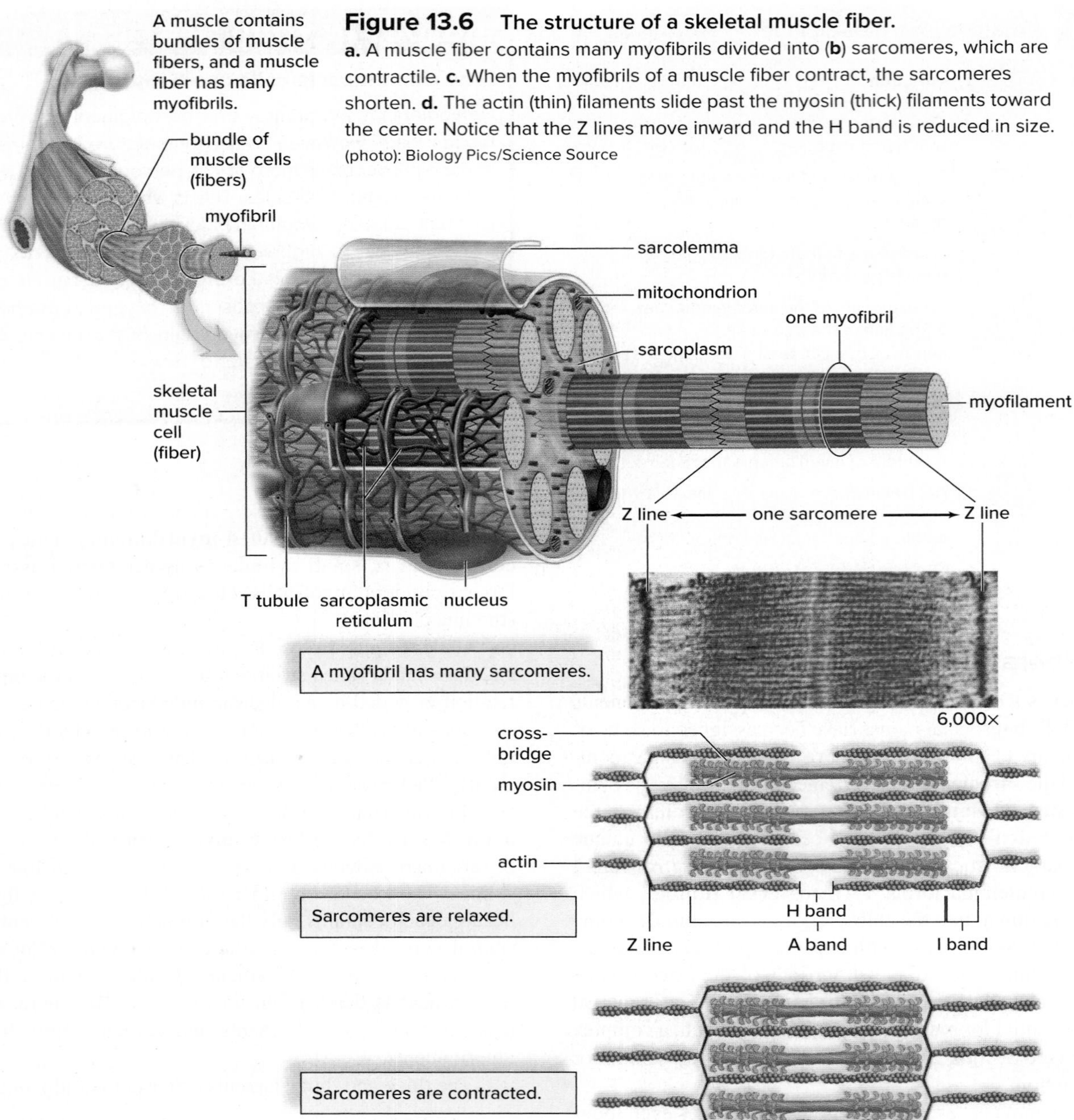

Figure 13.6 **The structure of a skeletal muscle fiber.** **a.** A muscle fiber contains many myofibrils divided into (**b**) sarcomeres, which are contractile. **c.** When the myofibrils of a muscle fiber contract, the sarcomeres shorten. **d.** The actin (thin) filaments slide past the myosin (thick) filaments toward the center. Notice that the Z lines move inward and the H band is reduced in size. (photo): Biology Pics/Science Source

Now the muscle fiber contracts as the sarcomeres within the myofibrils shorten. As you compare the relaxed sarcomere with the contracted sarcomere (Fig. 13.6*c*), note that the filaments themselves remain the same length. When a sarcomere shortens, the actin (thin) filaments approach one another as they slide past the myosin (thick) filaments. This causes the I band to shorten, the Z line to move inward, and the H band to almost or completely disappear (Fig. 13.6*d*). The sarcomere changes from a rectangular shape to a square as it shortens.

The movement of actin filaments in relation to myosin filaments is called the **sliding filament model** of muscle contraction. ATP supplies the energy for muscle contraction. Although the actin filaments slide past the myosin filaments, it is the myosin filaments that do the work. Myosin filaments break down ATP, and their cross-bridges pull the actin filament toward the center of the sarcomere.

As an analogy, think of yourself and a group of friends as myosin. Collectively, your hands are the cross-bridges, and you are pulling on a rope (actin) to get an object tied to the end of the rope (the Z line). As you pull the rope, you grab, pull, release, and then grab farther along on the rope.

Muscle Fiber Contraction

Muscle fibers are stimulated to contract by motor neurons whose axons are grouped together to form nerves. The axon of one

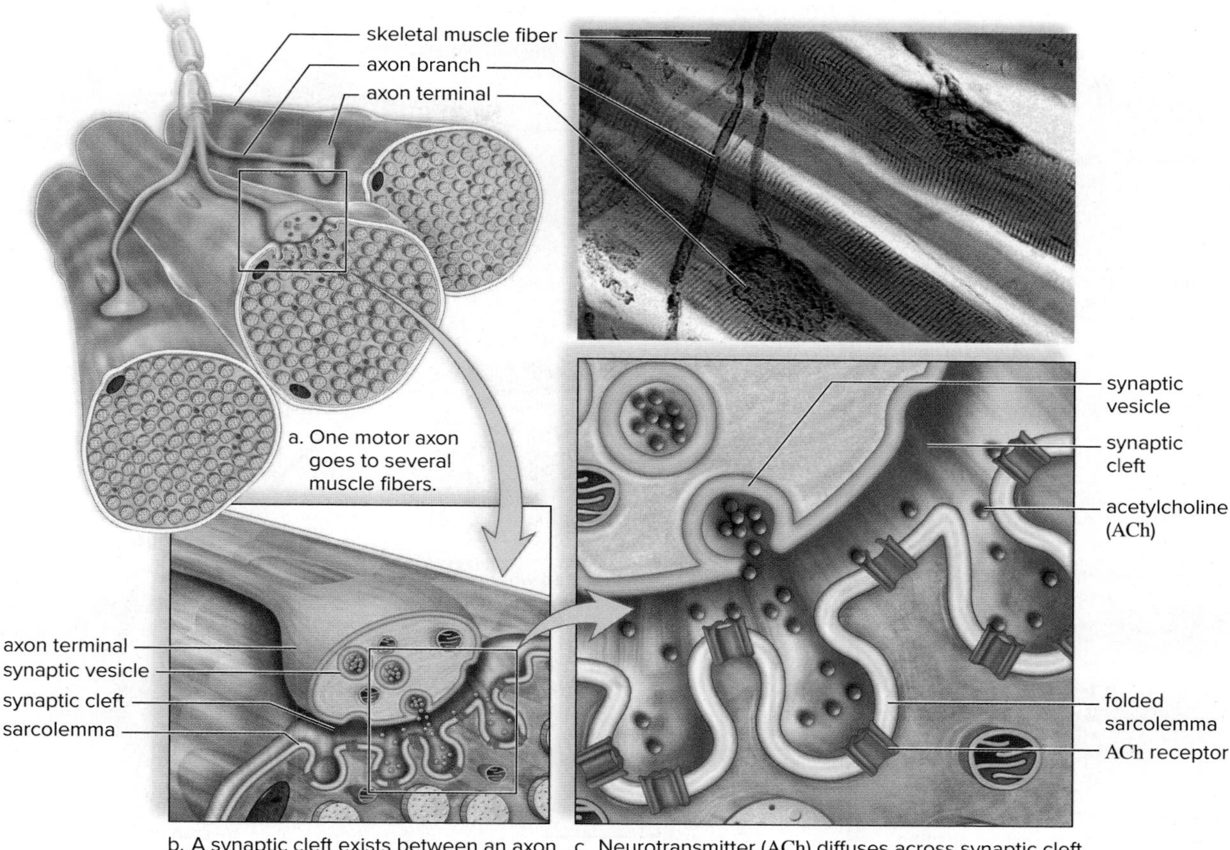

b. A synaptic cleft exists between an axon terminal and a muscle fiber. c. Neurotransmitter (ACh) diffuses across synaptic cleft and binds to receptors in sarcolemma.

Figure 13.7 Neuromuscular junctions.
a. The branch of a motor nerve fiber terminates in an axon terminal. **b.** A synaptic cleft separates the axon terminal from the sarcolemma of the muscle fiber. **c.** Nerve impulses traveling down a motor fiber cause synaptic vesicles to discharge acetylcholine, which diffuses across the synaptic cleft and binds to ACh receptors. Impulses travel down the T tubules of a muscle fiber, and the muscle fiber contracts.
(photo): Ed Reschke/Stone/Getty Images

motor neuron can stimulate from a few to several muscle fibers of a muscle, because each axon has several branches (Fig. 13.7*a*). Each branch of an axon ends in an axon terminal that lies in close proximity to the sarcolemma of a muscle fiber. A small gap, called a synaptic cleft, separates the axon terminal from the sarcolemma (Fig. 13.7*b*). This entire region is called a **neuromuscular junction.**

Axon terminals contain synaptic vesicles filled with the neurotransmitter acetylcholine (ACh). Nerve signals travel down the axons of motor neurons and arrive at an axon terminal. The signals trigger the synaptic vesicles to release ACh into the synaptic cleft (Fig. 13.7*c*). When ACh is released, it quickly diffuses across the cleft and binds to receptors in the sarcolemma. Now, the sarcolemma generates electrical signals that spread across the sarcolemma and down the T tubules. Recall that the T tubules lie adjacent to the sarcoplasmic reticulum, but the two structures are not connected. Nonetheless, signaling from the T tubules causes the release of Ca^{2+} from the sarcoplasmic reticulum, which leads to sarcomere contraction, as explained in Figure 13.8.

The Science feature "Botox and Wrinkles" explores how a drug called Botox, the trade name for a bacterial neurotoxin called botulinum toxin A, was discovered as a treatment for several medical conditions, including prevention of wrinkling on the face.

Two other proteins are associated with an actin filament. Threads of **tropomyosin** wind about an actin filament, covering binding sites for myosin located on each actin molecule. **Troponin** occurs at intervals along the threads. When Ca^{2+} is released from the sarcoplasmic reticulum, it combines with troponin. This causes the tropomyosin threads to shift their position, exposing myosin-binding sites. In other words, myosin can now bind to actin (Fig. 13.8*a*).

To fully understand muscle contraction, examine Figure 13.8*b* and notice the following:

1. The heads of a myosin filament have ATP-binding sites. At this site, ATP is hydrolyzed, or split, to form ADP and Ⓟ.
2. The ADP and Ⓟ remain on the myosin heads, and the heads attach to an actin-binding site. Joining myosin to actin forms temporary bonds called cross-bridges.

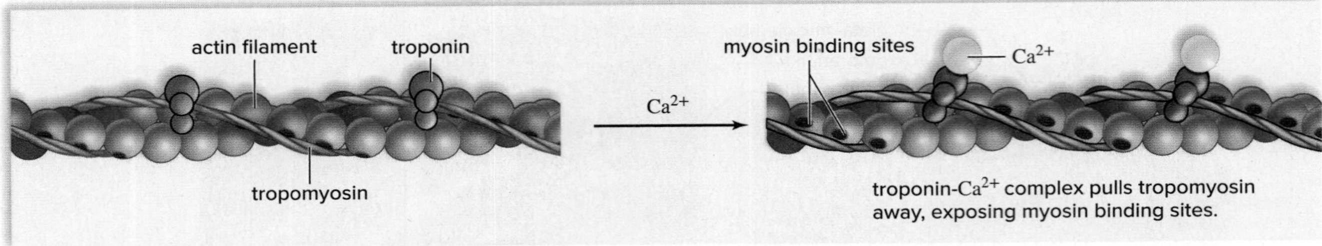

a. Function of Ca^{2+} ions in muscle contraction

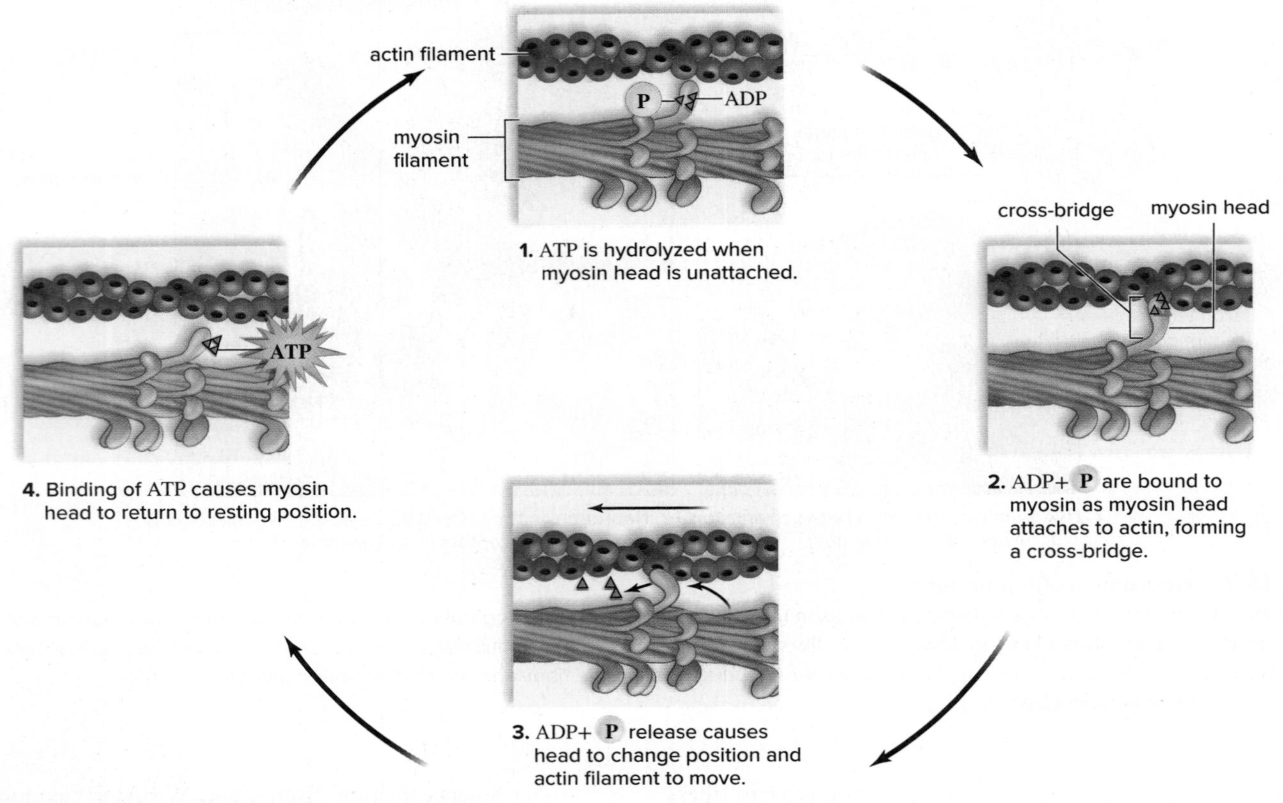

b. Function of cross-bridges in muscle contraction

Figure 13.8 The role of calcium ions and ATP during muscular contraction.
a. Calcium ions (Ca^{2+}) bind to troponin, exposing myosin-binding sites. **b.** Follow steps 1 through 4 to see how myosin uses ATP and does the work of pulling actin toward the center of the sarcomere.

3. Now, ADP and Ⓟ are released and the cross-bridges bend sharply. This is the power stroke that pulls the actin filament toward the center of the sarcomere.
4. When ATP molecules again bind to the myosin heads, the cross-bridges are broken. Myosin heads detach from the actin filament. This is the step that does not happen during rigor mortis (see the Science feature "Rigor Mortis" in Section 13.3). Relaxing the muscle is impossible, because ATP is needed to break the bond between an actin-binding site and the myosin cross-bridge.

In living muscle, the cycle begins again and myosin reattaches farther along the actin filament. The cycle recurs until calcium ions are actively returned to the calcium storage sites. This step also requires ATP.

CHECK YOUR PROGRESS 13.2

1. Explain the role of the myofibril, myofilament, and sarcomere in a muscle fiber.
2. Explain how the thin and thick filaments interact in the sliding filament model.
3. Describe the role of both ATP and calcium ions in muscle contraction.

BIOLOGY TODAY ▶ Science

Botox and Wrinkles

Several of the most important bacterial pathogens that cause human diseases—including cholera, diphtheria, tetanus, and botulism—do so by secreting potent toxins capable of sickening or killing their hosts. The botulinum toxin, produced by the bacterium *Clostridium botulinum,* is one of the most lethal substances known. Less than a microgram (μg) of the purified toxin can kill an average-size person, and 4 kilograms (kg) (8.8 pounds [lb]) would be enough to kill all humans on Earth! Given this scary fact, it seems that the scientists who discovered the lethal activity of this bacterial toxin nearly 200 years ago could never have anticipated that the intentional injection of a very dilute form of botulinum toxin (now known as Botox) would become the most common nonsurgical cosmetic procedure performed by many physicians. As with many breakthroughs in science and medicine, the pathway from thinking about botulism as a deadly disease to using botulinum toxin as a beneficial treatment involved the hard work of many scientists, mixed with a considerable amount of luck.

In the 1820s, a German scientist, Justinus Kerner, was able to prove that the deaths of several people had been caused by their consumption of spoiled sausage (in fact, botulism is named for the Latin word for "sausage," *botulus*). A few decades later, a Belgian researcher named Emile Pierre van Ermengem identified the specific bacterium responsible for producing the botulinum toxin, which can cause symptoms ranging from droopy eyelids to paralysis and respiratory failure.

By the 1920s, medical scientists at the University of California had obtained the toxin in pure form, which allowed them to determine that it acts by preventing nerves from communicating with muscles, specifically by interfering with the release of acetylcholine from the axon terminals of motor nerves.

Scientists soon began testing very dilute concentrations of the toxin as a treatment for conditions in which the muscles contract too much, such as crossed eyes or spasms of the facial muscles or vocal cords. In 1989, the FDA first approved diluted botulinum toxin (Botox) for treating specific eye conditions called blepharospasm (eyelid spasm) and strabismus (crossing of the eyes).

Right around this time, a lucky break occurred that eventually would open the medical community's eyes to the greater potential of the diluted toxin. A Canadian ophthalmologist, Jean Carruthers, had been using it to treat her patients' eye conditions when she noticed that some of their wrinkles had also subsided. One night at a family dinner, Dr. Carruthers shared this information with her husband, a dermatologist, who decided to investigate whether he could reduce the deep wrinkles of some of his patients by injecting the dilute toxin into their skin. The treatment worked well, and after trying it on several more patients (as well as on themselves!), the Canadian doctors spent several years presenting their findings at scientific meetings and in research journals. Although this was initially met with criticism by the scientific community, the Carrutherses eventually were able to convince the scientific community that diluted botulinum toxin was effective in treating wrinkles; however, they never patented it for that use, so they missed out on much of the almost $4 billion in annual sales the drug now earns for the company that did patent it.

The uses of diluted botulinum toxin seem to be growing since it was FDA approved for the treatment of frown lines in 2002 (Fig. 13A). In March 2010, it was approved for the treatment of muscle stiffness in people with upper limb spasticity, and the company has approval for as many as 90 uses of diluted botulinum toxin, including treatment of migraine headaches.

Questions to Consider

1. Considering that botulism is caused by a preformed toxin, how do you suppose it can be treated?
2. Do you think companies should be allowed to patent a naturally occurring molecule such as botulinum toxin? Why or why not?

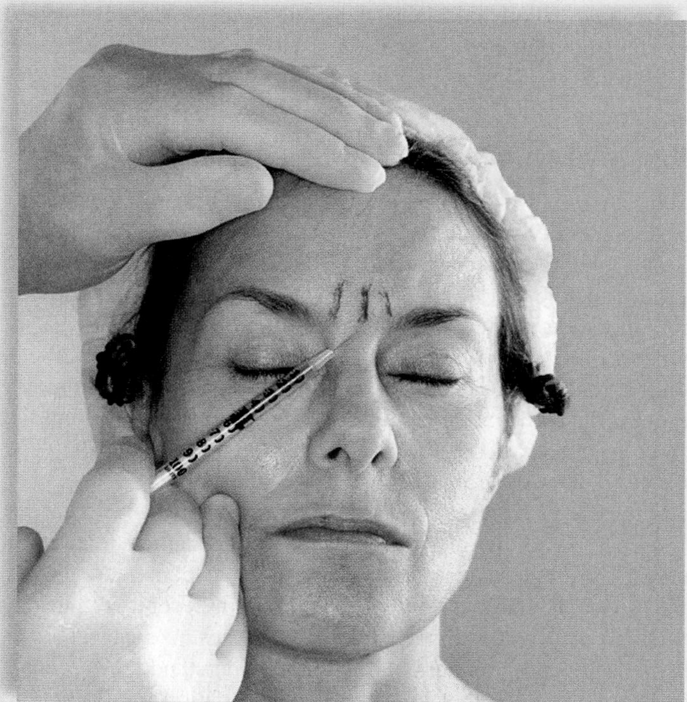

Figure 13A Botox Treatment.
This woman's wrinkles are being treated with diluted botulinum toxin.
Thinkstock/Comstock Images/Getty Images

CONNECTING THE CONCEPTS

For more information on ATP and how the nervous system controls the contraction of skeletal muscle, refer to the following discussions:

Figure 3.21 illustrates the ATP–ADP cycle.

Section 14.2 explains the role of neurotransmitters, such as acetylcholine, in the nervous system.

Figure 14.5 illustrates the action of neurotransmitters in the synaptic cleft.

13.3 Whole Muscle Contraction

LEARNING OUTCOMES

Upon completion of this section, you should be able to

1. List the stages of a muscle twitch and explain what is occurring in each stage.
2. Explain how summation and tetanus increase the strength of whole muscle contraction.
3. Summarize how muscle cells produce ATP for muscle contraction.
4. Distinguish between fast-twitch and slow-twitch muscle fibers.

In order for a whole muscle, such as the biceps or triceps, to contract, the individual muscle fibers must be activated by signals from the nervous system.

Muscles Have Motor Units

In Section 13.2, we explored how each axon within a nerve stimulates a number of muscle fibers. A nerve fiber with all the muscle fibers it innervates is called a **motor unit.** A motor unit operates on the principle of "all-or-none." Why? Because all the muscle fibers in a motor unit are stimulated at once. They all either contract or do not contract. What varies is the number of muscle fibers within a motor unit. For example, in the ocular muscles that move the eyes, the innervation ratio is one motor axon per 23 muscle fibers. By contrast, in the gastrocnemius muscle of the leg, the ratio is about one motor axon per 1,000 muscle fibers. Thus, moving the eyes requires finer control than moving the legs.

When a motor unit is stimulated by infrequent electrical impulses, a single contraction occurs. This response is called a **muscle twitch** and lasts only a fraction of a second. A muscle twitch is customarily divided into three stages. We can use our knowledge of muscle fiber contraction to understand these events. The latent period is the time between stimulation and initiation of contraction (Fig. 13.9*a*). During this time, we can imagine that the events that begin muscle contraction are occurring. The neurotransmitter acetylcholine (ACh) diffuses across the synaptic cleft, causing an electrical signal to spread across the sarcolemma and down the T tubules. The contraction period follows as calcium leaves the sarcoplasmic reticulum and myosin-actin cross-bridges form. As you know, the muscle shortens as it contracts. On the graph, the force increases as the muscle contracts. Finally, the relaxation period completes the muscle twitch. Myosin-actin cross-bridges are broken, and calcium returns to the sarcoplasmic reticulum. Force diminishes as the muscle returns to its former length.

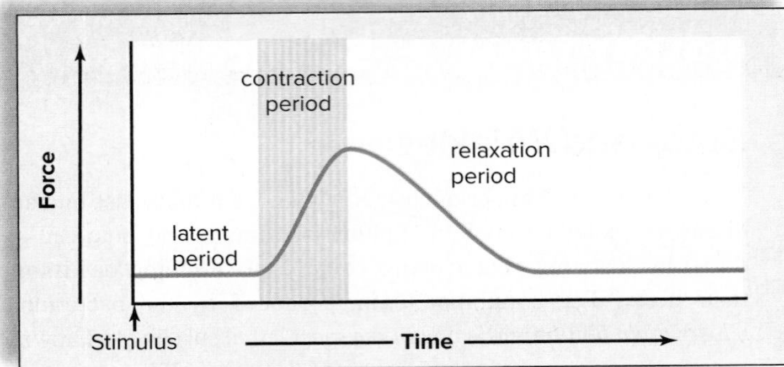

a.

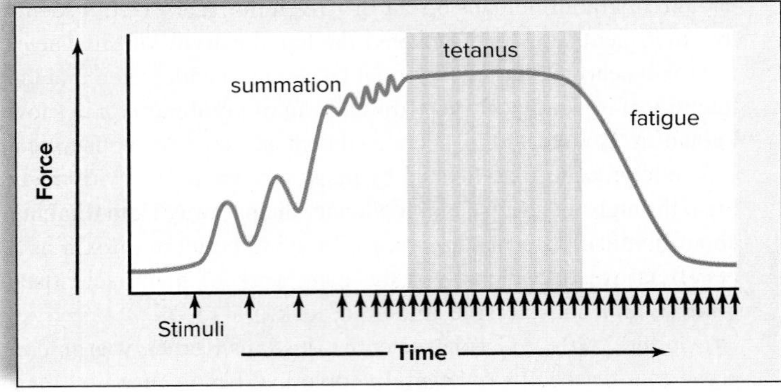

b.

Figure 13.9 The three phases of a single muscle twitch. **a.** Stimulation of a muscle by a single electrical signal results in a simple muscle twitch: first, a latent period, followed by contraction and relaxation. **b.** Repeated stimulation results in summation and tetanus, which creates greater force, because the motor unit cannot relax between stimuli.

If a motor unit is given a rapid series of stimuli, it can respond to the next stimulus without relaxing completely. *Summation* is increased muscle contraction until maximal sustained contraction, called **tetanus,** is achieved (Fig. 13.9*b*). Tetanus continues until the muscle fatigues due to depletion of energy reserves. Fatigue is apparent when a muscle relaxes, even though stimulation continues. The tetanus of muscle cells is not the same as the infection called tetanus. The infection called tetanus is caused by the bacterium *Clostridium tetani.* Death occurs because the muscles, including the respiratory muscles, become fully contracted and do not relax.

A whole muscle typically contains many motor units. As the intensity of nervous stimulation increases, more motor units in a muscle are activated. This phenomenon is known as *recruitment.* Maximum contraction of a muscle would require that all motor units be undergoing tetanic contraction. This rarely happens, because they could all fatigue at the same time. Instead, some motor units are contracting maximally while others are resting, allowing sustained contractions to occur.

Muscle Tone

One desirable effect of exercise is to have good **muscle tone.** Muscles that have good tone are firm and solid, as opposed to soft and flabby. The amount of muscle tone is dependent on muscle contraction. Some motor units are always contracted—but not enough to cause movement.

Energy for Muscle Contraction

Muscles can use various fuel sources for energy, and they have various ways of producing the ATP needed for muscle contraction.

Fuel Sources for Exercise

A muscle has four possible energy sources (Fig. 13.10). Two of these are stored in muscle (glycogen and triglycerides), and two are acquired from blood (glucose and fatty acids). The amount of each of these used depends on exercise intensity and duration. Figure 13.10 shows the percentage of energy derived from these sources due to submaximal exercise (65–75% of effort that an individual is capable of) over time. Notice that as the length of the exercise period is increased, use of muscle energy stores, such as glycogen and triglycerides, decreases and use of energy sources from the blood (glucose and fatty acids) increases.

Blood glucose and plasma fatty acids are delivered to muscles by circulating blood. Many of us exercise to maintain or lose weight. Therefore, we are particularly interested in increasing the use of plasma fatty acids as an energy source by muscle cells. Adipose tissue is the source of plasma fatty acids for muscle contraction. Figure 13.10 shows that the amount of fat burned increases when more time is spent in exercise. Therefore, a diet that restricts the amount of fat eaten, when combined with exercise, will decrease body fat. Submaximal exercise burns fat better than maximal exercise, for reasons we will now explore.

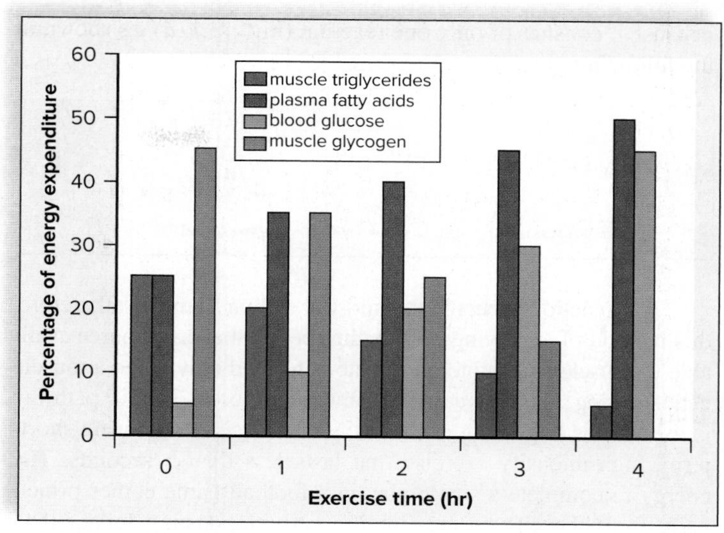

Figure 13.10 **The sources of energy for muscle contraction.** The percentage of energy derived from each of the four major fuel sources during submaximal exercise (65–75% of effort) is illustrated. The amount from plasma fatty acids increases during the time span shown.

Sources of ATP for Muscle Contraction

Muscle cells store limited amounts of ATP. Once stored ATP is used up, the cells have three ways to produce more ATP (Fig. 13.11). The three ways are (1) formation of ATP by the creatine phosphate (CP) pathway; (2) formation of ATP by fermentation; and (3) formation of ATP by cellular respiration, which involves the use of oxygen by mitochondria. Aerobic exercising depends on cellular respiration to supply ATP. Neither the CP pathway nor fermentation requires oxygen to form ATP; both are anaerobic processes.

The Creatine Phosphate Pathway The simplest and most rapid way for muscle to produce ATP is to use the CP pathway,

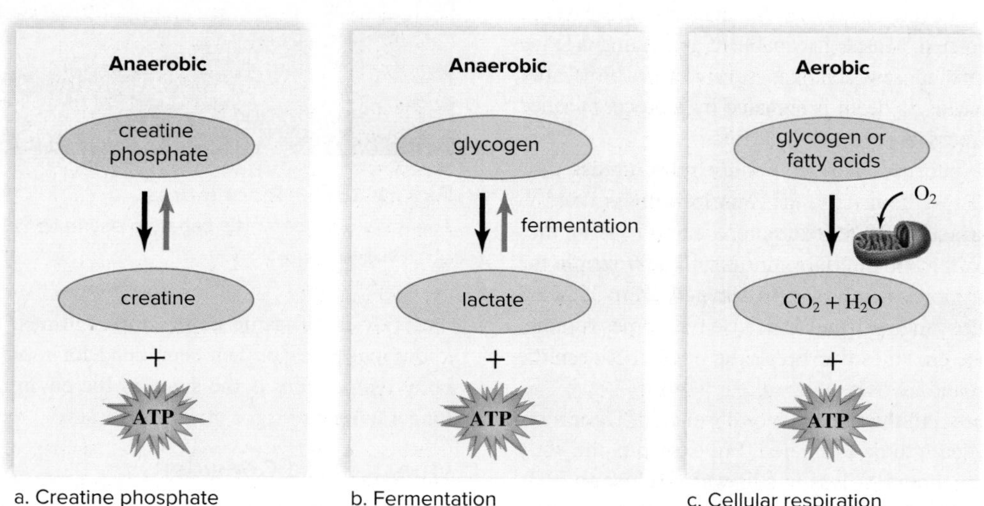

Figure 13.11 **The three pathways by which muscle cells produce ATP energy for contraction.**
a. When contraction begins, muscle cells break down creatine phosphate to produce ATP. When resting, muscle cells rebuild their supply of creatine phosphate (red arrow). **b.** Muscle cells also use fermentation to produce ATP quickly. When resting, muscle cells metabolize lactate, re-forming as much glucose and then glycogen as possible (red arrow). **c.** For the long term, muscle cells switch to cellular respiration to produce ATP aerobically.

because it consists of only one reaction (Fig. 13.11*a*), as shown in the following graphic:

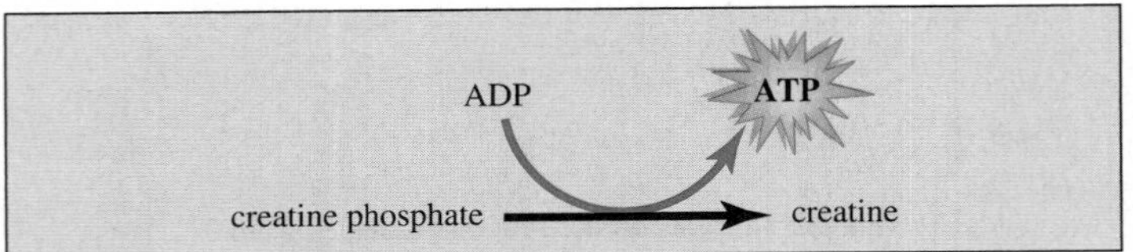

This reaction occurs in the midst of sliding filaments; therefore, this method of supplying ATP is the speediest energy source available to muscles. Creatine phosphate is formed only when a muscle cell is resting, and only a limited amount is stored. The CP pathway is used at the beginning of submaximal exercise and during short-term, high-intensity exercise that lasts less than 5 seconds. The energy to complete a single play in a football game comes principally from the CP system. Intense activities lasting longer than 5 seconds also make use of fermentation.

Fermentation The anaerobic processes of glycolysis and fermentation (see Section 3.6) produce two ATP molecules from the breakdown of glucose to lactate. This pathway is the one most likely to begin with glycogen. Hormones provide the signal to muscle cells to break down glycogen, making glucose available as an energy source.

Fermentation, like the CP pathway, is fast-acting, but it results in the buildup of lactate (Fig. 13.11*b*). We have all had the experience of heavy breathing following strenuous exercise. This continued intake of oxygen, called **oxygen debt,** is required, in part, to complete the metabolism of lactate and restore cells to their original energy state. The lactate is transported to the liver, where 20% of it is completely broken down to carbon dioxide and water. The ATP gained by this respiration is then used to reconvert 80% of the lactate to glucose and then glycogen. In persons who train, the number of mitochondria in individual muscles increases. There is a greater reliance on these additional mitochondria to produce ATP. Muscles rely less on fermentation as a result.

Cellular Respiration Cellular respiration is the slowest of all three mechanisms used to produce ATP. However, it is also the most efficient, typically producing several dozen molecules of ATP from each food molecule. As was discussed in Section 3.6, cellular respiration occurs in the mitochondria. Thus, the process is aerobic and oxygen is supplied by the respiratory system. In addition, a protein called **myoglobin** in muscle cells delivers oxygen directly

BIOLOGY TODAY ▶ Science

Rigor Mortis

When a person dies, the physiological events that accompany death occur in an orderly progression. Respiration ceases and the heart ultimately stops beating, and tissue cells begin to die. The first tissues to die are those with the highest oxygen requirement. Brain and nervous tissues have an extremely high requirement for oxygen. Deprived of oxygen, these cells typically die after only 6 minutes because of a lack of ATP. However, tissues that can produce ATP by fermentation (which does not require oxygen) can "live" for an hour or more before ATP is completely depleted. Muscle is capable of generating ATP by fermentation. Therefore, muscle cells can survive for a time after clinical death occurs. Muscle death is signaled by a process termed *rigor mortis,* the "stiffness of death" (Fig. 13B).

Stiffness occurs because muscles cannot relax unless they have a supply of ATP. Without ATP, the muscles remain fixed in their last state of contraction. If, for example, a murder victim dies while sitting at a desk, the body in rigor mortis will be frozen in the sitting position. Rigor mortis resolves approximately 24 to 36 hours after death. Muscles lose their stiffness because lysosomes rupture. The lysosomes release enzymes that break the bonds between the muscle proteins actin and myosin.

Body temperature and the presence or absence of rigor mortis allow the time of death to be estimated. For example, the body of someone dead for 3 hours or less is still warm (close to body temperature, 98.6°F [37°C]) and rigor mortis is absent. After approximately 3 hours, the body is significantly cooler than normal and rigor mortis begins to develop. The corpse of an individual dead at least 8 hours is in full rigor mortis, and the temperature of the body is the same as the surroundings. Forensic pathologists know that a person has been dead for more than 24 hours if the body temperature is the same as the environment and there is no longer a trace of rigor mortis.

Figure 13B Rigor mortis.
The level of rigor mortis can help estimate the time of death.
Justin Sullivan/Getty Images

Questions to Consider

1. At the level of the sarcomere, explain what is happening during the onset of rigor mortis.
2. How do you think the surrounding temperature influences the onset of rigor mortis?

to the mitochondria. Cellular respiration can make use of glucose from the breakdown of stored muscle glycogen, glucose taken up from blood, and/or fatty acids from fat digestion (Fig. 13.11*c*). Also, cellular respiration is more likely to supply ATP when exercise is submaximal in intensity. According to Figure 13.9, if you are interested in exercising to lose weight, you should do so at a lower intensity and for a longer amount of time. Many exercise programs now target these levels. In effect, they are all maximizing the use of triglycerides, or fat, for making ATP by cellular respiration.

When we die, these muscle cells are deprived of their ability to generate energy. As the Science feature "Rigor Mortis" explains, a series of events occurs that can help forensic scientists estimate the time of death.

Fast-Twitch and Slow-Twitch Muscle Fibers

We have seen that all muscle fibers metabolize aerobically and anaerobically. However, some muscle fibers use one method more than the other to provide myofibrils with ATP. Fast-twitch fibers tend to rely on the creatine phosphate pathway and fermentation, anaerobic means of supplying ATP to muscles. Slow-twitch fibers tend to prefer cellular respiration, which is aerobic.

Fast-Twitch Fibers

Fast-twitch fibers are usually anaerobic and seem to be designed for strength, because their motor units contain many fibers (Fig. 13.12). They provide explosions of energy and are most helpful in sports activities such as sprinting, weightlifting, swinging a golf club, or throwing a shot. Fast-twitch fibers are light in color, because they have fewer mitochondria, little or no myoglobin, and fewer blood vessels than do slow-twitch fibers. Fast-twitch fibers can develop maximum tension more rapidly than slow-twitch fibers can. In addition, their maximum tension is greater. However, their dependence on anaerobic energy leaves them vulnerable to an accumulation of lactate, which causes them to fatigue quickly.

Slow-Twitch Fibers

Despite having motor units with smaller numbers of muscle fibers, *slow-twitch fibers* have more stamina and a steadier "tug." These muscle fibers are most helpful in endurance sports, such as long-distance running, biking, jogging, and swimming. They produce most of their energy aerobically, so they tire only when their fuel supply is gone. Slow-twitch fibers have many mitochondria and are dark in color, because they contain myoglobin, the respiratory pigment found in muscles (Fig. 13.12). They are also surrounded by dense capillary beds and draw more blood and oxygen than fast-twitch fibers. Slow-twitch fibers have a low maximum tension, which develops slowly, but the muscle fibers are highly resistant to fatigue. Slow-twitch fibers have a substantial reserve of glycogen and fat, so their abundant mitochondria can maintain a steady, prolonged production of ATP when oxygen is available.

BIOLOGY IN YOUR LIFE

What causes muscles to be sore a few days after exercising?

Many of us have experienced delayed onset muscle soreness (DOMS), which generally appears some 24 to 48 hours after strenuous exercise. It is thought that DOMS is due to tissue injury and inflammation that takes several days to heal. Any movement you aren't used to can lead to DOMS, but it is especially associated with any activity that causes muscles to contract while they are lengthening. Examples include walking down stairs, running downhill, lowering weights, and the downward motion of squats and push-ups. To prevent DOMS, try warming up thoroughly and cooling down completely. Stretch after exercising. When beginning a new activity, start gradually and build up your endurance gradually. Avoid making sudden, major changes in your exercise routine.

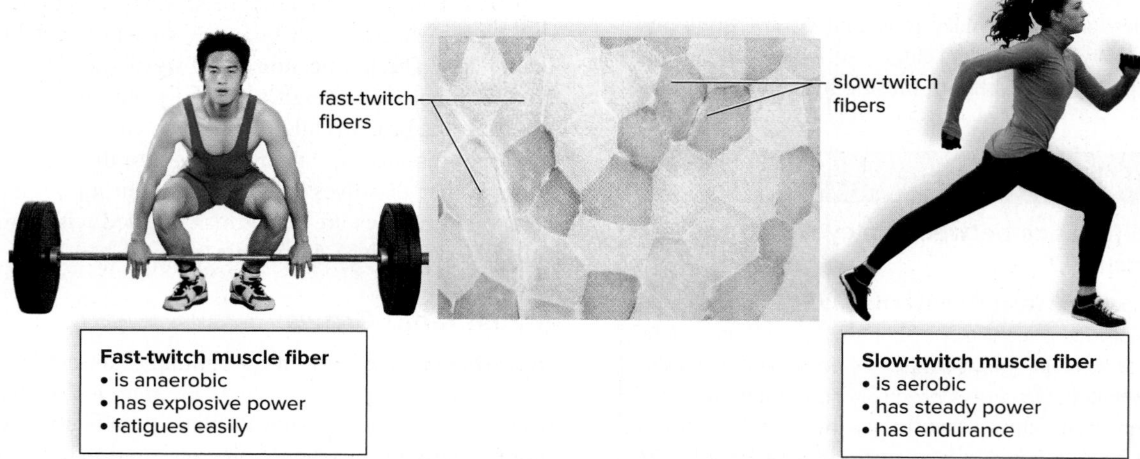
fast-twitch fibers
slow-twitch fibers
Fast-twitch muscle fiber
• is anaerobic
• has explosive power
• fatigues easily
Slow-twitch muscle fiber
• is aerobic
• has steady power
• has endurance

Figure 13.12 **Fast-twitch and slow-twitch muscle fibers differ in structure.**
If your muscles contain many fast-twitch fibers (light color), you would probably do better at a sport such as weightlifting. If your muscles contain many slow-twitch fibers (dark color), you would probably do better at a sport such as cross-country running.
(weightlifter): Isadora Getty Buyou/Image Source; (twitch fibers): Cultura Creative Ltd/Alamy Stock Photo; (runner): John Giustina/Purestock/Getty Images

CHECK YOUR PROGRESS 13.3

1. List the stages of a muscle twitch.
2. Contrast the activities of a single muscle twitch with the action of summation and tetanus.
3. Summarize how the CP pathway, fermentation, and cellular respiration produce ATP for muscle contraction.
4. Explain why weightlifters are not well adapted for distance running.

CONNECTING THE CONCEPTS

For more information on energy sources for muscle contraction and the pathways for generating ATP, refer to the following discussions:

Sections 2.4 and **2.5** describe the structure of carbohydrates and lipids and examine their function as energy nutrients.

Section 3.6 explores how ATP is generated by the cellular respiration and fermentation pathways.

Figure 3.21 illustrates the ATP–ADP cycle.

13.4 Muscular Disorders

LEARNING OUTCOMES

Upon completion of this section, you should be able to

1. Distinguish between common muscle conditions, such as strains and sprains.
2. Summarize the causes of fibromyalgia, muscular dystrophy, myasthenia gravis, and muscle cancer.

Muscular disorders are common for most people. However, some disorders can be life-threatening.

Common Muscular Conditions

Spasms are sudden and involuntary muscular contractions, most often accompanied by pain. Spasms can occur in smooth and skeletal muscles. A spasm of the smooth muscle in the intestinal tract is a type of colic sometimes called a bellyache. Multiple spasms of skeletal muscles are called a seizure, or **convulsion. Cramps** are strong, painful spasms, especially of the leg and foot, usually due to strenuous activity. Cramps can even occur when sleeping after a strenuous workout. **Facial tics,** such as periodic eye blinking, head turning, or grimacing, are spasms that can be controlled voluntarily, but only with great effort.

A **strain** is caused by stretching or tearing of a muscle. A **sprain** is a twisting of a joint, leading to swelling and injury, not only of muscles but also of ligaments, tendons, blood vessels, and nerves. The ankle and knee are often subject to sprains. **Tendinitis** (also spelled as *tendonitis*) is the inflammation of a tendon due to an injury, such as a sprain. Tendinitis may irritate the bursae underlying the tendon, causing **bursitis.**

As is presented in the Health feature "The Importance of Exercise," many common muscular conditions can be prevented by regular exercise.

BIOLOGY IN YOUR LIFE

What is the difference between an eyelid tic and an eyelid twitch?

The answer is based on whether the action can be controlled. If the individual is able to control the movement, even temporarily, it is called a tic. If the movement cannot be controlled, it is considered to be a twitch. No one is precisely sure what causes a tic, although it has been shown that tics are not connected with medications for attention deficit hyperactivity disorder (ADHD). Twitches are believed to be the result of signaling problems in a specific area of the brain. The severity of both tics and twitches may be influenced by stress and sleep problems.

Muscular Diseases

The following conditions are more serious and always require close medical care.

Myalgia and Fibromyalgia

Myalgia refers to achy muscles. The most common cause for myalgia is either overuse or overstretching of a muscle or group of muscles. Myalgia without a traumatic history is often due to viral infections. Myalgia may accompany *myositis* (inflammation of the muscles), either in response to viral infection or as an immune system disorder. **Fibromyalgia** is a chronic condition whose symptoms include widespread pain, tenderness, and stiffness of muscles. Its precise cause is not known; in some people, it occurs suddenly after an injury, while in others it has a more gradual progression.

Muscular Dystrophy

Muscular dystrophy is a broad term applied to a group of disorders characterized by a progressive degeneration and weakening of muscles. As muscle fibers die, fat and connective tissue take their place. **Duchenne muscular dystrophy,** the most common type, is inherited through a flawed gene on the X chromosome. The lack of a protein called dystrophin causes the condition. When dystrophin is absent, calcium leaks into the cell and activates an enzyme that dissolves muscle fibers. In an attempt to treat the condition, muscles are sometimes injected with immature muscle cells that do produce dystrophin.

Myasthenia Gravis

Myasthenia gravis is an autoimmune disease characterized by weakness that especially affects the muscles of the eyelids, face, neck, and extremities. Muscle contraction is impaired because the immune system mistakenly produces antibodies that destroy acetylcholine (ACh) receptors. In many cases, the first sign of the disease is a drooping of the eyelids and double vision. Treatment includes drugs that inhibit the enzyme that digests acetylcholine, so that ACh accumulates in neuromuscular junctions.

BIOLOGY TODAY ▶ **Health**

The Importance of Exercise

Exercise programs improve muscular strength, muscular endurance, and flexibility. Muscular strength is the force a muscle group (or muscle) can exert against a resistance in one maximal effort. Muscular endurance is judged by the ability of a muscle to contract repeatedly or to sustain a contraction for an extended period. Flexibility is tested by observing the range of motion about a joint.

Exercise also improves cardiorespiratory endurance. The heart rate and capacity increase, and the air passages dilate, so that the heart and lungs are able to support prolonged muscular activity. The blood level of high-density lipoprotein (HDL) increases. HDL is the molecule that slows the development of artherosclerotic plaques in blood vessels (see Section 5.7). Also, body composition—the proportion of protein to fat—changes favorably when you exercise.

Exercise also seems to help prevent certain types of cancer. Cancer prevention involves eating properly, not smoking, avoiding cancer-causing chemicals and radiation, undergoing appropriate medical screening tests, and knowing the early warning signs of cancer. However, studies show that people who exercise are less likely to develop colon, breast, cervical, uterine, and ovarian cancers.

Physical training with weights can improve the density and strength of bones and the strength and endurance of muscles in all adults, regardless of age. Even men and women in their eighties and nineties can make substantial gains in bone and muscle strength that help them lead more independent lives. Exercise helps prevent osteoporosis, a condition in which the bones are weak and tend to break (see Section 12.5). Exercise promotes the activity of osteoblasts in young as well as older people. The stronger the bones when a person is young, the less chance of osteoporosis as that person ages. Exercise helps prevent weight gain, not only because the level of activity increases but also because muscles metabolize faster than other tissues. As a person becomes more muscular, the body is less likely to accumulate fat.

Exercise relieves depression and enhances the mood. Some people report that exercise actually makes them feel more energetic. Further, after exercising, particularly in the late afternoon, people sleep better that night. Self-esteem rises because of improved appearance, as well as other factors that are not well understood. For example, vigorous exercise releases endorphins, hormonelike chemicals known to alleviate pain and provide a feeling of tranquility.

A sensible exercise program is one that provides all these benefits without the detriments of a too strenuous program. Overexertion can be harmful to the body and may result in sports injuries, such as lower back strains or torn ligaments of the knees. The beneficial programs suggested in Table 13A are tailored according to age.

Dr. Arthur Leon at the University of Minnesota performed a study involving 12,000 men, and the results showed that only moderate exercise is needed to lower the risk of a heart attack by one-third. In another study, conducted by the Institute for Aerobics Research in Dallas, Texas, which included 10,000 men and more than 3,000 women, even a little exercise was found to lower the risk of death from cardiovascular diseases and cancer. Increasing daily activity by walking to the corner store instead of driving and by taking the stairs instead of the elevator can improve your health.

Questions to Consider

1. At the level of the muscle fiber, how does exercise increase muscle strength?
2. How might an overly ambitious workout damage muscle fibers?

Table 13A Staying Fit

Exercise	Children, 7–12	Teenagers, 13–18	Adults, 19–55
Amount	Vigorous activity 1–2 hr daily	Vigorous activity 1 hr, 3–5 days a week; otherwise, ½ hr daily moderate activity	Vigorous activity 1 hr, 3 days a week; otherwise, ½ hr daily moderate activity
Purpose	Free play	Build muscle with calisthenics	Exercise to prevent lower back pain: aerobics, stretching, or yoga
Organized	Build motor skills through team sports, dancing, or swimming	Continue team sports, dancing, hiking, or swimming	Do aerobic exercise to control buildup of fat cells
Group	Enjoy more exercise outside of physical education classes	Pursue sports that can be enjoyed for a lifetime: tennis, swimming, or horseback riding	Find exercise partners: join a running club, a bicycle club, or an outing group
Family	Participate in family outings: bowling, boating, camping, or hiking	Take active vacations: hike, bicycle, or cross-country ski	Initiate family outings: bowling, boating, camping, or hiking

(children): Rawpixel.com/Shutterstock

(playing basketball): Nancy Ney/Photodisc/Getty Images

(biking): Stockbyte/Getty Images

Muscle Cancer

Sarcomas are cancers that originate in connective tissues, such as those found in muscles. Soft tissue sarcomas occur in both smooth and skeletal muscles. One of the more common forms of smooth muscle cancer is leiomyoma, which occurs in the uterine wall. Rhabdomyosarcomas are a rare form of cancer that originate in the skeletal muscle or move into the muscle from another location in the body. Both of these types of sarcomas may be either benign or malignant.

CHECK YOUR PROGRESS 13.4

1. Distinguish between a strain and a sprain.
2. Compare and contrast the potential causes of myalgia and myasthenia gravis.
3. Discuss the potential symptoms of muscular dystrophy.

CONNECTING THE CONCEPTS

For background information on the physiology of these diseases, refer to the following discussions:

Section 7.3 describes the inflammatory response.

Section 7.5 examines how an autoimmune response causes diseases in humans.

Section 21.4 provides additional information on sex-linked inheritance.

13.5 Homeostasis

LEARNING OUTCOMES

Upon completion of this section, you should be able to

1. Summarize the role of the muscular and skeletal systems in movement.
2. Summarize the role of the muscular system in body temperature homeostasis.

In this section, our discussion centers on the contribution of the muscular system to homeostasis (Fig. 13.13). In many cases, the muscular system works closely with the skeletal system—for example, in the protection of body parts and movement.

Both Systems Produce Movement

Movement is essential to maintaining homeostasis. The skeletal and muscular systems work together to enable body movement. This is most evidently illustrated by what happens when skeletal muscles contract and pull on the bones to which they are attached, causing movement at joints. Body movement of this sort allows us to respond to certain types of changes in the environment. For instance, if you are sitting in the sun and start to feel hot, you can get up and move to a shady spot.

The muscular and skeletal systems work for other types of movements that are just as important for maintaining homeostasis. Contraction of skeletal muscles associated with the jaw and tongue allows you to grind food with the teeth. The rhythmic smooth muscle contractions of peristalsis move ingested materials through the digestive tract. These processes are necessary for supplying the body's cells with nutrients. The ceaseless beating of your heart, which propels blood into the arterial system, is caused by the contraction of cardiac muscle. Contractions of skeletal muscles in the body, especially those associated with breathing and leg movements, aid in the process of venous return by pushing blood back toward the heart. This is why soldiers and members of marching bands are cautioned not to lock their knees when standing at attention. The reduction in venous return causes a drop in blood pressure, which can result in fainting. The pressure exerted by skeletal muscle contraction also helps squeeze interstitial fluid into the lymphatic capillaries, where it is referred to as lymph.

Both Systems Protect Body Parts

The skeletal system plays an important role by protecting the soft internal organs of your body. The brain, heart, lungs, spinal cord, kidneys, and liver and most of the endocrine glands are shielded by the skeleton. In particular, the nervous and endocrine organs must be defended so they can carry out activities necessary for homeostasis.

The skeletal muscles pad and protect the bones, and the tendons and bursae associated with skeletal muscles reinforce and cushion the joints. Muscles of the abdominal wall offer additional protection to the soft internal organs. Examples of these muscles include the rectus abdominis and external oblique muscles illustrated in Figure 13.5.

Muscles Help Maintain Body Temperature

The muscular system helps regulate body temperature. When you are very cold, smooth muscle constricts inside the blood vessels supplying the skin. Thus, the amount of blood close to the surface of the body is reduced. This helps conserve heat in the body's core, where vital organs lie. If you are cold enough, you may start to shiver. Shivering is caused by involuntary skeletal muscle contractions. This is initiated by temperature-sensitive neurons in the hypothalamus of the brain. Skeletal muscle contraction requires ATP, and using ATP generates heat. You may also notice that you get goose bumps when you are cold. This is because arrector pili muscles contract. These tiny bundles of smooth muscle attached to the hair follicles cause the hairs to stand up. This is not very helpful in keeping humans warm, but it is quite effective in our furrier fellow mammals. Think of a cat or dog outside on a cold winter day. Its fur is a better insulator when standing up than when lying flat. Goose bumps can also be a sign of fear. Although a human with goose bumps may not look very impressive, a frightened or aggressive animal whose fur is

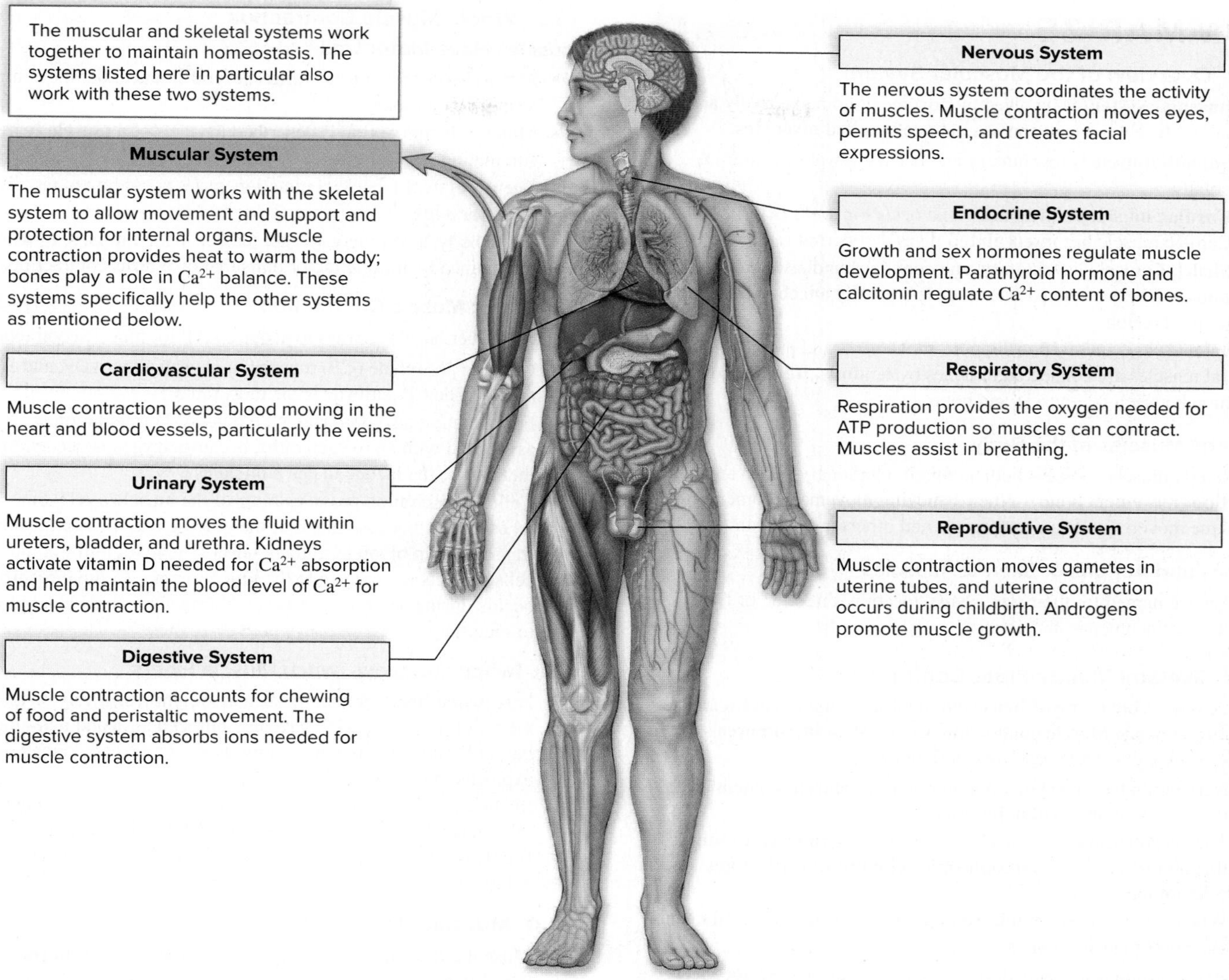

The muscular and skeletal systems work together to maintain homeostasis. The systems listed here in particular also work with these two systems.

Muscular System

The muscular system works with the skeletal system to allow movement and support and protection for internal organs. Muscle contraction provides heat to warm the body; bones play a role in Ca^{2+} balance. These systems specifically help the other systems as mentioned below.

Cardiovascular System

Muscle contraction keeps blood moving in the heart and blood vessels, particularly the veins.

Urinary System

Muscle contraction moves the fluid within ureters, bladder, and urethra. Kidneys activate vitamin D needed for Ca^{2+} absorption and help maintain the blood level of Ca^{2+} for muscle contraction.

Digestive System

Muscle contraction accounts for chewing of food and peristaltic movement. The digestive system absorbs ions needed for muscle contraction.

Nervous System

The nervous system coordinates the activity of muscles. Muscle contraction moves eyes, permits speech, and creates facial expressions.

Endocrine System

Growth and sex hormones regulate muscle development. Parathyroid hormone and calcitonin regulate Ca^{2+} content of bones.

Respiratory System

Respiration provides the oxygen needed for ATP production so muscles can contract. Muscles assist in breathing.

Reproductive System

Muscle contraction moves gametes in uterine tubes, and uterine contraction occurs during childbirth. Androgens promote muscle growth.

Figure 13.13 **The muscular system and homeostasis.**
The muscular system works with these body systems to assist in homeostasis.

standing on end looks bigger and (it is hoped) more intimidating to a predator or rival.

CHECK YOUR PROGRESS 13.5

1. Summarize the importance of movement in homeostasis.
2. Summarize how the muscular system works to maintain body temperature.
3. Explain how the muscular system interacts with the digestive system.

CONNECTING THE CONCEPTS

For more information on calcium and body temperature homeostasis, refer to the following discussions:

Section 4.8 explores how the body maintains homeostasis using feedback mechanisms.

Figure 4.17 examines how the hypothalamus is involved in body temperature regulation.

Section 16.3 describes how the thyroid and parathyroid glands are involved in calcium homeostasis.

CONCLUSION

Eliud Kipchoge's efforts are amazing, but while many of us may never run a marathon, the same physiological principles that are at work in Kipchoge's body during a race occur as we go about our daily tasks. Given the importance of movement to all aspects of our lives, and our developing understanding of movement to our health, it is important we understand how the skeletal and muscular systems function.

SUMMARIZE

13.1 Overview of the Muscular System

The **muscular system** is involved in movement, both externally and internally. Muscle tissue is composed of cells called **myocytes.**

- **Smooth muscle** is involuntary and occurs in walls of internal organs.
- **Cardiac muscle** is involuntary and occurs in walls of the heart. Cardiac muscle has **intercalated discs** that permit rapid contraction.
- **Skeletal muscle** is voluntary, and contains bundles of cells called **muscle fibers** arranged into fascicles, usually attached by tendons to the skeleton.

Skeletal muscle is involved in support, movement, and protection. Skeletal muscles are connected to bones by **tendons. Bursae** provide a cushion between the muscle and bone.

Skeletal Muscles of the Body

All skeletal muscles possess both an **origin** (stationary point) and an **insertion** (movement point). When achieving movement, some muscles are prime movers, some are synergists, and others are antagonists.

Names and Actions of Skeletal Muscles

Muscles are named for their size, shape, location, direction of fibers, number of attachments, and action.

13.2 Skeletal Muscle Fiber Contraction

Muscle fibers contain **myofibrils,** and myofibrils contain **actin** and **myosin** filaments. Muscle contraction occurs when **sarcomeres** shorten and actin filaments slide past myosin filaments.

- Nerve impulses travel down motor neurons and stimulate muscle fibers at **neuromuscular junctions.**
- The **sarcolemma** of a muscle fiber forms **T (transverse) tubules** that almost touch the **sarcoplasmic reticulum,** which stores calcium ions.
- When calcium ions are released into muscle fibers, actin filaments slide past myosin filaments.
- At a neuromuscular junction, synaptic vesicles release acetylcholine (neurotransmitter), which diffuses across the synaptic cleft.
- When acetylcholine (ACh) is received by the sarcolemma, electrical signals begin and lead to the release of calcium.
- Calcium ions bind to **troponin,** causing **tropomyosin** proteins to shift, thus exposing myosin-binding sites.
- Myosin filaments break down ATP and attach to actin filaments, forming cross-bridges.
- When ADP and Ⓟ are released, cross-bridges change their positions.
- This **sliding filament model** pulls actin filaments to the center of a sarcomere.

13.3 Whole Muscle Contraction

Muscles Have Motor Units

- A muscle contains **motor units:** several fibers under the control of a single motor axon.
- Motor unit contraction is described in terms of a **muscle twitch,** summation, and **tetanus.**
- The strength of muscle contraction varies according to recruitment of motor units.
- In the body, a continuous slight tension, called **muscle tone,** is maintained by muscle motor units that take turns contracting.

Energy for Muscle Contraction

A muscle fiber has three ways to acquire ATP for muscle contraction:

- Creatine phosphate (CP) transfers a phosphate to ADP, and ATP results. The CP pathway is the most rapid.
- Fermentation also produces ATP quickly. Fermentation is associated with an **oxygen debt,** because oxygen is needed to metabolize the lactate that accumulates.
- Cellular respiration provides most of the muscle's ATP but takes longer, because much of the glucose and oxygen must be transported in blood to mitochondria. The **myoglobin** in muscle cells delivers the oxygen to the mitochondria. Cellular respiration occurs during aerobic exercise and burns fatty acids in addition to glucose.

Fast-Twitch and Slow-Twitch Muscle Fibers

- Fast-twitch fibers, for sports such as weightlifting, rely on anaerobic means of acquiring ATP; have few mitochondria and myoglobin, but motor units contain more muscle fibers; and are known for explosive power but fatigue quickly.
- Slow-twitch fibers, for sports such as running and swimming, rely on aerobic respiration to acquire ATP and have a plentiful supply of mitochondria and myoglobin, which gives them a dark color.

13.4 Muscular Disorders

- Muscular disorders include **spasms, convulsions, cramps,** and **facial tics.**
- Muscular system injuries include **strains, sprains, tendinitis,** and **bursitis.**
- Diseases of the muscular system include **myalgias (fibromyalgia); muscular dystrophy (Duchenne muscular dystrophy); myasthenia gravis;** and cancer of the muscles **(sarcomas).**

13.5 Homeostasis

- The muscles and bones produce movement and protect body parts.
- The muscles produce the heat that gives us a constant body temperature.

ENGAGE

THINKING CRITICALLY

1. The dystrophin protein is located between the sarcolemma and the outer myofilaments of the muscle. It is responsible for conducting the force of the muscle contraction from the myofilaments to the connective tissue of the muscle. In Kate's case, a mutation in this protein was causing the symptoms of muscular dystrophy.
   a. Why would a loss of dystrophin protein cause weakness and a loss of coordination?
   b. Muscular dystrophy is frequently referred to as a muscle-wasting disease, in which the muscles lose mass over time. How would a defect in dystrophin contribute to the wasting of muscle tissue?
2. You learned about rigor mortis in the Science feature "Rigor Mortis" (Section 13.3). Perhaps you're also a fan of crime scene shows on television. If so, you know that the onset of rigor mortis in a deceased person can be influenced by a number of factors. Consider the following:
   a. If a body was rapidly cooled after death, how would this affect the timing of rigor mortis?
   b. Discuss what factors, besides cooling, might delay or accelerate the onset of rigor mortis.
3. Rigor mortis is usually complete within 1 to 2 days after death (depending on environmental variables). Why would rigor mortis diminish after several days?

MAKING IT RELEVANT

1. Do you think there is a limit as to how fast a human can run a marathon? What factors may determine that limit?
2. How do you think high-impact sports, such as marathons, change the way the body utilizes energy in the muscles? How would that change the marathon runner's diet?
3. In this chapter, we discussed skeletal muscle, but how do you think running may also influence the cardiac and smooth muscles?

Find answers to all of the chapter questions at connect.mheducation.com

CHAPTER 14

Nervous System

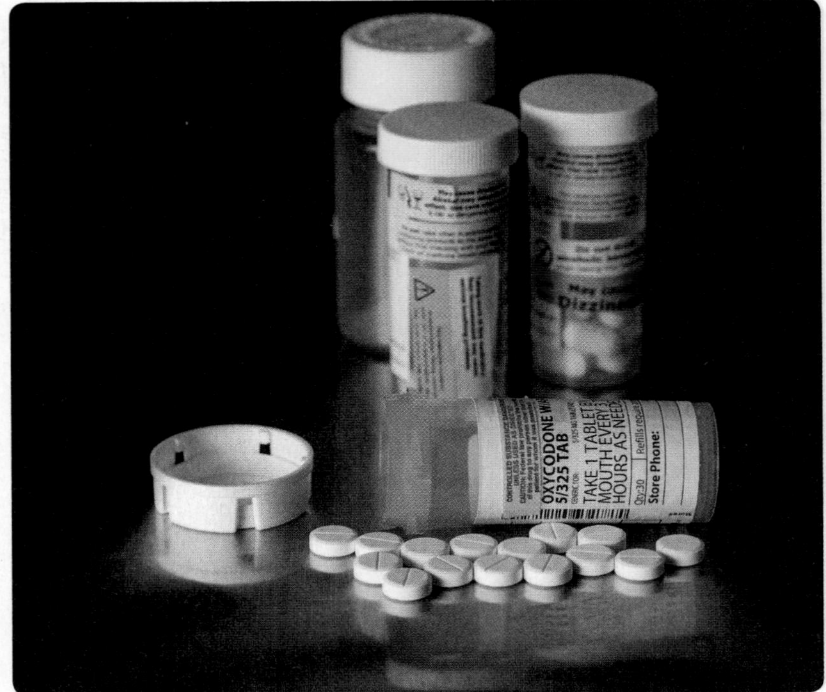

Steve Heap/Shutterstock

CHAPTER OUTLINE

BEFORE YOU BEGIN

Before beginning this chapter, take a few moments to review the following discussions:

Section 2.1 How does an ion differ from an atom of an element?

Section 3.3 How does the sodium–potassium pump move ions across the plasma membrane?

Section 4.1 What is the function of nervous tissue in the body?

Opioids and the Nervous System

Each day, approximately 130 people die from an opioid overdose in the United States. The addiction and misuse of opioids has become a national crisis that impacts the social and economic welfare of our country.

The opioid system is a component of the central nervous system that, within humans, controls pain, reward, and addictive behaviors. Opioid receptors belong to a group of transmembrane proteins. When the receptors are engaged by an opioid like morphine or heroin, the pain pathway is altered and feelings of euphoria and pleasure can result. Three main receptors—mu, delta, and kappa—are responsible for enabling opioids to exert their effect. Mu receptors are molecular switches that trigger the brain reward system. Delta receptors appear to play a role in determining an individual's emotional state and kappa receptors are associated with pain relief.

Morphine is the most widely used opioid to control pain after surgery or for individuals who suffer from chronic pain. Morphine acts on the mu receptor and therefore has the potential for abuse and addiction. A number of drugs may be prescribed to combat opioid abuse. These drugs bind to the opioid receptors and eliminate withdrawal symptoms.

In this chapter, we will explore the structure and function of the nervous system, which is the target of pain killers such as opioids.

As you read through the chapter, think about the following questions:

1. How do cellular receptors play a role in the response of the nervous system to stimuli?
2. What areas of the central nervous system are most affected by pain killers such as opioids?

14.1 Overview of the Nervous System

LEARNING OUTCOMES

Upon completion of this section, you should be able to

1. Distinguish between the central nervous system and the peripheral nervous system with regard to location and function.
2. List the three types of neurons and provide a function for each.
3. Summarize the activities that generate and propagate an action potential.
4. Explain the role of neurotransmitters and the process of synaptic integration.

The **nervous system** is responsible for the reception and processing of sensory information from both the external and the internal environments. The nervous system has two major divisions. The major structures of the nervous system are shown in Figure 14.1.

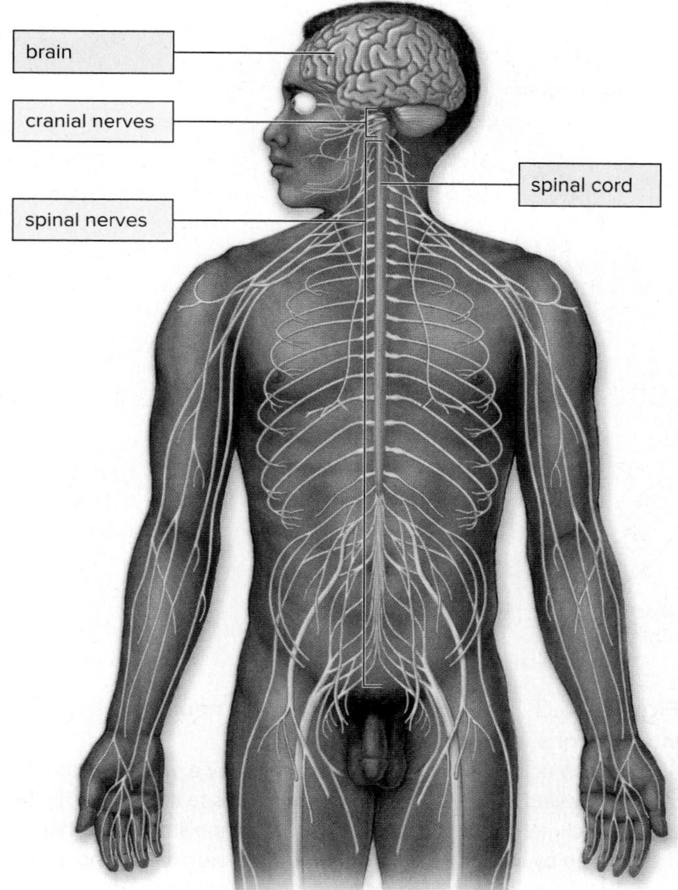

Figure 14.1 The central nervous system.
The central nervous system (CNS) consists of the brain and spinal cord. The peripheral nervous system (PNS) consists of the nerves, which lie outside the CNS.

The **central nervous system (CNS)** consists of the brain and spinal cord. The brain is completely surrounded and protected by the skull. It connects directly to the spinal cord, similarly protected by the vertebral column. The **peripheral nervous system (PNS)** consists of nerves. Nerves lie outside the CNS. The division between the CNS and the PNS is arbitrary. The two systems work together and are connected to each other (Fig. 14.2).

The nervous system has three specific functions:

- The nervous system receives sensory input. Sensory receptors in skin and other organs respond to external and internal stimuli by generating nerve signals that travel by way of the PNS to the CNS. For example, if you smell baking cookies, olfactory (smell) receptors in the nose use the PNS to transmit that information to the CNS.
- The CNS performs information processing and integration, summing up the input it receives from all over the body. The CNS reviews the information, stores the information as memories, and creates the appropriate motor responses. The smell of those baking cookies evokes memories of their taste.
- The CNS generates motor output. Nerve signals from the CNS go by way of the PNS to the muscles, glands, and organs, all in response to the cookies. Signals to the salivary glands make you salivate. Your stomach generates the acid and enzymes needed to digest the cookies—even before you've had a bite. The CNS also coordinates the movement of your arms and hands as you reach for the cookies.

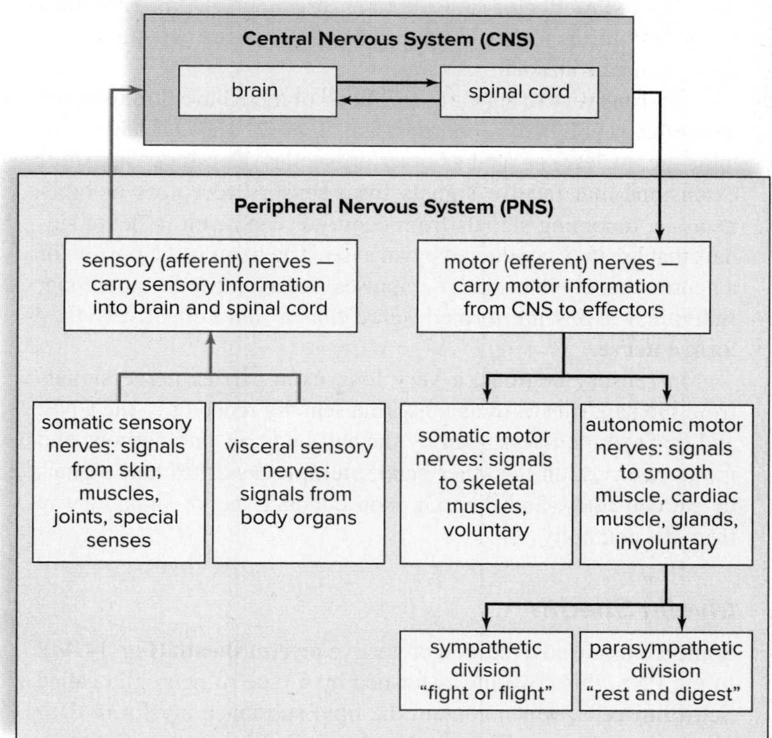

Figure 14.2 Organization of the nervous system.
The red arrows are the pathways by which the CNS receives sensory information. The black arrows are the pathways by which the CNS communicates information with the PNS.

Nervous Tissue

Nervous tissue contains two types of cells: neurons and neuroglia. **Neurons** are the cells that transmit nerve impulses between parts of the nervous system; **neuroglia,** sometimes called glial cells, support and nourish neurons.

Neuroglia (see Section 4.4) greatly outnumber neurons in the brain. There are several types of neuroglia in the CNS, each with specific functions. *Microglia* are phagocytic cells that help remove bacteria and debris, whereas *astrocytes* provide metabolic and structural support directly to the neurons. The myelin sheath is formed from the membranes of tightly spiraled neuroglia. In the PNS, *Schwann cells* perform this function, leaving gaps called nodes of Ranvier. In the CNS, neuroglia cells called *oligodendrocytes* form the myelin sheath.

The Anatomy of a Neuron

Classified according to function, the three types of neurons are sensory neurons, interneurons, and motor neurons (Fig. 14.3). Their functions are best described relative to the CNS. A **sensory neuron** takes nerve signals from a sensory receptor to the CNS. **Sensory receptors** are special structures that detect changes in the environment. An **interneuron** lies entirely within the CNS. Interneurons can receive input from sensory neurons and from other interneurons in the CNS. Thereafter, they sum up all the information received from other neurons before they communicate with motor neurons. A **motor neuron** takes nerve impulses away from the CNS to an effector (muscle fiber, organ, or gland). **Effectors** carry out our responses to environmental changes, whether these are external or internal.

Neurons vary in appearance, but all of them have three distinct structures: a cell body, dendrites, and an axon. The **cell body** contains the nucleus, as well as other organelles. **Dendrites** are short extensions that receive signals from sensory receptors or other neurons. Incoming signals from dendrites can result in nerve signals that are then conducted by an axon. The **axon** is the portion of a neuron that conducts nerve impulses. An axon can be quite long. Individual axons are termed *nerve fibers,* and collectively they form a **nerve.**

In sensory neurons, a very long axon carries nerve signals from the dendrites associated with a sensory receptor to the CNS, and this axon is interrupted by the cell body. In interneurons and motor neurons, on the other hand, multiple dendrites take signals to the cell body, and then an axon conducts nerve signals away from the cell body.

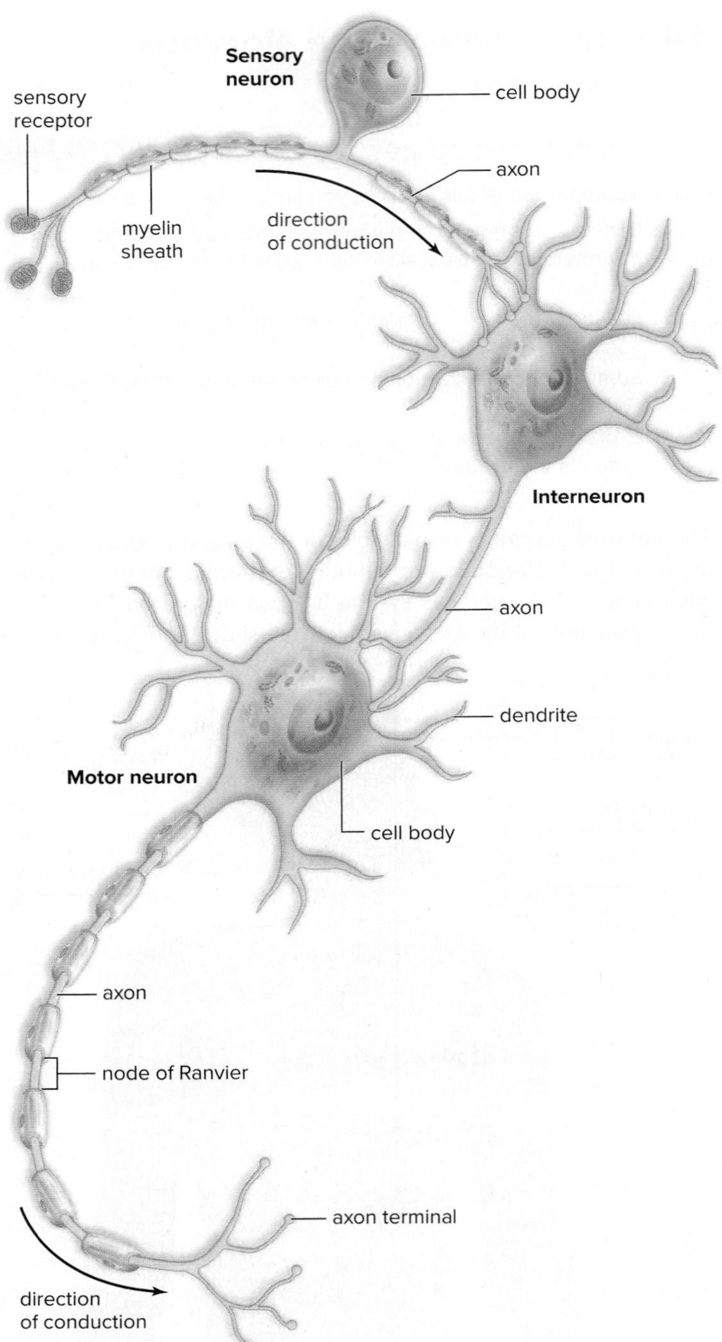

Figure 14.3 The structure of sensory neurons, interneurons, and motor neurons.
a. A sensory neuron has a long axon covered by a myelin sheath that takes nerve impulses all the way from dendrites to the CNS. **b.** In the CNS, some interneurons, such as this one, have a short axon that is not covered by a myelin sheath. **c.** A motor neuron has a long axon covered by a myelin sheath that takes nerve impulses from the CNS to an effector.

Myelin Sheath

Some axons are covered by a protective **myelin sheath** (Fig. 14.4*a*). In the PNS, this covering is formed by a type of neuroglia called **Schwann cells,** which contain the lipid substance myelin in their plasma membranes. The myelin sheath develops when Schwann cells wrap themselves around an axon as many as 100 times, and in this way lay down many layers of plasma membrane. Because each Schwann cell myelinates only part of an axon, the myelin sheath is interrupted. The gaps where there is no myelin sheath are called the

BIOLOGY TODAY ▶ Science

Nerve Regeneration and Stem Cells

In humans, axons outside the brain and spinal cord can regenerate, but axons inside these organs cannot (Fig. 14A). After injury, axons in the human central nervous system (CNS) degenerate, resulting in permanent loss of nervous function. Interestingly, about 90% of the cells in the brain and the spinal cord are not even neurons. They are neuroglia cells. In nerves outside the brain and spinal cord, the neuroglia cells are Schwann cells that help axons regenerate. The neuroglia cells in the CNS include microglial cells, oligodendrocytes, and astrocytes, and they inhibit axon regeneration.

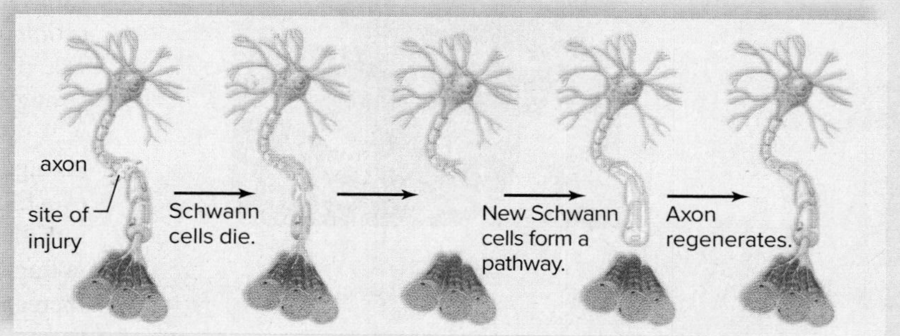

Figure 14A Regeneration of nerve cells.
Outside the CNS, nerves regenerate because new neuroglia called Schwann cells form a pathway for axons to reach a muscle. In the CNS, comparable neuroglia called oligodendrocytes do not have this function.

The spinal cord contains its own stem cells. When the spinal cord is injured in experimental animals, these stem cells proliferate. But instead of becoming functional neurons, they become neuroglia cells. Researchers are trying to understand the process that triggers the stem cells to become neuroglia cells. In the future, this understanding could allow manipulation of stem cells into neurons.

In early experiments with neural stem cells in the laboratory, scientists at Johns Hopkins University caused embryonic stem (ES) cells to differentiate into spinal cord motor neurons, the type of nerve cell that causes muscles to contract. The motor neurons then produced axons. When grown in the same dish with muscle cells, the motor neurons formed neuromuscular junctions and even caused muscle contractions. The cells were then transplanted into the spinal cords of rats with spinal cord injuries. Some of the transplanted cells survived for longer than a month within the spinal cord. However, no improvement in symptoms was seen and no functional neuron connections were made.

In later experiments by the same research group, paralyzed rats were first treated with drugs and nerve growth factors to overcome inhibition from the central nervous system. These techniques significantly increased the success of the transplanted neurons. Amazingly, axons of transplanted neurons reached the muscles, formed neuromuscular junctions, and provided partial relief from the paralysis. Research is being done on the use of both the body's own stem cells and laboratory-grown stem cells to repair damaged CNS neurons. Though many questions remain, the current results are promising.

Questions to Consider

1. What is the likely reason neurons cannot simply be transplanted from other areas of the body?
2. How might this research also help patients with neurodegenerative diseases, such as Parkinson's disease?

nodes of Ranvier (Fig 14.4*b*). Schwann cells are small, and because a single axon may be several feet long (if it runs from the spinal cord to the foot, for example), several hundred or more Schwann cells may be required to myelinate a single axon.

The Science feature "Nerve Regeneration and Stem Cells" explores how these Schwann cells participate in nerve regeneration.

Long axons tend to have a myelin sheath, but short axons do not. The gray matter of the CNS is gray because it contains no myelinated axons; the white matter of the CNS is white because it does. In the PNS, myelin gives nerve fibers their white, glistening appearance and serves as an excellent insulator. When the myelin breaks down, as happens in **multiple sclerosis (MS),** then it becomes more difficult for the neurons to transmit information. In effect, MS "short-circuits" the nervous system. The myelin sheath also plays an important role in nerve regeneration within the PNS. If an axon is accidentally severed, the myelin sheath remains and serves as a passageway for new fiber growth.

The Physiology of a Neuron

Nerve impulses are the electrochemical changes that convey information within the nervous system. In the past, nerve impulses could be studied only in neurons that had been removed from the human body or from other organisms. More advanced techniques now enable researchers to study nerve impulses in single, intact nerve cells.

Resting Potential

Think of all the devices, such as your cell phone and laptop, that are battery-powered. Every battery is an energy source manufactured by separating positively charged ions across a membrane from negative ions. The battery's *potential energy* can be used to perform work—for example, using your phone or lighting a flashlight. A resting neuron also has potential energy, much like a fully charged battery. This energy, called the **resting potential,**

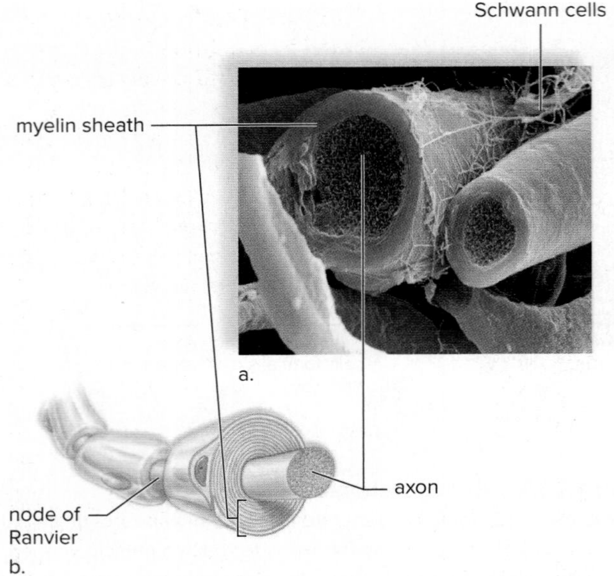

Figure 14.4 Myelin sheath.
a. In the PNS, a myelin sheath forms when Schwann cells wrap themselves around an axon. **b.** Nodes of Ranvier are gaps between the sections of the myelin sheath.
(a): Steve Gschmeissner/Science Photo Library/Alamy Stock Photo

exists because the plasma membrane is *polarized:* Positively charged ions are stashed outside the cell, with negatively charged ions inside.

As Figure 14.5*a* shows, the outside of the cell is positive because positively charged sodium ions (Na^+) gather around the outside of the plasma membrane. At rest, the neuron's plasma membrane is permeable to potassium, but not to sodium. Thus, positively charged potassium ions (K^+) contribute to the positive charge by diffusing out of the cell to join the sodium ions. The inside of the cell is negative in relation to the exterior of the cell because of the presence of large, negatively charged proteins and other molecules that remain inside the cell because of their size.

Like a battery, the neuron's resting potential energy can be measured in volts. Whereas a D-size flashlight battery has 1.5 volts, a nerve cell typically has 0.070 volt, or 70 millivolts (mV), of stored energy (Fig. 14.5*a*). By convention, the voltage measurement is always a negative number. This is because scientists compare the inside of the cell—where negatively charged proteins and other large molecules are clustered—to the outside of the cell—where positively charged sodium and potassium ions are gathered.

Just like rechargeable batteries, neurons must maintain their resting potential to be able to work. To do so, neurons actively transport sodium ions out of the cell and return potassium ions to the cytoplasm. A protein carrier in the membrane, called the **sodium–potassium pump,** pumps sodium ions (Na^+) out of the neuron and potassium ions (K^+) into the neuron (see Section 3.3). This action effectively "recharges" the cell so that, like a fresh battery, it can perform work.

Action Potential

The resting potential energy of the neuron can be used to perform the work of the neuron: conduction of nerve impulses. The process of conduction is termed an **action potential,** and it occurs in the axons of neurons. A **stimulus** activates the neuron and begins the action potential. For example, a stimulus for pain neurons in the skin would be the prick of a sharp pin. However, the stimulus must be strong enough to cause the cell to reach **threshold,** the voltage that will result in an action potential. In Figure 14.5*b,* the threshold voltage is around −55 mV. An action potential is an all-or-nothing event. Once threshold is reached, the action potential happens automatically and completely. On the other hand, if the threshold voltage is never reached, the action potential does not occur. Increasing the strength of a stimulus (such as pressing harder with the pin) does not change the strength of an action potential. However, it may cause more action potentials to occur in a given period. As a result, the person may perceive that pain has increased.

Sodium Gates Open Protein channels specific for sodium ions are located in the plasma membrane of the axon. When an action potential begins in response to a threshold stimulus, these protein channels open and sodium ions rush into the cell. Adding positively charged sodium ions causes the inside of the axon to become positive compared to the outside (Fig. 14.5*c*). This change is called **depolarization,** because the charge (polarity) inside the axon changes from negative to positive.

Potassium Gates Open Almost immediately after depolarization, the channels for sodium close and a separate set of potassium protein channels opens. Potassium flows rapidly from the cell. As positively charged potassium ions exit the cell, the inside of the cell becomes negative again because of the presence of large, negatively charged ions trapped inside the cell. This change in polarity is called **repolarization,** because the inside of the axon resumes a negative charge as potassium exits the axon (Fig. 14.5*d*). Finally, the sodium–potassium pump completes the action potential. Potassium ions are returned to the inside of the cell and sodium ions to the outside, and resting potential is restored.

Graph of an Action Potential

To visualize such rapid fluctuations in voltage across the axonal membrane, researchers generally find it useful to plot the voltage changes over time (Fig. 14.5*e*). During depolarization, the voltage increases from −70 mV to −55 mV to between +30 and +35 mV as sodium ions move to the inside of the axon. In repolarization, the opposite change occurs when potassium ions leave the axon. The entire process is very rapid, requiring only 3 to 4 milliseconds (ms) to complete.

Propagation of an Action Potential

If an axon is unmyelinated, an action potential at one locale stimulates an adjacent part of the axon membrane to produce an action potential. Conduction along the entire axon in this fashion can be rather slow—approximately 1 meter/second (1 m/s) in thin axons—because each section of the axon must be stimulated.

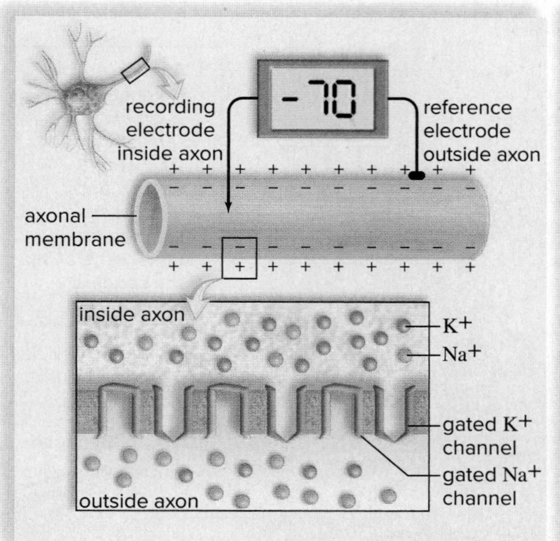

a. Resting potential: Na^+ outside the axon, K^+ and large anions inside the axon. Separation of charges polarizes the cell and causes the resting potential.

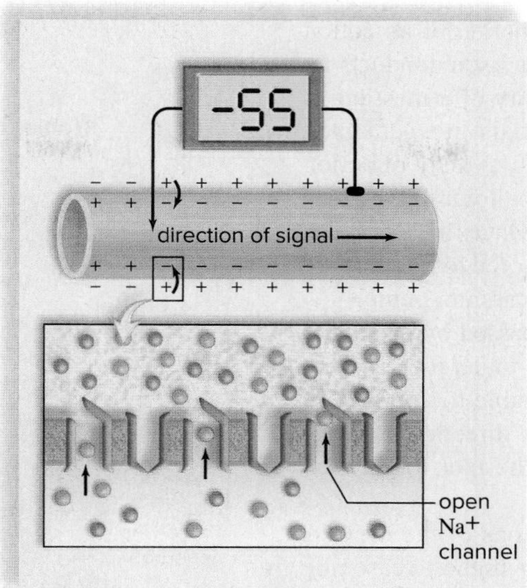

b. Stimulus causes the axon to reach its threshold; the axon potential increases from –70 to –55. The action potential has begun.

Figure 14.5 **Generation of an action potential.**
a. Resting potential occurs when a neuron is not conducting a nerve impulse. During an action potential, (**b**) the stimulus causes the cell to reach its threshold. **c.** Depolarization is followed by (**d**) repolarization. **e.** A graph depicting the generation of an action potential.

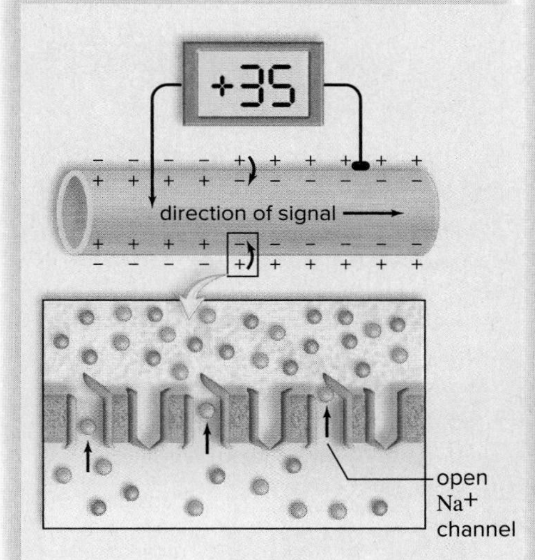

c. Depolarization continues as Na^+ gates open and Na^+ moves inside the axon.

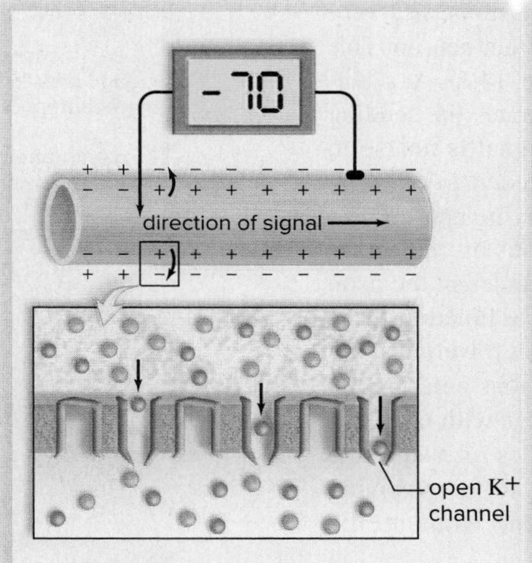

d. Action potential ends: repolarization occurs when K^+ gates open and K^+ moves to outside the axon. The sodium–potassium pump returns the ions to their resting positions.

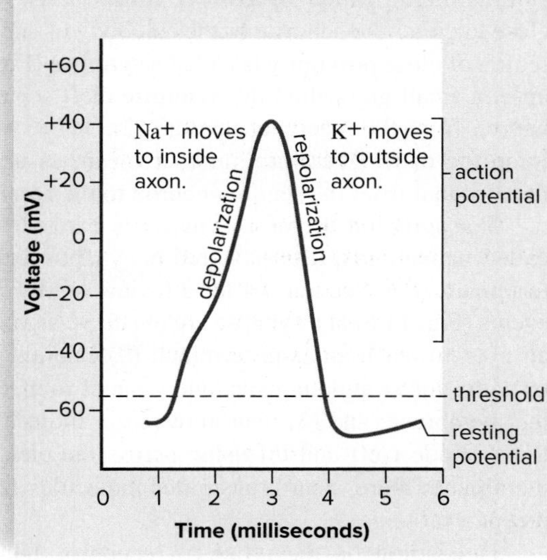

e. An action potential can be visualized if voltage changes are graphed over time.

In myelinated fibers, an action potential at one node of Ranvier causes an action potential at the next node, jumping over the entire myelin-coated portion of the axon. This type of conduction is called **saltatory conduction** (*saltatio* is a Latin word that means "to jump") and is much faster. In thick, myelinated fibers, the rate of transmission is more than 100 m/s. Regardless of whether an axon is myelinated or not, its action potentials are self-propagating. Each action potential generates another, along the entire length of the axon.

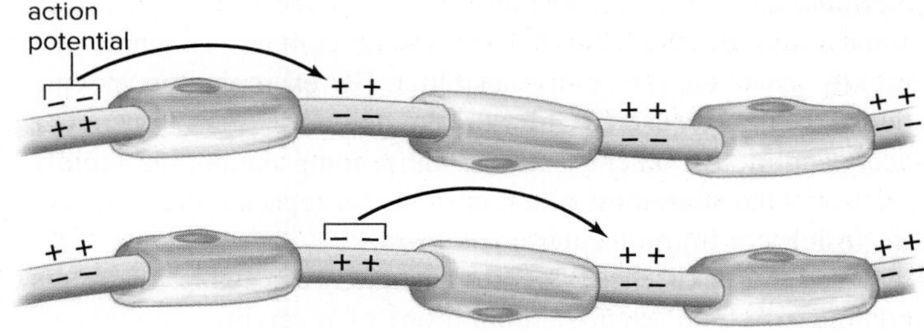

Like the action potential itself, conduction of an action potential is an all-or-none event—either an axon conducts its action potential or it does not. The intensity of a message is determined by how many action potentials are generated within a given time. An axon can conduct a volley of action potentials very quickly, because only a small number of ions are exchanged with each action potential. Once the action potential is complete, the ions are rapidly restored to their proper place through the action of the sodium–potassium pump.

As soon as the action potential has passed by each successive portion of an axon, that portion undergoes a short **refractory period,** during which it is unable to conduct an action potential. This ensures the one-way direction of a signal from the cell body down the length of the axon to the axon terminal.

It is interesting to note that all functions of the nervous system, from our deepest emotions to our highest reasoning abilities, are dependent on the conduction of nerve signals.

The Synapse

Every axon branches into many fine endings, each tipped by a small swelling called an **axon terminal.** Each terminal lies very close to either the dendrite or the cell body of another neuron. This region of close proximity is called a **synapse** (Fig. 14.6). At a synapse, a small gap called the **synaptic cleft** separates the sending neuron from the receiving neuron. The nerve signal is unable to jump the cleft. Therefore, another means is needed to pass the nerve signal from the sending neuron to the receiving neuron.

Transmission across a synapse is carried out by molecules called **neurotransmitters,** stored in synaptic vesicles in the axon terminals. (See Section 3.4 for a review of vesicle function.) The events (Fig. 14.6) at a synapse are (1) nerve signals traveling along an axon to reach an axon terminal; (2) calcium ions entering the terminal and stimulating synaptic vesicles to merge with the sending membrane; and (3) neurotransmitter molecules releasing into the synaptic cleft and diffusing across the cleft to the receiving membrane; there, neurotransmitter molecules bind with specific receptor proteins.

Depending on the types of receptors, the response of the receiving neuron can be toward excitation or toward inhibition. In Figure 14.7, excitation occurs because the neurotransmitter, such as acetylcholine (ACh), has caused the sodium gate to open. Sodium ions diffuse into the receiving neuron. Inhibition would occur if a neurotransmitter caused potassium ions to exit the receiving neuron.

Once a neurotransmitter has been released into a synaptic cleft and has initiated a response, it is removed from the cleft. In some synapses, the receiving membrane contains enzymes that rapidly inactivate the neurotransmitter. For example, the enzyme **acetylcholinesterase (AChE)** breaks down the neurotransmitter acetylcholine. In other synapses, the sending membrane rapidly reabsorbs the neurotransmitter, possibly for repackaging in synaptic vesicles or for molecular breakdown.

The short existence of neurotransmitters at a synapse prevents continuous stimulation (or inhibition) of receiving membranes.

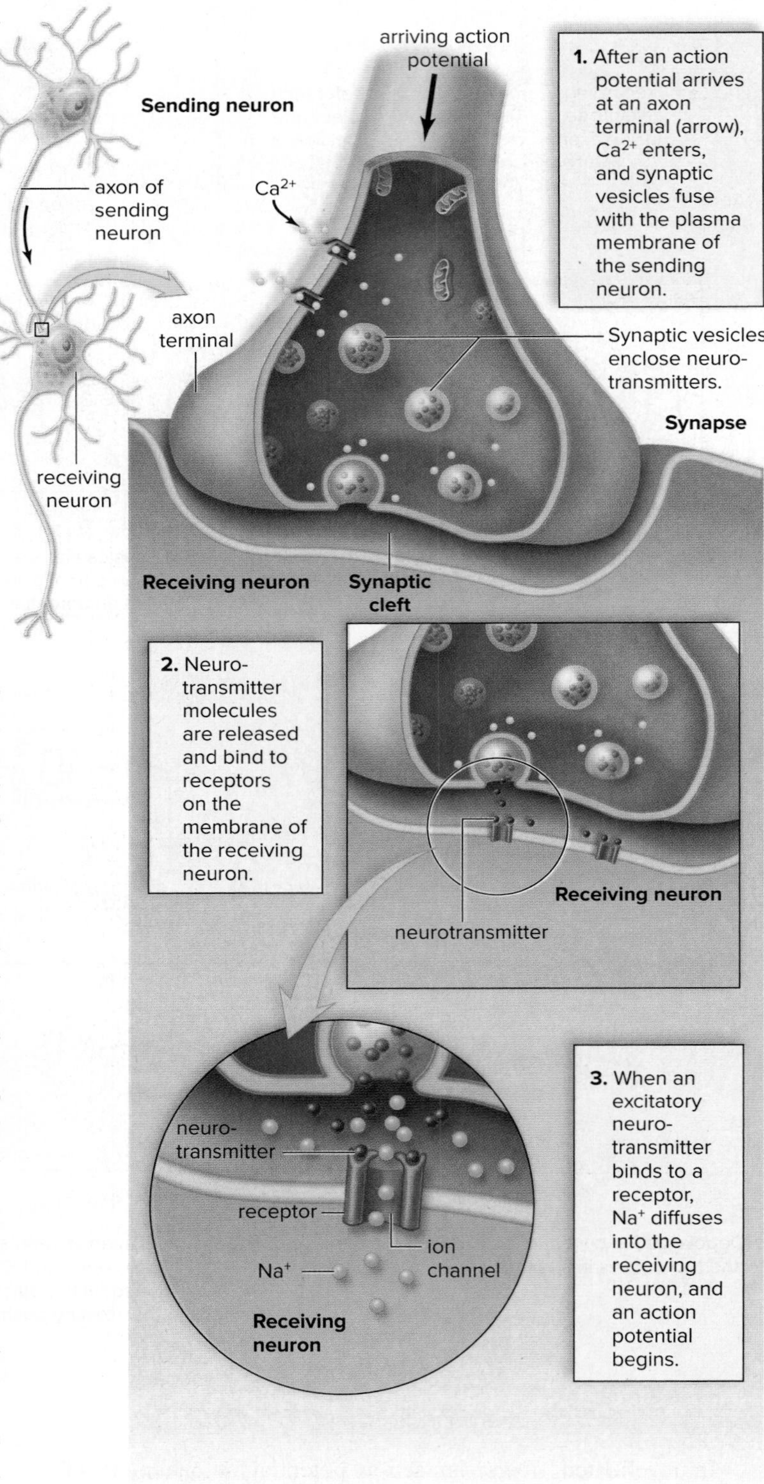

Sending neuron
axon of sending neuron
receiving neuron
arriving action potential
1. After an action potential arrives at an axon terminal (arrow), Ca^{2+} enters, and synaptic vesicles fuse with the plasma membrane of the sending neuron.
Ca^{2+}
axon terminal
Synaptic vesicles enclose neuro-transmitters.
Synapse
Receiving neuron
Synaptic cleft
2. Neuro-transmitter molecules are released and bind to receptors on the membrane of the receiving neuron.
Receiving neuron
neurotransmitter
3. When an excitatory neuro-transmitter binds to a receptor, Na^+ diffuses into the receiving neuron, and an action potential begins.
neuro-transmitter
receptor
ion channel
Na^+
Receiving neuron

Figure 14.6 Signal transmission at the synapse.
Transmission across a synapse from one neuron to another occurs when a neurotransmitter is released, diffuses across a synaptic cleft, and binds to a receptor in the membrane of the receiving neuron.

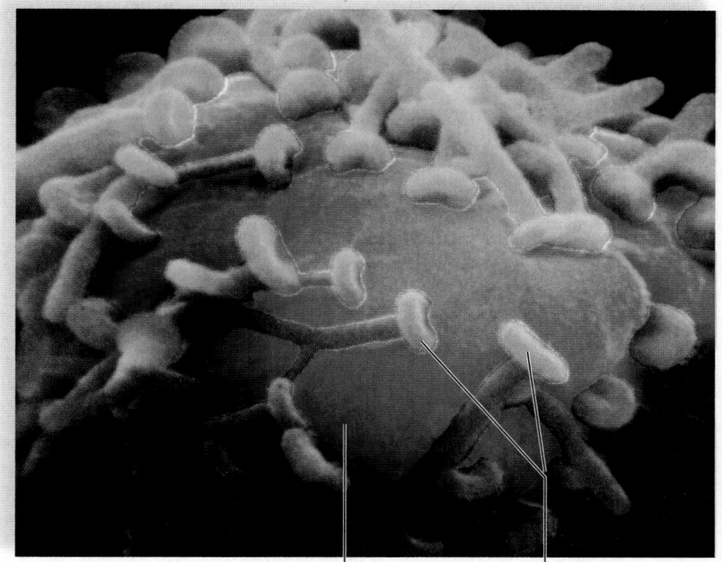

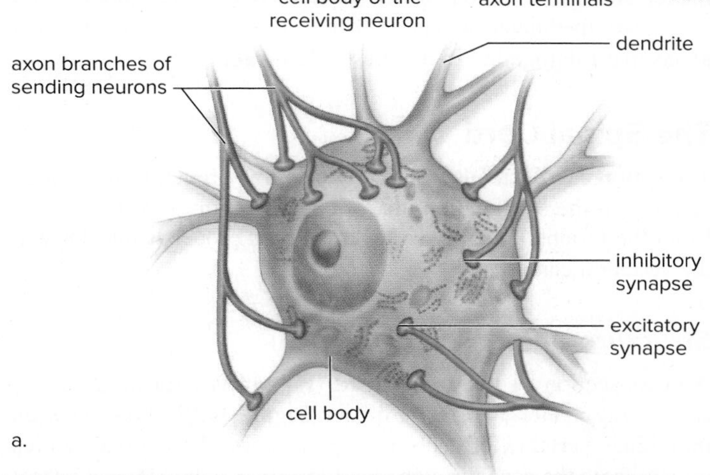

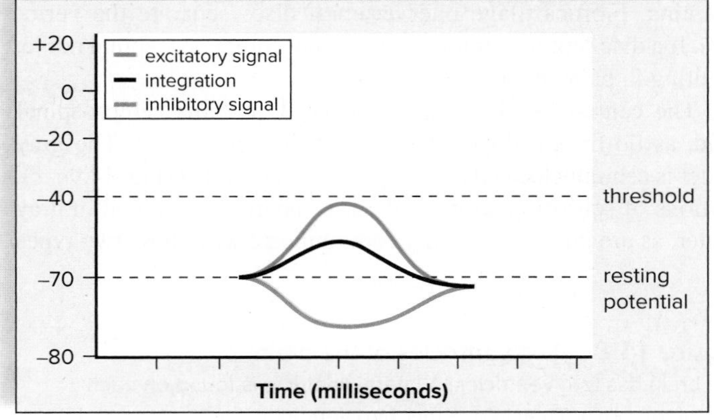

Figure 14.7 **Integration of excitatory and inhibitory signals at the synapse.**
a. Inhibitory signals and excitatory signals are summed up in the dendrite and cell body of the postsynaptic neuron. Only if the combined signals cause the membrane potential to rise above threshold does an action potential occur. **b.** In this example, threshold was not reached.
(photo) (a): Omikron/Science Source

The receiving cell needs to be able to respond quickly to changing conditions. If the neurotransmitter were to linger in the cleft, the receiving cell would be unable to respond to a new signal from a sending cell.

Neurotransmitter Molecules

More than 100 substances are known or suspected to be neurotransmitters. Some of the more common ones in humans are acetylcholine, norepinephrine, dopamine, serotonin, glutamate, and GABA (gamma-aminobutyric acid). Neurotransmitters transmit signals between nerves. Nerve-muscle, nerve-organ, and nerve-gland synapses also communicate using neurotransmitters.

Acetylcholine (ACh) and **norepinephrine** are active in both the CNS and PNS. In the PNS, these neurotransmitters act at synapses called neuromuscular junctions. We will explore the structure of the neuromuscular junctions in Section 13.2.

In the PNS, ACh excites skeletal muscle but inhibits cardiac muscle. It has either an excitatory or inhibitory effect on smooth muscle or glands, depending on their location.

Norepinephrine generally excites smooth muscle. In the CNS, norepinephrine is important to dreaming, waking, and mood. **Serotonin** is involved in thermoregulation, sleeping, emotions, and perception. Many drugs that affect the nervous system act at the synapse. Some interfere with the actions of neurotransmitters, and other drugs prolong the effects of neurotransmitters (see Section 14.5).

BIOLOGY IN YOUR LIFE

How do SSRIs work?

Selective serotonin reuptake inhibitors (SSRIs) are a class of drugs widely used to treat depression and anxiety. They work within the synapses of the brain by blocking the reabsorption (reuptake) of serotonin after it is released with the synapse. The exact mechanism by which this occurs is still not completely understood, but it is widely recognized that this class of drugs interacts with the reuptake receptors on the surface of the neurons.

Synaptic Integration

A single neuron has a cell body and may have many dendrites (Fig. 14.7*a*). All can have synapses with many other neurons. Therefore, a neuron is on the receiving end of many signals, which can either be excitatory or inhibitory. Recall that an excitatory neurotransmitter produces an excitatory signal by opening sodium gates at a synapse. This drives the neuron closer to its threshold (illustrated by the green line in Fig. 14.7*b*). If threshold is reached, an action potential is inevitable. On the other hand, an inhibitory neurotransmitter drives the neuron farther from an action potential (red line in Fig. 14.7*b*) by opening the gates for potassium.

Neurons integrate these incoming signals. **Integration** is the summing up of excitatory and inhibitory signals. If a neuron receives enough excitatory signals (either from different synapses or at a rapid rate from a single synapse) to outweigh the inhibitory ones, chances are the axon will transmit a signal. On the other hand, if a neuron receives more inhibitory than excitatory signals, summing these signals may prohibit the axon from reaching threshold and then depolarizing (the solid black line in Fig. 14.7*b*).

CHECK YOUR PROGRESS 14.1

1. Describe the three types of neurons, and list the three main parts of a neuron.
2. Describe how a nerve impulse is propagated.
3. Summarize how a nerve impulse is transmitted from one neuron to the next.

CONNECTING THE CONCEPTS

For more information on neurons and the nervous system, refer to the following discussions:

Section 4.4 explores how stem cells may be used to regenerate nervous tissue.

Figure 13.7 illustrates the role of the synapse in the neuromuscular junction.

Section 15.1 explains how the peripheral nervous system sends information to and from the central nervous system.

14.2 The Central Nervous System

LEARNING OUTCOMES

Upon completion of this section, you should be able to

1. Identify the structures of the spinal cord and provide a function for each.
2. Identify the structures of the brain and provide a function for each.
3. Identify the lobes and major areas of the human brain.
4. Distinguish between the functions of the primary motor and the primary somatosensory areas of the brain.

The spinal cord and the brain make up the central nervous system (CNS), where sensory information is received and motor control is initiated. Both the spinal cord and the brain are protected by bone. The spinal cord is surrounded by vertebrae, and the brain is enclosed by the skull. Also, both the spinal cord and the brain are wrapped in protective membranes known as **meninges** (*sing.*, meninx). *Meningitis* is an infection of the meninges and may be caused by either bacterial or viral pathogens. The spaces between the meninges are filled with **cerebrospinal fluid,** which cushions and protects the CNS. In a spinal tap (lumbar puncture), a small amount of this fluid is withdrawn from around the spinal cord for laboratory testing. Cerebrospinal fluid is also contained within the ventricles of the brain and in the central canal of the spinal cord. The brain has four **ventricles,** interconnecting chambers that produce and serve as a reservoir for cerebrospinal fluid (Fig. 14.8). Normally, any excess cerebrospinal fluid drains away into the cardiovascular system. However, blockages can occur. In an infant, the brain can enlarge due to cerebrospinal fluid accumulation, resulting in a condition called hydrocephalus ("water on the brain"). If cerebrospinal fluid collects in an adult, the brain cannot enlarge. Instead, it is pushed against the skull. Such situations cause severe brain damage and can be fatal unless quickly corrected.

The CNS is composed of two types of nervous tissue—gray matter and white matter. **Gray matter** contains cell bodies and short, nonmyelinated axons. **White matter** contains myelinated axons that run together in bundles called **tracts.**

The Spinal Cord

The **spinal cord** extends from the base of the brain through a large opening in the skull called the foramen magnum (see Fig. 12.4). From the foramen magnum, the spinal cord proceeds inferiorly in the vertebral canal.

Structure of the Spinal Cord

A cross-section of the spinal cord (Fig. 14.9*a*) shows a central canal, gray matter, and white matter. Figure 14.9*b* shows how an individual vertebra protects the spinal cord. The spinal nerves project from the cord through small openings called intervertebral foramina. Fibrocartilage intervertebral discs separate the vertebrae. If a disc ruptures or herniates, it may compress a spinal nerve, resulting in pain and a loss of mobility.

The central canal of the spinal cord contains cerebrospinal fluid, as do the meninges that protect the spinal cord. The gray matter is centrally located and shaped like the letter *H* (Fig. 14.9*a, c*). Portions of sensory neurons and motor neurons are found in gray matter, as are interneurons that communicate with these two types

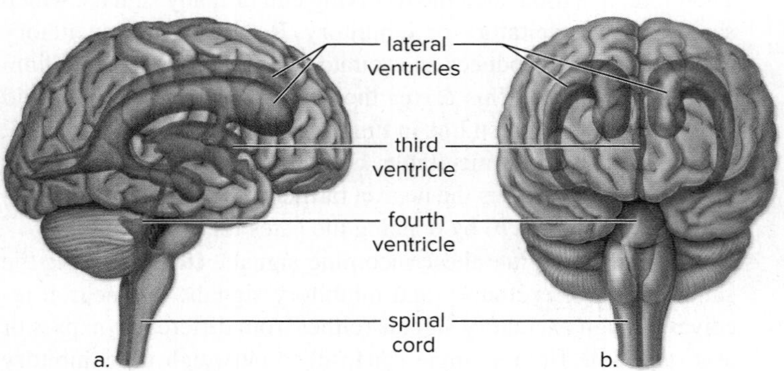

Figure 14.8 The ventricles of the brain.
The brain has four ventricles. A lateral ventricle is found on each side of the brain. They join at the third ventricle. The third ventricle connects with the fourth ventricle superiorly; the central canal of the spinal cord joins the fourth ventricle inferiorly. All structures are filled with cerebrospinal fluid. **a.** Lateral view of ventricles seen through a transparent brain. **b.** Anterior view of ventricles seen through a transparent brain.

of neurons. The dorsal root of a spinal nerve contains sensory fibers entering the gray matter. The ventral root of a spinal nerve contains motor fibers exiting the gray matter. The dorsal and ventral roots join before the spinal nerve leaves the vertebral canal (Fig. 14.9*c, d*), forming a mixed nerve. Spinal nerves are a part of the PNS.

The white matter of the spinal cord occurs in areas around the gray matter. The white matter contains ascending tracts taking information to the brain (primarily located posteriorly) and descending tracts taking information from the brain (primarily located anteriorly). Many tracts cross just after they enter and exit the brain, so the left side of the brain controls the right side of the body. Likewise, the right side of the brain controls the left side of the body.

Functions of the Spinal Cord

The spinal cord provides a means of communication between the brain and the peripheral nerves that leave the cord. When someone touches your hand, sensory receptors generate nerve signals that pass through sensory fibers to the spinal cord and up ascending tracts to the brain (see Fig. 14.2, red arrows).

The gate control theory of pain proposes that the tracts in the spinal cord have "gates" and that these gates control the flow of pain messages from the peripheral nerves to the brain. Depending on how the gates process a pain signal, the pain message can be allowed to pass directly to the brain or can be prevented from reaching the brain. Pain messages may also be blocked by other inputs, such as those received from touch receptors or endorphins.

The brain coordinates the voluntary control of our limbs. Motor signals originating in the brain pass down descending tracts to the spinal cord and out to our muscles by way of motor fibers (see Fig. 14.2, black arrows). Therefore, if the spinal cord is severed, we experience a loss of sensation and a loss of voluntary control—paralysis. If the cut occurs in the thoracic region, the lower body and legs are paralyzed, a condition known as *paraplegia.* If the injury is in the neck region, all four limbs are usually affected, a condition called *quadriplegia.*

Reflex Actions The spinal cord is the center for thousands of *reflex arcs* (see Fig. 14.18). A stimulus causes sensory receptors to generate signals that travel in sensory axons to the spinal cord. Interneurons integrate the incoming data and relay signals to motor neurons. A response to the stimulus occurs when motor axons cause skeletal muscles to contract. Motor neurons in a reflex arc may also affect smooth muscle, organs, or glands. Each interneuron in the spinal cord synapses with numerous other neurons. From there, interneurons send signals to other interneurons and motor neurons.

Similarly, the spinal cord creates reflex arcs for the internal organs. For example, when blood pressure falls, internal receptors in the carotid arteries and aorta generate nerve signals that pass through sensory fibers to the cord and then up an ascending tract to a cardiovascular center in the brain. Thereafter, nerve signals pass down a descending tract to the spinal cord. Motor signals then cause blood vessels to constrict, so that the blood pressure rises.

white matter
gray matter
central canal
a.
10×

spinal cord
vertebra
gray matter
white matter
dorsal root
dorsal root ganglion
spinal nerve
ventral root
vertebra
b.

central canal
dorsal root
dorsal root ganglion
spinal nerve
ventral root
dorsal
ventral
gray matter
white matter
meninges
c.

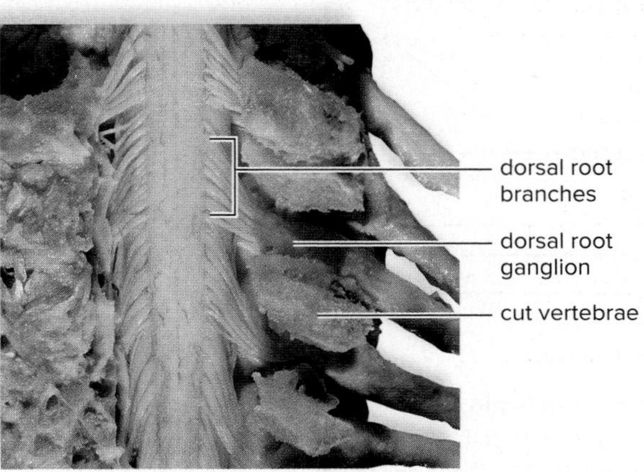

d. Dorsal view of spinal cord and dorsal roots of spinal nerves

Figure 14.9 The organization of white and gray matter in the spinal cord and the spinal nerves.
a. Cross-section of the spinal cord, showing arrangements of white and gray matter. **b.** Spinal nerves originating from the spinal cord. **c.** The spinal cord is protected by vertebrae. **d.** Spinal nerves emerging from the cord.

(a): Scientifica/Corbis Documentary/Getty Images; (d): Rebecca Gray/Don Kincaid/Wise Anatomy Collection/McGraw Hill

The Brain

The human **brain** has been called the last great frontier of biology. The goal of modern neuroscience is to understand the structure and function of the brain's various parts so well that it will be possible to prevent or correct the thousands of mental disorders that cause human suffering. This section gives only a glimpse of what is known about the brain and the modern avenues of research.

We discuss the parts of the brain with reference to the cerebrum, the diencephalon, the cerebellum, and the brain stem. The brain's four ventricles (see Fig. 14.8) are called, in turn, the two lateral ventricles, the third ventricle, and the fourth ventricle. It may be helpful for you to associate the cerebrum with the two lateral ventricles, the diencephalon with the third ventricle, and the brain stem and cerebellum with the fourth ventricle (Fig. 14.10*a*).

The Cerebrum

The **cerebrum** is the largest portion of the brain in mammals, including humans. The cerebrum is the last center to receive sensory input and carry out integration before commanding voluntary motor responses. It communicates with and coordinates the activities of the other parts of the brain.

Cerebral Hemispheres Just as the human body has two halves, so does the cerebrum. These halves are called the left and right **cerebral hemispheres** (Fig. 14.10*b*). A deep groove called the longitudinal fissure divides the left and right cerebral hemispheres. The two cerebral hemispheres communicate via the **corpus callosum,** an extensive bridge of nerve tracts.

The characteristic appearance of the cerebrum is the result of thick folds, called *gyri* (*sing.,* gyrus) separated by shallow grooves called *sulci* (*sing.,* sulcus). The sulci divide each hemisphere into lobes (Fig. 14.11). The *frontal lobe* is the most anterior of the lobes (directly behind the forehead). The *parietal lobe* is posterior to the frontal lobe. The *occipital lobe* is posterior to the parietal lobe (at the rear of the head). The *temporal lobe* lies inferior to the frontal and parietal lobes (at the temple and the ear).

The Cerebral Cortex The **cerebral cortex** is a thin, highly convoluted outer layer of gray matter that covers the cerebral hemispheres. Recall that gray matter consists of neurons whose axons are not myelinated. The cerebral cortex contains over 1 billion cell bodies and is the region of the brain that accounts for sensation, voluntary movement, and all the thought processes we associate with consciousness.

Primary Motor and Sensory Areas of the Cortex The cerebral cortex contains motor areas and sensory areas, as well as association areas. The **primary motor area** is in the frontal lobe just anterior to (before) the central sulcus. Voluntary commands to skeletal muscles begin in the primary motor area, and each part of the body is controlled by a certain section (Fig. 14.12*a*). In this illustration, notice that large areas of the cerebral cortex are devoted

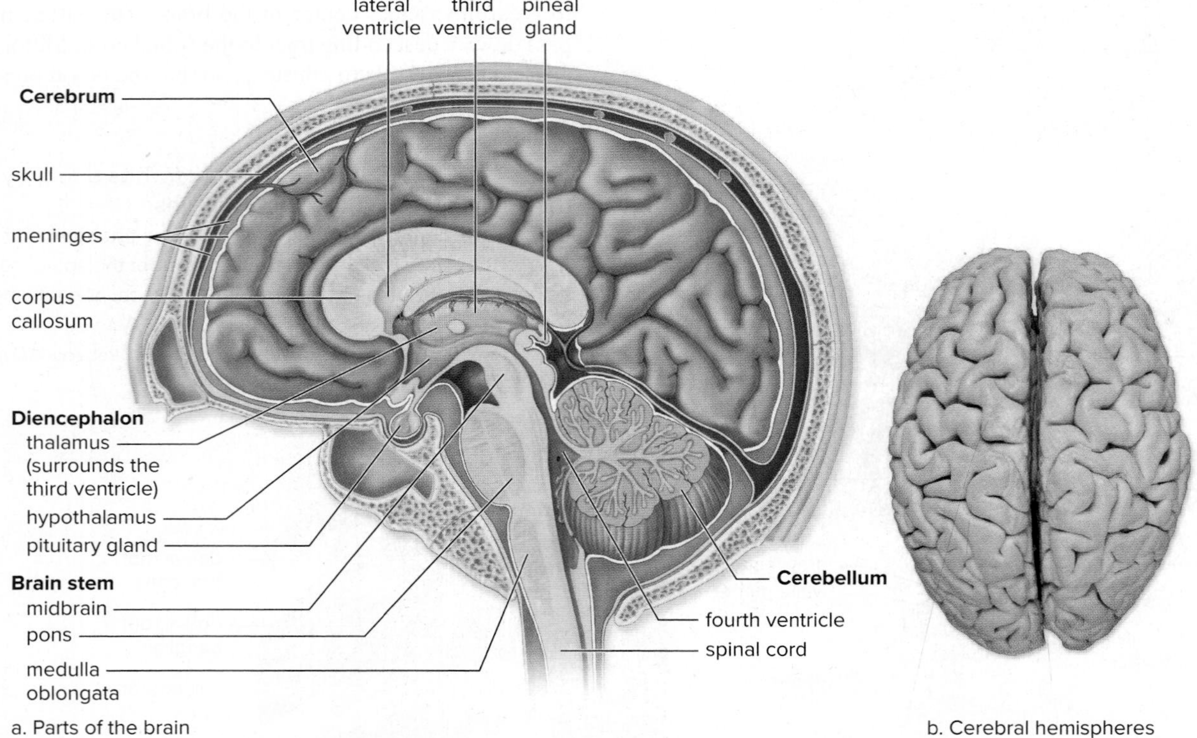

Figure 14.10 The human brain.

a. The cerebrum is the largest part of the brain in humans. **b.** Viewed from above, the cerebrum has left and right cerebral hemispheres. The hemispheres are connected by the corpus callosum.

(b): Christine Eckel/McGraw Hill

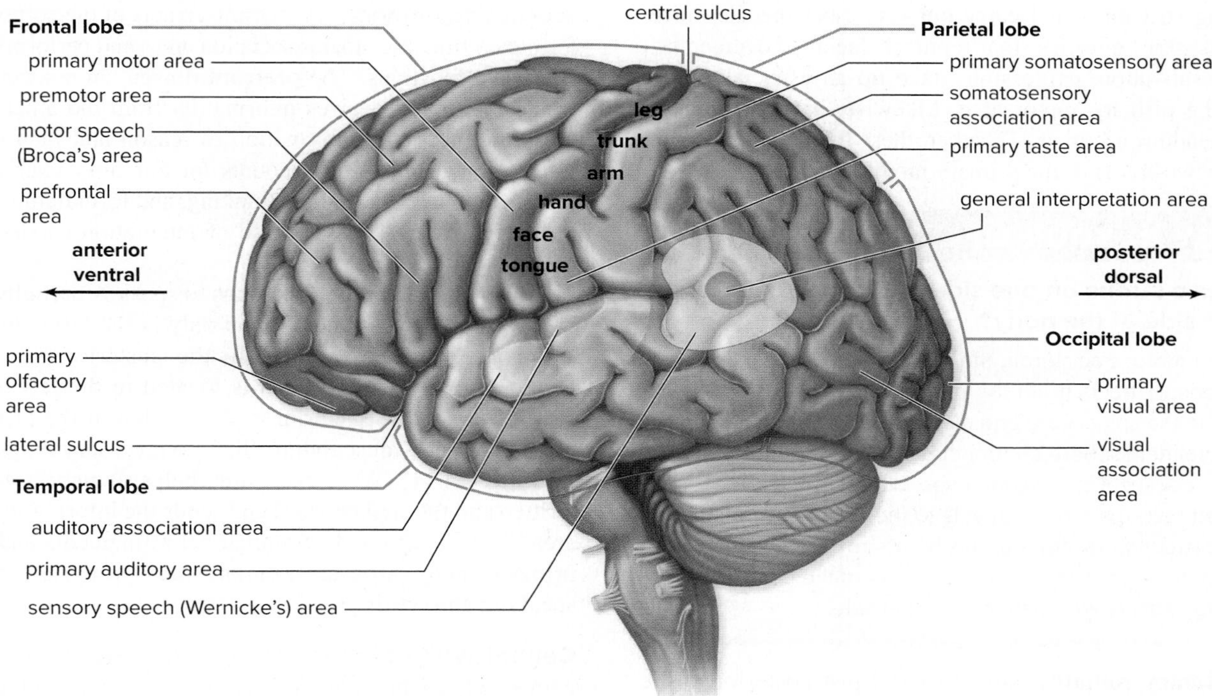

Figure 14.11 The lobes of the cerebral hemispheres.

Each cerebral hemisphere is divided into four lobes: frontal, parietal, temporal, and occipital. Centers in the frontal lobe control movement and higher reasoning, as well as the smell sensation. Somatic sensing is carried out by parietal lobe neurons, and those of the temporal lobe receive sound information. Visual information is received and processed in the occipital lobe.

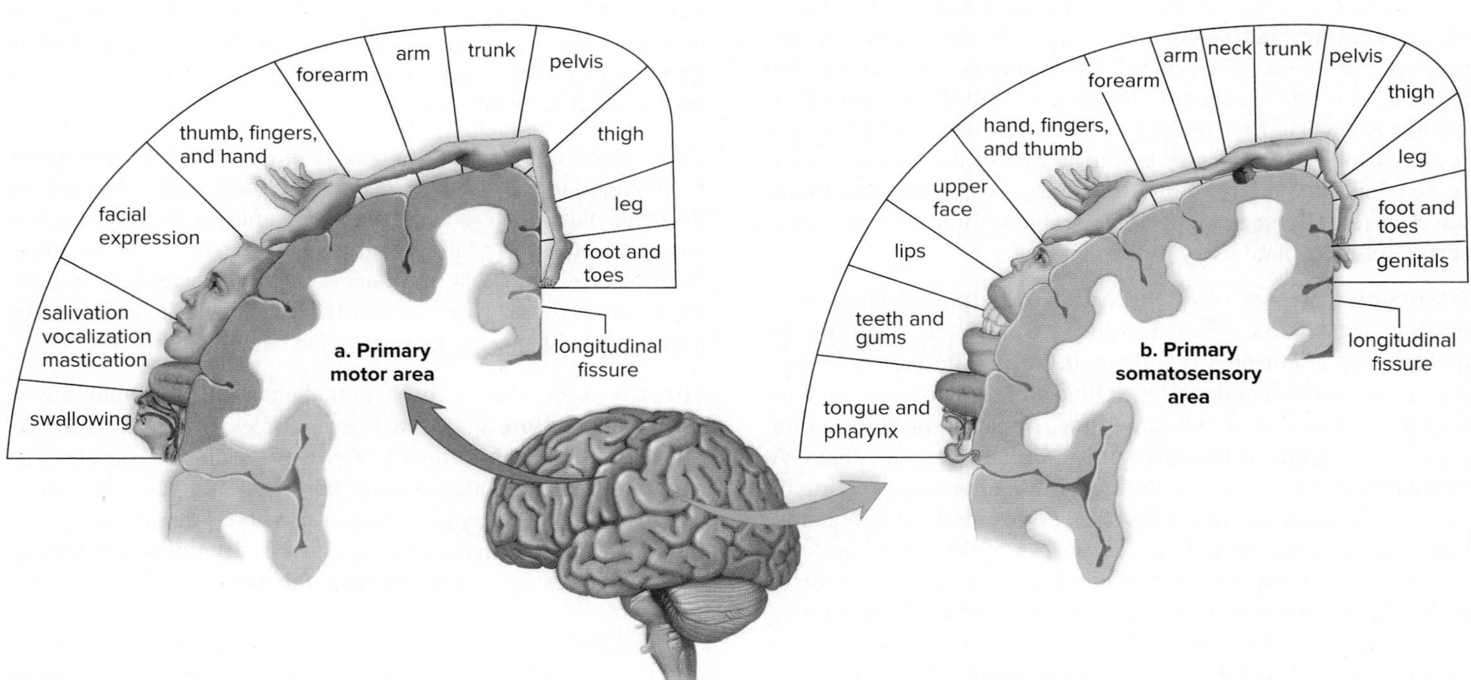

Figure 14.12 The primary motor and primary somatosensory areas of the brain.

a. The primary motor area (blue) is located in the frontal lobe, adjacent to (**b**) the primary somatosensory area in the parietal lobe. The primary taste area is colored pink. The size of each body region shown indicates the relative amount of cortex devoted to control of that body region.

to controlling structures that carry out very fine, precise movements. Thus, the muscles that control facial movements—swallowing, salivation, expression—take up an especially large portion of the primary motor area. Likewise, hand movements require tremendous accuracy. Together, these two structures command nearly two-thirds of the primary motor area.

BIOLOGY IN YOUR LIFE

How does a stroke on one side of the brain affect the other side of the body?

Descending motor tracts (from the primary motor area) and ascending sensory tracts (from the primary somatosensory area) cross over in the spinal cord and medulla. Motor neurons in the right cerebral hemisphere control the left side of the body, and vice versa, because of crossing-over. Likewise, the sensation from the left half of the body travels to the right cerebral hemisphere. Destruction of brain tissue by a stroke interferes with outgoing motor signals to the opposite side of the body, as well as incoming sensory information from that side.

The **primary somatosensory area** is just posterior to the central sulcus in the parietal lobe. Sensory information from the skin and skeletal muscles arrives here, where each part of the body is sequentially represented (Fig. 14.12*b*). Like the primary motor cortex, large areas of the primary sensory cortex are dedicated to those body areas with acute sensation. Once again, the face and hands require the largest proportion of the sensory cortex.

Reception areas for the other primary sensations—taste, vision, hearing, and smell—are located in other areas of the cerebral cortex (see Fig. 14.11). The primary taste area in the parietal lobe (pink) accounts for taste sensations. Visual information is received by the primary visual cortex (blue) in the occipital lobe. The primary auditory area in the temporal lobe (green) accepts information from our ears. Smell sensations travel to the primary olfactory area (yellow) found on the deep surface of the frontal lobe.

Association Areas **Association areas** are places where integration occurs and where memories are stored. Anterior to the primary motor area is a premotor area. The premotor area organizes motor functions for skilled motor activities, such as walking and talking at the same time. Next, the primary motor area sends signals to the cerebellum, which integrates them. A momentary lack of oxygen during birth can damage the motor areas of the cerebral cortex, resulting in cerebral palsy, a condition characterized by a spastic weakness of the arms and legs. The *somatosensory association area,* located just posterior to the primary somatosensory area, processes and analyzes sensory information from the skin and muscles. The *visual association area* in the occipital lobe associates new visual information with stored visual memories. It might "decide," for example, if we have seen a face, scene, or symbol before. The *auditory association area* in the temporal lobe performs the same functions with regard to sounds.

Processing Centers Processing centers of the cortex receive information from the other association areas and perform higher-level analytical functions. The **prefrontal area,** an association area in the frontal lobe, receives information from the other association areas and uses this information to reason and plan our actions. Integration in this area accounts for our most cherished human abilities. Reasoning, critical thinking, and formulating appropriate behaviors are possible because of integration carried out in the prefrontal area.

The unique ability of humans to speak is partially dependent on two processing centers found only in the left cerebral cortex. **Wernicke's area** is located in the posterior part of the left temporal lobe. **Broca's area** is located in the left frontal lobe. Broca's area is just anterior to the portion of the primary motor area for speech musculature (lips, tongue, larynx, and so forth) (see Fig. 14.11). Wernicke's area helps us understand both the written and the spoken word and sends the information to Broca's area. Broca's area adds grammatical refinements and directs the primary motor area to stimulate the appropriate muscles for speaking and writing.

Central White Matter Much of the rest of the cerebrum is composed of white matter. Myelination occurs and white matter develops as a child grows. Progressive myelination enables the brain to grow in size and complexity. For example, as neurons become myelinated within tracts designed for language development, children become more capable of speech. Descending tracts from the primary motor area communicate with lower brain centers, and ascending tracts from lower brain centers send sensory information up to the primary somatosensory area. Tracts within the cerebrum also take information among the different sensory, motor, and association areas pictured in Figure 14.11. The corpus callosum contains tracts that join the two cerebral hemispheres.

Basal Nuclei Though the majority of each cerebral hemisphere is composed of tracts, there are masses of gray matter deep within the white matter. These **basal nuclei** integrate motor commands to ensure that the proper muscle groups are stimulated or inhibited. Integration ensures that movements are coordinated and smooth. **Parkinson's disease** (see Section 18.5) is believed to be caused by degeneration of specific neurons in the basal nuclei.

The Diencephalon The hypothalamus and thalamus are in the **diencephalon,** a region that encircles the third ventricle. The **hypothalamus** forms the floor of the third ventricle. The hypothalamus is an integrating center that helps maintain homeostasis. It regulates hunger, sleep, thirst, body temperature, and water balance. The hypothalamus controls the pituitary gland and thereby serves as a link between the nervous and endocrine systems.

The **thalamus** consists of two masses of gray matter located in the sides and roof of the third ventricle. The thalamus is on the receiving end for all sensory input except the sense of smell. Visual, auditory, and somatosensory information arrives at the thalamus via the cranial nerves and tracts from the spinal cord. The thalamus integrates this information and sends it on to the appropriate portions of the cerebrum. The thalamus is involved in arousal of the cerebrum, and it participates in higher mental functions, such as memory and emotions.

The pineal gland, which secretes the hormone melatonin, is located in the diencephalon. Presently, there is much popular interest in the role of melatonin in our daily rhythms. Some researchers believe it can help alleviate jet lag or insomnia. Scientists are also interested in the possibility that the hormone may regulate the onset of puberty.

The Cerebellum

The **cerebellum** lies under the occipital lobe of the cerebrum and is separated from the brain stem by the fourth ventricle. The cerebellum has two portions joined by a narrow median portion. Each portion is primarily composed of white matter. In a longitudinal section, the white matter has a treelike pattern called *arbor vitae.* Overlying the white matter is a thin layer of gray matter that forms a series of complex folds.

The cerebellum receives sensory input from the eyes, ears, joints, and muscles about the present position of body parts. It also receives motor output from the cerebral cortex about where these parts should be located. After integrating this information, the cerebellum sends motor signals by way of the brain stem to the skeletal muscles. In this way, the cerebellum maintains posture and balance. It also ensures that all the muscles work together to produce smooth, coordinated, voluntary movements. The cerebellum assists in the learning of new motor skills, such as playing the piano or hitting a baseball.

The Brain Stem

The tracts cross in the **brain stem,** which contains the midbrain, the pons, and the medulla oblongata (see Fig. 14.10*a*). The **midbrain** acts as a relay station for tracts passing between the cerebrum and the spinal cord or cerebellum. It also has reflex centers for visual, auditory, and tactile responses. The **pons** ("bridge" in Latin) contains bundles of axons traveling between the cerebellum and the rest of the CNS. In addition, the pons functions with the medulla oblongata to regulate breathing rate. Reflex centers in the pons coordinate head movements in response to visual and auditory stimuli.

The **medulla oblongata** contains a number of reflex centers for regulating heartbeat, breathing, and vasoconstriction (blood pressure). It also contains the reflex centers for vomiting, coughing, sneezing, hiccuping, and swallowing. The medulla oblongata lies just superior to the spinal cord, and it contains tracts that ascend or descend between the spinal cord and higher brain centers. Recall that tracts are groups of axons that travel together. Ascending tracts convey sensory information. Motor information is transmitted on descending tracts.

The Reticular Formation The **reticular formation** is a complex network of *nuclei,* which are masses of gray matter, and fibers that extends the length of the brain stem (Fig. 14.13). The reticular formation is a major component of the reticular activating system (RAS). The RAS receives sensory signals and sends

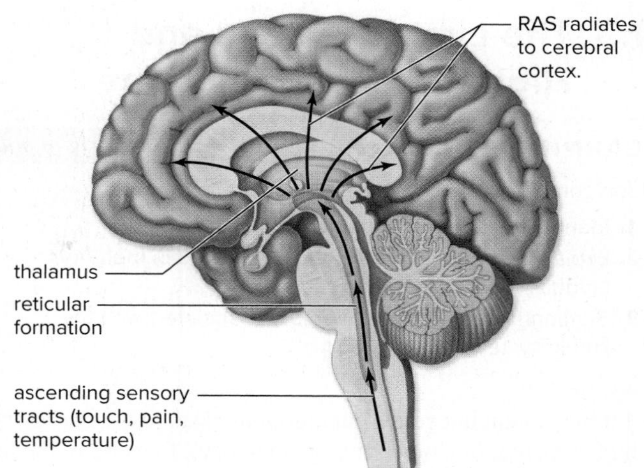

Figure 14.13 **The reticular formation of the brain.** The reticular formation receives and sends on motor and sensory information to various parts of the CNS. One portion, the reticular activating system (RAS) (see arrows), arouses the cerebrum and, in this way, controls alertness versus sleep.

them to higher centers. Motor signals received by the RAS are sent to the spinal cord.

The RAS arouses the cerebrum via the thalamus and causes a person to be alert. If you want to awaken the RAS, surprise it with sudden stimuli, such as an alarm clock ringing, bright lights, smelling salts, or cold water splashed on your face. The RAS can filter out unnecessary sensory stimuli, explaining why you can study with the TV on. Similarly, the RAS allows you to take a test without noticing the sounds of the people around you—unless the sounds are particularly distracting. To inactivate the RAS, remove visual or auditory stimuli, allowing yourself to become drowsy and drop off to sleep. General anesthetics function by artificially suppressing the RAS. A severe injury to the RAS can cause a person to become comatose, from which recovery may be impossible.

CHECK YOUR PROGRESS 14.2

1. List the functions of the spinal cord.
2. Summarize the major regions of the brain and describe the general function of each.
3. Relate how the RAS aids in homeostasis.

CONNECTING THE CONCEPTS

For more information on the central nervous system, refer to the following discussions:

Section 10.5 examines how the central nervous system controls breathing.

Section 18.5 explores how aging and diseases such as Alzheimer's disease influence the brain.

Sections 23.3 and **23.4** outline how the size of the brain has changed over the course of human evolution.

14.3 The Limbic System and Higher Mental Functions

LEARNING OUTCOMES

Upon completion of this section, you should be able to

1. Identify the structures of the limbic system.
2. Explain how the limbic system is involved in memory, language, and speech.
3. Summarize the types of memory associated with the limbic system.

The limbic system integrates our emotions (fear, joy, sadness) with our higher mental functions (reason, memory). Because of the limbic system, activities such as sexual behavior and eating seem pleasurable, and mental stress can cause high blood pressure.

The Limbic System

The **limbic system** is an evolutionarily ancient group of linked structures deep within the cerebrum. It is a functional grouping rather than an anatomical one (Fig. 14.14). The limbic system blends primitive emotions and higher mental functions into a united whole. As already noted, it accounts for why activities such as sexual behavior and eating seem pleasurable. Conversely, unpleasant sensations or emotions (pain, frustration, hatred, despair) are translated by the limbic system into a stress response.

Two significant structures in the limbic system are the amygdala and the hippocampus. The **amygdala,** in particular, can cause experiences to have emotional overtones, and it creates the sensation of fear. This center can use past knowledge fed to it by association areas to assess a current situation. If necessary, the amygdala can trigger the fight-or-flight reaction. So if you are out late at night and you turn to see someone in a ski mask following you, the amygdala may immediately cause you to start running. The frontal cortex can override the limbic system, cause you to rethink the situation, and prevent you from acting out strong reactions.

The **hippocampus** is believed to play a crucial role in learning and memory. The hippocampal region acts as an information gateway during the learning process. It determines what information about the world is to be sent to memory and how this information is to be encoded and stored by other regions in the brain. Most likely, the hippocampus can communicate with the frontal cortex, because we know that memories are an important part of our decision-making processes.

Higher Mental Functions

As in other areas of biological research, brain research has progressed due to technological breakthroughs. Neuroscientists now have a wide range of techniques at their disposal for studying the human brain, including modern technologies that allow us to record its functioning.

Memory and Learning

Just as the connecting tracts of the corpus callosum are evidence that the two cerebral hemispheres work together, so the limbic system indicates that cortical areas may work with lower centers to produce learning and memory. **Memory** is the ability to hold a thought in mind or to recall events from the past, ranging from a word we learned only yesterday to an early emotional experience that has shaped our lives. **Learning** takes place when we retain and use past memories.

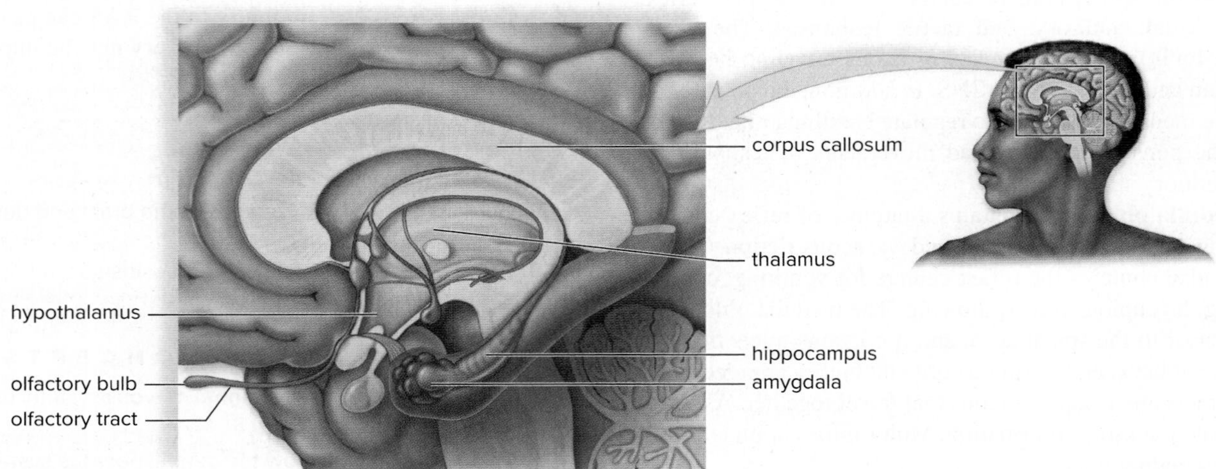

Figure 14.14 The regions of the brain associated with the limbic system.
In the limbic system (purple), structures deep within each cerebral hemisphere and surrounding the diencephalon join higher mental functions, such as reasoning, with more primitive feelings, such as fear and pleasure. Therefore, primitive feelings can influence our behavior, but reason can also keep them in check.

Types of Memory We have all tried to remember a seven-digit telephone number for a short time. If we say we are trying to keep it in the forefront of our brain, we are exactly correct. The prefrontal area, active during **short-term memory,** lies just posterior to our forehead! There are some telephone numbers that we have memorized. In other words, they have gone into **long-term memory.** Think of a telephone number you know by heart, and try to bring it to mind without also thinking about the place or person associated with that number. Most likely you cannot. Typically, long-term memory is a mixture of what is called **semantic memory** (numbers, words, etc.) and **episodic memory** (persons, events, etc.).

Skill memory is another type of memory that can exist independent of episodic memory. Skill memory is involved in performing motor activities such as riding a bike or playing ice hockey. When a person first learns a skill, more areas of the cerebral cortex are involved than after the skill is perfected. In other words, you have to think about what you are doing when you learn a skill, but later the actions become automatic. Skill memory involves all the motor areas of the cerebrum below the level of consciousness.

Long-Term Memory Storage and Retrieval Our long-term memories are apparently stored in bits and pieces throughout the sensory association areas of the cerebral cortex. Visual perceptions are stored in the vision association area, sounds are stored in the auditory association area, and so forth. As previously mentioned, the hippocampus serves as a bridge between the sensory association areas (where memories are stored) and the prefrontal area (where memories are used). The prefrontal area communicates with the hippocampus when memories are stored and when these memories are brought to mind. Some memories are emotionally charged because the amygdala seems to be responsible for fear conditioning and associating danger with sensory stimuli received from various parts of the brain.

BIOLOGY IN YOUR LIFE

What is amnesia?

Amnesia results from disruption of the memory pathways and can be temporary or permanent. In anterograde amnesia, injury to the limbic system separates long-term memories of events that occurred prior to the injury from events that occur in the here and now. A person with anterograde amnesia might carry on a conversation about past events (memories of a long-ago birthday) but be unable to recall a breakfast menu from that morning. In retrograde amnesia, a blow to the head or similar injury abolishes all memories for a variable time before the injury. For example, a head injury occurring during a car accident may abolish all memories from hours to days prior to the accident.

Long-Term Potentiation Though it is helpful to know the memory functions of various portions of the brain, an important step toward curing mental disorders is understanding memory on the cellular level. After synapses have been used intensively for a short time, they release more neurotransmitters than before. This phenomenon, called *long-term potentiation,* may be involved in memory storage.

Language and Speech

Language depends on semantic memory. Therefore, we would expect some of the same areas in the brain to be involved in both memory and language. Any disruption of these pathways could contribute to an inability to comprehend our environment and use speech correctly.

Seeing and hearing words depends on sensory centers in the occipital and temporal lobes, respectively. Damage to Wernicke's area (see Section 14.2) results in the inability to comprehend speech. Damage to Broca's area, on the other hand, results in the inability to speak and write. The functions of the visual cortex, Wernicke's area, and Broca's area are shown in Figure 14.15.

One interesting aside pertaining to language and speech is the recognition that the left brain and the right brain may have different functions. Recall that the left hemisphere contains both Broca's area and Wernicke's area (see Section 14.2). As you might expect, it appears that the left hemisphere plays a role of great importance in language functions. The role of the isolated left hemisphere can be studied in patients after surgery to sever the corpus callosum. This procedure is used for seizure control in patients with epilepsy. After surgery, the patient is said to have split-brain syndrome, because there is no longer direct communication between the two cerebral hemispheres. If an individual with this syndrome views an object with only the right eye, its image will be sent only to the right hemisphere. This person will be able to choose the proper object for a particular use—scissors to cut paper, for example—but will be unable to name that object.

Researchers now believe that the hemispheres process the same information differently. The left hemisphere is more global, whereas the right hemisphere is more specific in its approach. However, research also indicates that the classification of "right-brained" versus "left-brained" for individuals is probably not an accurate indication of an individual's brain activity.

CHECK YOUR PROGRESS 14.3

1. Summarize the function of the limbic system.
2. List what limbic system structures are involved in the fight-or-flight reaction, learning, and long-term memory.
3. Describe the relationship between the left and right sides of the brain and language and speech.

CONNECTING THE CONCEPTS

For more information on these topics, refer to the following discussion:

Section 18.5 examines the effects of aging on the body, including the nervous system.

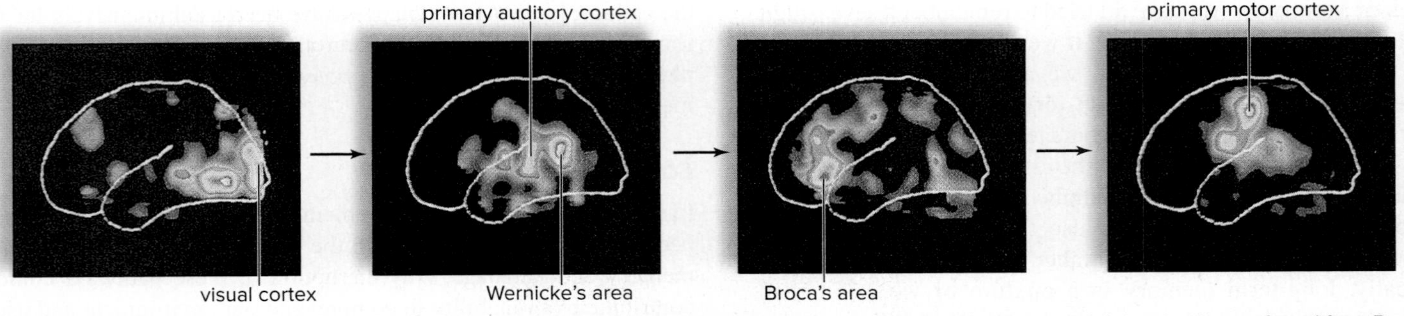

Figure 14.15 **The areas of the brain involved in reading.**
These functional images were captured by a high-speed computer during a PET (positron-emission tomography) scan of the brain. A radioactively labeled solution is injected into the subject, and then the subject is asked to perform certain activities. Cross-sectional images of the brain generated by the computer reveal where activity is occurring because the solution is preferentially taken up by active brain tissue and not by inactive brain tissue. These PET images show the cortical pathway for reading words and then speaking them. Red indicates the most active areas of the brain, and blue indicates the least active areas.
(all): Courtesy of Marcus Raichle

14.4 The Peripheral Nervous System

LEARNING OUTCOMES

Upon completion of this section, you should be able to

1. Describe the series of events during a spinal reflex.
2. Distinguish between the somatic and autonomic divisions of the peripheral nervous system.
3. Distinguish between the sympathetic and parasympathetic divisions of the autonomic division.

The peripheral nervous system (PNS), which lies outside the central nervous system, contains the nerves. Nerves are designated as cranial nerves when they arise from the brain and are termed spinal nerves when they arise from the spinal cord. In any case, all nerves carry signals to and from the CNS. So right now, your eyes are sending messages by way of a cranial nerve to the brain, allowing you to read this text. When you're finished, your brain will direct the muscles in your fingers, by way of the spinal cord and a spinal nerve, to proceed to the next chapter.

Figure 14.16 illustrates the anatomy of a nerve. The cell body and the dendrites of neurons are in either the CNS or the ganglia. **Ganglia** (*sing.*, ganglion) are collections of nerve cell bodies outside the CNS. The axons of neurons project from the CNS and form the spinal cord. In other words, nerves, whether cranial or spinal, are composed of axons, the long part of neurons.

Humans have 12 pairs of **cranial nerves** attached to the brain. By convention, the pairs of cranial nerves are referred to by Roman numerals (Fig. 14.17). Some cranial nerves are sensory nerves—they contain only sensory fibers; some are motor nerves that contain only motor fibers; others are mixed nerves that contain both sensory and motor fibers. Cranial nerves are largely concerned with the head, neck, and facial regions of the body. However, the vagus nerve (X) has branches not only to the pharynx and larynx but also to most of the internal organs. It arises from the brain

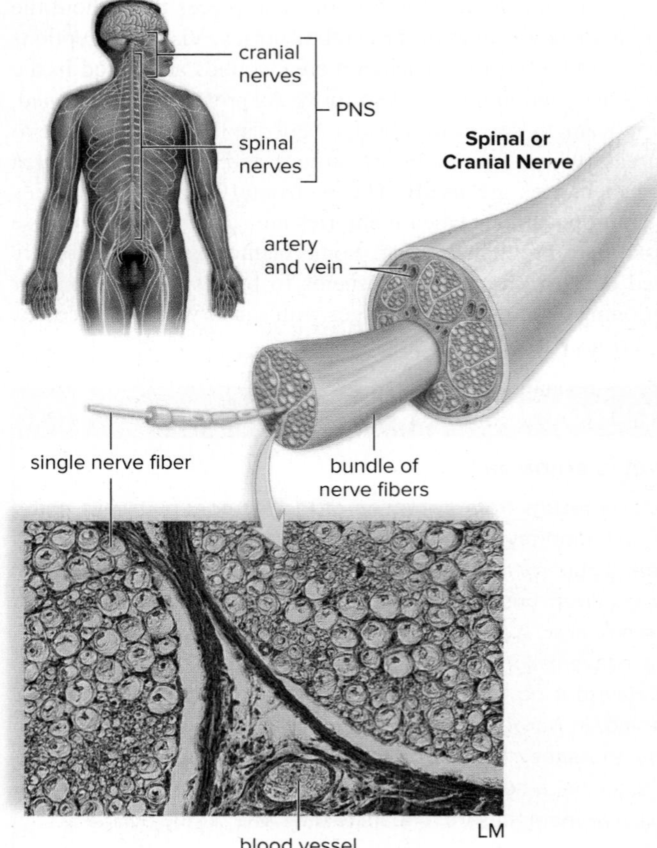

Figure 14.16 **The structure of a nerve.**
The peripheral nervous system consists of the cranial nerves and the spinal nerves. A nerve is composed of bundles of axons separated from one another by connective tissue.
(photo): PASIEKA/Science Photo Library/Getty Images

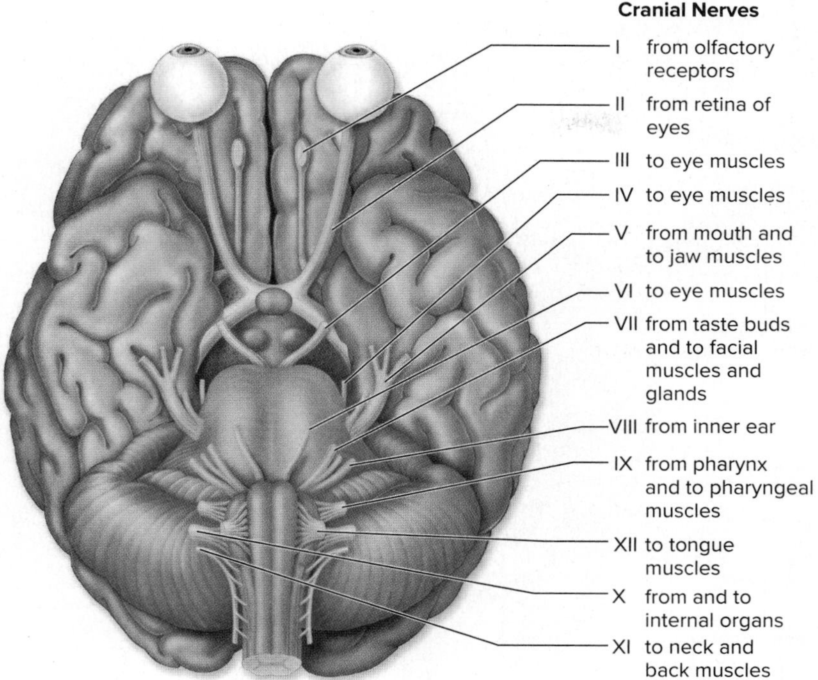

Figure 14.17 The cranial nerves.
Overall, cranial nerves receive sensory input from, and send motor outputs to, the head region. The spinal nerves receive sensory input from, and send motor outputs to, the rest of the body. Two important exceptions are the vagus nerve, X, which communicates with internal organs, and the spinal accessory nerve, XI, which controls neck and back muscles.

stem—specifically, the medulla oblongata, which communicates with the hypothalamus. These two parts of the brain control the internal organs.

The **spinal nerves** of humans emerge from either side of the spinal cord (see Fig. 14.9). There are 31 pairs of spinal nerves. The roots of a spinal nerve physically separate the axons of sensory neurons from the axons of motor neurons, forming an arrangement resembling a letter *Y*. The posterior root of a spinal nerve contains sensory fibers that direct sensory receptor information inward (toward the spinal cord). The cell body of a sensory neuron is in a posterior-root ganglion (also termed a dorsal-root ganglion). The anterior (also termed ventral) root of a spinal nerve contains motor fibers that conduct impulses outward (away from the cord) to the effectors. Observe in Figure 14.9 that the anterior and posterior roots join to form a spinal nerve. All spinal nerves are called mixed nerves, because they contain both sensory and motor fibers. Each spinal nerve serves the particular region of the body in which it is located. For example, the intercostal muscles of the rib cage are innervated by thoracic nerves.

BIOLOGY IN YOUR LIFE

How does aspirin work?

Aspirin is made of a chemical called acetylsalicylic acid (ASA). Damaged tissue produces large amounts of a type of fatty acid called prostaglandin. Prostaglandin acts as a signal to the peripheral nervous system that tissue damage has occurred, which the brain interprets as pain. Prostaglandins are manufactured in the cell by an enzyme called COX (cyclooxygenase). ASA reduces the capabilities of this enzyme, thus lowering the amount of prostaglandin produced and the perception of pain.

The Somatic System

The PNS has divisions: the somatic system and the autonomic system. The nerves in the **somatic system** serve the skin, skeletal muscles, and tendons (see Fig. 14.2). The somatic system sensory nerves take sensory information from external sensory receptors to the CNS. Motor commands leaving the CNS travel to skeletal muscles via somatic motor nerves.

Not all somatic motor actions are voluntary. Some are automatic. Automatic responses to a stimulus in the somatic system are called **reflexes.** A reflex occurs quickly, without your even having to think about it. For example, a reflex may cause you to blink your eyes in response to a flash of light, without your willing it. We will study the path of a reflex, because it allows us to study in detail the path of nerve signals to and from the CNS.

The Reflex Arc

Figure 14.18 illustrates the path of a reflex that involves only the spinal cord. If your hand touches a sharp pin, sensory receptors in the skin generate nerve signals that move along sensory fibers through the posterior (dorsal) root ganglia toward the spinal cord. Sensory neurons that enter the cord posteriorly pass signals on to many interneurons. Some of these interneurons synapse with motor neurons whose short dendrites and cell bodies are in the spinal cord. Nerve signals travel along these motor fibers to an effector, which brings about a response to the stimulus. In this case, the effector is a muscle, which contracts so that you withdraw your hand from the pin. Various other reactions are also possible—you will most likely look at the pin, wince, and cry out in pain. This whole series of responses occurs because some of the interneurons involved carry nerve signals to the brain. The brain makes you aware of the stimulus and directs these other reactions to it. In

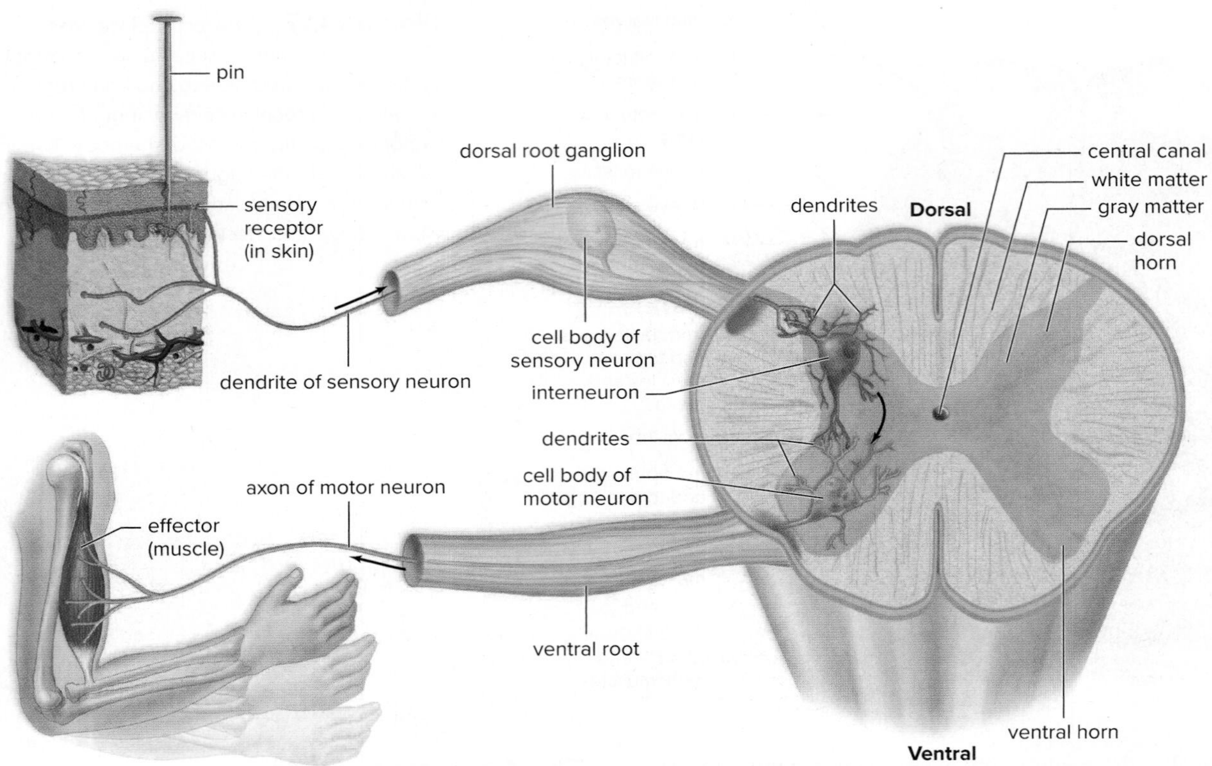

Figure 14.18 A spinal reflex arc.
A stimulus (e.g., a sharp pin) causes sensory receptors in the skin to generate nerve signals that travel in sensory axons to the spinal cord. Interneurons integrate data from sensory neurons and then relay signals to motor neurons, causing contraction of a skeletal muscle and movement of the hand away from the stimulus.

other words, you don't feel pain until the brain receives the information and interprets it.

The Autonomic System

The **autonomic system** is also in the PNS (see Fig. 14.2). The autonomic system regulates the activity of cardiac and smooth muscles, organs, and glands. The system is divided into the sympathetic and parasympathetic divisions (Fig. 14.19). Activation of these two systems generally causes opposite responses.

Although their functions are different, the two divisions share some features: (1) They usually function in an involuntary manner; (2) they innervate all internal organs; and (3) they use two neurons and one ganglion for each impulse. The first neuron has a cell body within the CNS and a preganglionic fiber that enters the ganglion. The second neuron has a cell body within a ganglion and a postganglionic fiber that leaves the ganglion.

Reflex actions, such as those that regulate blood pressure and breathing rate, are especially important to the maintenance of homeostasis. These reflexes begin when the sensory neurons in contact with internal organs send messages to the CNS. They are completed by motor neurons within the autonomic system.

Sympathetic Division

Most preganglionic fibers of the **sympathetic division** arise from the middle portion of the spinal cord. They terminate almost immediately in ganglia that lie near the cord.

The sympathetic division is especially important during emergency situations when you might be required to fight or take flight. It accelerates the heartbeat and dilates the bronchi—active muscles, after all, require a ready supply of glucose and oxygen. Sympathetic neurons inhibit the digestive organs, as well as the kidneys and urinary bladder; the activities of these organs—digestion, defecation, and urination—are not immediately necessary if you're under attack. The neurotransmitter released by the postganglionic axon is primarily norepinephrine (NE). The structure of NE is like that of epinephrine (adrenaline), an adrenal medulla hormone that usually increases heart rate and contractility.

Parasympathetic Division

The **parasympathetic division** includes a few cranial nerves (e.g., the vagus nerve), as well as fibers that arise from the sacral (bottom) portion of the spinal cord. Therefore, this division is often referred to as the craniosacral portion of the autonomic system. In the parasympathetic division, the preganglionic fiber is long, and the postganglionic fiber is short because the ganglia lie near or within the organ.

The parasympathetic division, sometimes called the housekeeper division, promotes all the internal responses we associate with a relaxed state. For example, it causes the pupil of the eye to contract, promotes digestion of food, and slows heart rate. It has been suggested that the parasympathetic system could be called the *rest-and-digest* system. The neurotransmitter used by the parasympathetic division is acetylcholine (ACh).

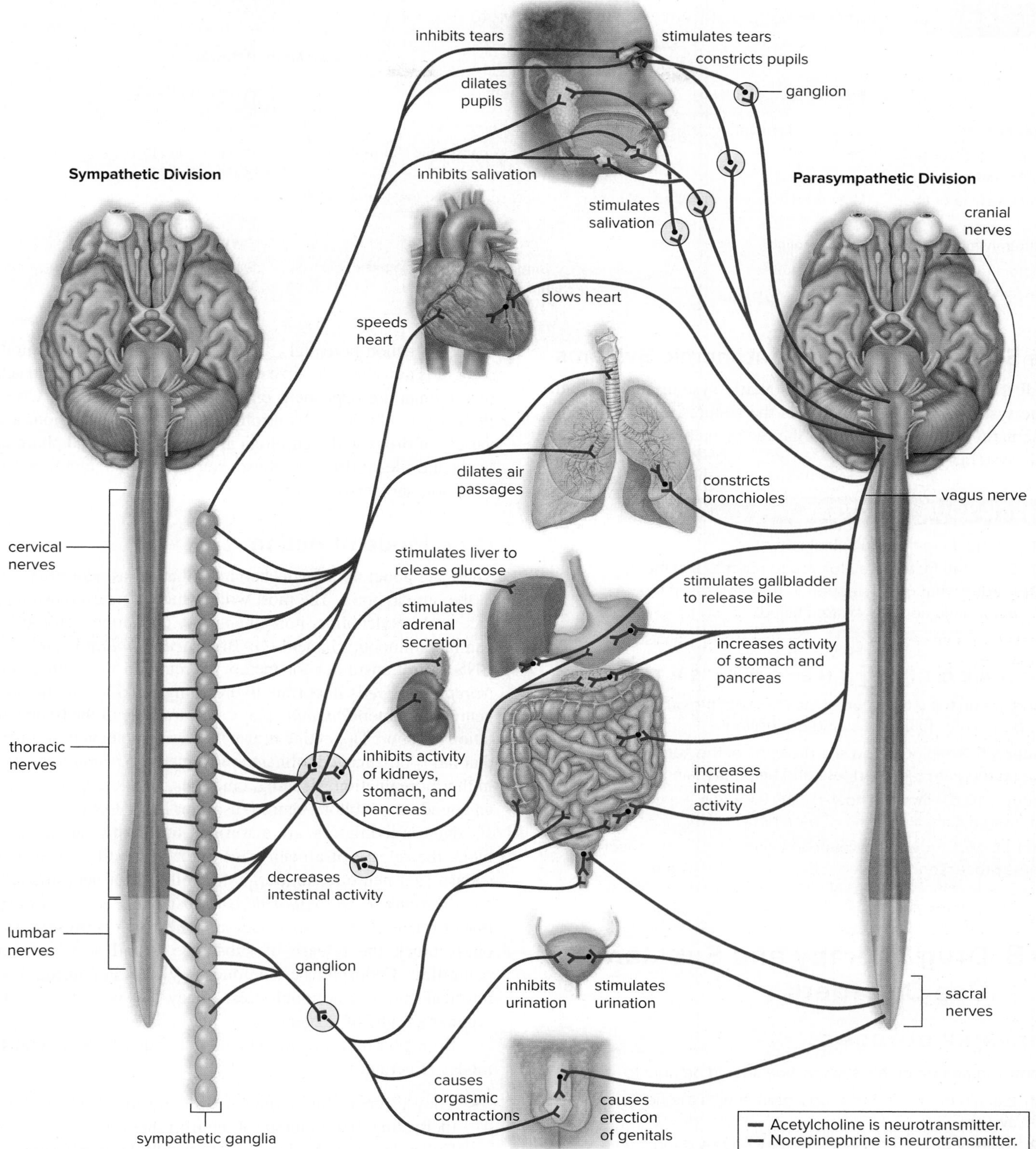

Figure 14.19 The two divisions of the autonomic nervous system.
Sympathetic preganglionic fibers (*left*) arise from the thoracic and lumbar portions of the spinal cord; parasympathetic preganglionic fibers (*right*) arise from the cranial and sacral portions of the spinal cord. Each system innervates the same organs but has contrary effects.

Table 14.1 Comparison of Somatic Motor and Autonomic Motor Pathways

	Somatic Motor Pathway	Autonomic Motor Pathways: Sympathetic	Autonomic Motor Pathways: Parasympathetic
Type of control	Voluntary/involuntary	Involuntary	Involuntary
Number of neurons per message	One	Two (preganglionic shorter than postganglionic)	Two (preganglionic longer than postganglionic)
Location of motor fiber	Most cranial nerves and all spinal nerves	Thoracolumbar spinal nerves	Cranial (e.g., vagus) and sacral spinal nerves
Neurotransmitter	Acetylcholine	Norepinephrine	Acetylcholine
Effectors	Skeletal muscles	Smooth and cardiac muscle, glands, and organs	Smooth and cardiac muscle, glands, and organs

The Somatic Versus the Autonomic Systems

Recall that the PNS includes the somatic system and the autonomic system. Table 14.1 compares the features and functions of the somatic motor pathway with the motor pathways of the autonomic system.

CHECK YOUR PROGRESS 14.4

1. Contrast cranial and spinal nerves.
2. Detail the fastest way for you to react to a stimulus.
3. Predict what could happen to homeostasis if the autonomic nervous system failed.

CONNECTING THE CONCEPTS

For more on the interaction of the PNS with the other systems of the body, refer to the following discussions:

Section 5.3 explores how the divisions of the autonomic system regulate the heart rate and help maintain homeostasis.

Section 10.5 examines how signals between the brain and the diaphragm control the rate of breathing.

Section 15.1 provides an overview of the types of sensory inputs processed by the peripheral nervous system.

14.5 Drug Therapy and Substance Use Disorders

LEARNING OUTCOMES

Upon completion of this section, you should be able to

1. Explain the ways that drugs interact with the nervous system.
2. Classify drugs as to whether they have a depressant, stimulant, or psychoactive effect on the nervous system.
3. List the long-term effects of drug use on the body.

As you are reading these words, synapses throughout your brain are organizing, integrating, and cataloging the information you take in. Neurotransmitters at these synapses control the firing of countless action potentials, thus creating a network of neural circuits. It is amazing to realize that all thoughts, feelings, and actions of a human are dependent on neurotransmitters in the CNS and PNS. By modifying or controlling synaptic transmission, a wide variety of drugs with neurological activity, both legal pharmaceuticals and illegal drugs of abuse, can alter mood, emotional state, behavior, and personality.

Drug Mode of Action

There are about 40 known chemicals that act as neurotransmitters in the human brain. The most widely studied neurotransmitters to date are acetylcholine, norepinephrine, dopamine, serotonin, and gamma-aminobutyric acid (GABA). *Acetylcholine* is an essential CNS neurotransmitter for memory circuits in the limbic system. *Norepinephrine* is important to dreaming, waking, and mood. The neurotransmitter *dopamine* plays a central role in the brain's regulation of mood. Dopamine is also the basal nuclei neurotransmitter that helps organize coordinated movements. *Serotonin* is involved in thermoregulation, sleeping, emotions, and perception. *GABA* is an abundant inhibitory neurotransmitter in the CNS.

Neuromodulators are naturally occurring molecules that block the release of a neurotransmitter or modify a neuron's response to a neurotransmitter. Two well-known neuromodulators are *substance P* and *endorphins.* Substance P is a neuropeptide that is released by sensory neurons when pain is present. Endorphins block the release of substance P and serve as natural painkillers. Endorphins are produced by the brain during times of physical and/or emotional stress. They are associated with the "runner's high" of joggers.

Both pharmaceuticals and illegal drugs have several basic modes of action:

- They promote the action of a neurotransmitter, usually by increasing the amount of neurotransmitter at a synapse. Examples include drugs such as alprazolam (Xanax) and diazepam (Valium), which increase GABA. These medications are used for panic attacks and anxiety. Reduced levels of norepinephrine and serotonin are linked to depression. Drugs such as fluoxetine (Prozac), paroxetine (Paxil), and duloxetine (Cymbalta) allow norepinephrine and/or serotonin to accumulate at the synapse, which explains their effectiveness as antidepressants. Alzheimer's disease causes a slow, progressive loss of memory (see Section 18.5). Drugs used for Alzheimer's disease allow acetylcholine to accumulate at synapses in the limbic system.

- They interfere with or decrease the action of a neurotransmitter. For instance, antipsychotic drugs used for the treatment of schizophrenia decrease the activity of dopamine. The caffeine in coffee, chocolate, and tea keeps us awake by interfering with the effects of inhibitory neurotransmitters in the brain.
- They replace or mimic a neurotransmitter or neuromodulator. The opiates—namely, codeine, heroin, and morphine—bind to endorphin receptors and in this way reduce pain and produce a feeling of well-being.

Ongoing research into neurophysiology and neuropharmacology (the study of nervous system function and the way drugs work in the nervous system) continues to provide evidence that mental illnesses are caused by imbalances in neurotransmitters. These studies will undoubtedly improve treatments for mental illness, as well as provide insight into substance use disorders.

Substance Use Disorders

Like mental illness, drug use is linked to neurotransmitter levels. As mentioned previously, the neurotransmitter dopamine is essential for mood regulation. Dopamine plays a central role in the working of the brain's built-in *reward circuit.* The reward circuit is a collection of neurons that, under normal circumstances, promotes healthy, pleasurable activities, such as consuming food. It's possible to become addicted to behaviors such as eating, spending, or gambling because the behaviors stimulate the reward circuit and make us feel good. Individuals with substance use disorders take drugs that artificially affect the reward circuit to the point that these persons neglect their basic physical needs in favor of continued drug use.

In addition to other criteria, **substance use disorder** is apparent when a person takes a drug at a dose level and under circumstances that increase the potential for a harmful effect. People with substance use disorders are apt to display a psychological and/or physical dependence on the drug. Psychological dependence is apparent when a person craves the drug, spends time seeking the drug, and takes it regularly. With physical dependence, formerly called "addiction," the person has become tolerant to the drug. More is needed to get the same effect, and withdrawal symptoms occur when the person stops taking the drug. This is true not only of teenagers and adults but also newborn babies of mothers who use drugs. Alcohol, drugs, and tobacco can all adversely affect the developing embryo, fetus, or newborn.

Table 14.2 outlines some of the drugs we will be examining in this section.

Table 14.2 Drug Influence on the CNS

Substance	Effect	Mode of Transmission
Alcohol	Depressant	Drink
Nicotine	Stimulant	Smoke or chew
Cocaine	Stimulant	Sniff/snort, inject, or smoke
Methamphetamine/ Ecstasy	Stimulant	Smoke or take pill
Heroin	Depressant	Sniff/snort, inject, or smoke
Marijuana/K2	Psychoactive	Smoke or consume

Alcohol

With the possible exception of caffeine (see the Health feature "Caffeine: Good or Bad for You?"), alcohol is the most used and abused drug among America's teenagers. According to recent national surveys, 30% of high school students reported drinking some alcohol (down from 37.4% in 2014), and 14% binge drank (five-plus drinks in one setting) during the 30 days preceding the survey. Among adults, 86.4% reported they had consumed alcohol during their lifetime, with 56% stating they had used alcohol in the past month. Notably, 80% of college-age young adults drink. According to the CDC, underage drinking in college contributes to almost 4,300 deaths per year and over 119,000 emergency room visits.

Alcohol acts as a *depressant* on many parts of the brain by increasing the action of GABA (gamma-aminobutyric), an inhibitory neurotransmitter. Depending on the amount consumed, the effects of alcohol on the brain can lead to a feeling of relaxation, lowered inhibitions, impaired concentration and coordination, slurred speech, and vomiting. If the blood level of alcohol becomes too high, coma or death can occur.

When ingested, ethanol acts as a drug in the brain by influencing the action of GABA and other neurotransmitters such as serotonin and dopamine. Alcohol is primarily metabolized in the liver, where it disrupts the normal workings of this organ so fats cannot be broken down. Fat accumulation, the first stage of liver deterioration, begins after only a single night of heavy drinking. If heavy drinking continues, fibrous scar tissue is deposited during the next stage of liver damage. If heavy drinking stops at this point, the liver may still recover and become normal again. If not, the final and irrevocable stage, cirrhosis of the liver, occurs. Liver cells die, harden, and turn orange (*cirrhosis* means "orange").

Alcohol is a carbohydrate, and as such it can be converted into energy for the body to use. However, alcoholic beverages lack the vitamins, minerals, essential amino acids, and fatty acids the body needs. For this reason, many alcoholics are vitamin-deficient, undernourished, and prone to illness.

Based upon extensive research, the Surgeon General of the United States recommends that pregnant women drink no alcohol at all. Alcohol crosses the placenta freely and causes fetal alcohol syndrome in newborns, which is characterized by intellectual disability and various physical defects.

Nicotine

Although, according to the CDC, the numbers have been decreasing since 2005, in 2019, 14.0% of adults and 7.8% of 18-to-20-year-olds in the United States smoked cigarettes. Cigarette smoking is

BIOLOGY TODAY ▶ Health

Caffeine: Good or Bad for You?

Red Bull. Rockstar. Monster. Full Throttle. Walk down the beverage aisle of most U.S. grocery stores, and the colorful labels of these and other "energy drinks" compete for your attention (Fig. 14B). That's no surprise—the United States is the world's largest consumer of energy drinks, totaling roughly 1.25 billion units in 2019.

Around 90% of American adults report using caffeine every day. Caffeine, or 1,3,7-trimethylxanthine, occurs naturally in over 60 plant species worldwide. In plants, it is thought to function as a natural pesticide, killing certain insects that attempt to feed on the plant. It is naturally present in coffee, tea, and chocolate. It is also added to soft drinks and energy drinks, possibly to add flavor, though studies seem to prove that most people cannot taste the difference when caffeine is added to a caffeine-free beverage.

For humans, caffeine is a central nervous system stimulant. It readily crosses the blood-brain barrier, where it seems to block the effects of adenosine, which it resembles chemically. In the brain, adenosine normally seems to suppress brain activity, and by blocking this effect, caffeine can increase alertness. However, in response to continuing doses of caffeine, brain cells adjust by producing more adenosine receptors, so that increased doses of caffeine are needed for the same effect. If a regular user suddenly stops ingesting caffeine, withdrawal symptoms—such as headache, inability to concentrate, and insomnia—may ensue within 12 to 24 hours and last from 1 to 5 days.

Americans still get most of their caffeine from that tried-and-true source, the cup of coffee, which averages about 100 mg of caffeine. By comparison, a 12-oz can of Diet Coke contains about 38 mg (about 10 mg more than regular Coca-Cola), Mountain Dew has 55 mg, and Diet Pepsi Max has 69 mg. Energy drinks vary even more, with Red Bull at 80 mg, and Full Throttle and Monster doubling that to around 160. At the extreme end of the spectrum, a 20-oz bottle of Fixx Energy Extreme contains 400 mg of caffeine!

Increasingly, scientists and physicians have become concerned that the combination of high doses of caffeine in energy drinks, coupled with a high intake of drinks by some individuals, may place drinkers at a possible risk for caffeine intoxication. As a stimulant, high doses of caffeine can have serious consequences. Adverse effects seen with high doses of caffeine include nervousness, irritability, tremors, insomnia, headaches, and high blood pressure. High levels of caffeine can interfere with the normal operation of the heart, causing palpitations and irregular heartbeat. Caffeine reduces the absorption of iron from the intestine, and because it acts as a diuretic, it increases calcium loss in the urine. Some individuals, perhaps 20%, are more sensitive to lower levels of caffeine, so even a few milligrams may cause problems for them.

Figure 14B Energy drinks.
A collection of some of the more common energy drinks in today's market.
Ricochet Creative Productions, LLC/McGraw Hill

Pregnant and nursing women should also be careful to limit their caffeine intake. Fortunately, caffeine-induced deaths are rare. The lethal dose for adults has been estimated at 5,000 mg.

So there is definitely a downside to caffeine use (or abuse). But might there be an upside? Some studies have shown that caffeine consumption, in moderation, may have some health benefits. For example, women who drank two to three cups of caffeinated coffee per day had a 25% lower risk of death from heart disease, and women who drank five to seven cups per week had a 7% lower risk of death from all causes than nondrinkers. For men, although the benefits were not statistically significant, the scientists found no health risk to drinking up to seven cups of coffee per day. Other studies have suggested a link between caffeine and increased athletic and academic performance, as well as a reduced risk of Parkinson's disease, migraine headaches, and even diabetes. So although the debate over caffeine's risks versus benefits may never be completely resolved, for many people it is possible that consumption of a moderate amount of caffeine may end up doing more good than harm.

Questions to Consider

1. Estimate how much caffeine you consume per day. What effects do you notice after consuming caffeine?
2. Would you agree that manufacturers should be required to display the caffeine content of soft drinks and energy drinks on the label? Why or why not?

responsible for over 480,000 deaths per year. While this has traditionally involved using tobacco cigarettes, increasingly this is now associated with "vaping," the use of e-cigarettes.

When tobacco is smoked or chewed, nicotine is rapidly delivered throughout the body. It causes a release of epinephrine from the adrenal glands, increasing blood sugar and causing the initial feeling of stimulation. As blood sugar falls, depression and fatigue set in, causing the individual to seek more nicotine. In the CNS, nicotine stimulates neurons to release dopamine, a neurotransmitter that promotes a temporary sense of pleasure, and reinforces dependence on the drug. About 70% of people who try smoking become addicted.

As mentioned in earlier chapters, smoking is strongly associated with serious diseases of the cardiovascular and respiratory systems. Once addicted, however, only 10–20% of people who smoke are able to quit. Most medical approaches to quitting smoking involve the administration of nicotine in safer forms, such as skin patches, gum, or a newly developed nicotine inhaler, so that withdrawal symptoms can be minimized while dependence is gradually reduced. Several antinicotine vaccines (such as NicVAX) are currently in development or in early clinical trials. These vaccines stimulate the production of antibodies that prevent nicotine from entering the brain.

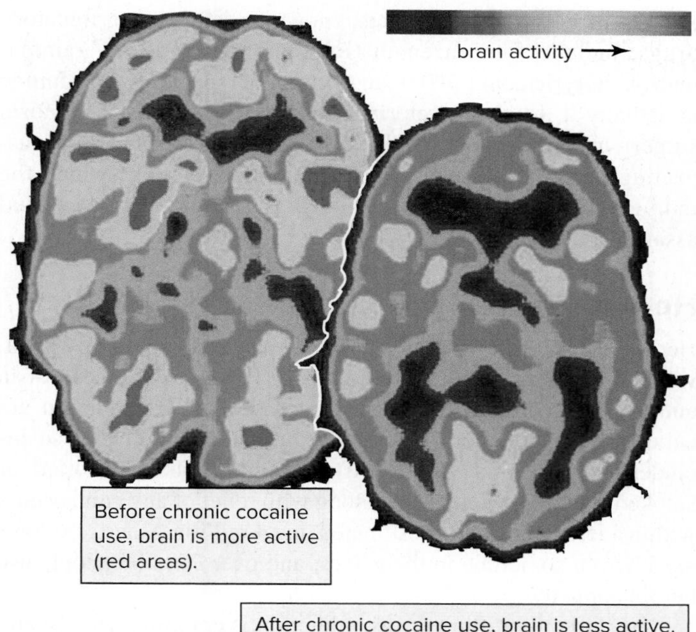
brain activity →
Before chronic cocaine use, brain is more active (red areas).
After chronic cocaine use, brain is less active.

Figure 14.20 Cocaine use.
Brain activity before and after the use of cocaine.
(both photos): Brookhaven National Laboratory/Science Source

Cocaine and Crack

Cocaine is an alkaloid derived from the shrub *Erythroxylon coca*. Approximately 35 million Americans have used cocaine by sniffing/snorting, injecting, or smoking. Cocaine is a powerful stimulant in the CNS that interferes with the reuptake of dopamine at synapses, increasing overall brain activity. The result is a rush of a sense of well-being that lasts from 5 to 30 minutes. However, long-term use of cocaine causes a loss of metabolic functions in the brain (Fig. 14.20).

"Crack" is the name often given to cocaine that is processed to a free-base form for smoking. The term *crack* refers to the crackling sound heard when the drug is smoked. Smoking allows high doses of the drug to reach the brain rapidly, providing an intense and immediate high, or "rush." Approximately 8 million Americans use crack.

A cocaine binge is a period in which a person takes the drug at ever-higher doses. The person becomes hyperactive, with little desire for food or sleep, but has an increased sex drive. This is followed by a crash period, characterized by fatigue, depression, irritability, and a lack of interest in sex. In fact, men who use cocaine often become impotent.

Cocaine is highly addictive; with continued use, the brain makes less dopamine to compensate for a seemingly endless supply. The individual experiences withdrawal symptoms and an intense craving for cocaine. Overdosing on cocaine can cause cardiac and/or respiratory arrest.

Methamphetamine and Ecstasy

Methamphetamine and ecstasy have been classified as club or party drugs because of their frequent use at clubs, parties, concerts, and other outings, but these drugs can be highly addictive and harmful. Methamphetamine (commonly called meth or crank) is a powerful CNS stimulant. Meth is often produced in makeshift home laboratories, usually starting with ephedrine or pseudoephedrine, common ingredients in many cold and asthma medicines. As a result, many states have passed laws making these medications more difficult to purchase. The number of toxic chemicals used to prepare the drug makes a former meth lab site hazardous to humans and to the environment. Over 9 million people in the United States have used methamphetamine at least once. It is available as a powder that can be snorted or as crystals (crystal meth or ice) that can be smoked.

The structure of methamphetamine is similar to that of dopamine, and the most immediate effect of taking meth is a rush of euphoria, energy, alertness, and elevated mood. However, this is typically followed by a state of agitation that, in some individuals, leads to violent behavior. Chronic use can result in what is called an amphetamine psychosis, characterized by paranoia, hallucinations, irritability, and aggressive, erratic behavior.

Ecstasy is the name commonly used for MDMA (methylenedioxymethamphetamine), which is chemically similar to methamphetamine. Many people say that "X," taken as a pill that looks like an aspirin or candy, increases their feelings of well-being and love for other people. However, it has many of the same side effects as other stimulants, plus it can interfere with temperature regulation, leading to hyperthermia, high blood pressure, and seizures. Although deaths from alcohol abuse are more common, ecstasy is identified as a cause of accidental death in young adults each year.

Drugs with sedative effects, known as date rape or predatory drugs, include flunitrazepam (Rohypnol, or roofies), gamma-hydroxybutyric acid (GHB), and ketamine (special K). Ketamine is actually a drug that veterinarians sometimes use to perform surgery on animals. Any of these drugs can be given to an unsuspecting person, and may cause a dreamlike state in which the individual is unable to move, and thus is vulnerable to sexual assault.

Heroin

Heroin is derived from the resin or sap of the opium poppy plant, which is widely grown in a region from Turkey to Southeast Asia and in parts of Latin America. Drugs derived from opium are called opiates, or more commonly, *opioids*. This class also includes morphine and codeine. After heroin is injected, snorted, or smoked, a feeling of euphoria, along with relief of any pain, occurs within a few minutes. It is estimated that 4 million Americans have used heroin sometime in their lives, and over 300,000 people use heroin annually.

As with other illicit drugs, addiction is common. Heroin and opioids bind to receptors meant for the endorphins, naturally occurring neurotransmitters that kill pain and produce feelings of tranquility. With repeated use, the body's production of endorphins decreases. Tolerance develops, so the user needs to take more of the drug just to prevent withdrawal symptoms (tremors, restlessness, cramps, vomiting), and the original euphoria is no longer felt. People who use heroin long term are at increased risk for acquiring hepatitis, HIV/AIDS, and various bacterial infections from the use of shared needles. People who use heroin heavily may experience convulsions and even death by respiratory arrest.

Heroin addiction can be treated with synthetic opiate compounds, such as methadone or buprenorphine and naloxone (Suboxone), that decrease withdrawal symptoms and block heroin's effects. However, methadone itself can be addictive, and methadone-related deaths are on the rise.

Marijuana and K2

The dried flowering tops, leaves, and stems of the marijuana plant, *Cannabis sativa,* contain and are covered by a resin that is rich in THC (tetrahydrocannabinol). Marijuana can be ingested, but usually it is smoked in a cigarette called a "joint," or in pipes or other paraphernalia. An estimated 65 million Americans have used marijuana, making it the most commonly used illegal drug in the United States. As of 2020, 15 states have legalized marijuana for recreational use, and all but 5 states have either decriminalized or made marijuana available for medical purposes, such as treating cancer, AIDS, or glaucoma.

Researchers have found that THC binds to a receptor for anandamide, a naturally occurring neurotransmitter that is important for short-term memory processing, and perhaps for feelings of contentment. A person who occasionally uses marijuana experiences mild euphoria, along with alterations in vision and judgment. Heavy use can cause hallucinations, anxiety, depression, paranoia, and psychotic symptoms. Research is underway to identify the effects of long-term marijuana use on the brain, as well as on the effects of secondhand marijuana smoke on the respiratory system.

In recent years, awareness has been increasing about a synthetic compound called K2, or spice. Originally synthesized by an organic chemist at Clemson University, K2 is about ten times as potent as THC. The chemical is typically sprayed onto a mixture of other herbal products and smoked. However, because there is no regulation of how it is produced, the amount of K2 itself, or contaminants, can vary greatly. This may account for the several reports of serious medical problems and even deaths among people who have used K2.

CHECK YOUR PROGRESS 14.5

1. Contrast drug therapy and illicit drug use.
2. List how the use of drugs, including alcohol and nicotine, affects the nervous system.
3. Detail several modes of action of pharmaceutical and illegal drugs.

CONNECTING THE CONCEPTS

For more on the long-term effects of drug use on the systems of the body, refer to the following discussions:

Section 5.7 explores the negative long-term effects of smoking on the cardiovascular system.

Section 11.4 provides information on how alcohol acts as a diuretic in the urinary system.

Section 20.2 examines the relationship between smoking and alcohol use and the increased risk of cancer.

CONCLUSION

In this chapter, we explored the structure and function of the nervous system. As we learned, the nervous system utilizes nerves to relay information, in the form of nerve impulses, from the tissues and sense organs of the body to the brain and spinal cord for processing. There, this information is processed, and then sent—in the form of nerve impulses—to the tissues and organs of the body.

A variety of substances and drugs, such as opioids, have the ability to interfere with the relaying or processing of this information. By understanding how these compounds work on the cellular level, it is possible for medical researchers to target specific processing pathways, such as those responsible for pain or anxiety and depression. However, in many cases, these drugs may also be abused, creating problems such as addiction for the individual.

SUMMARIZE

14.1 Overview of the Nervous System

The **nervous system**

- Is divided into the **central nervous system (CNS)** and the **peripheral nervous system (PNS).**
- Has three functions: (1) reception of input, (2) integration of data, and (3) generation of motor output.

Nervous Tissue

Nervous tissue contains the following two types of cells: **neurons** and **neuroglia:**

- Neurons transmit nerve signals using **action potentials.**
- Neuroglia nourish and support neurons.

The Anatomy of a Neuron

A neuron is composed of **dendrites,** a **cell body,** and an **axon.** The axons of neurons may be clustered into **nerves.** There are three types of neurons:

- **Sensory neurons** take nerve signals from **sensory receptors** to the CNS.
- **Interneurons** occur within the CNS.
- **Motor neurons** take nerve signals from the CNS to **effectors** (muscles or glands).

Myelin Sheath

- Long axons are covered by a **myelin sheath,** which is formed by the neuroglia cells. Gaps in the myelin sheath are called **nodes of Ranvier.**
- **Multiple sclerosis (MS)** occurs when the myelin sheath breaks down, causing a short-circuiting of nerve signals.

The Physiology of a Neuron

Nerve impulses move information within the nervous system. The generation of a nerve impulse is based on the polarity across the membrane of the neuron.

- *Resting potential:* There is more Na^+ outside the axon and more K^+ inside the axon. The axon does not conduct a signal. The **resting potential** is maintained by active transport using the **sodium–potassium pump.**
- *Action potential:* On receipt of a **stimulus** strong enough to overcome the **threshold,** a change in polarity across the axonal membrane as a nerve signal occurs: When Na^+ gates open, Na^+ moves to the inside of the axon, and a **depolarization** occurs. When K^+ gates open, K^+ moves to the outside of the axon, and a **repolarization** occurs.
- *Signal propagation:* The presence of the myelin sheath speeds the movement of the nerve signal by **saltatory conduction.** After the action potential has passed, a **refractory period** occurs during which no additional action potentials may be processed.

The Synapse

- At the end of each axon is an **axon terminal,** which borders the **synapse** between another neuron or target cell.
- When a neurotransmitter is released into a **synaptic cleft,** transmission of a nerve impulse occurs.
- Binding of the **neurotransmitter** to receptors in the receiving membrane causes excitation or inhibition.
- Enzymes, such as **acetylcholinesterase (AChE),** assist in removing the neurotransmitter from the synaptic cleft.

Neurotransmitters

- Neurotransmitters, such as **acetylcholine, norepinephrine,** and **serotonin,** are used to convey signals across the synapses.
- **Integration** is the summing of excitatory and inhibitory signals.

14.2 The Central Nervous System

The CNS receives and integrates sensory input and formulates motor output. The CNS consists of the spinal cord and brain. The CNS is protected by the **meninges,** which are filled with **cerebrospinal fluid.** The same fluid fills the four **ventricles** of the brain. In the CNS, **gray matter** contains cell bodies and nonmyelinated fibers. **White matter** contains myelinated axons organized as **tracts.**

The Spinal Cord

- The **spinal cord** is responsible for conduction of information to and from the **brain** and carries out reflex actions.

The Brain

- *The cerebrum:* The **cerebrum** has two **cerebral hemispheres** connected by the **corpus callosum.**
- Sensation, reasoning, learning and memory, and language and speech take place in the cerebrum.
- The **cerebral cortex** of each cerebral hemisphere has four lobes: frontal, parietal, occipital, and temporal.
- The **primary motor area** in the frontal lobe sends out motor commands to lower brain centers, which pass them on to motor neurons.
- The **primary somatosensory area** in the parietal lobe receives sensory information from lower brain centers in communication with sensory neurons.
- **Association areas** are located in all the lobes. The **prefrontal area** in the frontal lobe is involved in reasoning and planning of actions.
- **Wernicke's area** and **Broca's area** are two processing centers involved in speech.

Basal nuclei: The **basal nuclei** integrate commands to the muscles to coordinate movement. **Parkinson's disease** is associated with the degradation of neurons in this area.

The diencephalon: The **diencephalon** contains both the hypothalamus and the thalamus. The **hypothalamus** controls homeostasis. The **thalamus** sends sensory input to the cerebrum.

The cerebellum: The **cerebellum** coordinates skeletal muscle contractions.

The brain stem: The **brain stem** includes the midbrain, the pons, and the medulla oblongata.

- The **medulla oblongata** and **pons** have centers for breathing and the heartbeat.
- The **midbrain** serves as a relay station between the cerebrum and spinal cord or cerebellum.
- The **reticular formation** is part of the reticular activating system (RAS), which transfers sensory signals to higher processing centers in the brain.

14.3 The Limbic System and Higher Mental Functions

- The **limbic system,** located deep in the brain, is involved in determining emotions and higher mental functions, such as **learning.**
- The **amygdala** determines when a situation deserves the emotion we call "fear."
- The **hippocampus** is particularly involved in storing and retrieving memories.

- A **memory** may be processed as either **short-term memory** or **long-term memory.** Long-term memory may be classified as either **semantic memory** or **episodic memory. Skill memory** is involved with processes such as riding a bike.

14.4 The Peripheral Nervous System

- The PNS contains only nerves and **ganglia** (*sing.*, **ganglion**).
- **Cranial nerves** take impulses to and from the brain.
- **Spinal nerves** take impulses to and from the spinal cord.
- The PNS is divided into the somatic system and the autonomic system.

The Somatic System

The **somatic system** serves the skin, skeletal muscles, and tendons.

- Some actions are due to **reflexes,** which are automatic and involuntary.
- Other actions are voluntary and originate in the cerebral cortex.

The Autonomic System

The **autonomic system** is further divided into the **sympathetic division** and the **parasympathetic division.**

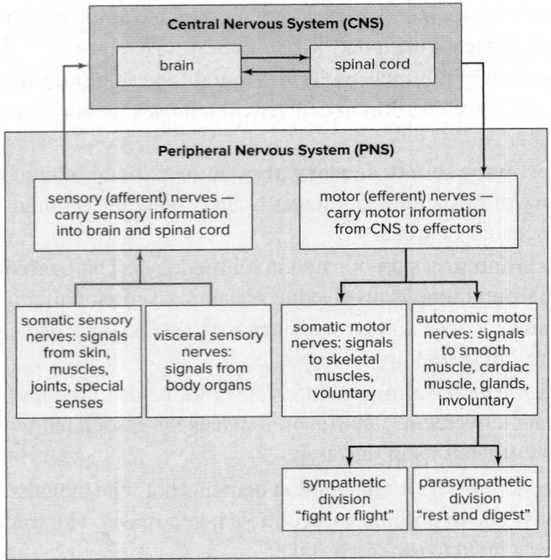

Sympathetic division: responses that occur during times of stress

Parasympathetic division: responses that occur during times of relaxation

- Actions in these divisions are involuntary and automatic.
- These divisions innervate internal organs.
- Two neurons and one ganglion are used for each impulse.

14.5 Drug Therapy and Substance Use Disorders

- Neurotransmitters, such as acetylcholine, norepinephrine, dopamine, and serotonin, play an important role in moving signals within the nervous system.
- Neuromodulators block the release of a neurotransmitter.
- Neurological drugs promote, prevent, or mimic the action of a particular neurotransmitter.
- Drugs, such as alcohol, nicotine, and marijuana, may have depressant, stimulant, or psychoactive effects.
- Dependency occurs when the body compensates for the presence of neurological drugs.

ENGAGE

THINKING CRITICALLY

1. How do you suppose scientists and physicians have determined which areas of the brain are responsible for different activities? (See Figures 14.11 and 14.12 for examples.)
2. Dopamine is a key neurotransmitter in the brain. Patients with Parkinson's disease suffer due to a lack of this chemical, whereas abusers of drugs such as nicotine, cocaine, and methamphetamine enjoy an enhancement of dopamine activity. Would these drugs be a possible treatment, or even a cure, for Parkinson's disease? Why or why not?
3. What are some factors that make brain diseases such as Alzheimer's disease, Parkinson's disease, and MS so difficult to treat?
4. Explain the following: How does the bite of a black widow spider, which injects a powerful AChE inhibitor, cause muscle cramps, salivation, fast heart rate, and high blood pressure?

MAKING IT RELEVANT

1. Based on what you have learned, how do you think your nervous system interacts with opioids?
2. Do you think prescription-based opioids should be prescribed to patients suffering from chronic pain or other ailments? What limitations would you impose?
3. You may be aware that not all people respond the same to opioids. From what you have learned in this chapter, what may be some factors that explain this variation in response?

Find answers to all of the chapter questions at connect.mheducation.com

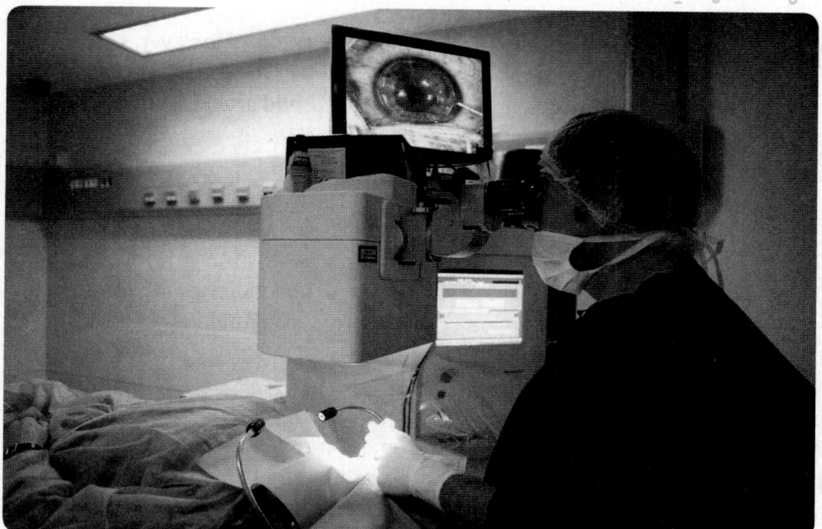
Amélie Benoist/Science Source

CHAPTER 15

Senses

Improving Your Eyesight

Chances are, you or one of your close friends wears glasses. In fact, 150 million people in the United States (over 64% of the population) wear eyeglasses to correct vision problems. If you are one of them, you may be considering eye surgery to remove your need for glasses.

LASIK, which stands for laser-assisted in situ keratomileusis, is a quick and relatively painless procedure that involves the use of a laser to permanently change the shape of the cornea. During the procedure, a small flap of tissue (the conjunctiva) is cut away from the front of the eye. The flap is folded back, exposing the cornea, allowing the surgeon to remove a defined amount of tissue from the cornea. Each pulse of the laser removes a small amount of corneal tissue, allowing the surgeon to flatten or increase the steepness of the curve of the cornea. After the procedure, the flap of tissue is put back into place and allowed to heal on its own.

To be an ideal candidate for this type of surgery, you should be over 18 years of age and have two consecutive annual eye exams that indicated your vision is relatively stable. While there may be a small amount of discomfort from the procedure, it is generally safe, and almost 80% of patients improve their vision to the point that they no longer need glasses.

In this chapter, we will explore not only the structure and function of the eye, but also the other sense organs that contribute information to our central nervous system for interpretation.

As you read through the chapter, think about the following questions:

1. What is the role of the cornea in vision?
2. How does the eye normally adjust to looking at objects at different distances?

CHAPTER OUTLINE

BEFORE YOU BEGIN

Before beginning this chapter, take a few moments to review the following discussions:

Section 14.1 What are the roles of the central and peripheral nervous systems in the body?

Section 14.2 What is the role of the primary somatosensory area of the cerebral cortex?

Section 14.2 How does the cerebellum help maintain balance?

15.1 Overview of Sensory Receptors and Sensations

LEARNING OUTCOMES

Upon completion of this section, you should be able to

1. List the four categories of sensory receptors and describe what stimulus each responds to.
2. Distinguish between perception and sensation.
3. Explain the purpose of integration and sensory adaptation.

A **sensory receptor** is able to convert a signal from the environment, called a stimulus, into a nerve impulse. This conversion is commonly referred to as *sensory transduction.* Some sensory receptors are modified neurons, and others are specialized cells closely associated with neurons. Sensory receptors may detect stimuli originating from both the internal and external environments. **Exteroceptors** are sensory receptors that detect stimuli from outside the body, such as those that result in taste, smell, vision, hearing, and equilibrium (Table 15.1). **Interoceptors** receive stimuli from inside the body. Examples of interoceptors are the baroreceptors (also called pressoreceptors) that respond to changes in blood pressure, osmoreceptors that monitor the body's water-salt balance, and chemoreceptors that monitor the pH of the blood.

Interoceptors are directly involved in homeostasis and are regulated by a negative feedback mechanism (see Fig. 4.15). For example, when blood pressure rises, baroreceptors signal a regulatory center in the brain. The brain responds by sending out nerve signals to the arterial walls, causing their smooth muscle to relax. The blood pressure then falls. Once blood pressure is returned to normal, the baroreceptors are no longer stimulated.

Exteroceptors, such as those in the eyes, ears, and skin, continuously send messages to the central nervous system. In this way, they keep us informed regarding the conditions of the external environment.

Types of Sensory Receptors

Sensory receptors in humans can be classified into four categories: chemoreceptors, photoreceptors, mechanoreceptors, and thermoreceptors.

Chemoreceptors respond to chemical substances in the immediate vicinity. As Table 15.1 indicates, taste and smell, which detect external stimuli, use chemoreceptors. However, so do various other organs sensitive to internal stimuli. Chemoreceptors that monitor blood pH are located in the carotid arteries and aorta. If the pH lowers, the breathing rate increases. As more carbon dioxide is exhaled, the blood pH rises. **Nociceptors** (also referred to as pain receptors) are a type of chemoreceptor. They are naked dendrites that respond to chemicals released by damaged tissues. Nociceptors are protective, because they alert us to possible danger. For example, without the pain associated with appendicitis, we might never seek the medical help needed to avoid a ruptured appendix.

Photoreceptors respond to light energy. Our eyes contain photoreceptors that are sensitive to light rays and thereby provide us with a sense of vision. Stimulation of the photoreceptors known as rod cells results in black-and-white vision. Stimulation of the photoreceptors known as cone cells results in color vision.

Mechanoreceptors are stimulated by mechanical forces, which most often result in pressure of some sort. When we hear, airborne sound waves are converted to pressure waves in the fluids of the inner ear that can be detected by mechanoreceptors. Mechanoreceptors are responding to pressure waves when we detect changes in gravity and motion, helping us keep our balance. These receptors are in the vestibule and semicircular canals of the inner ear.

The sense of touch depends on pressure receptors sensitive to either strong or slight pressure. Baroreceptors located in certain arteries detect changes in blood pressure, and stretch receptors in the lungs detect the degree of lung inflation. Proprioceptors respond to the stretching of muscle fibers, tendons, joints, and ligaments. Signals from proprioceptors make us aware of the position of our limbs.

Thermoreceptors in the hypothalamus and skin are stimulated by changes in temperature. They respond to both heat and cold and play a major role in the regulation of internal body temperature (see Fig. 4.17).

How Sensation Occurs

Sensory receptors respond to environmental stimuli by generating nerve signals. When the nerve signals arrive at the cerebral cortex of the brain, **sensation,** the conscious perception of stimuli, occurs.

As discussed in Section 14.4, sensory receptors are the first element in a reflex arc. We are aware of a reflex action only when sensory information reaches the brain. At that time, the brain

Table 15.1 Exteroceptors

Sensory Receptor	Stimulus	Category	Sense	Sensory Organ
Taste cells	Chemicals	Chemoreceptor	Taste	Taste bud
Olfactory cells	Chemicals	Chemoreceptor	Smell	Olfactory epithelium
Rod cells and cone cells in retina	Light rays	Photoreceptor	Vision	Eye
Hair cells in spiral organ of the inner ear	Sound waves	Mechanoreceptor	Hearing	Ear
Hair cells in semicircular canals of the inner ear	Motion	Mechanoreceptor	Rotational equilibrium	Ear
Hair cells in vestibule of the inner ear	Gravity	Mechanoreceptor	Gravitational equilibrium	Ear

integrates this information with other information received from other sensory receptors. Consider what happens if you burn yourself and quickly remove your hand from a hot stove. The brain receives information not only from your skin but also from your eyes, your nose, and all sorts of sensory receptors.

Some sensory receptors are free nerve endings or encapsulated nerve endings, and others are specialized cells closely associated with neurons. Often, the plasma membrane of a sensory receptor contains receptor proteins that react to the stimulus. For example, the receptor proteins in the plasma membrane of chemoreceptors bind to certain chemicals. When this happens, ion channels open, and ions flow across the plasma membrane. If the stimulus is sufficient, nerve signals begin and are carried by a sensory nerve fiber in the PNS to the CNS (Fig. 15.1). The stronger the stimulus, the greater the frequency of nerve signals. Nerve signals that reach the spinal cord first are conveyed to the brain by ascending tracts. If nerve signals finally reach the cerebral cortex, sensation occurs.

All sensory receptors initiate nerve signals. The sensation that results depends on the part of the brain receiving the nerve signals.

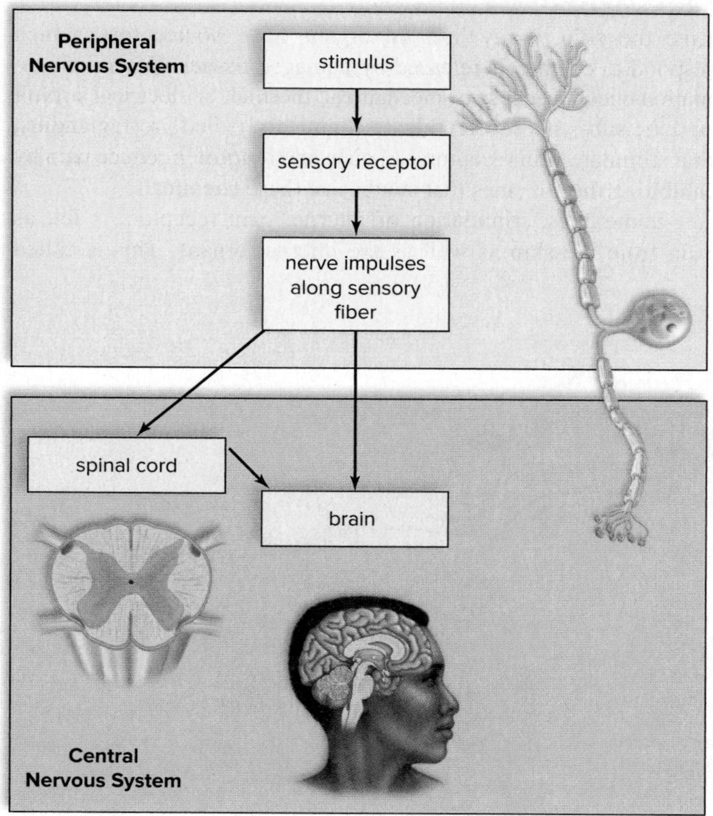

Figure 15.1 The role of the CNS and PNS in sensation and sensory perception.
After detecting a stimulus, sensory receptors initiate nerve signals in the peripheral nervous system (PNS). These signals give the central nervous system (CNS) information about the external and internal environments. The CNS integrates all incoming information, and then initiates a motor response to the stimulus.

Nerve signals that begin in the optic nerve eventually reach the visual areas of the cerebral cortex. Thereafter, we see objects. Nerve signals that begin in the auditory nerve eventually reach the auditory areas of the cerebral cortex. We hear sounds when the auditory cortex is stimulated. If it were possible to switch these nerves, stimulation of the eyes would result in hearing!

Before sensory receptors initiate nerve signals, they also carry out **integration,** the summing up of signals. One type of integration is called **sensory adaptation,** which is a decrease in response to a stimulus over time. We have all had the experience of smelling an odor when we first enter a room and then later not being aware of it. When sensory adaptation occurs, sensory receptors send fewer impulses to the brain. Without these impulses, the sensation of the stimuli is decreased. The functioning of our sensory receptors makes a significant contribution to homeostasis. Without sensory input, we would not receive information about our internal and external environments. This information leads to appropriate reflex and voluntary actions to keep the internal environment constant.

CHECK YOUR PROGRESS 15.1

1. Describe the functions of the four types of sensory receptors.
2. Distinguish between sensation and integration.
3. Summarize the importance of sensory receptors in the maintenance of homeostasis in the body.

CONNECTING THE CONCEPTS

For more information on the regions of the brain associated with sensation, refer to the following discussions:

Section 14.2 describes the location and function of the reticular activating system (RAS).

Figure 14.12 illustrates the somatosensory regions of the cerebral cortex.

Figure 14.18 illustrates the portions of the peripheral nervous system involved in a reflex arc.

15.2 Somatic Senses

LEARNING OUTCOMES

Upon completion of this section, you should be able to

1. Distinguish between proprioceptors and cutaneous receptors with regard to function.
2. State the location and general function of each type of cutaneous receptor.
3. Explain the role of nociceptors and summarize the type of sensory input they detect.

Senses whose receptors are associated with the skin, muscles, joints, and viscera are termed the *somatic senses.* These receptors can be categorized into three types: proprioceptors, cutaneous receptors, and pain receptors. All of these send nerve impulses via the spinal cord to the primary somatosensory areas of the cerebral cortex (see Fig. 14.12).

Proprioceptors

Proprioceptors are mechanoreceptors involved in reflex actions that maintain muscle tone, and thereby the body's equilibrium and posture. For example, proprioceptors called *muscle spindles* are embedded in muscle fibers (Fig. 15.2). If a muscle relaxes too much, the muscle spindle stretches, generating nerve impulses that cause the muscle to contract slightly. Conversely, when muscles are stretched too much, proprioceptors called *Golgi tendon organs,* buried in the tendons that attach muscles to bones, generate nerve impulses that cause the muscles to relax. Both types of receptors act together to maintain a functional degree of muscle tone. The knee-jerk reflex, which involves muscle spindles, offers an opportunity for physicians to test a reflex action. The information sent by muscle spindles to the CNS is used to maintain the body's equilibrium and posture. Proper balance and body position are maintained, despite the force of gravity always acting on the skeleton and muscles.

Cutaneous Receptors

The skin is composed of two layers: the epidermis and the dermis (see Section 4.7). The dermis contains **cutaneous receptors** (Fig. 15.3), which make the skin sensitive to touch, pressure, pain, and temperature (warmth and cold). The dermis is a mosaic of these tiny receptors, as you can determine by slowly passing a metal probe over your skin. At certain points, you will feel touch or pressure; at others, you will feel heat or cold (depending on the probe's temperature).

Several types of cutaneous receptors are sensitive to fine touch. These receptors give a person specific information, such as the location of the touch, as well as its shape, size, and texture. *Meissner corpuscles* and *Krause end bulbs* are concentrated in the fingertips, palms, lips, tongue, nipples, penis, and clitoris. *Merkel discs* are found where the epidermis meets the dermis. A free nerve ending called a *root hair plexus* winds around the base of a hair follicle. This receptor responds if the hair is touched.

Two types of cutaneous receptors sensitive to pressure are Pacinian corpuscles and Ruffini endings. *Pacinian corpuscles* are onion-shaped sensory receptors that lie deep inside the dermis. *Ruffini endings* are encapsulated by sheaths of connective tissue and contain lacy networks of nerve fibers.

Temperature receptors are simply free nerve endings in the epidermis. Some free nerve endings are responsive to cold; others respond to warmth. Cold receptors are far more numerous than warmth receptors, but the two types have no known structural differences.

Pain Receptors

Like the skin, many internal organs have nociceptors, which respond to chemicals released by damaged tissues. When inflammation occurs because of mechanical, thermal, or electrical stimuli or toxic substances, cells release chemicals, called prostaglandins, that stimulate pain receptors. Aspirin and ibuprofen reduce pain by inhibiting the enzymes that synthesize these chemicals.

Sometimes, stimulation of internal pain receptors is felt as pain from the skin as well as the internal organs. This is called

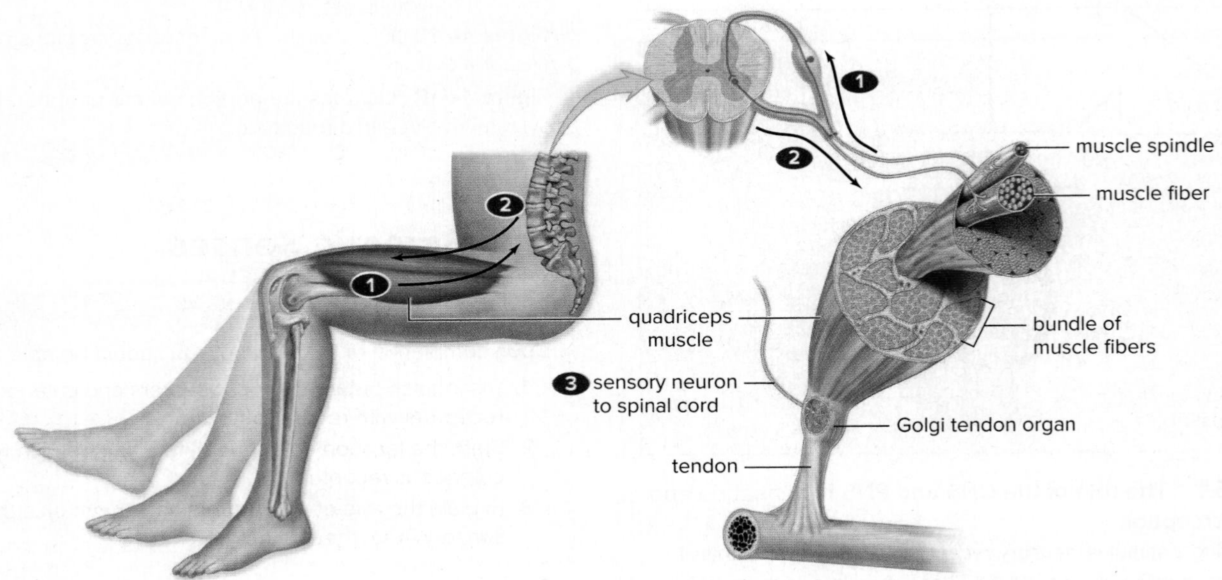

Figure 15.2 The action of proprioceptors.
1. When a muscle is stretched, muscle spindles send sensory nerve impulses to the spinal cord. **2.** Motor nerve impulses from the spinal cord cause slight muscle contraction. **3.** When tendons are stretched excessively, Golgi tendon organs cause muscle relaxation.

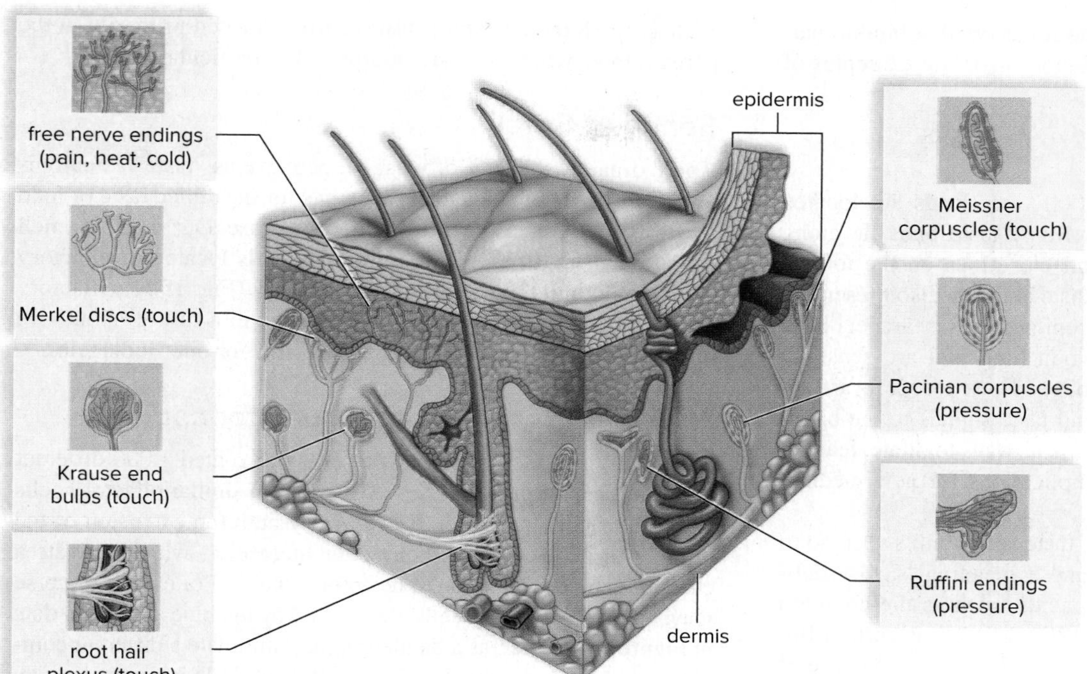

Figure 15.3 Sensory receptors of the skin. The general function of each sensory receptor is shown here. However, receptors are not always this specialized. For example, microscopic examination of the skin of the ear shows only free nerve endings (pain receptors), yet the skin of the ear is sensitive to all sensations.

referred pain. Some internal organs have a referred pain relationship with areas in the skin of the back, groin, and abdomen. For example, pain from the heart is often felt in the left shoulder and arm. This most likely happens when nerve impulses from the pain receptors of internal organs travel to the spinal cord and synapse with neurons also receiving impulses from the skin. Frequently, this type of referred pain is more common in men than in women. The nonspecific symptoms that women often experience during a heart attack may delay a diagnosis.

BIOLOGY IN YOUR LIFE

What is the difference between phantom sensation and phantom pain?

Suppose a person loses a foot and a leg due to an injury. In addition to dealing with the loss of a limb, a person who has undergone amputation often must cope with the phenomenon of phantom sensation or phantom pain—or both. Phantom sensation is a painless awareness of the amputated limb. For example, a patient whose foot and lower leg have been removed may have an itchy or tingly sensation in the "foot," even though the foot is no longer there. Similarly, phantom pain can be sensed as originating from the absent body part. Researchers believe that any stimulus (such as a touch) to the stump will fool the brain into a perceived sensation, because the brain has received signals from the leg and foot for such a long time.

Phantom sensation may last for years but usually disappears without treatment. Phantom pain must be treated with a combination of medication, massage, and physical therapy.

CHECK YOUR PROGRESS 15.2

1. Describe how the body uses proprioceptors to indicate the position of the arms and legs.
2. Summarize the role of each type of cutaneous receptor.
3. Explain why the sensation of pain is important for the maintenance of homeostasis.

CONNECTING THE CONCEPTS

For more information on the material in this section, refer to the following discussions:

Figure 4.11 provides a more detailed look at the structure of human skin.

Section 13.2 provides an overview of muscle fiber contraction.

Section 14.2 presents the gate control theory of how the brain responds to input from pain receptors.

15.3 Senses of Taste and Smell

LEARNING OUTCOMES

Upon completion of this section, you should be able to

1. Compare and contrast the senses of taste and smell.
2. Identify the structures of the tongue and the olfactory areas of the nose.
3. Summarize how the brain receives taste and odor information.

Taste and smell are called chemical senses because their receptors are sensitive to molecules in the food we eat and the air we breathe.

Chemoreceptors are plasma membrane receptors that bind to particular molecules. Taste cells and olfactory cells are examples of chemoreceptors.

Sense of Taste

In adult humans, approximately 10,000 **taste buds** are located primarily on the tongue (Fig. 15.4). Many taste buds lie along the walls of the papillae. These small elevations on the tongue are visible to the naked eye. Isolated taste buds are also present on the hard palate, the pharynx, and the epiglottis. Researchers have identified chemoreceptors in the human lung that are sensitive only to chemicals that normally taste bitter. These receptors are not clustered in buds, and they do not send taste signals to the brain. Stimulation of these receptors causes the airways to dilate, leading the researchers to speculate about implications for new medications to treat diseases such as asthma.

Humans have five main types of taste receptors: sweet, sour, salty, bitter, and umami (from the Japanese, meaning "savory, delicious"). Foods rich in certain amino acids, such as the common seasoning monosodium glutamate (MSG), as well as certain flavors of cheese, beef broth, and some seafood, produce the taste of umami. Taste buds for each of these tastes are located throughout the tongue, although certain regions may be slightly more sensitive to particular tastes. Food can stimulate more than one of these types of taste buds. The brain appears to survey the overall pattern of incoming sensory impulses and to take a "weighted average" of their taste messages as the perceived taste.

How the Brain Receives Taste Information

Taste buds open at a *taste pore* (Fig. 15.4*c*). They have supporting cells and a number of elongated taste cells that end in microvilli. When molecules bind to receptor proteins of the microvilli, nerve signals are generated in sensory nerve fibers that go to the brain. Signals reach the gustatory (taste) cortex, located primarily in the parietal lobe, where they are interpreted as particular tastes.

Sense of Smell

Approximately 80–90% of what we perceive as "taste" actually is due to the sense of smell. This accounts for the dulled taste of food when we have a head cold or a stuffed-up nose. Our sense of smell depends on 10 to 20 million **olfactory cells** located in olfactory epithelia high in the roof of the nasal cavity (Fig. 15.5). Olfactory cells are modified neurons. Each cell ends in a tuft of about five olfactory cilia, which bear receptor proteins for odor molecules.

How the Brain Receives Odor Information

Each olfactory cell has only 1 out of an estimated 1,000 different types of receptor proteins. Nerve fibers from similar olfactory cells lead to the same neuron in the olfactory bulb (an extension of the brain). An odor contains many odor molecules, which activate a characteristic combination of receptor proteins. For example, a rose may stimulate olfactory cells, designated by the blue and green dots in Figure 15.5, whereas a dandelion may stimulate a different combination. An odor's signature in the olfactory bulb is determined by which neurons are stimulated. When the neurons communicate this information via the olfactory tract to the olfactory areas of the cerebral cortex, we know we have smelled either a rose or a carnation.

The olfactory cortex is located in the temporal lobe. Some areas of the olfactory cortex receive smell sensations, and other areas contain olfactory memories.

Have you ever noticed that a certain aroma vividly brings to mind a certain person or place and can re-create emotions you feel about that person or place? For example, a smell of a certain food may remind you of a favorite vacation. This is because the olfactory bulbs have direct connections with the limbic system and its centers for emotion and memory (see Section 14.3). One investigator

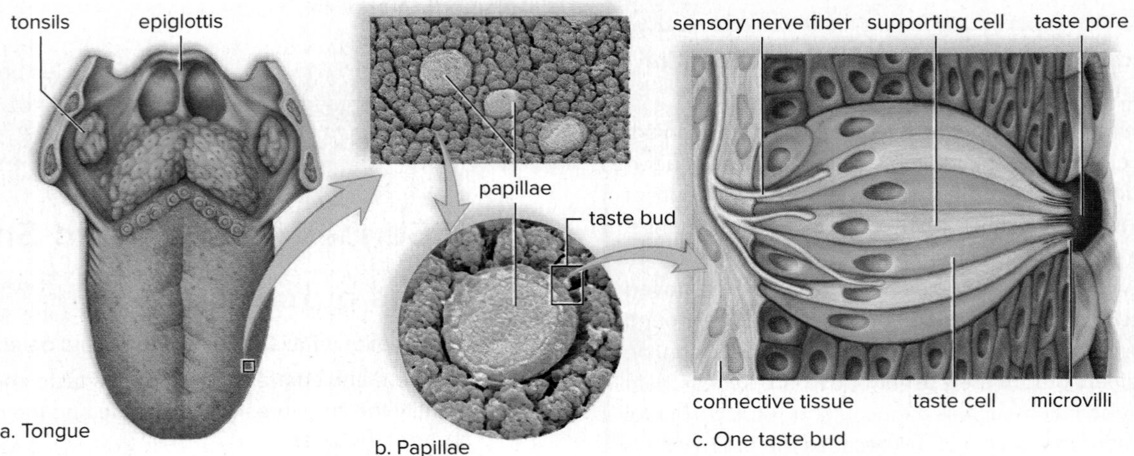

Figure 15.4 The tongue and the sense of taste.
a. Papillae on the tongue contain taste buds sensitive to sweet, sour, salty, bitter, and umami. **b.** Photomicrograph and enlargement of the papillae. **c.** Taste buds occur along the walls of the papillae. Taste cells in microvilli possess receptor proteins for certain molecules. When molecules bind to the receptor proteins, nerve signals are generated and go to the brain, where the sensation of taste occurs.
(b, both): Clouds Hill Imaging Ltd./Corbis Documentary/Getty Images

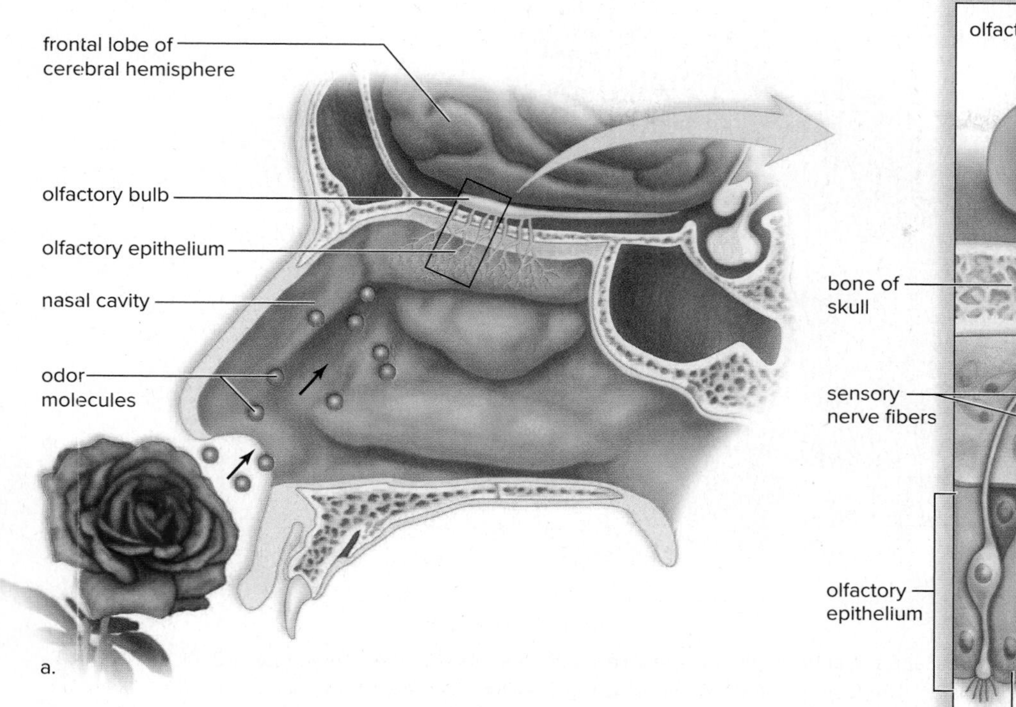

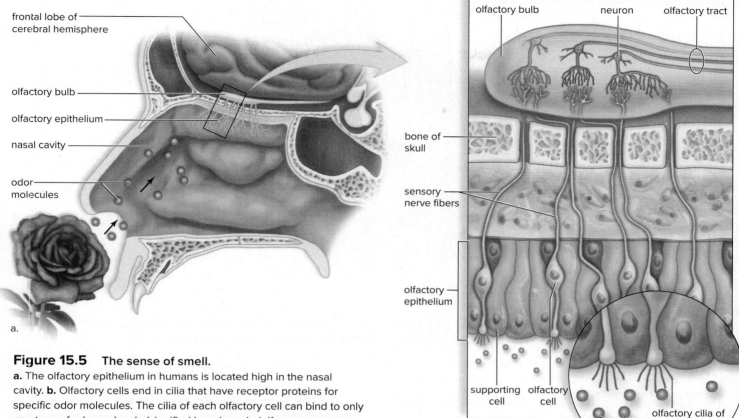

Figure 15.5 The sense of smell.
a. The olfactory epithelium in humans is located high in the nasal cavity. **b.** Olfactory cells end in cilia that have receptor proteins for specific odor molecules. The cilia of each olfactory cell can bind to only one type of odor molecule (signified here by color). If a rose causes olfactory cells to be stimulated by "blue" and "green" odor molecules, then neurons designated by blue and green in the olfactory bulb are activated. The primary olfactory area of the cerebral cortex interprets the pattern of stimulation as the scent of a rose.

showed that when subjects smelled an orange while viewing a painting, they later recalled memories of the painting more vividly and had many deep feelings about the painting. We know that the number of olfactory cells declines with age. This can be dangerous if an older person can't smell smoke or a gas leak.

CHECK YOUR PROGRESS 15.3

1. Identify the structures of the tongue and nose involved in the senses of taste and smell.
2. Compare and contrast the function of the chemoreceptors on the tongue and in the nose.
3. Summarize the pathway of sensory information regarding taste and smell from the receptors to the brain.

CONNECTING THE CONCEPTS

For more information on chemoreceptors, refer to the following discussions:

Section 10.5 describes the function of the respiratory center in the medulla oblongata.

Section 14.3 explains the role of the limbic system in maintaining memories, such as smell and taste.

15.4 Sense of Vision

LEARNING OUTCOMES

Upon completion of this section, you should be able to

1. Identify the structures of the human eye.
2. Explain how the eye focuses on near and far objects.
3. Describe the role of photoreceptors in vision.
4. Summarize the abnormalities of the eye that produce vision problems.

Vision requires the work of the eyes and the brain. As we will see, integration of stimuli occurs in the eyes before nerve signals are sent to the brain. Still, researchers estimate that at least a third of the cerebral cortex takes part in processing visual information.

Anatomy and Physiology of the Eye

The eye is an elongated sphere about 2.5 cm in diameter. It has three layers, or coats: the sclera, the choroid, and the retina (Fig. 15.6). The outer layer is made up of the white, fibrous **sclera,** and the transparent **cornea,** which is made of collagen fibers. The cornea is known as the window of the eye.

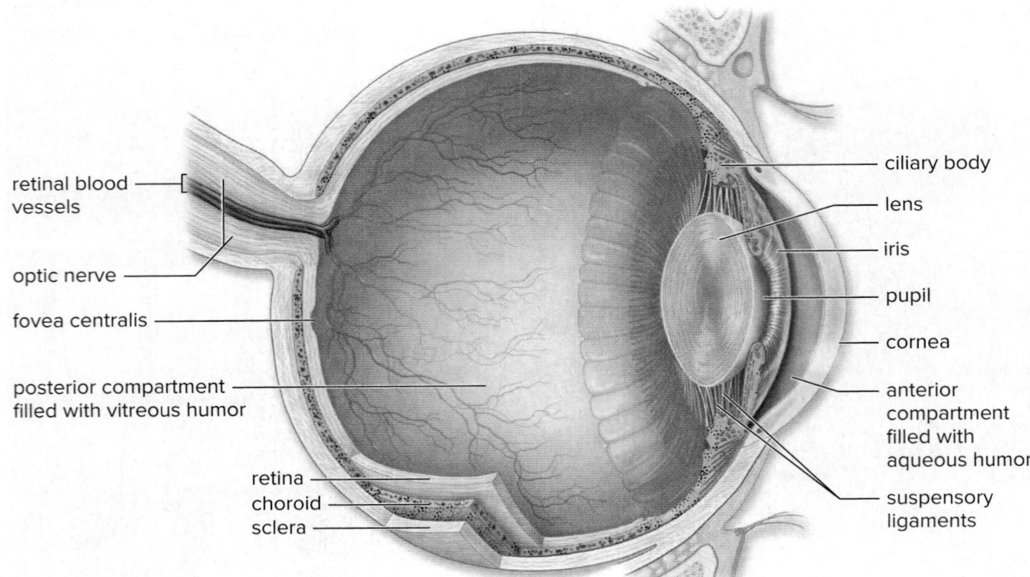

Figure 15.6 The structures of the human eye.
The sclera (the outer layer of the eye) becomes the cornea, and the choroid (the middle layer) is continuous with the ciliary body and the iris. The retina (the inner layer) contains the photoreceptors for vision. The fovea centralis is the region where vision is most acute.

The **choroid** is the thin, middle coat. It has an extensive blood supply, and its dark pigment absorbs stray light rays that photoreceptors have not absorbed. This helps visual acuity. Toward the front, the choroid becomes the doughnut-shaped **iris.** The iris regulates the size of the **pupil,** a hole in the center of the iris through which light enters the eye. The color of the iris (and therefore the color of the eyes) correlates with its pigmentation. Heavily pigmented eyes are brown, and lightly pigmented eyes are green or blue. Behind the iris, the choroid thickens and forms the circular ciliary body. The ciliary body contains the ciliary muscle, which controls the shape of the lens for near and far vision.

BIOLOGY IN YOUR LIFE

What is pinkeye?

At some point in their lives, most people have had conjunctivitis, or pinkeye. Conjunctivitis is the inflammation of a mucous membrane called the conjunctiva, which covers the eye (except the cornea) and the inner part of the eyelid. The purpose of the conjunctiva is to lubricate the eye and keep it from drying out. In the case of viral conjunctivitis, the most common type, this membrane becomes inflamed as part of an immune response against viral pathogens. Viral conjunctivitis is highly contagious; individuals with the condition must be careful not to spread the disease. However, not all conjunctivitis is contagious; allergies and other medical conditions can cause pinkeye-like symptoms. Treatment usually involves the use of eyedrops that help lubricate the eye and reduce inflammation.

The **lens** is attached to the ciliary body by suspensory ligaments and divides the eye into two compartments. The anterior compartment is in front of the lens, and the posterior compartment is behind it. The anterior compartment is filled with a clear, watery fluid called the **aqueous humor.** A small amount of aqueous humor is continually produced each day. Normally, it leaves the anterior compartment by way of tiny ducts. When a person has **glaucoma,** these drainage ducts are blocked and aqueous humor builds up. If glaucoma is not treated, the resulting pressure compresses the arteries that serve the nerve fibers of the retina, where photoreceptors are located. The nerve fibers begin to die because of lack of nutrients, and the person gradually loses their vision. Eventually, total blindness can result.

The third layer of the eye, the **retina,** is located in the posterior compartment. This compartment is filled with a clear, gelatinous material called the **vitreous humor.** The vitreous humor holds the retina in place and supports the lens. The retina contains photoreceptors called rod cells and cone cells. The rods are very sensitive to light, but they do not detect color. Therefore, at night or in a darkened room, we see only shades of gray. The cones, which require bright light, are sensitive to different wavelengths of light. This sensitivity gives us the ability to distinguish colors. The retina has a very special region called the **fovea centralis** where cone cells are densely packed. Light is normally focused on the fovea when we look directly at an object. This is helpful because the sharpest images are produced by the fovea centralis. Sensory fibers from the retina form the **optic nerve,** which takes nerve signals to the visual cortex.

Table 15.2 summarizes the major structures of the eye and their functions.

Table 15.2 Structures of the Eye

Structure	Function
Sclera	Protects and supports the eye
Cornea	Refracts light rays
Pupil	Admits light
Choroid	Absorbs stray light
Ciliary body	Holds lens in place, accommodation
Iris	Regulates light entrance
Retina	Contains photoreceptors for sight
Rod cells	Make black-and-white vision possible
Cone cells	Make color and acute vision possible
Fovea centralis	Contains mostly cones for acute vision
Other	
Lens	Refracts and focuses light rays
Humors	Transmit light rays and support the eye
Optic nerve	Transmits impulses to the visual cortex

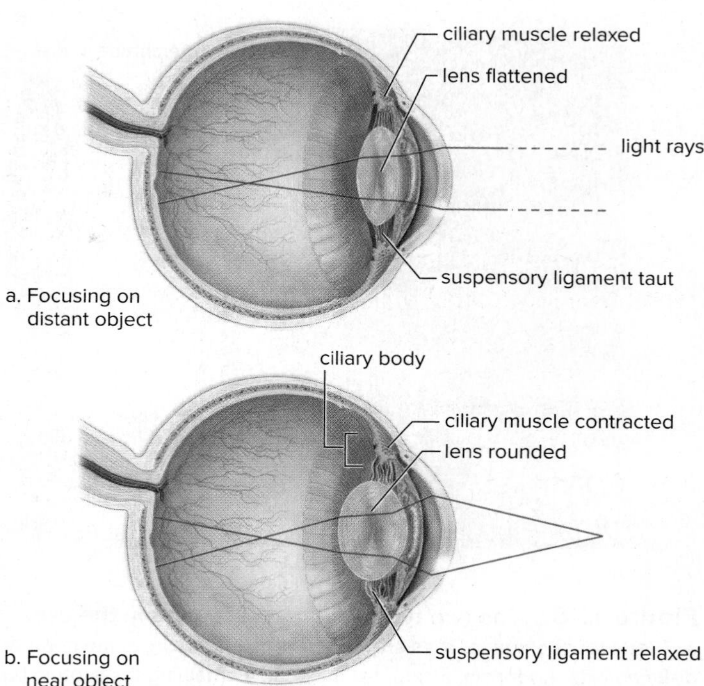

Figure 15.7 Focusing light on the retina.
Light rays from each point on an object are bent by the cornea and the lens in such a way that an inverted and reversed image of the object forms on the retina. **a.** When focusing on a distant object, the lens is flat because the ciliary muscle is relaxed and the suspensory ligament is taut. **b.** When focusing on a near object, the lens accommodates—it becomes rounded because the ciliary muscle contracts, causing the suspensory ligament to relax.

Function of the Lens

The cornea, assisted by the lens and the humors, focuses images on the retina. Focusing starts with the cornea and continues as the rays pass through the lens and the humors. The image produced is much smaller than the object, because light rays are bent (refracted) when they are brought into **focus.** If the eye is too long or too short, the person may need corrective lenses to bring the image into focus. The image on the retina is inverted (upside down) and reversed from left to right.

Visual accommodation occurs for close vision. During visual accommodation, the lens changes its shape to bring the image into focus on the retina. The shape of the lens is controlled by the ciliary muscle, within the ciliary body. When we view a distant object, the ciliary muscle is relaxed, causing the suspensory ligaments attached to the ciliary body to be taut. The ligaments put tension on the lens and cause it to remain relatively flat (Fig. 15.7*a*). When we view a near object, the ciliary muscle contracts, releasing the tension on the suspensory ligaments. The lens becomes round and thick due to its natural elasticity (Fig. 15.7*b*). Thus, contraction or relaxation of the ciliary muscle allows the image to be focused on the retina. Close work requires contraction of the ciliary muscle, so it often causes muscle fatigue, known as eyestrain. Eyestrain is more common after the age of 40 because the lens loses some of its elasticity and is unable to accommodate. It is also common among those who work with computers because the intense focusing causes the person to blink less, allowing the eyes to dry out. Eyedrops and/or corrective lenses, either eyeglasses or contact lenses, may be necessary to reduce eyestrain.

Visual Pathway to the Brain

The pathway for vision begins once light has been focused on the photoreceptors in the retina. Some integration occurs in the retina, where nerve signals begin before the optic nerve transmits them to the brain.

Function of Photoreceptors Figure 15.8*a* illustrates the structure of the photoreceptors called **rod cells** and **cone cells.** Both rods and cones have an outer segment joined to an inner segment by a short stalk. Pigment molecules are embedded in the membrane of the many disks present in the outer segment. Synaptic vesicles are located at the synaptic endings of the inner segment.

The visual pigment in rods is a deep purple pigment called rhodopsin (Fig. 15.8*b*). **Rhodopsin** is a complex molecule made up of the protein opsin and a light-absorbing molecule called **retinal,** a derivative of vitamin A. When a rod absorbs light, rhodopsin splits into opsin and retinal. This leads to a cascade of reactions and the closure of ion channels in the rod cell's plasma membrane. The release of inhibitory transmitter molecules from the rod's synaptic vesicles ceases. Thereafter, signals go to other neurons in the retina. Rods are very sensitive to light and, therefore, are suited to night vision. Carrots, and other orange and yellow vegetables, are rich in vitamin A, so it is true that eating carrots can improve your night vision. Rod cells are plentiful throughout the retina, except the fovea. Therefore, rods also provide us with peripheral vision and perception of motion.

The cones, on the other hand, are located primarily in the fovea and are activated by bright light. They allow us to detect the fine detail and the color of an object. Color vision depends on three types of cones, which contain pigments called the B (blue),

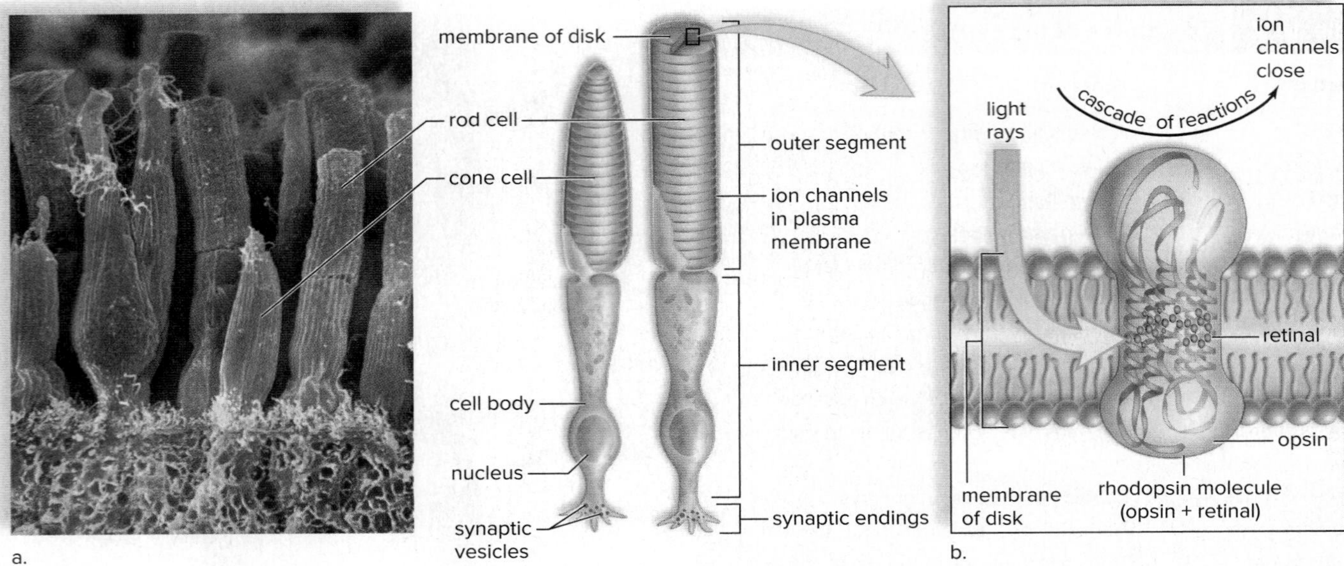

Figure 15.8 **The two types of photoreceptors in the eye.**
a. The outer segment of rods and cones contains stacks of membranous disks, which contain visual pigments. **b.** In rods, the membrane of each disk contains rhodopsin, a complex molecule containing the protein opsin and the pigment retinal. When rhodopsin absorbs light energy, it splits, releasing retinal, which sets in motion a cascade of reactions that causes ion channels in the plasma membrane to close. Thereafter, nerve signals go to the brain.
(a): Omikron/Science Source

G (green), and R (red) pigments. Each pigment is made up of retinal and opsin, but there is a slight difference in the opsin structure of each. This accounts for their individual absorption patterns. Various combinations of cones are believed to be stimulated by in-between shades of color.

BIOLOGY IN YOUR LIFE

Why does rubbing your closed eyes produce "stars"?

The eye is a flexible container filled with fluid and a soft, gelatinous material. Compressing the eyes by rubbing them increases pressure in the eyes. In turn, the photoreceptors of the eye are stimulated by the increased eye pressure. When the nerve signals are conveyed to the brain, the brain senses "vision." We "see stars" because nerve signals from the eyes can only result in sight.

Function of the Retina The retina has three layers of neurons (Fig. 15.9). The layer closest to the choroid contains the rod cells and cone cells. A layer of bipolar cells covers the rods and cones. The innermost layer contains ganglion cells, whose sensory fibers become the optic nerve. Only the rod cells and cone cells are sensitive to light; therefore, light must penetrate to the back of the retina before the rods and cones are stimulated.

The rod cells and cone cells synapse with the bipolar cells. Next, signals from bipolar cells stimulate ganglion cells whose axons become the optic nerve. Notice in Figure 15.9 that there are many more rod cells and cone cells than ganglion cells. Although the precise number is not known, the retina has around 150 million rod cells and 6.5 million cone cells, but only 1 million ganglion cells. The sensitivity of cones versus rods is mirrored by how directly they connect to ganglion cells. As many as 150 rods may activate the same ganglion cell. No wonder the stimulation of rods results in vision that is blurred and indistinct. In contrast, some cone cells in the fovea centralis activate only one ganglion cell. This explains why cones, especially in the fovea centralis, provide us with a sharper, more detailed image of an object.

As signals pass to bipolar cells and ganglion cells, integration occurs. Therefore, considerable processing occurs in the retina before ganglion cells generate nerve signals. Ganglion cells converge to form the optic nerve, which transmits information to the visual cortex. Additional integration occurs in the visual cortex.

Blind Spot Figure 15.9 also shows that there are no rods and cones where the optic nerve exits the retina. Therefore, no vision is possible in this area. You can prove this to yourself by putting a dot to the right of center on a piece of paper. Use your right hand to move the paper slowly toward your right eye, and make sure you look straight ahead. The dot will disappear at one point—this is your right eye's **blind spot.** The two eyes together provide complete vision because the blind spot for the right eye is not the same as the blind spot for the left eye. The blind spot for the right eye is right of center, and the blind spot for the left eye is left of center.

From the Retina to the Visual Cortex To reach the visual cortex, nerve impulses are carried by the optic nerves from the

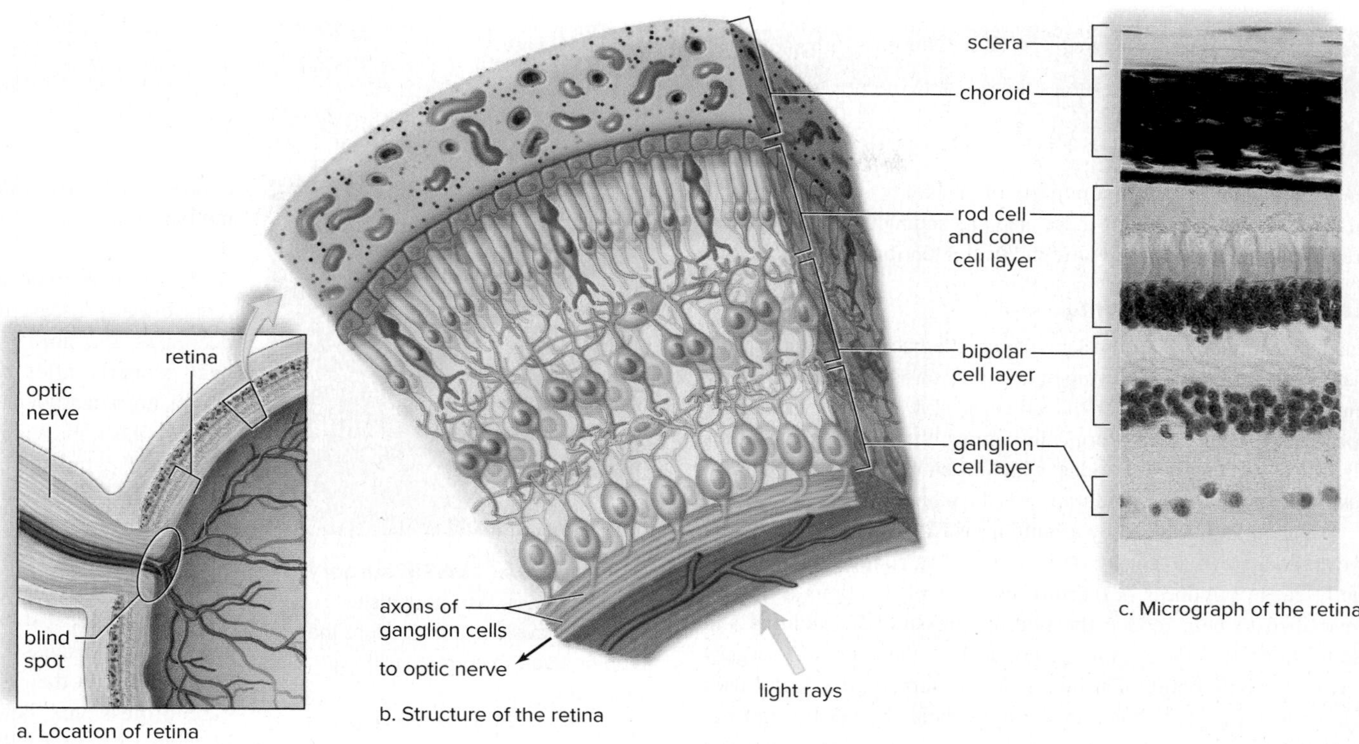

Figure 15.9 **The structure of the retina.**
a. The retina is the inner layer of the eye. **b.** Rod and cone cells, located at the back of the retina nearest the choroid, synapse with bipolar cells, which synapse with ganglion cells. Integration of signals occurs at these synapses. Cone cells, in general, distinguish more detail than do rod cells. **c.** Micrograph shows that the sclera and choroid are relatively thin compared to the retina, which has several layers of cells.
(c): Dennis Strete/McGraw Hill

eyes to the optic chiasma (Fig. 15.10). The **optic chiasma** has an X shape, formed by a crossing-over of optic nerve fibers. After exiting the optic chiasma, the optic nerves continue as **optic tracts.** Fibers from the right half of each retina converge and continue on together in the right optic tract. Similarly, the nerve fibers from the left half of each retina join to form the left optic tract, traveling together to the brain.

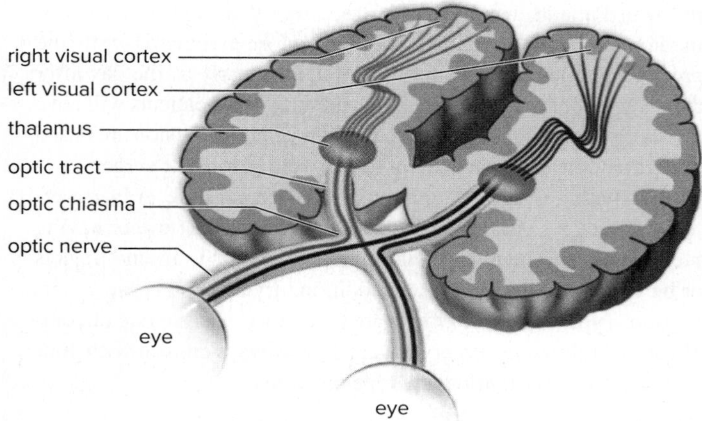

Figure 15.10 **The function of the optic chiasma.**
Because of the optic chiasma, data from the right half of each retina go to the right visual cortex, and data from the left half of the retina go to the left visual cortex. These data are then combined to allow us to see the entire visual field.

The optic tracts sweep around the hypothalamus, and most fibers synapse with neurons in nuclei (masses of neuron cell bodies) within the thalamus. Axons from the thalamic nuclei form optic radiations that take nerve impulses to the *visual cortex* within the occipital lobe. The image is split in the visual cortex. This division of incoming information happens because the right visual cortex receives information from the right optic tract, and the left visual cortex receives information from the left optic tract. For good depth perception, the right and left visual cortices communicate with each other. Also, because the image is inverted and reversed, it must be righted in the brain for us to correctly perceive the visual field.

Abnormalities of the Eye

Color blindness and changes in the physical shape of the eye are two of the more common vision abnormalities. There are several forms of color blindness, all of which are attributed to a genetic mutation. In most instances, only one type of cone is defective or is deficient in number. The most common mutation is the inability to see the colors red and green. The gene for red-green color blindness is on the X chromosome; therefore, males (who possess only one X chromosome) are more susceptible (see Section 21.5). This

BIOLOGY TODAY ▶ Health

Correcting Vision Problems

Poor vision can be due to a number of problems, some more serious than others. Several of these, such as cataracts and glaucoma, are conditions that often require medical attention.

Cataracts and Glaucoma

Cataracts develop when the lens of the eye becomes cloudy. Normally, the lens is clear, allowing light to pass through easily. A cloudy lens allows less light to reach the retina and slowly causes vision loss. Fortunately, a doctor can surgically remove the cloudy lens and replace it with a clear plastic lens, which often restores the light level passing through the lens and improves the patient's vision.

Glaucoma is caused by a buildup of fluid pressure inside the eye and may lead to a decrease in vision. The condition may eventually cause blindness. Eyedrops and oral medications are often prescribed to help reduce the interior pressure. If eyedrops and medications are not capable of controlling the pressure, surgery may be the only option. During glaucoma surgery, the doctor uses a laser to create tiny holes in the eye where the cornea and iris meet. This increases fluid drainage from the eye and decreases the pressure inside the eye.

The Benefits of LASIK Surgery

For many people, a sign of aging is the slow and steady decrease of their ability to see up close, a condition called presbyopia. Difficulty in reading small print, or reading in low-light conditions, is usually the first sign of presbyopia. The condition tends to begin in the late thirties and is common by age 55. Reading in low-light situations becomes more difficult, and letters begin to look fuzzy when reading close up. Many people who have presbyopia experience headaches while reading. Although, historically, people adjusted by using a magnifying lens, today, most people wear bifocal lenses. Bifocals are designed to correct vision at a distance of 12 to 18 inches. These lenses work well for most people while reading, but pose a problem for those who use a computer. Computer monitors are usually 19 to 24 inches away. This forces bifocal lens wearers to constantly move their head up and down in an attempt to switch between the close and distant viewing sections of the bifocals. Another solution is to wear contact lenses with one eye corrected to see close objects and the other eye corrected to see distant objects. The same type of correction can be done with LASIK surgery (Fig. 15A). LASIK, which stands for *laser-assisted in situ keratomileusis,* is generally a safe and effective treatment option for a wide array of vision problems.

LASIK is a quick and relatively painless procedure that involves the use of a laser to permanently change the shape of the cornea. For the majority of patients, LASIK improves their vision and reduces their dependency on corrective lenses. The ideal LASIK candidate is over 18 years of age and has had a stable contact or glasses prescription for at least 2 years. Patients need to have a cornea thick enough to allow the surgeon to safely create a clean corneal flap of appropriate depth. Typically, patients who have common vision problems (nearsightedness, astigmatism, or farsightedness) respond well to LASIK. Anyone who suffers from any disease that decreases the ability to heal properly after surgery is not a candidate for LASIK. Also, individuals who have cataracts, advanced glaucoma, or corneal or other eye diseases are generally not considered for LASIK either.

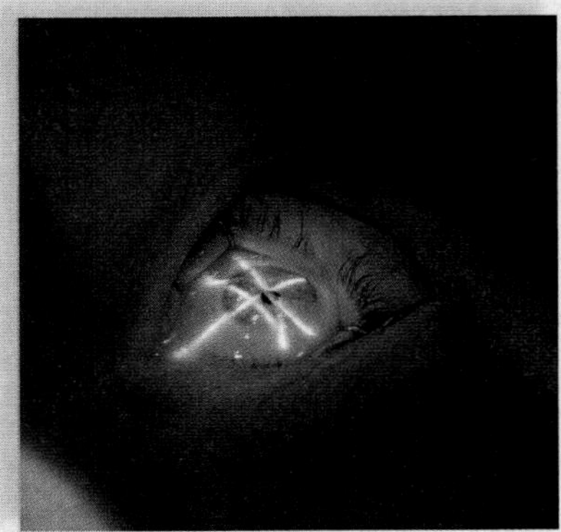

Figure 15A LASIK surgery. LASIK, or laser-assisted in situ keratomileusis, is a procedure that can be used to correct vision problems.
Arctic-Images/Stone/Getty Images

Candidates should thoroughly discuss the procedure with their eye-care professional before electing to have LASIK. People need to realize that the goal of LASIK is to reduce their dependency on glasses or contact lenses, not to eliminate them completely.

The LASIK Procedure

During the LASIK procedure, a small flap of tissue (the conjunctiva) is cut away from the front of the eye. The flap is folded back, exposing the cornea, allowing the surgeon to remove a defined amount of tissue from the cornea. Each pulse of the laser removes a small amount of corneal tissue, allowing the surgeon to flatten or increase the steepness of the curve of the cornea. After the procedure, the flap of tissue is put back into place and allowed to heal on its own. Patients who have LASIK surgery receive eyedrops or medications to help relieve the discomfort associated with the procedure. Improvements to vision begin as early as the day after the surgery, but typically take 2 to 3 months. Most patients will have vision close to 20/20, but the chances for improved vision are based in part on how good the person's eyes were before the surgery.

As with any surgery, complications are possible. Adverse effects include a sensation of having something in the eye or having blurred vision. The individual might also see halos around objects or be very sensitive to glare. In addition, dryness can cause eye irritation. Typically, these effects are temporary, and the rate of complications following surgery is very low. Always consult with your doctor before considering any type of surgery.

Questions to Consider

1. Using Figure 15.11 as a guide, explain how LASIK surgery corrects the flow of light into the eye.
2. What problems might be experienced by people who wear contacts that cause the two eyes to focus at different distances?

abnormality affects 5–8% of the male population. If the eye lacks cones that respond to red wavelengths, green colors are accentuated, and vice versa.

Distance Vision

If you can see from 20 ft what a person with normal vision can see from 20 ft, you are said to have 20/20 vision. Persons who can see close objects but can't see the letters on an optometrist's chart from 20 ft are said to be nearsighted. People who are **nearsighted** can see close objects better than they can see objects at a distance. The shape of the eye in these individuals is elongated, and when they attempt to look at a distant object, the image is brought to focus in front of the retina (Fig. 15.11*a*). They can see close objects because their lens can compensate for the elongated shape of the eye. To see distant objects, these people can wear concave lenses, which spread the light rays, so that the image focuses on the retina.

Persons who can easily see the optometrist's chart but cannot see close objects well are **farsighted.** These individuals can see distant objects better than they can see close objects. The shape of their eye is shortened, and when they try to see close objects, the image is focused behind the retina (Fig. 15.11*b*). When the object is distant, the lens can compensate for the shortened shape of the eye. When the object is close, these persons can wear convex lenses to increase the bending of light rays, so that the image can be focused on the retina.

When the cornea or lens is uneven, the image is fuzzy. The light rays cannot be evenly focused on the retina. This condition, called **astigmatism,** can be corrected by an unevenly ground lens to compensate for the uneven cornea (Fig. 15.11*c*).

As we introduced in the chapter opener, many people today opt to have LASIK surgery instead of wearing lenses. LASIK surgery is discussed in the Health feature "Correcting Vision Problems."

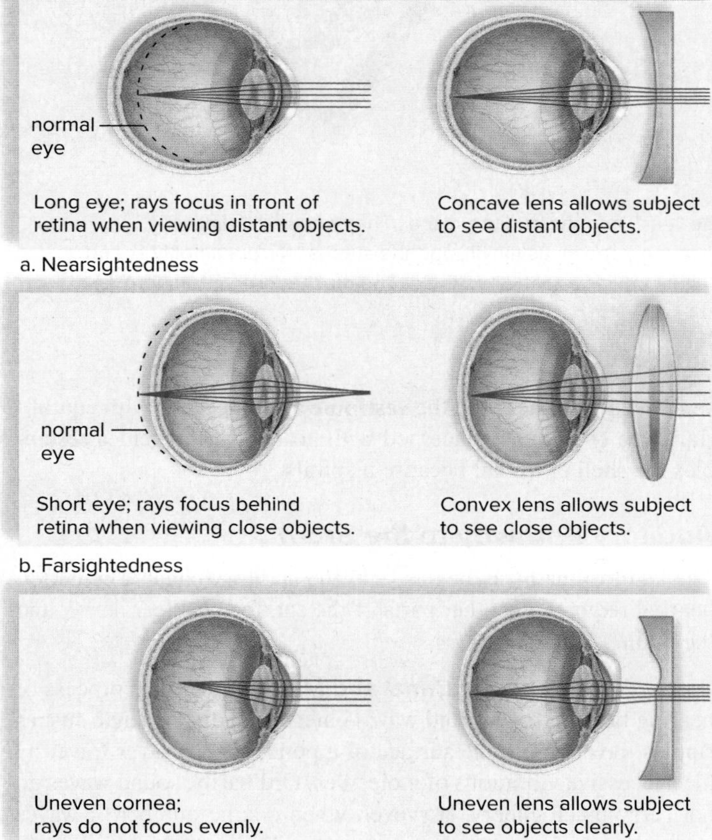
normal eye
Long eye; rays focus in front of retina when viewing distant objects.
Concave lens allows subject to see distant objects.
a. Nearsightedness
normal eye
Short eye; rays focus behind retina when viewing close objects.
Convex lens allows subject to see close objects.
b. Farsightedness
Uneven cornea; rays do not focus evenly.
Uneven lens allows subject to see objects clearly.
c. Astigmatism

Figure 15.11 How corrective lenses correct vision problems. **a.** A concave lens in persons who are nearsighted focuses light rays on the retina. **b.** A convex lens in persons who are farsighted focuses light rays on the retina. **c.** An uneven lens in persons with astigmatism focuses light rays on the retina.

CHECK YOUR PROGRESS 15.4

1. Identify the structures of the eye and provide a function of each.
2. Describe the two types of photoreceptors and state the function of each.
3. Summarize the movement of sensory information from the photoreceptors to the visual cortex.

CONNECTING THE CONCEPTS

For more information on the material presented in this section, refer to the following discussions:

Table 9.8 describes the function and dietary sources of vitamin A.

Section 14.2 describes the function of the visual association area in the cerebral cortex of the brain.

Section 21.5 explores the pattern of inheritance associated with color blindness.

15.5 Sense of Hearing

LEARNING OUTCOMES

Upon completion of this section, you should be able to

1. Identify the structures of the ear involved in hearing.
2. Summarize how sound waves are converted into nerve signals.
3. Describe the pathway of sensory information from the ear to the brain.

The ear has two sensory functions: hearing and balance (equilibrium). The sensory receptors for both of these are located in the inner ear. Each consists of **hair cells** with **stereocilia** (*sing.,* stereocilium), which are long, stiff microvilli that are sensitive to mechanical stimulation. The stereocilia act as mechanoreceptors.

Anatomy and Physiology of the Ear

Figure 15.12 shows that the ear has three divisions: outer, middle, and inner. The **outer ear** consists of the **pinna** (external flap) and the **auditory canal.** The opening of the auditory canal is lined with

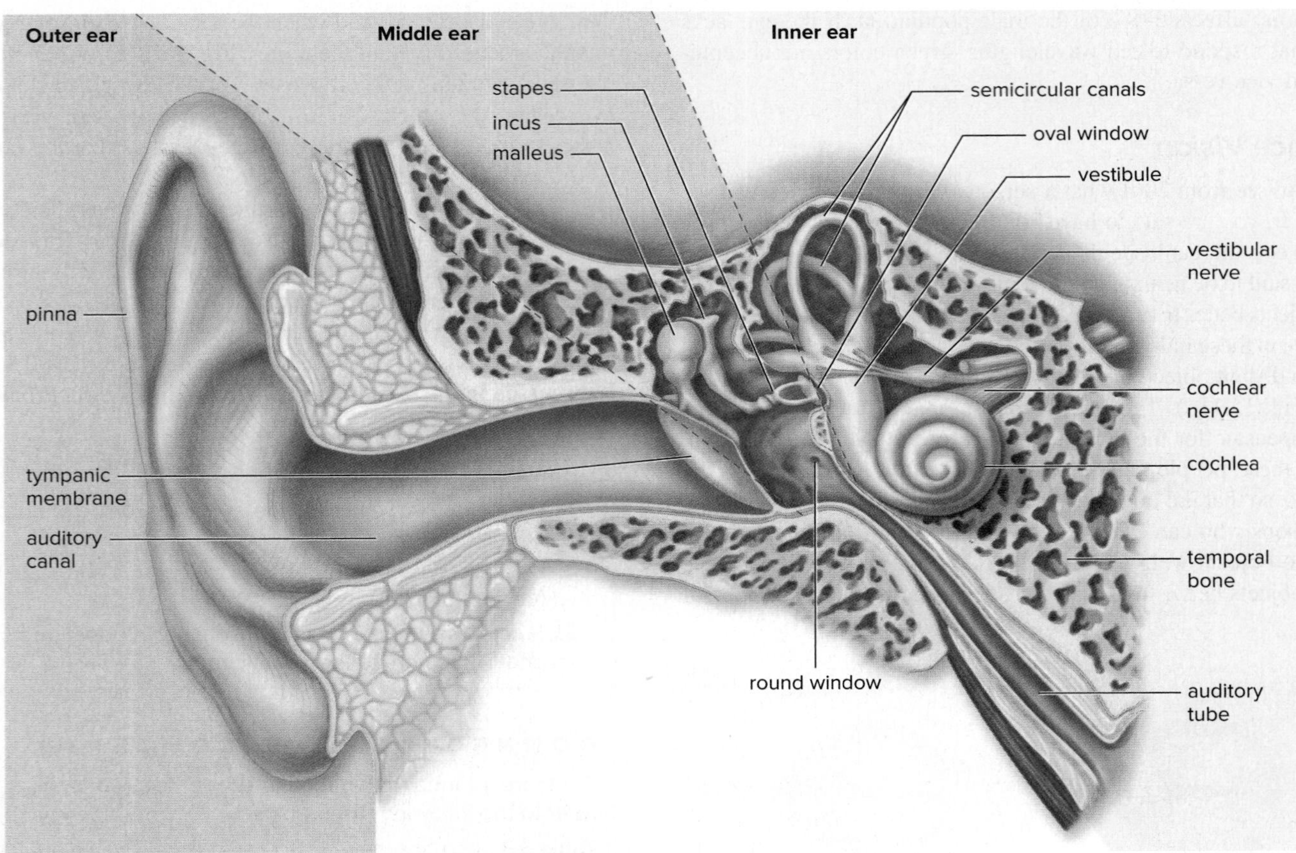

Figure 15.12 The three divisions of the human ear.
The external ear consists of the pinna (the structure commonly referred to as the "ear") and the auditory canal. The tympanic membrane separates the external ear from the middle ear. In the middle ear, the malleus (hammer), the incus (anvil), and the stapes (stirrup) amplify sound waves. In the inner ear, the mechanoreceptors for equilibrium are in the semicircular canals and the vestibule. The mechanoreceptors for hearing are in the cochlea.

fine hairs and sweat glands. Modified sweat glands are located in the upper wall of the canal. They secrete earwax, a substance that helps guard the ear against the entrance of foreign materials, such as air pollutants.

The **middle ear** begins at the **tympanic membrane** (eardrum) and ends at a bony wall containing two small openings covered by membranes. These openings are called the **oval window** and the **round window.** Three small bones are found between the tympanic membrane and the oval window. Collectively, they are called the **ossicles.** Individually, they are called the **malleus** (hammer), the **incus** (anvil), and the **stapes** (stirrup) because their shapes resemble these objects. The malleus adheres to the tympanic membrane, and the stapes touches the oval window. An **auditory tube,** also called the eustachian or pharyngotympanic tube, extends from the middle ear to the nasopharynx. Its purpose is to equalize air pressure across the tympanic membrane. When changing elevation, such as in an airplane, the act of chewing gum, yawning, or swallowing opens the auditory tubes wider. As this occurs, we often feel the ears "pop."

Whereas the outer ear and the middle ear contain air, the inner ear is filled with fluid. The **inner ear** has three areas: The **semicircular canals** and the **vestibule** are concerned with equilibrium; the **cochlea** is concerned with hearing. The cochlea resembles the shell of a snail because it spirals.

Auditory Pathway to the Brain

The auditory pathway begins with the auditory canal. Thereafter, hearing requires the other parts of the ear, the cochlear nerve, and the brain.

Through the Auditory Canal and Middle Ear The process of hearing begins when sound waves enter the auditory canal. Just as ripples travel across the surface of a pond, sound waves travel by the successive vibrations of molecules. Ordinarily, sound waves do not carry much energy. However, when a large number of waves strike the tympanic membrane, it moves back and forth (vibrates) ever so slightly. As you know, the auditory ossicles attach to one another: malleus to incus, incus to stapes. The malleus is attached to the inner wall of the tympanic membrane. Thus, vibrations of the tympanic membrane cause vibration of the malleus and, in turn, the incus and stapes. The magnitude of the original pressure wave increases significantly as the vibrations move along the

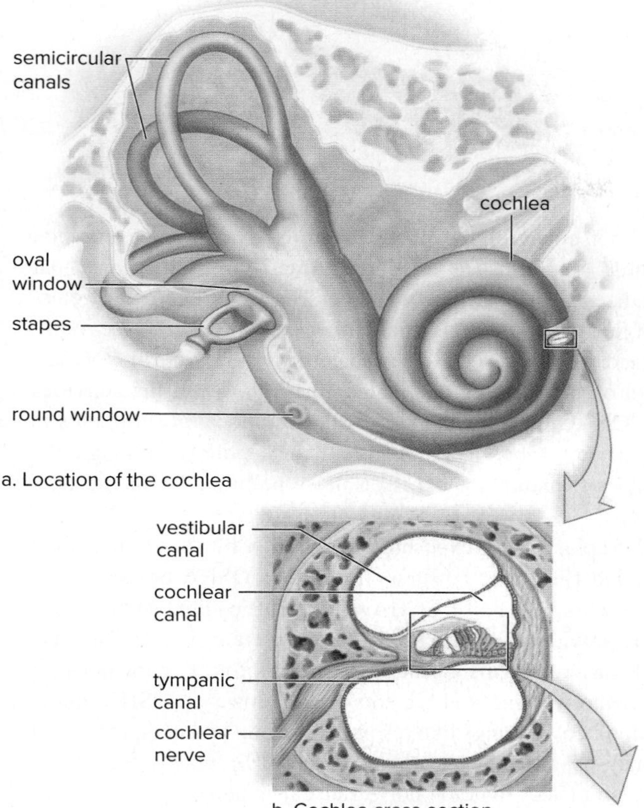

a. Location of the cochlea

b. Cochlea cross-section

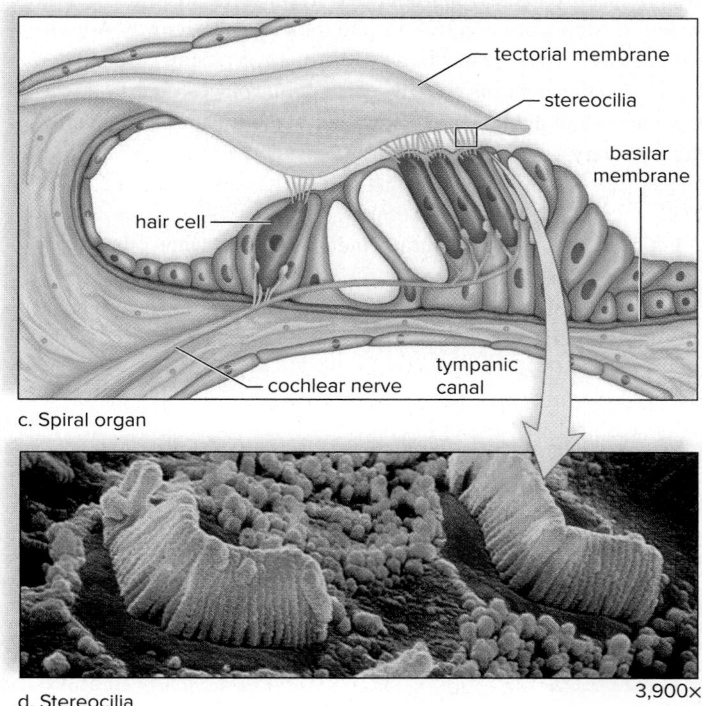

c. Spiral organ

d. Stereocilia

Figure 15.13 How the spiral organ (organ of Corti) translates sound waves into nerve signals.
a. The spiral organ (organ of Corti) is located within the (**b**) cochlea. **c.** The spiral organ consists of hair cells resting on the basilar membrane, with the tectorial membrane above. Pressure waves moving through the canals cause the basilar membrane to vibrate. This causes the stereocilia embedded in the tectorial membrane to bend. Nerve impulses traveling in the cochlear nerve result in hearing. **d.** A micrograph of the stereocilia.
(photo): Prof. P.M. Motta/Univ. "La Sapienza," Rome/Science Source

auditory ossicles. The pressure is multiplied about 20 times. Finally, the stapes strikes the membrane of the oval window, causing it to vibrate. In this way, the pressure is passed to the fluid within the cochlea.

BIOLOGY IN YOUR LIFE

What are "ear tubes"?

The auditory tubes of children tend to be oriented more horizontally than those of adults. Because of this, fluid may accumulate in the tubes, allowing for an infection to occur. These infections are called otitis media, and they are often painful. Extended cases of otitis media may produce long-term hearing loss.

A procedure called a tympanostomy places small tubes in the tympanic membrane, allowing these fluids to drain more easily, thus reducing the chance of infection. In most cases, the tubes fall out of the membrane over time, but sometimes they need to be removed by a physician.

From the Cochlea to the Auditory Cortex By examining the cochlea in cross-section (Fig. 15.13), you can see that it has three canals. The sensory organ for hearing, called the **spiral organ** (or the *organ of Corti*), is located in the cochlear canal. The spiral organ consists of little hair cells and a gelatinous material called the *tectorial membrane.* The hair cells sit on the *basilar membrane*, and their stereocilia are embedded in the tectorial membrane.

When the stapes strikes the membrane of the oval window, pressure waves move from the vestibular canal to the tympanic canal across the basilar membrane. The basilar membrane moves up and down, and the stereocilia of the hair cells embedded in the tectorial membrane bend. Then, nerve signals begin in the **cochlear nerve** and travel to the brain. When they reach the auditory cortex in the temporal lobe, they are interpreted as a sound.

Each part of the spiral organ is sensitive to different wave frequencies, or pitch. Near the tip, the spiral organ responds to low pitches, such as those of a tuba. Near the base (beginning), it responds to higher pitches, such as those of a bell or a whistle. The nerve fibers from each region along the length of the spiral organ lead to slightly different areas in the auditory cortex. The pitch sensation we experience depends upon which region of the basilar membrane vibrates and which area of the auditory cortex is stimulated.

Volume is a function of the amplitude (strength) of sound waves. Loud noises cause the fluid within the vestibular canal to exert more pressure and the basilar membrane to vibrate to a greater extent. The resulting increased stimulation is interpreted by the brain as volume. As discussed in the Health feature "Noise Pollution," noise levels above 85 decibels (Table 15.3) may cause permanent hearing loss.

BIOLOGY TODAY ▶ Health

Noise Pollution

Though we can sometimes tune out its presence, unwanted noise is all around us. Noise pollution is noise from the environment that is annoying, distracting, and potentially harmful. It comes from airplanes, cars, lawn mowers, machinery, and our own loud music and that of our neighbors. It is present at our workplaces, in public spaces like amusement parks, and at home. Its prevalence allows loud noise to have a potentially high impact on our welfare.

Noise and Health

How does noise affect human health? Perhaps the greatest worry about noise pollution is that exposure to loud (over 85 decibels) or chronic noises can damage cells of the inner ear and cause hearing loss (Fig. 15B). Loud noises, such as loud music at concerts, can cause damage to our spiral organ and diminish hearing.

Noise can affect well-being by other means, too. Data from studies of environmental noise can be difficult to interpret because of the presence of other confounding factors, including physical or chemical pollution. The tolerance level for noise also varies from person to person. Nonetheless, laboratory and field studies show that noise may be detrimental in nonauditory ways. Its effects on mental health include annoyance, inability to concentrate, and increased irritability. Long-term noise exposure from air or car traffic may impair cognitive ability, language learning, and memory in children. Noise often causes loss of sleep and reduced productivity and can induce stress. Additionally, several studies have demonstrated a link between noise pollution and cardiovascular health, specifically hypertension.

Regulating Noise Pollution

Noise pollution has been a concern for several decades. In 1972, the Noise Control Act was passed as a means for coordinating federal noise control and research and to develop noise emission standards. The aim was to protect Americans from "noise that jeopardizes their health or welfare." The Environmental Protection Agency (EPA) had federal authority to regulate noise pollution, and its Office of Noise Abatement and Control (ONAC) worked on establishing noise guidelines. However, the activities of the ONAC were transferred to state and local governments in 1981. Today, there is no national noise policy, although the EPA does maintain standards on noise pollution on its website: www.epa.gov.

Workplace noise exposure is controlled by the Occupational Safety and Health Administration (OSHA). OSHA has set guidelines for workplace noise. OSHA regulations require that protective gear be provided if sound levels exceed certain values. This may include noise-reducing earmuffs and other protective methods for people who work around big equipment. However, OSHA guidelines don't cover things like telephone ringing and computer noise that may be present in a nonindustrial environment such as an open-plan office. Aviation noise and traffic noise reduction plans are overseen by the Department of Transportation, the Federal Aviation Administration (FAA), and the Federal Highway Administration (FHWA), respectively. Local governments often have legislation that controls noise levels in public places, such as downtown areas and public parks. However, without national standards, the laws vary by location.

Questions to Consider

1. Given that noise pollution induces stress, what other body systems may be affected?
2. At a local level, what do you think could be done to curb noise pollution in your neighborhood?

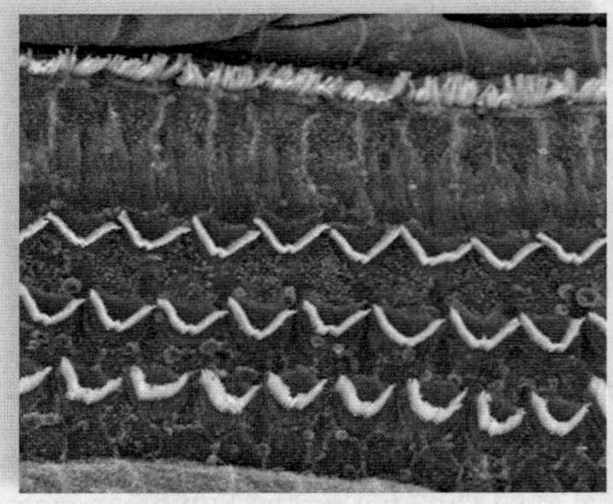
a.

b.

Figure 15B Loud noise damages the hair cells in the spiral organ.
a. Normal hair cells in the spiral organ of a guinea pig. **b.** Damaged cells. This damage occurred after 24-hour exposure to a noise level equivalent to that at a rock concert (see Table 15.3). Hearing is permanently impaired because lost cells will not be replaced, and damaged cells may also die.

(both): Dr. Joseph E Hawkins/University of Michigan/Kresage Hearing Research Institute

Table 15.3 Noises that Affect Hearing

Type of Noise	Sound Level (Decibels)	Effect
"Boom car," jet engine, shotgun, rock concert	Over 125	Beyond threshold of pain; potential for hearing loss high
Nightclub, thunderclap	Over 120	Hearing loss likely
Earbuds in external ear canal	110–120	Hearing loss likely
Chain saw, pneumatic drill, jackhammer, symphony orchestra, snowmobile, garbage truck, cement mixer	100–200	Regular exposure of more than 1 min risks permanent hearing loss
Farm tractor, newspaper press, subway, motorcycle	90–100	Fifteen minutes of unprotected exposure potentially harmful
Lawn mower, food blender	85–90	Continuous daily exposure for more than 8 hrs can cause hearing damage
Diesel truck, average city traffic noise	80–85	Annoying; constant exposure may cause hearing damage

CHECK YOUR PROGRESS 15.5

1. Identify the structures of the ear involved in hearing and provide a function for each.
2. Describe the role of mechanoreceptors in the sense of hearing.
3. Summarize how the spiral organ translates sound waves to nerve impulses.

CONNECTING THE CONCEPTS

For more information on the material in this section, refer to the following discussions:

Section 14.2 describes the function of the cerebral cortex area of the brain in hearing.

Figure 14.16 illustrates the structure of a nerve.

15.6 Sense of Equilibrium

LEARNING OUTCOMES

Upon completion of this section, you should be able to

1. Explain how mechanoreceptors are involved in the sense of equilibrium.
2. Identify the structures of the ear involved in the sense of equilibrium.
3. Distinguish between rotational and gravitational equilibrium.

The vestibular nerve originates in the semicircular canals, saccule, and utricle. It takes nerve signals to the brain stem and cerebellum (Fig. 15.14). Through its communication with the brain, the vestibular nerve helps us achieve equilibrium, but other structures in the body are also involved. For example, in Section 15.5, we mentioned that proprioceptors are necessary for maintaining our equilibrium. Vision, if available, usually provides extremely helpful input the brain can act upon. To explain, let's take a look at the two sets of mechanoreceptors for equilibrium.

Rotational Equilibrium Pathway

Mechanoreceptors in the **semicircular canals** detect rotational and/or angular movement of the head—**rotational equilibrium** (Fig. 15.14*a*). The three semicircular canals are arranged so there is one in each dimension of space. The base, or *ampulla,* of each of the three canals is slightly enlarged. Little hair cells, whose stereocilia are embedded within a gelatinous material called a cupula, are found within the ampullae. Each ampulla responds to head rotation in a different plane of space because of the way the semicircular canals are arranged. As fluid within a semicircular canal flows over and displaces a cupula, the stereocilia of the hair cells bend. This causes a change in the pattern of signals carried by the vestibular nerve to the brain. The brain uses information from the hair cells within each ampulla of the semicircular canals to maintain equilibrium. Appropriate motor output to various skeletal muscles can correct our present position in space as needed.

Why does spinning around cause you to become dizzy? When we spin, the cupula slowly begins to move in the same direction we are spinning, and bending of the stereocilia causes hair cells to send messages to the brain. As time goes by, the cupula catches up to the rate we are spinning, and the hair cells no longer send messages to the brain. When we stop spinning, the slow-moving cupula continues to move in the direction of the spin and the stereocilia bend again, indicating we are moving. Yet the eyes know we have stopped. The mixed messages sent to the brain cause us to feel dizzy.

Gravitational Equilibrium Pathway

The mechanoreceptors in the utricle and saccule detect movement of the head in the vertical or horizontal planes, or **gravitational equilibrium.** The **utricle** and **saccule** are two membranous sacs located in the inner ear near the semicircular canals. Both of these sacs contain little hair cells whose stereocilia are embedded within a gelatinous material called an *otolithic membrane* (Fig. 15.14*b*). Calcium carbonate ($CaCO_3$) granules, or **otoliths,** rest on this membrane. The utricle is especially sensitive to horizontal (back-and-forth) movements and the bending of the head, and the saccule responds best to vertical (up-and-down) movements.

When the body is still, the otoliths in the utricle and the saccule rest on the otolithic membrane above the hair cells. When the head bends or the body moves in the horizontal and vertical planes, the otoliths are displaced. The otolithic membrane sags, bending the stereocilia of the hair cells beneath. If the stereocilia move toward the largest stereocilium, called the *kinocilium,* nerve impulses

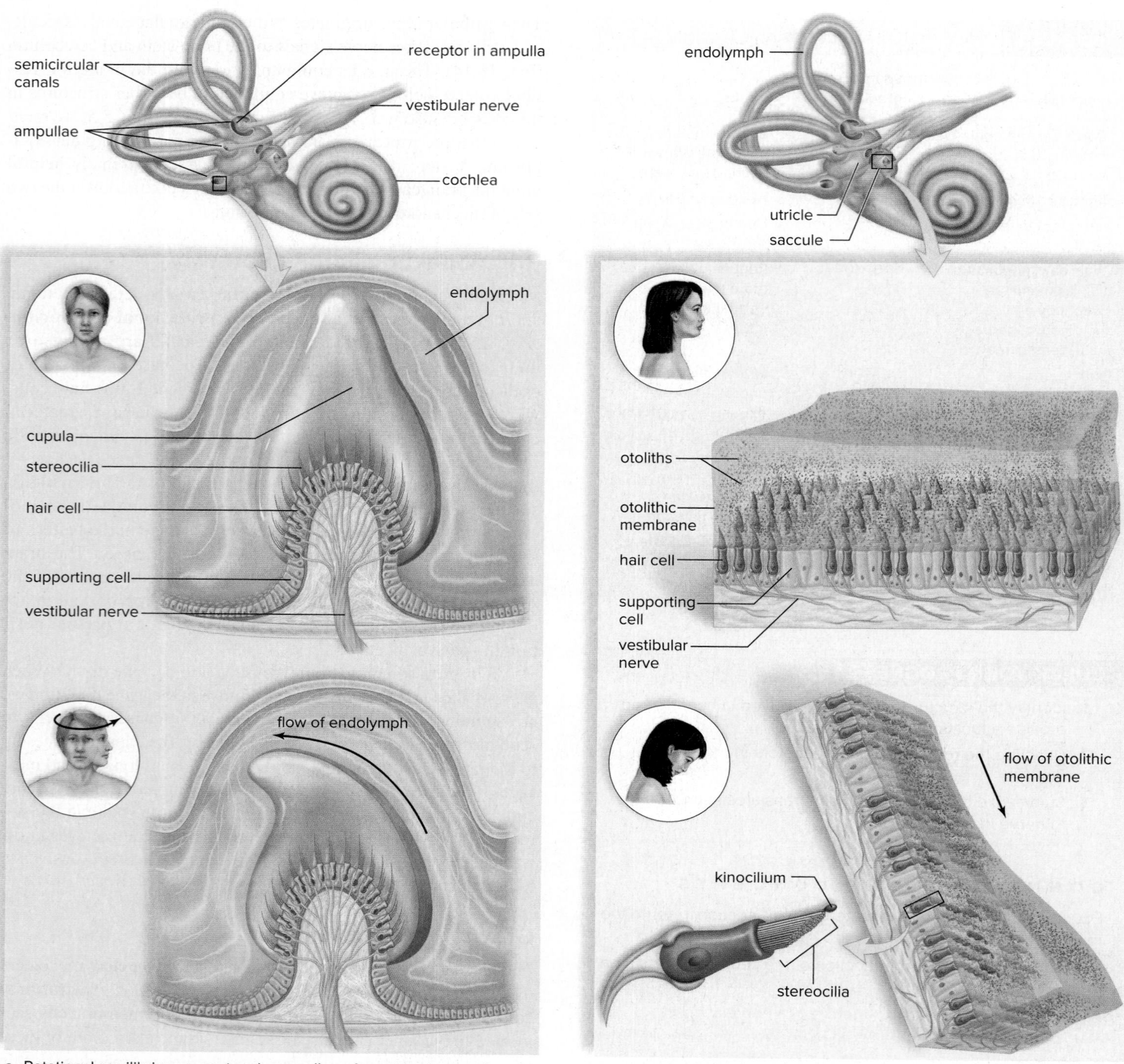

Figure 15.14 The mechanoreceptors of the inner ear and the sense of balance.
a. Rotational equilibrium is coordinated by receptors in the ampullae of the semicircular canals. **b.** Gravitational equilibrium is coordinated by receptors in the utricule and saccule located near the semicircular canals.

increase in the vestibular nerve. If the stereocilia move away from the kinocilium, nerve impulses decrease in the vestibular nerve. The frequency of nerve impulses in the vestibular nerve indicates whether you are moving up or down.

These data reach the cerebellum, which uses them to determine the direction of the movement of the head at that moment. Remember that the cerebellum (see Section 14.2) is vital to maintaining balance and gravitational equilibrium. The cerebellum processes information from the inner ear (the semicircular canals, utricle, and saccule), as well as visual and proprioceptive inputs. In addition, the motor cortex in the frontal lobe of the brain signals where the limbs should be located at any particular moment. After integrating all these nerve inputs, the cerebellum coordinates skeletal muscle contraction to correct our position in space if necessary.

Continuous stimulation of the stereocilia can contribute to motion sickness, especially when messages reaching the brain conflict with visual information from the eyes. Imagine you are standing inside a ship that is tossing up and down on the waves. Your visual inputs signal that you are standing still, because you can see the wall in front of you and that wall isn't moving. However, the inputs from all three sensory areas of the inner ear tell your brain you are moving up and down and from side to side. If you can match the two sets of information coming into the brain, you will begin to feel better. Thus, it makes sense to stand on deck if possible, so that visual signals and inner-ear signals both tell your brain that you're moving. Some antihistamine drugs, such as dimenhydrinate (Dramamine), reduce the excitability of the receptors in the inner ear, thus reducing the impulses received by the cerebellum, and alleviating motion sickness.

CHECK YOUR PROGRESS 15.6

1. State the location and function of the structures involved in maintaining balance.
2. Describe how rotational equilibrium is achieved.
3. Contrast rotational and gravitational equilibrium and explain how the two work together to maintain balance.

CONNECTING THE CONCEPTS

For more information on the sense of equilibrium, refer to the following discussions:

Section 14.1 examines the structure of a neuron and the generation of a nerve impulse.

Section 14.2 explains the role of the cerebellum in the processing of sensory information regarding balance.

CONCLUSION

In this chapter, we have explored how the senses interact with the nervous system to relay information about our world to the brain for interpretation. As with any body system, advances in medical procedures, such as LASIK, allow physicians to correct many of the problems associated with the sense organs.

SUMMARIZE

15.1 Overview of Sensory Receptors and Sensations

Signal transduction begins with the detection of stimuli by **sensory receptors.** These receptors may detect stimuli from within the body **(interoceptors)** or the external environment **(exteroceptors).** In general, receptors are classified by the types of stimuli they detect:

- **Chemoreceptors** detect chemical stimuli. **Nociceptors** are a form of chemoreceptor that detects pain.
- **Photoreceptors** detect light stimuli.
- **Mechanoreceptors** detect stimuli generated by mechanical forces.
- **Thermoreceptors** detect stimuli caused by changes in temperature.

All of these classes function as follows:

- **Sensory receptors** perform **integration** of the incoming signals. They then initiate nerve signals to the spinal cord and/or brain. **Sensory adaptation** may occur if the stimuli are repeated continuously.
- **Sensation** occurs when nerve signals reach the cerebral cortex.
- Perception is an interpretation of sensations.

15.2 Somatic Senses

Somatic senses are associated with the skin, muscles, joints, and viscera. The sensory receptors associated with the somatic senses include the following:

- Proprioceptors (mechanoreceptors) are involved in reflex actions and help maintain equilibrium and posture.
- **Cutaneous receptors** in the skin sense touch, pressure, and temperature.
- Nociceptors detect pain by responding to chemical signals from damaged tissues.

15.3 Senses of Taste and Smell

Taste and smell are due to chemoreceptors stimulated by molecules in the environment.

Sense of Taste

Receptors for taste are found primarily on the **taste buds.** Microvilli of taste cells have receptor proteins for molecules that cause the brain to distinguish sweet, sour, salty, bitter, and umami.

Sense of Smell

The cilia of **olfactory cells** have receptor proteins for molecules that cause the brain to distinguish odors.

15.4 Sense of Vision

Vision depends on the eye, the optic nerves, and the visual areas of the cerebral cortex.

Anatomy and Physiology of the Eye

The eye has three layers:

- The **sclera** (outer layer) protects and supports the eye.
- The **choroid** (middle, pigmented layer) absorbs stray light rays.
- The **retina** (inner layer) contains the rod cells (sensory receptors for dim light) and cone cells (sensory receptors for bright light and color).

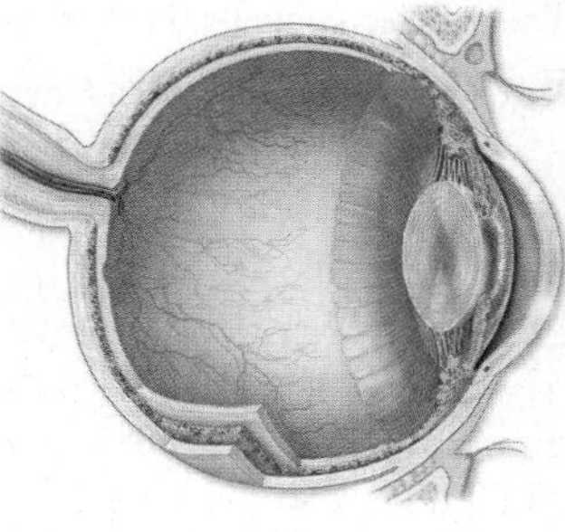

- *Function of the Lens:* Light enters the eye through the **pupil,** the size of which is regulated by the **iris.** The **lens,** with assistance from the **cornea, aqueous humor,** and **vitreous humor,** brings the light rays to **focus** on the retina, typically on the **fovea centralis** region of the retina. To see a close object, **visual accommodation** occurs as the lens becomes round and thick.

- *Photoreceptors:* Two types of photoreceptors are located on the retina: **rod cells** (black-and-white vision) and **cone cells** (color vision). Both contain **rhodopsin,** which includes retinal (vitamin A). An area called the **blind spot** lacks rods and cones.
- *Visual Pathway to the Brain:* The visual pathway begins when light strikes photoreceptors (rod cells and cone cells) in the retina. The **optic nerves** carry nerve impulses from the eyes to the **optic chiasma.** The nerve impulse leaves the optic chiasma along **optic tracts** to the thalamus before reaching the primary vision area in the occipital lobe of the brain.

Abnormalities of the Eye

Vision problems may be caused by a buildup of pressure in the eye (glaucoma), genetic factors (color blindness), or the shape of the eye (which can result in being **nearsighted, farsighted,** or having **astigmatism**).

15.5 Sense of Hearing

Hearing depends on the ear, the cochlear nerve, and the auditory areas of the cerebral cortex.

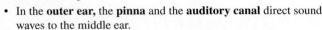

Anatomy and Physiology of the Ear

The ear has three parts:

- In the **outer ear,** the **pinna** and the **auditory canal** direct sound waves to the middle ear.
- In the **middle ear,** the **tympanic membrane** (including the **oval window** and **round window**), and the **ossicles** (**malleus, incus,** and **stapes**) amplify sound waves.
- In the **inner ear,** the **semicircular canals** and **vestibule** detect rotational equilibrium; the utricle and saccule detect gravitational equilibrium; and the **cochlea** houses the spiral organ, which contains mechanoreceptors, **hair cells** with **stereocilia,** for hearing.

The **auditory tube** (or eustachian tube) helps equalize pressure across the tympanic membrane.

Auditory Pathway to the Brain: The auditory pathway begins when the outer ear receives and the middle ear amplifies sound waves that then strike the oval window membrane.

- The mechanoreceptors for hearing are hair cells on the basilar membrane of the **spiral organ.**
- Nerve signals begin in the **cochlear nerve** and are carried to the primary auditory area in the temporal lobe of the cerebral cortex.

15.6 Sense of Equilibrium

The ear also contains mechanoreceptors for equilibrium.

Rotational Equilibrium Pathway

- **Rotational equilibrium** is due to mechanoreceptors (hair cells) in the semicircular canals that detect rotational and/or angular movement of the head.

Gravitational Equilibrium Pathway

- **Gravitational equilibrium** is due to mechanoreceptors (hair cells) in the utricle and saccule that detect head movement in the vertical or horizontal planes. Calcium carbonate granules called **otoliths** assist in this process.

ENGAGE

THINKING CRITICALLY

1. Which receptors are activated when you enjoy supper in a pizza restaurant?
2. Besides the blood pH mentioned, which other homeostatic conditions are monitored by chemoreceptors?
3. Some sensory receptors, such as those for taste, smell, and pressure, readily undergo the process of sensory adaptation, or decreased response to a stimulus. In contrast, receptors for pain are less prone to adaptation. Why does this make good biological sense? What do you think happens to children who are born without the ability to feel pain normally?
4. Airport and construction workers are likely to be exposed to continuous, loud noises. What would you predict the long-term effect on their hearing to be? Why?
5. The acoustic and vestibular nerves travel together to the brain. If a tumor grows on this combined nerve, which sensations will be affected?
6. Stem cells are currently being used to treat some forms of age-related macular degeneration (AMD). When placed in the retina, these unspecialized cells divide and assume the roles of the damaged retinal cells. How might stem cell therapy be used to treat damage to other senses, such as noise-related damage to hearing? What would be some challenges to this approach?

MAKING IT RELEVANT

1. How has your vision changed over time? Based on what you know about the structure of the eye, what factors do you think were involved in those changes?
2. Some animals can see wavelengths of light, such as infrared, that humans can't. How do you think your interactions with the environment would change if you could see infrared wavelengths?
3. Would you consider LASIK surgery to correct your vision? Why or why not?

Find answers to all of the chapter questions at connect.mheducation.com

Ricochet Creative Productions, LLC/McGraw Hill

CHAPTER

16

Endocrine System

Hormone Disruptors

You may have seen the label "BPA-free" on water bottles and plastic containers in stores. Or maybe you have heard news reports of concerns regarding contact with chemicals and plastics and human health. In most cases, this centers around a chemical called BPA (bisphenol A). BPA is used in the food and plastics industry as a lining on the inside of food and water containers. Because of this, it often enters the body through the digestive system. In the body, BPA mimics a form of estrogen called estradiol. While low levels of BPA in foods do not seem to cause any concerns, elevated levels have been associated with blood pressure, immunological, and reproductive problems in both sexes.

What you may not know is that some hormone disrupters play an important role in regulating pest species. Hormones regulate the development (metamorphosis) of many insects. One of these is called juvenile hormone. Methoprene, a common compound found in flea sprays, is an insect growth regulator that interferes with the juvenile hormone of insects such as fleas and mosquitoes. While methoprene does not kill the insects directly, it prevents their ability to develop from eggs to larvae and then adults.

In this chapter, we will explore the structure and function of the endocrine system, and the importance of the hormones it produces in human physiology.

As you read through the chapter, think about the following questions:

1. Why do animals, such as humans, have such a wide variety of hormones?
2. How does the nervous system work with the endocrine system to control body functions?
3. How do feedback mechanisms help control blood glucose levels?

CHAPTER OUTLINE

BEFORE YOU BEGIN

Before beginning this chapter, take a few moments to review the following discussions:

Section 2.5 What is the structure of a steroid?

Section 4.8 How are negative feedback mechanisms involved in homeostasis?

Section 14.2 What is the role of the hypothalamus in the nervous system?

16.1 Endocrine Glands

LEARNING OUTCOMES

Upon completion of this section, you should be able to

1. Distinguish between the mode of action of a neurotransmitter and that of a hormone.
2. Distinguish between endocrine and exocrine glands.
3. Identify the organs and glands of the endocrine system.
4. Compare the actions of peptide and steroid hormones.

The organs of the **endocrine system** (Fig. 16.1) are responsible for the production of chemical signals, called **hormones,** that are involved in the regulation of the other organs in the body. The endocrine system works very closely with the nervous system to maintain homeostasis in the body.

There is a difference in function between an endocrine gland and an exocrine gland. **Exocrine glands** have ducts and secrete their products into these ducts. The glands' products are carried to the interior of other organs or outside the body. The accessory glands of the digestive system (see Section 9.4) are good examples of the exocrine glands. For example, the salivary glands send

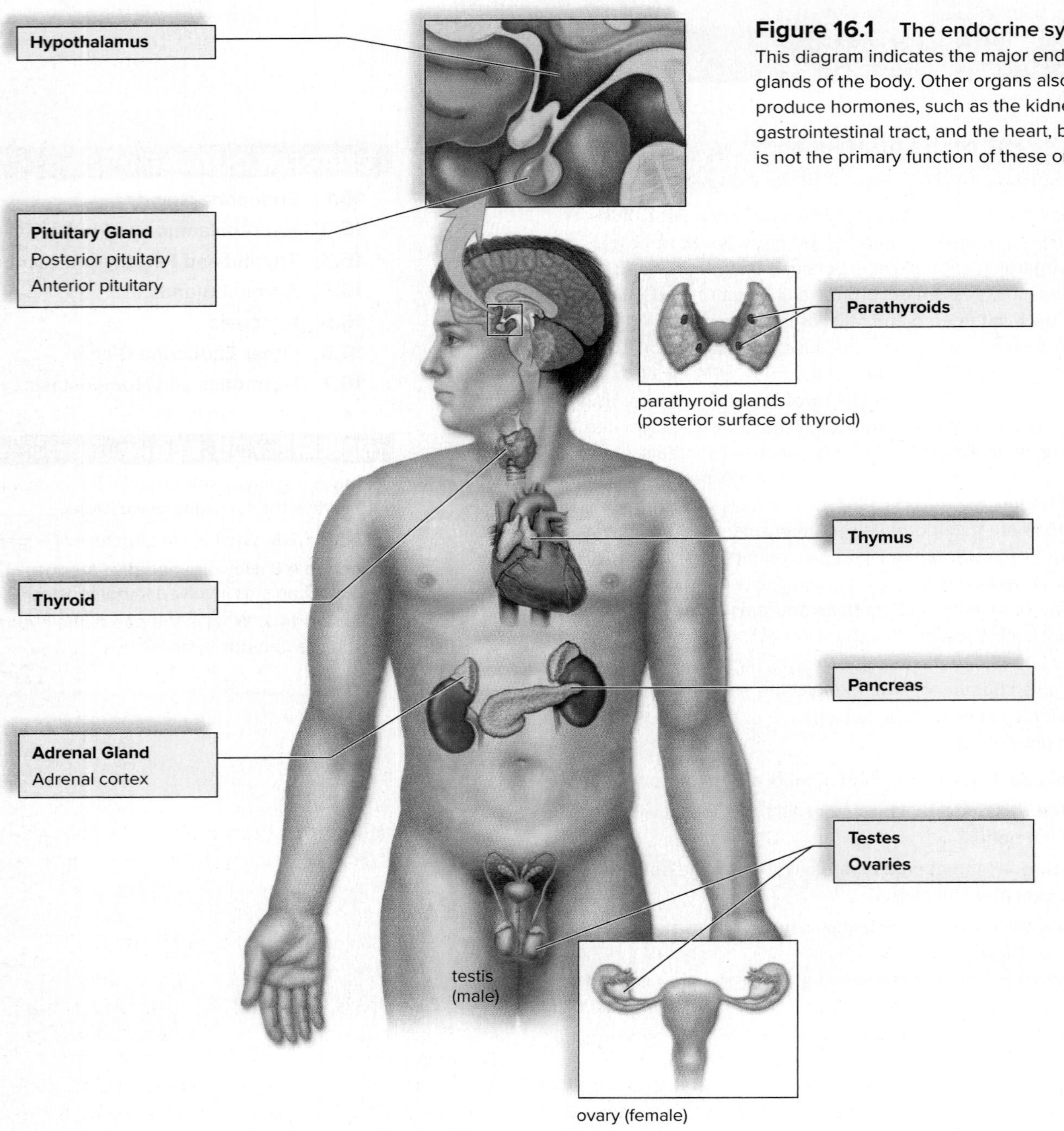

Figure 16.1 **The endocrine system.** This diagram indicates the major endocrine glands of the body. Other organs also produce hormones, such as the kidneys, the gastrointestinal tract, and the heart, but this is not the primary function of these organs.

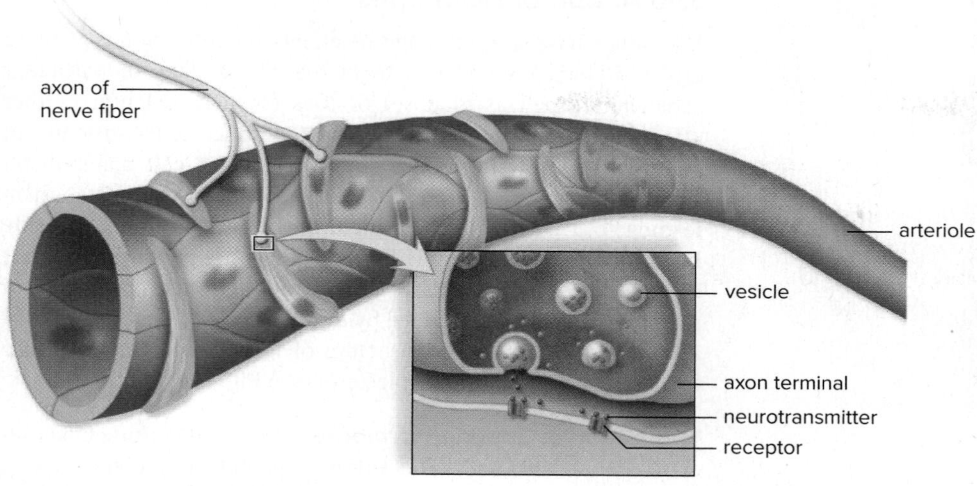

a. Reception of a neurotransmitter

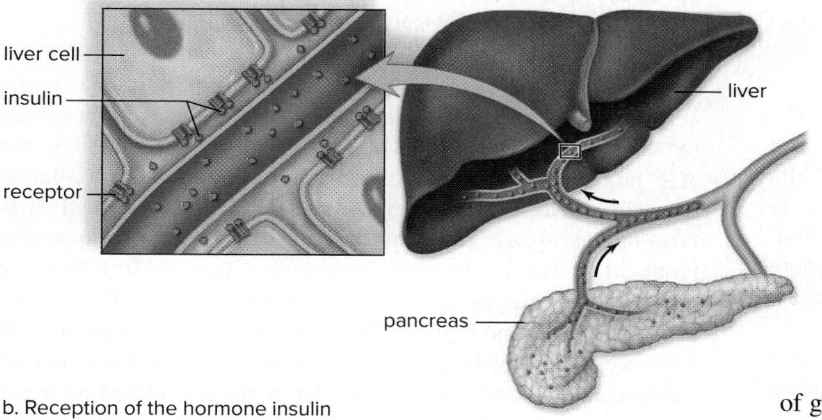

b. Reception of the hormone insulin

Figure 16.2 Action of neurotransmitters and hormones. **a.** Nerve impulses passing along an axon cause the release of a neurotransmitter. The neurotransmitter, a chemical signal, binds to a receptor and causes the wall of an arteriole to constrict. **b.** The hormone insulin, a chemical signal, travels in the cardiovascular system from the pancreas to the liver, where it binds to a receptor and causes the liver cells to store glucose as glycogen.

saliva into the mouth by way of the salivary ducts. In contrast, **endocrine glands** secrete their products into the bloodstream, which delivers them throughout the body. Only certain cells, called target cells, can respond to a specific hormone. A target cell for a particular hormone has a receptor protein for that hormone. The hormone and the receptor protein bind together like a key that fits a lock. The target cell then responds to that hormone.

Comparison of the Endocrine and Nervous Systems

The nervous system and endocrine system both use chemical signals when they respond to changes that might affect homeostasis. However, they have different means of delivering these signals (Fig. 16.2). As discussed in Section 14.1, the nervous system is composed of neurons. In this system, sensory receptors detect changes in the internal and external environments. The central nervous system (CNS) then integrates the information and responds by stimulating muscles and glands. Communication depends on nerve signals, conducted in axons, and neurotransmitters, which cross synapses. Axon conduction occurs rapidly, as does the diffusion of a neurotransmitter across the short distance of a synapse. In other words, the nervous system is organized to respond rapidly to stimuli. This is particularly useful if the stimulus is an external event that endangers our safety—we can move quickly to avoid being hurt.

The endocrine system functions differently than the nervous system. The endocrine system is largely composed of glands (see Fig. 16.1). These glands secrete hormones, which are carried by the bloodstream to target cells throughout the body. It takes time to deliver hormones, and it takes time for cells to respond. The effect initiated by the endocrine system is longer lasting. In other words, the endocrine system is organized for a slow but prolonged response.

Both the nervous system and the endocrine system make use of negative feedback mechanisms (see Section 4.8). If the blood pressure falls, sensory receptors signal a control center in the brain. This center sends out nerve signals to the arterial walls, so that they constrict, and blood pressure rises. Now the sensory receptors are no longer stimulated, and the feedback mechanism is inactivated. Similarly, a rise in blood glucose level causes the pancreas to release insulin. This, in turn, promotes glucose uptake by the liver, muscles, and other cells of the body (see Fig. 16.2). When the blood glucose level falls, the pancreas no longer secretes insulin.

Hormones Are Chemical Signals

Like other chemical signals, hormones are a means of communication between cells, between body parts, and even between individuals. They affect the metabolism of cells that have receptors to receive them (Fig. 16.3).

The importance of these receptors can be demonstrated by examining a condition called *androgen insensitivity syndrome.*

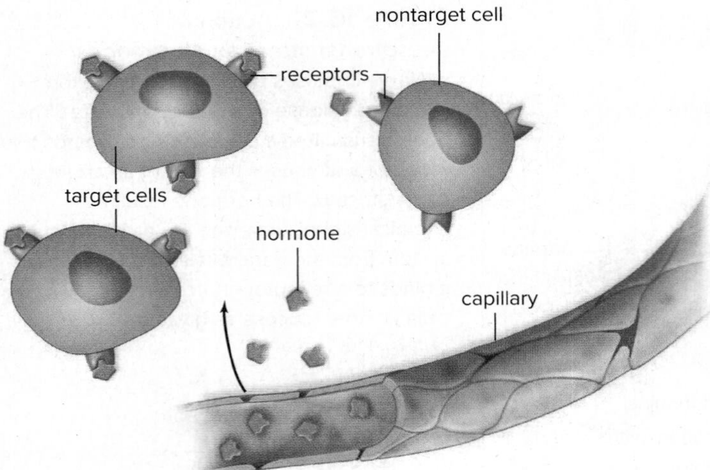

Figure 16.3 Hormones target specific cells.
Most hormones are distributed by the bloodstream to target cells. Target cells have receptors for the hormones, and a hormone combines with a receptor like a key fits a lock.

Individuals with this syndrome have both X and Y sex chromosomes. Because they possess a Y chromosome, they produce the sex hormone testosterone (see Section 16.6), even though the testes usually remain in the abdominal cavity. However, the body cells lack receptors for testosterone, and therefore do not respond to the hormone. Therefore, the individuals appear to have female physical traits, although genetically they are males.

Table 16.1 summarizes the hormones of the endocrine system and provides the functions and targets of these hormones in the body.

Like testosterone, most hormones act at a distance between body parts. They travel in the bloodstream from the gland that produced them to their target cells. Also considered to be hormones are the secretions produced by neurosecretory cells in the hypothalamus of the brain. They travel in the capillary network that runs between the hypothalamus and the pituitary gland. Some of these secretions stimulate the pituitary to secrete its hormones, and others prevent it from doing so.

Not all hormones act between body parts. As we will see, prostaglandins are a good example of *local hormones.* After prostaglandins are produced, they are not carried elsewhere in the bloodstream. Instead, they affect neighboring cells, sometimes promoting pain and inflammation. Also, growth factors are local hormones that promote cell division and mitosis.

Chemical signals that influence the behavior of other individuals are called **pheromones.** Nonhuman animals rely heavily on pheromones for communication—to mark one's territory and to attract a mate. Humans produce pheromones, too. Researchers have isolated a pheromone released by men that reduces premenstrual nervousness and tension in women. Women who live in the same household often have menstrual cycles in synchrony. This is likely caused by the armpit secretions of a woman who is menstruating, affecting the menstrual cycles of other women in the household.

The Action of Hormones

Hormones have a wide range of effects on cells. Some of these effects induce a target cell to increase its uptake of particular substances (such as glucose) or ions (such as calcium). Other effects bring about an alteration of the target cell's structure in some way. A few hormones simply influence cell metabolism. Growth hormone is a peptide that influences cell metabolism leading to a change in the structure of bone. The term **peptide hormone** is used to include hormones that are peptides, proteins, glycoproteins, and modified amino acids. Growth hormone is a protein produced and secreted by the anterior pituitary. All **steroid hormones** have a similar structure of four carbon rings because they are all derived from cholesterol (see Fig. 2.20).

The Action of Peptide Hormones Most endocrine glands secrete peptide hormones. The actions of peptide hormones can vary depending on the type of target cell. Peptide hormones do not have the ability to cross the plasma membrane, and therefore must interact with a receptor on the surface of the membrane.

As an example, we will explore what happens when the hormone epinephrine binds to a plasma membrane receptor of a muscle cell (Fig. 16.4). In muscle cells, the reception of epinephrine leads to the breakdown of glycogen to glucose, which provides energy for ATP production. The immediate result of binding is the formation of **cyclic adenosine monophosphate (cAMP).** Cyclic AMP contains one phosphate group attached to adenosine at two locations, producing a circular, or cyclic, molecule. Cyclic AMP activates a protein kinase enzyme in the cell. This enzyme, in turn, activates another enzyme, and so forth. The series of enzymatic reactions that follows cAMP formation is called an *enzyme cascade*. Each enzyme can be used over and over at every step of the cascade, so more enzymes are involved. Finally, many molecules of glycogen are broken down to glucose, which enters the bloodstream.

Typical of a peptide hormone, epinephrine never enters the cell. Therefore, the hormone is called the first messenger; cAMP, which sets the metabolic machinery in motion, is called the **second messenger.** To explain this terminology, let's imagine that the adrenal medulla, which produces epinephrine, is like a company's home office that sends out a courier (the hormone epinephrine is the first messenger) to a factory (the cell). The courier doesn't have a pass to enter the factory, so upon arrival at the factory, the courier tells a supervisor through the intercom that the home office wants the factory to produce a particular product. The supervisor (cAMP, the second messenger) enters a command in the computer that instructs the machinery (the enzymatic pathway) to make the product.

The Action of Steroid Hormones Only the adrenal cortex, the ovaries, and the testes produce steroid hormones. Thyroid hormones belong to a class of molecules called the amines. Amines act in a manner similar to the steroid hormones, even though they have a different structure. Steroid hormones do not bind to plasma membrane receptors. Because they are hydrophobic (see Section 2.5), steroids are able to enter the cell in the same manner as lipids (Fig. 16.5).

Once inside, a steroid hormone binds to a receptor, usually in the nucleus but sometimes in the cytoplasm. Inside the

Table 16.1 Principal Endocrine Glands and the Hormones They Produce

Endocrine Gland	Hormone Released	Target Tissues/Organs	Chief Functions
Hypothalamus	Hypothalamic-releasing	Anterior pituitary	Regulates anterior pituitary hormones
Pituitary gland			
Posterior pituitary	Antidiuretic (ADH)	Kidneys	Stimulates water reabsorption by kidneys
	Oxytocin	Uterus, mammary glands	Stimulates uterine muscle contraction, release of milk by mammary glands
Anterior pituitary	Thyroid-stimulating (TSH)	Thyroid	Stimulates thyroid
	Adrenocorticotropic (ACTH)	Adrenal cortex	Stimulates adrenal cortex
	Gonadotropic (FSH, LH)	Gonads	Egg and sperm production, sex hormone production
	Prolactin (PRL)	Mammary glands	Milk production
	Growth (GH)	Soft tissues, bones	Cell division, protein synthesis, bone growth
	Melanocyte-stimulating (MSH)	Melanocytes in skin	Unknown function in humans; regulates skin color in lower vertebrates
Thyroid	Thyroxine (T_4) and triiodothyronine (T_3)	All tissues	Increase metabolic rate, regulate growth and development
	Calcitonin	Bones, kidneys	Lowers blood calcium level
Parathyroids	Parathyroid (PTH)	Bones, kidneys, small intestine	Raises blood calcium level
Adrenal gland			
Adrenal cortex	Glucocorticoids (cortisol)	All tissues	Raise blood glucose level, stimulate breakdown of protein
	Mineralocorticoids (aldosterone)	Kidneys	Reabsorb sodium and excrete potassium
	Sex hormones	Gonads, skin, muscles, bones	Stimulate reproductive organs and bring about sex characteristics
Adrenal medulla	Epinephrine and norepinephrine	Cardiac and other muscles	Are released in emergency situations, raise blood glucose level
Pancreas	Insulin	Liver, muscles, adipose tissue	Lowers blood glucose level, promotes glycogen formation
	Glucagon	Liver, muscles, adipose tissue	Raises blood glucose level
Gonads			
Testes	Androgens (testosterone)	Gonads, skin, muscles, bones	Stimulate male sex characteristics
Ovaries	Estrogens, progesterone, small amounts of testosterone	Gonads, skin, muscles, bones	Stimulate female sex characteristics
Thymus	Thymosins	T lymphocytes	Stimulate production and maturation of T lymphocytes
Pineal gland	Melatonin	Brain	Controls circadian rhythms, possibly involved in maturation of sexual organs

nucleus, the hormone–receptor complex binds with DNA and activates certain genes. Messenger RNA (mRNA) moves to the ribosomes in the cytoplasm, and protein (e.g., enzyme) synthesis follows (see Section 22.2). To continue our analogy, a steroid hormone is like a courier who has a pass to enter the factory (the cell). Once inside, it makes contact with the plant manager (DNA), who sees to it that the factory (cell) is ready to produce a product.

An example of a steroid hormone is aldosterone, which is produced by the adrenal glands. Aldosterone targets the kidneys, where it helps regulate the water-salt balance of the blood. In general, steroid hormones act more slowly than peptide hormones, because it takes more time to synthesize new proteins than to activate enzymes already present in cells. Their action, however, typically lasts longer.

CHECK YOUR PROGRESS 16.1

1. State the role of a hormone.
2. Compare and contrast the nervous and endocrine systems with regard to function and the types of signals used.
3. Summarize the differences between a peptide hormone and a steroid hormone.
4. Explain why second messenger systems are needed for peptide hormones.

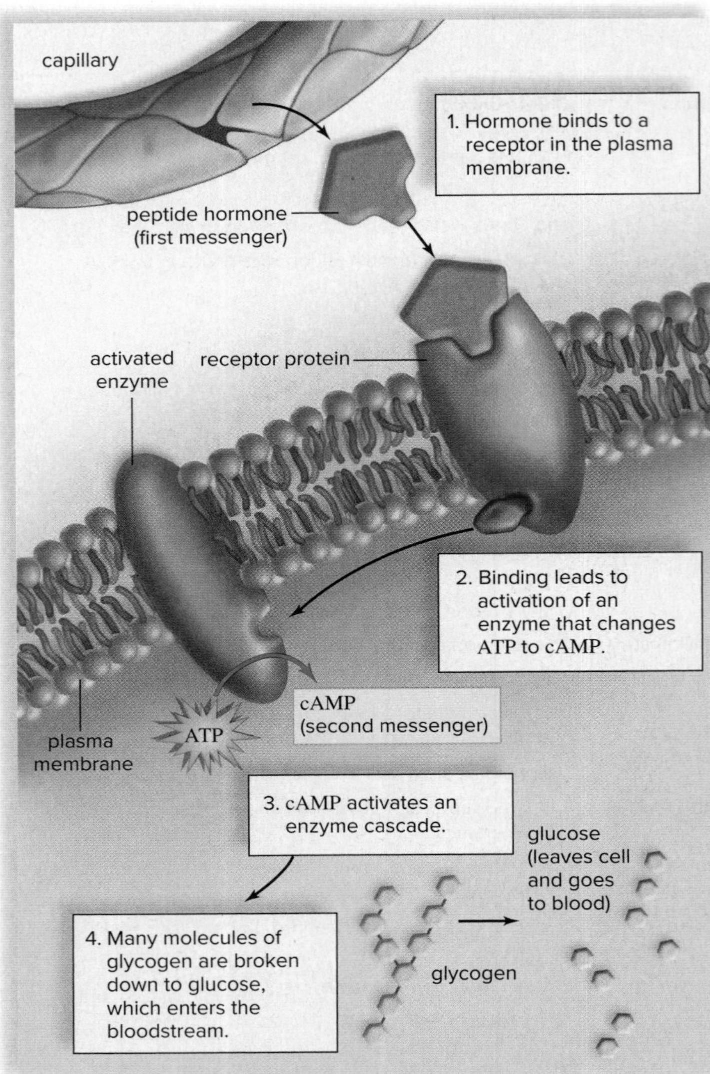

Figure 16.4 Action of a peptide hormone.
A peptide hormone (first messenger) binds to a receptor in the plasma membrane. Thereafter, cyclic AMP (second messenger) forms and activates an enzyme cascade.

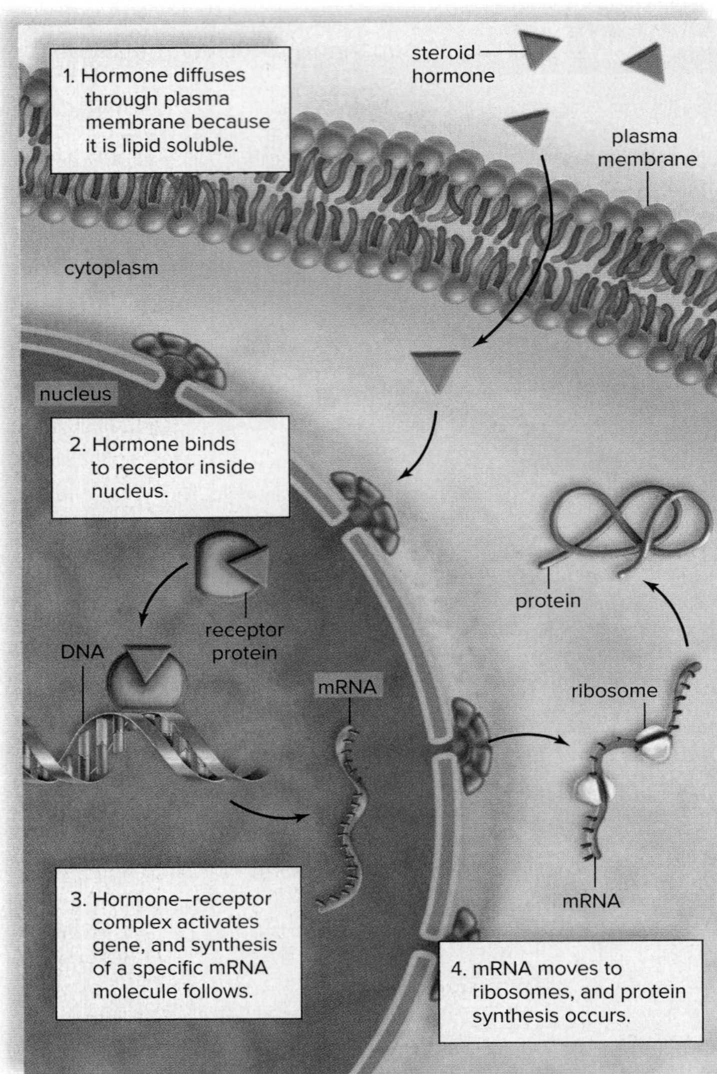

Figure 16.5 Action of a steroid hormone.
A steroid hormone passes directly through the target cell's plasma membrane before binding to a receptor in the nucleus or cytoplasm. The hormone–receptor complex binds to DNA, and gene expression follows.

CONNECTING THE CONCEPTS

For more information on the interactions in this section, refer to the following discussions:

Sections 2.5 and **2.6** summarize the roles of steroids and proteins in the body.

Section 3.3 explores the structure of the plasma membrane and the proteins associated with it.

Section 14.2 describes the location and function of the hypothalamus, which integrates the nervous and endocrine systems.

16.2 Hypothalamus and Pituitary Gland

LEARNING OUTCOMES

Upon completion of this section, you should be able to

1. Explain the role of the hypothalamus in the endocrine system.
2. List the hormones produced by the anterior and posterior pituitary glands and provide a function for each.
3. Summarize the conditions produced by excessive and inadequate levels of the major hormones.

The **hypothalamus** acts as the link between the nervous and endocrine systems. It regulates the internal environment through communications with the autonomic nervous system. For example, it helps control body temperature and water-salt balance. The hypothalamus also controls the glandular secretions of the **pituitary gland.** The pituitary, a small gland about 1 cm in diameter, is connected to the hypothalamus by a stalklike structure. The pituitary has two portions: the posterior and the anterior pituitary. Although the anterior and posterior pituitary glands are connected, they operate as separate physiological glands.

Posterior Pituitary

Neurons in the hypothalamus called neurosecretory cells produce the hormones **antidiuretic hormone (ADH)** and **oxytocin** (Fig. 16.6). These hormones pass through axons into the **posterior pituitary,** where they are stored in axon endings.

Certain neurons in the hypothalamus are sensitive to the water-salt balance of the blood. When these cells determine that the blood is too concentrated, ADH is released from the posterior pituitary. On reaching the kidneys, ADH causes more water to be reabsorbed into

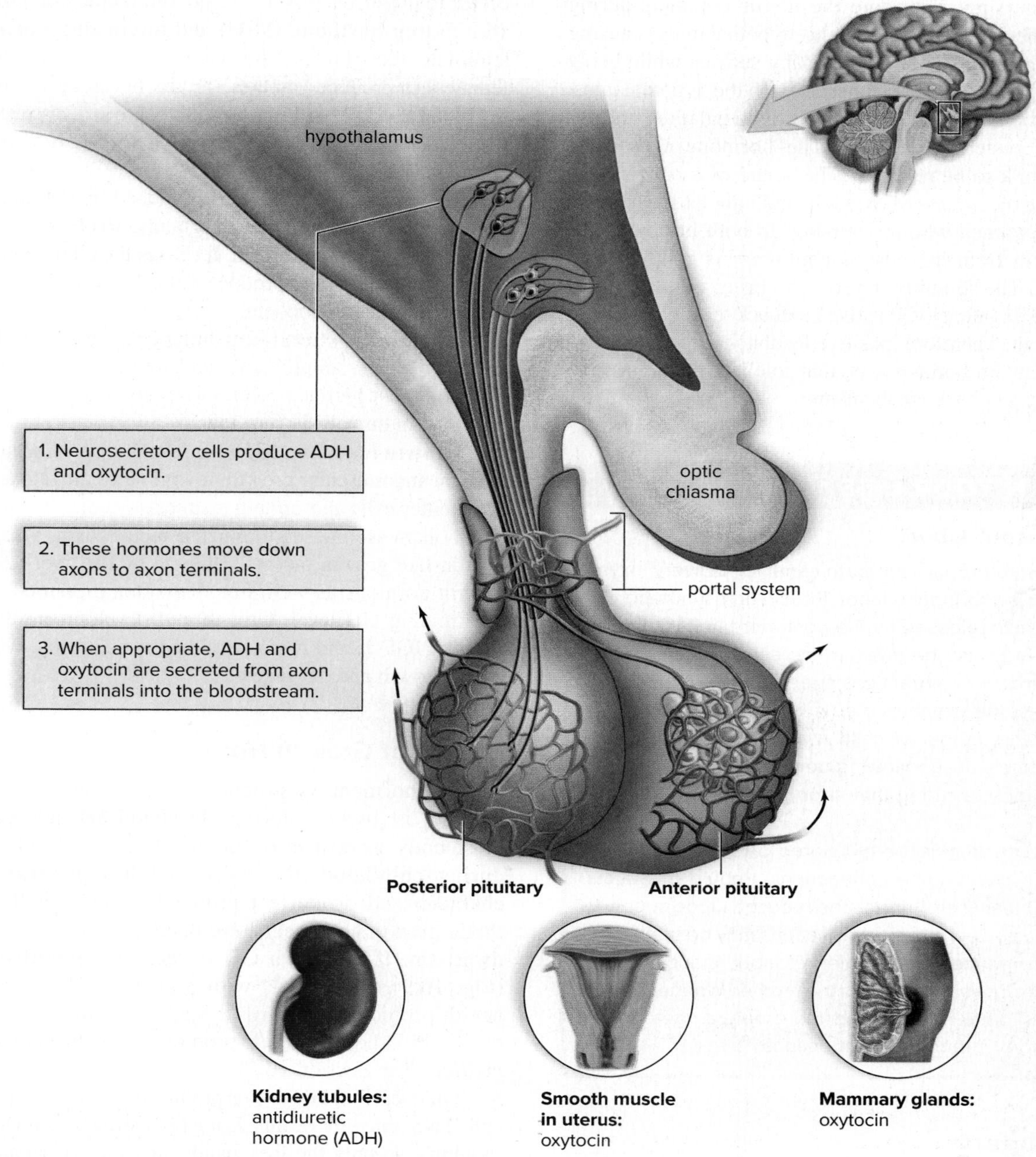
hypothalamus
1. Neurosecretory cells produce ADH and oxytocin.
2. These hormones move down axons to axon terminals.
3. When appropriate, ADH and oxytocin are secreted from axon terminals into the bloodstream.
optic chiasma
portal system
Posterior pituitary
Anterior pituitary
Kidney tubules: antidiuretic hormone (ADH)
Smooth muscle in uterus: oxytocin
Mammary glands: oxytocin

Figure 16.6 Hormones produced by the hypothalamus and posterior pituitary.
The hypothalamus produces two hormones, ADH and oxytocin, stored and secreted by the posterior pituitary.

kidney capillaries, decreasing urine volume. As the blood becomes dilute, ADH is no longer released. This is an example of control by negative feedback, because the effect of the hormone (to dilute blood) acts to shut down the release of the hormone. Negative feedback maintains stable conditions and homeostasis.

Inability to produce ADH causes *diabetes insipidus.* A person with this type of diabetes produces copious amounts of urine. Excessive urination results in severe dehydration and loss of important ions from the blood. The condition can be corrected by the administration of ADH.

Oxytocin, the other hormone made in the hypothalamus, causes uterine contraction during childbirth and milk letdown when a baby is nursing. The more the uterus contracts during labor, the more nerve signals reach the hypothalamus, causing oxytocin to be released. Similarly, as a baby suckles while being breastfed, nerve signals from breast tissue reach the hypothalamus. As a result, oxytocin is produced by the hypothalamus and released from the posterior pituitary. The hormone causes the woman's breast milk to be released. The sound of a baby crying may also stimulate the release of oxytocin and milk letdown, much to the chagrin of women who are nursing. In both instances, the release of oxytocin from the posterior pituitary is controlled by positive feedback. The stimulus continues to bring about an effect that ever increases in intensity. Positive feedback terminates due to some external event. Therefore, positive feedback mechanisms are rarely used to maintain homeostasis; that role is typically associated with negative feedback mechanisms.

BIOLOGY IN YOUR LIFE

What is "induced" labor?

After medication to prepare the birth canal for delivery, oxytocin (Pitocin) is used to induce labor. Pitocin is a synthetic version of the oxytocin released by the posterior pituitary. During labor, oxytocin may also be given to increase the strength of contractions. Stronger contractions speed the labor process if necessary (e.g., if the woman's uterus is contracting poorly or if the health of the mother or child is at risk during delivery). Oxytocin is routinely used following delivery to minimize postpartum bleeding by ensuring that strong uterine contractions continue.

The use of oxytocin must be monitored carefully, because it may cause excessive uterine contractions. Should this occur, the uterus could tear itself. Further, the reduced blood supply to the fetus caused by very strong contractions may be fatal to the baby. Though it reduces the duration of labor, inducing labor with oxytocin can be very painful for the mother. Whenever possible, physicians prefer gentler and more natural methods to induce labor and/or strengthen contractions.

Anterior Pituitary

A portal system, consisting of two capillary systems connected by a vein, lies between the hypothalamus and the **anterior pituitary.** The hypothalamus controls the anterior pituitary by producing hypothalamic-releasing and hypothalamic-inhibiting hormones, which pass from the hypothalamus to the anterior pituitary by way of the portal system (Fig. 16.7). Examples are *thyroid-releasing hormone (TRH)* and *thyroid-inhibiting hormone (TIH).* The TRH stimulates the anterior pituitary to secrete thyroid-stimulating hormone, and the TIH inhibits the pituitary from secreting thyroid-stimulating hormone.

Four of the seven hormones produced by the anterior pituitary have an effect on other glands. **Thyroid-stimulating hormone (TSH)** stimulates the thyroid to produce the thyroid hormones. **Adrenocorticotropic hormone (ACTH)** stimulates the adrenal cortex to produce cortisol. The **gonadotropic hormones—follicle-stimulating hormone (FSH)** and **luteinizing hormone (LH)**—stimulate the gonads (the testes in males and the ovaries in females) to produce gametes and sex hormones. In each instance, the blood level of the last hormone in the sequence exerts negative feedback control over the secretion of the first two hormones (Fig. 16.8).

The other three hormones produced by the anterior pituitary do not affect other endocrine glands. **Prolactin** is produced in quantity only after childbirth. It causes the mammary glands in the breasts to develop and produce milk. It also plays a role in carbohydrate and fat metabolism.

Melanocyte-stimulating hormone causes skin-color changes in many fishes, amphibians, and reptiles having melanophores, skin cells that produce color variations. The concentration of this hormone in humans is very low.

Growth hormone (GH), or somatotropic hormone, promotes skeletal and muscular growth. It stimulates the rate at which amino acids enter cells and protein synthesis occurs. It also promotes fat metabolism as opposed to glucose metabolism. The production of insulin-like growth factor 1 (IGF-1) by the liver is stimulated by growth hormone as well. IGF-1 is often measured as a means of determining GH level. Growth and development are also stimulated by IGF-1, and it may well be the means by which GH influences growth and development.

Effects of Growth Hormone

Growth hormone is produced by the anterior pituitary. The quantity is greatest during childhood and adolescence, when most body growth is occurring. If too little GH is produced during childhood, the individual has **pituitary dwarfism,** characterized by perfect proportions but small stature. Synthetic growth hormones have been used to treat some forms of dwarfism. If too much GH is secreted, **gigantism** may result (Fig. 16.9). Individuals with gigantism often have additional health problems, primarily because GH has a secondary effect on the blood sugar level, promoting an illness called *diabetes mellitus* (see Section 16.5).

On occasion, GH is overproduced in the adult and a condition called **acromegaly** results. Long bone growth is no longer possible in adults, so only the feet, hands, and face (particularly the chin, nose, and eyebrow ridges) can respond, and these portions of the body become overly large (Fig. 16.10).

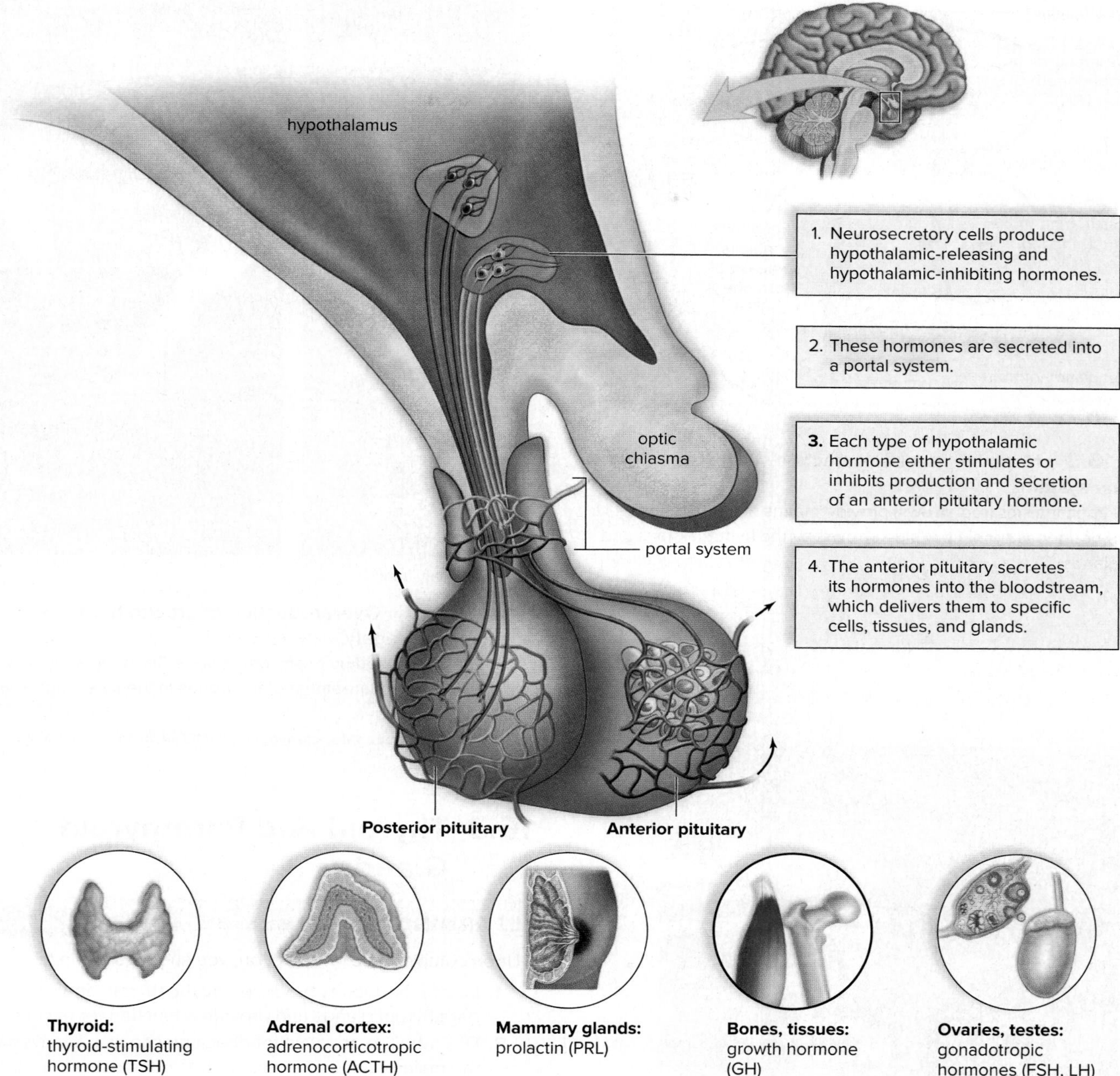
hypothalamus
1. Neurosecretory cells produce hypothalamic-releasing and hypothalamic-inhibiting hormones.
2. These hormones are secreted into a portal system.
optic chiasma
3. Each type of hypothalamic hormone either stimulates or inhibits production and secretion of an anterior pituitary hormone.
portal system
4. The anterior pituitary secretes its hormones into the bloodstream, which delivers them to specific cells, tissues, and glands.
Posterior pituitary
Anterior pituitary
Thyroid: thyroid-stimulating hormone (TSH)
Adrenal cortex: adrenocorticotropic hormone (ACTH)
Mammary glands: prolactin (PRL)
Bones, tissues: growth hormone (GH)
Ovaries, testes: gonadotropic hormones (FSH, LH)

Figure 16.7 **Hormones produced by the anterior pituitary.**
The hypothalamus controls the secretions of the anterior pituitary, and the anterior pituitary controls the secretions of the thyroid, adrenal cortex, and gonads, which are also endocrine glands.

CHECK YOUR PROGRESS 16.2

1. Explain how the endocrine system and nervous system communicate with one another.
2. List the hormones produced by the posterior pituitary and provide a function for each.
3. List the hormones produced by the anterior pituitary and provide a function for each.

CONNECTING THE CONCEPTS

For more information on the hormones presented in this section, refer to the following discussions:

Section 12.2 examines the influence of growth hormone on bone growth.

Section 17.2 describes the role of pituitary hormones in the production of sperm cells in males.

Section 17.4 describes the role of pituitary hormones in the female ovarian cycle.

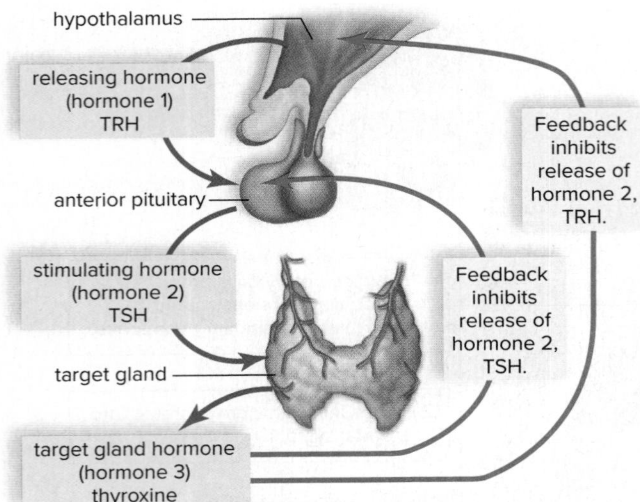

Figure 16.8 Negative feedback mechanisms in the endocrine system.
Feedback mechanisms (red arrows) provide means of controlling the amount of hormones produced (blue arrows) by the hypothalamus and pituitary glands.

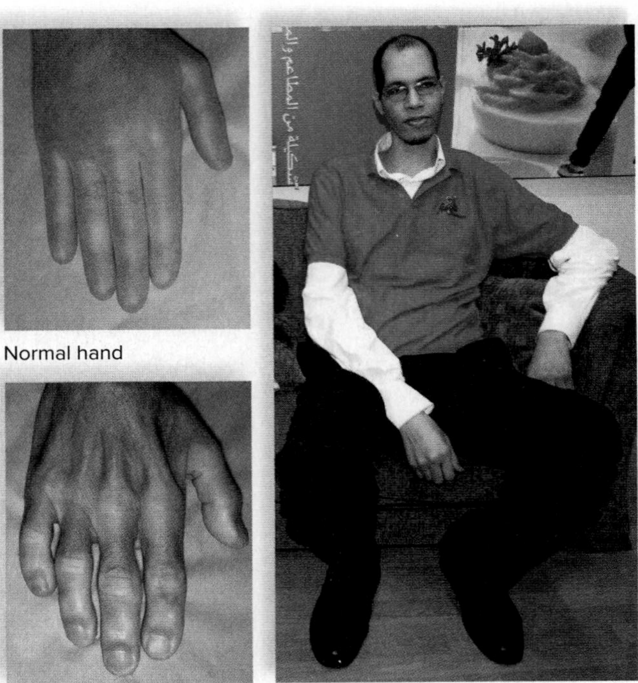

Figure 16.10 Overproduction of growth hormone in adults leads to acromegaly.
Acromegaly is caused by overproduction of GH in the adult. It is characterized by enlargement of the bones in the face, fingers, and toes as a person ages.
(both hands): Bob Tapper/Medical Images/DIOMEDIA; (man): Yasser Al-Zayyat/AFP/Getty Images

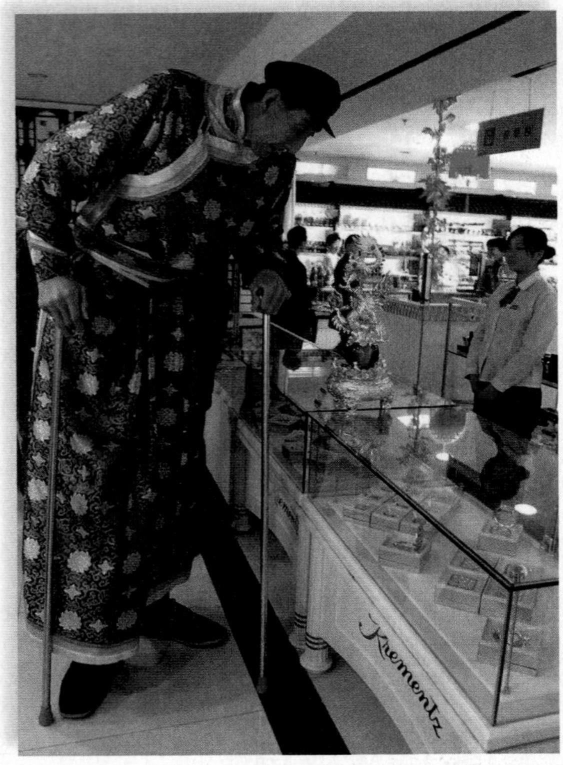

Figure 16.9 Growth hormone influences height.
Irregularities in growth hormone can lead to gigantism.
Xinhua News/Li Xin Xinhua/AP Images

16.3 Thyroid and Parathyroid Glands

LEARNING OUTCOMES

Upon completion of this section, you should be able to

1. List the hormones produced by the thyroid and parathyroid glands and provide a function for each.
2. Describe the negative feedback mechanism involved in the maintenance of blood calcium homeostasis.
3. Summarize the diseases and conditions associated with the thyroid and parathyroid glands.

The **thyroid gland** is a large gland located in the neck, where it is attached to the trachea just below the larynx (see Fig. 16.1). The parathyroid glands are embedded in the posterior surface of the thyroid gland.

Thyroid Gland

The thyroid gland regulates the metabolic rate of the body, and it has a role in calcium homeostasis. The thyroid gland is composed of a large number of follicles, each containing thyroid cells filled with **triiodothyronine (T_3)**, which contains three iodine atoms, and **thyroxine (T_4)**, which contains four.

Effects of Thyroid Hormones

To produce triiodothyronine (T_3) and thyroxine (T_4), the thyroid gland actively requires iodine. The concentration of iodine in the thyroid gland can increase to as much as 25 times that in the blood. If iodine is lacking in the diet, the thyroid gland is unable to produce the thyroid hormones. In response to constant stimulation by TSH from the anterior pituitary, the thyroid enlarges, resulting in a condition called **endemic goiter** (Fig. 16.11*a*). In the 1920s, it was discovered that the use of iodized salt allows the thyroid to produce the thyroid hormones and, therefore, helps prevent goiter. However, iodine deficiencies are still common in many parts of the world, with an estimated 2 billion people still experiencing some degree of deficiency.

While thyroid hormones increase the metabolic rate, they do not have a target organ. Instead, they stimulate all cells of the body to metabolize at a faster rate. More glucose is broken down, and more energy is used.

If the thyroid fails to develop properly, a condition called **congenital hypothyroidism** results (Fig. 16.11*b*). Individuals with this condition are short and stocky and have had extreme hypothyroidism (undersecretion of thyroid hormone) since infancy or childhood. Thyroid hormone therapy can initiate growth, but unless treatment is begun within the first 2 months of life, intellectual disability results. The occurrence of hypothyroidism in adults produces the condition known as **myxedema.** Lethargy, weight gain, loss of hair, slower pulse rate, lowered body temperature, and thickness and puffiness of the skin are characteristics of myxedema. The administration of adequate doses of thyroid hormones restores normal function and appearance.

In the case of **hyperthyroidism** (oversecretion of thyroid hormone), the thyroid gland is overactive and enlarges, forming a goiter. This type of goiter is called **exophthalmic goiter** (Fig. 16.11*c*). The eyes protrude because of edema in eye socket tissues and swelling of the muscles that move the eyes. The patient usually becomes hyperactive, nervous, and irritable and experiences insomnia. Surgical removal or destruction of a portion of the thyroid by means of radioactive iodine is sometimes effective in curing the condition. Hyperthyroidism can also be caused by a thyroid tumor, usually detected as a lump during physical examination. Again, the treatment is surgery in combination with administration of radioactive iodine. The prognosis for most patients is excellent.

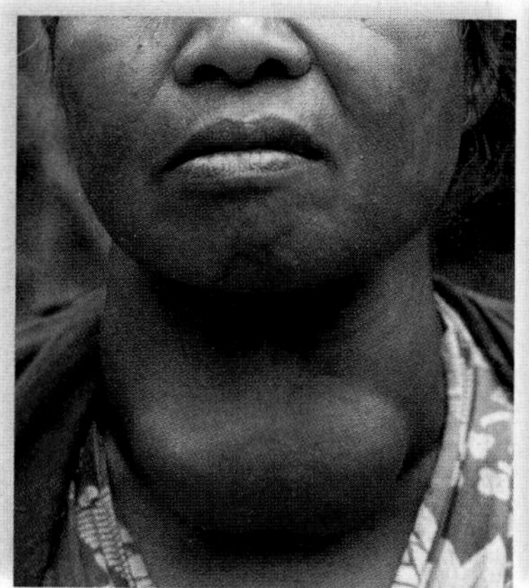

a. Endemic goiter

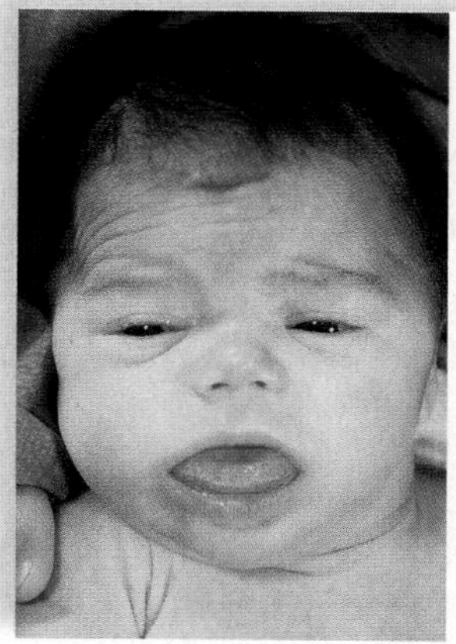

b. Congenital hypothyroidism

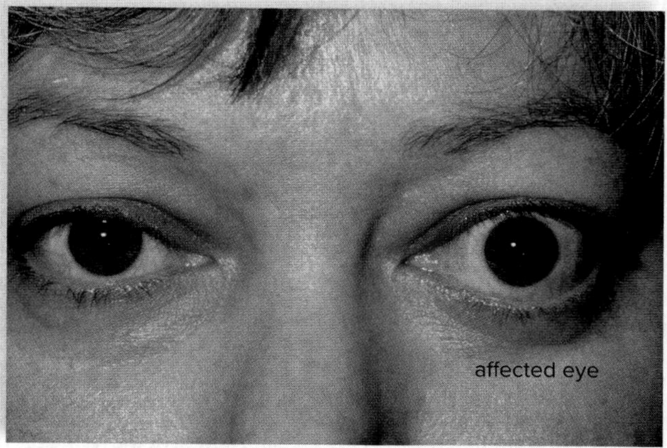

c. Exophthalmic goiter

Figure 16.11 **Endemic goiter, hypothyroidism, and exopthalmic goiter.**
a. An enlarged thyroid gland is often caused by a lack of iodine in the diet. Without iodine, the thyroid is unable to produce its hormones, and continued anterior pituitary stimulation causes the gland to enlarge. **b.** Individuals who develop hypothyroidism during infancy or childhood do not grow and develop as others do. Unless medical treatment is begun, the body is short and stocky; intellectual disabilities are also likely. **c.** In exophthalmic goiter, a goiter is due to an overactive thyroid and the eyes protrude because of edema in eye socket tissue.

Calcitonin

Calcium ions (Ca^{2+}) play a significant role in both nervous conduction and muscle contraction. They are also necessary for blood clotting. The blood calcium level is regulated in part by **calcitonin,** a hormone secreted by the thyroid gland when the blood calcium level rises (Fig. 16.12). The primary effect of calcitonin is to bring about the deposit of calcium ions in the bones. It also temporarily reduces the activity and number of osteoclasts. When the blood calcium level lowers to normal, the thyroid's release of calcitonin is inhibited.

Parathyroid Glands

Parathyroid hormone (PTH), produced by the **parathyroid glands,** causes the blood calcium level to increase. A low blood calcium level stimulates the release of PTH, which promotes the activity of osteoclasts and the release of calcium from the bones. PTH also activates vitamin D in the kidneys. Activated vitamin D, a hormone sometimes called *calcitriol,* then promotes calcium reabsorption by the kidneys. The absorption of calcium ions from the intestine is also stimulated by calcitriol. These effects bring the blood calcium level back to the normal range, and PTH secretion stops.

Many years ago, the four parathyroid glands were sometimes mistakenly removed during thyroid surgery because of their size and location. Gland removal caused insufficient PTH production,

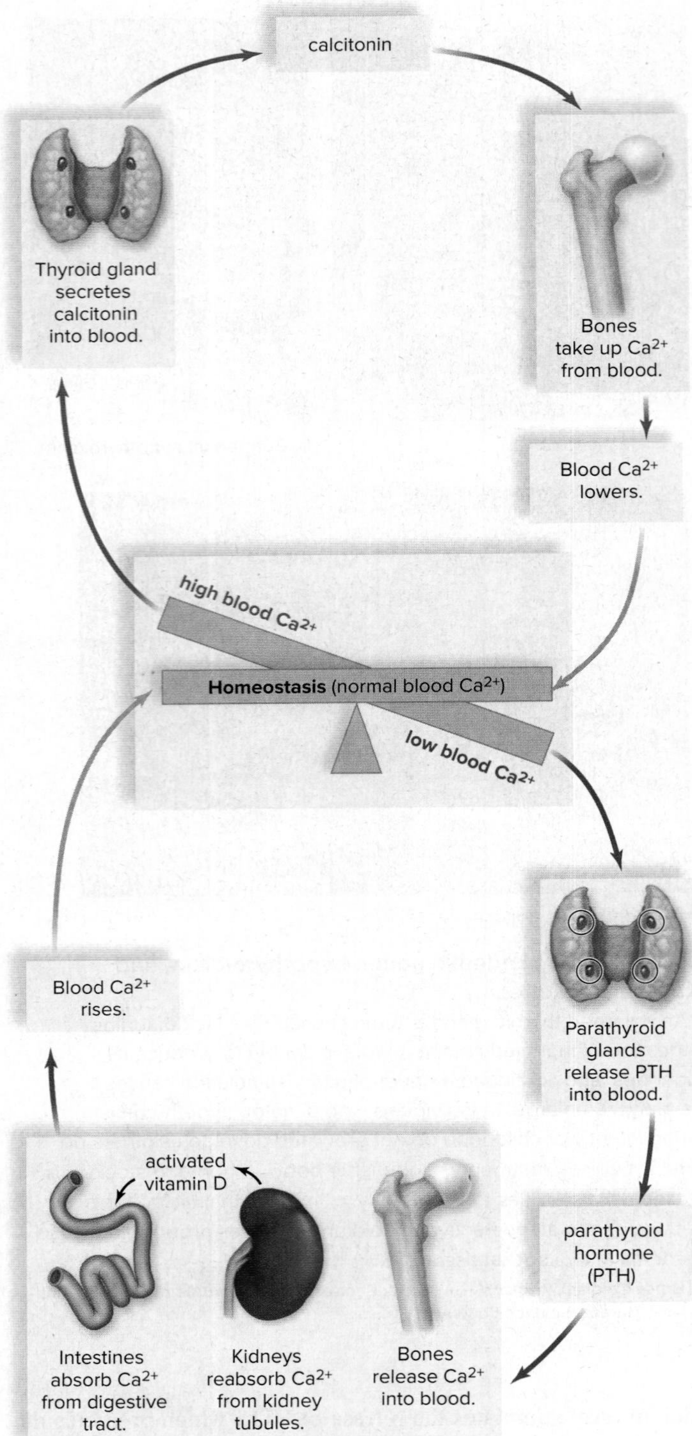

Figure 16.12 Blood calcium homeostasis.
Top: When the blood calcium level is high, the thyroid gland secretes calcitonin. Calcitonin promotes the uptake of calcium ions (Ca^{2+}) by the bones; therefore, the blood calcium level returns to normal. *Bottom:* When the blood calcium level is low, the parathyroid glands release parathyroid hormone (PTH). PTH causes the bones to release calcium ions (Ca^{2+}). It also causes the kidneys to reabsorb Ca^{2+} and activate vitamin D; thereafter, the intestines absorb Ca^{2+}. Therefore, the blood calcium level returns to normal.

which resulted in *hypoparathyroidism*. Hypoparathyroidism causes a dramatic drop in blood calcium, followed by excessive nerve excitability. Nerve signals happen spontaneously and without rest, causing a phenomenon called tetany. In *tetany*, the body shakes from continuous muscle contraction. Without treatment, severe hypoparathyroidism causes seizures, heart failure, and death.

Untreated *hyperparathyroidism* (oversecretion of PTH) can result in osteoporosis because of continuous calcium release from the bones. Hyperparathyroidism may also cause formation of calcium kidney stones.

When a bone is broken, homeostasis is disrupted. For the fracture to heal, osteoclasts will have to destroy old bone, and osteoblasts will have to lay down new bone. Many factors influence the formation of new bone, including parathyroid hormone, calcitonin, and vitamin D. The calcium needed to repair the fracture is made readily available as new blood capillaries penetrate the fractured area.

CHECK YOUR PROGRESS 16.3

1. Explain how the hormones of the thyroid gland influence the metabolic rate.
2. Describe how calcitonin and parathyroid hormones interact to regulate blood calcium levels.
3. Distinguish between hyperthyroidism and hyperparathyroidism with regard to the effects on the body.

CONNECTING THE CONCEPTS

For more information on the importance of calcium, refer to the following discussions:

Section 12.5 explains the role of the bones in maintaining calcium homeostasis.

Section 13.2 examines how calcium ions are involved in muscle contraction.

Section 14.1 explores how calcium ions are involved in the activity of a neural synapse.

16.4 Adrenal Glands

LEARNING OUTCOMES

Upon completion of this section, you should be able to

1. List the hormones produced by the adrenal medulla and adrenal cortex and provide a function for each.
2. Explain how the adrenal cortex is involved in the stress response.
3. Distinguish between mineralocorticoid and glucocorticoid hormones.

The **adrenal glands** sit atop the kidneys (see Fig. 16.1). Each adrenal gland consists of an inner portion called the **adrenal medulla** and an outer portion called the **adrenal cortex** (Fig. 16.13).

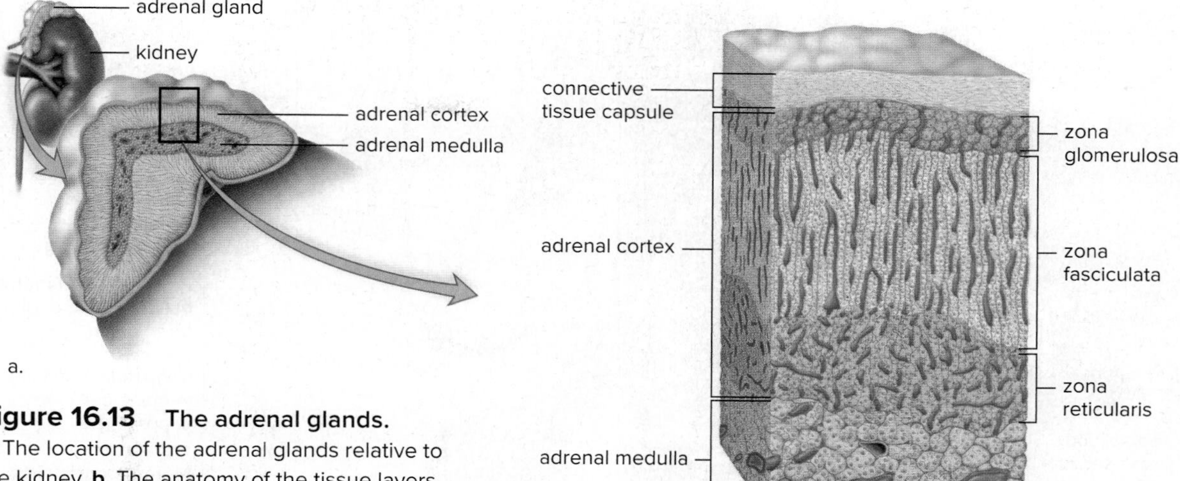

Figure 16.13 The adrenal glands.
a. The location of the adrenal glands relative to the kidney. **b.** The anatomy of the tissue layers within the adrenal glands.

These portions, like the anterior and the posterior pituitary, are two functionally distinct endocrine glands. The adrenal medulla is under nervous control. Portions of the adrenal cortex are under the control of corticotropin-releasing hormone (CRH) from the hypothalamus and ACTH, an anterior pituitary hormone. Stress of all types, including emotional and physical trauma, prompts the hypothalamus to stimulate a portion of the adrenal glands.

Adrenal Medulla

The hypothalamus initiates nerve signals that travel by way of the brain stem, spinal cord, and preganglionic sympathetic nerve fibers to the adrenal medulla. These signals stimulate the adrenal medulla to secrete its hormones. The cells of the adrenal medulla are thought to be modified postganglionic neurons.

Epinephrine (adrenaline) and **norepinephrine** (noradrenaline) are the hormones produced by the adrenal medulla. These hormones rapidly bring about all the body changes that occur when an individual reacts to an emergency situation in a fight-or-flight manner. These hormones provide a short-term response to stress (Fig. 16.14*a*).

Adrenal Cortex

The adrenal cortex is divided into three regions (see Fig. 16.13*b*). These are the zona glomerulosa, the zona fasciculata, and the zona reticularis. In contrast to the adrenal medulla, the hormones produced by the adrenal cortex provide a long-term response to stress (Fig. 16.14*b*). The two major types of hormones produced by the adrenal cortex are the glucocorticoids and the mineralocorticoids. The adrenal cortex also secretes a small amount of sex hormones in both males and females.

Glucocorticoids

The **glucocorticoids,** whose secretion is controlled by ACTH, regulate carbohydrate, protein, and fat metabolism. Glucocorticoids are produced in the adrenal cortex. **Cortisol** is a glucocorticoid that is active in the stress response and the repair of damaged tissues in the body. Glucocorticoids raise the blood glucose level in at least two ways. (1) They promote the breakdown of muscle proteins to amino acids, taken up by the liver from the bloodstream. The liver then converts these excess amino acids to glucose, which enters the blood. (2) They promote the metabolism of fatty acids rather than carbohydrates, and this spares glucose.

The glucocorticoids also counteract the inflammatory response that leads to pain and swelling. Very high levels of glucocorticoids in the blood can suppress the body's defense system, including the inflammatory response that occurs at infection sites. Cortisone and other glucocorticoids can relieve swelling and pain from inflammation. However, by suppressing pain and immunity, they can also make a person highly susceptible to injury and infection.

Mineralocorticoids

The **mineralocorticoids** regulate ion (electrolyte) balances in the body and are primarily produced by the zona glomerulosa in the adrenal cortex. **Aldosterone** is the most important of the mineralocorticoids. Aldosterone primarily targets the kidney, where it promotes renal absorption of sodium ions (Na^+) and renal excretion of potassium ions (K^+).

The secretion of mineralocorticoids is not controlled by the anterior pituitary. When the blood sodium level and pressure are low, the kidneys secrete **renin** (Fig. 16.15). Renin is an enzyme that converts the plasma protein angiotensinogen to angiotensin I. Angiotensin I is changed to angiotensin II by a converting enzyme found in lung capillaries. Angiotensin II stimulates the adrenal cortex to release aldosterone. The effect of this system, called the renin-angiotensin-aldosterone system, is to raise blood pressure in two ways. Angiotensin II constricts the arterioles, and aldosterone causes the kidneys to reabsorb sodium ions (Na^+). When the blood sodium level rises, water is reabsorbed, in part because the hypothalamus secretes ADH (see Section 16.2). Reabsorption means

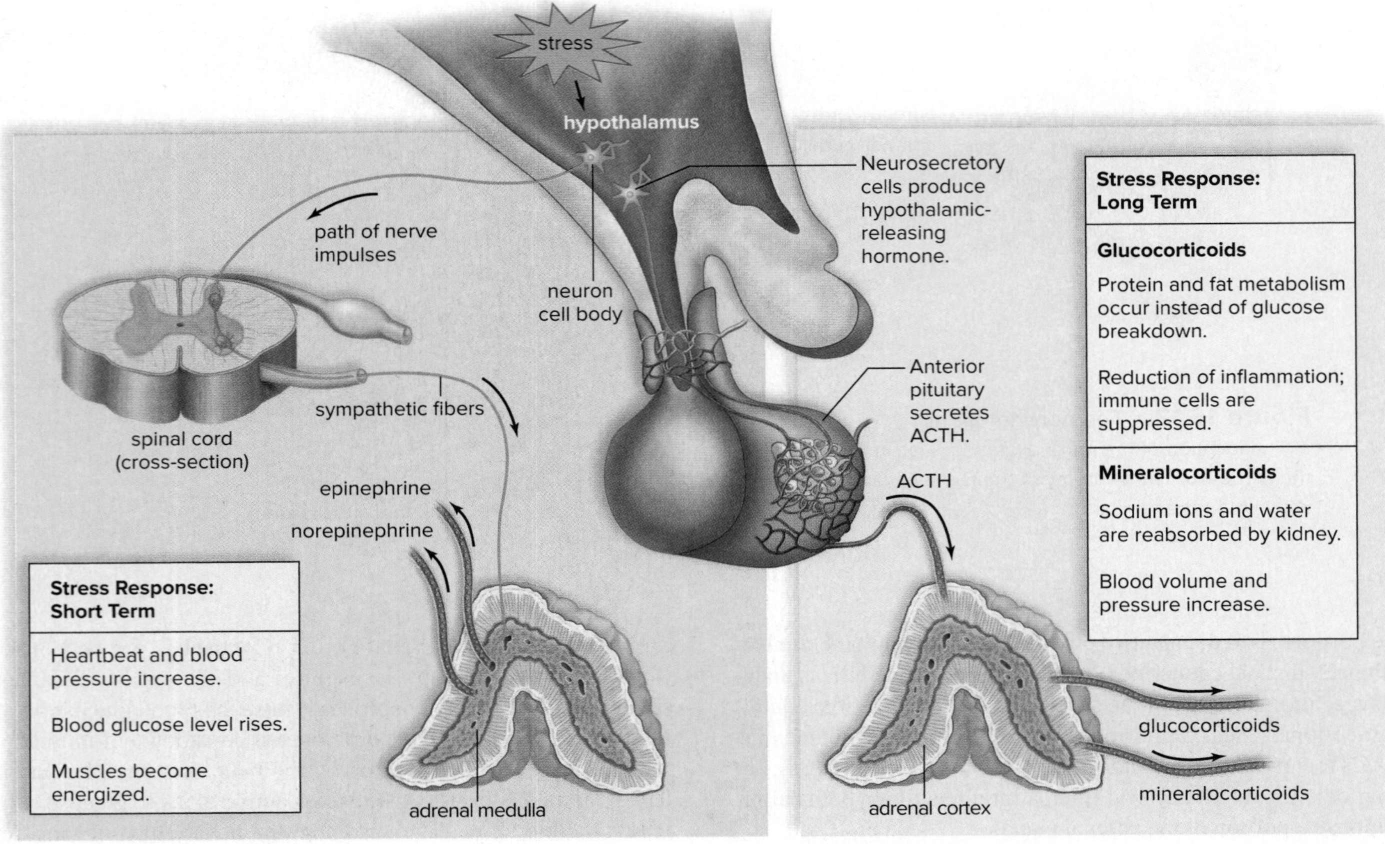

Figure 16.14 **Response of the adrenal medulla and the adrenal cortex to stress.**
Both the adrenal medulla and the adrenal cortex are under the control of the hypothalamus when they help us respond to stress. **a.** Nervous stimulation causes the adrenal medulla to provide a rapid but short-term stress response. **b.** The adrenal cortex provides a slower but long-term stress response. ACTH causes the adrenal cortex to release glucocorticoids. Independently, the adrenal cortex releases mineralocorticoids.

that water enters kidney capillaries and, thus, the blood. Then, blood pressure increases to normal.

Recall that we studied the role of the kidneys in maintaining blood pressure (see Section 11.4). At that time, we mentioned that if the blood pressure rises due to the reabsorption of sodium ions (Na^+), the atria of the heart are apt to stretch. Due to a great increase in blood volume, cardiac cells release a chemical called atrial natriuretic hormone (ANH), which inhibits the secretion of aldosterone from the adrenal cortex. In other words, the heart is one of the various organs in the body that release a hormone, but obviously this is not its major function. Therefore, the heart is not included as an endocrine gland in Figure 16.1. The effect of this ANH is to cause *natriuresis,* the excretion of sodium ions (Na^+). When sodium ions are excreted, so is water; therefore, blood pressure lowers to normal.

Sex Steroids

In addition to glucocorticoids, the adrenal cortex secrete small amounts of sex hormones called **gonadocorticoids.** These include male sex hormones **(androgens)** and female sex hormones (estrogen). The primary androgen hormone is **dehydroepiandrosterone (DHEA),** which is a precursor for **testosterone,** the primary male sex hormone. While primarily active in males following puberty, androgens do play a role in the sexual development of both males and females. In addition, these regions produce small amounts of **estradiol,** a form of **estrogen.** Although most estrogen in females is produced by the ovaries, the adrenal estradiol does play an important role in regulating growth of the skeleton in puberty and maintaining bone mass.

Malfunction of the Adrenal Cortex

When the blood level of glucocorticoids is low due to hyposecretion, it is called **Addison's disease.** The presence of excessive but ineffective ACTH causes a bronzing of the skin, because ACTH, like MSH, can lead to a buildup of melanin (Fig. 16.16). Without the glucocorticoids, glucose cannot be replenished when a stressful situation arises. Even a mild infection can lead to death. In some cases, hyposecretion of aldosterone results in a loss of sodium and water. Low blood pressure and, possibly, severe dehydration can develop as a result. Left untreated, Addison's disease can be fatal.

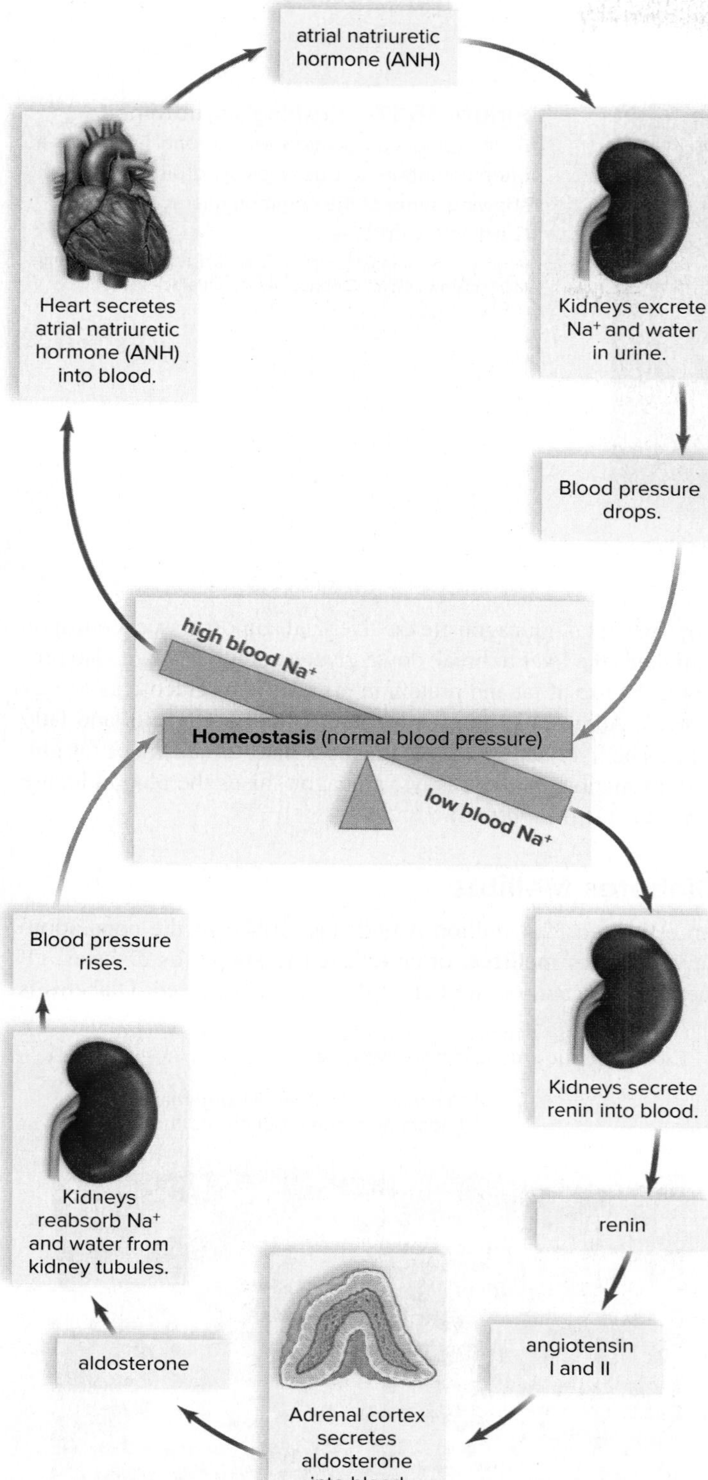
atrial natriuretic hormone (ANH)
Heart secretes atrial natriuretic hormone (ANH) into blood.
Kidneys excrete Na^+ and water in urine.
Blood pressure drops.
high blood Na^+
Homeostasis (normal blood pressure)
low blood Na^+
Blood pressure rises.
Kidneys secrete renin into blood.
renin
Kidneys reabsorb Na^+ and water from kidney tubules.
angiotensin I and II
aldosterone
Adrenal cortex secretes aldosterone into blood.

Figure 16.15 **Regulation of blood pressure is under hormonal control.**
Bottom: When the blood sodium level is low, a low blood pressure causes the kidneys to secrete renin. Renin leads to the secretion of aldosterone from the adrenal cortex. Aldosterone causes the kidneys to reabsorb sodium ions (Na^+), and water follows, so that blood volume and pressure return to normal. *Top:* When a high blood sodium level accompanies a high blood volume, the heart secretes atrial natriuretic hormone (ANH). ANH causes the kidneys to excrete sodium ions (Na^+), and water follows. The blood volume and pressure return to normal.

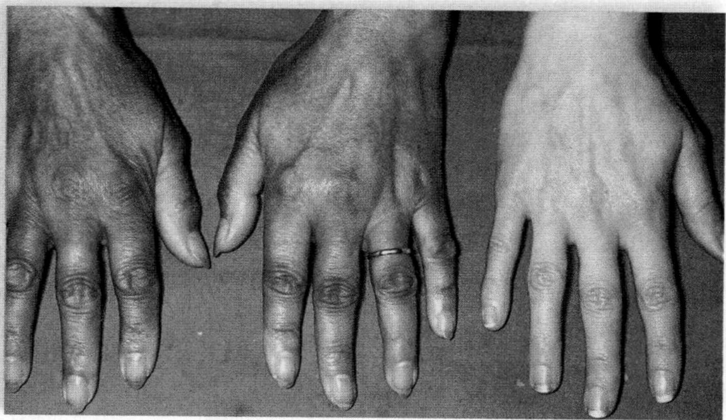

Figure 16.16 **Addison's disease.**
Addison's disease is characterized by a peculiar bronzing of the skin in all areas of the body, not just those exposed to sunlight. Note the color of the hands on the left and center compared with the hand of an individual without the disease on the right.
BSIP/Science Source

Excessive levels of glucocorticoids result in **Cushing's syndrome** (Fig. 16.17). This disorder can be caused by tumors that affect either the pituitary gland, resulting in excess ACTH secretion, or the adrenal cortex itself. The most common cause, however, is the administration of glucocorticoids to treat other conditions (e.g., to suppress chronic inflammation). Regardless of the source, excess glucocorticoids cause muscle protein to be metabolized and subcutaneous fat to be deposited in the midsection. Excess production of adrenal male sex hormones in women may result in masculinization, including an increase in body hair, deepening of the voice, and beard growth. Depending on the cause, treatment of Cushing's syndrome may involve a careful reduction in the amount of cortisone being taken, the use of cortisol-inhibiting drugs, or surgery to remove any existing pituitary or adrenal tumor.

CHECK YOUR PROGRESS 16.4

1. List the hormones produced by the adrenal glands, and indicate whether they are produced by the adrenal cortex or the adrenal medulla.
2. Summarize the involvement of the adrenal glands during a stress response.
3. Contrast the roles of glucocorticoids and mineralocorticoids in the body.

CONNECTING THE CONCEPTS

For more information on the hormones produced by the adrenal glands, refer to the following discussions:

Section 5.3 describes how epinephrine and norepinephrine influence the heart rate.

Section 11.4 examines how aldosterone is involved in maintaining the water-salt balance of the body fluids.

a.

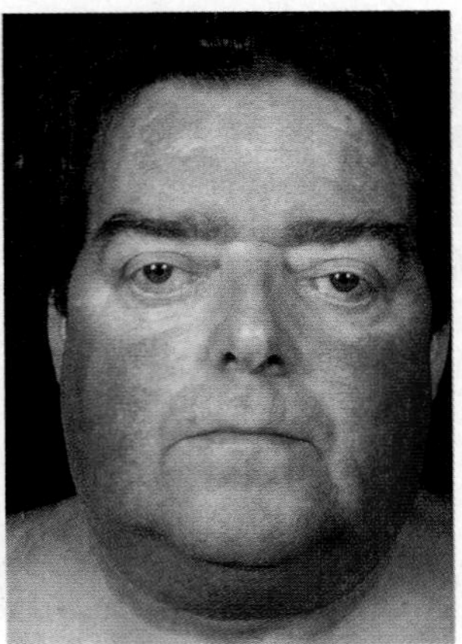
b.

Figure 16.17 **Cushing's syndrome.**
a. The tumors associated with adrenal hyperplasia often contribute to Cushing's syndrome. **b.** A man showing some of the common characteristics of Cushing's syndrome.
(a): Dennis K. Burns, MD/Travis G. Brown, MD/Walter L. Kemp, MD/McGraw Hill; (b): Biophoto Associates/Science Source

16.5 Pancreas

LEARNING OUTCOMES

Upon completion of this section, you should be able to

1. Explain how the pancreas functions as both an endocrine and an exocrine gland.
2. Describe how the pancreatic hormones help maintain blood glucose homeostasis.
3. Distinguish between type 1 and type 2 diabetes mellitus.

The **pancreas** is a fish-shaped organ that stretches across the abdomen behind the stomach and near the duodenum of the small intestine. It is composed of both exocrine and endocrine tissue. The exocrine tissue produces and secretes enzymes and other compounds involved in digestion. These are delivered to the small intestine by the pancreatic duct (see Section 9.4). The endocrine tissue is called the **pancreatic islets** (islets of Langerhans). As Figure 16.18 illustrates, each pancreatic islet is surrounded by exocrine tissue. Within each islet are a variety of cell types, several of which play an important role in the endocrine functions of this organ. A cells are responsible for the secretion of the hormone glucagon, whereas B cells (not to be confused with the B cells of the immune system) secrete insulin. A third cell type, D cells, releases somatostatin, a hormone that is released at the same time as insulin to regulate the digestive processes.

Unlike most other endocrine organs, the pancreas is not under pituitary control, but instead responds directly to changes in blood glucose levels. **Insulin** is secreted by the B cells when the blood glucose level is high, which usually occurs just after eating. Insulin stimulates the uptake of glucose by cells, especially liver cells, muscle cells, and adipose tissue cells. In liver and muscle cells, glucose is then stored as glycogen. In muscle cells, the glucose supplies energy for muscle contraction. Glucose enters the metabolic pool in fat cells and thereby supplies glycerol for the formation of fat. In these various ways, insulin lowers the blood glucose level (Fig. 16.19, *top*).

Glucagon is secreted by the A cells of the pancreas, usually between eating, when the blood glucose level is low. The major target tissues of glucagon are the liver and adipose tissue. Glucagon stimulates the liver to break down glycogen to glucose. It also promotes the use of fat and protein in preference to glucose as energy sources. Adipose tissue cells break down fat to glycerol and fatty acids. The liver takes these up and uses them as substrates for glucose formation. In these ways, glucagon raises the blood glucose level (Fig. 16.19, *bottom*).

Diabetes Mellitus

An estimated 32.4 million Americans (10.4% of the population) have **diabetes mellitus,** often referred to simply as diabetes. Of these, over 8 million are believed to be undiagnosed. Diabetes is

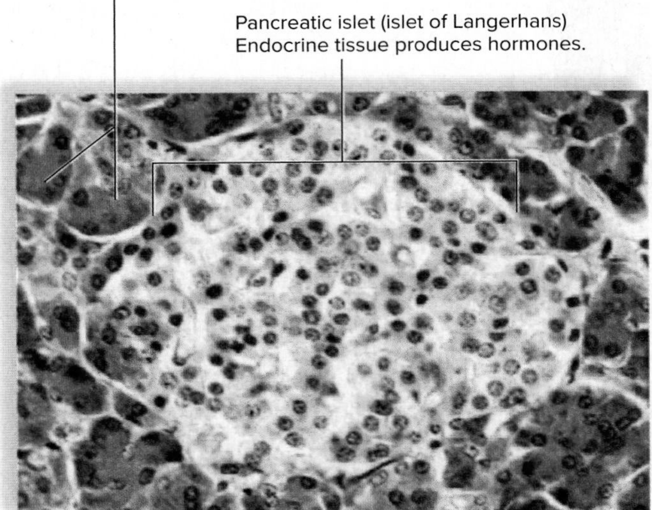
Exocrine tissue produces digestive juice.
Pancreatic islet (islet of Langerhans)
Endocrine tissue produces hormones.
80×

Figure 16.18 **The endocrine and exocrine tissues of the pancreas.**
This light micrograph shows that the pancreas has two types of cells. The exocrine tissue produces a digestive juice, and the endocrine tissue produces the hormones insulin and glucagon.
Victor P. Eroschenko

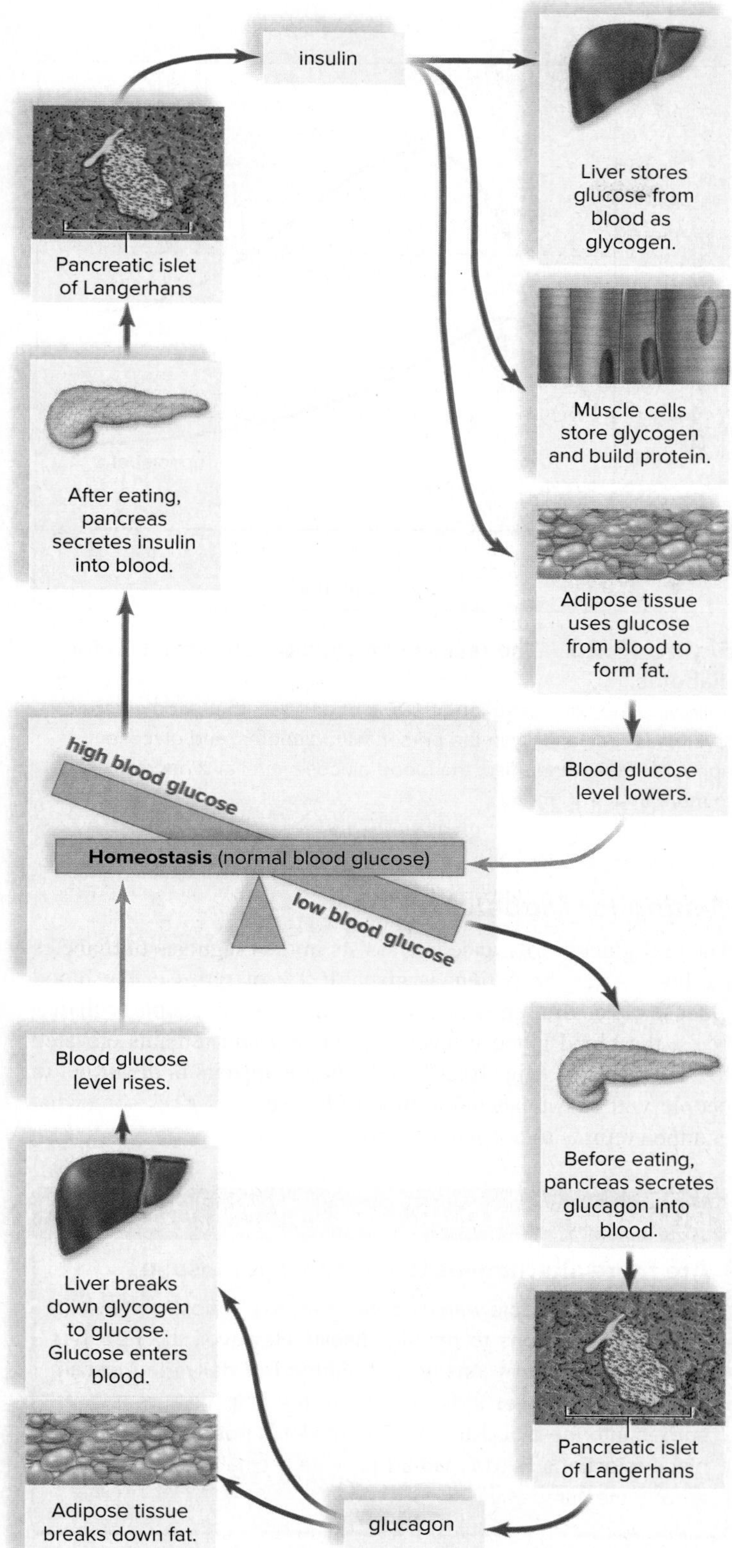

Figure 16.19 **Blood glucose homeostasis.** *Top:* When the blood glucose level is high, the pancreas secretes insulin. Insulin promotes the storage of glucose as glycogen and the synthesis of proteins and fats. Therefore, insulin lowers the blood glucose level. *Bottom:* When the blood glucose level is low, the pancreas secretes glucagon. Glucagon acts opposite to insulin; therefore, glucagon raises the blood glucose level to normal.

characterized by the body's inability to maintain blood glucose homeostasis (Fig. 16.19), resulting in an excess of glucose in the blood. This creates a number of problems in the body with homeostasis. As the blood glucose level rises, glucose, along with water, is excreted in the urine. The term *mellitus,* from Greek, refers to "honey" or "sweetness." As a result, people with diabetes urinate frequently and are always thirsty. Other symptoms of diabetes include fatigue, constant hunger, and weight loss.

The high blood glucose levels often cause an increase in blood pressure due to osmosis, and as a result, this can damage the small capillaries of the kidneys, eyes, and other areas of the circulatory system. People with diabetes often experience vision problems due to diabetic retinopathy and swelling in the lens of the eye. If untreated, individuals with diabetes often develop serious and even fatal complications. Sores that don't heal develop into severe infections. Blood vessel damage causes kidney failure, nerve destruction, heart attack, or stroke.

Types of Diabetes

There are two types of diabetes. Type 1 diabetes is sometimes called juvenile diabetes or insulin-dependent diabetes mellitus (IDDM). Type 2 diabetes is also known as adult-onset diabetes, or non-insulin-dependent diabetes mellitus (NIDDM). Although the causes of these forms of diabetes are different, they can occur in children or adults.

Type 1 Diabetes In type 1 diabetes, the pancreas is not producing enough insulin. This condition is believed to be brought on by exposure to an environmental agent, most likely a virus, whose presence causes cytotoxic T cells to destroy the pancreatic islets as part of an autoimmune response (see Section 7.5). The body turns to the metabolism of fat, which leads to the buildup of ketones in the blood, called *ketoacidosis,* which increases the acidity of the blood and can lead to coma and death.

Individuals with type 1 diabetes must have daily insulin injections. These injections control the diabetic symptoms but still can cause problems because the blood sugar level may swing between hypoglycemia (low blood glucose) and hyperglycemia (high blood glucose). Without testing the blood glucose level, it is difficult to be certain which of these is present, because the symptoms can be similar. These symptoms include perspiration, pale skin, shallow breathing, and anxiety. Whenever these symptoms appear, immediate attention is required to bring the blood glucose back within the normal range. If the problem is hypoglycemia, the treatment is one or two glucose tablets, hard candy, or orange juice. If the problem is hyperglycemia, the treatment is insulin. Better control of blood glucose levels can often be achieved with an insulin pump, a small device worn outside the body that is connected to a plastic catheter inserted under the skin.

Because diabetes is such a common problem, many researchers are working to develop more effective methods for treating diabetes. Recently, progress has been made in the development of an artificial pancreas, which would act as an automated system to provide insulin based on real-time changes in blood sugar levels. It is also possible to transplant a working pancreas, or even fetal pancreatic islet cells, into patients with type 1 diabetes. Another possibility is xenotransplantation, in which insulin-producing islet cells of another species, such as pigs, are placed inside a capsule that allows insulin to exit but prevents the immune system from attacking the foreign cells. Finally, researchers are close to testing a vaccine that could block the immune system's attack on the islet cells, perhaps by inducing the T cells capable of suppressing these responses.

Type 2 Diabetes Most adults with diabetes have type 2 diabetes. Often, the patient is overweight or obese, and adipose tissue produces a substance that impairs insulin receptor function. However, complex genetic factors can be involved, as shown by the tendency for type 2 diabetes to occur more often in certain families or even ethnic groups. For example, the condition is 77% more common in African Americans than in non-Hispanic whites.

Normally, the binding of insulin to its plasma membrane receptor causes the number of protein carriers for glucose to increase, causing more glucose to enter the cell. In individuals with type 2 diabetes, insulin still binds to its receptor, but the number of glucose carriers does not increase. Therefore, the cell is said to be insulin-resistant.

It is possible to prevent or at least control type 2 diabetes by adhering to a low-fat, low-sugar diet and exercising regularly. If this fails, oral drugs are available that stimulate the pancreas to secrete more insulin and enhance the metabolism of glucose in the liver and muscle cells. Millions of Americans may have type 2 diabetes without being aware of it, yet the effects of untreated type 2 diabetes are as serious as those of type 1 diabetes.

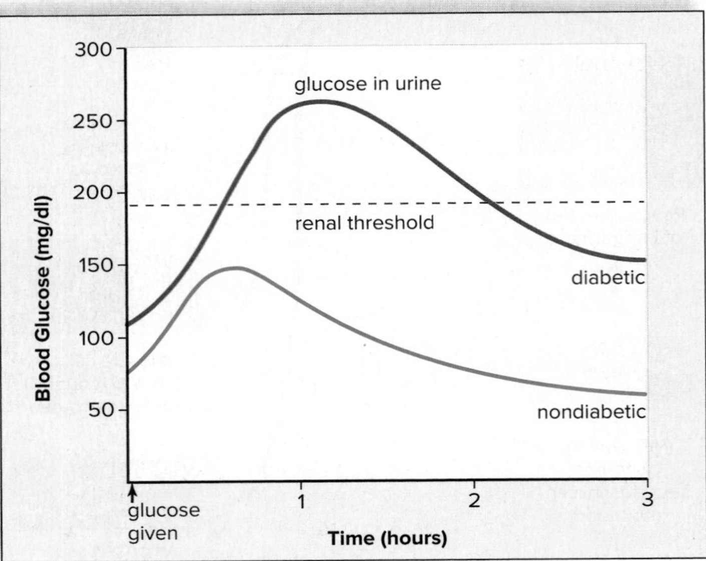

Figure 16.20 The results of a glucose tolerance test for diabetes.
Following the administration of 100 g of glucose, the blood glucose level rises dramatically in the person with diabetes, and glucose appears in the urine. Also, the blood glucose level at 2 hours is equal to more than 200 mg/dl.

BIOLOGY IN YOUR LIFE

What is gestational diabetes, and what causes it?

Women who were not diabetic prior to pregnancy but have high blood glucose during pregnancy have *gestational* diabetes. Gestational diabetes affects a small percentage of women who are pregnant. This form of diabetes is caused by insulin resistance—body insulin concentration is normal, but cells fail to respond normally. Gestational diabetes and insulin resistance generally develop later in the pregnancy. Carefully planned meals and exercise often control this form of diabetes, but insulin injections may be necessary.

If the woman is not treated, additional glucose crosses the placenta, causing high blood glucose in the fetus. The extra energy in the fetus is stored as fat, resulting in macrosomia, or a larger-than-average weight. Delivery of a very large baby can be dangerous for both the infant and the mother; thus, a cesarean section is often necessary. Complications after birth are common for these babies. Further, there is a greater risk that the child will become obese and develop type 2 diabetes mellitus later in life.

Gestational diabetes usually goes away after the birth of the child. However, once a woman has experienced gestational diabetes, she has a greater chance of developing it again during future pregnancies. These women also tend to develop type 2 diabetes later in life.

Testing for Diabetes

The oral glucose tolerance test assists in the diagnosis of diabetes mellitus. After the patient is given 100 g of glucose, the blood glucose concentration is measured at intervals. In people with diabetes, the blood glucose level rises greatly and remains elevated for several hours (Fig. 16.20), and glucose appears in the urine. In people without diabetes, the blood glucose level rises somewhat and then returns to normal after about 2 hours.

BIOLOGY IN YOUR LIFE

Are there alternatives to injections for insulin?

Until recently, people with diabetes had to rely mostly on insulin pumps or injections to receive insulin. However, the FDA has approved an insulin inhaler as a method of delivering insulin. The inhaler provides a dry powder to the lungs, where it is absorbed into the bloodstream. The inhaler is not designed to replace injections but to instead provide a small dose of insulin around mealtimes.

CHECK YOUR PROGRESS 16.5

1. Distinguish between the exocrine and endocrine functions of the pancreas.
2. Describe how the pancreatic hormones interact to regulate blood glucose levels.
3. Explain the difference in the relationship of the pancreas to type 1 and type 2 diabetes.

BIOLOGY TODAY ▶ Science

Identifying Insulin as a Chemical Messenger

In 1920, physician Frederick Banting decided to try to isolate insulin in order to identify it as a chemical messenger. Previous investigators had been unable to do this, because the enzymes in the digestive juices destroyed insulin (a protein) during the isolation procedure. Banting hit upon the idea of ligating (tying off) the pancreatic duct, which he knew from previous research would lead to the degeneration only of the cells that produce digestive juices and not of the pancreatic islets (islets of Langerhans), where insulin is made. His professor, J. J. Macleod, made a laboratory available to him at the University of Toronto and assigned a graduate student, Charles Best, to assist him.

Banting and Best had limited funds and spent that summer working, sleeping, and eating in the lab. By the end of the summer, they had obtained pancreatic extracts that did lower the blood glucose level in dogs with diabetes. Macleod then brought in biochemists, who purified the extract. Insulin therapy for the first human patient began in 1922, and large-scale production of purified insulin from pigs and cattle followed. The basic experimental system used by Banting and Best is shown in Table 16A.

For their discovery, Banting and Macleod received the Nobel Prize in Physiology or Medicine in 1923. The amino acid sequence of insulin was determined in 1953. Insulin is now synthesized using recombinant DNA technology, using bacteria, such as *Escherichia coli,* to produce the hormone. The availability of recombinant insulin (Fig. 16A), sometimes called synthetic insulin, has played a major role in improving the health of people with diabetes around the world.

Questions to Consider

1. What are some advantages, and potential disadvantages, of producing a medicine destined to be injected into humans (such as insulin) in a bacterium such as *E. coli*?
2. Some people oppose the use of animals for medical research. Do you think insulin would have eventually been discovered without animal experimentation? Why or why not?

Table 16A Experimental System Used by Banting and Best

Procedure	Results
1. Identify the source of the chemical.	Pancreatic islets are source.
2. Identify the effect to be studied.	Presence of pancreatic secretions in body lowers blood glucose.
3. Isolate the chemical.	Insulin isolated from pancreatic secretions.
4. Show that the chemical has the desired effect.	Insulin lowers blood glucose.

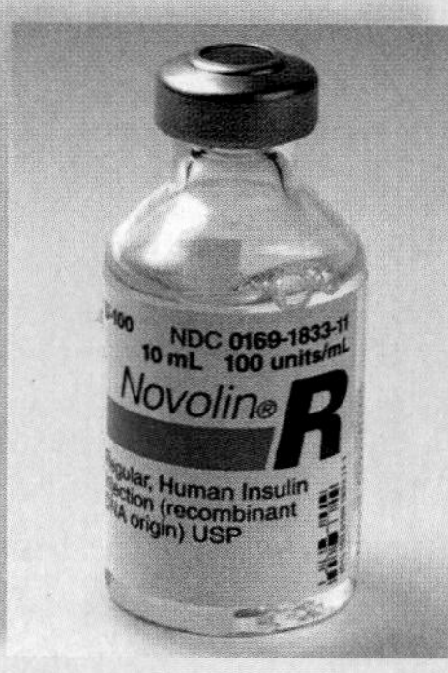

Figure 16A Synthetic insulin. Insulin is now a product of recombinant engineering and biotechnology.
Jill Braaten/McGraw Hill

CONNECTING THE CONCEPTS

For additional information on the various forms of diabetes, refer to the following discussions:

Section 4.8 examines how feedback mechanisms are involved in maintaining blood glucose homeostasis.

Section 9.6 explains the body mass index (BMI), an indicator that is used to determine obesity and the subsequent risk of diabetes.

Section 11.3 examines the influence of diabetes on the urinary system.

16.6 Other Endocrine Glands

LEARNING OUTCOMES

Upon completion of this section, you should be able to

1. List the hormones produced by the sex organs, thymus, and pineal gland and provide a function for each.
2. List the hormones produced by glands and organs outside of the endocrine system.

The male testes and female ovaries, collectively called the **gonads,** produce hormones and therefore are considered endocrine glands. In addition, the thymus and pineal gland, as well as some other tissues in the body, have endocrine functions.

Testes and Ovaries

The activity of the testes and ovaries is controlled by the hypothalamus and pituitary. The **testes** (*sing.,* testis) are located in the scrotum, and the **ovaries** are located in the pelvic cavity. The testes produce androgens (male sex hormones), such as **testosterone.** The ovaries produce **estrogen** and **progesterone,** the female sex hormones. These hormones feed back to control the hypothalamic secretion of gonadotropin-releasing hormone (GnRH). The pituitary gland secretion of follicle-stimulating hormone (FSH) and luteinizing hormone (LH), the gonadotropic hormones (Fig. 16.21), is controlled by feedback from the sex hormones, too. The activities of FSH and LH are discussed in more detail in Section 17.4. The ovaries also produce a small amount of testosterone.

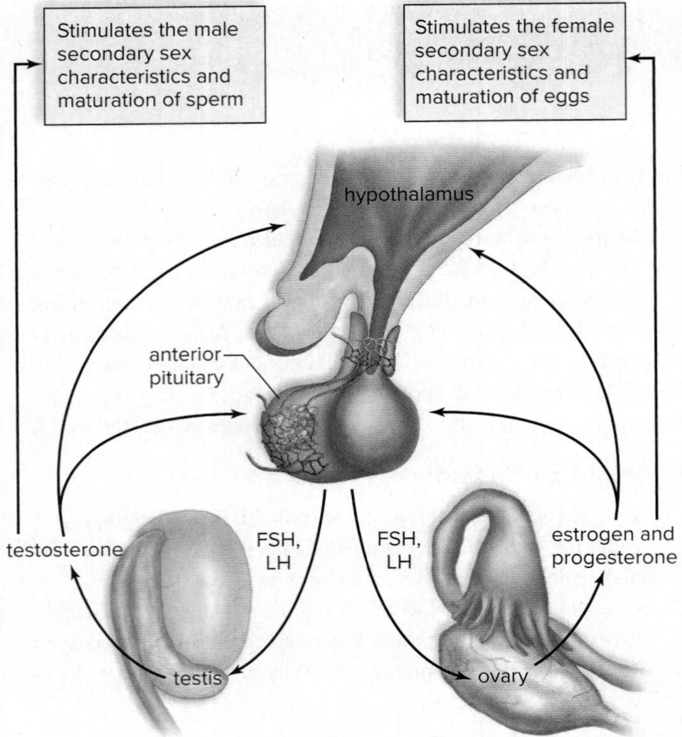

Figure 16.21 **The hormones produced by the testes and the ovaries.**
The testes and ovaries secrete the sex hormones. The testes secrete testosterone, and the ovaries secrete estrogens and progesterone. In each sex, secretion of GnRH from the hypothalamus and secretion of FSH and LH from the pituitary are controlled by their respective hormones.

Under the influence of the gonadotropic hormones, the testes begin to release increased amounts of testosterone at the time of puberty. Testosterone stimulates the growth of the penis and the testes. Testosterone also brings about and maintains the male secondary sex characteristics that develop during puberty. These include the growth of facial, axillary (underarm), and pubic hair. It prompts the larynx and the vocal cords to enlarge, causing the voice to lower. Testosterone also stimulates oil and sweat glands in the skin. It is largely responsible for acne and body odor. Another side effect of testosterone is baldness. Although females, like males, inherit genes for baldness, baldness is seen more often in males because of the presence of testosterone. Testosterone is partially responsible for the muscular strength of males, and this is why some athletes take supplemental amounts of **anabolic steroids,** which are either testosterone or related chemicals.

The female sex hormones, estrogens (often referred to in the singular) and progesterone, have many effects on the body. In particular, estrogen secreted at the time of puberty stimulates the growth of the uterus and the vagina. Estrogen is necessary for egg maturation and is largely responsible for the secondary sex characteristics in females. These include female body hair and fat distribution. In general, females have a more rounded appearance than males because of a greater accumulation of fat beneath the skin. Also, the pelvic girdle is wider in females than in males, resulting in a larger pelvic cavity. Both estrogen and progesterone are required for breast development and for regulation of the uterine cycle. This includes monthly menstruation (discharge of blood and mucosal tissues from the uterus).

Thymus

The lobular **thymus** lies just beneath the sternum (see Fig. 16.1). This organ reaches its largest size and is most active during childhood. With aging, the organ gets smaller and becomes fatty. Lymphocytes that originate in the bone marrow and then pass through the thymus are transformed into T lymphocytes. The lobules of the thymus are lined by epithelial cells that secrete hormones called **thymosins.** These hormones aid in the differentiation of lymphocytes packed inside the lobules. Although thymosins ordinarily work in the thymus, research is investigating ways that they could be used in patients with AIDS or cancer to enhance T-lymphocyte function.

Pineal Gland

The **pineal gland,** located in the brain (see Fig. 16.1), produces the hormone **melatonin,** primarily at night. Melatonin is involved in our daily sleep-wake cycle. Normally, we grow sleepy at night when melatonin levels increase and awaken once daylight returns and melatonin levels are low (Fig. 16.22). Daily 24-hour cycles such as this are called **circadian rhythms.** These rhythms are controlled by a biological clock located in the hypothalamus.

Animal research suggests that melatonin also regulates sexual development. In keeping with these findings, it has been noted that children whose pineal glands have been destroyed due to brain tumors experience early puberty.

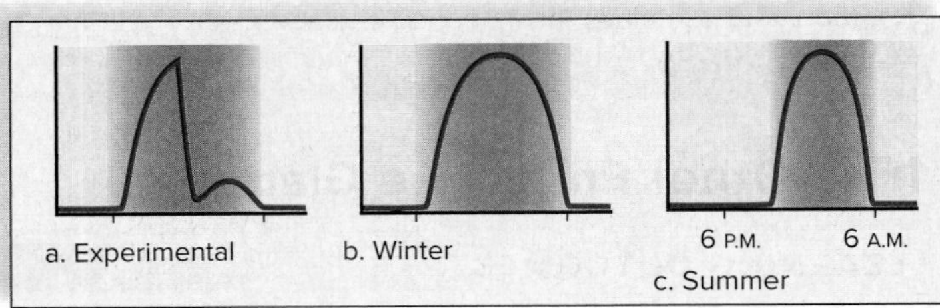

Figure 16.22 **Melatonin production changes by season.**
Melatonin production is greatest at night when we are sleeping. **a.** Light suppresses melatonin production. Melatonin is secreted for a longer time in the (**b**) winter than in the (**c**) summer.
(photo): Evelyn Jo Johnson

Hormones from Other Organs or Tissues

Some organs not usually considered endocrine glands secrete hormones. We have already mentioned that the kidneys secrete renin and that the heart produces atrial natriuretic hormone (see Section 16.4); recall also that the stomach and the small intestine produce peptide hormones that regulate digestive secretions. A number of other types of tissues produce hormones.

Erythropoietin

In response to a low oxygen blood level, the kidneys secrete **erythropoietin (EPO).** Erythropoietin stimulates red blood cell formation in the red bone marrow. A greater number of red blood cells results in increased blood oxygen. A number of different types of organs and cells also produce peptide growth factors, which stimulate cell division and mitosis. Growth factors can be considered hormones because they act on cell types with specific receptors to receive them. Some are released into the blood; others diffuse to nearby cells.

Leptin

Leptin is a protein hormone produced by adipose tissue. Leptin acts on the hypothalamus, where it signals satiety, or fullness. Individuals with obesity may have high blood levels of leptin. It is possible that the leptin they produce is ineffective because of a genetic mutation or because their hypothalamic cells lack a suitable number of receptors for leptin.

Prostaglandins

Prostaglandins are potent chemical signals produced in cells from arachidonate, a fatty acid. Prostaglandins are not distributed in the blood. They act locally, quite close to where they were produced. They are often produced by a tissue where damage has occurred, resulting in the sensation of pain (see Section 15.2). In the uterus, prostaglandins cause muscles to contract. Therefore, they are implicated in the pain and discomfort of menstruation in some women. Also, prostaglandins mediate the effects of pyrogens, chemicals believed to reset the temperature regulatory center in the brain. Aspirin reduces body temperature and controls pain because of its effect on prostaglandins.

Certain prostaglandins reduce gastric secretion and have been used to treat gastric reflux. Others lower blood pressure and have been used to treat hypertension. Still others inhibit platelet aggregation and have been used to prevent thrombosis. However, different prostaglandins have contrary effects, and it has been very difficult to standardize their use. Therefore, prostaglandin therapy is still considered experimental.

CHECK YOUR PROGRESS 16.6

1. Summarize the role of testosterone and estrogen in the body.
2. Explain the relationship between melatonin and the sleep-wake cycle.
3. Describe the response of the body to low levels of oxygen in the blood.

CONNECTING THE CONCEPTS

For more information on the hormones presented in this section, refer to the following discussions:

Section 6.2 illustrates the role of erythropoietin in the manufacture of new red blood cells.

Section 9.4 examines the role of the digestive hormones.

Chapter 17 explores the role of the male and female sex hormones.

16.7 Hormones and Homeostasis

LEARNING OUTCOMES

Upon completion of this section, you should be able to

1. Summarize how the endocrine and nervous systems respond to external changes in the body.
2. Summarize how the endocrine and nervous systems respond to internal changes in the body.

The nervous and endocrine systems exert control over the other systems and thereby maintain homeostasis (Fig. 16.23).

Responding to External Changes

The nervous system is particularly able to respond to changes in the external environment. Some responses are automatic, as you can verify by trying this: Hold a piece of clear plastic in front of your face. Get someone to gently toss a soft object, such as a wadded-up piece of paper, at the plastic. Can you prevent yourself from blinking? This reflex protects your eyes.

The eyes and other organs that have sensory receptors provide us with valuable information about the external environment. The central nervous system, on the receiving end of millions of bits of information, integrates information, compares it with previously stored memories, and "decides" on the proper course of action. The nervous system often responds to changes in the external environment through body movement. It gives us the ability to stay in as moderate an environment as possible. Otherwise, we test the ability of the nervous system to maintain homeostasis despite extreme conditions.

Responding to Internal Changes

The governance of internal organs usually requires that the nervous and endocrine systems work together. This usually occurs below the level of consciousness. Subconscious control often depends on reflex actions that involve the hypothalamus and the medulla oblongata. Let's take blood pressure as an example. After a 3-mile run, you decide to sit down under a tree to rest a bit. When you stand up to push off again, you feel faint. The feeling quickly passes, because the medulla oblongata responds to input from the baroreceptors in the aortic arch and carotid arteries. The sympathetic system immediately acts to increase heart rate and constrict the blood vessels, so your blood pressure rises. Sweating may have upset the water-salt balance of your blood.

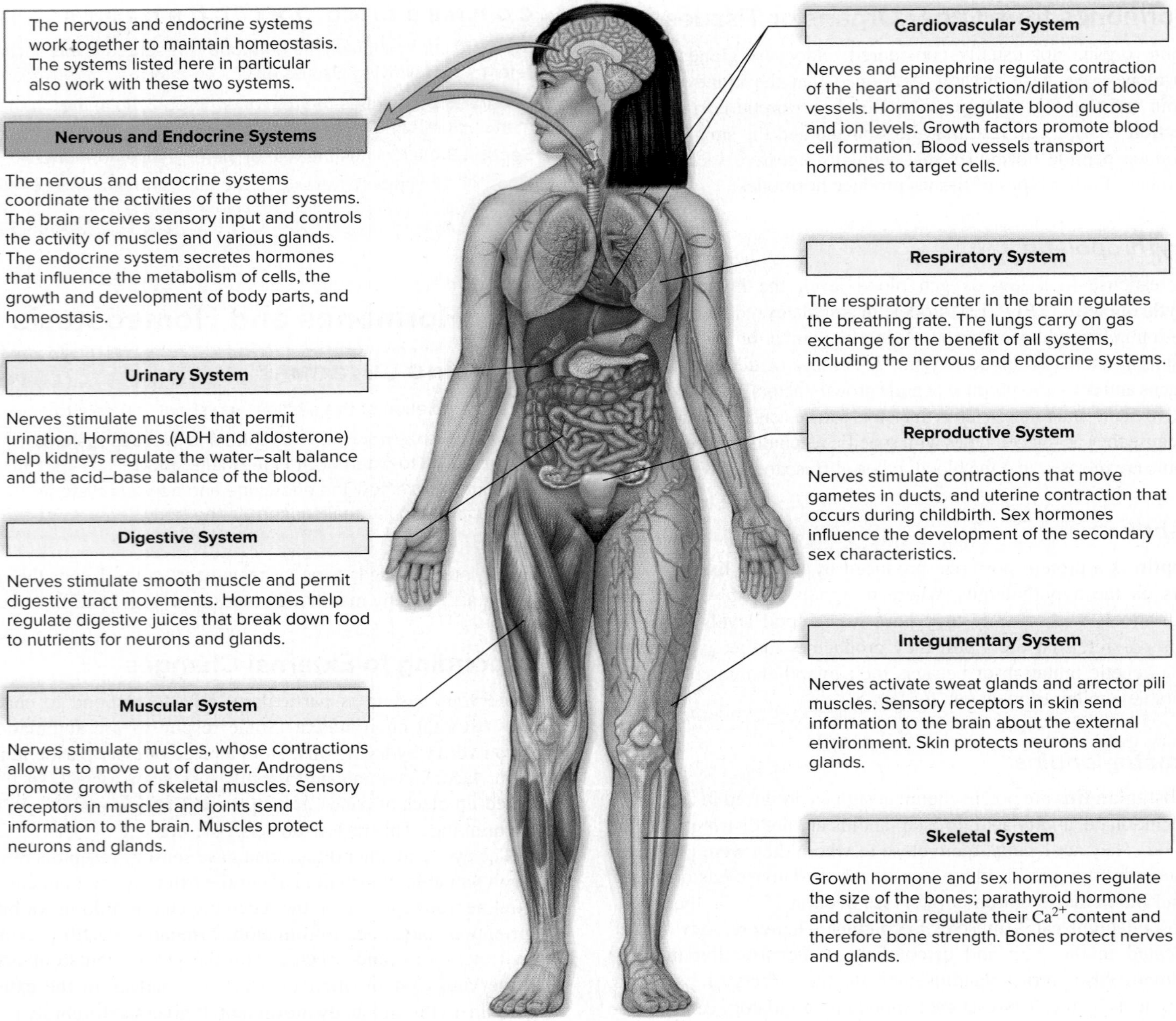

The nervous and endocrine systems work together to maintain homeostasis. The systems listed here in particular also work with these two systems.

Nervous and Endocrine Systems

The nervous and endocrine systems coordinate the activities of the other systems. The brain receives sensory input and controls the activity of muscles and various glands. The endocrine system secretes hormones that influence the metabolism of cells, the growth and development of body parts, and homeostasis.

Urinary System

Nerves stimulate muscles that permit urination. Hormones (ADH and aldosterone) help kidneys regulate the water–salt balance and the acid–base balance of the blood.

Digestive System

Nerves stimulate smooth muscle and permit digestive tract movements. Hormones help regulate digestive juices that break down food to nutrients for neurons and glands.

Muscular System

Nerves stimulate muscles, whose contractions allow us to move out of danger. Androgens promote growth of skeletal muscles. Sensory receptors in muscles and joints send information to the brain. Muscles protect neurons and glands.

Cardiovascular System

Nerves and epinephrine regulate contraction of the heart and constriction/dilation of blood vessels. Hormones regulate blood glucose and ion levels. Growth factors promote blood cell formation. Blood vessels transport hormones to target cells.

Respiratory System

The respiratory center in the brain regulates the breathing rate. The lungs carry on gas exchange for the benefit of all systems, including the nervous and endocrine systems.

Reproductive System

Nerves stimulate contractions that move gametes in ducts, and uterine contraction that occurs during childbirth. Sex hormones influence the development of the secondary sex characteristics.

Integumentary System

Nerves activate sweat glands and arrector pili muscles. Sensory receptors in skin send information to the brain about the external environment. Skin protects neurons and glands.

Skeletal System

Growth hormone and sex hormones regulate the size of the bones; parathyroid hormone and calcitonin regulate their Ca^{2+} content and therefore bone strength. Bones protect nerves and glands.

Figure 16.23 The nervous system and endocrine system interact to control homeostasis. The nervous and endocrine systems work together to regulate and control the other systems.

If so, the hormone aldosterone from the adrenal cortex will act on the kidney tubules to conserve sodium ions (Na^+), and water reabsorption will follow. The hypothalamus can also help by sending antidiuretic hormone (ADH) to the posterior pituitary gland, which releases it into the blood. ADH actively promotes water reabsorption by the kidney tubules.

Recall from Section 14.5 that certain drugs, such as alcohol, can affect ADH secretion. When you consume alcohol, it is quickly absorbed across the stomach lining into the bloodstream, where it travels to the hypothalamus and inhibits ADH secretion. When ADH levels fall, the kidney tubules absorb less water. The result is increased production of dilute urine. Excessive water loss, or dehydration, is a disturbance of homeostasis. This is why drinking alcohol when you are exercising or perspiring heavily on a hot day is not a good idea. Instead of keeping you hydrated, an alcoholic beverage, such as beer, has the opposite effect.

Controlling the Reproductive System

Few systems intrigue us more than the reproductive system, which couldn't function without nervous and endocrine control. The hypothalamus controls the anterior pituitary, which controls the release of hormones from the testes and the ovaries and the production of their gametes. The nervous system directly controls the muscular contractions of the ducts that propel the sperm. Contractions of the uterine tubes, which move a developing embryo to the uterus, where development continues, are stimulated by the nervous system, too. Without the positive feedback cycle involving oxytocin produced by the hypothalamus, birth might not occur.

The Neuroendocrine System

The nervous and endocrine systems work so closely together that they form what is sometimes called the neuroendocrine system. As we have seen, the hypothalamus certainly bridges the regulatory activities of the nervous and endocrine systems. In addition to producing the hormones released by the posterior pituitary, the hypothalamus produces hormones that control the anterior pituitary. The nerves of the autonomic system, which control other organs, are acted upon directly by the hypothalamus. The hypothalamus truly belongs to both the nervous and endocrine systems. Indeed, it is often and appropriately referred to as a neuroendocrine organ.

CHECK YOUR PROGRESS 16.7

1. Summarize the role of the endocrine system in maintaining homeostasis.
2. Explain how the body restores its water-salt balance after it has lost water and salt through sweating.
3. Explain why the nervous and endocrine systems are integrated with one another.

CONNECTING THE CONCEPTS

For more information on the organ systems presented in this section, refer to the following discussions:

Section 5.3 examines the factors that regulate heart rate.

Section 11.4 explains the role of aldosterone and ADH on the function of the kidney.

Section 14.2 explores the roles of the hypothalamus and medulla oblongata in the CNS.

CONCLUSION

As we have learned, hormones act as the means by which the body can regulate the majority of the body systems. As chemical signals, these hormones have the ability to target specific cells, tissues, or organs, as is the case with insulin, or provide a much broader control over organ systems, as happens with the sex hormones.

We are beginning to understand that some chemicals made by humans have the ability to mimic, or at times disrupt, the action of hormones naturally produced by the body. In the case of BPA, evidence suggests that this chemical mimics estrogens, and thus can have a widespread detrimental effect on the body in large doses.

SUMMARIZE

16.1 Endocrine Glands

The **endocrine system** works with the nervous system to regulate the activities of the other body systems. **Endocrine glands** secrete hormones into the bloodstream. From there, they are distributed to target organs or tissues. This differs from **exocrine glands,** which secrete products into ducts.

- **Hormones,** a type of chemical signal, usually act at a distance between body parts. Hormones are either peptides or steroids.
- **Pheromones** are chemical signals that influence the behavior of another individual.
- Reception of a **peptide hormone** at the plasma membrane activates an enzyme cascade inside the cell. Peptide hormones typically use **second messenger** systems, such as **cyclic adenosine monophosphate (cAMP).**
- **Steroid hormones** combine with a receptor, and the complex attaches to and activates DNA. Protein synthesis follows.

16.2 Hypothalamus and Pituitary Gland

The endocrine system is controlled by the **hypothalamus,** which regulates the secretions of the **pituitary gland.** Neurosecretory cells in the hypothalamus produce **antidiuretic hormone (ADH)** and **oxytocin,** which are stored in axon endings in the **posterior pituitary** until released.

- The hypothalamus produces hypothalamic-releasing and hypothalamic-inhibiting hormones, which pass to the anterior pituitary by way of a portal system.
- The **anterior pituitary** produces several types of hormones, including **thyroid-stimulating hormone (TSH), adrenocorticotropic hormone (ACTH), gonadotropic hormones, follicle-stimulating hormone (FSH), luteinizing hormone (LH), prolactin, melanocyte-stimulating hormone,** and **growth hormone (GH).** Some of these stimulate other hormonal glands to secrete hormones.
- Endocrine disorders associated with growth hormones include **pituitary dwarfism, gigantism,** and **acromegaly.**

16.3 Thyroid and Parathyroid Glands

The **thyroid gland** requires iodine to produce **triiodothyronine (T_3)** and **thyroxine (T_4),** which increase the metabolic rate.

- If iodine is available in limited quantities, **endemic goiter** develops. **Congenital hypothyroidism** occurs if the thyroid does not develop correctly.

- In adults, **hypothyroidism** leads to **myxedema,** while **hyperthyroidism** results in an **exophthalmic goiter.**
- The thyroid gland produces **calcitonin,** which helps lower the blood calcium level.
- The **parathyroid glands** secrete **parathyroid hormone (PTH),** which raises the blood calcium level.

16.4 Adrenal Glands

The **adrenal glands** respond to stress.

Adrenal Medulla

The **adrenal medulla** immediately secretes **epinephrine** and **norepinephrine.** Heartbeat and blood pressure increase, blood glucose level rises, and muscles become energized.

Adrenal Cortex

The **adrenal cortex** produces the **glucocorticoids (cortisol),** the **mineralocorticoids (aldosterone),** and **gonadocorticoids (dehydroepiandrosterone [DHEA]), androgens,** and **estradiol (estrogen)**. The glucocorticoids regulate carbohydrate, protein, and fat metabolism and suppress the inflammatory response. Mineralocorticoids are influenced by **renin** from the kidneys and regulate water and salt balance, leading to increases in blood volume and blood pressure.

- Problems with the adrenal cortex may result in **Addison's disease** or **Cushing's syndrome.**

16.5 Pancreas

The **pancreas** contains both endocrine and exocrine cells. The **pancreatic islets** secrete the hormones insulin and glucagon.

- **Insulin** lowers the blood glucose level.
- **Glucagon** raises the blood glucose level.
- **Diabetes mellitus** is due to the failure of the pancreas to produce insulin or the failure of the cells to take it up.

16.6 Other Endocrine Glands

Other endocrine glands also produce hormones:

- The **testes** and **ovaries (gonads)** produce the sex hormones. Male sex hormones are the androgens **(testosterone);** female sex hormones are the **estrogens** and **progesterone. Anabolic steroids** mimic the action of testosterone.
- The **thymus** secretes **thymosins,** which stimulate T-lymphocyte production and maturation.
- The **pineal gland** produces **melatonin,** which may be involved in **circadian rhythms** and the development of the reproductive organs.

Some organs and tissues also produce hormones:

- Kidneys produce **erythropoietin (EPO).**
- Adipose tissue produces **leptin,** which acts on the hypothalamus.
- **Prostaglandins** are produced within cells and act locally.

16.7 Hormones and Homeostasis

The nervous and endocrine systems exert control over the other systems and thereby maintain homeostasis.

- The nervous system is able to respond to the external environment after receiving data from the sensory receptors. Sensory receptors are present in such organs as the eyes and ears.
- The nervous and endocrine systems work together to govern the subconscious control of internal organs. This control often depends on reflex actions involving the hypothalamus and medulla oblongata.
- The nervous and endocrine systems work so closely together that they form what is sometimes called the neuroendocrine system.

ENGAGE

BioNOW

Want to know how this science is relevant to your life? Check out the BioNOW video below.

Quail Hormones

McGraw Hill

How do the nervous and endocrine systems of the quail work together to initiate a response to the changing environment?

THINKING CRITICALLY

Blood tests are a way to diagnose any number of endocrine disorders because hormones are transported by the circulatory system. GH and IGF-1 can be checked to determine if deficiencies are the reason for a child's slow growth. Blood levels of TSH, T_3, and T_4 provide information about thyroid function. Some tests, such as the glucose tolerance test, do not directly measure the level of hormones (insulin). Instead, they indirectly monitor whether an endocrine gland is performing correctly by measuring specific compounds in the blood.

1. How is follicle-stimulating hormone similar to growth hormone with regard to how their target cells respond to their signals?
2. It is possible to diagnose hypothyroidism by high levels of TSH in the blood. Explain what would cause a high TSH level. (*Hint:* You may want to consider what happens to TSH when the activity of the thyroid is normal.)
3. Why would a person with diabetes urinate frequently and always be thirsty?
4. Many diets advertise that they are specifically designed for individuals with diabetes. How would these diets be different from a "normal" diet?

MAKING IT RELEVANT

1. While popular culture believes that humans produce hormones, research has had a difficult time identifying many examples. Why do you think this may be the case?
2. BPA is a chemical used in the manufacture of plastics that acts as a hormone disruptor in humans. It is suspected in causing fertility problems. Suppose you were to initiate a research study on BPA. What human hormones would you include in that study?
3. Why do you think it is harder to understand the role of hormones than the chemical signals of the nervous system?

Find answers to all of the chapter questions at connect.mheducation.com

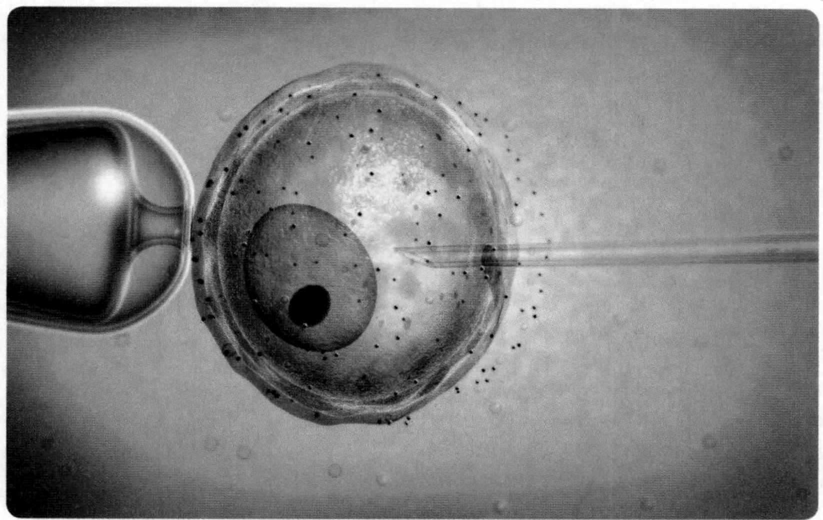

MedicalRF.com

CHAPTER 17

Reproductive System

Three Parents—One Baby

In vitro fertilization (IVF) technology has been used for many years to help couples conceive a child. The process involves taking an egg from the mother and fertilizing it with paternal sperm to create embryos that are then implanted into the mother (or a surrogate) to carry the child to term. A new technique has been proposed that allows for a donor egg to be used in cases where the mother's cells contain defective genes in the mitochondria.

Mitochondria are organelles inside a cell that generate ATP energy which the cell requires for metabolism. These organelles contain genetic material (DNA) that codes for 37 genes, 14 of which are associated with specific proteins related to efficient ATP production. Any defect in these genes leads to serious conditions such as Alpers' disease and various mitochondrial myopathies (muscle disorders). While numerous other genes found in the nucleus are related to mitochondria, it is this smaller set of genes located in the mitochondria themselves that have become a matter of controversy. At issue is an innovative therapy to prevent genetic diseases directly tied to these mitochondrial genes.

A form of in vitro fertilization creates what is sometimes called a "three-parent baby," because a third party donates an egg to be fertilized with a maternal nucleus and paternal sperm. The donor's nuclear genes are removed, but the genes inside the mitochondria remain behind. The resulting baby has all of the nuclear genes of the mother and father, but the 37 genes found in the mitochondria belong to the donor of the original egg cell.

In this chapter, we will explore the structure and function of the reproductive system in humans, as well as some of the diseases that may cause individuals to need processes such as IVF.

As you read through the chapter, think about the following questions:

1. Which sex normally contributes the mitochondrial genes to the offspring?
2. How does IVF differ from other assisted reproductive technologies?

CHAPTER OUTLINE

BEFORE YOU BEGIN

Before beginning this chapter, take a few moments to review the following discussions:

Section 8.1 What factors contribute to an increased risk of an HIV infection?

Section 16.6 Where is testosterone produced, and what is its function in the male body?

Section 16.6 Where are estrogen and progesterone produced, and what are their functions in the female body?

17.1 Human Life Cycle

LEARNING OUTCOMES

Upon completion of this section, you should be able to

1. List the functions of the human reproductive system.
2. Describe the human life cycle and explain the role of mitosis and meiosis in this cycle.

Unlike the other systems of the body, the **reproductive system** is quite different between males and females. In both males and females, the reproductive system is responsible for the production of gametes, the cells that combine to form a new individual of the species. In females, the reproductive system has the added function of protecting and nourishing the developing fetus until birth. The reproductive organs, or genitals, have the following functions:

- Males produce sperm within testes, and females produce eggs within ovaries.
- Males nurture and transport the sperm in ducts until they exit the penis. Females transport the eggs in uterine tubes to the uterus.
- The male penis functions to deliver sperm to the female vagina, which receives the sperm. The vagina also transports menstrual fluid to the exterior and acts as the birth canal.
- The uterus of the female allows the fertilized egg to develop within her body. After birth, the female breast provides nourishment in the form of milk.
- The testes and ovaries produce the sex hormones. The sex hormones have a profound effect on the body, because they bring about masculinization or feminization of various features. In females, the sex hormones also allow a pregnancy to continue.

Unlike many other animals, humans are not reproductively capable at birth. Instead, they undergo a sequence of events called *puberty,* during which a child becomes a sexually competent young adult. The reproductive system does not begin to fully function until puberty is complete. Sexual maturity typically occurs between the ages of 10 and 14 in girls and 12 and 16 in boys. At the completion of puberty, the individual is capable of producing children.

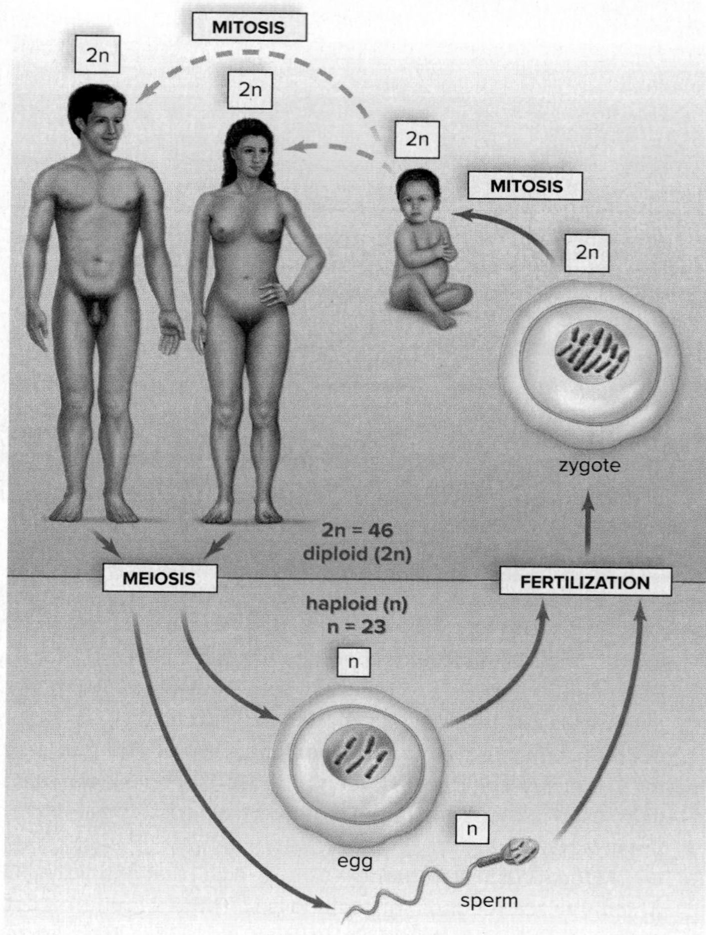

Figure 17.1 **The human life cycle.**
The human life cycle has two types of cell division: mitosis, in which the chromosome number stays constant, and meiosis, in which the chromosome number is reduced. During growth or cell repair, mitosis ensures that each new cell has 46 chromosomes. During production of sex cells, the chromosome number is reduced from 46 to 23. Therefore, an egg and a sperm each have 23 chromosomes, so that when the sperm fertilizes the egg, the new cell, called a zygote, has 46 chromosomes.

Mitosis and Meiosis

Before examining the two different forms of cell division that occur during the human life cycle, it is important to recognize that our genetic instructions, or DNA, are distributed among 46 chromosomes within the nucleus. These 46 chromosomes exist in 23 pairs, with each pair containing a contribution from both the male and female parent. Most of the cell types in the body have 46 chromosomes. During the majority of our life cycle, our cells divide by a process called **mitosis** (see Section 19.3). Mitosis is *duplication division,* meaning that each of the cells that exit mitosis has the same complement of 46 chromosomes. In other words, when a cell divides, it produces exact copies of itself by mitosis, much as a copier machine does with a page of notes. In the life cycle of a human, mitosis is the type of cell division that plays an important role during growth and repair of tissues (Fig. 17.1).

For the purposes of reproduction, special cells in the body undergo a type of cell division called **meiosis.** Meiosis takes place only in the testes of males during the production of sperm and in the ovaries of females during the production of eggs. Meiosis has two functions (see Section 19.4), the first of which is called *reduction division.* During meiosis, the chromosome number is reduced from the normal 46 chromosomes, called the diploid or 2n number, down to 23 chromosomes, called the haploid or n number of chromosomes. This process requires two successive divisions, called meiosis I and meiosis II, and is involved in the formation of **gametes,** or sex cells. As explained in Section 19.4, meiosis also introduces genetic variation, thus ensuring that the new individual is not an exact copy of either parent.

Following meiosis, the haploid cells develop into either sperm (males) or eggs (females). The flagellated sperm is small compared to the egg. It is specialized to carry only chromosomes as it swims to the egg. The egg is specialized to await the arrival of a sperm and to provide the new individual with cytoplasm in addition to chromosomes. The fusing of the egg and sperm form a cell called the **zygote.** Because a sperm has 23 chromosomes and the egg has 23 chromosomes, the zygote has 46 chromosomes altogether. Without meiosis, the chromosome number in each generation would double, and the cells would no longer be able to function.

BIOLOGY IN YOUR LIFE

What types of human cells do not have 46 chromosomes?

In humans, the cell types that do not have the standard 23 pairs of chromosomes are the red blood cells and the cells of the liver. Recall from Section 6.2 that red blood cells lack a nucleus; therefore, they do not have any chromosomes. Cells in the liver, called hepatocytes, typically have more than three copies of each chromosome (giving them 69 or more chromosomes). This condition is called polyploidy, and it is believed this gives the liver its ability to degrade toxic compounds.

CHECK YOUR PROGRESS 17.1

1. Compare the functions of the reproductive system in males and females.
2. Contrast the two types of cell division in the human life cycle.
3. Explain the location of meiosis in males and females.

CONNECTING THE CONCEPTS

For more information on the topics presented in this section, refer to the following discussions:

Section 16.6 provides an introduction to the sex hormones.

Sections 19.3 and **19.4** examine the stages of mitosis and meiosis.

Section 19.5 compares the processes of mitosis and meiosis.

17.2 Male Reproductive System

LEARNING OUTCOMES

Upon completion of this section, you should be able to

1. Identify the structures of the male reproductive system and provide a function for each.
2. Describe the location and stages of spermatogenesis.
3. Summarize how hormones regulate the male reproductive system.

The male reproductive system includes the organs listed in Table 17.1 and shown in Figure 17.2.

Table 17.1 Male Reproductive Organs

Organ	Function
Testes	Produce sperm and sex hormones
Epididymides	Ducts where sperm mature and some sperm are stored
Vasa deferentia	Conduct and store sperm
Seminal vesicles	Contribute nutrients and fluid to semen
Prostate gland	Contributes fluid to semen
Urethra	Conducts sperm
Bulbourethral glands	Contribute mucus-containing fluid to semen
Penis	Organ of sexual intercourse

The male gonads, or primary sex organs, are paired **testes** (*sing.*, testis), suspended within sacs called the **scrotum.** Sperm produced by the testes mature within the **epididymis** (*pl.*, epididymides), a tightly coiled duct lying just outside each testis. Maturation seems to be required for sperm to swim to the egg. When sperm leave an epididymis, they enter a **vas deferens** (*pl.*, vasa deferentia), also called the ductus deferens. The sperm may be stored for a time in the vas deferens. Each vas deferens passes into the abdominal cavity, where it curves around the bladder and empties into an ejaculatory duct. The ejaculatory ducts enter the **urethra.**

At the time of ejaculation, sperm leave the penis in a fluid called **semen.** The seminal vesicles, the prostate gland, and the bulbourethral glands add secretions to the semen. A pair of **seminal vesicles** lie at the base of the bladder, and each has a duct that joins with a vas deferens. **Bulbourethral glands** (also called Cowper's glands) are pea-sized organs that lie posterior to the prostate on either side of the urethra. Their secretion makes the semen gelatinous. The **prostate gland** is a single, doughnut-shaped gland that surrounds the upper portion of the urethra just below the bladder. In older men, the prostate can enlarge and squeeze off the urethra, making urination painful and difficult. This condition is discussed in more detail in the Health feature "Urinary Difficulties Due to an Enlarged Prostate" in Section 11.5.

Each component of semen has a particular function. Sperm are more viable in a basic solution; semen, milky in appearance, has a slightly basic pH (about 7.5). Swimming sperm require energy; semen contains the sugar fructose, which serves as an energy source. Semen also contains prostaglandins, chemicals that cause the uterus to contract. These contractions help propel the sperm toward the egg.

The Penis and Male Orgasm

The **penis** (Fig. 17.3) is the male organ of sexual intercourse. It also contains the urethra of the urinary system. The penis has a long shaft and an enlarged tip called the *glans penis.* The layer of skin covering the glans penis, called the *foreskin,* may be removed surgically by **circumcision** shortly after birth. This is usually done for religious reasons or perceived health benefits, including easier

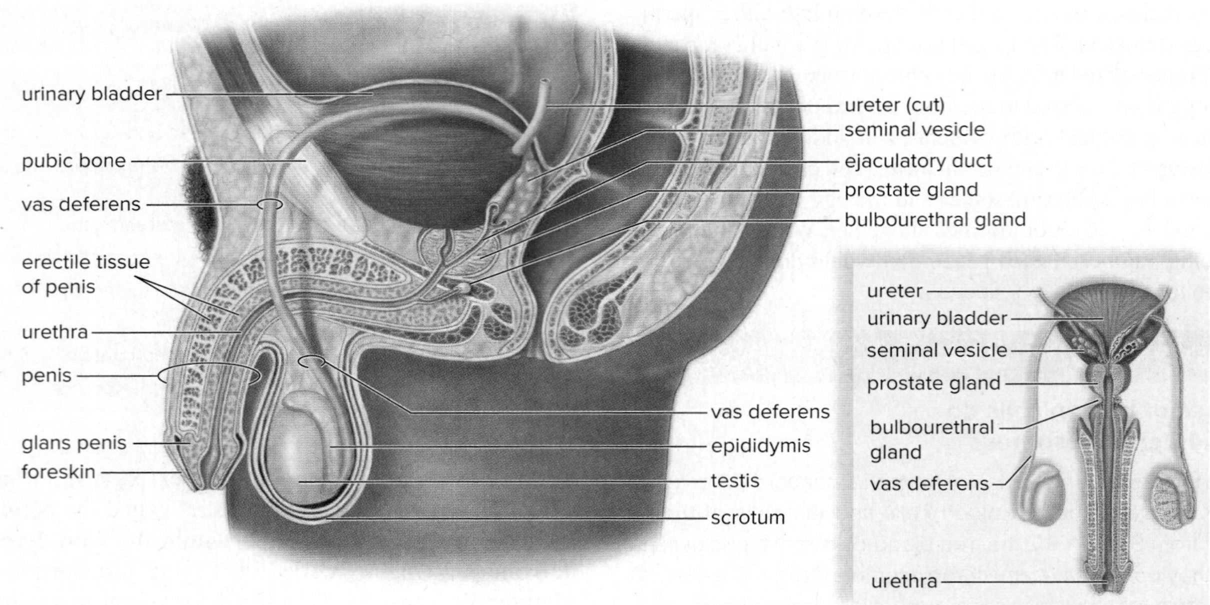

Figure 17.2 **The male reproductive system.**
The testes produce sperm. The seminal vesicles, the prostate gland, and the bulbourethral glands provide a fluid medium for the sperm, which move from the vas deferens through the ejaculatory duct to the urethra in the penis. The foreskin (prepuce) is removed when a penis is circumcised.

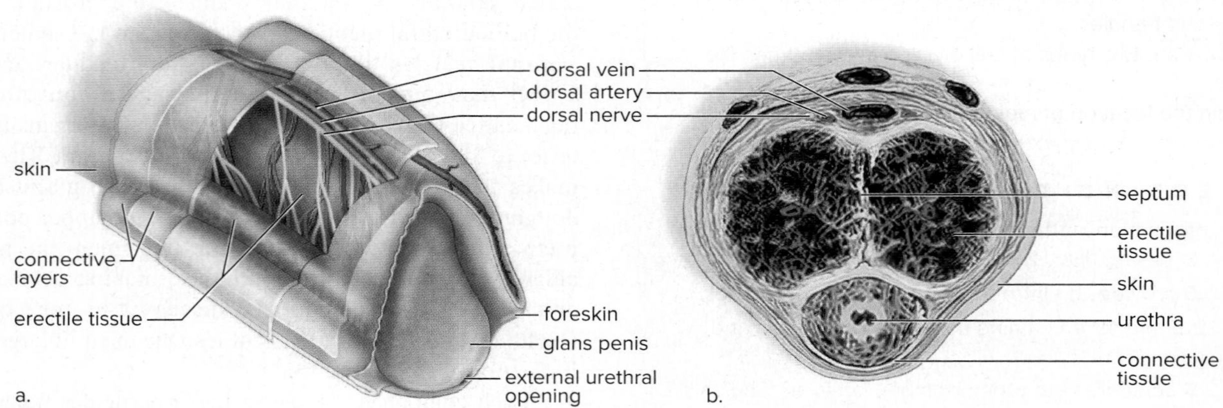

Figure 17.3 **The structure of the penis.**
a. The shaft of the penis ends in an enlarged tip called the glans penis. In uncircumcised males, this is partially covered by a foreskin (prepuce).
b. Micrograph of shaft in cross-section showing location of erectile tissue.
(b): Anatomical Travelogue/Science Source

hygiene, decreased urinary tract infections, and reduced risk of penile cancer. A study of 3,000 Ugandan men showed that compared to men who were uncircumcised, men who were circumcised were 25–35% less likely to contract HIV, human papillomavirus, or genital herpes. However, opponents of the procedure focus on the risks, including pain and potential loss of sensitivity in the penis, and the American Academy of Pediatrics' position is that the benefits are not sufficient to recommend routine neonatal circumcision.

Spongy, erectile tissue containing distensible blood spaces extends through the shaft of the penis. During sexual arousal, autonomic nerves release nitric oxide (NO). This stimulus leads to the production of cGMP (cyclic guanosine monophosphate), a high-energy compound similar to ATP. The cGMP causes the smooth muscle of incoming arterial walls to relax and the erectile tissue to fill with blood. The veins that take blood away from the penis are compressed, and the penis becomes erect.

Erectile dysfunction (ED) (formerly called *impotency*) is the inability to achieve or maintain an erection suitable for sexual intercourse. ED may be caused by a number of factors, including poor blood flow, certain medications, and many illnesses. Medications for the treatment of erectile dysfunction inhibit the enzyme that breaks down cGMP, ensuring that a full erection will take place. Some of these medications can cause vision problems, because the same enzyme occurs in the retina. During an erection, a sphincter closes off the bladder, so that no urine enters the urethra.

As sexual stimulation intensifies, sperm enter the urethra from each vas deferens, and the glands contribute secretions to the seminal fluid. Once semen is in the urethra, rhythmic muscle contractions cause it to be expelled from the penis in spurts (ejaculation).

The contractions that expel semen from the penis are a part of male orgasm, the physiological and psychological sensations that occur at the climax of sexual stimulation. The psychological sensation of pleasure is centered in the brain. However, the physiological reactions involve the reproductive organs and associated muscles, as well as the entire body. Marked muscular tension is followed by contraction and relaxation. Following ejaculation and/or loss of sexual arousal, the penis returns to its normal flaccid state. Usually, a period of time, called the refractory period, follows during which stimulation does not bring about an erection. The length of the refractory period increases with age.

There may be in excess of 100 million sperm in the 3.5 ml of semen expelled during ejaculation. The sperm count can be much lower than this, however, and fertilization of the egg by a sperm can still take place.

Male Gonads: The Testes

The testes, which produce sperm as well as the male sex hormones, lie outside the abdominal cavity of the male, within the scrotum. The testes begin their development inside the abdominal cavity. They descend into the scrotal sacs through the inguinal canal during the last 2 months of fetal development. If the testes do not descend and the male is not treated or operated on to place the testes in the scrotum, sterility (the inability to produce offspring) usually follows. This is because the internal temperature of the body is too high to produce viable sperm. The scrotum helps regulate the temperature of the testes by holding them closer to or farther away from the body.

BIOLOGY IN YOUR LIFE

Boxers or briefs?

The scrotum's role in male physiology is to keep the temperature of the testes lower than body temperature. The lower temperature is necessary for normal sperm production. It might follow that the man's type of underwear can change that temperature, affecting sperm production. However, research has not supported this assumption. The style of underwear worn by a man, loose or close fitting, has not been shown to affect sperm count or fertility significantly.

Seminiferous Tubules

A longitudinal section of a testis shows that it is composed of compartments, called lobules, each of which contains one to three tightly coiled **seminiferous tubules** (Fig. 17.4*a*). A microscopic cross-section of a seminiferous tubule reveals it is packed with cells undergoing **spermatogenesis** (Fig. 17.4*b*), the production of sperm.

During the production of sperm, *spermatogonia* divide to produce *primary spermatocytes* (2n). One of these cells does not proceed with the remainder of spermatogenesis and instead serves as a stem cell, allowing spermatogenesis to continue throughout the lifetime of the male. The other primary spermatocyte moves away from the outer wall, increases in size, and undergoes meiosis I to produce *secondary spermatocytes*. Each secondary spermatocyte has only 23 chromosomes (Fig. 17.4*c*). Secondary spermatocytes (n) undergo meiosis II to produce four *spermatids,* each of which also has 23 chromosomes. Spermatids then develop into sperm. Note the presence of **Sertoli cells** (purple), which support, nourish, and regulate the process of spermatogenesis. It takes approximately 74 days for sperm to undergo development from spermatogonia to sperm.

Mature **sperm,** or spermatozoa, have three distinct parts: a *head*, a *middle piece,* and a *tail* (Fig. 17.4*d*). Mitochondria in the middle piece provide energy for the movement of the tail, which is a flagellum. The head contains a nucleus covered by a cap called the *acrosome,* which stores enzymes needed to penetrate the egg. The ejaculated semen of a normal human male contains several hundred million sperm, but only one sperm normally enters an egg. Sperm usually do not live more than 48 hours in the female genital tract.

Interstitial Cells

The male sex hormones, the androgens, are secreted by cells that lie between the seminiferous tubules. These cells are called **interstitial cells.** The most important of the androgens is testosterone, whose functions are discussed next.

Hormonal Regulation in Males

The hypothalamus has ultimate control of the testes' sexual function, because it secretes a hormone called gonadotropin-releasing hormone (GnRH) (see Section 16.2). GnRH stimulates the anterior pituitary to secrete the gonadotropic hormones. There are two gonadotropic hormones, **follicle-stimulating hormone (FSH)** and **luteinizing hormone (LH),** which are present in both males and females. In males, FSH promotes the production of sperm in the seminiferous tubules. LH in males controls the production of testosterone by the interstitial cells.

All these hormones are involved in a negative feedback relationship that maintains the fairly constant production of sperm and testosterone (Fig. 17.5). When the amount of testosterone in the blood rises to a certain level, it causes the hypothalamus and anterior pituitary to decrease their respective secretion of GnRH and LH. As the level of testosterone begins to fall, the hypothalamus increases its secretion of GnRH and the anterior pituitary increases

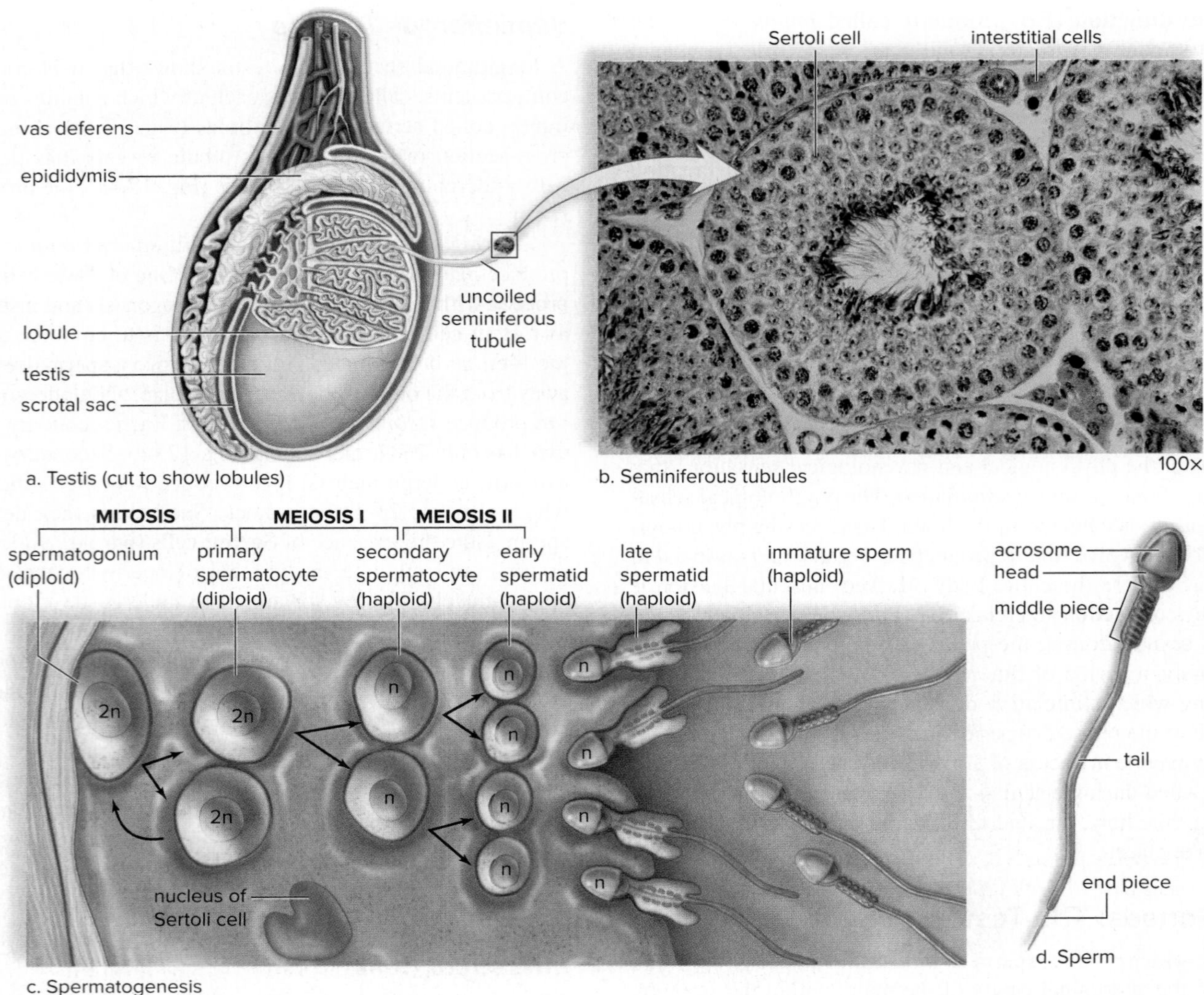

Figure 17.4 Spermatogenesis produces sperm cells.
a. The lobules of a testis contain seminiferous tubules. **b.** Electron micrograph of a cross-section of the seminiferous tubules, where spermatogenesis occurs. Note the location of interstitial cells in clumps among the seminiferous tubules. **c.** Diagrammatic representation of spermatogenesis, which occurs in the walls of tubules. **d.** A sperm has a head, a middle piece, and a tail. The nucleus is in the head, capped by the enzyme-containing acrosome.

its secretion of LH. These stimulate the interstitial cells to produce testosterone. A similar feedback mechanism maintains the continuous production of sperm. The Sertoli cells in the wall of the seminiferous tubules produce a hormone called *inhibin* that blocks GnRH and FSH secretion when appropriate (Fig. 17.5).

Testosterone, the main sex hormone in males, is essential for the normal development and functioning of the organs listed in Table 17.1. Testosterone also brings about and maintains the male secondary sex characteristics that develop at the time of puberty. Males are generally taller than females and have broader shoulders and longer legs relative to trunk length. The deeper voices of males compared with those of females are due to a larger larynx with longer vocal cords. The Adam's apple, part of the larynx, is usually more prominent in males than in females. Testosterone causes males to develop noticeable hair on the face, the chest, and occasionally other regions of the body, such as the back. A related chemical also leads to the receding hairline and male-pattern baldness that occur in males.

Testosterone is responsible for the greater muscular development in males. Knowing this, both males and females sometimes take anabolic steroids, either testosterone or related steroid hormones resembling testosterone. Health problems involving the kidneys, the cardiovascular system, and hormonal imbalances can arise from such use.

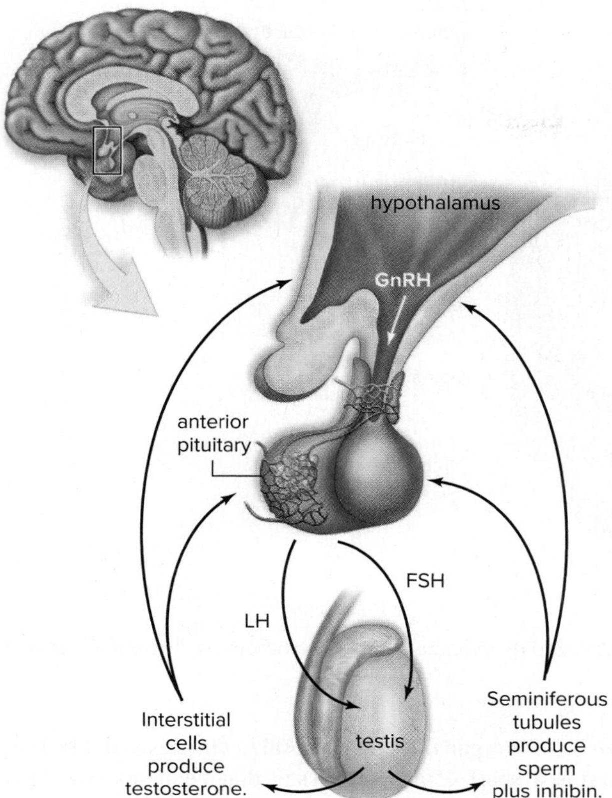

Figure 17.5 The hormones that control the production of sperm and testosterone by the testes.
Gonadotropin-releasing hormone (GnRH) stimulates the anterior pituitary to secrete the gonadotropic hormones: Follicle-stimulating hormone (FSH) stimulates the production of sperm, and luteinizing hormone (LH) stimulates the production of testosterone. Testosterone and inhibin exert negative feedback control over the hypothalamus and the anterior pituitary, and this regulates the level of testosterone in the blood and the production of sperm by the testes.

CHECK YOUR PROGRESS 17.2

1. List the structures of the male reproductive system, and then trace the movement of sperm through the system.
2. Describe the process of spermatogenesis.
3. Explain the importance of testosterone to the male reproductive system.

CONNECTING THE CONCEPTS

For more information on the topics presented in this section, refer to the following discussions:

Figure 2.20 provides the chemical structure of testosterone.

Section 16.6 provides additional information on the male sex hormones.

Section 19.4 examines how meiosis reduces the chromosome number during spermatogenesis.

17.3 Female Reproductive System

LEARNING OUTCOME

Upon completion of this section, you should be able to

1. Identify the structures of the female reproductive system and provide a function for each.

The female gonads are paired **ovaries** that lie in shallow depressions, one on each side of the upper pelvic cavity. The ovaries produce **eggs,** also called *ova* (*sing.,* ovum), and the female sex hormones estrogen and progesterone. The female reproductive system includes the organs listed in Table 17.2 and shown in Figure 17.6.

The Genital Tract

The **uterine tubes,** also called the *oviducts* or *fallopian tubes,* extend from the uterus to the ovaries. However, the uterine tubes are not attached to the ovaries. Instead, they have fingerlike projections called **fimbriae** (*sing.,* fimbria) that sweep over the ovaries. When an egg (ovum) bursts from an ovary during ovulation, it is usually swept into a uterine tube by the combined action of the fimbriae and the beating of cilia that line the uterine tube.

Once in the uterine tube, the egg is propelled slowly by ciliary movement and tubular muscle contraction toward the uterus. An egg lives approximately 6 to 24 hours, unless fertilization occurs. Fertilization, and therefore zygote formation, usually takes place in the uterine tube. A developing embryo normally arrives at the uterus after several days, and then **implantation** occurs. During implantation, the embryo embeds in the uterine lining, which has been prepared to receive it.

The **uterus** is a thick-walled, muscular organ about the size and shape of an inverted pear (Fig. 17.6). Normally, it lies above and is tipped over the urinary bladder. The uterine tubes join the uterus at its upper end; at its lower end, the **cervix** enters the vagina nearly at a right angle.

Cancer of the cervix is a common form of cancer in women. Early detection is possible by means of a *Pap test,* which requires the removal of a few cells from the region of the cervix for microscopic examination. If the cells are cancerous, a physician may recommend a *hysterectomy.* A hysterectomy is the removal of the uterus, including the cervix. Removal of the ovaries in addition to the uterus is termed an *ovariohysterectomy*

Table 17.2 Female Reproductive Organs

Organ	Function
Ovaries	Produce eggs and sex hormones
Uterine tubes	Conduct eggs; location of fertilization
Uterus	Houses developing fetus
Cervix	Contains opening to uterus
Vagina	Receives penis during sexual intercourse; serves as birth canal and as an exit for menstrual flow

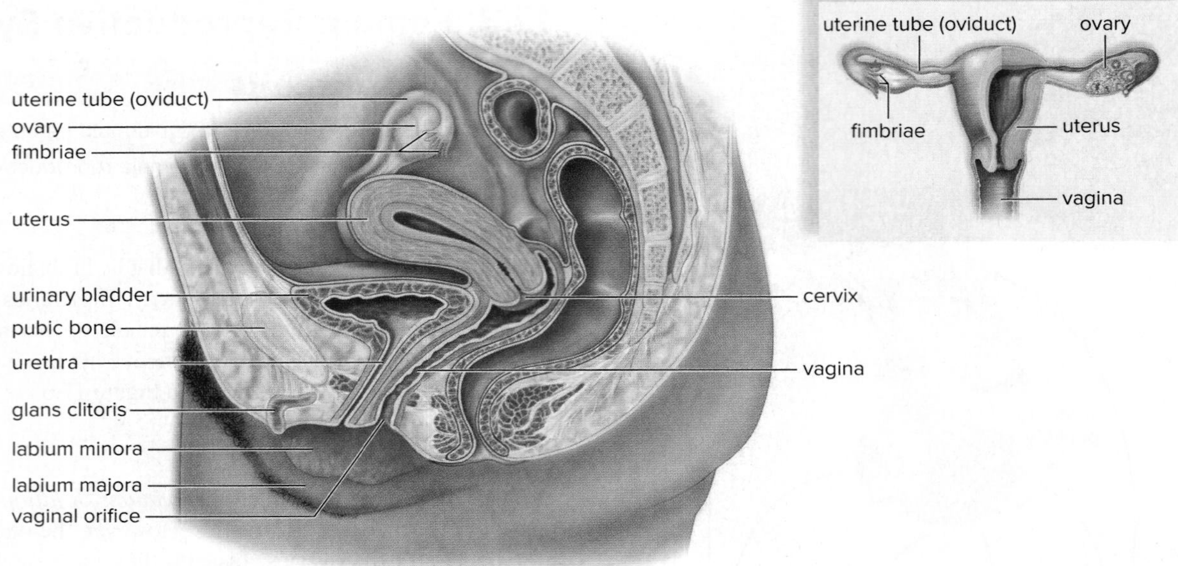

Figure 17.6 **The female reproductive system.**
The ovaries usually release one egg a month; fertilization occurs in the uterine tubes, and development occurs in the uterus. The vagina is the birth canal, as well as the organ of sexual intercourse and the outlet for menstrual flow.

(radical hysterectomy). The vagina remains, so the woman can still engage in sexual intercourse.

Development of the embryo and fetus normally takes place in the uterus. This organ, sometimes called the womb, is approximately 5 cm wide in its usual state. It is capable of stretching to over 30 cm wide to accommodate a growing fetus. The lining of the uterus is called the **endometrium.** The endometrium supplies nutrients needed for embryonic and fetal development. The endometrium has two layers: a functional layer that is shed during each menstrual period, and a basal layer of reproducing cells. In the nonpregnant female, the functional layer of the endometrium varies in thickness according to a monthly reproductive cycle called the uterine cycle.

A small opening in the cervix leads to the vaginal canal. The **vagina** is a tube that lies at a 45° angle to the small of the back. The mucosal lining of the vagina lies in folds and can extend. This is especially important when the vagina serves as the birth canal, and it facilitates sexual intercourse when the vagina receives the penis. The vagina also acts as an exit for menstrual flow. Several different types of bacteria normally reside in the vagina and create an acidic environment. While this environment is protective against the possible growth of pathogenic bacteria, sperm prefer the basic environment provided by seminal fluid.

External Genitals

The external genital organs of the female are known collectively as the **vulva** (Fig. 17.7). The vulva includes two large, hair-covered folds of skin called the *labia majora*. The labia majora extend backward from the *mons pubis,* a fatty prominence underlying the pubic hair. The *labia minora* are two small folds lying just inside the labia majora. They extend forward from the vaginal opening to encircle and form a foreskin for the glans clitoris. The *glans clitoris* is the organ of sexual arousal in females and, like the penis, contains a shaft of erectile tissue that becomes engorged with blood during sexual stimulation.

The cleft between the labia minora contains the openings of the *urethra* and the *vagina*. The vagina may be partially closed by a ring of tissue called the *hymen*. The hymen is ordinarily ruptured by sexual intercourse or by other types of physical activities. If remnants of the hymen persist after sexual intercourse, they can be surgically removed.

The urinary and reproductive systems in the female are entirely separate. For example, the urethra carries only urine, and the vagina serves only as the birth canal, the organ for sexual intercourse, and the outlet for menstrual flow.

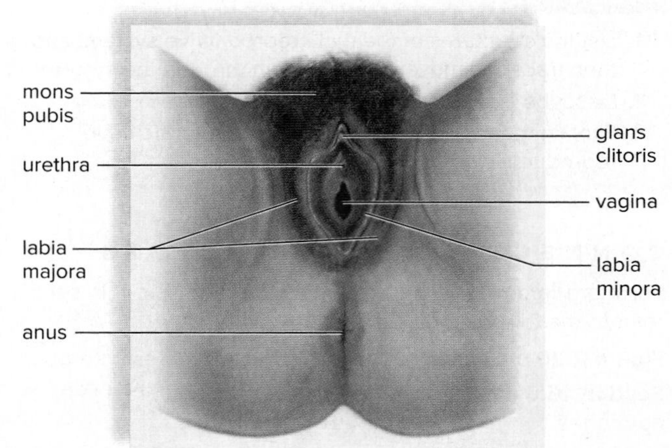

Figure 17.7 **The external genitals of a female.**
The external genitals of the female include the labia majora, labia minora, and glans clitoris. These organs are also referred to as the vulva.

Orgasm in Females

Upon sexual stimulation, the labia minora, the vaginal wall, and the clitoris become engorged with blood. The breasts also swell, and the nipples become erect. The labia majora enlarge, redden, and spread away from the vaginal opening.

The vagina expands and elongates. Blood vessels in the vaginal wall release small droplets of fluid that seep into the vagina and lubricate it. Mucus-secreting glands beneath the labia minora on either side of the vagina also provide lubrication for entry of the penis into the vagina. Although the vagina is the organ of sexual intercourse in females, the clitoris plays a significant role in the female sexual response. The extremely sensitive clitoris can swell to two or three times its usual size. The thrusting of the penis and the pressure of the pubic symphyses of the partners stimulate the clitoris.

Orgasm occurs at the height of the sexual response. Blood pressure and pulse rate rise, breathing quickens, and the walls of the uterus and uterine tubes contract rhythmically. A sensation of intense pleasure is followed by relaxation when organs return to their normal size. Females have no refractory period, and multiple orgasms can occur during a single sexual experience.

CHECK YOUR PROGRESS 17.3

1. Distinguish the structures of the female reproductive system that (a) produce the egg, (b) transport the egg, (c) house a developing embryo, and (d) serve as the birth canal.
2. Explain the purpose of the vagina and uterus in the female reproductive system.
3. Discuss why the urinary and reproductive systems are separate in a female.

CONNECTING THE CONCEPTS

For more information on the topics presented in this section, refer to the following discussions:

Section 18.1 outlines the steps in the fertilization of an egg by a sperm cell.

Section 18.2 examines the stages of fetal development in the uterus.

Sections 20.1 and **20.2** examine the characteristics of cancer cells and the causes of cancer.

17.4 The Ovarian Cycle

LEARNING OUTCOMES

Upon completion of this section, you should be able to

1. List the stages of the ovarian cycle and explain what is occurring in each stage.
2. Describe the process of oogenesis.
3. Summarize how estrogen and progesterone influence the ovarian cycle.

Hormone levels cycle in the female on a monthly basis, and the ovarian cycle drives the uterine cycle, as discussed in this section.

Ovarian Cycle: Nonpregnant

An ovary contains many **follicles,** and each one contains an immature egg called an **oocyte.** A female is born with as many as 2 million follicles, but the number has reduced to 300,000 to 400,000 by the time of puberty. Only a small number of follicles (about 400) ever mature, because a female usually produces only one egg per month during her reproductive years. As the follicle matures during the **ovarian cycle,** it changes from a primary to a secondary, and then to a vesicular (Graafian) follicle (Fig. 17.8). Epithelial cells of a *primary follicle* surround a *primary oocyte.* Pools of follicular fluid bathe the oocyte in a *secondary follicle.* In a *vesicular follicle,* the fluid-filled cavity increases to the point that the follicle wall balloons out on the surface of the ovary.

Figure 17.9 traces the steps of **oogenesis.** A primary oocyte undergoes meiosis I, and the resulting cells are haploid with 23 chromosomes each. One of these cells is called a **polar body.** A polar body is a sort of cellular "trash can," because its function is simply to hold discarded chromosomes. The secondary oocyte undergoes meiosis II, but only if it is first fertilized by a sperm cell. If the secondary oocyte remains unfertilized, it never completes meiosis and will die shortly after being released from the ovary.

When appropriate, the vesicular follicle bursts, releasing the oocyte (often called an egg) surrounded by a clear membrane. This process is referred to as **ovulation.** Once a vesicular follicle has lost the oocyte, it develops into a **corpus luteum,** a glandlike structure. If the egg is not fertilized, the corpus luteum disintegrates.

As we discussed in Section 17.3, the ovaries produce eggs and the female sex hormones estrogen and progesterone. A primary follicle produces estrogen, and a secondary follicle produces estrogen and some progesterone. The corpus luteum produces progesterone and some estrogen.

Phases of the Ovarian Cycle

Similar to the testes, the hypothalamus has ultimate control of the ovaries' sexual function, because it secretes gonadotropin-releasing hormone, or GnRH. GnRH stimulates the anterior pituitary to produce FSH and LH, and these hormones control the ovarian cycle. The gonadotropic hormones are not present in constant amounts. Instead, they are secreted at different rates during the cycle. For simplicity's sake, it is convenient to emphasize that during the first half, or *follicular phase,* FSH promotes the development of follicles that primarily secrete estrogen (Fig. 17.10). As the estrogen level in the blood rises, it exerts negative feedback control over the anterior pituitary secretion of FSH. The follicular phase then comes to an end.

The estrogen spike at the end of the follicular phase has a positive feedback effect on the hypothalamus and pituitary gland. As a result, GnRH from the hypothalamus increases. A corresponding surge of LH is released from the anterior pituitary. The LH surge triggers ovulation at about day 14 of a 28-day cycle.

Next, the *luteal phase* begins. During the luteal phase of the ovarian cycle, LH promotes the development of the corpus luteum.

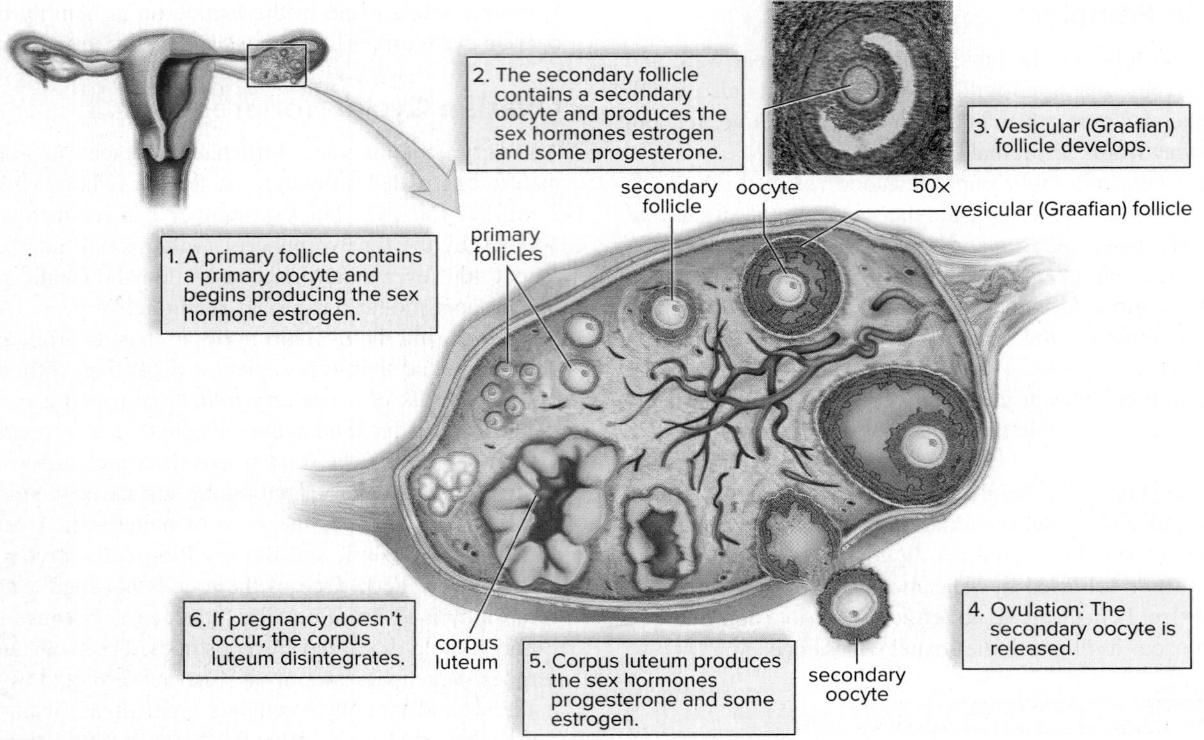

Figure 17.8 **The ovarian cycle.**

A single follicle goes through all six stages in one place in the ovary. As the follicle matures, layers of follicle cells surround a secondary oocyte. Eventually, the mature follicle ruptures, and the secondary oocyte is released. The follicle then becomes the corpus luteum, which eventually disintegrates.

(photo): ©Ed Reschke

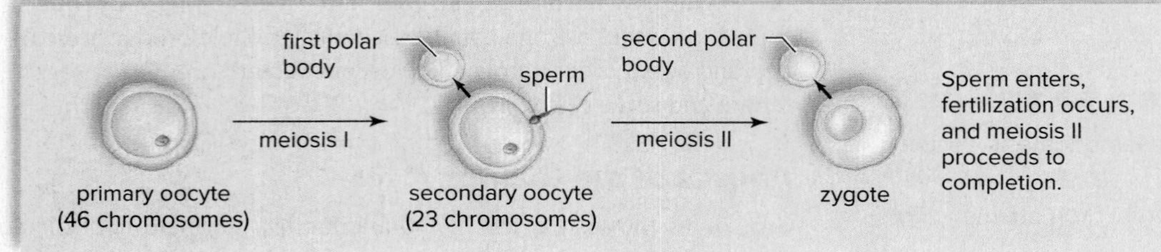

Figure 17.9 **Oogenesis produces egg cells.**

During oogenesis, the chromosome number is reduced from 46 to 23. Oogenesis produces a functional egg cell and nonfunctional polar bodies.

The corpus luteum secretes high levels of progesterone and some estrogen. When pregnancy does not occur, the corpus luteum regresses and a new cycle begins with menstruation (Fig. 17.11).

Estrogen and Progesterone

Estrogen and **progesterone** affect not only the uterus but other parts of the body as well. Estrogen is largely responsible for the secondary sex characteristics in females, including body hair and fat distribution. In general, females have a more rounded appearance than males because of a greater accumulation of fat beneath the skin. Like males, females develop axillary and pubic hair during puberty. In females, the upper border of pubic hair is horizontal, but in males, it tapers toward the navel. Both estrogen and progesterone are also required for breast development. Other hormones stimulate the breasts. Prolactin is involved in milk production following pregnancy, and oxytocin induces milk letdown when a baby begins to nurse.

BIOLOGY IN YOUR LIFE

Do women make testosterone?

The adrenal glands and ovaries of women make small amounts of testosterone. Women's low testosterone levels may affect the libido, or sex drive. The use of supplemental testosterone to restore a woman's libido has not been well researched.

By the way, men make estrogen, too. Some estrogen is produced by the adrenal glands. Androgens are also converted to estrogen by enzymes in the gonads and peripheral tissues. Estrogen may prevent osteoporosis in males.

The pelvic girdle is wider and deeper in females, so the pelvic cavity usually has a larger relative size compared with that of males. This means that females have wider hips than males and their thighs converge at a greater angle toward the knees. The female pelvis tilts forward, so females tend to have more of a lower back curve than males, an abdominal bulge, and protruding buttocks.

Menopause, the period in a woman's life during which the ovarian cycle ceases, is likely to occur between ages 45 and 55. The ovaries are no longer responsive to the gonadotropic hormones produced by the anterior pituitary, and the ovaries no longer

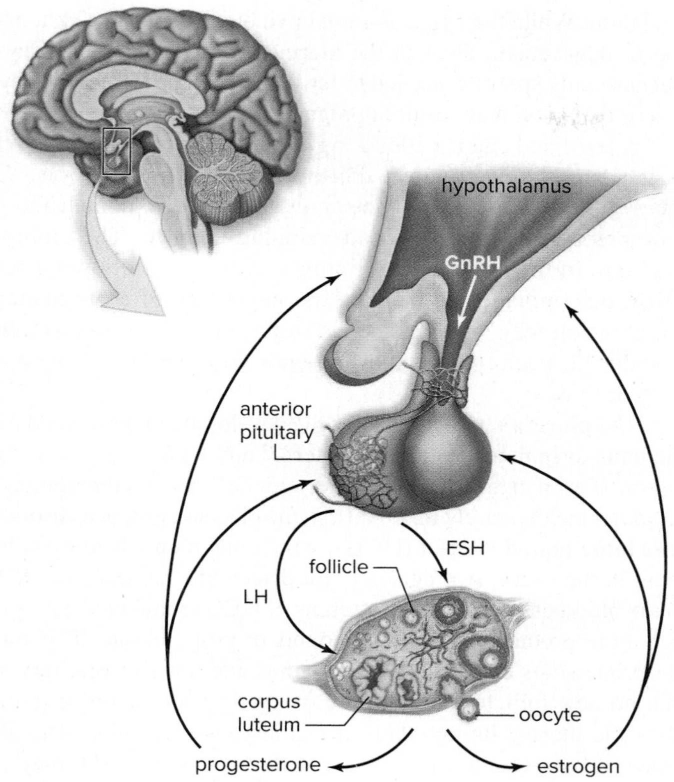

Figure 17.10 The hormones that control the production of estrogen and progesterone by the ovaries.
The hypothalamus produces gonadotropin-releasing hormone (GnRH). GnRH stimulates the anterior pituitary to produce follicle-stimulating hormone (FSH) and luteinizing hormone (LH). FSH stimulates the follicle to produce primarily estrogen, and LH stimulates the corpus luteum to produce primarily progesterone. Estrogen and progesterone maintain the sexual organs (e.g., uterus) and the secondary sex characteristics, and they exert feedback control over the hypothalamus and the anterior pituitary. Feedback control regulates the relative amounts of estrogen and progesterone in the blood.

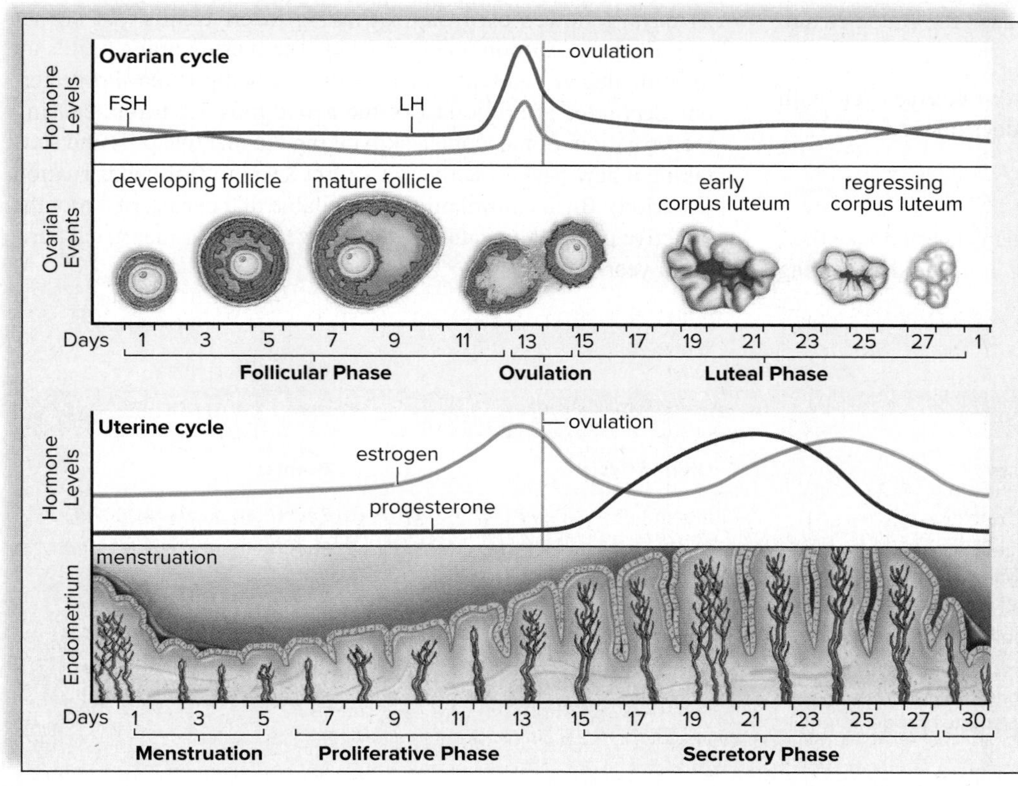

Figure 17.11 Female hormone levels during the ovarian and uterine cycles.
During the follicular phase, FSH released by the anterior pituitary promotes the maturation of a follicle in the ovary. The ovarian follicle produces increasing levels of estrogen, which causes the endometrium to thicken during the proliferative phase of the uterine cycle. After ovulation and during the luteal phase of the ovarian cycle, LH promotes the development of the corpus luteum. Progesterone, in particular, causes the endometrial lining to become secretory. Menses, due to the breakdown of the endometrium, begins when progesterone production declines to a low level.

secrete estrogen or progesterone. At the onset of menopause, menstruation becomes irregular, but as long as it occurs, it is still possible for a woman to conceive. Therefore, a woman is usually not considered to have completed menopause until menstruation is absent for a year.

Uterine Cycle: Nonpregnant

The female sex hormones—estrogen and progesterone—have numerous functions. One function of these hormones affects the endometrium, causing the uterus to undergo a cyclical series of events known as the **uterine cycle** (Fig. 17.11). Twenty-eight-day cycles are divided as follows:

- *Days 1–5.* A low level of estrogen and progesterone in the body causes the endometrium to disintegrate and its blood vessels to rupture. On day 1 of the cycle, a flow of blood and tissues, known as the menses, passes out of the vagina during **menstruation,** also called the menstrual period.
- *Days 6–13.* Increased production of estrogen by a new ovarian follicle in the ovary causes the endometrium to thicken and become vascular and glandular. This is called the proliferative phase of the uterine cycle.
- *Day 14.* For a 28-day cycle, ovulation usually occurs on this day.
- *Days 15–28.* Increased production of progesterone by the corpus luteum in the ovary causes the endometrium of the uterus to double or triple in thickness (from 1 mm to 2–3 mm). The uterine glands mature and produce a thick mucoid secretion in response to increased progesterone. This is called the secretory phase of the uterine cycle. The endometrium is now prepared to receive the developing embryo. If this does not occur, the corpus luteum in the ovary regresses. The low level of progesterone in the female body results in the endometrium breaking down during menstruation.

Table 17.3 compares the stages of a 28-day uterine cycle with those of the ovarian cycle when pregnancy does not occur.

Fertilization and Pregnancy

Following unprotected sexual intercourse, many sperm make their way into the uterine tubes, where the egg is located following ovulation. While the egg may remain viable for only 12–24 hours, sperm may remain alive in the uterine tubes for up to six days. Because only sperm is needed to fertilize the egg, intercourse days before ovulation may result in pregnancy.

A fertilized egg is called a *zygote*. Development begins even as the zygote travels down the uterine tube to the uterus. As the zygote divides, it becomes an *embryo*. The endometrium is now prepared to receive the developing embryo. The embryo implants in the endometrial lining several days following fertilization. Implantation signals the beginning of a pregnancy. An abortion may be spontaneous (referred to as a miscarriage) or induced. Each type of abortion ends with the loss of the embryo or fetus.

The **placenta,** which sustains the developing embryo and later the fetus, originates from both maternal and fetal tissues. It is the region of exchange of molecules between fetal and maternal blood, although the two rarely mix. At first, the placenta produces **human chorionic gonadotropin (HCG),** which maintains the corpus luteum in the ovary. A pregnancy test detects the presence of HCG in the blood or urine. Rising amounts of HCG stimulate the corpus luteum to produce increasing amounts of progesterone. This progesterone shuts down the hypothalamus and anterior pituitary so that no new follicles begin in the ovary. The progesterone maintains the uterine lining where the embryo now resides. The absence of menstruation is a signal to the woman that she may be pregnant (Fig. 17.12).

Eventually, the placenta produces progesterone and some estrogen. The corpus luteum is no longer needed and thus regresses.

Many women use birth control pills to prevent pregnancy (see Section 17.5). The most commonly used pills include active pills, containing a synthetic estrogen and progesterone, taken for 21 days, followed by 7 days of taking inactive pills that do not contain these hormones (Fig. 17.13). The uterine lining builds up to some degree while the active pills are being taken. Progesterone decreases after the last of the active pills are taken, causing menstruation. Some women skip taking the inactive pills and start taking a new pack of active pills right away to skip menstruation (a period). Birth control pills are available that consist of 3 months of active pills. Women taking them have only four menstrual periods a year.

Table 17.3 Ovarian and Uterine Cycles

Ovarian Cycle	Events	Uterine Cycle	Events
Follicular phase—Days 1–13*	FSH secretion begins.	Menstruation—Days 1–5	Endometrium breaks down.
	Follicle maturation occurs. Estrogen secretion is prominent.	Proliferative phase—Days 6–13	Endometrium rebuilds.
Ovulation—Day 14*	LH spike occurs.		
Luteal phase—Days 15–28*	LH secretion continues. Corpus luteum forms and secretes progesterone.	Secretory phase—Days 15–28	Endometrium thickens, and glands are secretory.

*Assuming a 28-day cycle.

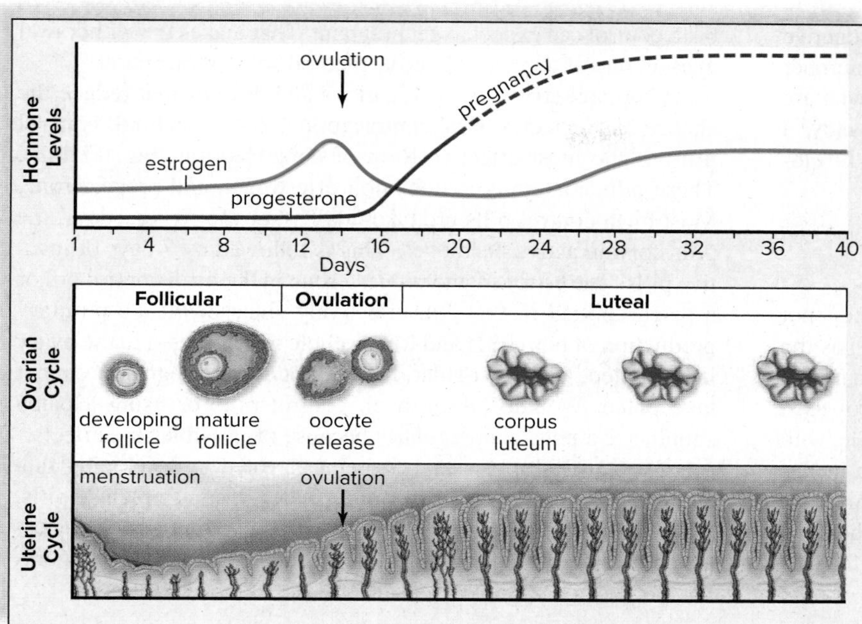

Figure 17.12 **The effect of pregnancy on the corpus luteum and endometrium.**
If pregnancy occurs, the corpus luteum does not regress. Instead, the corpus luteum is maintained and secretes increasing amounts of progesterone. Therefore, menstruation does not occur, and the uterine lining, where the embryo resides, is maintained.

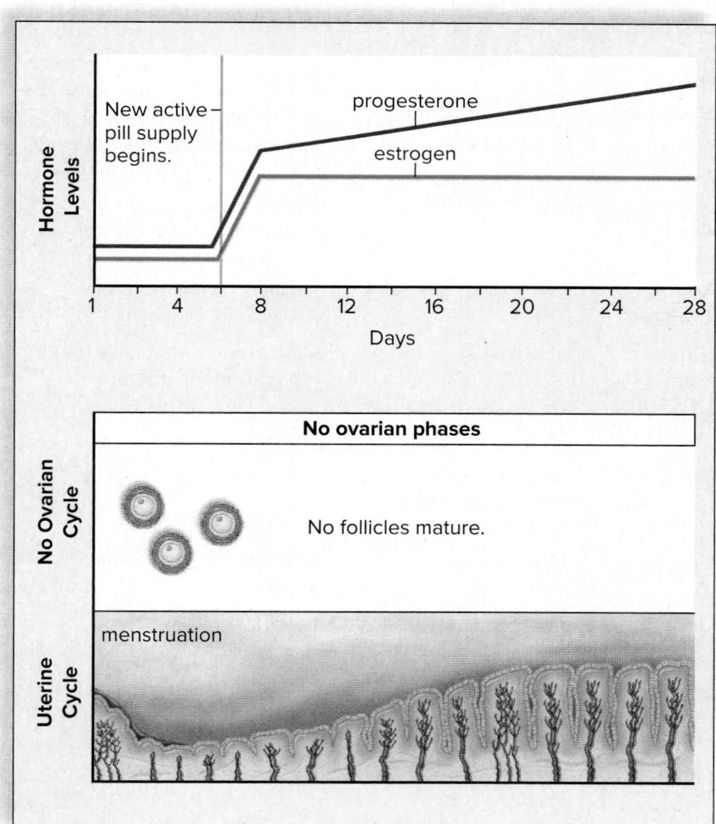

Figure 17.13 **The effect of birth control pills on the ovarian cycle.**
Active pills cause the uterine lining to build up, and this lining is shed when inactive pills are taken. Feedback inhibition of the hypothalamus and anterior pituitary means that the ovarian cycle does not occur.

CHECK YOUR PROGRESS 17.4

1. Summarize the roles of estrogen and progesterone in the ovarian and uterine cycles.
2. Describe the changes that occur in the ovarian and uterine cycles during pregnancy.
3. Describe the changes that occur in the ovarian and uterine cycles when birth control pills are used.

CONNECTING THE CONCEPTS

For more information on the topics presented in this section, refer to the following discussions:

Section 16.6 provides additional information on the male sex hormones.

Section 18.1 outlines the steps in the fertilization of an egg by a sperm cell.

Section 19.4 examines how meiosis reduces the chromosome number during oogenesis.

17.5 Control of Reproduction

LEARNING OUTCOMES

Upon completion of this section, you should be able to

1. List the forms of birth control and summarize how each reduces the chances of fertilization of an egg by a sperm cell.
2. Explain the causes of infertility.
3. Describe how the use of assisted reproductive technologies can increase the chances of conceiving a child.

Several means are available to reduce or enhance our reproductive potential. **Birth control methods** are used to regulate the number of children an individual or a couple has. For individuals who are experiencing infertility, or an inability to achieve pregnancy, a number of assisted reproductive technologies may be used to increase the chances of conceiving a child.

Birth Control Methods

The most reliable method of birth control is abstinence—not engaging in sexual intercourse. This form of birth control has the added advantage of preventing transmission of sexually transmitted diseases. Table 17.4 lists other means of birth control used in the United States and rates their effectiveness. For example, with the birth control pill, we expect 98% effectiveness, which means that, in a given year, 2% of sexually active women using this form of birth control may get pregnant. In comparison, the withdrawal method is 75% effective. Thus, 25% of women using this form of birth control can expect to get pregnant. That makes the withdrawal method one of the least effective methods of contraception.

Contraceptives are medications and devices that reduce the chance of pregnancy. Oral contraception, known as **birth control pills,** is the most effective form of contraception (Fig. 17.14*a*). These pills contain a combination of estrogen and progesterone. Most birth control pills are taken daily. For the first 21 days, the pills contain active hormones. This is followed by 7 days of inactive pills. The estrogen and progesterone in the birth control pill or a patch applied to the skin effectively shuts down the pituitary production of both FSH and LH. Follicle development in the ovary is prevented. Because ovulation does not occur, pregnancy cannot take place. Women taking birth control pills or using a patch should see a physician regularly because of possible side effects.

A great deal of research is being devoted to developing safe and effective hormonal birth control for men. Implants, pills, patches, and injections are being explored as ways to deliver testosterone and/or progesterone at adequate levels to suppress sperm

Table 17.4 Common Birth Control Methods*

Name	Procedure	Methodology	Effectiveness	Risk
Abstinence	Refrain from sexual intercourse	No sperm in vagina	100%	None
Vasectomy	Vasa deferentia cut and tied	No sperm in semen	99%	Irreversible sterility
Tubal ligation	Uterine tubes cut and tied	No oocytes in uterine tube	99%	Irreversible sterility
Oral contraception	Hormone medication taken daily	Anterior pituitary does not release FSH and LH	About 91%	Increased risk of heart attack, stroke, and thromboembolism
Contraceptive implants	Tubes of progestin (form of progesterone) implanted under skin	Anterior pituitary does not release FSH and LH	More than 99%	Similar to other hormone treatments; rare problems with insertion/removal
Contraceptive injections/ patch	Injections of hormones	Anterior pituitary does not release FSH and LH	About 91%	Similar to other hormone treatments
Vaginal contraceptive ring	Ring inserted into vagina each month	Anterior pituitary does not release FSH and LH	About 91%	May be somewhat lower than other hormone treatments
Intrauterine device (IUD)	Plastic coil inserted into uterus by physician	Prevents implantation	About 99%	PID†, rare problems with insertion/removal
Diaphragm	Latex cup inserted into vagina to cover cervix before intercourse	Blocks entrance of sperm to uterus	About 88%; increases when combined with spermicide	Latex, spermicide allergy
Cervical cap	Latex cap held by suction over cervix	Delivers spermicide near cervix	About 71–86%	UTI‡, latex or spermicide allergy
Male condom	Latex sheath fitted over erect penis	Traps sperm and prevents STDs	About 85%	Latex allergy
Female condom	Polyurethane liner fitted inside vagina	Blocks entrance of sperm to uterus and prevents STDs	About 79%	Latex allergy
Coitus interruptus (withdrawal)	Penis withdrawn before ejaculation	Prevents sperm from entering	About 78%	None
Spermicidal jellies, creams, or foams	Spermicidal products inserted before intercourse	Kill a large number of sperm	About 71%	UTI‡, vaginitis, allergy
Natural family planning	Day of ovulation determined by record-keeping, various methods of testing	Intercourse avoided on certain days of the month	About 76–88%	None

*Assuming a 28-day cycle; † = pelvic inflammatory disease; ‡ = urinary tract infection.

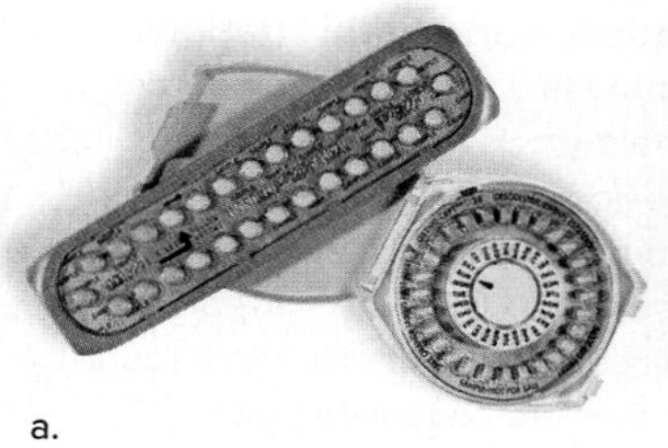
a.

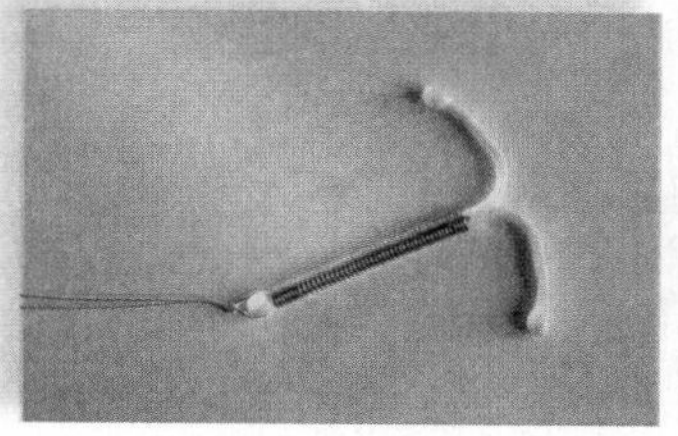
b.

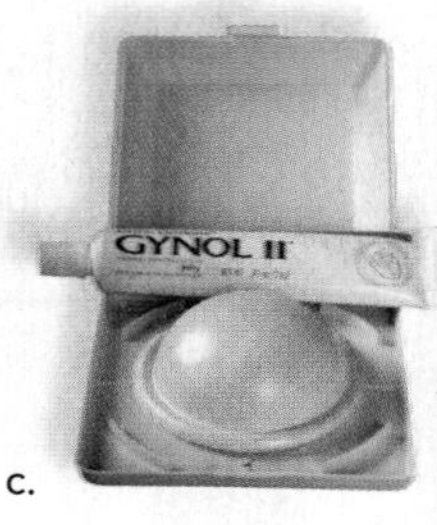

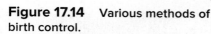

c.

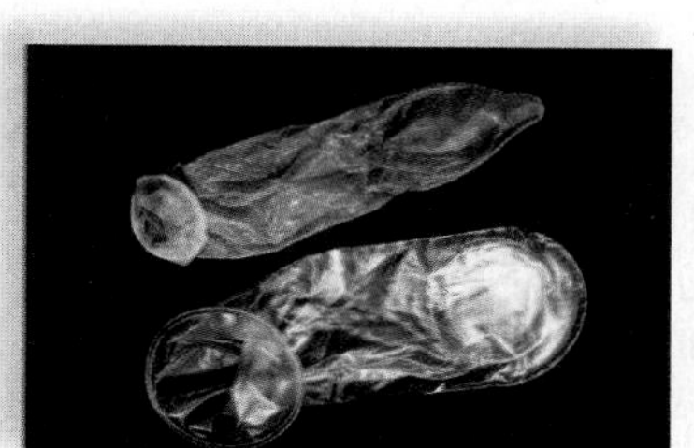
d.

e.

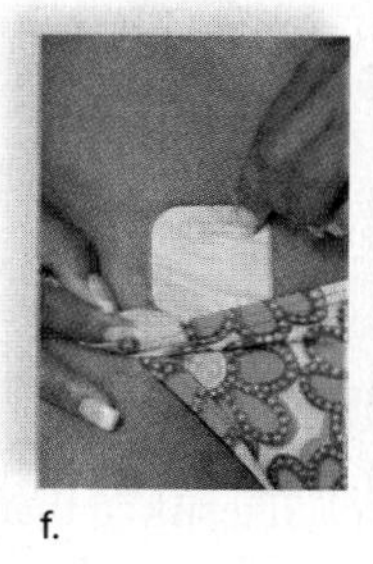
f.

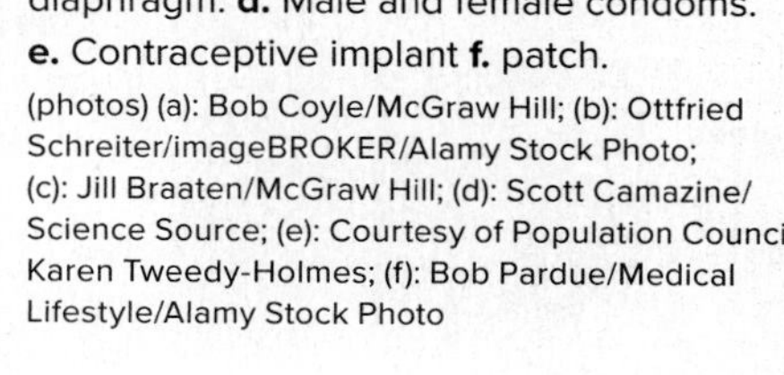
Figure 17.14 Various methods of birth control.
a. Oral contraception (birth control pills). **b.** Intrauterine device. **c.** Spermicidal jelly and diaphragm. **d.** Male and female condoms. **e.** Contraceptive implant **f.** patch.
(photos) (a): Bob Coyle/McGraw Hill; (b): Ottfried Schreiter/imageBROKER/Alamy Stock Photo; (c): Jill Braaten/McGraw Hill; (d): Scott Camazine/Science Source; (e): Courtesy of Population Council/Karen Tweedy-Holmes; (f): Bob Pardue/Medical Lifestyle/Alamy Stock Photo

production. Even the most successful formulations are still in the experimental stage and are unlikely to be available outside of clinical trials for at least a few more years.

An **intrauterine device (IUD)** is a small piece of molded plastic, and sometimes copper, that is inserted into the uterus by a physician (Fig. 17.14*b*). IUDs alter the environment of the uterus and uterine tubes to reduce the possibility of fertilization. If fertilization should occur, implantation cannot take place.

The **diaphragm** is a soft latex cup with a flexible rim that lodges behind the pubic bone and fits over the cervix (Fig. 17.14*c*). Each woman must be properly fitted by a physician, and the diaphragm can be inserted into the vagina no more than 2 hours before sexual relations. Also, it must be used with spermicidal jelly or cream and should be left in place at least 6 hours after sexual relations. The cervical cap is a minidiaphragm.

The male and female **condoms** offer some protection against sexually transmitted diseases in addition to helping prevent pregnancy (Fig. 17.14*d*). Female condoms consist of a large polyurethane tube with a flexible ring that fits onto the cervix. The open end of the tube has a ring that covers the external genitals. A male condom is most often a latex sheath that fits over the erect penis. The ejaculate is trapped inside the sheath and thus does not enter the vagina. When used in conjunction with a spermicide, the protection is better than with the condom alone.

Contraceptive implants and patches (Fig. 17.14*e, f*) use a synthetic progesterone to prevent ovulation by disrupting the ovarian cycle. Most versions consist of a single capsule that remains effective for about 3 years. Contraceptive injections are available as progesterone only or a combination of estrogen and progesterone. The length of time between injections can vary from 1 to several months.

Contraceptive vaccines, also referred to as *immunocontraception,* have been researched for some time now, but none are currently available for humans. Generally, these have focused on decreasing the viability of the gametes (egg or sperm) produced in the body, impairing their function, or impeding development after fertilization. Studies in other mammals indicate this approach is feasible, but due to variations in the human immune system between individuals, immunocontraception is not proving as effective as other birth control measures.

Emergency Contraception

Emergency contraception, or "morning-after pills," consists of medications that can prevent pregnancy after unprotected intercourse. The expression "morning-after" is a misnomer, in that some treatments can be started up to 5 days after unprotected intercourse.

The first FDA-approved medication produced for emergency contraception was a kit called Preven. Preven includes four synthetic progesterone pills; two are taken up to 72 hours after unprotected intercourse, and two more are taken 12 hours later. The hormone upsets the normal uterine cycle, making it difficult for an embryo to implant in the endometrium. One study estimated that Preven was 85% effective in preventing unintended pregnancies. The Preven kit also includes a pregnancy test; women are instructed to take the test first before using the hormone, because the medication is not effective on an established pregnancy.

In 2006, the FDA approved another drug, called Plan B One-Step, which is up to 89% effective in preventing pregnancy if taken within 72 hours after unprotected sex. It is available without a prescription to women age 17 and older. In August 2010, ulipristal acetate (also known as ella) was also approved for emergency contraception. It can be taken up to 5 days after unprotected sex, and studies indicate it is somewhat more effective than Plan B One-Step. Unlike Plan B One-Step, however, a prescription is required.

Mifepristone, also known as RU-486 or the "abortion pill," can cause the loss of an implanted embryo by blocking the progesterone receptors of endometrial cells. This causes the endometrium to slough off, carrying the embryo with it. When taken in conjunction with a prostaglandin to induce uterine contractions, RU-486 is 95% effective at inducing an abortion up to the 49th day of gestation. Because of its mechanism of action, the use of RU-486 is more controversial compared to other medications, and while it is currently available in the United States for early medical abortion, it is not approved for emergency contraception.

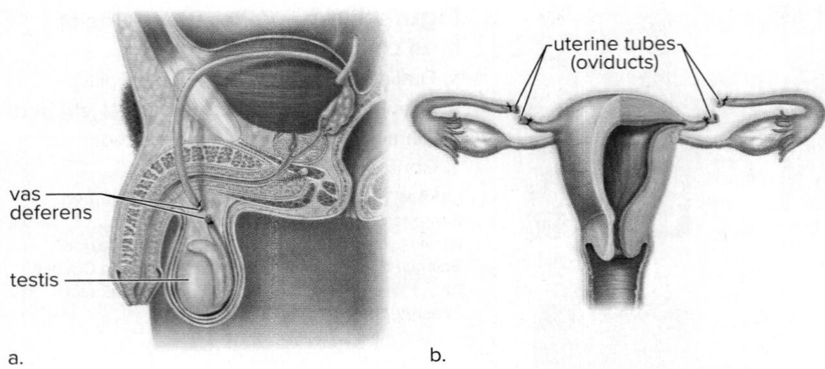

Figure 17.15 **Vasectomies and tubal ligations.** **a.** Vasectomy involves making two small cuts in the skin of the scrotum. Each vas deferens is lifted out and cut. The cut ends are tied or sealed with an electrical current. The openings in the scrotum are closed with stitches. **b.** During tubal ligation, one or two small incisions are made in the abdomen. Using instruments inserted through the incisions, the uterine tubes are coagulated (burned), sealed shut with cautery, or cut and tied. The skin incision is then stitched closed.

Surgical Methods

Vasectomy and tubal ligation are two methods used to bring about sterility, the inability to reproduce (Fig. 17.15). **Vasectomy** consists of cutting and sealing the vas deferens from each testis so that the sperm are unable to reach the seminal fluid ejected at the time of orgasm. The sperm are then largely reabsorbed. Following this operation, which can be done in a doctor's office, the amount of ejaculate remains normal because sperm account for only about 1% of the volume of semen. Also, there is no effect on the secondary sex characteristics, because testosterone continues to be produced by the testes.

Tubal ligation consists of cutting and sealing the uterine tubes. Pregnancy rarely occurs, because the passage of the egg through the uterine tubes has been blocked. Using a method called laparoscopy, which requires only two small incisions, the surgeon inserts a small, lighted telescope to view the uterine tubes and a small surgical blade to sever them.

BIOLOGY IN YOUR LIFE

Are vasectomies 100% effective?

Vasectomies and tubal ligations are considered to be permanent forms of birth control. However, many men do not realize that it is still possible to father a child for several months following a vasectomy. This is because, after the procedure, some sperm remain in the vas deferens. Males who have had a vasectomy need to use alternate forms of birth control for 1 to 2 months or until their physician has performed a follow-up sperm count and verified that sperm are no longer present in the ejaculate. In very rare situations, the vas deferens may reconnect, allowing sperm to once again be ejaculated. While the only 100% effective form of contraception is abstinence, vasectomies are considered to be over 99.8% effective.

It is best to view a vasectomy or tubal ligation as permanent. Even following successful reconnection, fertility is usually reduced by about 50%.

Infertility

Infertility is the failure of a couple to achieve pregnancy after 1 year of regular, unprotected intercourse. Estimates of the prevalence of infertility vary, but most professional organizations predict that around 15% of all couples are infertile. The cause of infertility can be evenly attributed to the male and female partners.

Causes of Infertility

The most frequent cause of infertility in males is low sperm count and/or a large proportion of abnormal sperm, which can be due to environmental influences. It appears that a sedentary lifestyle coupled with smoking and alcohol consumption is most often the cause of male infertility. When males spend most of the day driving or sitting in front of a computer or TV, the testes' temperature remains too high for adequate sperm production.

Body weight appears to be the most significant factor in causing female infertility. In women of normal weight, fat cells produce a hormone called leptin, which stimulates the hypothalamus to release GnRH. FSH release and normal follicle development follow. In women who are overweight, leptin levels are higher, which impacts GnRH and FSH. The ovaries of many women who are overweight contain many small follicles that fail to ovulate. Other causes of infertility in females are blocked uterine tubes due to pelvic inflammatory disease (see Section 17.6) and endometriosis. **Endometriosis** is the presence of uterine tissue outside the uterus, particularly in the uterine tubes and on the abdominal organs. Backward flow of menstrual fluid allows living uterine cells to establish themselves in the abdominal cavity. The cells go through the usual uterine cycle, causing pain and structural abnormalities that make it more difficult for a woman to conceive.

Sometimes the causes of infertility can be corrected by medical intervention, so that couples can have children. If no obstruction is apparent and body weight is normal, it is possible to give females fertility drugs. These drugs are gonadotropic hormones that stimulate the ovaries and bring about ovulation. Such hormone treatments may cause multiple ovulations and multiple births, as discussed in the Diversity in Science feature "Should Infertility Be Treated?"

Many couples who cannot reproduce in the usual manner adopt a child. Others sometimes try one of the assisted reproductive technologies discussed in the following paragraphs.

Assisted Reproductive Technologies

Assisted reproductive technologies consist of techniques used to increase the chances of pregnancy. Often, sperm and/or eggs are retrieved from the testes and ovaries, and fertilization takes place in a clinical or laboratory setting.

BIOLOGY TODAY ▶ Diversity in Science

Should Infertility Be Treated?

Every day, couples make plans to start or expand their families, yet for many, their dreams might not be realized because conception is difficult or impossible. Before seeking medical treatment for infertility, a couple might want to decide how far they are willing to go to have a child. Here are some of the possible risks.

Some of the Procedures Used

If a man has low sperm count or motility, artificial or intrauterine insemination of his partner with a large number of specially selected sperm may be done to stimulate pregnancy. Although there are dangers in all medical procedures, artificial insemination is generally safe.

If a woman is infertile because of physical abnormalities in her reproductive system, she may be treated surgically. Whereas surgeries are now very sophisticated, they nonetheless have risks, including bleeding, infection, organ damage, and adverse reactions to anesthesia. Similar risks are associated with collecting eggs for in vitro fertilization (IVF). To ensure the collection of several eggs, a woman may be placed on hormone-based medications that stimulate egg production. Such medications may cause ovarian hyperstimulation syndrome—enlarged ovaries and abdominal fluid accumulation. In mild cases, the only symptom is discomfort, but in severe cases (though rare), a woman's life may be endangered. In any case, the fluid has to be drained.

Usually, IVF involves the creation of many embryos; the healthiest-looking ones are transferred into the woman's body. Others may be frozen for future attempts at establishing pregnancy, given to other infertile couples, donated for research, or destroyed. Of those that are transferred, none, one, or all might develop into fetuses. The significant increase in multifetal pregnancies in the United States in the last 15 years has been largely attributed to fertility treatment (Fig. 17A). Though the number of triplet and higher-number multiple pregnancies started to level off in 1999, twin pregnancies continue to climb.

They may seem like a dream come true, but multifetal pregnancies are difficult. The mother is more likely to develop complications, such as gestational diabetes and high blood pressure, than are women carrying single babies. Positioning of the babies in the uterus may make vaginal delivery less likely, and there is likely a chance of preterm labor. Babies born prematurely face numerous hardships. Infant death and long-term disabilities are also more common with multiple births. This is true even of twins. Even if all babies are healthy, parenting "multiples" poses unique challenges.

What Happens to Frozen Embryos?

Despite potential trials, thousands of people undergo fertility treatment every year. Its popularity has brought a number of ethical issues to light. For example, the estimated high numbers of stored

Figure 17A Reproductive technologies. Some reproductive technologies may lead to multiple births.
Nancy R. Cohen/Photodisc/Getty Images

frozen embryos (a few hundred thousand in the United States) has generated debate about their fate, complicated by the fact that the long-term viability of frozen embryos is not well understood. Scientists may worry that embryos donated to other couples are ones screened out from one implantation and not likely to survive. Some religious groups strongly oppose destruction of these embryos or their use in research. Patients for whom the embryos were created generally feel that they should have sole rights to make decisions about their fate. However, a fertility clinic may no longer be receiving monetary compensation for the storage of frozen embryos and may be unable to contact the couples for whom they were produced. The question then becomes whether the clinic now has the right to determine their fate.

Who Should Be Treated?

Additionally, because fertility treatment is voluntary, is it ever acceptable to turn some people away? What if the prospect of a satisfactory outcome is very slim or almost nonexistent? This may happen when one of the partners is ill or the woman is at an advanced age. Should a physician go ahead with treatment even if it might endanger a woman's (or baby's) health? Those in favor of limiting treatment argue that a physician has a responsibility to prevent potential harm to a patient. On the other hand, there is concern that if certain people are denied fertility for medical reasons, might they be denied for other reasons also, such as race, religion, sexuality, or income?

Questions to Consider

1. Should couples go to all lengths to have children even if it could endanger the life of one or both spouses?
2. Should couples with "multiples" due to infertility treatment receive assistance from private and public services?
3. To what lengths should society go to protect frozen embryos?

Artificial Insemination by Donor (AID) During artificial insemination, sperm are placed in the vagina by a physician. Sometimes a woman is artificially inseminated by her partner's sperm. This is especially helpful if the partner has a low sperm count, because the sperm can be collected over time and concentrated, so that the sperm count is sufficient to result in fertilization. Often, however, a woman is inseminated by sperm acquired from a donor who is a complete stranger to her. At times, a combination of partner and donor sperm is used.

A variation of AID is *intrauterine insemination (IUI)*. In IUI, fertility drugs are given to stimulate the ovaries. Then, the donor's sperm are placed in the uterus, rather than in the vagina.

If the prospective parents wish, sperm can be sorted into those believed to be X-bearing or Y-bearing to increase the chances of having a child of the desired sex. Fertilization of an egg with an X-bearing sperm results in a female child. Fertilization by a Y-bearing sperm yields a male child.

In Vitro Fertilization (IVF) During **in vitro fertilization (IVF),** conception occurs in laboratory glassware. Ultrasound machines can now spot follicles in the ovaries that hold immature eggs; therefore, the latest method is to forgo the administration of fertility drugs and retrieve immature eggs by using a needle. The immature eggs are then brought to maturity in glassware, after which concentrated sperm are added. After about 2 to 4 days, the embryos are ready to be transferred to the uterus of the woman, who is now in the secretory phase of her uterine cycle. If desired, the embryos can be tested for a genetic disease, and only those found to be free of disease will be used. If implantation is successful, development is normal and continues to term.

Gamete Intrafallopian Transfer (GIFT) The term *gamete* refers to a sex cell, either a sperm or an egg. Gamete intrafallopian transfer (GIFT) was devised to overcome the low success rate (15–20%) of in vitro fertilization. The method is the same as in vitro fertilization, except the eggs and the sperm are placed in the uterine tubes immediately after they have been brought together. GIFT has the advantage of being a one-step procedure for the woman—the eggs are removed and reintroduced all at the same time. A variation on this procedure is to fertilize the eggs in the laboratory and then place the zygotes in the uterine tubes.

Surrogate Mothers Some women are contracted and paid to have babies. These women are called surrogate mothers. The sperm and even the egg can be contributed by the contracting parents.

Intracytoplasmic Sperm Injection In this highly sophisticated procedure, a single sperm is injected into an egg (Fig. 17.16). It is used effectively when a man has severe infertility problems.

CHECK YOUR PROGRESS 17.5

1. List the major forms of birth control in order of effectiveness.
2. Explain why vasectomies and tubal ligations are permanent forms of birth control.
3. Distinguish between an IVF and a GIFT procedure to compensate for infertility.

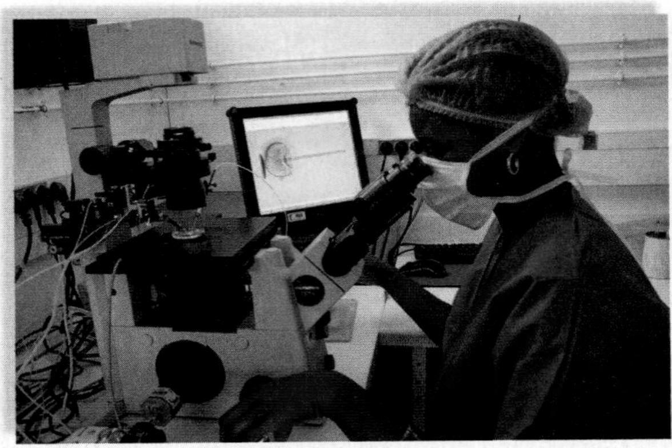

Figure 17.16 Intracytoplasmic sperm injection.
A microscope connected to a computer monitor is used to carry out intracytoplasmic sperm injection. A pipette holds the egg steady while a needle (not visible) introduces the sperm into the egg.

CONNECTING THE CONCEPTS

For more information on the hormones presented in this section, refer to the following discussions:

Section 16.2 explains the role of the gonadotropic hormones.

Section 16.6 describes the hormones produced by the female reproductive system.

17.6 Sexually Transmitted Diseases

LEARNING OUTCOMES

Upon completion of this section, you should be able to

1. Distinguish between sexually transmitted diseases (STDs) caused by viruses and those caused by bacteria.
2. Describe the causes and treatments of selected STDs.

Sexually transmitted diseases (STDs), sometimes referred to as sexually transmitted infections (STIs), are caused by viruses, bacteria, fungi, and parasites.

STDs Caused by Viruses

Among STDs caused by viruses, effective treatment is available for AIDS (acquired immunodeficiency syndrome) and genital herpes. However, treatment for HIV/AIDS and genital herpes cannot presently eliminate the virus from the person's body. Drugs used for treatment can only slow the replication of the viruses. Thus, neither viral disease is presently curable. Further, antiviral drugs have serious, debilitating side effects on the body.

HIV Infections

In Section 8.2, we explored the relationship between the HIV virus and AIDS, as well as some of the more common forms of treatment. At present, there is no vaccine to prevent an HIV infection (although several are in trials), nor is there a cure for AIDS. The

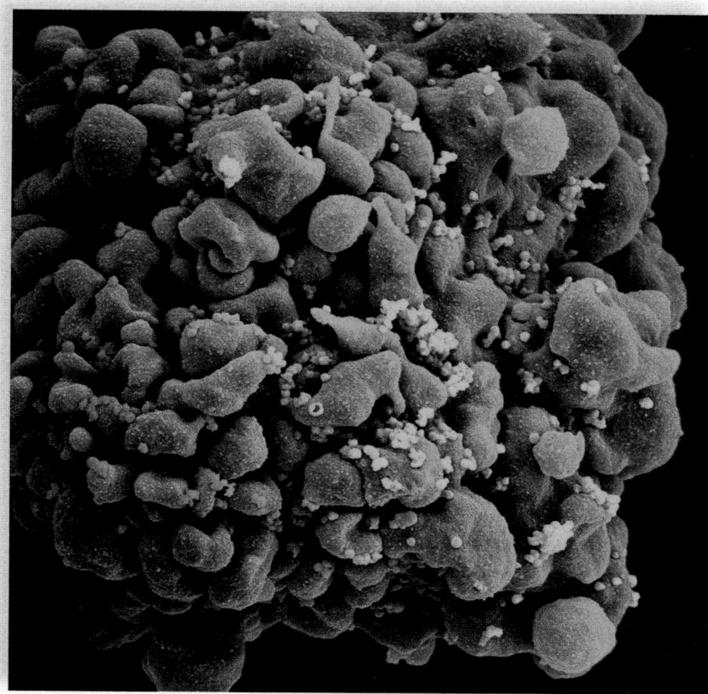

Figure 17.17 Cells infected by the HIV virus.
HIV viruses (yellow) can infect helper T cells (blue), as well as macrophages, which work with helper T cells to stem the infection.
National Institute of Allergy and Infectious Diseases (NIAID)/NIH/USHHS

best course of action is to follow the guidelines for preventing transmission of STDs outlined in the Health feature "Preventing Transmission of STDs."

The primary host for HIV is a helper T lymphocyte, or helper T cell (Fig. 17.17), although macrophages are also infected by the virus. The helper T cells are the very cells that stimulate an immune response (see Section 17.3), so loss of these cells causes the immune system to become severely impaired in persons with AIDS. During the first stage of an HIV infection, symptoms are few, but the individual is highly contagious. Several months to several years after infection, the helper T-lymphocyte count falls. Following this decrease, infections, such as other sexually transmitted diseases, begin to appear. In the last stage of infection, called AIDS, the helper T-cell count falls way below normal. At least one opportunistic infection is present. Such diseases have the opportunity to occur only because the immune system is severely weakened. Persons with AIDS typically die from an opportunistic disease, such as *Pneumocystis* pneumonia.

There is no cure for AIDS. A treatment called highly active antiretroviral therapy (HAART) is usually able to stop HIV reproduction to the extent that the virus becomes undetectable in the blood. The medications must be continued indefinitely, because as soon as HAART is discontinued, the virus rebounds.

Genital Warts

An estimated 79 million Americans are currently infected with the *human papillomavirus (HPV)*. There are over 100 types of HPV. Most cause warts, and about 30 types cause genital warts, which are sexually transmitted. Genital warts may appear as flat or raised warts on the penis and/or foreskin of males, and on the vulva, vagina, and/or cervix of females. Note that if the wart, or warts, are only on the cervix, there may be no outward signs or symptoms of the disease. Newborns can also be infected with HPV during passage through the birth canal.

Individuals currently infected with visible warts may have those growths removed by surgery, freezing, or burning with lasers or acids. However, visible warts that are removed may recur. A vaccine has been released for the human papillomaviruses that most commonly cause genital warts. This development is an extremely important step in the prevention of cancer, as well as in the prevention of the warts themselves. Genital warts, and specifically the HIV virus, are associated with cancer of the cervix, as well as tumors of the vulva, vagina, anus, and penis. Researchers believe that these viruses may be involved in up to 90% of all cases of cancer of the cervix. HPV vaccinations, which are recommended for both women and men before the age of 26, might make such cancers a thing of the past.

Genital Herpes

Genital herpes is caused by herpes simplex virus. Type 1 usually causes cold sores and fever blisters, whereas type 2 more often causes genital herpes (Fig. 17.18).

Persons usually get infected with herpes simplex virus 2 when they are adults. Some people exhibit no symptoms. Others may experience a tingling or itching sensation before blisters appear on the genitals. Once the blisters rupture, they leave painful ulcers, which may take between 5 days and 3 weeks to heal. The blisters may be accompanied by fever; pain on urination; swollen lymph nodes in the groin; and in women, a copious discharge. At this time, the individual has an increased risk of acquiring an HIV infection.

After the ulcers heal, the disease is only latent, and blisters can recur, although usually at less frequent intervals and with milder symptoms. Fever, stress, sunlight, and menstruation are associated with recurrence of symptoms. Exposure to herpes in the birth canal can cause an infection in the newborn, which leads to neurological disorders and even death. Birth by cesarean section prevents this possibility. There are antiviral drugs available that reduce the number and length of outbreaks. However, these drugs are not a cure for genital herpes. Latex or polyurethane condoms are recommended by the FDA to prevent the transmission of the virus to sexual partners.

Hepatitis

Hepatitis infects the liver and can lead to liver failure, liver cancer, and death. Six known viruses cause hepatitis, designated A, B, C, D, E, and G. Hepatitis A is usually acquired from sewage-contaminated drinking water, but this infection can also be sexually transmitted through oral-anal contact. Hepatitis B is spread through sexual contact and by blood-borne transmission (accidental needlestick on the job, a contaminated blood transfusion, infected needles while injecting illegal drugs, from mother to fetus, etc.).

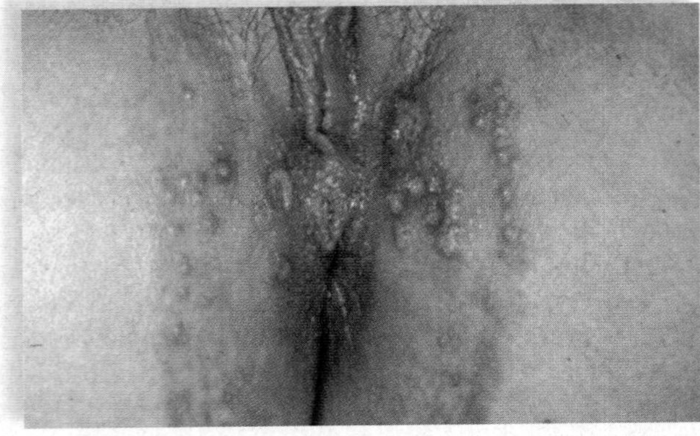

a.

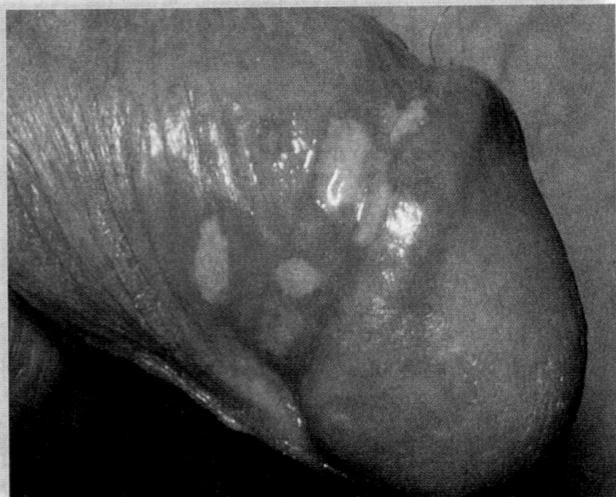

b.

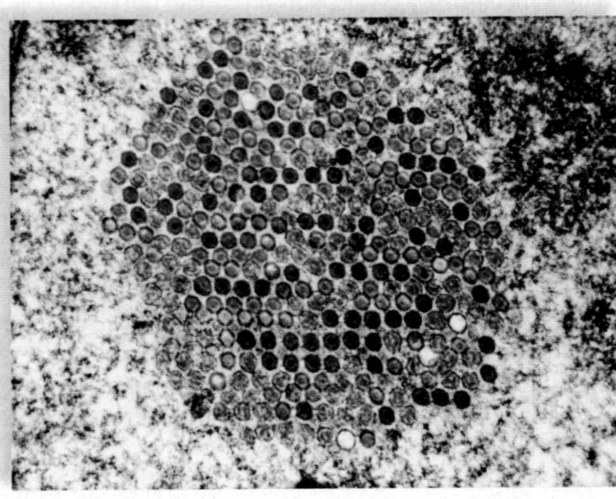

c.

Figure 17.18 **Herpes simplex virus 2 and genital herpes.** Several types of viruses are associated with herpes. Genital herpes is usually caused by herpes simplex virus 2. Symptoms of genital herpes include an outbreak of blisters, which can be present on the labia of females (**a**), or on the penis of males (**b**). **c.** A photomicrograph of cells infected with the herpes simplex virus.

(a): Bob Tapper/Medical Images/DIOMEDIA; (b): Clinical Photography, Central Manchester University Hospitals NHS Foundation Trust, UK/Science Source; (c): David M. Phillips/Science Source

Simultaneous infection with hepatitis B and HIV is common, because both share the same routes of transmission. Fortunately, a combined vaccine is available for hepatitis A and B. It is recommended that all children receive the vaccine to prevent infection, and that adults receive vaccinations throughout their lives (see Section 7.4). Hepatitis C (also called *non-A, non-B hepatitis*) causes most cases of posttransfusion hepatitis. Hepatitis D and G are sexually transmitted, and hepatitis E is acquired from contaminated water. Screening of blood and blood products can prevent transmission of hepatitis viruses during a transfusion. Proper water-treatment techniques can prevent contamination of drinking water.

STDs Caused by Bacteria

Only STDs caused by bacteria are curable with antibiotics. Antibiotic resistance acquired by these bacteria may require treatment with extremely strong drugs for an extended period to achieve a cure.

Chlamydia

Chlamydia is named for the tiny bacterium that causes it: *Chlamydia trachomatis* (Fig. 17.19). The incidence of new chlamydial infections has steadily increased since 1984.

Chlamydial infections of the lower reproductive tract are usually mild or asymptomatic, especially in women. About 18 to 21 days after infection, men may experience a mild burning sensation on urination and a mucoid discharge. Women may have a vaginal discharge, along with the symptoms of a urinary tract infection. Chlamydia also causes cervical ulcerations, which increase the risk of acquiring HIV.

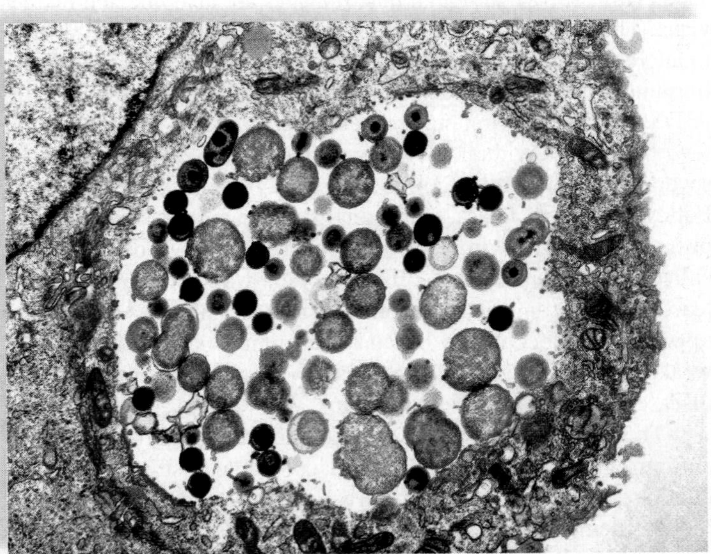

Figure 17.19 **Chlamydial infection.** The different stages of a *Chlamydia trachomatis* infection inside a cell are stained red, brown, and black.

Biomedical Imaging Unit, Southampton General Hospital/Science Source

BIOLOGY TODAY ▶ Health

Preventing Transmission of STDs

Sexual Activities Transmit STDs

- Abstain from sexual intercourse or develop a long-term monogamous (always the same partner) sexual relationship with a partner who is free of STDs (Fig. 17B).
- Refrain from having multiple sex partners or having relations with someone who has multiple sex partners. If you have sex with two people and each of these persons has sex with two people, and so forth, the number of individuals involved becomes quite large.
- Be aware that behaviors associated with intravenous drug use (e.g., needle sharing) may increase the risk of AIDS and hepatitis B, which can then be transmitted sexually to other partners. Be aware that anyone who already has another sexually transmitted disease is more susceptible to an HIV infection.
- Be aware that certain types of sexual activities are associated with an increased risk of HIV infection. Anal intercourse (in which the penis is inserted into the rectum) may increase the risk of HIV. The lining of the rectum is thin, and infected CD4 T cells can easily enter the body there. Also, the rectum is supplied with many blood vessels, and insertion of the penis into the rectum is likely to cause tearing and bleeding that facilitate the entrance of HIV. The vaginal lining is thick and difficult to penetrate, but the lining of the uterus is only one cell thick at certain times of the month and does allow CD4 T cells to enter.
- Males who are uncircumcised are more likely to become infected than males who are circumcised. This is because vaginal secretions, viruses, and bacteria may remain under the foreskin for a longer time.

Figure 17B Transmission of STDs.
Sexual activities can increase the transmission of STDs
(left): Igormakarov/Shutterstock; (right): Laura Doss/Image Source/Getty Images

Figure 17C Sharing needles transmits STDs.
The use of shared needles can transmit many forms of STDs, including HIV and hepatitis.
Don Mason/Brand X Pictures/Getty Images

Practice Safer Sex

- Always use a latex condom during sexual intercourse if you are not in a monogamous relationship. Be sure to follow the directions supplied by the manufacturer for the use of a condom. At one time, people who used condoms were advised to use nonoxynol-9 in conjunction with a condom, but testing shows that this spermicide has no effect on viruses, including HIV.
- Be aware of the risks associated with fellatio (kissing and insertion of the penis into a partner's mouth) and cunnilingus (kissing and insertion of the tongue into the vagina), because they may be a means of transmission. The mouth and gums often have cuts and sores that facilitate catching an STD.
- Practice penile, vaginal, oral, and hand cleanliness. Be aware that hormonal contraceptives make the female genital tract receptive to the transmission of sexually transmitted diseases, including HIV.
- Be cautious about using alcohol or any drug that may prevent you from being able to control your behavior.

Drug Use May Transmit HIV

- Stop, if necessary, or do not start the habit of injecting drugs into your veins. Be aware that HIV and hepatitis B can be spread by blood-to-blood contact.
- If you are struggling with a substance use disorder and are unable to stop using drugs, always use a new sterile needle for injection or one that has been cleaned in bleach (Fig. 17C).

Questions to Consider

1. Why might the use of female contraceptives actually increase the chances of contracting HIV?
2. Which cells in the blood act as a host for HIV?

If the infection is misdiagnosed or if a woman does not seek medical help, there is a particular risk of the infection spreading from the cervix to the uterine tubes, so that pelvic inflammatory disease (PID) results. This very painful condition can result in blockage of the uterine tubes, with the possibility of sterility and infertility. If a baby comes in contact with chlamydia during birth, inflammation of the eyes or pneumonia can result.

Gonorrhea

Gonorrhea is caused by the bacterium *Neisseria gonorrhoeae.* Diagnosis in the male is not difficult, because typical symptoms are pain upon urination and a thick, greenish-yellow urethral discharge. In females, a latent infection leads to pelvic inflammatory disease (PID), which may result in damage to the uterus, ovaries, and other reproductive structures. If a baby is exposed during birth, an eye infection leading to blindness can result. All newborns are given eyedrops to prevent this possibility.

Gonorrhea proctitis, an infection of the anus characterized by anal pain and blood or pus in the feces, also occurs in patients. Oral-genital contact can cause infection of the mouth, throat, and tonsils. Gonorrhea can spread to internal parts of the body, causing heart damage or arthritis. If, by chance, the person touches infected genitals and then touches their eyes, a severe eye infection can result. Up to now, gonorrhea was curable by antibiotic therapy. However, resistance to antibiotics is becoming more and more common, and *Neisseria gonorrhoeae* is now classified as a "superbug," meaning it has developed resistance to a variety of antibiotics.

Syphilis

Syphilis is caused by a bacterium called *Treponema pallidum* (Fig. 17.20). As with many other bacterial diseases, penicillin is an effective antibiotic. Syphilis has three stages, often separated by latent periods, during which the bacteria are resting before multiplying again. During the primary stage, a hard chancre (ulcerated sore with hard edges) indicates the site of infection. The chancre usually heals spontaneously, leaving little scarring. During the secondary stage, the person breaks out in a rash that does not itch and may even appear on the palms of the hands and the soles of the feet. Hair loss and infectious gray patches on the mucous membranes may also occur. These symptoms disappear of their own accord.

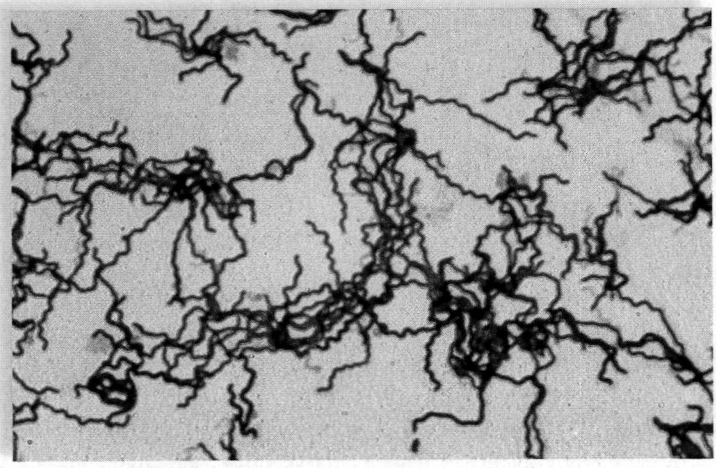

Figure 17.20 **Syphilis.**
Treponema pallidum, the cause of syphilis.
Melba Photo Agency/Alamy Stock Photo

The tertiary stage lasts until the patient dies. During this stage, syphilis may affect the cardiovascular system by causing aneurysms, particularly in the aorta. In other instances, the disease may affect the nervous system, resulting in psychological disturbances. Also, gummas—large, destructive ulcers—may develop on the skin or within the internal organs.

Congenital syphilis is caused by syphilitic bacteria crossing the placenta. The child is born blind and/or with numerous anatomical malformations. Control of syphilis depends on prompt and adequate treatment of all new cases. Therefore, it is crucial for all sexual contacts to be traced so they can be treated. Diagnosis of syphilis can be made by blood tests or by microscopic examination of fluids from lesions.

BIOLOGY IN YOUR LIFE

Can you catch an STD from a toilet seat?

When HIV/AIDS was first identified in the mid-1980s, many people were concerned about being infected by the virus on toilet seats. Toilet seats are plastic and inert, so they're not very hospitable to disease-causing organisms. If you're deciding on whether to hover or sit, remember that sitting on a toilet seat will not give you an STD.

Vaginal Infections

The term *vaginitis* is used to describe any vaginal infection or inflammation. It is the most commonly diagnosed gynecologic condition. Bacterial vaginosis (BV) is believed to cause 40–50% of the cases of vaginitis in the United States. Overgrowth of certain bacteria inhabiting the vagina causes vaginosis. A common culprit is the bacterium *Gardnerella vaginosis.* Overgrowth of this organism and subsequent symptoms can occur for nonsexual reasons. However, males without symptoms can pass on the bacterium to women, who do experience symptoms.

The symptoms of BV are vaginal discharge that has a strong odor, a burning sensation during urination, and/or itching or pain in the vulva. Some women with BV have no signs of the infection. How women acquire these infections is not well understood. Having a new sex partner or multiple sex partners seems to increase the risk of getting BV, but females who are not sexually active get BV as well. Douching also appears to increase the incidence of BV. Women with BV are more susceptible to infection by other STDs, including HIV, herpes, chlamydia, and gonorrhea. Pregnant women with BV are at greater risk of premature delivery.

The yeast *Candida albicans,* and a protozoan, *Trichomonas vaginalis,* are two other causes of vaginitis. *Candida albicans* is normally found living in the vagina. Under certain circumstances, its growth increases above normal, causing vaginitis. For example, women taking birth control pills or antibiotics may be prone to yeast infections. Both can alter the normal balance of vaginal organisms, causing a yeast infection. A yeast infection causes a thick, white, curdlike vaginal discharge and is accompanied by itching of the vulva and/or vagina. Antifungal medications inserted into the vagina are used to treat yeast infections. Trichomoniasis, caused by *Trichomonas vaginalis,* affects both males and females. The urethra is usually the site of infection in males. Males with trichomoniasis are often asymptomatic and pass the parasite to their partner during sexual intercourse. Symptoms of trichomoniasis in females are a foul-smelling, yellow-green, frothy discharge and itching of the vulva/vagina. Having trichomoniasis greatly increases the risk of infection by HIV. Prescription drugs are used to treat trichomoniasis, but if one partner remains infected, reinfection will occur. It is recommended that both partners in a sexual relationship be treated and abstain from having sex until the treatment is completed.

CHECK YOUR PROGRESS 17.6

1. Explain which condition can occur due to a chlamydial or gonorrheal infection.
2. Identify a medical condition in women that is associated with genital warts.
3. Discuss the causes of most STDs.

CONNECTING THE CONCEPTS

For more information on the topics presented in this section, refer to the following discussions:

Section 8.1 explores the structure of both viruses and bacteria.

Section 8.2 provides a detailed examination of the HIV virus, its replication, and the disease AIDS.

Section 8.4 examines how antibiotic resistance occurs and its consequences in the treatment of disease.

CONCLUSION

The three-parent in vitro fertilization procedure is up for review by the FDA to be approved for clinical studies. However, in 2015, the United Kingdom became the first country to approve three-parent IVF to prevent the inheritance of genetic diseases. Despite its acceptance in the UK, this procedure has been a source of controversy among many parties interested in reproductive issues.

While popularized in the media as three-parent babies, the genes in question amount to just 37 out of the estimated 19,000 genes in a human cell. Therefore, many argue that this does not justify calling it a third-parent baby because the donated mitochondrial genes are insignificant in number compared to the rest of the genome derived from the parents.

This is just the start, however. Additional technologies are being developed that may be even more controversial. In 2015, researchers announced that it may be possible to fertilize an egg using another egg, thus eliminating the need for sperm. While the deployment of these technologies may be years away, there is already opposition developing to changing the one egg–one sperm traditional view of reproduction.

SUMMARIZE

17.1 Human Life Cycle

The **reproductive system** is responsible for the production of **gametes** in both sexes. In females, the system also provides the location for fertilization. Following **zygote** formation, the female reproductive system protects and nourishes the developing fetus.

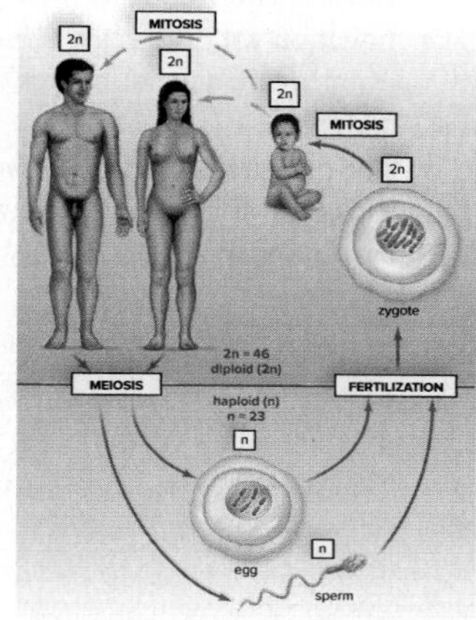

The life cycle of higher organisms requires two types of cell division:

- **Mitosis,** the growth and repair of tissues
- **Meiosis,** the production of gametes

17.2 Male Reproductive System

The external genitals of males are

- The **penis** (organ of sexual intercourse)
- The **scrotum,** which contains the **testes**

Spermatogenesis, occurring in **seminiferous tubules** of the testes, produces **sperm.**

- **Sertoli cells** regulate the process of spermatogenesis.
- The **epididymis** stores mature sperm cells. A mature sperm consists of a head containing the acrosome, a middle section containing mitochondria, and a tail.
- Sperm pass from the **vas deferens** to the **urethra.**
- The **seminal vesicles, prostate gland,** and **bulbourethral glands** secrete fluids that aid the sperm.
- Sperm and secretions are called **semen** (seminal fluid).

Orgasm in males results in ejaculation of semen from the penis.

Circumcision is the surgical removal of the foreskin. **Erectile dysfunction (ED)** is a condition in which the male is unable to achieve or sustain an erection.

Hormonal Regulation in Males

- Hormonal regulation, involving secretions from the hypothalamus, the anterior pituitary, and the testes, maintains a fairly constant level of testosterone.
- **Follicle-stimulating hormone (FSH)** from the anterior pituitary promotes spermatogenesis.
- **Luteinizing hormone (LH)** from the anterior pituitary promotes **testosterone** production by **interstitial cells.**

17.3 Female Reproductive System

Oogenesis occurring within the **ovaries** typically produces one mature follicle each month.

- This follicle balloons out of the ovary and bursts, releasing an **egg** (ovum) that is moved by the **fimbriae** into the **uterine tubes.**
- The uterine tubes lead to the **uterus,** where **implantation** of the zygote and development occur. The **endometrium** is the lining of the uterus, which participates in the formation of the placenta.
- The **cervix** is the end of the uterus, which links to the vagina.
- The female external genital area is called the vulva. It includes the vaginal opening, the clitoris, the labia minora, and the labia majora.
- The **vagina** is the organ of sexual intercourse and the birth canal in females.

Orgasm in females culminates in contractions of the uterus and uterine tubes.

17.4 The Ovarian Cycle

Ovarian Cycle: Nonpregnant

- **Oogenesis** in females produces **oocytes** (egg cells) and **polar bodies.**
- The **ovarian cycle** is under the hormonal control of the hypothalamus and the anterior pituitary.
- During the cycle's first half, FSH from the anterior pituitary causes maturation of a **follicle** that secretes estrogen and some progesterone.
- After **ovulation** and during the cycle's second half, LH from the anterior pituitary converts the follicle into the **corpus luteum.**
- The corpus luteum secretes progesterone and some estrogen.
- **Menopause** represents that stage of a woman's life when the ovarian cycle ceases.

Uterine Cycle: Nonpregnant

Estrogen and progesterone regulate the **uterine cycle.**

- **Estrogen** causes the endometrium to rebuild.
- Ovulation usually occurs on day 14 of a 28-day cycle.
- **Progesterone** produced by the corpus luteum causes the endometrium to thicken and become secretory.
- A low level of hormones causes the endometrium to break down as **menstruation** occurs.

Fertilization and Pregnancy

If fertilization takes place, the embryo implants in the thickened endometrium.

- The corpus luteum is maintained because of **human chorionic gonadotropin (HCG)** production by the **placenta;** therefore, progesterone production does not cease.
- Menstruation usually does not occur during pregnancy.

17.5 Control of Reproduction

Contraceptives are **birth control methods** that reduce the chance of pregnancy.

- A few of these are the **birth control pill, intrauterine device (IUD), diaphragm,** and **condom.**
- Contraceptive vaccines, implants, and injections are becoming increasingly available.
- Surgical procedures, such as a **vasectomy** or **tubal ligation,** make the individual sterile.

Assisted reproductive technologies may help couples who are experiencing **infertility.** Infertility may be caused by a number of factors, including **endometriosis** in females and alcohol consumption and smoking in males. Some examples of assisted reproductive technologies include:

- Artificial insemination by donor (AID)
- **In vitro fertilization (IVF)**
- Gamete intrafallopian transfer (GIFT)
- Intracytoplasmic sperm injection

17.6 Sexually Transmitted Diseases

STDs are caused by viruses, bacteria, fungi, and parasites.

STDs Caused by Viruses

- AIDS is caused by HIV (human immunodeficiency virus).
- Genital warts are caused by human papillomaviruses. These viruses cause warts or lesions on genitals and are associated with certain cancers.
- Genital herpes is caused by herpes simplex virus 2; it causes blisters on genitals.
- Hepatitis is caused by hepatitis viruses A, B, C, D, E, and G. Hepatitis A and E are usually acquired from contaminated water; B and C are from blood-borne transmission; and B, D, and G are sexually transmitted.

STDs Caused by Bacteria

- Chlamydia is caused by *Chlamydia trachomatis.*
- Gonorrhea is caused by *Neisseria gonorrhoeae.*
- Syphilis is caused by *Treponema pallidum.* It has three stages, with the third stage resulting in death.

Vaginal Infections

- Bacterial vaginosis commonly results from bacterial overgrowth. *Gardnerella vaginosis* often causes such infections.
- Infection with the yeast *Candida albicans* also occurs because of overgrowth, and antibiotics or hormonal contraceptives trigger this condition.
- The parasite *Trichomonas vaginalis* also causes vaginosis. This type affects both men and women, though men are often asymptomatic.

ENGAGE

THINKING CRITICALLY

1. Female athletes who train intensively often stop menstruating. The important factor appears to be the reduction of body fat below a certain level. Give a possible evolutionary explanation for a relationship between body fat in females and reproductive cycles.
2. The average sperm count in males is now lower than it was several decades ago. The reasons for this lower sperm count are not known. What data might be helpful in order to formulate a testable hypothesis?
3. Women who use birth control pills appear to have a lower risk of developing ovarian cancer, whereas the use of fertility-enhancing drugs (which increase the number of follicles that develop) may increase a woman's risk. Speculate about how these therapies might affect a woman's risk of developing ovarian cancer.

MAKING IT RELEVANT

1. New molecular tools, such as CRISPR (see Section 22.3), are allowing for direct genetic modifications to embryos. If you were a potential parent, under what circumstances would you want to modify the genetics of your offspring?
2. Why might some people state that the use of reproductive technologies represents an "unnatural" process? What are your thoughts on this?
3. In the near future, it may be possible for human reproduction to occur completely outside of the mother. How might this be beneficial for the developing fetus, and what might be the drawbacks?

Find answers to all of the chapter questions at connect.mheducation.com

CHAPTER 18

Development and Aging

Yuri_Arcurs/iStock/Getty Images

CHAPTER OUTLINE

BEFORE YOU BEGIN

Before beginning this chapter, take a few moments to review the following discussions:

Section 17.2 How does spermatogenesis produce sperm cells?

Section 17.4 How does oogenesis produce egg cells?

Section 17.4 What are the roles of estrogen and progesterone in the female reproductive system?

The Genetics of a Long Life

From the time we are born, our bodies begin to age. Due to advances in medicine and nutrition, our life span expectancy has increased from about 45 years of age in 1900, to just under 79 years of age in the United States today. Increasingly, more individuals are living past the age of 100 (called centenarians). In the United States, there are over 80,000 individuals, or around 0.02% of the population, who are centenarians. The rate is almost triple that in Japan and Okinawa.

In the past several years, researchers have begun to use new molecular techniques to unravel some of the mysteries as to why some individuals live past the age of 100. A variation of one gene, *FOX03A*, has been identified to be more prevalent in centenarians than in the general population. This gene regulates the insulin pathways of the body and appears to control the genetic mechanisms that protect cells against free radicals. Both insulin regulation and protection against free radicals have been known for some time to enhance longevity in a variety of organisms. Interestingly, *FOX03A* is also believed to be involved in the process of apoptosis and may help protect the body against cancer. Although researchers do not think that *FOX03A* is the sole gene for longevity, it is providing a starting point for larger genomic studies on human aging.

In this chapter, we will explore what happens to the human body from the time we are conceived through the development of old age.

As you read through the chapter, think about the following questions:

1. What genetic factors control the process of development in humans?
2. What are the major causes of aging at the cellular and physiological levels?

18.1 Fertilization

LEARNING OUTCOME

Upon completion of this section, you should be able to

1. Describe the steps in the fertilization of an egg cell by a sperm.

In Chapter 17, we examined the structure and function of the reproductive system in males and females. One of the functions of a reproductive system is to produce gametes (egg and sperm cells) for the production of a new individual. **Fertilization** is the union of a sperm and an egg to form a **zygote,** the first cell of that new individual (Fig. 18.1).

Steps of Fertilization

The tail of a sperm is a flagellum, which enables the sperm to swim toward the egg. The middle piece contains energy-producing mitochondria. The head contains a nucleus capped by a membrane-bound acrosome. The acrosome is an organelle containing digestive enzymes. Only the nucleus from the sperm head fuses with the egg nucleus.

The plasma membrane of the egg is surrounded by an extracellular matrix termed the *zona pellucida.* In turn, the zona pellucida is surrounded by a few layers of adhering follicular cells, collectively called the *corona radiata.* These cells nourished the egg when it was in a follicle of the ovary.

During fertilization, several sperm penetrate the corona radiata. Several sperm attempt to penetrate the zona pellucida, but only one sperm enters the egg. The acrosome plays a role in allowing sperm to penetrate the zona pellucida. After a sperm head binds tightly to the zona pellucida, the acrosome releases digestive enzymes that forge a pathway for the sperm through the zona pellucida. When a sperm binds to the egg, the plasma membranes of egg and sperm fuse and the nucleus of the sperm enters the egg. Fusion of the sperm nucleus and the egg nucleus follows.

To ensure proper development, only one sperm should enter an egg. Prevention of polyspermy (entrance of more than one sperm) depends on changes in the egg's plasma membrane and in the zona pellucida. When a sperm comes in contact with the egg, a rapid release of Na^+ ions depolarizes the egg's plasma membrane,

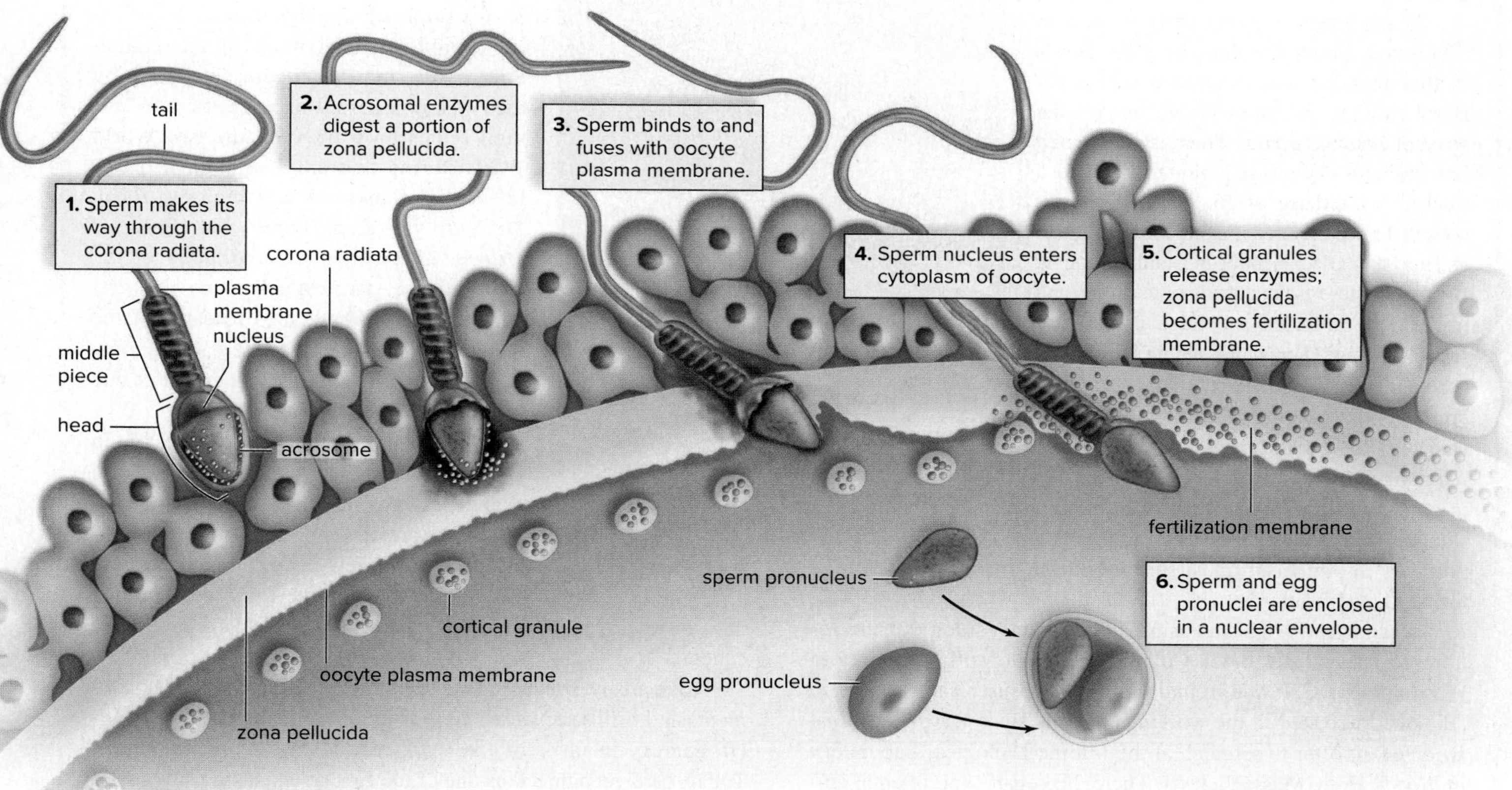

Figure 18.1 Fertilization.
At the start of fertilization, a single sperm is drawn into the egg by microvilli of the egg's plasma membrane. With the help of enzymes from the acrosome, the sperm makes its way through the zona pellucida. After the sperm binds to the plasma membrane of the egg, changes occur that prevent other sperm from entering the egg. Fertilization is complete when the sperm pronucleus and the egg pronucleus contribute their chromosomes to the zygote.

preventing the binding of any other sperm. In addition, vesicles called cortical granules release enzymes that cause the zona pellucida to become an impenetrable fertilization membrane. Now sperm cannot bind to the zona pellucida, either.

As the Diversity in Science feature "Understanding Fertilization" explores, much of our understanding of how fertilization occurs is due to the work of the biologist Ernest Everett Just, a pioneer in the early studies of developmental biology.

BIOLOGY TODAY ▶ Diversity in Science

Understanding Fertilization

In the early twentieth century, pathways in the sciences for Black Americans were few and far between, often due to the racial prejudice that halted advancement in academia for nonwhite scientists. But Ernest Everett Just, a pioneering biologist who uncovered the secrets of cells, not only became one of the most prominent biologists of his generation, but also helped set the foundation for understanding the process of fertilization. His findings would support the work of a generation of future scientists.

Ernest Everett Just (Fig.18A) was born in Charleston, South Carolina, in 1883. Best's mother founded and directed a school for Black children on James Island, just off the coast of South Carolina. There, she educated her son and encouraged him to become a teacher. By the age of 15, Just had already achieved a certification making him eligible to teach at any Black school in South Carolina. But Just's interests lay outside of teaching, and in 1900 he attended a college preparatory school in New Hampshire, where he was the school's only Black student. This eventually brought him to Dartmouth, where Just graduated as the only magna cum laude in his class, majoring in biology. Eager to advance further in academia, Just nevertheless found himself shut out from almost all faculty and teaching positions in American universities—both in the North and South.

Figure 18A **Earnest Just.**
Earnest Just conducted some of the early investigations into the biology of fertilization.
Photo Researchers/Science History Images/Alamy Stock Photo

Just instead began teaching English and biology at the renowned Historically Black College (HBC) Howard University in Washington, DC. It was around this time that Just's career began to take off. Interested in the workings of cells since Dartmouth, Just accepted an offer to research at the Marine Biological Laboratory in Woods Hole, Massachusetts. There, he began experimental embryonic research on marine invertebrates, specifically marine worms, with a special interest in the nature of the female egg cell. His research found important roles of the ectoplasm, or surface of the egg, in fertilization, and showed that a sperm has as an equal probability of entering an egg at any point on its surface, rather than being predetermined.

These findings, which Just would later publish as part of a PhD. dissertation at the University of Chicago, would help propel understanding of the egg's role in fertilization forward, and would later be used as a foundation for work by other scientists in developmental biology. But even after achieving a PhD. and the prestigious Spingarn Medal, awarded to African Americans who had achieved the highest accomplishments in their field, Just still struggled to find any university to bring him on as a professor due to his race.

Unable to find work in the United States, Just moved to Europe, which by then was in a period of scientific and cultural renaissance between the two World Wars. During this time, he published two influential books on cell biology, *Basic Methods for Experiments on Eggs of Marine Animals* and *The Biology of the Cell Surface,* and even became the first American to be invited to research at the Kaiser Wilhelm Institute in Berlin, Germany, a position that was cut short due to the rise of Nazism in 1933.

Just spent most of the rest of his life in Europe, chiefly in France. During World War II, he was held as a prisoner of war, but afterward returned to Howard University, one of the few institutions that would allow him to continue his research. Just died only a year after his return to the States from pancreatic cancer.

Like many Black scientists of his time, Just's accomplishments and brilliance were overlooked through much of the twentieth century in favor of the work of his white contemporaries. Today, he is recognized as one of the first scientists to truly understand the role of the cell's surface in an organism. He also expanded scientists' understanding of the role of eggs in the fertilization process. More recently, Just has been recognized in symposia at the University of Chicago and Dartmouth for his scientific and professional accomplishments in the face of overwhelming racial prejudice in the sciences.

CHECK YOUR PROGRESS 18.1

1. Describe the steps in fertilization.
2. Distinguish between the functions of the corona radiata and the zona pellucida.
3. Explain what prevents multiple sperm from fertilizing the same egg.

CONNECTING THE CONCEPTS

For more information on egg and sperm cells, refer to the following discussions:

Section 17.2 explains how sperm are produced by spermatogenesis.

Section 17.4 explains how egg cells are produced by oogenesis.

18.2 Embryonic Development

LEARNING OUTCOMES

Upon completion of this section, you should be able to

1. Recognize how cleavage, growth, morphogenesis, and differentiation all play a role in development.
2. Identify the extraembryonic membranes and provide a function for each.
3. Identify the organ systems formed from each of the primary germ layers.
4. Summarize the key events that occur at each stage of pre-embryonic and embryonic development.

Human development proceeds from pre-embryonic to embryonic development and then through fetal development. Table 18.1 outlines the major events during development.

Table 18.1 Human Development

Time	Events for Mother	Events for Baby
Pre-embryonic Development		
First week	Ovulation occurs.	Fertilization occurs. Cell division begins and continues. Chorion appears.
Embryonic Development		
Second week	Symptoms of early pregnancy (nausea, breast swelling, and fatigue) are present. Blood pregnancy test is positive.	Implantation occurs. Amnion and yolk sac appear. Embryo has tissues. Placenta begins to form.
Third week	First menstruation is missed. Urine pregnancy test is positive. Symptoms of early pregnancy continue.	Nervous system begins to develop. Allantois and blood vessels are present. Placenta is well formed.
Fourth week		Limb buds form. Heart is noticeable and beating. Nervous system is prominent. Embryo has a tail. Other systems form.
Fifth week	Uterus is the size of a hen's egg. Mother feels frequent need to urinate due to pressure of growing uterus on her bladder.	Embryo is curved. Head is large. Limb buds show divisions. Nose, eyes, and ears are noticeable.
Sixth week	Uterus is the size of an orange.	Fingers and toes are present. Skeleton is cartilaginous.
Second month	Uterus can be felt above the pubic bone.	All systems are developing. Bone is replacing cartilage. Facial features are becoming refined. Embryo is about 38 mm (1.5 in.) long.
Fetal Development		
Third month	Uterus is the size of a grapefruit.	Gender can be distinguished by ultrasound. Fingernails appear.
Fourth month	Fetal movement is felt by a mother who has previously been pregnant.	Skeleton is visible. Hair begins to appear. Fetus is about 150 mm (6 in.) long and weighs about 170 grams (6 oz).
Fifth month	Fetal movement is felt by a mother who has not previously been pregnant. Uterus reaches up to level of umbilicus, and pregnancy is obvious.	Protective cheesy coating called vernix caseosa begins to be deposited. Heartbeat can be heard.
Sixth month	Doctor can tell where baby's head, back, and limbs are. Breasts have enlarged, nipples and areolae are darkly pigmented, and colostrum is produced.	Body is covered with fine hair called lanugo. Skin is wrinkled and reddish.
Seventh month	Uterus reaches halfway between umbilicus and rib cage.	Testes descend into scrotum. Eyes are open. Fetus is about 300 mm (12 in.) long and weighs about 1,350 grams (3 lb).
Eighth month	Weight gain is averaging about a pound a week. Standing and walking are difficult for the mother because her center of gravity is thrown forward.	Body hair begins to disappear. Subcutaneous fat begins to be deposited.
Ninth month	Uterus is up to rib cage, causing shortness of breath and heartburn. Sleeping becomes difficult.	Fetus is ready for birth. It is about 530 mm (20.5 in.) long and weighs about 3,400 grams (7.5 lb).

Processes of Development

The following processes occur during the development of a human embryo:

- **Cleavage.** Immediately after fertilization, the zygote begins to divide, so that there are first 2; then 4, 8, 16, and 32 cells; and so forth. An increase in size does not accompany these divisions. Cell division during cleavage is mitotic, and each cell receives a full complement of chromosomes and genes.
- **Growth.** During embryonic development, cell division is accompanied by an increase in the size of the daughter cells.
- **Morphogenesis.** Morphogenesis is the shaping of the embryo and is first evident when certain cells are seen to move, or migrate, in relation to other cells. By these movements, the embryo begins to assume various shapes.
- **Differentiation.** When cells take on a specific structure and function, differentiation occurs. The first system to become visibly differentiated is the nervous system.

BIOLOGY IN YOUR LIFE

How is a baby's due date calculated?

The due date for the arrival of a baby is calculated from the first day of the woman's last menstrual cycle before pregnancy. From conception to birth is approximately 266 days. Conception occurs approximately 14 days after the menstrual cycle begins (assuming ovulation occurs in the middle of the menstrual cycle). This gives a total of 280 days until the due date, or approximately 40 weeks.

To estimate the actual date, a calculation called Naegele's rule is often used:

1. Use the first day of the last period as a starting point.
2. Subtract 3 months from the month in which the period occurred.
3. Add 7 days to the first day of the last period.

For example, if a woman's last period started on January 1, her baby's approximate due date is October 8. Ultrasound exams are also frequently used to verify the baby's due date.

Stages of Development

Pre-embryonic development encompasses the events of the first week; **embryonic development** begins with the second week and lasts until the end of the second month.

Pre-embryonic Development

The events of the first week of development are shown in Figure 18.2.

Immediately after fertilization, the zygote divides repeatedly as it passes down the uterine tube to the uterus. At this point, the zygote is referred to as an **embryo.** A **morula** is a compact ball of embryonic cells that becomes a **blastocyst.** The many cells of the blastocyst arrange themselves so that there is an **inner cell mass** surrounded by an outer layer of cells. The inner cell mass will eventually become the **fetus.**

Each cell in the inner cell mass has the genetic capability of becoming any type of tissue. Sometimes, during development, the cells of the morula separate or the inner cell mass splits and two embryos are present rather than one. If all goes well, these two embryos will be identical twins, because they have inherited exactly the same chromosomes. Fraternal twins arise when two different eggs are fertilized by two different sperm. They do not have identical chromosomes.

Extraembryonic Membranes

The **extraembryonic membranes** are not part of the embryo and fetus. Instead, as implied by their name, they are outside the embryo (Fig. 18.3). The names of the extraembryonic membranes in humans are named for their general function in animals, such as birds and reptiles, that produce eggs with shells. In these animals, the *chorion* lies next to the shell and carries on gas exchange. The *amnion* contains the protective amniotic fluid, which bathes the developing embryo. The *allantois* collects nitrogenous wastes. The *yolk sac* surrounds the *yolk,* which provides nourishment.

The functions of the extraembryonic membranes are slightly different in humans, because humans develop inside the uterus. The extraembryonic membranes and their functions in humans follow.

- The **chorion** develops into the fetal half of the **placenta,** the organ that provides the embryo/fetus with nourishment and oxygen and takes away its waste. The *chorionic villi* are fingerlike projections of the chorion that increase the absorptive area of the chorion. Blood vessels within the chorionic villi are continuous with the umbilical blood vessels.
- The **allantois,** like the yolk sac, extends away from the embryo. It accumulates the small amount of urine produced by the fetal kidneys and later gives rise to the urinary bladder. For now, its blood vessels become the umbilical blood vessels, which take blood to and from the fetus. The umbilical arteries carry oxygen-poor blood from the fetus to the placenta, and the umbilical vein carries oxygen-rich blood from the placenta to the fetus.
- The **yolk sac** is the first embryonic membrane to appear. In animals that have eggs encased by shells, such as birds, the yolk sac contains *yolk,* which is the food for the developing embryo. In mammals such as humans, this function is taken over by the placenta, and thus the yolk sac contains little yolk. However, the yolk sac contains plentiful blood vessels. It is the first site of blood cell formation.
- The **amnion** enlarges as the embryo and then the fetus enlarges. It contains fluid to cushion and protect the embryo, which develops into a fetus.

Embryonic Development

The second week begins the process of implantation. Embryonic development lasts until the end of the second month of development. At the end of embryonic development, the embryo is easily recognized as human.

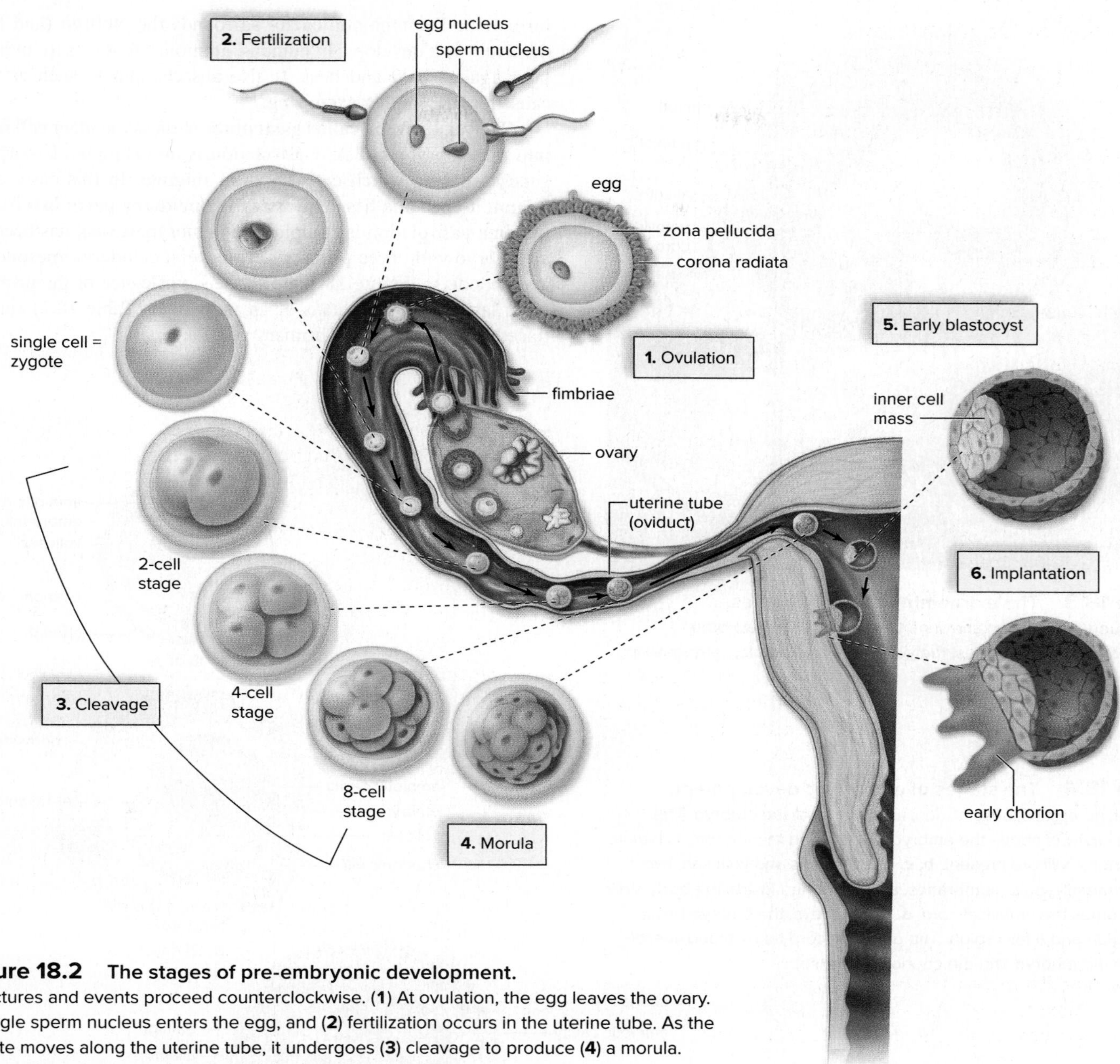

Figure 18.2 **The stages of pre-embryonic development.** Structures and events proceed counterclockwise. (**1**) At ovulation, the egg leaves the ovary. A single sperm nucleus enters the egg, and (**2**) fertilization occurs in the uterine tube. As the zygote moves along the uterine tube, it undergoes (**3**) cleavage to produce (**4**) a morula. (**5**) The blastocyst forms and (**6**) implants in the uterine lining.

Second Week At the end of the first week, the embryo usually begins the process of implanting itself in the wall of the uterus. When **implantation** is successful, a woman is clinically pregnant. On occasion, it happens that the embryo implants itself in a location other than the uterus, usually one of the uterine tubes. This is called an *ectopic pregnancy.* Because the uterine tubes are unable to expand to adjust for the growing embryo, this form of pregnancy is not successful and can pose health risks for the mother. During implantation, the chorion secretes enzymes to digest away some of the tissue and blood vessels of the endometrium of the uterus. The chorion also begins to secrete **human chorionic gonadotropin (HCG),** the hormone that is the basis for the pregnancy test. HCG acts as luteinizing hormone (LH) in that it maintains the corpus luteum past the time it normally disintegrates. It is being stimulated, so the corpus luteum secretes progesterone, which maintains the endometrial wall. The endometrium is maintained, so the expected menstruation does not occur.

The embryo is now about the size of the period at the end of this sentence. As the week progresses, the inner cell mass becomes the *embryonic disk,* and two more extraembryonic membranes form (Fig. 18.4*a, b*). The yolk sac is the first site of blood cell

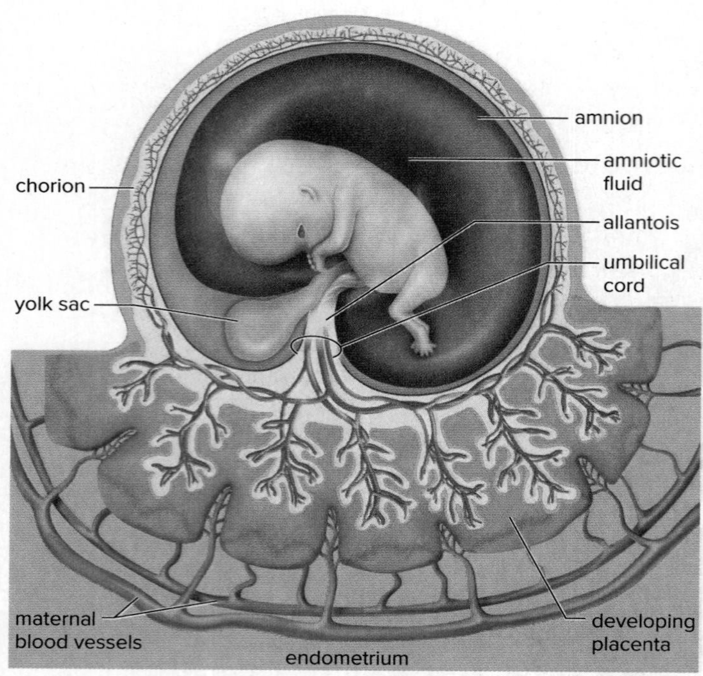

Figure 18.3 **The extraembryonic membranes.** The chorion and amnion surround the embryo. The two other extraembryonic membranes, the yolk sac and allantois, contribute to the umbilical cord.

formation. The amniotic cavity surrounds the embryo (and then the fetus) as it develops. In humans, amniotic fluid acts as an insulator against cold and heat. It also absorbs shock, such as that caused by the mother exercising.

The major event, called **gastrulation,** turns the inner cell mass into the embryonic disk. Gastrulation is an example of morphogenesis, during which cells move or migrate. In this case, cells migrate to become tissue layers called **primary germ layers.** By the time gastrulation is complete, the embryonic disk has become an embryo with three primary germ layers: ectoderm, mesoderm, and endoderm. Figure 18.5 shows the significance of the primary germ layers. All the organs of an individual (Table 18.2) can be traced back to one of the primary germ layers.

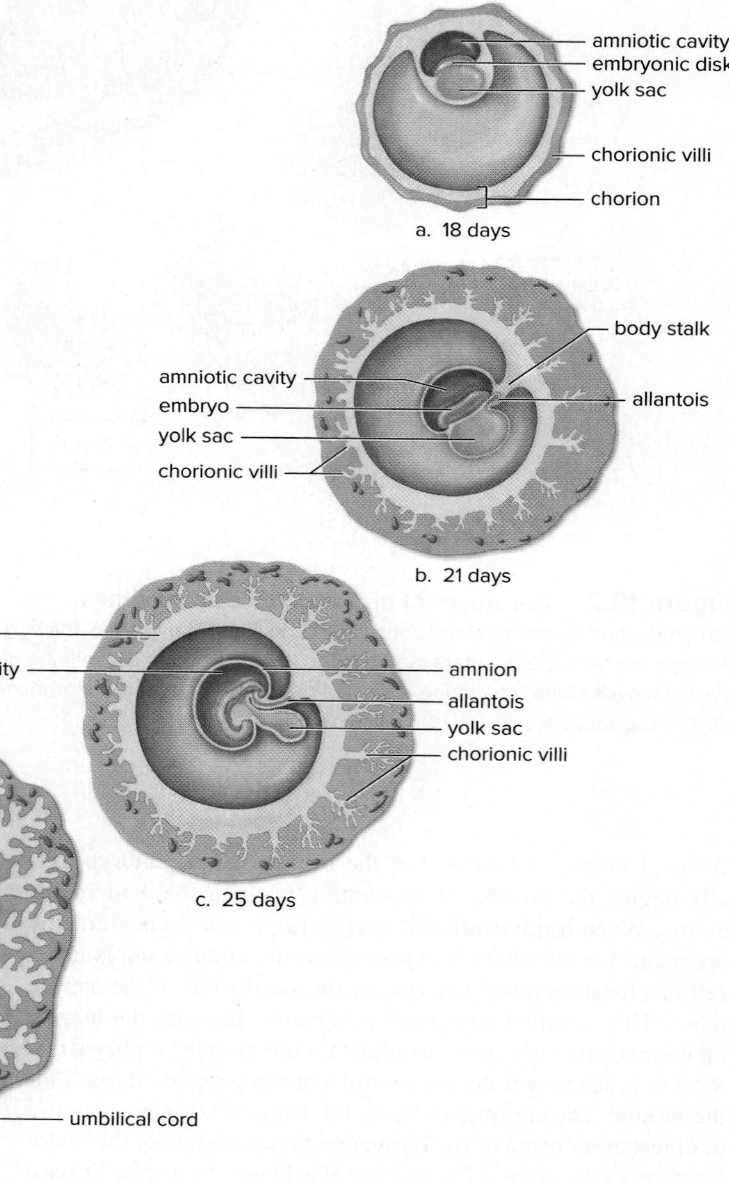

Figure 18.4 **The stages of embryonic development.** **a.** At first, no organs, only tissues, are present in the embryo. The amniotic cavity is above the embryonic disk, and the yolk sac is below. The chorionic villi are present. **b, c.** The allantois and yolk sac, two more extraembryonic membranes, are positioned inside the body stalk as it becomes the umbilical cord. **d.** At 35+ days, the embryo has a head region and a tail region. The umbilical cord takes blood vessels between the embryo and the chorion (placenta).

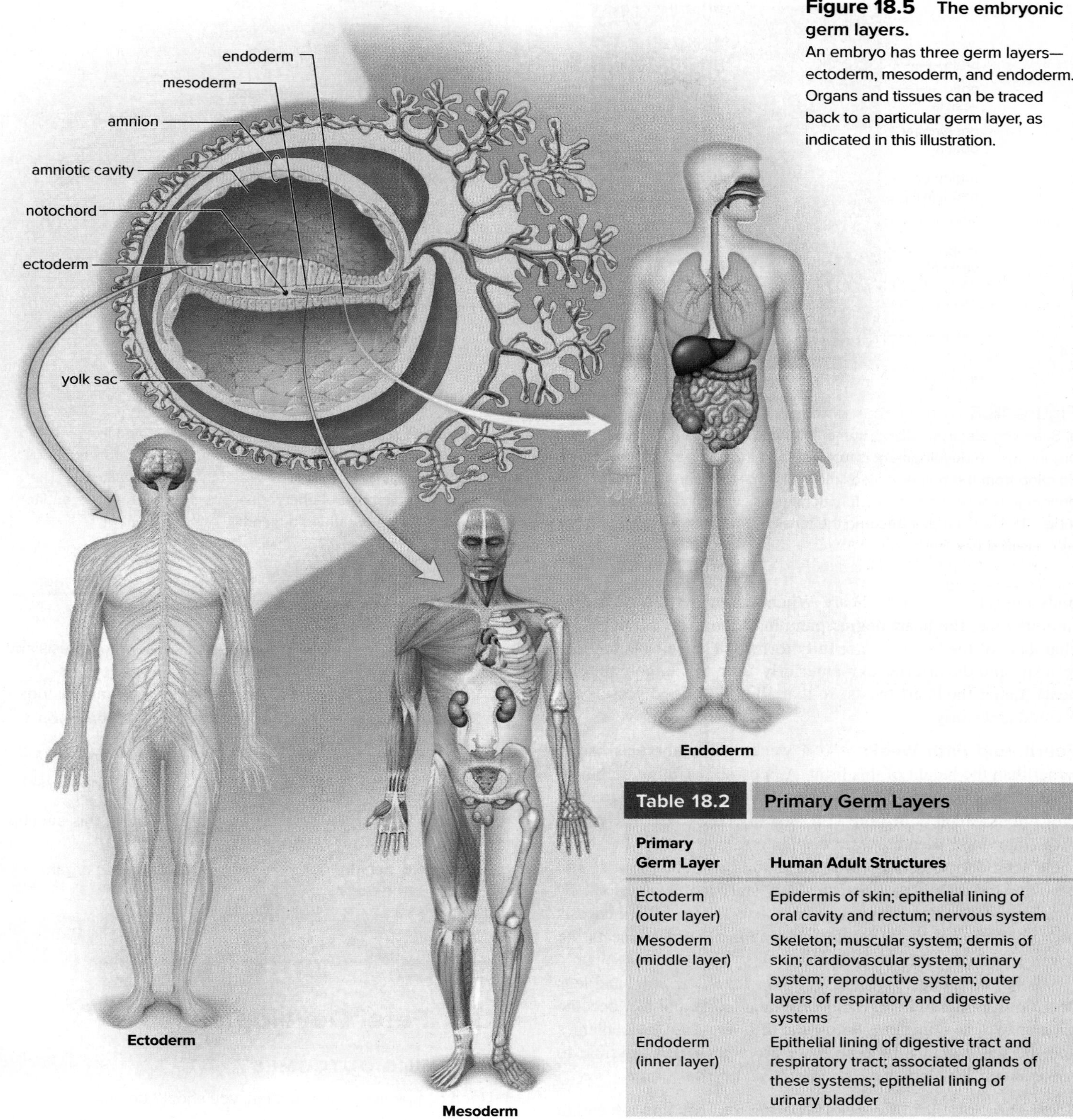

Figure 18.5 **The embryonic germ layers.**
An embryo has three germ layers—ectoderm, mesoderm, and endoderm. Organs and tissues can be traced back to a particular germ layer, as indicated in this illustration.

Table 18.2 Primary Germ Layers

Primary Germ Layer	Human Adult Structures
Ectoderm (outer layer)	Epidermis of skin; epithelial lining of oral cavity and rectum; nervous system
Mesoderm (middle layer)	Skeleton; muscular system; dermis of skin; cardiovascular system; urinary system; reproductive system; outer layers of respiratory and digestive systems
Endoderm (inner layer)	Epithelial lining of digestive tract and respiratory tract; associated glands of these systems; epithelial lining of urinary bladder

Third Week Two important organ systems make their appearance during the third week. The nervous system is the first organ system to be visually evident. At first, a thickening appears along the entire posterior length of the embryo. Then, the center begins to fold inward, forming a pocket. The edges are called *neural folds*. When the neural folds meet at the midline, the pocket becomes a tube, called the neural tube. The neural tube later develops into the brain and the spinal cord.

Development of the heart begins in the third week and continues into the fourth week. At first, cells from both sides of the

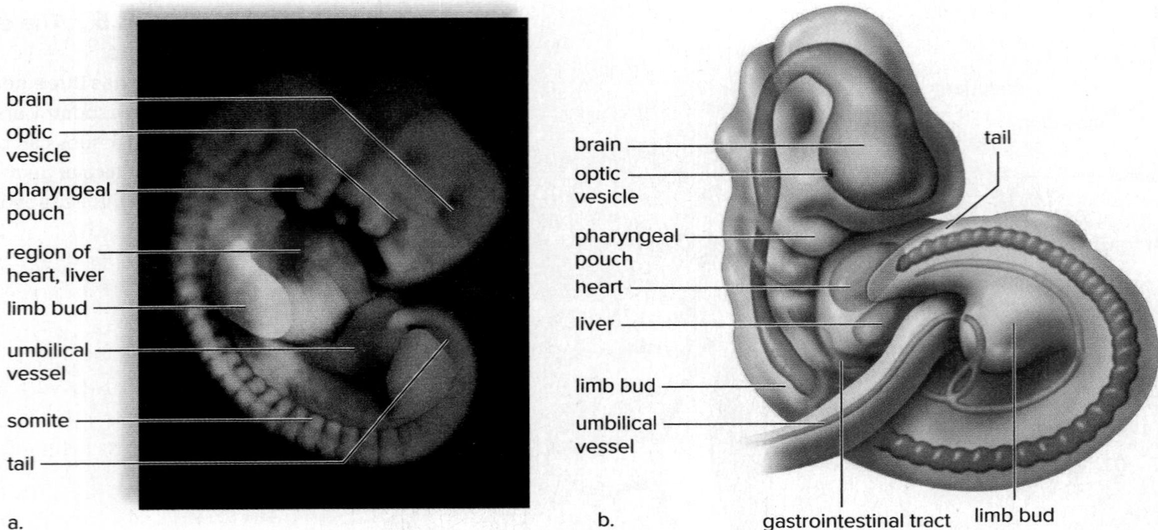

Figure 18.6 The human embryo after 5 weeks of development.
a. Scanning electron micrograph of a human embryo after 5 weeks. **b.** The embryo is curled, so that the head touches the heart and liver, the two organs whose development is further along than the rest of the body. The organs of the gastrointestinal tract are forming, and the arms and legs develop from the bulges called limb buds. The tail is an evolutionary remnant; its bones regress and become those of the coccyx (tailbone). The pharyngeal pouches become functioning gills in fishes and amphibian larvae; in humans, the first pair of pharyngeal pouches become the auditory tubes. The second pair become the tonsils, and the third and fourth become the thymus and the parathyroid glands.
(a): Anatomical Travelogue/Science Source

body migrate to form the heart. When these fuse to form a continuous tube, the heart begins pumping blood, even though the chambers of the heart are not fully formed. The veins enter posteriorly, and the arteries exit anteriorly from this largely tubular heart. Later, the heart twists, so that all major blood vessels are located anteriorly.

Fourth and Fifth Weeks At 4 weeks, the embryo is barely larger than the height of this print. A body stalk (future umbilical cord) connects the embryo to the chorion, which has treelike projections called **chorionic villi** (see Fig. 18.4*c, d*). The fourth extraembryonic membrane, the allantois, lies within the body stalk. Its blood vessels become the umbilical blood vessels. The head and tail then lift up, and the body stalk moves anteriorly by constriction. Once this process is complete, the **umbilical cord** is fully formed (see Fig. 18.4*d*). The umbilical cord connects the developing embryo to the placenta.

Soon, limb buds appear (Fig. 18.6). Later, the arms and legs develop from the limb buds, and even the hands and feet become apparent. At the same time, during the fifth week, the head enlarges and the sense organs become more prominent. It is possible to make out the developing eyes and ears, and even the nose.

Sixth Through Eighth Weeks During the sixth through eighth weeks of development, the embryo changes to a form easily recognized as a human. Concurrent with brain development, the head achieves its normal relationship with the body as a neck region develops. The nervous system is developed well enough to permit reflex actions, such as a startle response to touch. At the end of this period, the embryo is about 38 mm (1.5 in.) long and weighs no more than an aspirin tablet, even though all organ systems have been established.

CHECK YOUR PROGRESS 18.2

1. Distinguish between the processes of morphogenesis and differentiation.
2. Describe the function of the extraembryonic membranes.
3. Summarize what occurs at each stage of pre-embryonic development and embryonic development.

CONNECTING THE CONCEPTS

For more information on the topics presented in this section, refer to the following discussions:

Section 4.6 summarizes the function of each of the organ systems in the body.

Section 17.4 examines the roles of HCG and progesterone in pregnancy.

18.3 Fetal Development

LEARNING OUTCOMES

Upon completion of this section, you should be able to

1. State the roles of progesterone and estrogen in fetal development.
2. Describe the flow of blood in a fetus and explain the role of the placenta.
3. Summarize the major events in the development of the fetus from 3 to 9 months.
4. Explain the process by which the male and female reproductive organs develop.

The **placenta** is the source of progesterone and estrogen during pregnancy. These hormones have two functions: (1) Because of negative feedback on the hypothalamus and anterior pituitary, they prevent any new follicles from maturing; and (2) they maintain the endometrium. Menstruation does not usually occur during pregnancy.

The placenta has a fetal side contributed by the chorion and a maternal side consisting of uterine tissue (Fig. 18.7*a*). The blood of the mother and blood of the fetus never mix, because exchange always takes place across the villi via diffusion. Carbon dioxide and other wastes move from the fetal side to the maternal side. Nutrients and oxygen move from the maternal side to the fetal side of the placenta.

As discussed in the Health feature "Preventing and Testing for Birth Defects," harmful chemicals can cross the placenta, and this is of particular concern during the embryonic period, when various structures are first forming. Each organ or part seems to have a sensitive period during which a substance can alter its normal development and function.

Fetal Circulation

The umbilical cord stretches between the placenta and the fetus. It is the lifeline of the fetus because it contains the umbilical arteries and vein (Fig. 18.7*b*). Blood in the fetal aorta travels to its various branches, including the iliac arteries. The iliac arteries connect to the *umbilical arteries* carrying oxygen (O_2)-poor blood to the placenta. The *umbilical vein* carries blood rich in nutrients and O_2 from the placenta to the fetus. The umbilical vein enters the liver and then joins the *ductus venosus* (venous duct). This merges with the inferior vena cava, a vessel that returns blood to the right

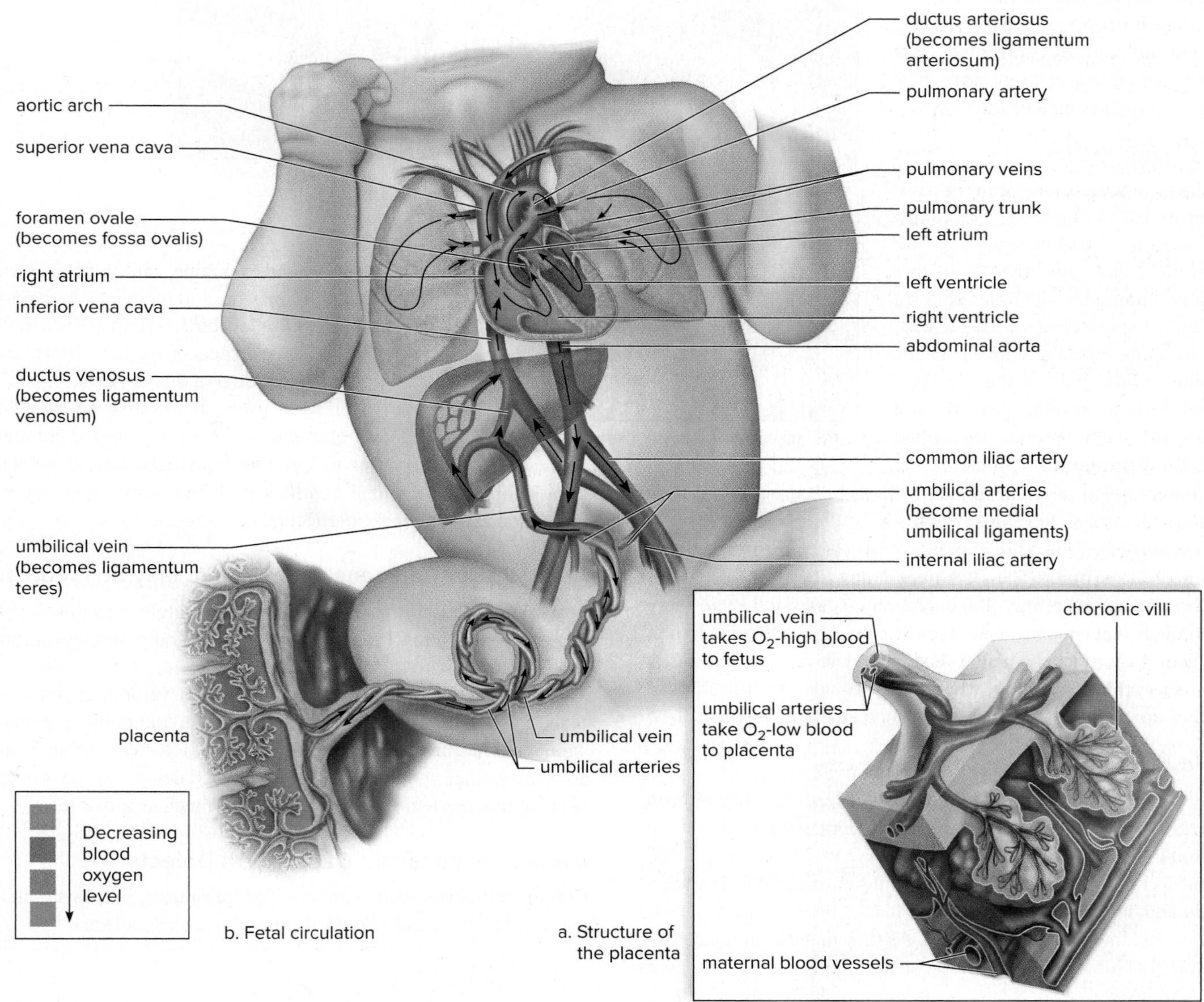

Figure 18.7 The placenta and fetal circulation.
a. At the placenta, an exchange of molecules between fetal and maternal blood takes place across the walls of the chorionic villi. **b.** The flow of blood in the fetus differs from that in the adult (see Fig. 5.11) due to presence of the placenta.

BIOLOGY TODAY ▶ Health

Preventing and Testing for Birth Defects

Birth defects, or congenital disorders, are abnormal conditions that are present at birth. They are one of the leading causes of infant deaths. According to the Centers for Disease Control and Prevention (CDC), about 1 in 33 babies born in the United States has a birth defect. Genetic birth defects can sometimes be detected before birth by a variety of methods (Fig. 18B). However, these methods are not without risk.

Some birth defects are not serious, and not all can be prevented. But women can take steps to increase their chances of delivering a healthy baby.

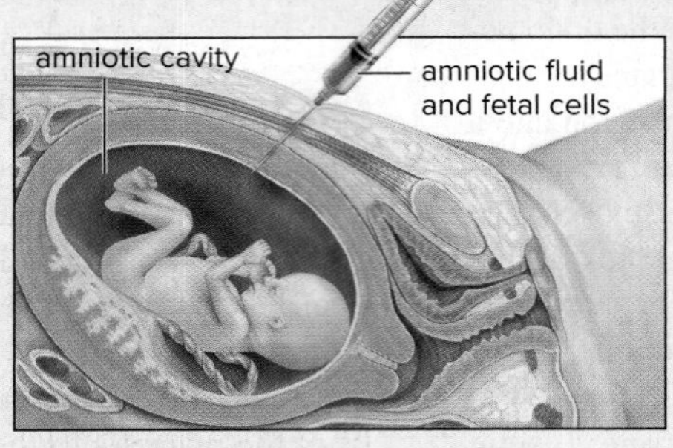

a. Amniocentesis

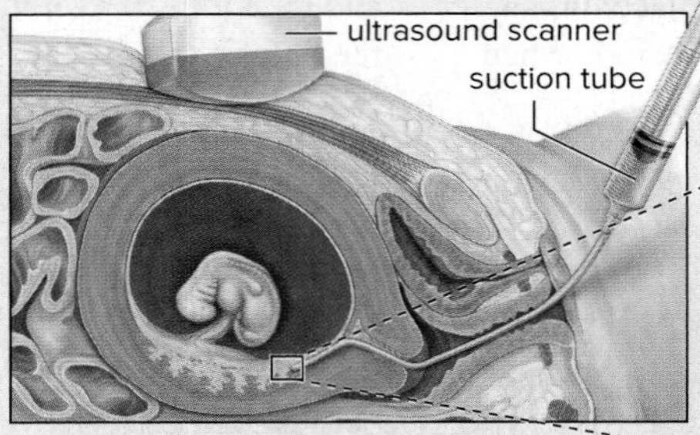

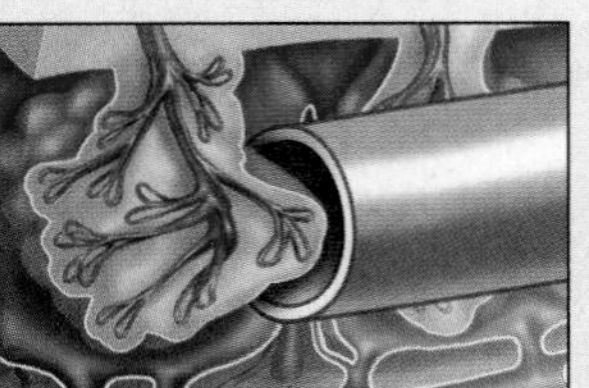

b. Chorionic villus sampling

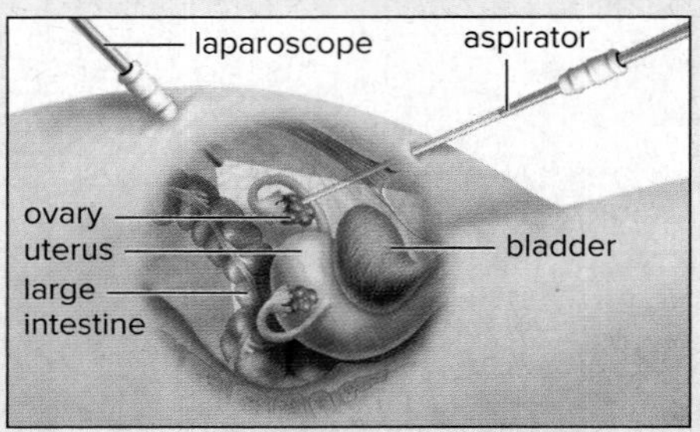

c. Preimplantation genetic diagnosis

Figure 18B **Methods for genetic defect testing before birth.** About 20% of all birth defects are due to genetic or chromosomal abnormalities, which may be detected before birth. **a.** Amniocentesis is usually performed from the fifteenth to the seventeenth week of pregnancy. **b.** Chorionic villus sampling is usually performed from the eighth to the twelfth week of pregnancy. **c.** Preimplantation genetic diagnosis can be performed prior to in vitro fertilization, either on oocytes that have been collected from the woman or on the early embryo.

Eat a Healthy Diet

Certain birth defects may occur because of nutritional deficiencies. For example, women of childbearing age are urged to make sure they consume adequate amounts of folic acid (a B vitamin) to prevent neural tube defects, such as spina bifida and anencephaly. In spina bifida, part of the vertebral column fails to develop properly and cannot adequately protect the spinal cord. With anencephaly, most of the fetal brain fails to develop. Infants with anencephaly are stillborn or survive for only a few days after birth.

Fortunately, folic acid is plentiful in leafy green vegetables, nuts, and citrus fruits. The CDC recommends that all women of childbearing age get at least 400 micrograms (μg) of folic acid every day through supplements, in addition to eating a healthy diet rich in folic acid. Unfortunately, neural tube birth defects can occur just a few weeks after conception, when many women are still unaware that they are pregnant—especially if the pregnancy is unplanned.

Avoid Alcohol, Smoking, and Drug Use

Alcohol consumption during pregnancy is a leading cause of birth defects. In severe instances, the baby is born with fetal alcohol syndrome (FAS), estimated to occur in 0.2 to 2.0 of every 1,000 live births in the United States. Many children with FAS are underweight and have an abnormally small head, abnormal facial development, and intellectual disabilities. As they mature, children with FAS often exhibit a short attention span, impulsiveness, and poor judgment, as well as problems with learning and memory. Heavy alcohol use also reduces a woman's folic acid level, increasing the risk of neural tube defects.

Cigarette smoking causes many birth defects. Babies born to mothers who smoke typically have low birth weight and are more likely to have defects of the face, heart, and brain than children of nonsmokers.

Illegal drugs should also be avoided. For example, cocaine causes blood pressure fluctuations that deprive the fetus of oxygen. Babies exposed to cocaine may have problems with vision and coordination and may have intellectual disabilities.

Alert Medical Personnel If You Are or May Be Pregnant

Several medications that are safe for healthy adults may pose a risk to a developing fetus. Pregnant women who require immunizations should consult with their physicians.

Because the rapidly dividing cells of a developing embryo or fetus are very susceptible to damage from radiation, pregnant women should avoid unnecessary X-rays. If X-rays are unavoidable, the woman should notify the X-ray technician that she is pregnant, so that her fetus can be protected as much as possible.

Avoid Infections that Cause Birth Defects

Certain pathogens such as rubella, toxoplasmosis, herpes simplex, cytomegalovirus, and Zika virus may cause birth defects.

Question to Consider

1. Besides tobacco, alcohol, and illegal drugs, what other potential risks should a pregnant woman avoid? Why?

atrium. This mixed blood enters the heart, and most of it is shunted to the left atrium through the *foramen ovale* (oval opening). The left ventricle pumps this blood into the aorta. Oxygen-poor blood that enters the right atrium is pumped into the pulmonary trunk. It then joins the aorta by way of the *ductus arteriosus* (arterial duct). Therefore, most blood entering the right atrium bypasses the lungs.

Various circulatory changes occur at birth due to the tying of the cord and the expansion of the lungs:

- Inflation of the lungs. This reduces the resistance to blood flow through the lungs, resulting in an increased amount of blood flow from the right atrium to the right ventricle and into the pulmonary arteries. Now gas exchange occurs in the lungs, not at the placenta. Oxygen-rich blood returns to the left side of the heart through the pulmonary veins.
- An increase in blood flow from the pulmonary veins to the left atrium. This increases the pressure in the left atrium, causing a flap to cover the foramen ovale. Even if this mechanism fails, passage of blood from the right atrium to the left atrium rarely occurs, because either the opening is small or it closes when the atria contract.
- The ductus arteriosus closes at birth, because endothelial cells divide and block off the duct.
- Remains of the ductus arteriosus and parts of the umbilical arteries and vein later are transformed into connective tissue.

BIOLOGY IN YOUR LIFE

When can the heartbeat of a fetus first be detected?

A fetal heart will begin forming from tissues in the chest of the fetus first by forming a tube structure, which will later develop into the chambers of the heart. By the fifth week of fetal development, the heart has formed; it is too small to hear but it can be seen on an ultrasound. By week 10, the heart is fully developed and is beating at a rate of 150 to 195 beats per minute. The sounds of the heart at this point are often referred to as fetal heart tones (FHTs) and are very rapid due to the heart's small size; however, eventually they will settle into a rate of 120 to 160 beats per minute (usually after the twelfth week) and may even beat in synch with the mother's rate. The fetal heart can be heard through the end of the first trimester and into the beginning of the second using an amplification machine called a Doppler instrument, which bounces harmless sound waves off the heart. After that point, depending on the position of the fetus, a stethoscope can detect the heartbeat as the fetus and its heart get larger.

Events of Fetal Development

Fetal development includes the third through the ninth months of development. At this time, the fetus is recognizably human, but many refinements still need to be added. The fetus usually increases in size and gains the weight it needs to live as an independent individual.

Due to the rapid development of organs and tissues, the fetus is especially susceptible to environmental influences, such as chemicals and radiation. While procedures such as ultrasounds provide an indication of the overall rate of development and potential physical problems, there are also several methods of testing the fetus for genetic abnormalities. The Health feature "Preventing and Testing for Birth Defects," explores some of the more common options.

Third and Fourth Months

At the beginning of the third month, the fetal head is still very large relative to the rest of the body. The nose is flat, the eyes are far apart, and the ears are well formed. Head growth begins to slow down as the rest of the body increases in length. Fingernails, nipples, eyelashes, eyebrows, and hair on the head appear.

Cartilage begins to be replaced by bone as ossification centers appear in most of the bones. Cartilage remains at the ends of the long bones, and ossification is not complete until age 18 or 20 years. The skull has six large, membranous areas called **fontanels.** These permit a certain amount of flexibility as the head passes through the birth canal, and they allow rapid growth of the brain during infancy. Progressive fusion of the skull bones causes the fontanels to close, usually by 2 years of age.

Sometime during the third month, it is possible to distinguish males from females. As discussed later in this section, the presence of an *SRY* gene, usually on the Y chromosome, leads to the development of testes and male genitals. Otherwise, ovaries and female genitals develop. At this time, either testes or ovaries are located within the abdominal cavity. Later, in the last trimester of fetal development, the testes descend into the scrotal sacs (scrotum). Sometimes the testes fail to descend. In that case, an operation may be done later to place them in their proper location.

During the fourth month, the fetal heartbeat is loud enough to be heard when a physician applies a stethoscope to the mother's abdomen. At the end of this month, the fetus is about 152 mm (6 in.) in length and weighs about 171 g (6 oz).

Fifth Through Seventh Months

During the fifth through seventh months (Fig. 18.8), the mother begins to feel fetal movement. At first there is only a fluttering sensation, but as the fetal legs grow and develop, kicks and jabs are felt. The fetus, though, is in the fetal position, with the head bent down and in contact with the flexed knees.

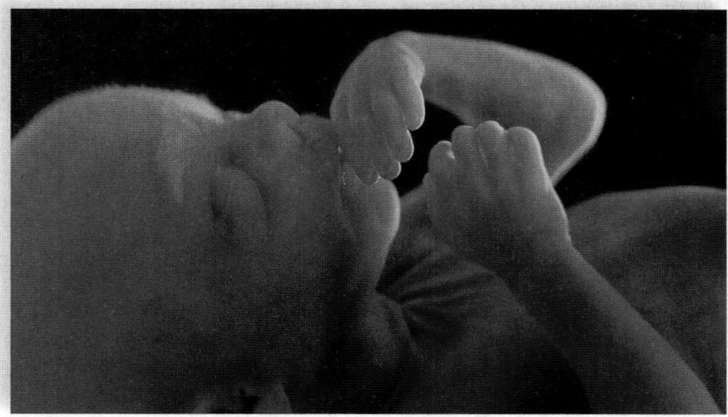

Figure 18.8 **A 5- to 7-month-old fetus.** The wrinkled skin is covered by fine hair.
James Stevenson/Science Source

BIOLOGY IN YOUR LIFE

Can a baby hear in the womb?

A baby's ears begin to develop around 8 weeks but are not fully formed. At 18 weeks, the bones of the skull and middle ear, as well as their nerve connections to the brain, have developed so that a baby can hear. At this time, sounds such as the mother's heartbeat are heard. At 25 weeks, the baby listens to voices and recognizes the mother's voice in particular. The baby's heart rate will slow slightly—a sign that her voice comforts her baby.

For the rest of the pregnancy, the baby's sense of hearing transmits information from the outside world. Soft music lulls the baby to sleep. Loud sounds startle and wake the baby. However, all sounds reaching the baby in the womb are muffled. The baby's ears are filled with amniotic fluid, and the outer ear is covered with a waxy coating that protects the baby's skin.

The wrinkled, translucent skin is covered by a fine down called **lanugo.** This, in turn, is coated with a white, greasy, cheeselike substance called **vernix caseosa,** which probably protects the delicate skin from the amniotic fluid. The eyes are now able to fully open.

At the end of this period, the fetus' length has increased to about 300 mm (12 in.), and it weighs about 1,380 g (3 lb). It is possible that the baby will survive if born now.

Eighth Through Ninth Months

At the end of 9 months, the fetus is about 530 mm (20.5 in.) long and weighs about 3,400 g (7.5 lb). Weight gain is due largely to an accumulation of fat beneath the skin. Full-term babies have the best chance of survival. Premature babies are subject to various challenges, such as respiratory distress syndrome (because their lungs are underdeveloped), jaundice, and infections.

As the end of development approaches, the fetus usually rotates, so that the head is pointed toward the cervix. However, if the fetus does not turn, a breech birth (rump first) is likely. It is very difficult for the cervix to expand enough to accommodate this form of birth, and asphyxiation of the baby is more likely to occur. Thus, a *cesarean section* (incision through the abdominal and uterine walls) may be prescribed for delivery of the fetus.

Development of Male and Female Sex Organs

The sex of an individual is determined at the moment of fertilization. Males have a pair of chromosomes designated as X and Y, and females have two X chromosomes. On the Y chromosome, a gene called *SRY* (*s*ex-determining *r*egion of the *Y*) determines whether the gonadal tissue in the embryo will develop into the male or female sex organs. The protein encoded by the *SRY* gene acts as a regulatory mechanism to control the expression, or function, of other developmental genes in the body (see Section 22.2).

Development of the Sex Organs

The development of the internal and external sex organs depends on the presence or absence of the *SRY* gene.

Internal Sex Organs During the first several weeks of development, it is impossible to tell by external inspection whether the unborn child is a boy or a girl. Gonads don't start developing until the seventh week. The tissue that gives rise to the gonads is called *indifferent,* because it can become testes or ovaries, depending on the action of hormones.

In Figure 18.9, notice that at 6 weeks, males and females have the same types of ducts. During this indifferent stage, an embryo has the potential to develop into a male or a female. If the *SRY* gene is present, a protein called *testis-determining factor* is produced that regulates the initial development of the testes. The **testosterone** produced by the testes (see Section 16.6) stimulates the Wolffian ducts to become male genital ducts. The Wolffian ducts enter the urethra, which belongs to both the urinary system and the reproductive system in males. An anti-Müllerian hormone causes the Müllerian ducts to regress. In the absence of an *SRY* gene, ovaries (rather than testes) develop from the same indifferent tissue. Now the Wolffian ducts regress, and because of an absence of testosterone, the Müllerian ducts develop into the uterus and uterine tubes. Estrogen has no effect on the Wolffian duct, which degenerates in females. A developing vagina also extends from the uterus. There is no connection between the urinary and genital systems in females.

At 14 weeks, the primitive testes or ovaries are located deep inside the abdominal cavity. An inspection of the interior of the ovaries would indicate that they already contain large numbers of tiny follicles, each having an ovum. Toward the end of development, in males the testes descend into the scrotal sac, while in females the ovaries remain in the abdominal cavity.

BIOLOGY IN YOUR LIFE

How is Zika virus related to birth defects?

The first cases of Zika virus were reported in Africa in 1952, but the virus had been largely unknown in the Western Hemisphere until it was reported in Brazil in 2015.

The virus is transmitted by a bite from an infected *Aedes* mosquito, and it can also be sexually transmitted from males who are infected to females. For most people, infection with the Zika virus produces mild symptoms, such as fevers, rashes, or joint pain. Some individuals do not experience any symptoms.

However, in a small number of cases, women who are pregnant and have been infected with the Zika virus have given birth to children with microcephaly. Microcephaly is a form of birth defect where the infant's head and brain are abnormally small. This can cause a number of developmental problems, including seizures, intellectual disabilities, and vision problems. There is no cure for microcephaly.

The exact method by which Zika virus may cause microcephaly is still being investigated. However, recent findings suggest the virus interferes with the proteins produced by genes associated with brain development, such as the *Ankle2* gene. This may lead scientists to develop methods of protecting this protein, in order to reduce the chances of microcephaly.

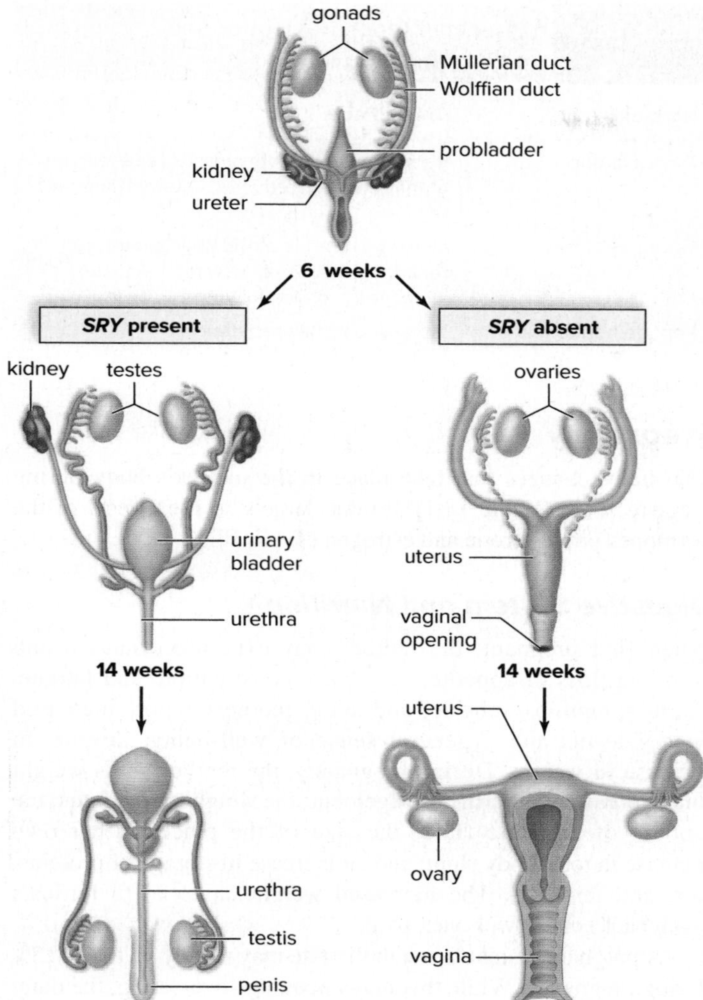

Figure 18.9 Development of the internal sex organs. The formation of the internal male and female sex organs is largely determined by the presence or absence of the *SRY* gene on the Y chromosome.

External Sex Organs Figure 18.10 shows the development of the external sex organs (genitals). These tissues are also indifferent at first—they can develop into either male or female sex organs. At 6 weeks, a small bud appears between the legs; this can develop into the male penis or the female clitoris. At 9 weeks, a *urogenital groove* bordered by two swellings appears. By 14 weeks, this groove has disappeared in males, and the scrotum has formed from the original swellings. In females, the groove persists and becomes the vaginal opening. Labia majora and labia minora are present instead of a scrotum. These changes are due to the presence or absence of the hormone dihydrotestosterone (DHT), which is manufactured in the adrenal glands and prostate glands from testosterone.

Abnormal Development of the Sex Organs

It's not correct to say that all XY individuals develop into males. Some XY individuals become females (XY female syndrome). Similarly, some XX individuals develop into males (XX male

> **BIOLOGY IN YOUR LIFE**
>
> **What happens if the *SRY* gene does not function correctly?**
>
> On the Y chromosome, the *SRY* (sex-determining region of the Y) gene produces a protein that will cause Sertoli cells in the testes to produce Müllerian-inhibiting substance (MIS). This causes Leydig cells in the testes to produce testosterone, which signals the development of the male sex organs (vasa deferentia, epididymides, penis, etc.). Without the *SRY* gene and this hormone cascade effect, female structures (uterus, uterine tubes, ovaries, etc.) will begin to form.

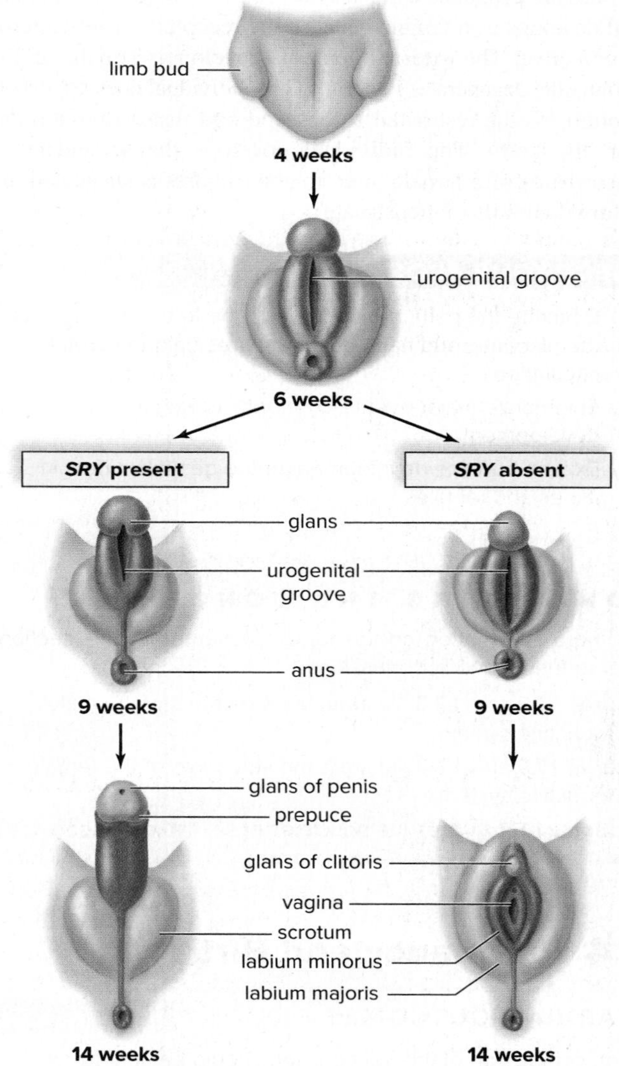

Figure 18.10 Development of the external sex organs. The presence or absence of the *SRY* gene on the Y chromosome plays an important role in the development of the external sex organs (or genitals).

syndrome). In individuals with XY female syndrome, a piece of the Y chromosome containing the *SRY* gene is missing (this is called a deletion). In individuals with XX male syndrome, the *SRY* gene has moved (this is called a translocation) to the X chromosome. The *SRY* gene causes testes to form, and then the testes secrete these hormones: (1) Testosterone stimulates development of the epididymides, vasa deferentia, seminal vesicles, and ejaculatory duct. (2) Anti-Müllerian hormone prevents further development of female structures and instead causes them to degenerate. (3) Dihydrotestosterone (DHT) directs the development of the urethra, prostate gland, penis, and scrotum.

Ambiguous Sex Determination The absence of any one or more of these hormones results in ambiguous sex determination. The individual has the external appearance of a female, although the gonads of a female are absent.

In *androgen insensitivity syndrome,* these three types of hormones are produced by testes during development, but the individual develops as a female because the receptors for testosterone are ineffective. The external genitalia develop as female, and the Wolffian duct degenerates internally. The individual does not develop a scrotum, so the testes fail to descend and instead remain deep within the body. The individual develops the secondary sex characteristics of a female, and no abnormality is suspected until the individual fails to menstruate.

CHECK YOUR PROGRESS 18.3

1. Describe the path of blood flow in the fetus, starting with the placenta, and name the structures unique to fetal circulation.
2. Summarize major events, by month, during fetal development.
3. Explain how the development of the genitals differs in males and females.

CONNECTING THE CONCEPTS

For more information on the topics presented in this section, refer to the following discussions:

Figures 17.2 and **17.3** illustrate the structures of the male reproductive system.

Figures 17.6 and **17.7** illustrate the structures of the female reproductive system.

Section 21.5 explores the principles of sex-linked inheritance.

18.4 Pregnancy and Birth

LEARNING OUTCOMES

Upon completion of this section, you should be able to

1. Explain the influence of progesterone and estrogen on female physiology during pregnancy.
2. Summarize the events that occur during each stage of birth.

Table 18.3 Effects of Placental Hormones on the Mother

Hormone	Chief Effects
Progesterone	Relaxation of smooth muscle; reduced uterine motility; reduced maternal immune response to fetus
Estrogen	Increased uterine blood flow; increased renin-angiotensin-aldosterone activity; increased protein biosynthesis by the liver
Peptide hormones	Increased insulin resistance

Pregnancy

The major changes that take place in the mother's body during pregnancy (see Table 18.1) are due largely to the effects of the hormones progesterone and estrogen (Table 18.3).

Digestive System and Nutrition

When first pregnant, the mother may experience nausea and vomiting, loss of appetite, heartburn, constipation, and fatigue. These symptoms subside, and some mothers report increased energy levels and a general sense of well-being, despite an increase in weight. During pregnancy, the mother gains weight due to breast and uterine enlargement; the weight of the fetus; the amount of amniotic fluid; the size of the placenta; her own increase in total body fluid; and an increase in storage of proteins, fats, and minerals. The increased weight can lead to lordosis (swayback) and lower back pain.

A pregnant woman's metabolic rate may rise by up to 10–15% during pregnancy. While this may encourage overeating, the daily diet of a pregnant woman needs to increase by only about 300 kcal to meet the energy needs of the developing fetus. Of far greater importance is the quality of foods in the diet, because there is a greater demand on the woman's body for nutrients such as iron, calcium, and proteins.

The Circulatory System

Aside from an increase in weight, many of the physiological changes in the mother are due to the presence of the placental hormones that support fetal development. Progesterone decreases uterine motility by relaxing smooth muscle, including the smooth muscle in the walls of arteries. The arteries expand, and this leads to a low blood pressure that sets in motion the renin-angiotensin-aldosterone mechanism, promoted by estrogen. Aldosterone activity promotes sodium and water retention, and blood volume increases until it reaches its peak sometime during weeks 28 to 32 of pregnancy. Altogether, blood volume increases from 5 liters to 7 liters—a 40% rise. An increase in the number of red blood cells follows. With the rise in blood volume, cardiac output increases by 20–30%. Blood flow to the kidneys, placenta, skin, and breasts rises significantly. Smooth muscle relaxation also explains the common gastrointestinal effects of pregnancy. The heartburn experienced by many is due to relaxation of the esophageal sphincter

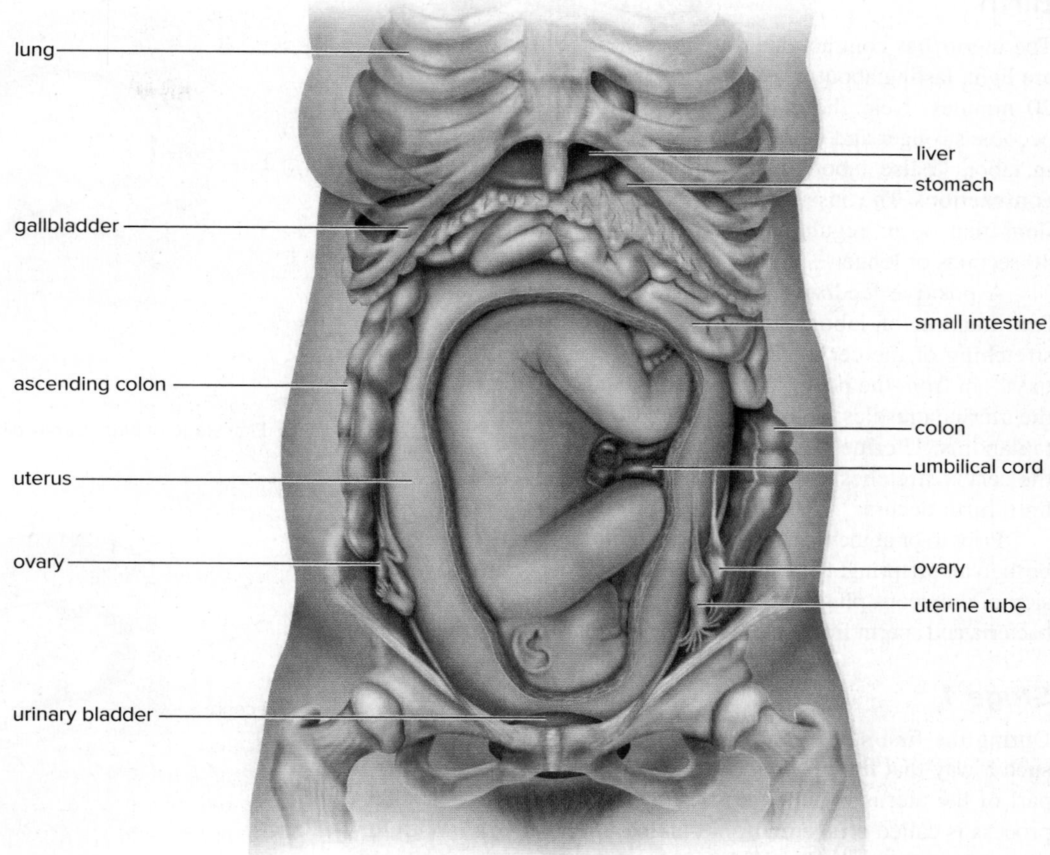

Figure 18.11 Changes to the internal anatomy of a pregnant woman.
The developing fetus compresses many of the organs in the body of the pregnant woman.

and reflux of stomach contents into the esophagus. Constipation is caused by a decrease in intestinal tract motility.

The Respiratory System

Of interest is the increase in pulmonary values in a pregnant woman. The bronchial tubes relax, but this alone cannot explain the typical 40% increase in vital capacity and tidal volume. The increasing size of the uterus from a nonpregnant weight of 60–80 g to 900–1,200 g contributes to an improvement in respiratory functions. The uterus comes to occupy most of the abdominal cavity, reaching nearly to the xiphoid process of the sternum. This increase in size not only pushes the intestines, liver, stomach, and diaphragm superiorly, but also widens the thoracic cavity. Compared with nonpregnant values, the maternal oxygen level changes little. Blood carbon dioxide levels fall by 20%, creating a concentration gradient favorable to the flow of carbon dioxide from fetal blood to maternal blood at the placenta.

Still Other Effects

The enlargement of the uterus may create problems. In the pelvic cavity, compression of the ureters and urinary bladder (Fig. 18.11) can result in stress incontinence, or the involuntary leakage of urine from the urinary tract. Compression of the inferior vena cava, especially when lying down, decreases venous return, and the results are edema and varicose veins.

Aside from the steroid hormones progesterone and estrogen, the placenta also produces some peptide hormones. One of these makes cells resistant to insulin, and the result can be gestational diabetes. Some of the integumentary changes observed during pregnancy are also due to placental hormones. "Stretch marks" typically form over the abdomen and lower breasts in response to increased steroid hormone levels, rather than stretching of the skin. Melanocyte activity also increases during pregnancy. As a result, many women develop a dark line, the linea nigra, that extends from the pubic region to the umbilical region (belly button). In addition, darkening of certain areas of the skin, including the face, neck, and breast areolae, is common.

BIOLOGY IN YOUR LIFE

Does the length or width of the linea nigra indicate the sex of a baby?

The linea nigra occurs due to the secretions of melanocytes in a pregnant woman. The line may be darker in fair-skinned women, and the length and width of the line may vary even between pregnancies. However, there is no correlation between the existence of the linea nigra and the sex, or any other characteristics, of the developing fetus.

Birth

The uterus has contractions throughout pregnancy. At first, these are light, lasting about 20 to 30 seconds and occurring every 15 to 20 minutes. Near the end of pregnancy, the contractions may become stronger and more frequent, so that a woman thinks she is in labor. "False labor" contractions are called **Braxton Hicks contractions.** The onset of true labor is marked by uterine contractions that occur regularly every 15 to 20 minutes and last for 40 seconds or longer.

A positive feedback mechanism can explain the onset and continuation of labor. Uterine contractions are induced by a stretching of the cervix, which also brings about the release of oxytocin from the posterior pituitary gland. Oxytocin stimulates the uterine muscles, both directly and through the action of prostaglandins. Uterine contractions push the fetus downward, and the cervix stretches even more. This cycle keeps repeating itself until birth occurs.

Prior to or at the first stage of **parturition,** the process of giving birth to an offspring, there can be a "bloody show" caused by expulsion of a mucous plug from the cervical canal. This plug prevented bacteria and sperm from entering the uterus during pregnancy.

Stage 1

During the first stage of labor, the uterine contractions occur in such a way that the cervical canal slowly disappears as the lower part of the uterus is pulled upward toward the baby's head. This process is called **effacement,** or "taking up the cervix." With further contractions, the baby's head acts as a wedge to assist with cervical dilation (Fig. 18.12*a*). If the amniotic membrane has not already ruptured, it is apt to do so during this stage, releasing the amniotic fluid, which leaks out of the vagina (an event sometimes referred to as "breaking water"). The first stage of parturition ends once the cervix is dilated completely.

Stage 2

During the second stage of parturition, the uterine contractions occur every 1 to 2 minutes and last about 1 minute each. They are accompanied by a desire to push, or bear down. As the baby's head gradually descends into the vagina, the mother's desire to push becomes greater. When the baby's head reaches the exterior, it turns, so that the back of the head is uppermost (Fig. 18.12*b*). To enlarge the vaginal orifice, an **episiotomy** is often performed. This incision, which enlarges the opening, is sewn together later. As soon as the head is delivered, the physician may hold the head and guide it downward while one shoulder and then the other emerges. The rest of the baby follows easily.

Once the baby is breathing normally, the umbilical cord is cut and tied, severing the child from the placenta. The stump of the cord shrivels and leaves a scar, the umbilicus (belly button).

Stage 3

The placenta, or **afterbirth,** is delivered during the third stage of parturition (Fig. 18.12*c*). About 15 minutes after delivery of the baby, uterine muscular contractions shrink the uterus and dislodge

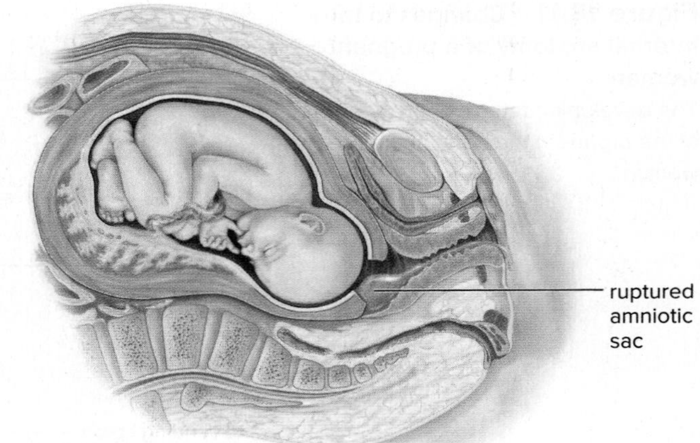

a. First stage of birth: Cervix dilates.

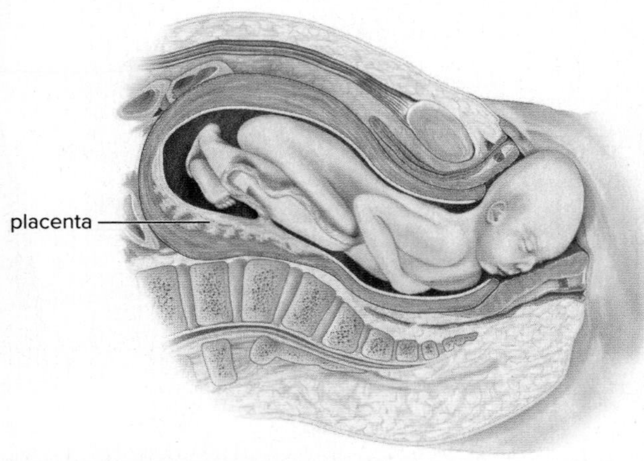

b. Second stage of birth: Baby emerges.

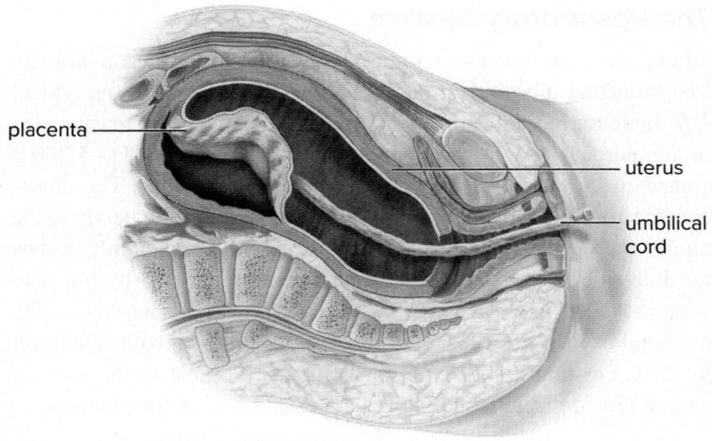

c. Third stage of birth: Afterbirth is expelled.

Figure 18.12 Stages of birth.
The stages of birth include: **a.** Dilation of cervix. **b.** Birth of baby. **c.** Expulsion of afterbirth.

the placenta. The placenta then is expelled into the vagina. As soon as the placenta and its membranes are delivered, the third stage of parturition is complete.

CHECK YOUR PROGRESS 18.4

1. Identify the hormonal changes that occur during pregnancy.
2. Maternal blood carbon dioxide levels fall by 20% during pregnancy. How does this benefit the fetus?
3. Describe the three stages of labor.

CONNECTING THE CONCEPTS

For more information on the content of this section, refer to the following discussions:

Section 4.8 explains positive feedback mechanisms.

Section 11.4 examines how aldosterone regulates urine formation in the kidneys.

Section 17.4 examines the role of the female sex hormones estrogen and progesterone.

18.5 Aging

LEARNING OUTCOMES

Upon completion of this section, you should be able to

1. Summarize the hypotheses on why humans age.
2. Summarize the effects of aging on the organ systems of the body.

Development does not cease once birth has occurred. It continues throughout the stages of life: infancy, childhood, adolescence, and adulthood. Infancy, the toddler years, and the preschool years are times of remarkable growth. During the birth to 5-year-old stage, humans acquire gross motor and fine motor skills. These include the ability to sit up and then to walk, as well as to hold a spoon and manipulate small objects. Language usage begins during this time and will become increasingly sophisticated throughout childhood. As infants and toddlers explore their environment, their senses—vision, taste, hearing, smell, and touch—mature dramatically. Socialization is very important as a child forms emotional ties with its caregivers and learns to separate self from others. Babies do not all develop at the same rate, and there is a large variation in what is considered normal.

The preadolescent years, from 6 to 12 years of age, are a time of continued rapid growth and learning. Preadolescents form identities apart from parents, and peer approval becomes very important. Adolescence begins with the onset of puberty as the young person achieves sexual maturity. For girls, puberty begins between 10 and 14 years of age, whereas for boys it generally occurs between ages 12 and 16. During this time, the sex-specific hormones (see Section 16.6) cause the secondary sex characteristics to appear. Profound social and psychological changes are also associated with the transition from childhood to adulthood.

Aging encompasses the progressive changes from infancy until eventual death. Today, **gerontology,** the study of aging, is of great interest because there are now more older individuals in our society than ever before. The number is expected to rise dramatically; in the next half century, the number of people over age 65 will increase 147%. The human life span is judged to be a maximum of 120 to 125 years. The present goal of gerontology is not necessarily to increase the life span but to increase the health span, the number of years that an individual enjoys the full functions of all body parts and processes.

Cellular Aging

Aging is a complex process affected by multiple factors. Most scientists who study gerontology believe that aging is partly genetically preprogrammed. This idea is supported by the observation that longevity runs in families—that is, the children of long-lived parents tend to live longer than those of short-lived parents. As would also be expected, studies show that identical twins have a more similar life span than nonidentical twins.

Hormones

Many laboratory studies of aging have been performed in the nematode *Caenorhabditis elegans,* in which single-gene mutations have been shown to influence the life span. For example, mutations that decrease the activity of a hormone receptor similar to the insulin receptor more than double the life span of the worms, which also behave and look like much younger worms throughout their prolonged lives. Interestingly, small-breed dogs, such as poodles and terriers, which may live 15 to 20 years, have lower levels of an analogous receptor compared to large-breed dogs that live 6 to 8 years.

Telomeres

Studies of the behavior of cells grown in the lab also suggest a genetic influence on aging. Most types of differentiated cells can divide only a limited number of times. One factor that may control the number of cell divisions is the length of the *telomeres,* sequences of DNA, at the ends of chromosomes. Telomeres protect the ends of chromosomes from deteriorating or fusing with other chromosomes. Each time a cell divides, the telomeres normally shorten, and cells with shorter telomeres tend to undergo fewer divisions (see Section 19.2). Some cells, such as stem cells, possess an enzyme called telomerase, which replenishes the length of the telomeres, effectively making stem cells immortal. Cancer cells, which behave in a similar manner to stem cells, frequently possess an active telomerase enzyme, which allows them to replicate continuously (see Section 20.1). Studies using stem cells and cancer cells have begun to close in on the genetic factors that cause cellular aging. For example, in 2012 researchers used *gene therapy* (see Section 22.4) to introduce an active telomerase enzyme into mice, thus slowing the aging process.

Mitochondria and Diet

The mitochondria are the powerhouses of the cell (see Section 3.6). As the mitochondria harvest the energy contained in carbohydrates, fats, and proteins, they generate free radicals. Free radicals are unstable molecules that carry an extra electron. To become stable, free radicals donate an electron to another molecule, such as DNA, proteins (e.g., enzymes), or lipids found in plasma membranes. Eventually these molecules become unable to function, and the cell loses internal functions. This may lead to cell death. Scientists have determined that high-calorie diets increase the levels of free radicals, thus accelerating cellular aging. Multiple studies on model organisms, including mice, have supported that a low-calorie diet can extend the life span. It is also possible to reduce the negative effects of free radicals by increasing one's consumption of natural antioxidants, such as those present in brightly colored and dark-green vegetables and fruits. Chemicals in nuts, fish, shellfish, and red wine have also been shown to reduce our exposure to free radicals and slow the aging process.

However, if aging were mainly a function of genes, we would expect to see much less variation in life span among individuals of a given species than is actually seen. For this reason, experts have estimated that in most cases genes account only for about 25% of what determines the length of life.

Damage Accumulation

Another set of hypotheses propose that aging involves the accumulation of damage over time. In 1900, the average human life expectancy was around 45 years. A male born in the United States this year has a life expectancy of about 76 years, while a female has a life expectancy of 81 years. Because human genes have presumably not changed much in such a short time, most of this gain in life span is due to better medical care, along with the application of scientific knowledge about how to prolong our lives.

Two basic types of cellular damage can accumulate over time. The first type can be thought of as agents that are unavoidable—for example, the accumulation of harmful DNA mutations or the buildup of harmful metabolites. A second form involves the fact that proteins—such as the collagen fibers present in many support tissues—may become increasingly cross-linked as people age. This cross-linking may account for the inability of such organs as the blood vessels, heart, and lungs to function as they once did. Some researchers have now found that glucose has the tendency to attach to any type of protein, which is the first step in a cross-linking process. They are currently experimenting with drugs that can prevent cross-linking. However, other sources of cellular damage, such as a poor diet or exposure to the sun, may be avoidable.

Effect of Age on Body Systems

In the preceding chapters, we examined the structure and function of the major body systems. Aging reduces the ability of an organ system to perform these functions and in many cases impacts its ability to contribute to homeostasis. Therefore, it seems appropriate to first consider the effects of aging on the various body systems.

Integumentary System

As aging occurs, the skin becomes thinner and less elastic, because the number of elastic fibers decreases and the collagen fibers become increasingly cross-linked to each other, reducing their flexibility. There is also less adipose tissue in the subcutaneous layer; therefore, older people are more likely to feel cold. Together, these changes typically result in sagging and wrinkling of the skin.

As people age, the sweat glands also become less active, resulting in decreased tolerance to high temperatures. There are fewer hair follicles, so the hair on the scalp and the limbs thins out. Older people also experience a decrease in the number of melanocytes, making their hair gray and their skin pale. In contrast, some of the remaining pigment cells are larger, and pigmented blotches ("age spots") appear on the skin.

Cardiovascular System

Common problems with cardiovascular function are usually related to diseases, especially atherosclerosis. However, even with normal aging, the heart muscle weakens somewhat and may increase slightly in size as it compensates for its decreasing strength. The maximum heart rate decreases even among the most fit older athletes, and it takes longer for the heart rate and blood pressure to return to normal resting levels following stress. Some part of this decrease in heart function may also be due to blood leaking back through heart valves that have become less flexible.

Aging also affects the blood vessels. The middle layer of arteries contains elastic fibers, which, like collagen fibers in the skin, become more cross-linked and rigid with time. These changes, plus a frequent decrease in the internal diameter of arteries due to atherosclerosis, contribute to a gradual increase in blood pressure with age. Indeed, nearly 50% of older adults have chronic hypertension. Such changes are common in individuals living in Western industrialized countries but not in agricultural societies. This indicates that a diet low in cholesterol and saturated fatty acids, along with a sensible exercise program, may help prevent age-related cardiovascular disease.

Immune System

As people age, many of their immune system functions become compromised. Because a healthy immune system normally protects the entire body from infections, toxins, and at least some types of cancer, some investigators believe that losses in immune function can play a major role in the aging process.

The thymus is an important site for T-cell maturation. Beginning in adolescence, the thymus begins to involute, gradually decreasing in size and eventually becoming replaced by fat and connective tissue. The thymus of a 60-year-old adult is about 5% of the size of the thymus of a newborn, resulting in a decrease in the ability of older people to generate T-cell responses to new antigens. The evolutionary rationale for this may be that the thymus is energetically expensive for an organism to maintain. Compared to younger animals that must respond to a high number of new infections and other antigens, older animals have already responded to most of the antigens to which they will be exposed in their life.

Aging also affects other immune functions. Because most B-cell responses are dependent on T cells, antibody responses also begin to decline. This, in turn, may explain why older people do not respond as well to vaccinations as younger people do. This presents challenges in protecting older people against diseases such as influenza and pneumonia, which can otherwise be prevented by annual vaccination.

Not all immune functions decrease with age. The activity of natural killer cells, which are a part of the innate immune system, seems to change very little with age. Perhaps by investigating how these cells remain active throughout a normal human life span, researchers can learn to preserve other aspects of immunity in older adults.

Digestive System

The digestive system is perhaps less affected by the aging process than other systems. Because secretion of saliva decreases, more bacteria tend to adhere to the teeth, causing more decay and periodontal disease. Blood flow to the liver is reduced, resulting in less efficient metabolism of drugs or toxins. This means that, as a person gets older, less medication is needed to maintain the same level in the bloodstream.

Respiratory System

Cardiovascular problems are often accompanied by respiratory disorders, and vice versa. Decreasing elasticity of lung tissues means that ventilation is reduced. Because we rarely use the entire vital capacity, these effects may not be noticed unless the demand for oxygen increases, such as during exercise.

Urinary System

Blood supply to the kidneys is also reduced. The kidneys become smaller and less efficient at filtering wastes. Salt and water balance are difficult to maintain, and older people dehydrate faster than younger people. Urinary incontinence (lack of bladder control) increases with age, especially in women. In men, an enlarged prostate gland may reduce the diameter of the urethra, causing frequent or difficult urination.

Nervous System

Between the ages of 20 and 90, the brain loses about 20% of its weight and volume. Neurons are extremely sensitive to oxygen deficiency, and neuron death may be due not to aging itself but to reduced blood flow in narrowed blood vessels. However, contrary to previous scientific opinion, recent studies using advanced imaging techniques show that most age-related loss in brain function is

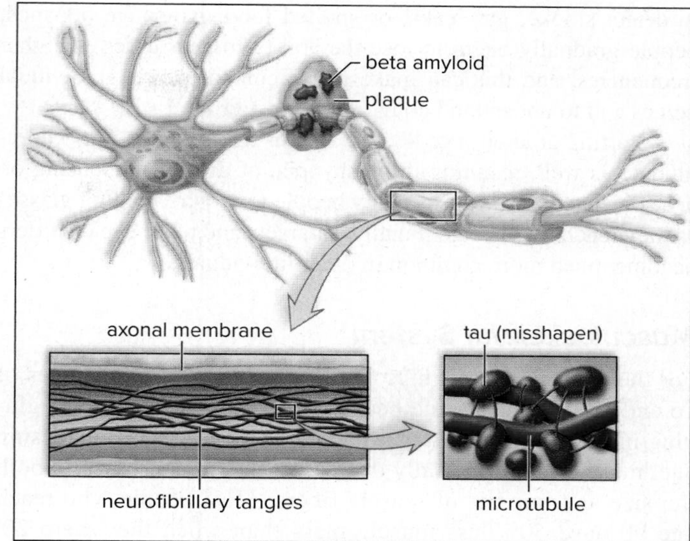

Figure 18.13 **Tau protein and Alzheimer's disease.** Some of the neurons of patients with Alzheimer's disease have beta amyloid plaques and neurofibrillary tangles. Affected neurons are present throughout the brain but concentrated in the hippocampus and amygdala.

not due to whatever loss of neurons is occurring. Instead, decreased function may occur due to alterations in complex chemical reactions or increased inflammation in the brain. For example, an age-associated decline in levels of dopamine can affect brain regions involved in complex thinking.

Alzheimer's disease is characterized by the presence of abnormally structured neurons and a reduced amount of acetylcholine (ACh), primarily in an area of the brain called the hippocampus (see Fig. 14.14). A neuron that has been affected by Alzheimer's disease has two characteristic features. Bundles of fibrous protein, called neurofibrillary tangles, extend from the axon to surround the nucleus of the neuron. Tangles form when the supporting protein, called tau, becomes malformed (Fig. 18.13) and twists the neurofibrils, which are normally straight. In addition, protein-rich accumulations called amyloid plaques envelop branches of the axon. The plaques grow so dense that they trigger an inflammatory reaction that causes neuron death.

Recent studies have confirmed that lifestyle factors can affect the aging brain. For example, animals on restricted-calorie diets developed fewer Alzheimer's-like changes in their brains. Other positive factors that may help maintain a healthy brain include attending college (the "use it or lose it" idea), exercising regularly, and getting sufficient sleep.

Sensory Systems

In general, with aging, more stimulation is needed for taste, smell, and hearing receptors to function as before. A majority of people over age 80 have a significant decline in their sense of smell, and about 15% suffer from anosmia, or a total inability to smell. The latter condition can be a serious health hazard, due to the inability to detect smoke, gas leaks, or spoiled food. After age 50, most people gradually begin to lose the ability to hear tones at higher frequencies, and this can make it difficult to identify individual voices and to understand conversation in a group.

Starting at about age 40, the lens of the eye does not accommodate as well, resulting in presbyopia, or difficulty focusing on near objects, which causes many people to require reading glasses as they reach middle age. Finally, cataracts and other eye disorders become much more common in older individuals.

Musculoskeletal System

For the average person, muscle mass peaks between the ages of 16 and 19 for females and between 18 and 24 for males. Beginning in the twenties or thirties, but accelerating with increasing age, muscle mass generally decreases, due to decreases in both the size and number of muscle fibers. Most people who reach age 90 have 50% less muscle mass than when they were 20. Although some of this loss may be inevitable, regular exercise can slow this decline.

Like muscles, bones tend to shrink in size and density with age. Due to compression of the vertebrae, along with changes in posture, most of us lose height as we age. Those who reach age 80 will be about 2 in. shorter than they were in their twenties. Women lose bone mass more rapidly than men do, especially after menopause. Osteoporosis is a common disease in older adults. Although some decline in bone mass is a normal result of aging, certain extrinsic factors are also important. A proper diet and a moderate exercise program have been found to slow the progressive loss of bone mass.

Endocrine System

As with the immune system, aging of the hormonal system can affect many organs of the body. These changes are complex, however, with some hormone levels tending to decrease with age, while others increase. The activity of the thyroid gland generally declines, resulting in a lower basal metabolic rate. The production of insulin by the pancreas may remain stable, but cells become less sensitive to its effects, resulting in a rise in fasting glucose levels of about 10 mg/dl each decade after age 50.

Human growth hormone (HGH) levels also decline with age, but it is very unlikely that taking HGH injections will "cure" aging, despite Internet claims. In fact, one study found that people with lower levels of HGH actually lived longer than those with higher levels.

Reproductive System

Testosterone levels are highest in men in their twenties. After age 30, testosterone levels decrease by about 1% per year. Extremely low testosterone levels have been linked to a decreased sex drive, excessive weight gain, loss of muscle mass, osteoporosis, general fatigue, and depression. However, the levels below which testosterone treatment should be initiated remain controversial. Testosterone replacement therapy, whether through injection, patches, or gels, is associated with side effects such as enlargement of the prostate, acne or other skin reactions, and the production of too many red blood cells.

Menopause, the period in a woman's life during which the ovarian and uterine cycles cease, usually occurs between ages 45 and 55. The ovaries become unresponsive to the gonadotropic hormones produced by the anterior pituitary, and they no longer secrete estrogen or progesterone. At the onset of menopause, the uterine cycle becomes irregular, but as long as menstruation occurs, it is still possible for a woman to conceive. Therefore, a woman is usually not considered to have completed menopause (and thus be infertile) until menstruation has been absent for a year.

The hormonal changes during menopause often produce physical symptoms such as "hot flashes" (caused by circulatory irregularities), dizziness, headaches, insomnia, sleepiness, and depression. To ease these symptoms, female hormone replacement therapy (HRT) was routinely prescribed until 2002, when a large clinical study showed that, in the long term, HRT caused more health problems than it prevented. For this reason, most doctors no longer recommend long-term HRT for the prevention of postmenopausal symptoms.

As a group, females live longer than males. It is likely that estrogen offers women some protection against cardiovascular disorders when they are younger. Males suffer a marked increase in heart disease in their forties, but an increase is not noted in females until after menopause, when women lead men in the incidence of stroke. Men remain more likely than women to have a heart attack at any age, however.

Conclusion

We have examined many adverse effects of aging; however, these effects are not inevitable. Diet and exercise are factors that are under our personal control. Just as it is wise to make the proper preparations to remain financially independent when older, it is also wise to realize that, biologically, successful aging begins with the health habits developed when we are younger.

CHECK YOUR PROGRESS 18.5

1. Briefly describe the hypotheses of why we age.
2. Summarize the effects of aging on the various body systems.
3. Discuss the best way to keep healthy, even though aging occurs.

CONNECTING THE CONCEPTS

For more information on the organ systems presented in this section, refer to the following discussions:

Section 5.1 provides an overview of the cardiovascular system.

Section 11.1 provides an overview of the urinary system.

Section 14.1 provides an overview of the nervous system.

CONCLUSION

Aging is a complex process that is influenced by factors such as genetics and our environments. The genetics of longevity are not associated with a single gene, such as *FOXO3A*. Rather, minor variations in a number of genes, and gene combinations, make contributions to our life span. By examining the genetic basis of diseases such as Alzheimer's disease, scientists are better able to determine how our genes affect aging at the cellular and physiological levels.

However, it is important to note that the environment also plays a major role. Exposure to the sun, the types of food we eat, and our behaviors all can affect our life span. Often, environmental factors interact with variations in genes, meaning that for some people, specific behaviors, such as drinking alcohol, may have a different effect on the aging process than for another individual with another combination of genes.

SUMMARIZE

18.1 Fertilization

Fertilization is the combination of an egg and sperm cell to produce a new individual, or **zygote.** During fertilization, the acrosome of a sperm releases enzymes that digest a pathway for the sperm through the zona pellucida. The sperm nucleus then enters the egg and fuses with the egg nucleus.

18.2 Embryonic Development

Cleavage, growth, morphogenesis, and **differentiation** are the processes of development. Development of the fetus may be divided into **pre-embryonic development** events (first week) and **embryonic development** events (second week and later).

Pre-embryonic Development

- Immediately after fertilization, the zygote begins to divide, becoming an **embryo.** As division continues, the embryo forms a **morula** and then a **blastocyst.** Within the blastocyst, the **inner cell mass** forms. This will become the **fetus.**
- The **extraembryonic membranes** (**chorion, allantois, yolk sac,** and **amnion**) begin to form.

Embryonic Development

- During the second week, **implantation** of the embryo occurs. Several hormones, including **human chorionic gonadotropin (HCG),** act on the uterus to adapt it for pregnancy. Within the embryo, **gastrulation** occurs, forming the **primary germ layers,** which will become the structures of the body.
- Starting in the third week, the development of organ systems begins, including the nervous system and circulatory system (heart).
- In the fourth week, the embryo connects to the chorion using **chorionic villi.** The formation of the **umbilical cord** establishes a connection to the placenta. The limb buds appear, and by the fifth week the sense organs develop in the head.

18.3 Fetal Development

At the end of the embryonic period, all organ systems are established and there is a mature and functioning **placenta.** The umbilical arteries and umbilical vein take blood to and from the placenta, where exchanges take place. Fetal development occurs during the third to ninth months.

Fetal Circulation

- Fetal circulation supplies the fetus with oxygen and nutrients and rids the fetus of carbon dioxide and wastes.
- The venous duct joins the umbilical vein to the inferior vena cava. The oval duct and arterial duct allow the blood to pass through the heart without going to the lungs. **Fetal development** extends from the third through the ninth months.

Third and Fourth Months

- During the third and fourth months, the skeleton is becoming ossified. In the skull, the **fontanels** will allow the head to pass through the birth canal.
- The sex of the fetus becomes distinguishable. If an *SRY* gene is present, **testosterone** directs the development of the testes and male sex organs. Otherwise, ovaries and female sex organs develop.

Fifth to Ninth Months

- During the fifth through the ninth months, the fetus continues to grow and to gain weight. At this point, the skin is covered by a fine down **(lanugo)** and a protective layer **(vernix caseosa).**

18.4 Pregnancy and Birth

Pregnancy

Major changes take place in the mother's body during pregnancy.

- Weight gain occurs as the uterus occupies most of the abdominal cavity.
- Many complaints, such as constipation, incontinence, heartburn, darkening of certain skin areas, and pregnancy-induced diabetes, are due to the presence of placental hormones.

Birth

A positive feedback mechanism that involves uterine contractions (including **Braxton Hicks contractions**) and oxytocin explains the onset and continuation of labor.

- During stage 1 of **parturition** (birth), **effacement** assists in the dilation of the cervix.
- During stage 2, the child is born. An **episiotomy** may assist in the widening of the vaginal orifice.
- During stage 3, the **afterbirth** is expelled.

18.5 Aging

Development after birth consists of infancy, childhood, adolescence, and adulthood. The science of **gerontology** examines the progressive changes that occur during **aging.** As we age, these changes contribute to an increased risk of infirmity, disease, and death.

Cellular Aging

Several factors contribute to aging at the cellular level.

- Telomeres contribute to the life span of cells.
- Receptors for certain hormones may not work efficiently.
- Free radicals and other metabolites cause damage to cellular components.

Effect of Age on Body Systems

- Deterioration of organ systems can be prevented or reduced in part by adhering to good health habits.

ENGAGE

THINKING CRITICALLY

1. Mitochondria contain their own genetic material. Mitochondrial mutations are inherited from mother to child, without any contribution from the father. Why?
2. At-home pregnancy tests check for the presence of HCG in a female's urine. Where does HCG come from? Why is HCG found in a pregnant woman's urine?
3. A variety of fertility tests are available for women to purchase over the counter—for example, at drugstores. Because more women now delay their first pregnancy until they are older, these tests are becoming more popular. Many of these tests incorporate antibodies that specifically react with hormones found in a woman's urine. What specific hormones could be measured in these tests, and how might these tests actually work?

MAKING IT RELEVANT

1. Suppose it was possible to identify specific alleles of aging genes for a greatly shortened, or lengthened, life span. Would you want to know this information about your genes?
2. How might an identification of aging genes also allow us to better understand the environmental influences of aging?
3. Why do you think animal species evolved an aging process? Why not make all individuals immortal?

Find answers to all of the chapter questions at connect.mheducation.com

Yuri Arcurs/iStockphoto/Getty Images

CHAPTER 19

Cell Division

p53 and the Cell Cycle

Why don't elephants get cancer? Elephants, like humans, are long-lived organisms. Yet, despite their longevity, recent studies have indicated that only about 5% of elephants will develop cancer in their lifetime, compared to up to 25% of humans.

Cancer results from a failure to control the cell cycle, a series of steps that all cells go through prior to initiating cell division. A gene called *p53* is an important component of that control mechanism. This gene belongs to a group called tumor suppressor genes. At specific points in the cell cycle, the proteins encoded by tumor suppressor genes check the DNA for damage. If the cells are damaged, they are not allowed to divide.

Humans have only one pair of *p53* genes (one from each parent). Luckily, you need only a single copy to regulate the cell cycle. But if both genes are not functioning properly, because of inheritance of a defective gene or mutations that inactivate a gene, they can't act as gatekeepers, and instead will allow cells to divide continuously. Unrestricted cell growth is a characteristic of cancer. In humans, mutations in the *p53* gene are associated with an increased risk of a number of cancers. Interestingly, elephants have 20 pairs of *p53* genes in their genome, which means it is very unlikely their cells will lose all of this gene's functionality.

In this chapter, we will explore how cell division is regulated, as well as how genes such as *p53* function in the regulation of the cycle.

As you read through the chapter, think about the following questions:

1. What are the roles of checkpoints in the cell cycle?
2. At which checkpoint do you think *p53* would normally be active?
3. Why would a failure of the checkpoints in the cell cycle result in cancer?

CHAPTER OUTLINE

BEFORE YOU BEGIN

Before beginning this chapter, take a few moments to review the following discussions:

Section 2.7 What is the structure of a DNA molecule? How does this structure differ from that of RNA?

Section 3.4 What is chromatin?

Section 3.5 What are the functions of microtubules and actin filaments in a cell?

19.1 Chromosomes

LEARNING OUTCOMES

Upon completion of this section, you should be able to

1. Distinguish between a chromosome and chromatin.
2. Explain the purpose of a karyotype.
3. Describe the purpose of the centromere in relation to the sister chromatids.

Although the nucleus of a human cell is only about 5–8 μm long, it holds all the genetic material necessary to direct all the functions in the body. The genetic material within the nucleus is arranged into **chromosomes,** structures that assist in the transmission of genetic information from one generation to the next. The instructions in each chromosome are contained within genes, which in turn are composed of DNA (see Section 22.1).

Chromosomes also contain proteins that assist in the organizational structure of the chromosome. Collectively, the DNA and proteins are called **chromatin.** Humans have 46 chromosomes, which occur in 23 pairs. Twenty-two of these pairs are called *autosomes.* All of the autosome chromosomes are found in both males and females. However, one pair of chromosomes is called the *sex chromosomes,* because this pair differs in males and females. Males have the X and Y sex chromosomes, and females have two X chromosomes. The presence of the *SRY* gene on the Y chromosome causes testes to develop in males (see Section 18.3).

Karyotypes

Physicians and prospective parents sometimes want to view an unborn child's chromosomes to determine whether a chromosomal abnormality exists. Any cell in the body except red blood cells, which lack a nucleus, can be a source of chromosomes for examination. In adults, it is easiest to obtain and use white blood cells separated from a blood sample for the purpose of looking at the chromosomes. For an examination of fetal chromosomes, a physician may recommend procedures such as chorionic villus sampling or amniocentesis. These processes are described more fully in the Health feature "Preventing and Testing for Birth Defects" in Section 18.3.

After a cell sample has been obtained, the cells are stimulated to divide in a culture medium. When a cell divides, chromatin condenses to form chromosomes. The nuclear envelope fragments, liberating the chromosomes. Next, a chemical is used to stop the division process when the chromosomes are most compacted and visible microscopically. Stains are applied to the slides, and the cells can be photographed with a camera attached to a microscope. Staining causes the chromosomes to have dark and light cross-bands of varying widths, and these can be used—in addition to size and shape—to help pair up the chromosomes. A computer is used to arrange the chromosomes in pairs (Fig. 19.1). The display is called a *karyotype.*

The karyotype in Figure 19.1 is that of a genetically typical male. Notice that the cell this sample was obtained from is diploid, meaning it has the full complement of 46 chromosomes. A form of

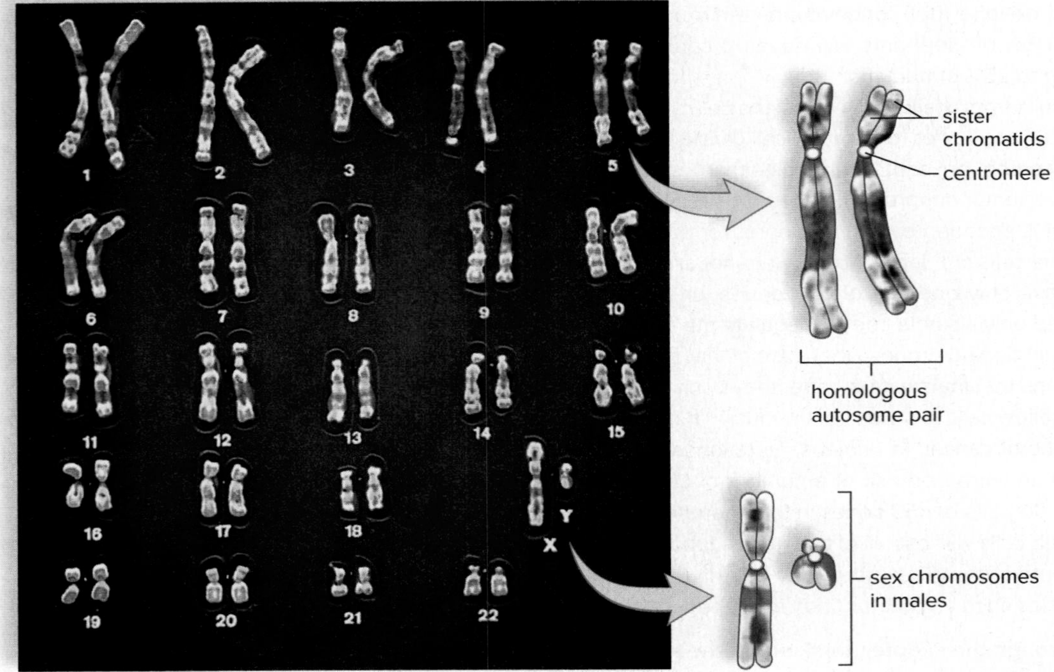

Figure 19.1 A karyotype of human chromosomes.
In body cells, the chromosomes occur in pairs. In a karyotype, the pairs have been numbered and arranged by size from largest to smallest. These chromosomes are duplicated, and each one is composed of two sister chromatids. This karyotype illustrates the 46 chromosomes of a male.
(photo): CNRI/Science Source

cell division called *mitosis* (see Section 19.3) begins when the fertilized egg starts dividing and ensures that every cell has 46 chromosomes. The majority of cells of the body undergo mitosis, but exceptions include red blood cells, sex cells, and liver cells.

The enlargement of a pair of chromosomes shows that in dividing cells each chromosome is composed of two identical parts, called **sister chromatids** (Fig. 19.1). Sister chromatids contain the same genes. *Genes* are the units of heredity that control traits, such as eye color and metabolism. Humans have about 20,000 different genes, and collectively they contain the instructions for how our bodies conduct the characteristics of life that we explored in Section 1.1.

The chromatids are held together at a region called the centromere. A **centromere** holds the chromatids together until cell division occurs. Cell division separates the sister chromatids, forming new independent chromosomes, sometimes called daughter chromosomes, that are then allocated to new cells. Once in the new cell, these chromosomes are replicated, forming new sister chromatids.

CHECK YOUR PROGRESS 19.1

1. Explain the purpose of chromosomes in a cell.
2. Describe how a karyotype can be used to determine the number of chromosomes in a cell.
3. Explain why sister chromatids are genetically the same.

CONNECTING THE CONCEPTS

For more information on the topics in this section, refer to the following discussions:

Section 3.4 examines the role of the nucleus in a cell.

Section 3.4 explains the relationship of chromatin to the chromosomes.

Section 18.3 describes the stages of fetal development.

19.2 The Cell Cycle

LEARNING OUTCOMES

Upon completion of this section, you should be able to

1. List the stages of the cell cycle and state the purpose of each.
2. Describe the purpose of the checkpoints in the cell cycle.
3. Distinguish between mitosis and cytokinesis.

The **cell cycle** is an orderly process that has two parts: interphase and cell division. To understand the cell cycle, it is necessary to understand the structure of a cell (see Fig. 3.4). A human cell has a plasma membrane, which encloses the cytoplasm, the content of the cell outside the nucleus. In the cytoplasm are organelles that carry out the various functions necessary to the life of the cell. Within the nucleus is the chromatin (DNA and associated proteins), organized into chromosomes. Prior to cell division, the chromatin is typically spread throughout the nucleus as a tangled mass of threads.

Interphase

As Figure 19.2 shows, most of the cell cycle is spent in **interphase.** This is the time when the organelles in the cell carry on their usual functions. As the cell continues through interphase, it gets ready to divide. The cell grows larger, the number of organelles doubles, and the amount of chromatin doubles as DNA replication occurs.

Interphase is divided into three main stages: the G_1 stage occurs before DNA replication; the S stage includes DNA replication; and the G_2 stage occurs after DNA replication. Originally, *G* stood for "gaps"—times during interphase when DNA synthesis was not occurring. But now that we know growth happens during these stages, the *G* can be thought of as standing for "growth." Let us see what specifically happens during these stages.

- *G_1 stage.* The cell returns to normal size and resumes its function in the body. A cell doubles its organelles (e.g., mitochondria and ribosomes), and it accumulates the materials needed for DNA synthesis.
- *S stage.* A copy is made of all the DNA in the cell. DNA replication occurs, so each chromosome consists of two identical DNA double-helix molecules. These molecules occur in the strands called *sister chromatids.*
- *G_2 stage.* The cell synthesizes the proteins needed for cell division, such as the protein found in microtubules. The role of microtubules in cell division is described in Section 19.3.

The amount of time the cell takes for interphase varies widely. Some cells, such as nerve and muscle cells, typically do not complete the cell cycle and are permanently arrested in G_1. These cells are said to have entered a G_0 stage. Embryonic cells spend very little time in G_1 and complete the cell cycle in a few hours.

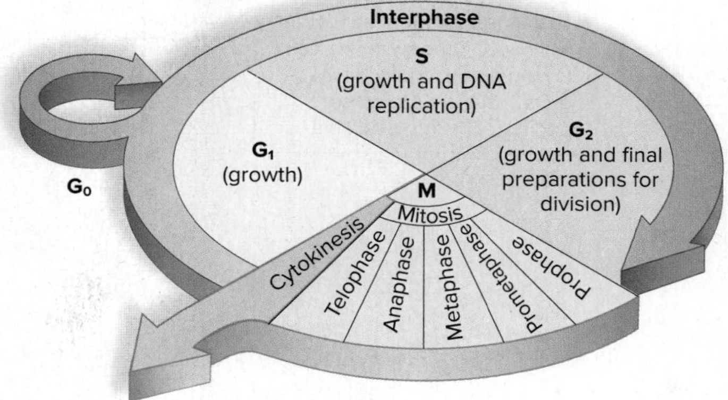

Figure 19.2 Stages of the cell cycle.
During interphase, which consists of stages G_1, S, and G_2, the cell gets ready to divide. During the mitotic stage, nuclear division and cytokinesis (cytoplasmic division) occur. The G_0 stage represents a holding stage outside the cell cycle.

Mitosis and Cytokinesis

Following interphase, the cell enters the cell division part of the cell cycle. Cell division has two stages: M (for mitosis, or mitotic) stage and cytokinesis. **Mitosis** is a type of nuclear division. While most cells of the human body undergo mitosis, a few do not. The exceptions are white blood cells (see Section 7.2) and skeletal muscle cells (see Section 12.1). Mitosis is also referred to as *duplication division,* because each new nucleus contains the same number and type of chromosomes as the former cell. **Cytokinesis** is division of the cytoplasm.

During mitosis, the sister chromatids of each chromosome separate, becoming chromosomes distributed to two daughter nuclei. When cytokinesis is complete, two daughter cells are now present. Actively dividing mammal cells usually require only about 4 hours to complete the mitotic stage.

The cell cycle, including interphase and cell division, occurs continuously in certain tissues. Right now your body is producing thousands of new red blood cells, skin cells, and cells that line your respiratory and digestive tracts. Mitosis is balanced by the process of **apoptosis,** or programmed cell death. Apoptosis occurs when cells are no longer needed or have become excessively damaged.

Cell Cycle Control

For a cell to reproduce successfully, the cell cycle must be controlled. The cell cycle is controlled by **checkpoints,** which can delay the cell cycle until certain conditions are met. The cell cycle has many checkpoints, but we will consider only three: G_1, G_2, and the mitotic checkpoint (Fig. 19.3). In addition, the cell cycle may be controlled by external factors, such as hormones and growth factors. Failure of the cell cycle control mechanisms may result in unrestricted cell growth, or cancer.

Checkpoints The *G_1 checkpoint* is especially significant, because if the cell cycle passes this checkpoint, the cell is committed to divide. If the cell does not pass this checkpoint, it can enter a holding phase called G_0, during which it performs its normal functions but does not divide. The proper growth signals, such as certain growth factors, must be present for a cell to pass the G_1 checkpoint. Additionally, the integrity of the cell's DNA is also checked. If the DNA is damaged, proteins such as p53 can stop the cycle at this checkpoint and place the cell in G_0 phase. G_0 phase acts as a holding phase; if the DNA can be repaired, the cell may reenter the cell cycle. If not, then internal mechanisms cause the cell to undergo apoptosis. The cell cycle halts momentarily at the *G_2 checkpoint* until the cell verifies that DNA has replicated. This prevents the initiation of the M stage unless the chromosomes are duplicated. Also, if DNA is damaged, as from exposure to solar (UV) radiation or X-rays, arresting the cell cycle at this checkpoint allows time for the damage to be repaired so it is not passed on to daughter cells.

Another cell cycle checkpoint occurs during the mitotic stage. The cycle hesitates between metaphase and anaphase to make sure the chromosomes are properly attached to the spindle and will be distributed accurately to the daughter cells. The cell cycle does not continue until every chromosome is ready for the nuclear division process.

External Control The cell cycle control system extends from the plasma membrane to particular genes in the nucleus. Some external signals, such as hormones and growth factors, can stimulate a cell to go through the cell cycle. At a certain time in the menstrual cycle of females, the hormone progesterone stimulates cells lining the uterus to prepare the lining for implantation of a fertilized egg. Epidermal growth factor stimulates skin in

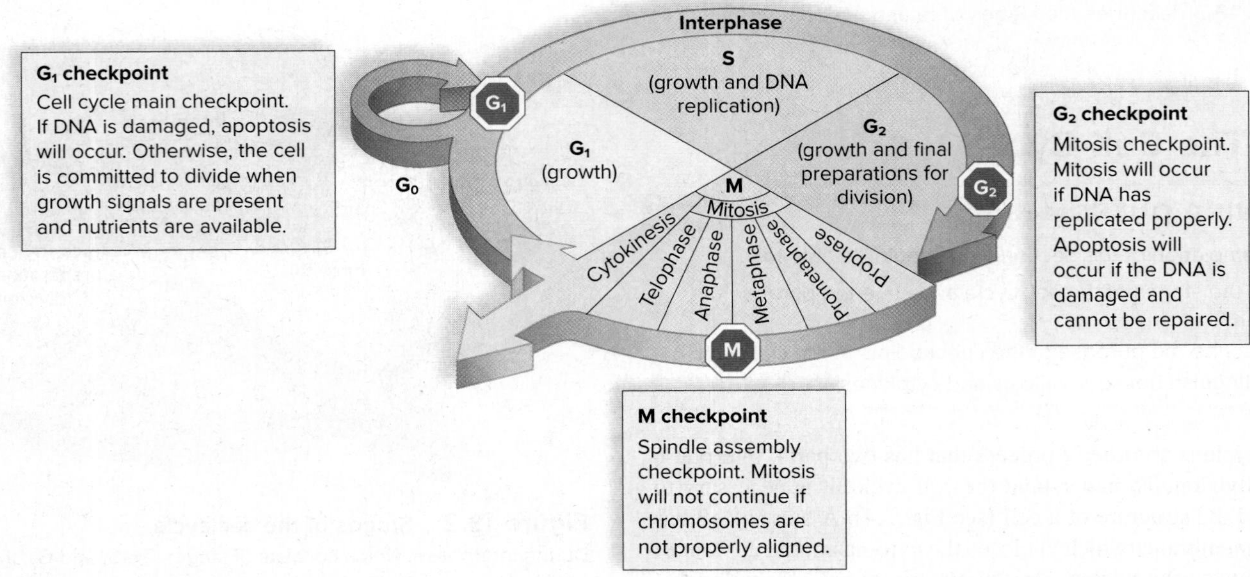

Figure 19.3 Control of the cell cycle.
Checkpoints regulate the progression of the cell through the cell cycle. This diagram shows three of the major checkpoints.

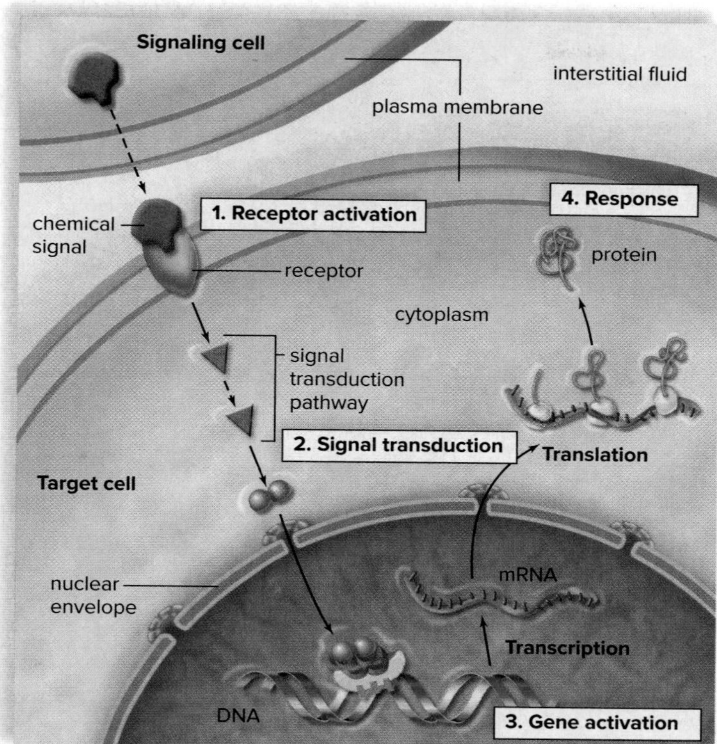

Figure 19.4 **External controls of the cell cycle.**
Growth factors stimulate a cell signaling pathway that stretches from the plasma membrane to the genes that regulate the occurrence of the cell cycle.

the vicinity of an injury to finish the cell cycle, thereby repairing damage.

As shown in Figure 19.4, during reception an external signal delivers a message to a specific receptor embedded in the plasma membrane of a receiving cell. The signal is then relayed from the receptor to proteins inside the cell's cytoplasm. The proteins form a pathway called the signal transduction pathway because they pass the signal from one to the other. The last signal activates genes in the nucleus of the cell. The expression of these genes may either stimulate or inhibit the cell cycle. Genes called proto-oncogenes stimulate the cell cycle, and genes called tumor suppressor genes inhibit the cell cycle. We will explore the action of these genes in more detail in Section 20.1.

CHECK YOUR PROGRESS 19.2

1. Describe the cell cycle, and list the locations of each phase and checkpoint.
2. Explain the purpose of the S phase in the cell cycle.
3. Explain how checkpoints help protect the cell against unregulated cell growth.
4. Summarize why external controls may be necessary to regulate the cell cycle.

CONNECTING THE CONCEPTS

For more information on the material presented in this section, refer to the following discussions:

Figure 16.5 illustrates how steroid hormones, such as progesterone, influence the internal activities of a cell.

Section 20.1 describes the differences between proto-oncogenes and tumor suppressor genes.

Section 20.2 explores how environmental factors, such as radiation, may cause cancer.

19.3 Mitosis

LEARNING OUTCOMES

Upon completion of this section, you should be able to

1. Explain the purpose of mitosis.
2. Explain the events that occur in each stage of mitosis.
3. State the purpose of cytokinesis.

The cell cycle, which includes mitosis, is very important to the well-being of humans. Mitosis is responsible for new cells in the developing embryo, fetus, and child. It is also responsible for replacement cells in an adult (Fig. 19.5). As we mentioned in Section 19.2, mitosis is often referred to as *duplication division,* because at the conclusion of mitosis the nuclei of the two new cells have the same number and types of chromosomes as the original cell. During mitosis, the cell that divides is called the **parent cell,** and the new cells are called **daughter cells.** Following mitosis, with the exception of rare mutations that may have occurred during DNA replication, the daughter cells are genetically identical to the parent cell.

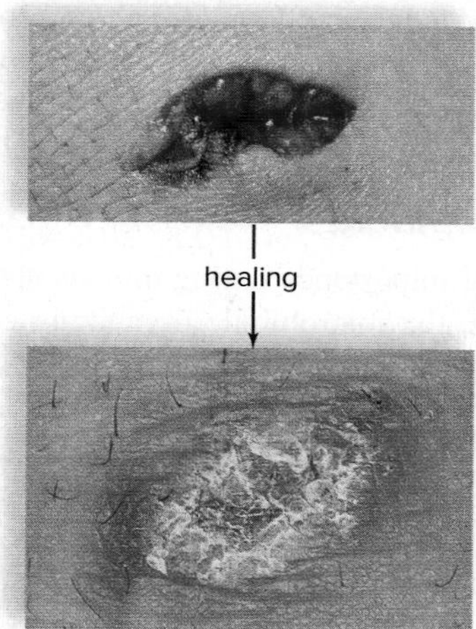

Figure 19.5 **The importance of mitosis.**
The cell cycle, including mitosis, occurs when humans grow and when tissues undergo repair.
(fresh wound): Scott Camazine/Science Source; (healing wound): Ted Kinsman/Science Source

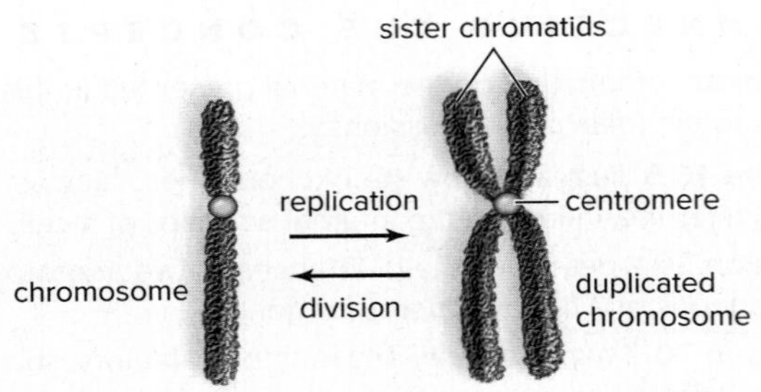

Figure 19.6 **Relationship between DNA replication and DNA division.**
The replication of a DNA molecule forms sister chromatids, whereas cell division separates the sister chromatids into new cells.

Overview of Mitosis

During S phase of the cell cycle, replication of the DNA occurs (see Section 22.1), thus duplicating the chromosomes. Each chromosome now contains two identical parts, called *sister chromatids,* held together at a centromere. They are called sister chromatids because they contain the same genes (Fig. 19.6).

As mitosis begins, the proteins in the chromatin assist in causing the chromosomes to become highly condensed. Once this occurs, the chromosomes become visible under a light microscope. Figure 19.7 gives an overview of mitosis. For simplicity, only four chromosomes are depicted. Notice that there are two copies of each chromosome (one maternal and one paternal), so in this case the **diploid (2n)** number of chromosomes is four.

During mitosis, the centromeres divide and the sister chromatids separate. Following separation during mitosis, each chromatid is called a *chromosome.* Each daughter cell gets a complete set of chromosomes and is diploid (2n). Therefore, each daughter cell receives the same number and types of chromosomes as the parent cell. Each daughter cell is genetically identical to the other and to the parent cell.

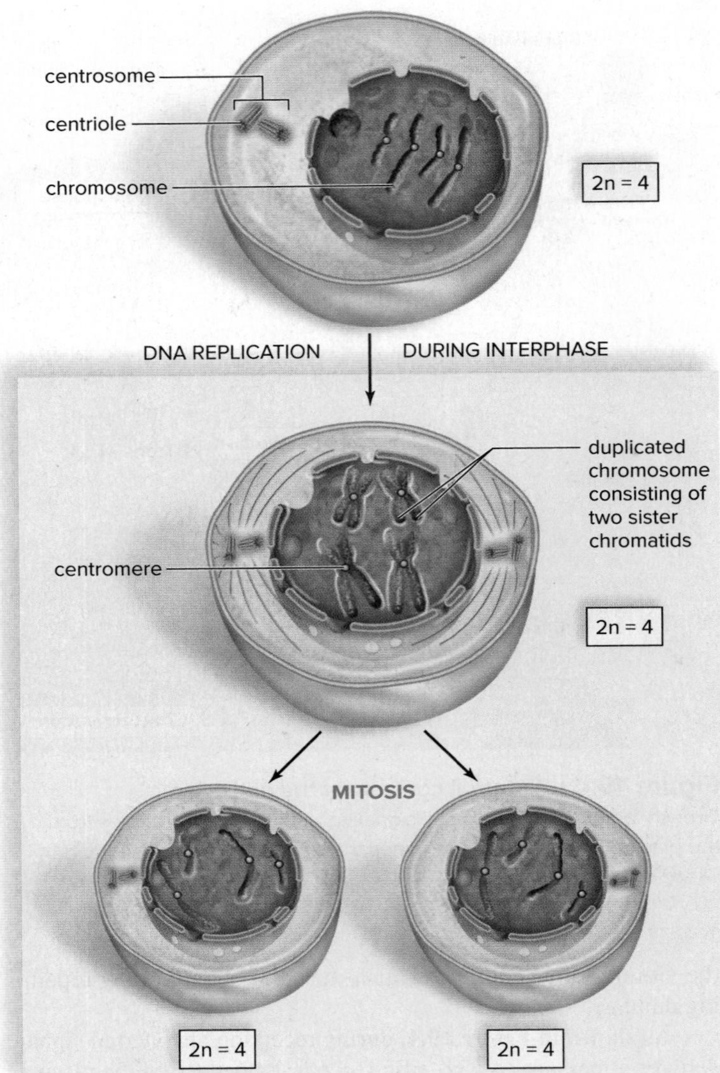

Figure 19.7 **An overview of mitosis.**
Following DNA replication, each chromosome is duplicated. When the centromeres split, the sister chromatids, now called chromosomes, move into daughter nuclei.

The Mitotic Spindle

Another event of importance during mitosis is the duplication of the **centrosome,** the microtubule organizing center of the cell. After centrosomes duplicate, they separate and form the poles of the **mitotic spindle,** where they assemble the microtubules that make up the spindle fibers. The chromosomes are attached to the spindle fibers at their centromeres. An array of microtubules called an *aster* (because it looks like a star) is also at the poles. Each centrosome contains a pair of **centrioles,** which consist of short cylinders of microtubules. The centrioles lie at right angles to one another. Centrioles are absent in plant cells, and their function in animals cells is not completely understood, although it is believed they assist in the formation of the spindle that separates the chromatids during mitosis.

Phases of Mitosis

As an aid in describing the events of mitosis, the process is divided into phases: prophase, prometaphase, metaphase, anaphase, and telophase. Although the stages of mitosis are depicted as if they were separate, they are continuous. One stage flows from the other with no noticeable interruption.

Prophase

Several events occur during **prophase** that visibly indicate the cell is preparing to divide (Fig. 19.8). The centrosomes outside the nucleus have duplicated, and they begin moving away from one another toward opposite ends of the nucleus. Spindle fibers appear between the separating centrosomes. The nuclear envelope begins to fragment. The nucleolus, a special region of the nucleus, disappears as the chromosomes coil and become condensed. The chromosomes are now clearly visible. Each is composed of two sister chromatids held together at a centromere.

Prometaphase

In **prometaphase,** the spindle fibers attach to the centromeres as the chromosomes continue to shorten and thicken. During prometaphase, chromosomes are randomly placed in the nucleus (Fig. 19.8).

Metaphase

During **metaphase,** the spindle is fully formed. The *metaphase plate* is a plane perpendicular to the axis of the spindle and equidistant from the poles. The chromosomes, attached to spindle fibers at their centromeres, line up at the metaphase plate during metaphase (Fig. 19.8).

Anaphase

At the start of **anaphase,** the centromeres uniting the sister chromatids divide. Then the sister chromatids separate, becoming chromosomes that move toward opposite poles of the spindle. Separation of the sister chromatids ensures that each cell receives a copy of each type of chromosome and thereby has a full complement of genes. Anaphase is characterized by the diploid (2n) number of chromosomes moving toward each pole. Remember that the number of centromeres indicates the number of chromosomes. Therefore, each pole receives four chromosomes: In Figure 19.8, two are shown in red and two are shown in blue.

Spindle Function in Anaphase The spindle brings about chromosomal movement. Two types of spindle fibers are involved in the movement of chromosomes during anaphase. One type extends from the poles to the equator of the spindle. There, they overlap. As mitosis proceeds, these fibers increase in length, which helps push the chromosomes apart. The chromosomes themselves are attached to other spindle fibers that extend from their centromeres to the poles. Because these fibers (composed of microtubules that can disassemble) become shorter as the chromosomes move toward the poles, they pull the chromosomes apart.

Spindle fibers, as stated earlier, are composed of microtubules. Microtubules can assemble and disassemble by the addition or subtraction of tubulin (protein) subunits. This is what enables spindle fibers to lengthen and shorten and what ultimately causes the movement of the chromosomes.

Telophase

Telophase begins when the chromosomes arrive at the poles. During telophase, the chromosomes become indistinct chromatin again. The spindle disappears as the nuclear envelope components reassemble in each cell. Telophase is characterized by the presence of two daughter nuclei.

Cytokinesis

Cytokinesis is the division of the cytoplasm and organelles. In human cells, a slight indentation called a **cleavage furrow** passes around the circumference of the cell. Actin filaments form a contractile ring; as the ring becomes smaller, the cleavage furrow pinches the cell in half. As a result, each cell becomes enclosed by its own plasma membrane.

CHECK YOUR PROGRESS 19.3

1. Explain how the chromosome number of the daughter cell compares with the chromosome number of the parent cell following mitosis.
2. List the phases of mitosis and explain what happens during each phase.
3. Describe how the cytoplasm is divided between the daughter cells following mitosis.

CONNECTING THE CONCEPTS

For more information on mitosis and cytokinesis, refer to the following discussions:

Section 3.4 examines the structure of the nucleus.

Section 3.5 describes the functions of both the microtubules and actin filaments in a nondividing cell.

19.4 Meiosis

LEARNING OUTCOMES

Upon completion of this section, you should be able to

1. List the stages of meiosis and describe what occurs in each stage.
2. Explain how meiosis increases genetic variation.
3. Differentiate between spermatogenesis and oogenesis with regard to occurrence and the number of functional gametes produced by each process.

Meiosis, or reduction division, reduces the chromosome number in the daughter cells. To do this, meiosis involves two consecutive cell divisions, without an intervening interphase. The end result is four daughter cells, each of which has one of each type of chromosome and, therefore, half as many chromosomes as the parent cell. The parent cell has the diploid (2n) number of chromosomes; the daughter cells have half this number, called the **haploid (n)** number of chromosomes. In addition, meiosis introduces genetic variation, which means that each of the resulting daughter cells is not a genetic replicate of the parent cell but, rather, possesses new combinations of the genetic material. In animals, including humans, the daughter cells that result from meiosis may go on to become the gametes.

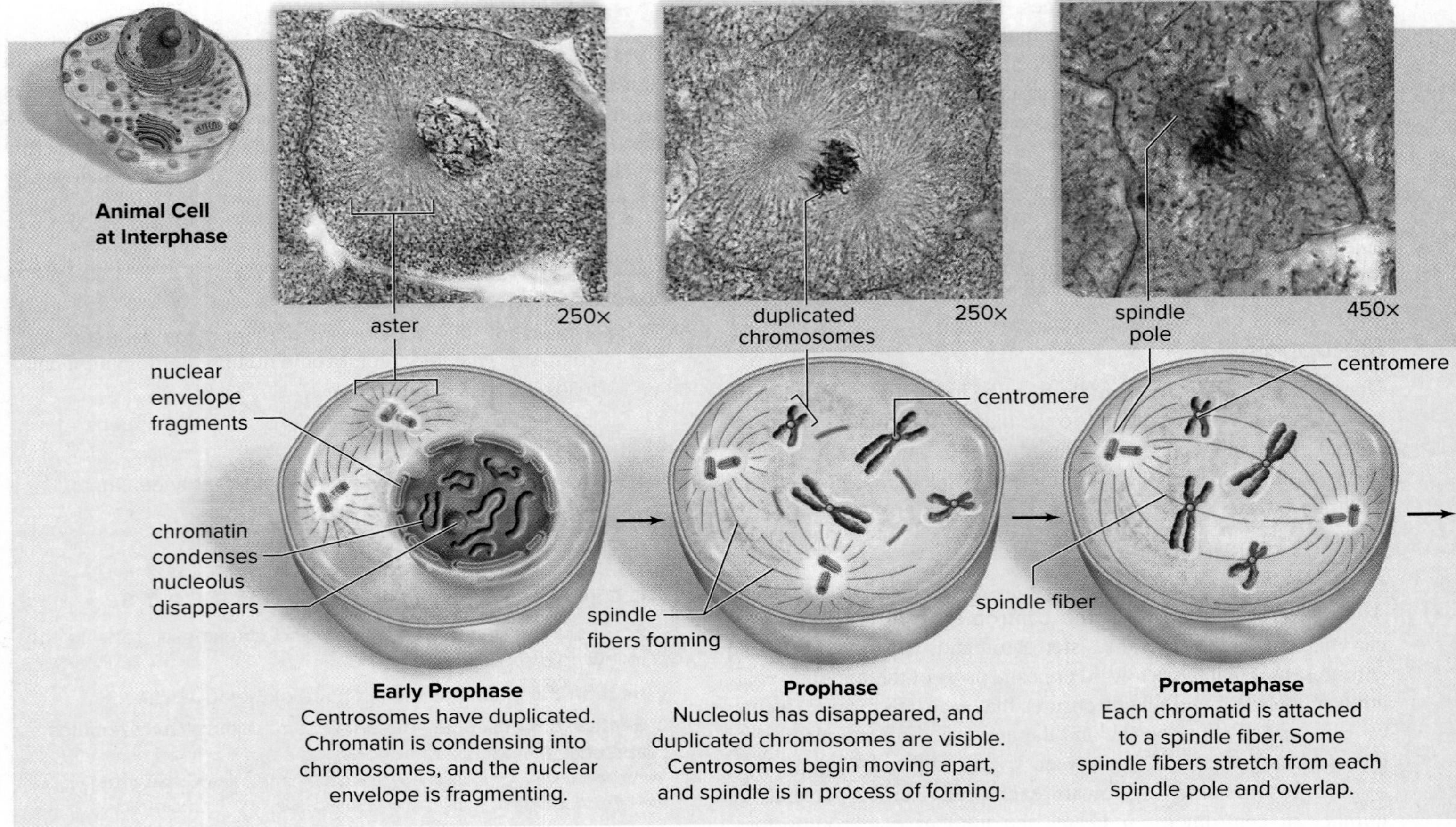

Figure 19.8 Stages of mitosis.
The stages of prophase, prometaphase, metaphase, anaphase, and telophase all act to sort the chromosomes for the new daughter cells.
(photos) (early prophase, prophase, metaphase, anaphase, telophase): Ed Reschke; (prometaphase): Michael Abbey/Science Source

Overview of Meiosis

At the start of meiosis, the parent cell is diploid (2n), and the chromosomes occur in pairs. For simplicity's sake, Figure 19.9 has only two pairs of chromosomes. In this figure, the diploid (2n) number of chromosomes is four chromosomes. The short chromosomes are one pair, and the long chromosomes are another. The members of a pair are called **homologous chromosomes,** or *homologues,* because they look alike and carry genes for the same traits, such as type of hair or color of eyes. Notice that the parent cell *(top)* has the diploid (2n) number of chromosomes; the daughter cells *(bottom)* have the haploid (n) number of chromosomes, equal to two chromosomes.

Meiosis I

The two cell divisions of meiosis are called *meiosis I* and *meiosis II.* Prior to meiosis I, DNA replication has occurred and the chromosomes are duplicated. Each chromosome consists of two chromatids held together at a centromere. During meiosis I (Fig. 19.10), the homologous chromosomes come together and line up side by side. This is called **synapsis,** and it results in an association of four chromatids that stay in close proximity during the first two phases of meiosis I. Synapsis is significant, because its occurrence leads to a reduction of the chromosome number.

There are pairs of homologous chromosomes at the equator during meiosis I because of synapsis. Only during meiosis I is it possible to observe paired chromosomes at the equator. When the members of these pairs separate, each daughter nucleus receives one member of each pair. Therefore, each daughter cell now has the haploid (n) number of chromosomes, as you can verify by counting its centromeres. Each chromosome, however, is still duplicated. No replication of DNA occurs between meiosis I and meiosis II. The time between meiosis I and meiosis II is called **interkinesis.**

BIOLOGY IN YOUR LIFE

How often do mistakes occur in meiosis?

It is estimated that 8% of all clinically recognized pregnancies have some form of chromosomal aberration. In a spontaneous abortion (typically referred to as a *miscarriage*), the frequency of chromosomal abnormalities rises to approximately 50%. Most of these are the result of errors during meiosis in parents with normal karyotypes.

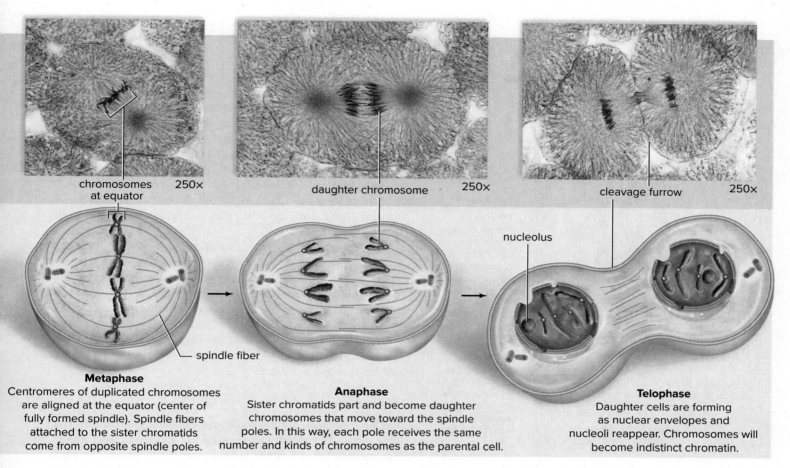

chromosomes at equator 250×

daughter chromosome 250×

cleavage furrow 250×

nucleolus

spindle fiber

Metaphase
Centromeres of duplicated chromosomes are aligned at the equator (center of fully formed spindle). Spindle fibers attached to the sister chromatids come from opposite spindle poles.

Anaphase
Sister chromatids part and become daughter chromosomes that move toward the spindle poles. In this way, each pole receives the same number and kinds of chromosomes as the parental cell.

Telophase
Daughter cells are forming as nuclear envelopes and nucleoli reappear. Chromosomes will become indistinct chromatin.

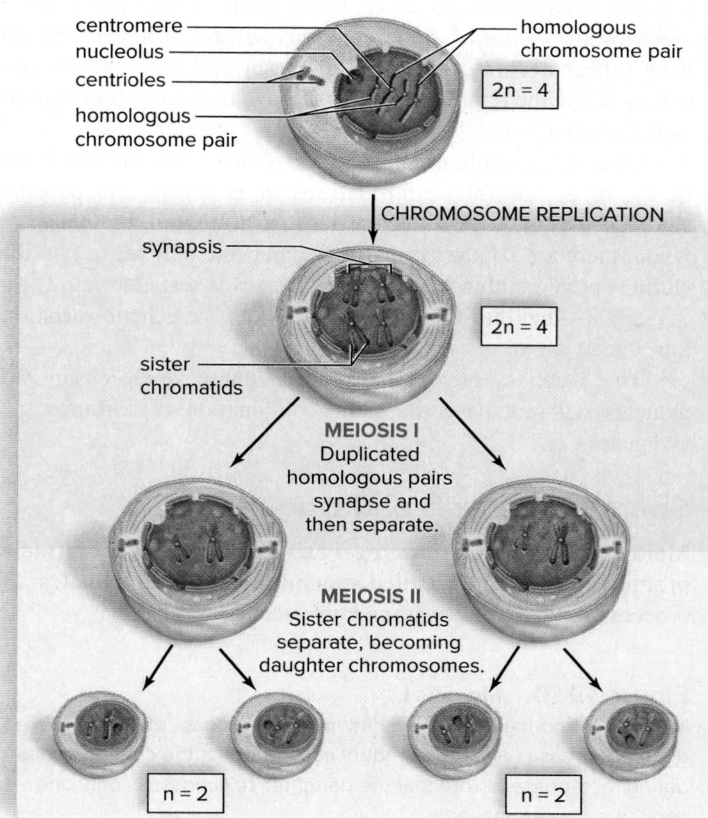

Meiosis II

During meiosis II (Fig. 19.11), the centromeres divide. The sister chromatids separate, becoming chromosomes that are distributed to daughter nuclei. In the end, each of four daughter cells has the n, or haploid, number of chromosomes. Each chromosome consists of one chromatid.

In humans, the daughter cells mature into gametes (sperm and egg) that fuse during fertilization. Fertilization restores the diploid number of chromosomes in the zygote, the first cell of the new individual. If the gametes carried the diploid instead of the haploid number of chromosomes, the chromosome number would double with each fertilization. After several generations, the zygote would be nothing but chromosomes.

Meiosis and Genetic Variation

Meiosis is a part of sexual reproduction. The process of meiosis ensures that the next generation of individuals will have the diploid number of chromosomes and a combination of genetic characteristics different from that of either parent. Though both meiosis I and meiosis II have the same four stages of nuclear division as did

Figure 19.9 **The results of meiosis.**
DNA replication is followed by meiosis I when homologous chromosomes pair and then separate. During meiosis II, the sister chromatids become chromosomes that move into daughter nuclei.

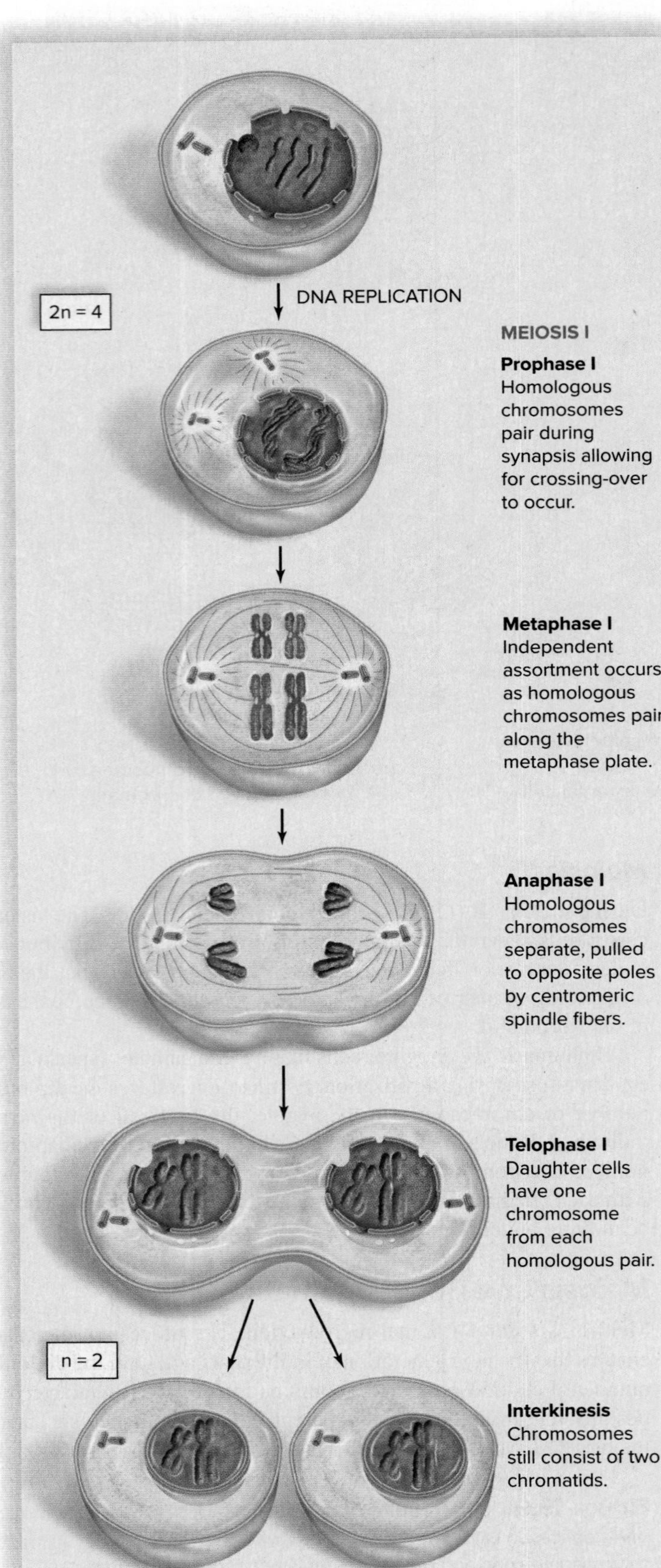

2n = 4
DNA REPLICATION
MEIOSIS I
Prophase I
Homologous chromosomes pair during synapsis allowing for crossing-over to occur.
Metaphase I
Independent assortment occurs as homologous chromosomes pair along the metaphase plate.
Anaphase I
Homologous chromosomes separate, pulled to opposite poles by centromeric spindle fibers.
Telophase I
Daughter cells have one chromosome from each homologous pair.
n = 2
Interkinesis
Chromosomes still consist of two chromatids.

mitosis (see Section 19.3), here we discuss only prophase I and metaphase I, because special events occur during these phases that introduce new genetic combinations into the daughter cells.

Prophase I

In prophase I, synapsis occurs, causing the homologous chromosomes to come together and line up side by side. Now, an exchange of genetic material may occur between the nonsister chromatids of the homologous pair (Fig. 19.12). This exchange is called **crossing-over.** Notice that in Figure 19.12 the crossing-over events (there may be more than one) have produced chromatids that are no longer identical. When the chromatids separate during meiosis II, the daughter cells receive chromosomes with recombined genetic material.

To appreciate the significance of crossing-over, it is necessary to realize that the members of a homologous pair can carry slightly different instructions for the same genetic trait. For example, one homologue may carry instructions for brown eyes and blond hair, and the corresponding homologue may carry instructions for blue eyes and red hair. Crossing-over causes the offspring to receive a different combination of instructions than the mother or the father received. Therefore, offspring can receive brown eyes and red hair or blue eyes and blond hair.

Metaphase I

During metaphase I, the homologous pairs align independently at the equator. This means that the maternal or paternal member may be oriented toward either pole. Figure 19.13 shows the eight possible orientations for a cell that contains only three pairs of chromosomes. Four of the orientations will result in gametes that have different combinations of maternal and paternal chromosomes, while the remaining cells will have the same combinations as the original cells.

Once all possible orientations are considered, the result will be 2^3, or 8, possible combinations of maternal and paternal chromosomes in the resulting gametes from this cell. In humans, in whom there are 23 pairs of chromosomes, the number of possible chromosomal combinations in the gametes is a staggering 2^{23}, or 8,388,608—and this does not even consider the genetic variations introduced due to crossing-over.

The events of prophase I and metaphase I help ensure that gametes will not have the same combination of chromosomes and genes.

Spermatogenesis and Oogenesis

Meiosis is a part of *gametogenesis*. Gametogenesis in males produces sperm and is called **spermatogenesis.** In females, the process is called **oogenesis,** and produces eggs.

Figure 19.10 Meiosis I.
Meiosis I introduces genetic variation by the process of crossing-over during prophase I and independent assortment of the chromosomes during metaphase I. Note that the daughter cells possess only one copy of each chromosome.

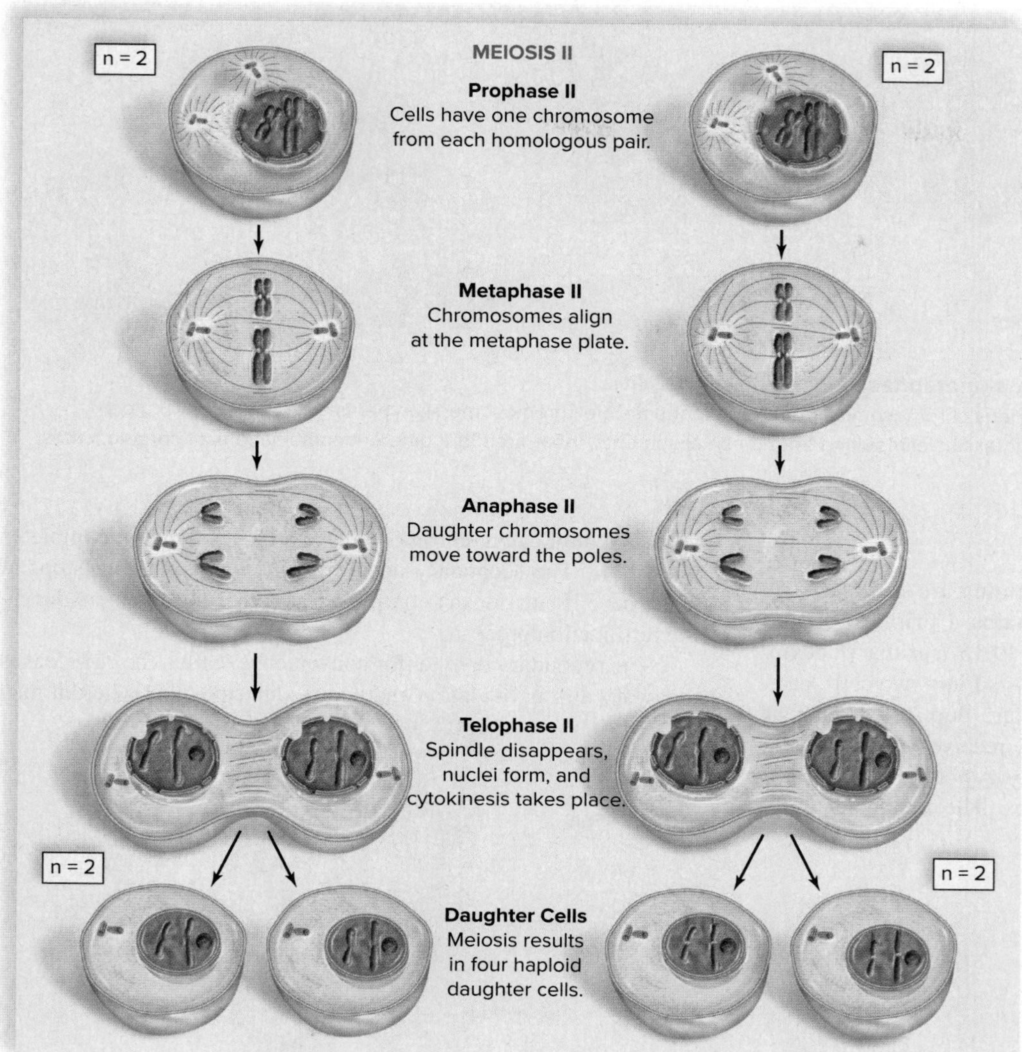

Figure 19.11 **Meiosis II.** During meiosis II, sister chromatids separate, becoming daughter chromosomes that are distributed to the daughter nuclei. Following meiosis II, there are four haploid daughter cells. Comparing the number of chromosomes in each daughter cell with the number in the parental cell at the start of meiosis I verifies that each daughter cell is haploid.

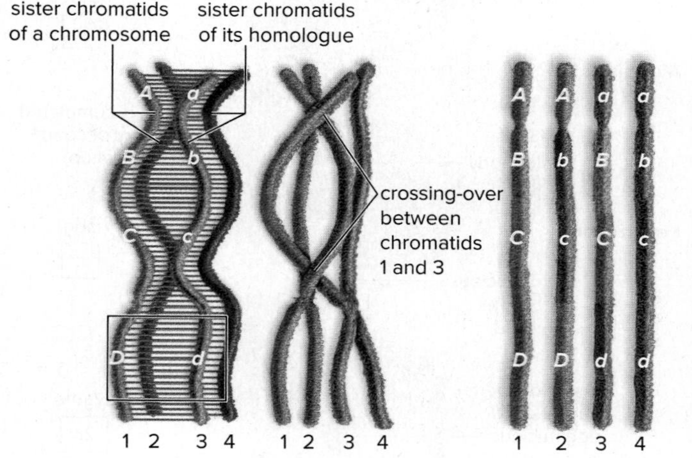

Figure 19.12 **Synapsis and crossing-over increase variability.** **a.** During meiosis I, duplicated homologous chromosomes undergo synapsis and line up with each other. **b.** During crossing-over, nonsister chromatids break and then rejoin in the manner shown. **c.** Two of the resulting chromosomes have a different combination of genes than they had before.

Spermatogenesis

After puberty, the time of life when the sex organs mature, spermatogenesis is continual in the testes of human males. As many as 300,000 sperm are produced per minute, or over 400 million per day.

Spermatogenesis is shown in Figure 19.14. The *primary spermatocytes,* which are diploid (2n), divide during meiosis I to form two *secondary spermatocytes,* which are haploid (n). Secondary spermatocytes divide during meiosis II to produce four *spermatids,* which are also haploid (n). What's the difference between the chromosomes in haploid secondary spermatocytes and those in haploid spermatids? The chromosomes in secondary spermatocytes are duplicated and consist of two chromatids, whereas those in spermatids consist of only one. Spermatids mature into sperm (spermatozoa). In human males, sperm have 23 chromosomes, the haploid number. The process of meiosis in males always results in four cells that become sperm. In other words, all four daughter cells—the spermatids—become sperm.

Figure 19.13 **Independent alignment at metaphase I increases variability.**
When a parent cell has three pairs of homologous chromosomes, there are eight possible chromosome alignments at the equator due to independent assortment. Among the 16 daughter nuclei resulting from these alignments, there are eight different combinations of chromosomes.

Oogenesis

The ovary of a female contains many immature follicles (see Fig. 17.8). Each of these follicles contains a primary oocyte arrested in prophase I. As shown in Figure 19.15, a primary oocyte, which is diploid (2n), divides during meiosis I into two cells, each of which is haploid. The chromosomes are duplicated. One of these cells, termed the *secondary oocyte,* receives almost all the cytoplasm. The other is the first polar body. A *polar body* acts as a trash can to hold discarded chromosomes. The first polar body contains duplicated chromosomes and occasionally completes meiosis II. The secondary oocyte begins meiosis II but stops at metaphase II and doesn't complete it unless a sperm enters during the fertilization process.

The secondary oocyte (for convenience, called the egg) leaves the ovary during ovulation and enters a uterine tube, where it may

SPERMATOGENESIS
Meiosis I
primary spermatocyte
2n
secondary spermatocytes
n
Meiosis II
spermatids
n
Metamorphosis and maturation
sperm
n

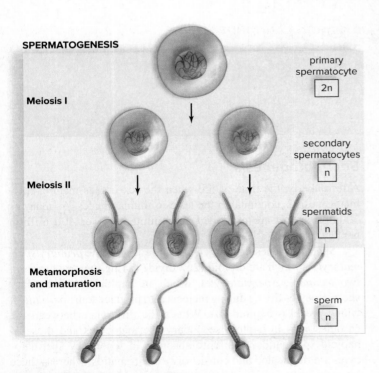

Figure 19.14 **Spermatogenesis.**
Spermatogenesis produces four viable sperm, each with 23 chromosomes. whereas oogenesis produces one egg and at least two polar bodies. In humans, both sperm and egg have 23 chromosomes each; therefore, following fertilization, the zygote has 46 chromosomes.

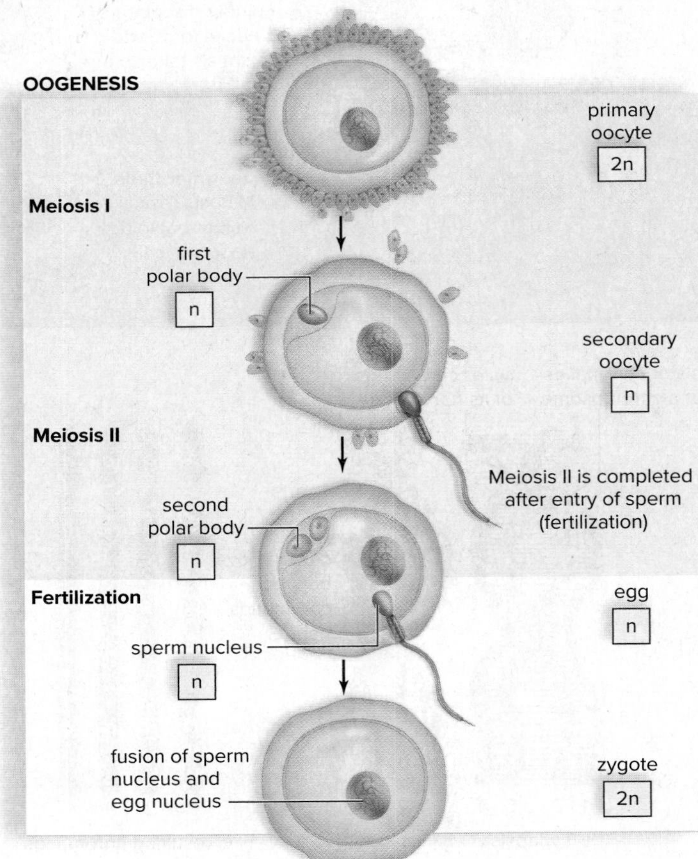

Figure 19.15 **Oogenesis.**
Oogenesis produces one egg and at least two polar bodies. The polar bodies and egg have 23 chromosomes. Following fertilization of the egg by a sperm, the zygote has 46 chromosomes.

be fertilized by a sperm. If so, the oocyte is activated to complete the second meiotic division. Following meiosis II, there is one egg and two or possibly three polar bodies. The mature egg has 23 chromosomes. The polar bodies disintegrate, which is a way to discard unnecessary chromosomes while retaining much of the cytoplasm in the egg.

One egg can be the source of identical twins if, after one division of the fertilized egg during development, the cells separate and each one becomes a complete individual. On the other hand, the occurrence of fraternal twins requires that two eggs be ovulated and then fertilized separately.

Significance of Meiosis

In animals, one function of meiosis is to keep the chromosome number constant from generation to generation. The gametes are haploid, so the zygote has only the diploid number of chromosomes.

An easier way to keep the chromosome number constant is to reproduce asexually. Single-celled organisms such as bacteria, protozoans, and yeasts (a fungi) reproduce by binary fission. Binary fission is a form of asexual reproduction, because one parent produces identical offspring. Binary fission is a quick and easy way to asexually reproduce many organisms within a short time. A bacterium can increase to over 1 million cells in about 7 hours, for example. Given this, why do organisms expend the energy to reproduce sexually? It takes energy to find a mate, carry out a courtship, and produce eggs or sperm that may never be used for reproductive purposes. A human male produces over 400 million sperm per day, and very few of these will fertilize an egg.

Sexual reproduction also introduces genetic variation into the gametes. Genetic variation ensures that offspring will be genetically different from each other and their parents. It occurs because of crossing-over (see Fig. 19.12) and independent alignment of chromosomes (see Fig. 19.13). Also, at the time of fertilization, parents contribute genetically different chromosomes to the offspring.

All environments are subject to a change in conditions. Those individuals able to survive in a new environment are able to pass on their genes. Environments are subject to change, so sexual reproduction is advantageous. It generates the diversity needed, so that at least a few will be suited to new and different environmental circumstances.

CHECK YOUR PROGRESS 19.4

1. Explain how, following meiosis, the chromosome number of the daughter cells compares to the chromosome number of the parent cell.
2. Explain how meiosis reduces the likelihood that gametes will have the same combination of chromosomes and genes.
3. Summarize the events during the two cell divisions of meiosis.
4. Compare and contrast the stages of oogenesis and spermatogenesis.

CONNECTING THE CONCEPTS

For more on the importance of meiosis, refer to the following discussions:

Figure 17.4 illustrates how meiosis relates to spermatogenesis.

Figure 17.9 demonstrates how meiosis produces eggs and polar bodies during oogenesis.

Figure 21.5 relates meiosis to the patterns of genetic inheritance.

19.5 Comparison of Meiosis and Mitosis

LEARNING OUTCOMES

Upon completion of this section, you should be able to

1. Distinguish between meiosis and mitosis with regard to the number of divisions and the number and chromosome content of the resulting cells.
2. Contrast the events of meiosis I and meiosis II with the events of mitosis.

Meiosis and mitosis are both nuclear divisions, but they differ in the number of cells produced and the genetic complement (haploid or diploid) of each of the daughter cells. Figure 19.16 provides a visual review of the similarities and differences between meiosis and mitosis.

General Comparison

DNA replication takes place only once prior to both meiosis and mitosis. Meiosis requires two nuclear divisions, but mitosis requires only one.

- Four daughter nuclei are produced by meiosis; following cytokinesis, there are four daughter cells. Mitosis followed by cytokinesis results in two daughter cells.
- The four daughter cells following meiosis are haploid (n) and have half the chromosome number of the parent cell (2n). The daughter cells following mitosis have the same chromosome number as the parent cell—the 2n, or diploid, number.
- The daughter cells from meiosis are not genetically identical to each other or to the parent cell. The daughter cells from mitosis are genetically identical to each other and to the parent cell.

The specific differences between these nuclear divisions can be categorized according to occurrence and process.

Occurrence

Meiosis occurs only at certain times in the life cycle of sexually reproducing organisms. In humans, it happens only in the reproductive organs and produces the gametes. Mitosis is more common because it occurs in all tissues during growth and repair. So, which type of cell division can lead to cancer? Mitosis, which can result in the proliferation of body cells. Abnormal rates of mitosis can lead to cancer.

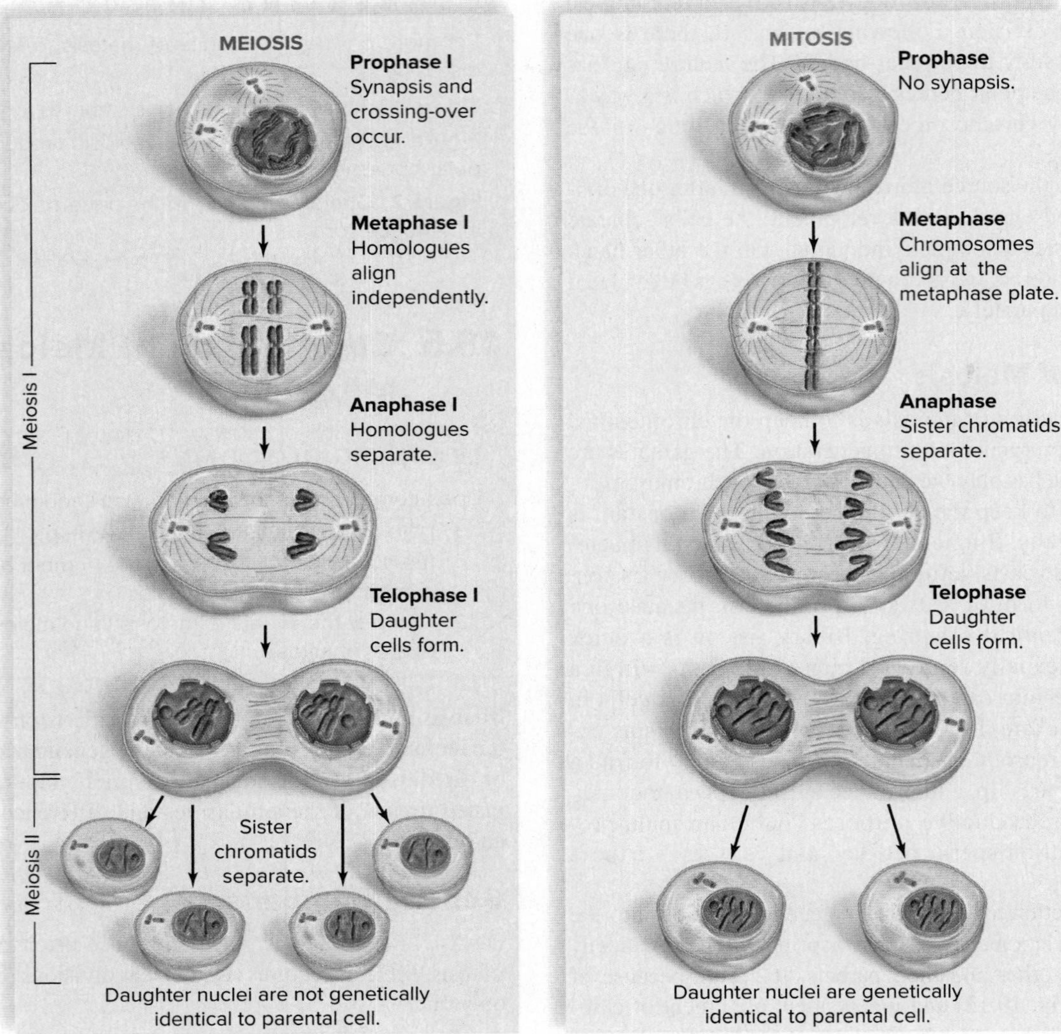

Figure 19.16 **A comparison of meiosis and mitosis.**
By comparing mitosis with meiosis, you can see why mitosis is referred to as duplication division and why meiosis is called reduction division. Only in metaphase I are the homologous chromosomes paired at the equator. Members of homologous chromosome pairs separate during anaphase I; therefore, the daughter cells are haploid. The blue chromosomes were inherited from the paternal parent, and the red chromosomes were inherited from the maternal parent. The exchange of color between nonsister chromatids represents the crossing-over that occurs during meiosis I.

Process

Comparison of Meiosis I with Mitosis

These events distinguish meiosis I from mitosis (Table 19.1):

- Homologous chromosomes pair and undergo crossing-over during prophase I of meiosis but not during mitosis.
- Paired homologous chromosomes align at the equator during metaphase I in meiosis. These paired chromosomes have four chromatids altogether. Individual chromosomes align at the equator during metaphase in mitosis. They each have two chromatids.
- This difference makes it easy to tell whether you are looking at mitosis, meiosis I, or meiosis II. For example, if a cell has 16 chromosomes, then 16 chromosomes are at the equator during mitosis but only 8 chromosomes during meiosis II. Only meiosis I has paired duplicated chromosomes at the equator.
- Homologous chromosomes (with centromeres intact) separate and move to opposite poles during anaphase I of meiosis. Centromeres split, and sister chromatids, now called chromosomes, move to opposite poles during anaphase in mitosis and meiosis II.

Comparison of Meiosis II with Mitosis

The events of meiosis II are like those of mitosis (Table 19.2) except that, in meiosis II, the nuclei contain the haploid number of chromosomes. If the parent cell has 16 chromosomes, then the cells undergoing meiosis II have 8 chromosomes, and the daughter cells have 8 chromosomes, for example.

Table 19.1 Comparison of Meiosis I with Mitosis

Meiosis I	Mitosis
Prophase I	*Prophase*
Pairing of homologous chromosomes	No pairing of chromosomes
Metaphase I	*Metaphase*
Homologous duplicated chromosomes at equator	Duplicated chromosomes at equator
Anaphase I	*Anaphase*
Homologous chromosomes separate.	Sister chromatids separate, becoming daughter chromosomes, which move to the poles.
Telophase I	*Telophase*
Two haploid daughter cells	Two diploid daughter cells, identical to the parent cell

Table 19.2 Comparison of Meiosis II with Mitosis

Meiosis II	Mitosis
Prophase II	*Prophase*
No pairing of chromosomes	No pairing of chromosomes
Metaphase II	*Metaphase*
Haploid number of duplicated chromosomes at equator	Duplicated chromosomes at equator
Anaphase II	*Anaphase*
Sister chromatids separate, becoming daughter chromosomes, which move to the poles.	Sister chromatids separate, becoming daughter chromosomes, which move to the poles.
Telophase II	*Telophase*
Four haploid daughter cells	Two daughter cells, identical to the parent cell

CHECK YOUR PROGRESS 19.5

1. List the similarities and differences between meiosis I and mitosis.
2. List the similarities and differences between meiosis II and mitosis.
3. Explain why a close examination of metaphase can indicate whether a cell is undergoing mitosis or meiosis.

CONNECTING THE CONCEPTS

For more on the roles of mitosis and meiosis, refer to the following discussions:

Section 17.2 examines the process of spermatogenesis and the male reproductive system.

Section 17.4 examines the process of oogenesis and the female reproductive system.

Section 20.1 explores how unrestricted mitosis causes cancer.

19.6 Chromosome Inheritance

LEARNING OUTCOMES

Upon completion of this section, you should be able to

1. Explain how nondisjunction produces monosomy and trisomy chromosome conditions.
2. Describe the causes and consequences of trisomy 21.
3. List the major syndromes associated with changes in the number of sex chromosomes.
4. Describe the effects of deletions, duplications, inversions, and translocations on chromosome structure.

Normally, an individual possesses 22 pairs of autosomes and two sex chromosomes in their cells. Each pair of these chromosomes carries genes for particular traits. These genes may be slightly different in the information they possess. These variations of the genes are called alleles. Changes in chromosome number or structure may change the combination of alleles for a trait in an organism. In most cases, this has a detrimental effect.

Changes in Chromosome Number

Some individuals are born with either too many or too few autosomes or sex chromosomes. This is most likely due to an error, called nondisjunction, during meiosis. **Nondisjunction** is the failure of the homologous chromosomes or daughter chromosomes to separate correctly during meiosis I and meiosis II, respectively. Nondisjunction may occur during meiosis I, when both members of a homologous pair go into the same daughter cell. It can also occur during meiosis II, when the sister chromatids fail to separate and both daughter chromosomes go into the same gamete.

Figure 19.17 assumes that nondisjunction has occurred during oogenesis. Some abnormal eggs have 24 chromosomes, whereas others have only 22 chromosomes. If an egg with 24 chromosomes is fertilized with a normal sperm, the result is called a **trisomy,** because one type of chromosome is present in three copies ($2n + 1$). If an egg with 22 chromosomes is fertilized with a normal sperm, the result is called a **monosomy,** because one type of chromosome is present in a single copy ($2n - 1$).

Normal development depends on the presence of exactly two of each type of chromosome. An abnormal number of autosomes causes a developmental abnormality. Monosomy of all but the X chromosome is fatal. The affected infant rarely develops to full term. Trisomy is usually fatal, though there are some exceptions. Among autosomal trisomies, only trisomy 21 (Down syndrome) has a reasonable chance of survival after birth.

The chances of survival are greater when trisomy or monosomy involves the sex chromosomes. In normal XX females, one of the X chromosomes becomes a darkly staining mass of chromatin called a **Barr body** (named after the person who discovered it). A Barr body is an inactive X chromosome. The Science feature "Inactivating X Chromosomes" provides additional information regarding Barr bodies.

We now know that the cells of females function with a single X chromosome just as those of males do. This is most likely the reason that a zygote with one X chromosome (Turner syndrome)

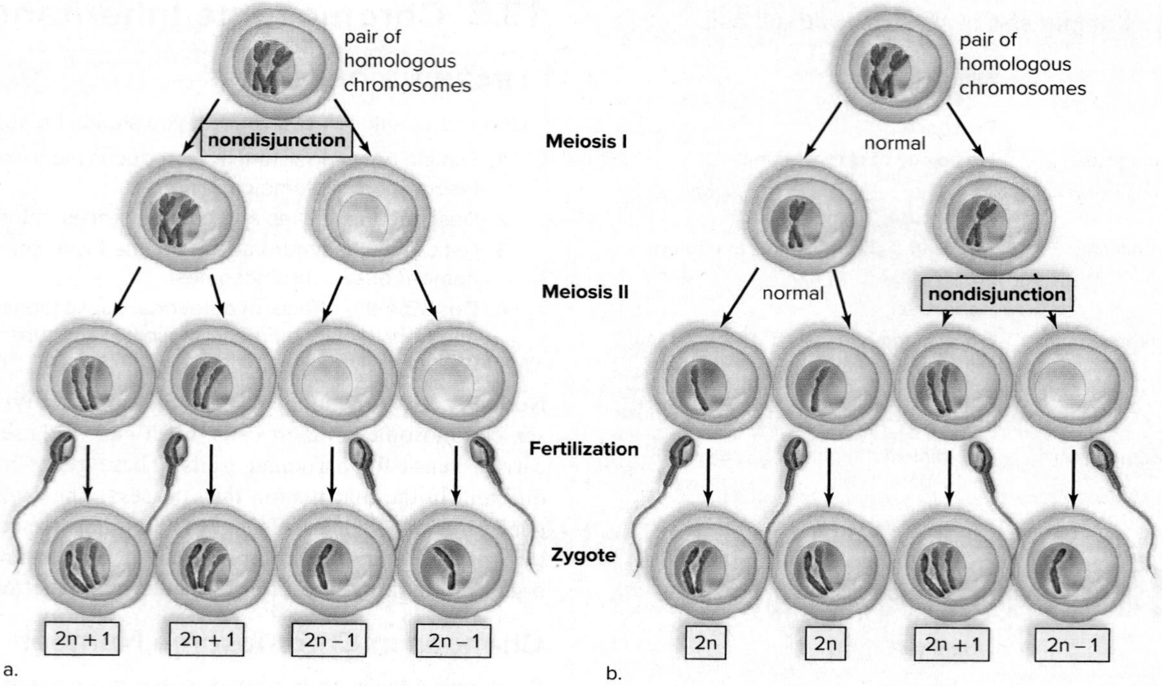

Figure 19.17 Consequences of nondisjunction.
Nondisjunction may occur in either the sperm or egg cells (shown here). **a.** During meiosis I, nondisjunction results in abnormal eggs that have one more or one less than the normal number of chromosomes. Fertilization of these abnormal eggs with normal sperm results in a zygote with abnormal chromosome numbers. **b.** Nondisjunction can also occur during meiosis II if the sister chromatids separate but the resulting daughter chromosomes go into the same daughter cell. The egg will then have one more or one less than the usual number of chromosomes. Fertilization of these abnormal eggs with normal sperm produces a zygote with abnormal chromosome numbers.

> **BIOLOGY IN YOUR LIFE**
>
> **Are there trisomies of the other chromosomes besides chromosome 21?**
>
> There are other chromosomal trisomies. However, because most chromosomes are much larger than chromosome 21, the abnormalities associated with three copies of these other chromosomes are much more severe than those found in Down syndrome. The extra genetic material causes profound congenital defects, resulting in fatality. Trisomies of the X and Y chromosomes appear to be exceptions to this, as noted in the text.
>
> Chromosome 8 trisomy occurs rarely. Fetuses with this condition generally do not survive to birth or die shortly after birth. There are also trisomies of chromosomes 13 (Patau syndrome) and 18 (Edwards syndrome). Again, these babies usually die within the first few days of life.

can survive. Then, too, all extra X chromosomes beyond a single one become Barr bodies. This explains why poly-X females and XXY males are seen fairly frequently. An extra Y chromosome, called Jacobs syndrome, is tolerated in humans, most likely because the Y chromosome carries few genes. Jacobs syndrome (XYY) is due to nondisjunction during meiosis II of spermatogenesis. We know this because two Ys are present only during meiosis II in males.

Down Syndrome: An Autosomal Trisomy

The most common autosomal trisomy seen among humans is Down syndrome, also called trisomy 21. Persons with Down syndrome usually have three copies of chromosome 21, because the egg had two copies instead of one. However, about 20% of the time the sperm contributes the extra chromosome 21. The chances of a woman having a child with Down syndrome increase rapidly with age, starting at about age 40. The reasons for this are still being investigated.

Although an older woman is more likely to have a child with Down syndrome, most babies with Down syndrome are born to women younger than age 40, because this is the age group having the most babies. Karyotyping can detect a child with Down syndrome. However, young women are not routinely encouraged to undergo the procedures necessary to get a sample of fetal cells (amniocentesis or chorionic villus sampling), because the risk of complications is greater than the likelihood of having a child with Down syndrome. Fortunately, a test based on substances in maternal blood can help identify fetuses who may need to be karyotyped.

Down syndrome is associated with some common characteristics, such as the following: a short stature; an eyelid fold; a flattened facial profile; stubby fingers; a wide gap between the first and second toes; a large, fissured tongue; a round head; and a palm crease known as the single transverse pal mar crease (STPC). Individuals with Down syndrome may experience developmental delays and intellectual disability, which vary in severity. However, with the help of

BIOLOGY TODAY ▶ **Science**

Inactivating X Chromosomes

Most people are familiar with tortoiseshell cats, whose fur contains patches of orange and black (Fig. 19A). These cats are genetic mosaics. A mosaic is formed by combining different pieces to form a whole (a stained glass window is one example). Likewise, in genetics, a mosaic is an individual whose cells have at least two—and sometimes more—different types of genetic expression. In the case of the tortoiseshell cat, the fur colors are due to the expression of different genes. Some of the hair cells of these cats express the paternal copy of the gene. If an orange-haired father's copy of the gene is activated, a patch of orange hair develops. In other cells, the maternal gene is activated. A calico kitten with a black mother will grow black patches of hair scattered among the orange. Were you aware that human females are also mosaics?

The nucleus of human cells contains 46 chromosomes arranged into a set of 23 pairs. One chromosome from each pair is maternal, and the other is paternal. Each of the chromosomes in the first 22 pairs resembles its mate. Further, each member of a pair contains the same genes as the other member. Sex chromosomes that determine a person's gender are the last pair. Females have two X chromosomes, and males have one X and one Y chromosome. The Y chromosome is very small and contains far fewer genes than the X chromosome. Almost all the genes on the X chromosome lack a corresponding gene on the Y chromosome. Thus, females have two copies of X genes, whereas males have only one. The body compensates for this extra dose of genetic material by inactivating one of the X chromosomes in each cell of the female embryo. Inactivation occurs early in development (at approximately the 100-cell stage). The inactivated X chromosome is called a Barr body, named after its discoverer. Barr bodies are highly condensed chromatin that appear as dark spots in the nucleus. Which X chromosome is inactivated in a given cell appears to be random. But every cell that develops from the original group of 100 cells will have the same inactivated X chromosome as its parent cell. Some of a woman's cells have inactivated the maternal X chromosome, while other cells have inactivated the paternal X chromosome—thus, she is a mosaic.

Problems with inactivation of the X chromosome in humans could be linked to the development of cancer. For example, women who have one defective copy of the breast cancer gene *BRCA1* have a greatly increased risk of developing breast and ovarian cancer. The BRCA1 protein produced from the gene is called a tumor suppressor. When the protein is functioning normally, it suppresses the development of cancer. The same protein is involved in X chromosome inactivation, although its exact role is uncertain. Presumably, increased cancer risk occurs because abnormal BRCA1 protein can neither inactivate the X chromosome nor function as a tumor suppressor.

Figure 19A Tortoiseshell cats.
The black and orange color patterns on a tortoiseshell cat are due to two different alleles on the X chromosome. Orange areas indicate where the black allele has been inactivated, and black regions are where the orange allele has been inactivated.
Anna Yakimova/evdoha/123RF

Questions to Consider

1. Why would having an extra set of X chromosome genes be a problem for a female?
2. If X inactivation compensates for an extra X chromosome, why do you think that males with Klinefelter syndrome (XXY) may have developmental problems?

interventions and supports, children with Down syndrome are able to achieve developmental milestones and live fulfilled lives as adults.

The genes that cause Down syndrome are located on the bottom third of chromosome 21 (Fig. 19.18). Extensive investigative work has been directed toward discovering the specific genes responsible for the characteristics of the syndrome. Thus far, investigators have discovered several genes that may account for various conditions seen in persons with Down syndrome. For example, they have located genes most likely responsible for the increased tendency toward leukemia, cataracts, accelerated rate of aging, and intellectual disabilities. The gene associated with intellectual disabilities, called the *Gart* gene, causes an increased level of purines in the blood, a finding associated with problems in intellectual development. One day, it may be possible to control the expression of the *Gart* gene even before birth, so that at least this symptom of Down syndrome does not appear.

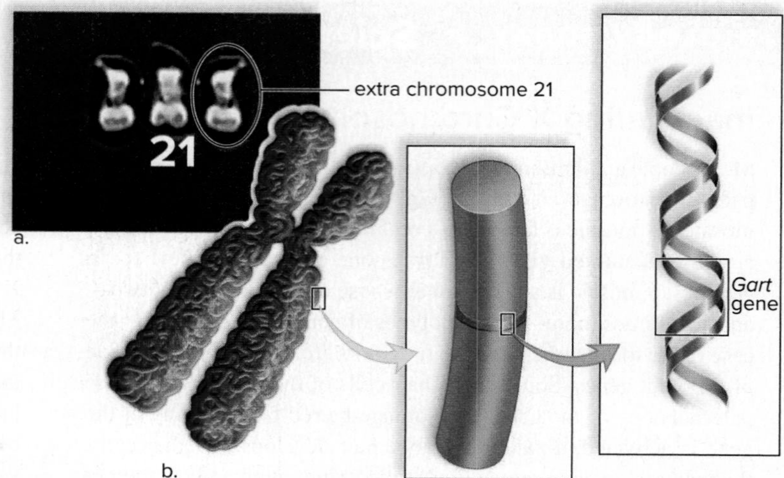

Figure 19.18 **Down syndrome.**
a. A partial karotype of an individual with Down syndrome shows an extra chromosome 21. **b.** DNA technologies have pinpointed the location of specific genes associated with the syndrome, such as the *Gart* gene.
(photo): CNRI/Science Source

BIOLOGY IN YOUR LIFE

Why is the age of a female a factor in Down syndrome?

One reason may be a difference in the timing of meiosis between males and females. Following puberty, males produce sperm continuously throughout their lives. In contrast, meiosis for females begins about 5 months after being conceived. However, the process is paused at prophase I of meiosis. Only after puberty are a selected few number of these cells allowed to continue meiosis as part of the female menstrual cycle. Because long periods of time may occur between the start and completion of meiosis, there is a greater chance that nondisjunction will occur; thus, as a female ages, there is a greater chance of producing a child with Down syndrome.

Changes in Sex Chromosome Number

An abnormal sex chromosome number is the result of inheriting too many or too few X or Y chromosomes. Figure 19.17 can also be used to illustrate nondisjunction of the sex chromosomes during oogenesis if you assume that the chromosomes shown represent X chromosomes. Nondisjunction during oogenesis or spermatogenesis can result in gametes that have too few or too many X or Y chromosomes.

A person with Turner syndrome (XO) is a female, and a person with Klinefelter syndrome (XXY) is a male. The term **syndrome** indicates that there are a group of symptoms that always occur together. This shows that, in humans, the presence of a Y chromosome, not the number of X chromosomes, determines maleness. The *SRY* gene, on the short arm of the Y chromosome, produces a hormone called *testis-determining factor.* This hormone plays a critical role in the development of male sex organs.

Turner Syndrome

From birth, an individual with Turner syndrome has only one sex chromosome, an X. In adult females, Turner syndrome is associated with physical features such as a short stature, a broad chest, and folds of skin on the back of the neck. The ovaries, uterine tubes, and uterus are very small and underdeveloped. Females with Turner syndrome do not undergo puberty or menstruate, and their breasts do not develop. However, some have given birth following in vitro fertilization using donor eggs. They usually do not have an intellectual disability and can lead healthy lives if they receive hormone supplements.

Klinefelter Syndrome

A male with Klinefelter syndrome has two or more X chromosomes in addition to a Y chromosome. The extra X chromosome(s) become(s) a Barr body. The approximate incidence for Klinefelter syndrome is 1 in every 500 to 1,000 males.

In males with Klinefelter syndrome, the testes and prostate gland are underdeveloped and facial hair is lacking. They may exhibit some breast development. Affected individuals have large hands and feet and very long arms and legs. They are usually slow to learn but do not have an intellectual disability unless they inherit more than two X chromosomes.

While males with Klinefelter syndrome exhibit no other major health abnormalities, they have an increased risk of some disorders, including breast cancer, osteoporosis, and lupus, which disproportionately affect females. Although men with Klinefelter syndrome typically do not need medical treatment, some have found that testosterone therapy helps increase muscle strength, sex drive, and concentration ability. Testosterone treatment, however, does not reverse the sterility associated with Klinefelter syndrome due to incomplete testicle development.

Females with Poly-X Syndrome

A female with poly-X syndrome has more than two X chromosomes and extra Barr bodies in the nucleus. Females with three X chromosomes have no distinctive phenotype, aside from a tendency to be tall and thin. Although some experience delayed motor and language development, most females with poly-X syndrome do not have intellectual disabilities. Some may have menstrual difficulties, but many menstruate regularly and are fertile. Their children usually have a normal karyotype.

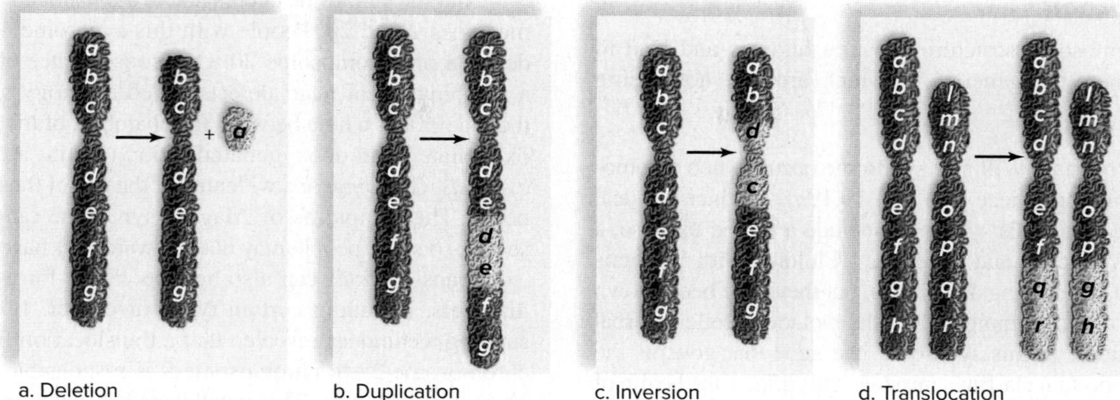

Figure 19.19 The various types of chromosomal mutations.
a. Deletion is the loss of a chromosome piece. **b.** Duplication occurs when the same piece is repeated within the chromosome. **c.** Inversion occurs when a piece of chromosome breaks loose and then rejoins in the reversed direction. **d.** Translocation is the exchange of chromosome pieces between nonhomologous pairs.

Females with more than three X chromosomes occur rarely. Unlike females with XXX chromosomes, females with XXXX chromosomes are usually tall and tend to have severe intellectual disabilities. Various physical abnormalities are seen, but they may menstruate normally.

Jacobs Syndrome

The condition of Jacobs syndrome (XXY) in males can only result from nondisjunction during spermatogenesis. Males with this syndrome are usually taller than average, have persistent acne, and tend to experience speech and reading problems, but they are fertile and may have children. Despite the extra Y chromosome, there is no difference in behavioral development between males with XYY chromosomes and those with XY chromosomes.

Changes in Chromosome Structure

Changes in chromosome structure are another type of chromosomal mutation. Various agents in the environment, such as radiation, certain organic chemicals, or even viruses, can cause chromosomes to break. Ordinarily, when breaks occur in chromosomes, the two broken ends reunite to give the same sequence of genes. Sometimes, however, the broken ends of one or more chromosomes do not rejoin in the same pattern as before. The results are various types of chromosomal mutation.

Changes in chromosome structure include deletions, duplications, inversions, and translocations of chromosome segments. A **deletion** occurs when an end of a chromosome breaks off or when two simultaneous breaks lead to the loss of an internal segment (Fig. 19.19*a*). Even when only one member of a pair of chromosomes is affected, a deletion often causes abnormalities.

A **duplication** is the presence of a chromosomal segment more than once in the same chromosome (Fig. 19.19*b*). An **inversion** has occurred when a segment of a chromosome is turned around 180° (Fig. 19.19*c*). While most inversions do not present problems for the individuals, because all of the genes are present, the reversed sequence of genes can lead to problems during prophase of meiosis when crossing-over occurs. Often, inversions may lead to the formation of deletions and duplications (Fig. 19.20).

A **translocation** is the movement of a chromosome segment from one chromosome to another nonhomologous chromosome (see Fig. 19.19*d*). In 5% of cases, a translocation that occurred in a previous generation between chromosomes 21 and 14 is the cause of Down syndrome. In other words, because a portion of chromosome 21 is now attached to a portion of chromosome 14, the individual has three copies of the alleles that bring about Down syndrome when they are present in triplet copy. In these cases, Down syndrome is not related to the age of the mother but, instead, tends to run in the family of either the father or the mother.

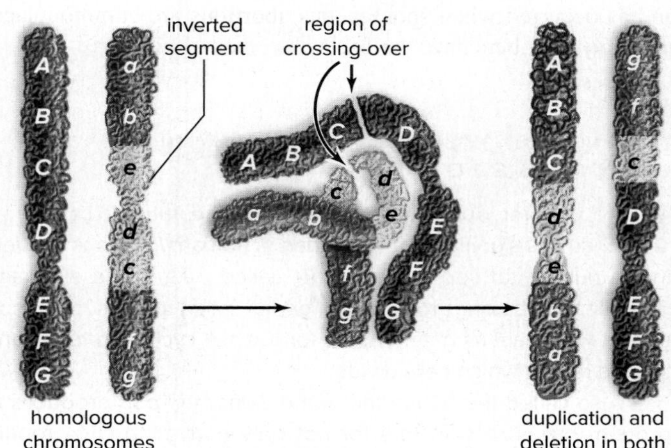

Figure 19.20 A chromosomal inversion.
Left: A segment of one homologue is inverted. In the shaded segment, *edc* occurs instead of *cde*. *Middle:* The two homologues can pair only when the inverted sequence forms an internal loop. After crossing-over, a duplication and a deletion can occur. *Right:* The homologue on the left has *AB* and *ab* sequences, and neither *fg* nor *FG* genes. The homologue on the right has *gf* and *FG* sequences, and neither *AB* nor *ab* genes.

Human Syndromes

Changes in chromosome structure occur in humans and lead to various syndromes, the genetics of which are just now being investigated.

Deletion Syndromes Williams syndrome occurs when chromosome 7 loses a tiny end piece (see Fig. 19.19*a*). Distinct physical features associated with this syndrome include a turned-up nose, a wide mouth, a small chin, and larger ears. Children with Williams syndrome often have learning disabilities, but they have been shown to excel in other areas. Common strengths include excellent verbal and musical abilities. In this syndrome, the gene that governs the production of the protein elastin is missing. This affects the health of the cardiovascular system and causes their skin to age prematurely. Many individuals with Williams syndrome are friendly and outgoing in temperament. Other common behavioral and psychological characteristics associated with this syndrome include anxiety, phobias, hyperactivity, and difficulty with attention and concentration, perhaps because of the loss of a gene for a protein normally active in the brain.

Cri du chat ("cat's cry") syndrome is seen when chromosome 5 is missing an end piece. This syndrome is associated with characteristics that include a smaller head, facial abnormalities, and intellectual disabilities. Abnormal development of the glottis and larynx results in the most characteristic symptom—the infant's cry resembles that of a cat.

Translocation Syndromes A person who has both of the chromosomes involved in a translocation (see Fig. 19.19*d*) has the normal amount of genetic material and is healthy, unless the chromosome exchange broke an allele into two pieces. The person who inherits only one of the translocated chromosomes will no doubt have only one copy of certain alleles and three copies of certain other alleles. A genetics counselor begins to suspect a translocation has occurred when spontaneous abortions are commonplace and family members have various syndromes.

Alagille syndrome occurs due to a translocation between chromosomes 2 and 20. People with this syndrome ordinarily have a deletion on chromosome 20. One consequence of this deletion is a combination of heart defects called *tetralogy of Fallot.* One of these defects is a hole between the chambers of the heart that allows oxygenated and deoxygenated blood to mix, a condition called *cyanosis. Clubbing,* or a widening of the tips of the fingers, may also occur. The symptoms of Alagille syndrome range from mild to severe, so some people may not be aware they have the syndrome.

Translocations can also be responsible for a variety of other disorders, including certain types of cancer. In the 1970s, new staining techniques revealed that a translocation from a portion of chromosome 22 to chromosome 9 is responsible for chronic myelogenous leukemia. This translocated chromosome was called the Philadelphia chromosome. In Burkitt lymphoma, a cancer common in children in equatorial Africa, a large tumor develops from lymph glands in the region of the jaw. This disorder involves a translocation from a portion of chromosome 8 to chromosome 14.

CHECK YOUR PROGRESS 19.6

1. Explain what causes an individual to have an abnormal number of chromosomes.
2. Describe the specific chromosome abnormality of a person with Down syndrome.
3. Distinguish between a translocation and an inversion.
4. Describe the nondisjunction events that would cause Turner and Jacobs syndromes.

CONNECTING THE CONCEPTS

For more information on the topics presented in this section, refer to the following discussions:

Section 18.3 explains how the *SRY* gene directs the formation of the male reproductive system.

Section 21.2 explores how chromosomes are involved in patterns of inheritance.

CONCLUSION

In the chapter opener, we asked why the rate of cancer in elephants is significantly lower than in humans. The answer lies in the number of copies of a gene, called *p53,* in the elephant genome. *p53* belongs to a class of genes called tumor suppressor genes, which act as gatekeepers for the cell cycle and thus control the rate at which cells divide.

Also called the "Guardian of the Genome," *p53* produces a protein that is responsible for not only activating DNA repair enzymes, but also stopping the cell cycle and placing the cell in the G_0 phase. In doing so, it helps regulate the rate at which cells divide and limits the probability that cells will become cancerous. While having extra copies of genes is not always advantageous, in this case, elephants have evolved a mechanism of decreasing their rates of cancer.

SUMMARIZE

19.1 Chromosomes

- The genetic material of the cell is organized as **chromosomes.** Chromosomes contain a combination of proteins and DNA called **chromatin.**
- Most human cells are diploid—therefore, chromosomes occur in pairs.
- Prior to mitosis, or duplication division, the chromosomes are replicated, forming **sister chromatids.** The sister chromatids are joined at the **centromere.**
- A karyotype is a visual display of an individual's chromosomes.

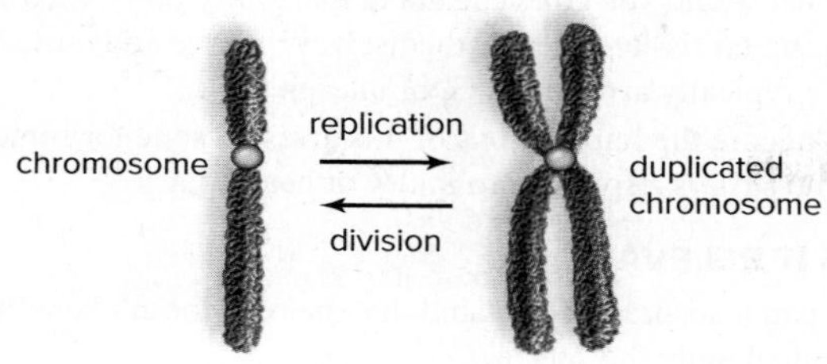

19.2 The Cell Cycle

The **cell cycle** occurs continuously and has several stages: G_1, S, G_2 (the **interphase** stages), and M (the mitotic stage), which includes **cytokinesis** and the stages of **mitosis.**

- In G_1, a cell doubles organelles and accumulates materials for DNA synthesis.
- In S, DNA replication occurs.
- In G_2, a cell synthesizes proteins needed for cell division.
- **Checkpoints** and external signals control the progression of the cell cycle. Cells that fail to pass checkpoints may enter G_0 phase and undergo **apoptosis.**

19.3 Mitosis

Mitosis is duplication division that ensures that the **daughter cells** have the **diploid (2n)** number and the same types of chromosomes as the **parent cell.** The **mitotic spindle** plays an important role in the separation of the sister chromatids during mitosis. The mitotic spindle is organized by the **centrosomes** of the cell. Centrosomes contain clusters of microtubules called **centrioles.**

The phases of mitosis are prophase, prometaphase, metaphase, anaphase, and telophase:

- **Prophase.** The nucleus dissolves and the chromosomes condense.
- **Prometaphase.** Chromosomes attach to spindle fibers.
- **Metaphase.** Chromosomes align at the equator.
- **Anaphase.** Chromatids separate, becoming chromosomes that move toward the poles.
- **Telophase.** Nuclear envelopes form around chromosomes; cytokinesis begins.

Cytokinesis is the division of cytoplasm and organelles following mitosis.

- Cytokinesis in animal cells involves the formation of a **cleavage furrow** to separate the cytoplasm.

19.4 Meiosis

Meiosis is reduction division that reduces the diploid (2n) chromosome number to a **haploid (n)** number. Meiosis involves two cell divisions—meiosis I and meiosis II.

Meiosis I

- **Homologous chromosomes** pair **(synapsis)** and then separate. **Interkinesis** follows meiosis I.

Meiosis II

- Sister chromatids separate, resulting in four cells with the haploid number of chromosomes that move into daughter nuclei.

Meiosis results in genetic recombination due to **crossing-over;** gametes have all possible combinations of chromosomes. Upon fertilization, the zygote is restored to a diploid number of chromosomes.

Spermatogenesis and Oogenesis

- **Spermatogenesis.** In males, spermatogenesis produces four viable sperm.
- **Oogenesis.** In females, oogenesis produces one egg and several polar bodies. Oogenesis goes to completion if the sperm fertilizes the developing egg.

19.5 Comparison of Meiosis and Mitosis

- In prophase I, homologous chromosomes pair; there is no pairing in mitosis.
- In metaphase I, homologous duplicated chromosomes align at the equator.
- In anaphase I, homologous chromosomes separate.

19.6 Chromosome Inheritance

Meiosis is a part of gametogenesis (spermatogenesis in males and oogenesis in females) and contributes to genetic diversity.

Changes in Chromosome Number

- **Nondisjunction** changes the chromosome number in gametes, resulting in **trisomy** (2n + 1) or **monosomy** (2n – 1).
- Autosomal syndromes include Down syndrome.

Changes in Sex Chromosome Number

- Nondisjunction during oogenesis or spermatogenesis can result in gametes that have too few or too many X or Y chromosomes.
- If more than one X chromosome is present in a cell, a **Barr body** may be formed.
- **Syndromes** include Turner, Klinefelter, poly-X, and Jacobs.

Changes in Chromosome Structure

- Chromosomal mutations can produce **deletions, duplications, inversions,** and **translocations.**
- These result in various syndromes, such as Williams, cri du chat (deletion), and Alagille, and certain cancers (translocation).

ENGAGE

BioNOW

Want to know how this science is relevant to your life? Check out the BioNOW video below:

- Cell Division

McGraw Hill

Why is it advantageous for cell division to halt in an organism at certain times, such as a plant in the winter?

THINKING CRITICALLY

1. Benign and cancerous tumors occur when the cell cycle control mechanisms no longer operate correctly. What types of genes may be involved in these cell cycle control mechanisms?
2. BPA is a chemical compound that has historically been used in the manufacture of plastic products. However, cells often mistake BPA compounds for hormones that accelerate the cell cycle. Because of this, BPA is associated with an increased risk of certain cancers.
   a. How might BPA interact with the cell cycle and its checkpoints?
   b. Why do you think that very small concentrations of BPA might have a large effect on the cell?
3. Explain how the separation of homologous chromosomes during meiosis affects the appearance of siblings (such that some resemble each other and others look very different from one another).
4. a. What would you conclude about the ability of nervous and muscular tissue to repair themselves if nerve and muscle cells are typically arrested in G_1 of interphase?
   b. What are the implications of this arrested state for someone who suffers a spinal cord injury or heart attack?

MAKING IT RELEVANT

1. Why can it accurately be stated that meiosis doesn't benefit an individual, only the species?
2. Why do organisms restrict meiosis to only specialized cells of the body? What would happen if any cell could conduct meiosis?
3. How would an understanding of meiosis benefit assessing potential genetic problems in future offspring?

Find answers to all of the chapter questions at connect.mheducation.com

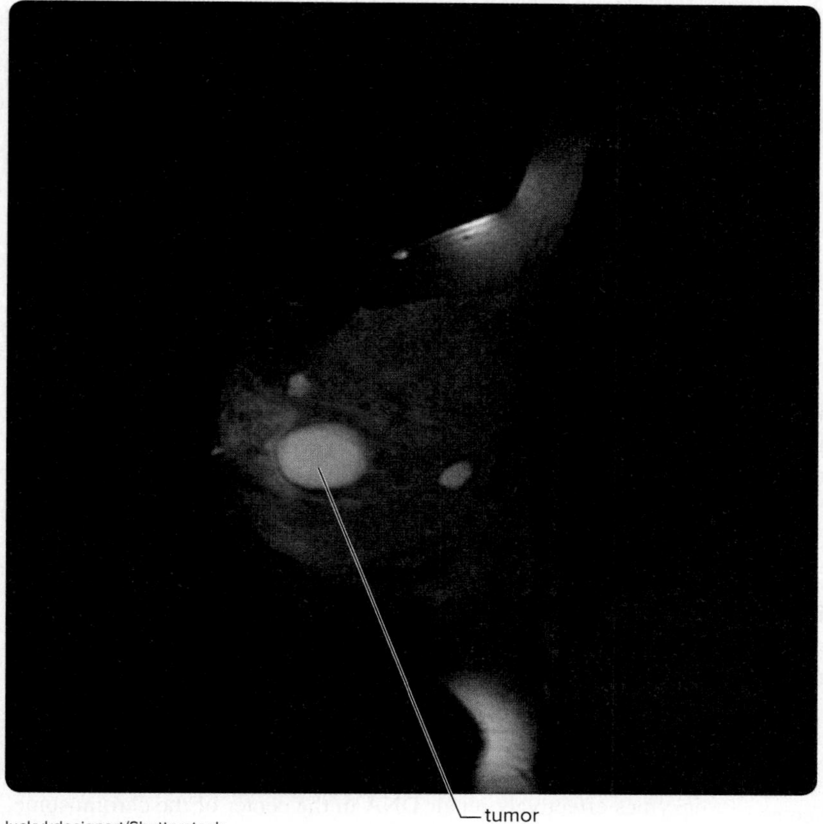

luckykdesignart/Shutterstock

CHAPTER 20

Cancer

Cancer

Chances are, someone you know has been diagnosed with cancer. Maybe that person is you. This year in the United States, there will be almost 1.8 million new cases of cancer. Cancer is the second-leading cause of death, behind heart disease, and it will claim over 600,000 lives this year. Almost 40% of us will be diagnosed with some form of cancer in our lives.

While those statistics sound ominous, the facts are that cancer is no longer as dangerous as it was a few decades ago. Since the 1990s, the death rates for cancer have been dropping by almost 1–2% per year. For many forms of cancer, especially more common forms such as breast cancer, colon cancer, prostate cancer, and melanomas (cancers of the skin), the 5-year survivor rates are over 90% if the disease is diagnosed early.

Our success against cancer is due to advances in our abilities to not only make the public aware of the biology of cancer, but also new methods of preventing and diagnosing cancer. New therapies, such as genome editing (CRISPR) technologies, and the development of more effective immunotherapies that enlist the assistance of our own immune systems, are having a significant impact on our ability to control this disease.

In earlier chapters, we explored the relationship between cancer and cell division. In this chapter, we will examine the causes, treatments, and prevention of cancer.

As you read through the chapter, think about the following questions:

1. What are the characteristics of cancer cells that distinguish them from normal cells?
2. Why do cancer cells form tumors?

CHAPTER OUTLINE

BEFORE YOU BEGIN

Before beginning this chapter, take a few moments to review the following discussions:

Section 9.6 What are antioxidants?

Section 19.2 What is the role of checkpoints in the cell cycle?

Section 19.2 What external factors may regulate cell division?

20.1 Overview of Cancer

LEARNING OUTCOMES

Upon completion of this section, you should be able to

1. Describe the characteristics of cancer cells that distinguish them from normal cells.
2. Distinguish between a proto-oncogene and a tumor suppressor gene with regard to their effects on the cell cycle.
3. Identify the common types of cancers and the body system with which each is associated.

Cancer is a disease characterized by uncontrolled cell growth. Although there are many different types of cancer, and their causes vary widely, most cancers are a result of a cell accumulating mutations that ultimately cause a loss of control over the cell cycle.

Characteristics of Cancer Cells

Although the effects of cancer are often noticed at the tissue, organ, or organismal level, cancer is ultimately a cellular disease. Despite a large number of different cancer types, cancer cells share general traits that distinguish them from normal cells.

Cancer Cells Lack Differentiation

Differentiation is the process of cellular development by which a cell acquires a specific structure and function. Red blood cells are examples of differentiated cells in the circulatory system. In comparison, cancer cells are nonspecialized and do not contribute to the functioning of a body part. A cancer cell does not look like a differentiated epithelial, muscle, nervous, or connective tissue cell. Instead, it looks distinctly abnormal.

Cancer Cells Have Abnormal Nuclei

The nucleus of normal cervical cells (Fig. 20.1*a*) differs from that of precancerous (Fig. 20.1*b*) and cancerous (Fig. 20.1*c*) cervical cells. The nuclei of cancer cells are enlarged and may contain an abnormal number of chromosomes. The nuclei of the cervical cancer cells have increased to the point that they take up most of the cell.

In addition to nuclear abnormalities, cancer cells often have chromosomal mutations (see Section 19.6). Some portions of the chromosomes may be duplicated, and/or some may be deleted. In addition, gene amplification (extra copies of specific genes) is seen much more frequently than in normal cells. Ordinarily, cells with damaged DNA undergo **apoptosis,** or programmed cell death. Cancer cells fail to undergo apoptosis, even though they are abnormal cells.

Tissues that divide frequently, such as those that line the respiratory and digestive tracts, are more likely to become cancerous. Cell division gives them the opportunity to undergo genetic mutations, each one making the cell more abnormal and giving it the ability to produce more of its own type.

Cancer Cells Have Unlimited Potential to Replicate

Ordinarily, cells divide about 60 to 70 times and then just stop dividing and eventually undergo apoptosis. Cancer cells are immortal and keep on dividing for an unlimited number of times.

Just as shoelaces are capped by small pieces of plastic, chromosomes in human cells end with special repetitive DNA sequences called **telomeres.** Specific proteins bind to telomeres in both normal and cancerous cells. These telomere proteins protect the ends of chromosomes from DNA repair enzymes. Though the enzymes effectively repair DNA in the center of the chromosome, they always tend to bind together the naked ends of chromosomes. In a normal cell, the telomeres get shorter after each cell cycle and protective telomere proteins gradually decrease. In turn, repair enzymes eventually cause the chromosomes' ends to bind together, causing the cell to undergo apoptosis. Telomerase is an enzyme that can rebuild telomere sequences and in that way prevent a cell from ever losing its potential to divide. The gene that codes for telomerase is constantly turned on in cancer cells, and telomeres are continuously rebuilt. The telomeres remain at a constant length, and the cell can keep dividing over and over.

Cancer Cells Form Tumors

Normal cells anchor themselves to a substratum and/or adhere to their neighbors. They exhibit *contact inhibition,* meaning that

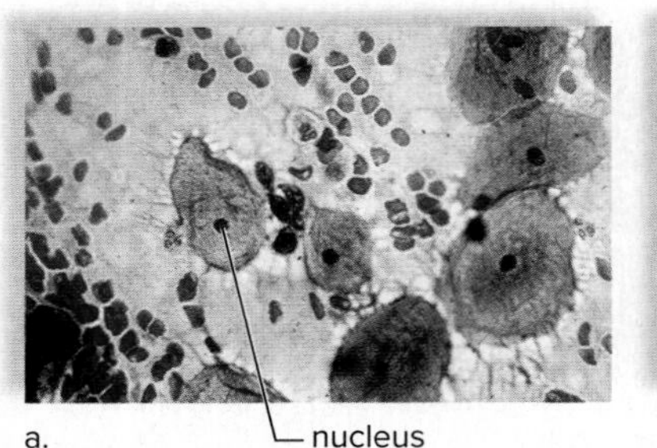

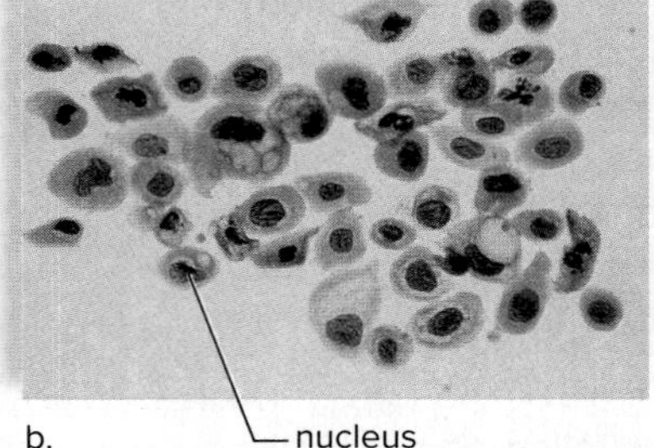

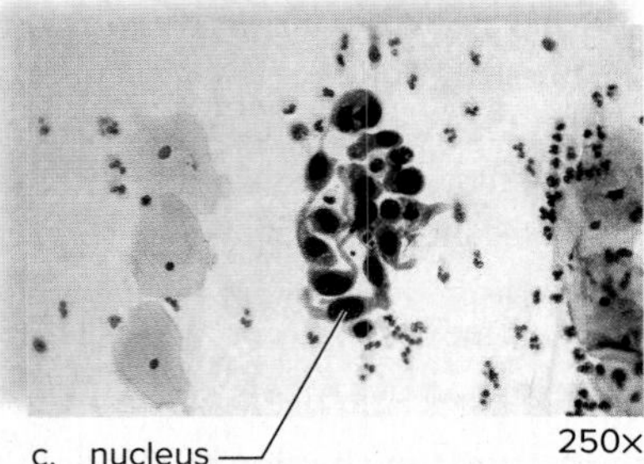

Figure 20.1 Changes in the nucleus of cancer cells.
a. Normal cervical cells. **b.** Precancerous cervical cells. **c.** Cancerous cervical cells.
(a): Biology Pics/Science Source; (b): SPL/Science Source; (c): Martin M. Rotker/Science Source

BIOLOGY IN YOUR LIFE

What's the difference between a benign and a malignant tumor?

A *benign* tumor is usually surrounded by a connective tissue capsule, which prevents the tumor from invading adjacent tissue. The cells of a benign tumor resemble normal cells fairly closely. Chances are you have one of these tumors. If you have a mole, or nevus, on your body, you have a benign tumor of the skin melanocytes. Cells from a mole closely resemble other melanocytes.

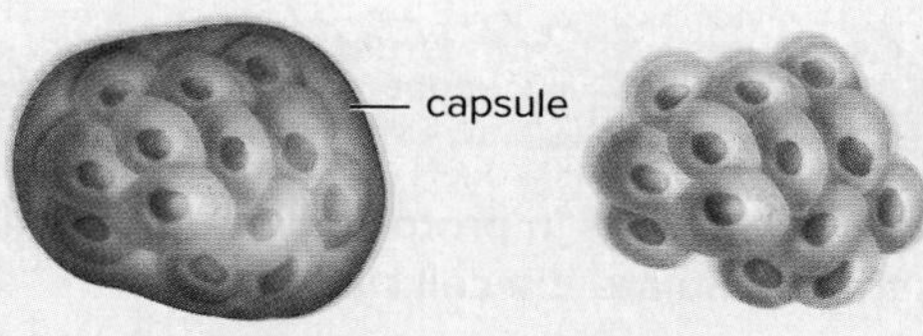

However, despite the term *benign,* this type of tumor isn't necessarily harmless. If it presses on normal tissue or restricts the normal tissue's blood supply, a benign tumor can be fatal. For example, a benign neuroma (nerve cell tumor) growing near the brain stem eventually affects control centers for heartbeat and respiration.

On the other hand, a malignant tumor is able to invade surrounding tissues and its cells don't resemble normal cells. By traveling in blood or lymphatic vessels, the tumor can spread throughout the body. As a general rule, badly deformed cells are most likely to spread. Thus, they are the most malignant.

Cancer in situ (in place) is a malignant tumor found in its place of origin. As yet, the cancer has not spread beyond the basement membrane, the nonliving material that anchors tissues to one another. If recognized and treated early, cancer in situ is usually curable.

when they come in contact with a neighbor, they stop dividing. Cancer cells have lost all restraint. They pile on top of one another and grow in multiple layers, forming a **tumor.** As cancer develops, the most aggressive cell becomes the dominant cell of the tumor.

Cancer Cells Disregard Growth Factors

Chemical signals between cells tell them whether or not they should be dividing. These chemical signals, called growth factors, are of two types: stimulatory growth factors and inhibitory growth factors. Cancer cells keep on dividing even when stimulatory growth factors are absent, and they do not respond to inhibitory growth factors.

Cancer Cells Gradually Become Abnormal

Figure 20.2 illustrates that **carcinogenesis,** the development of cancer, is a multistage process that can be divided into these three phases:

- *Initiation:* A single cell undergoes a mutation that causes it to begin to divide repeatedly (Fig. 20.2*a*).

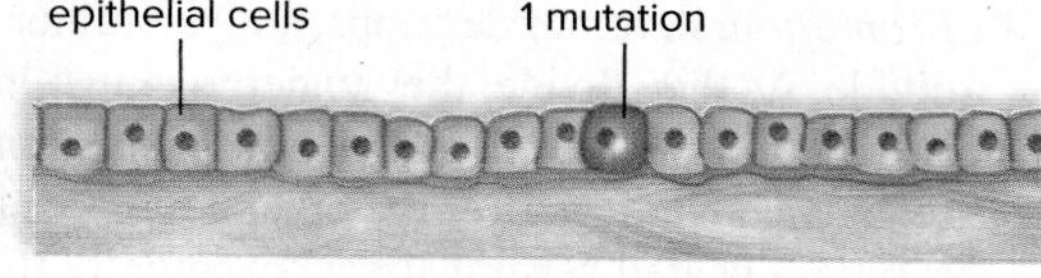

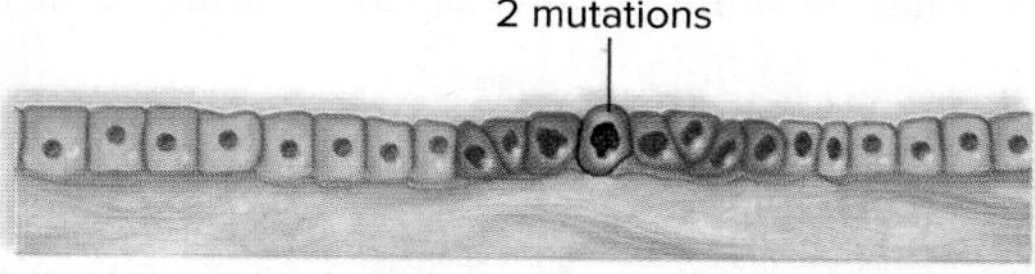

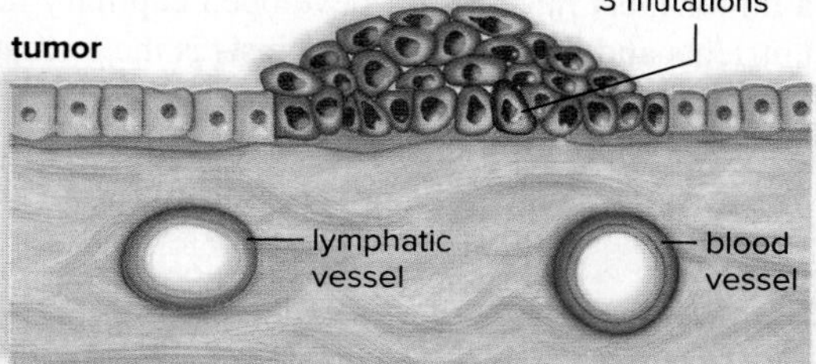

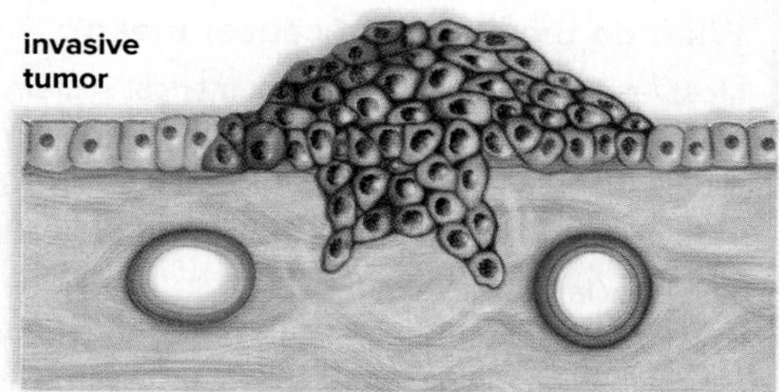

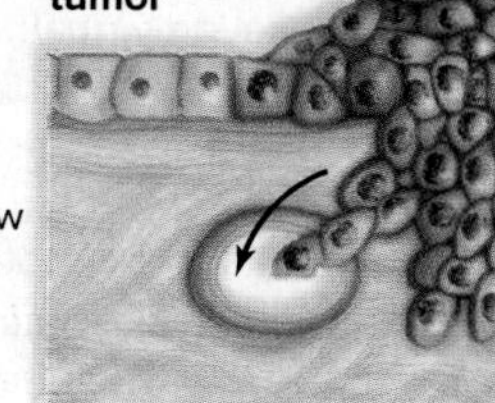

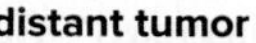

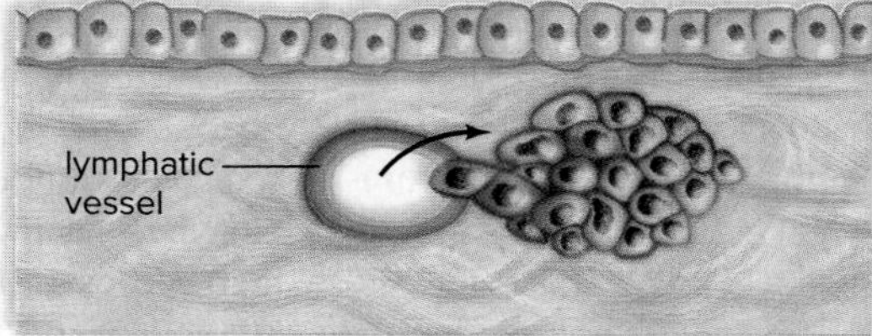

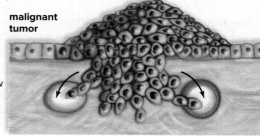

Figure 20.2 **Progression from a single mutation to a tumor.**
a. One cell (dark pink) in a tissue mutates. **b.** This mutated cell divides repeatedly and a cell (brown) with two mutations appears. **c.** A tumor forms and a cell with three mutations (purple) appears. **d.** This cell (purple), which takes over the tumor, can invade underlying tissue. **e.** Tumor cells invade lymphatic and blood vessels. **f.** A new tumor forms at a distant location.

- *Promotion:* A tumor develops, and the tumor cells continue to divide. As they divide, they undergo mutations (Fig. 20.2*b*, *c*).
- *Progression:* One cell undergoes a mutation that gives it a selective advantage over the other cells (Fig. 20.2*c*). This process is repeated several times; eventually there is a cell that has the ability to invade surrounding tissues (Fig. 20.2*d*, *e*).

Cancer Cells Undergo Angiogenesis and Metastasis

To grow larger than about a billion cells (about the size of a pea), a tumor must have a well-developed capillary network to bring it nutrients and oxygen. **Angiogenesis** is the formation of new blood vessels. The low oxygen content in the middle of a tumor may turn on genes coding for angiogenic growth factors that diffuse into the nearby tissues and cause new vessels to form.

BIOLOGY IN YOUR LIFE

What do the stages of cancer mean?

Most cancer diagnoses use a numerical system to indicate the degree to which cancer has spread in the body. While these differ slightly depending on the type of cancer, they generally use a 0–4 scale that is based on the following criteria:

- How large is the tumor?
- Has the tumor begun to invade nearby tissues?
- Is the cancer located in the nearby lymph nodes?
- Has the cancer moved to any other organs of the body?

The higher the cancer stage, the more severe the form of cancer, and the greater the risk to the individual.

Due to mutations, cancer cells tend to be motile. They have a disorganized internal cytoskeleton and lack intact actin filament bundles. To metastasize, cancer cells must make their way across the basement membrane and invade a blood vessel or lymphatic vessel. Invasive cancer cells are abnormally shaped (see Fig. 20.1*c*) and don't look at all like normal cells nearby. Cancer cells produce proteinase enzymes that degrade the basement membrane and allow them to invade underlying tissues. Malignancy occurs when cancer cells are found in nearby lymph nodes. When these cells begin new tumors far from the primary tumor, **metastasis** has occurred (Fig. 20.2*f*). Not many (maybe 1 in 10,000) cancer cells achieve this ability, but those that successfully metastasize to various parts of the body lower the prognosis (the predicted outcome of the disease) for recovery.

The Science feature "The Immortal Henrietta Lacks" discusses how cancer cells from one patient have played an important role in our understanding of the characteristics of cancer.

Cancer Results from Gene Mutation

Recall that the cell cycle consists of interphase, followed by mitosis. **Checkpoints** (see Fig. 19.3) in the cell cycle monitor the condition of the cell and regulate its ability to divide. Normally, a protein called *cyclin* directs the movement of a cell through the cell cycle. At each checkpoint, specific factors, such as DNA damage, are assessed by checkpoint proteins. However, mutations in these checkpoint proteins cause the cell to lose control of the cell cycle, resulting in cancer. The two classes of checkpoint proteins are as follows:

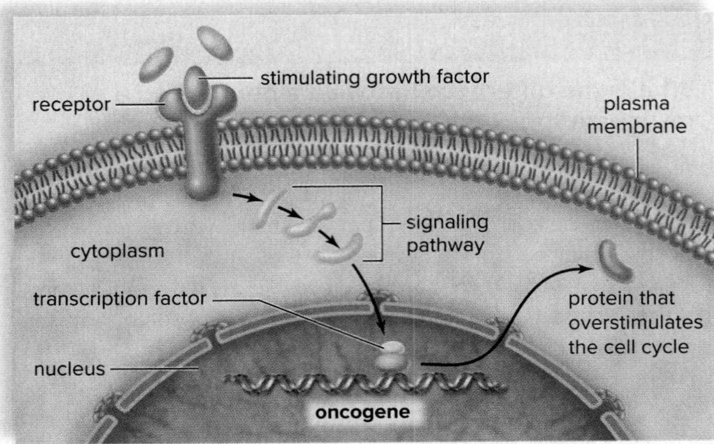

Figure 20.3 Mutations in proto-oncogenes produce oncogenes that stimulate the cell cycle.
Normally, proto-oncogenes stimulate cell division but are typically turned off in differentiated cells. A mutation may convert a proto-oncogene to an oncogene, which then produces a protein that overstimulates the cell cycle.

- **Proto-oncogenes** code for proteins that promote the cell cycle and prevent apoptosis. They are often likened to the gas pedal of a car, because they cause acceleration of the cell cycle.
- **Tumor suppressor genes** code for proteins that inhibit the cell cycle and promote apoptosis. They are often likened to the brakes of a car, because they inhibit acceleration.

Proto-oncogenes Become Oncogenes

When proto-oncogenes mutate, they become cancer-causing genes called **oncogenes.** These mutations can be called "gain-of-function," or dominant, mutations, because overexpression is the result (Fig. 20.3). Even though we possess two copies of each proto-oncogene, only one must be mutated to lose control of the cell cycle. In general, whatever a proto-oncogene does, an oncogene does it better.

A **growth factor** is a signal that activates a cell signaling pathway, resulting in cell division. Some proto-oncogenes code for a growth factor or for a receptor protein that receives a growth factor. When these proto-oncogenes become oncogenes, receptor proteins are easy to activate and may even be stimulated by a growth factor produced by the receiving cell. Several proto-oncogenes code for Ras proteins that promote mitosis by activating cyclin. These *Ras* oncogenes are typically found in many types of cancers. *Cyclin D* is a proto-oncogene that codes for cyclin directly. When this gene becomes an oncogene, cyclin is readily available all the time.

BIOLOGY TODAY ▶ **Science**

The Immortal Henrietta Lacks

The availability of human tissue cells is important for many areas of medical research. Unfortunately, growing human cells has historically been very difficult. While these cells can be coaxed to reproduce using a technique called tissue culture, they typically all die very rapidly, usually after dividing only a few times. However, metastatic cells (a form of cancer cells) can survive and thrive in tissue culture. The techniques used to grow human cells successfully in tissue culture are part of the legacy of Henrietta Lacks (Fig. 20A). The cancer that claimed her life ensured that a part of Henrietta will live forever.

Lacks was a young woman and the mother of five children. In February 1951, she experienced unexplained vaginal bleeding and sought help from a Baltimore hospital. Physicians found a quarter-sized tumor on Henrietta's cervix. Samples of the tumor were quickly obtained, then sent to the tissue culture laboratories at Johns Hopkins University. Though radiation treatment was attempted, the tumor ravaged Henrietta's body, appearing on all her major organs within months. After 8 months of suffering, she died in October 1951. She was survived by her husband and five children, three of whom were still in diapers.

Henrietta's tumor cells ended up in the laboratory of George and Margaret Gey at Johns Hopkins. The couple had been trying to culture human cells, with little success, for more than two decades. The cells from Henrietta Lacks' tumor, now termed *HeLa cells* (Fig. 20B), not only lived but multiplied like wildfire. At last, here was a source of human cells that grew rapidly and seemed almost immortal.

Figure 20A Henrietta Lacks (1920–1951).
Obstetrics & Gynaecology/SPL/Science Source

Using these cells, the Geys directed their research toward curing polio. Infantile paralysis, or polio, occurred in epidemics. In a small percentage of patients, it damaged the brain and spinal cord, causing paralysis of major muscle groups. If the diaphragm and other respiratory muscles were affected, the disease could be fatal. For the first time, the virus could be grown in human cells—HeLa cells—so that its characteristics could be studied. The results of these studies enabled Dr. Jonas Salk to develop a vaccine for polio. Today, polio is almost unheard of in the Western world.

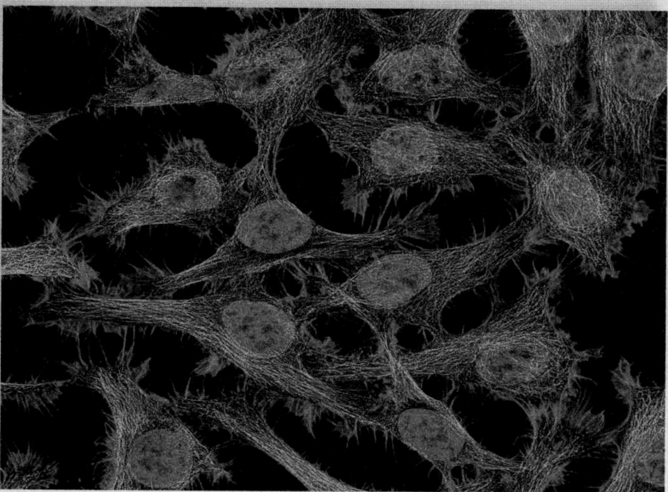

Figure 20B SEM of HeLa cells.
The term *HeLa* is derived from the letters of Henrietta Lacks' name.
National Institutes of Health (NIH)

Research with HeLa cells did not stop with the Geys. For over 50 years, these durable cells have been used worldwide to study many types of viruses, as well as leukemia and other cancers. The cells are human in origin, so they have also been the test subjects to determine the harmful effects caused by drugs or radiation. Effective testing was developed for chromosome abnormalities and hereditary diseases using HeLa. Samples of HeLa cells have even been launched in the space shuttle for experiments involving a zero-gravity environment. HeLa cell colonies can be found around the world. The cells can even be purchased from biological supply companies.

HeLa cells are almost too sturdy. In 1974, researchers discovered that HeLa cells, like bacteria, can be transmitted through the air, on a researcher's glove, or on contaminated glassware. This discovery led to better sterile techniques not only in the laboratory but also in operating rooms where cancerous tumors were removed.

In 2011, Henrietta's story was presented in a book, *The Immortal Life of Henrietta Lacks,* by Rebecca Sloot. The book has received multiple awards for its ability to portray the importance of Henrietta's cells to science.

Questions to Consider

1. What characteristics of cancer cells would make HeLa cells immortal?
2. What other uses do you think are possible for these cells?

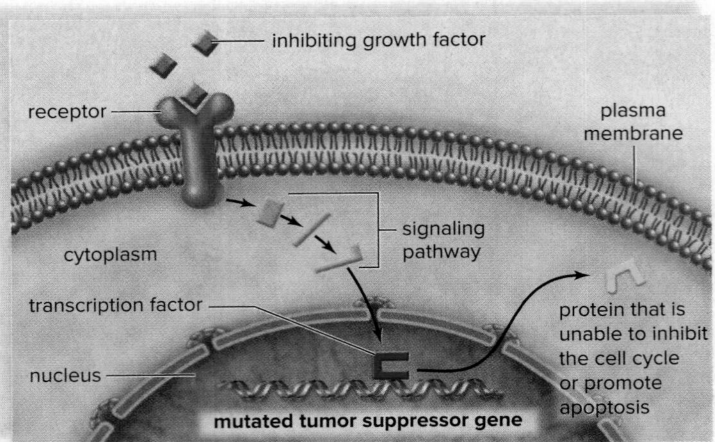

Figure 20.4 **Mutations in tumor suppressor genes cause a loss of cell cycle control.**
Normally, tumor suppressor genes code for a protein that inhibits the cell cycle. If mutations occur, the resulting protein loses the function of controlling the cell cycle.

Tumor Suppressor Genes Become Inactive

When tumor suppressor genes mutate, their products no longer inhibit the cell cycle or promote apoptosis. Therefore, these mutations can be called "loss-of-function," or recessive, mutations (Fig. 20.4). Unlike proto-oncogenes, both copies of the tumor suppressor gene in the cell must be mutated to lose cell cycle control.

Mutation of the tumor suppressor gene *Bax* is a good example. Its product, the protein Bax, promotes apoptosis. When *Bax* mutates, Bax protein is not present and apoptosis is less likely to occur. The *Bax* gene contains a line of eight consecutive G bases in its DNA. When the same base molecules are lined up in this fashion, the gene is more likely to be subject to mutation.

Another tumor suppressor protein, p53, activates DNA repair enzymes. At the same time, p53 turns on genes that stop the cell cycle from proceeding. If repair is impossible, the p53 protein promotes apoptosis. Apoptosis is an important way for carcinogenesis to be prevented. Many tumors are lacking in p53 activity.

The *BRCA1* gene codes for another DNA repair enzyme, one that is responsible for fixing breaks in the DNA molecule. In fact, it works very closely with the p53 protein. *BRCA1* mutations prevent the body from recognizing DNA damage, allowing the cells to progress through the cell cycle unchecked. *BRCA1* mutations are associated with a number of cancers, including breast cancer.

Types of Cancer

Statistics indicate that almost 40% of Americans will be diagnosed with cancer in their lifetime. Therefore, this is a topic of considerable importance to the health and well-being of every individual. **Oncology** is the study of cancer. A medical specialist in cancer is known as an *oncologist*. The patient's prognosis (probable outcome) depends on (1) whether the tumor has invaded surrounding tissues and (2) whether there are metastatic tumors in distant parts of the body.

Tumors are classified according to their place of origin. **Carcinomas** are cancers of the epithelial tissues, and adenocarcinomas are cancers of glandular epithelial cells. Carcinomas include cancer of the skin, breast, liver, pancreas, intestines, lung, prostate, and thyroid. **Sarcomas** are cancers that arise in muscles and connective tissue, such as bone and fibrous connective tissue. **Leukemias** are cancers of the blood, and **lymphomas** are cancers of lymphoid tissue. A blastoma is a cancer composed of immature cells. In Section 18.2, we observed that the embryo is formed from three primary germ layers: ectoderm, mesoderm, and endoderm. Each blastoma cell resembles the cells in its original primary germ layer. For example, a nephroblastoma has cells similar to mesoderm cells, because the kidney grows from mesoderm.

Common Cancers

Cancer occurs in all parts of the body, but some body systems and organs are more susceptible than others. In the respiratory system, lung cancer is the most common type. Overall, this is one of the most common types of cancer, and smoking is known to increase a person's risk for this disease. Smoking also increases the risk for cancer in the oral cavity.

In the digestive system, colorectal (colon/rectum) cancer is another common form of cancer. Other cancers of the digestive system include those of the pancreas, stomach, esophagus, and other organs. In the cardiovascular system, cancers include leukemia and plasma cell tumors. In the lymphatic system, cancers are classified as either Hodgkin's or non-Hodgkin's lymphoma. Hodgkin's lymphomas develop from mutated B cells. Non-Hodgkin's lymphomas can arise from B cells or T cells. Thyroid cancer is the most common type of tumor in the endocrine system.

Reproductive system cancers, such as breast cancer in women (although it occasionally also occurs in men) and prostate cancer in men, are some of the more common forms of cancer. Cancers of the cervix, ovaries, and other reproductive structures also occur in women. Other cancers of the male reproductive system include cancer of the testis and the penis. Bladder and kidney cancers are associated with the urinary system. Skin cancers include melanoma and basal and squamous cell carcinomas.

BIOLOGY IN YOUR LIFE

How does cancer cause death?

Cancer often causes death by interfering with the ability of the body to maintain homeostasis. For example, bone cancer may interfere with calcium homeostasis or the body's ability to produce red blood cells. The liver and pancreas play important roles in homeostasis, and thus cancers of these organs often cause death by altering the levels of important chemicals (hormones, nutrients) in the blood. Sometimes a growing tumor blocks an important pathway in the body, such as the lungs, the digestive tract, or an artery. In other cases, the tumor produces chemicals (metabolites) that are toxic to a certain group of tissues.

CHECK YOUR PROGRESS 20.1

1. List the characteristics of cancer cells that allow them to grow uncontrollably.
2. Describe how mutations in tumor suppressor genes and proto-oncogenes regulate the cell cycle.
3. Identify some of the more common types of cancer.

CONNECTING THE CONCEPTS

For more information on the topics in this section, refer to the following discussions:

Section 19.2 describes the role of the checkpoints of the cell cycle.

Section 22.2 describes how the information in a gene is expressed to form a protein.

20.2 Causes and Prevention of Cancer

LEARNING OUTCOMES

Upon completion of this section, you should be able to

1. Explain how heredity and the environment may both contribute to cancer.
2. Identify the genetic mechanisms of select forms of cancer.
3. Summarize how protective behaviors and diet can help prevent cancer.

A significant amount of research is currently being directed to the understanding of cancer, because once a probable cause is identified for a specific type of cancer, treatments and preventive measures may be developed. By studying patterns of cancer development in populations, scientists have determined that both heredity and environmental risk factors come into play. These discoveries have led to the development of new recommendations on how to prevent and treat cancer, which in turn has reduced the mortality rates for most forms of cancer (Fig. 20.5) Obviously, one's genetic inheritance can't currently be changed, but avoiding risk factors and following dietary guidelines can help prevent cancer.

Heredity

The first gene associated with breast cancer was discovered in 1990. Scientists named this gene *BRCA1* (*br*east *ca*ncer *1*), early onset. The gene is now called *br*east *ca*ncer susceptibility gene *1*. Later, they found that breast cancer can also be due to a breast cancer gene they called *BRCA2*. These genes are tumor suppressor genes that follow a recessive pattern of inheritance (see Section 21.3). We inherit two copies of every gene, one from each parent. If a mutated copy of *BRCA1* or *BRCA2* is inherited from either parent, a mutation in the other copy is required before predisposition to cancer is increased. Each cell in the body already has the single mutated copy, but cancer develops wherever the second mutation occurs. If the second mutation occurs in the breast, breast cancer may develop. Ovarian cancer may develop if a second cancer-causing mutation occurs in an ovary.

The *RB* gene is also a tumor suppressor gene. It takes its name from its association with retinoblastoma, a rare eye cancer that occurs almost exclusively in early childhood. In an affected child, a single mutated copy of the *RB* gene is inherited. A second mutation, this time to the other copy of the *RB* gene, causes the cancer to develop (Fig. 20.6). Retinoblastoma affecting a single eye is treated by removal of the eye, because total removal is more likely to result in a cure. Radiation, laser, and chemotherapy are options when both eyes are involved, but these treatments are less likely to produce a cure.

An abnormal *RET* gene, which predisposes an individual to thyroid cancer, can be passed from parent to child. *RET* is a proto-oncogene known to be inherited in an autosomal dominant manner (see Section 21.3), meaning that only one mutation is needed to increase a predisposition to cancer. The remainder of the mutations necessary for a thyroid cancer to develop are acquired (not inherited).

Environmental Carcinogens

A **mutagen** is an agent that causes mutations. A simple laboratory test—an Ames test—is used to determine whether a substance is mutagenic. A **carcinogen** is a chemical that causes cancer by being mutagenic. Some carcinogens cause only initiation. Others cause initiation and promotion.

Heredity can predispose a person to cancer, but whether it develops or not depends on environmental mutagens, such as the ones we will be discussing.

Radiation

Ionizing radiation, such as in radon gas, nuclear fuel, and X-rays, is capable of affecting DNA and causing mutations. Though not a form of ionizing radiation, ultraviolet light also causes mutations. Ultraviolet radiation in sunlight and tanning lamps is most likely responsible for the dramatic increases seen in skin cancer in the past several years. Today, at least six cases of skin cancer occur for every one case of lung cancer. Nonmelanoma skin cancers are usually curable through surgery. However, melanoma skin cancer tends to metastasize and is responsible for 1–2% of cancer deaths annually in the United States.

Another natural source of ionizing radiation is radon gas, which comes from the natural (radioactive) breakdown of uranium in soil, rock, and water. The Environmental Protection Agency recommends that every home be tested for radon, because it is the second leading cause of lung cancer in the United States. The combination of inhaling radon gas and smoking cigarettes can be particularly dangerous. A vent pipe system and fan, which pull radon from beneath the house and vent it to the outside, are the most common tools to rid a house of radon after the house is constructed.

We are well aware of the damaging effects of a nuclear bomb explosion or accidental emissions from nuclear power plants. For

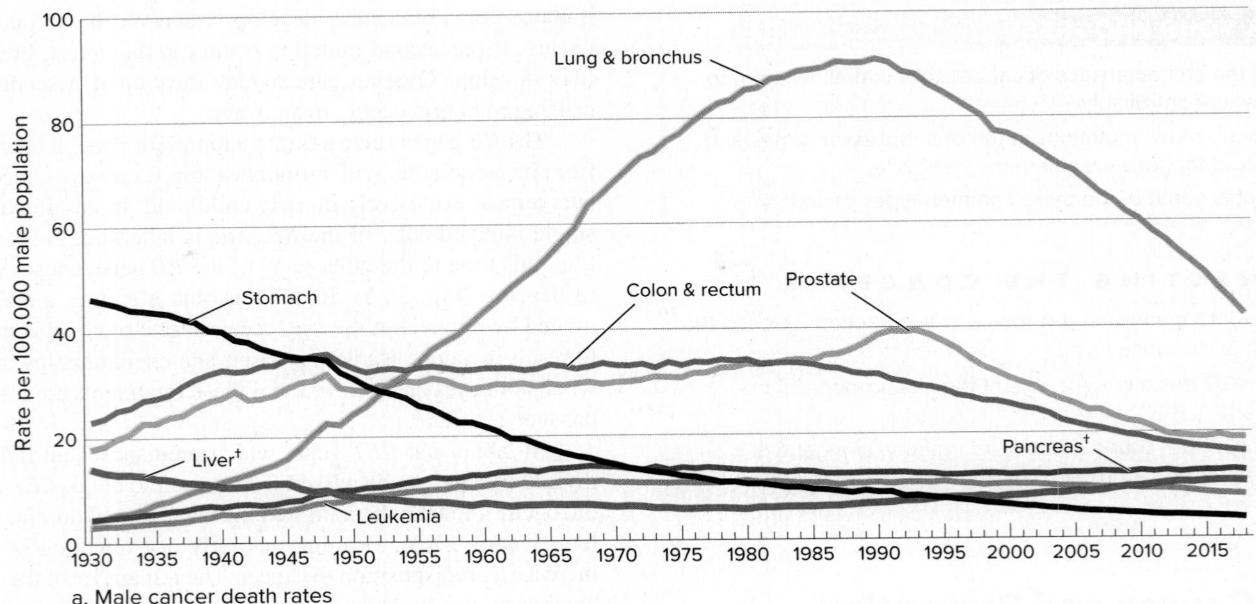

a. Male cancer death rates

†Mortality rates for pancreatic and liver cancers are increasing.

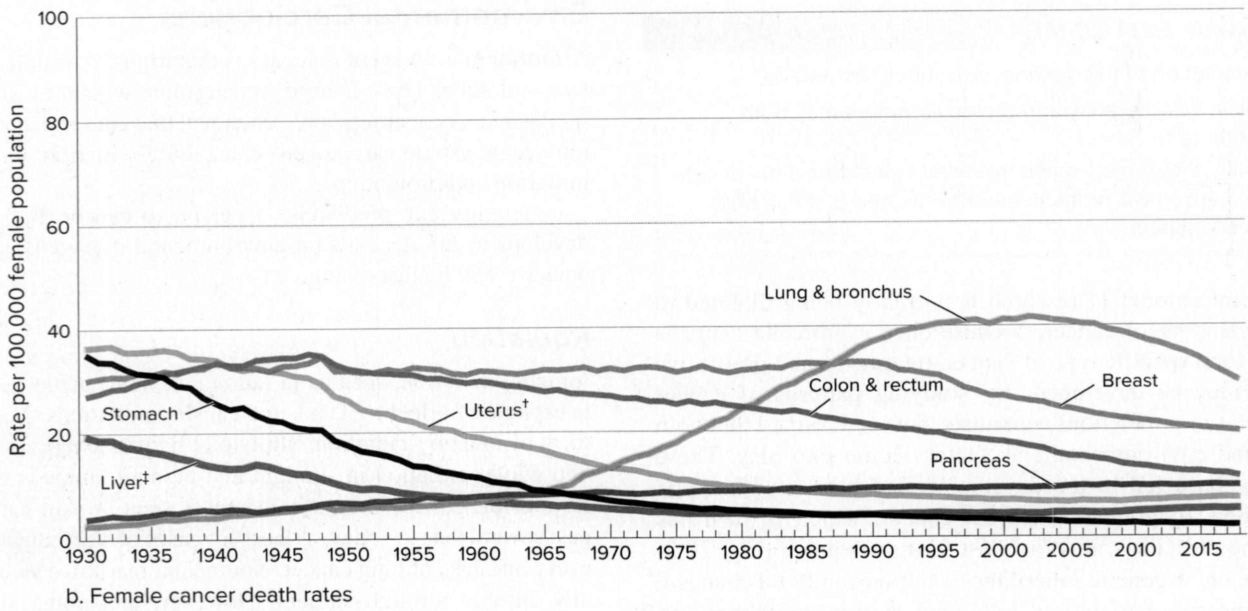

b. Female cancer death rates

†Uterus refers to uterine cervix and uterine corpus combined. ‡The mortality rate for liver cancer is increasing.

Figure 20.5 Cancer mortality.
The mortality rates for many forms of cancer have declined in both **(a)** males and **(b)** females from 1930 to 2017.
Source: American Cancer Society, Cancer Facts & Figures, 2017

example, cancer deaths are elevated in the vicinity of the Chernobyl Power Station (in Ukraine), which suffered a terrible accident in 1986. The 2011 incident at the Fukushima nuclear plant (in Japan) released radiation into the environment. Usually, however, diagnostic X-rays account for most of our exposure to artificial sources of radiation. The benefits of these procedures can far outweigh the possible risk, but it is still wise to avoid X-ray procedures that are not medically warranted. When X-rays are necessary for therapy, nearby noncancerous tissues should be shielded carefully.

Recently, there has been a great deal of public concern regarding the presumed danger of nonionizing radiation. This energy

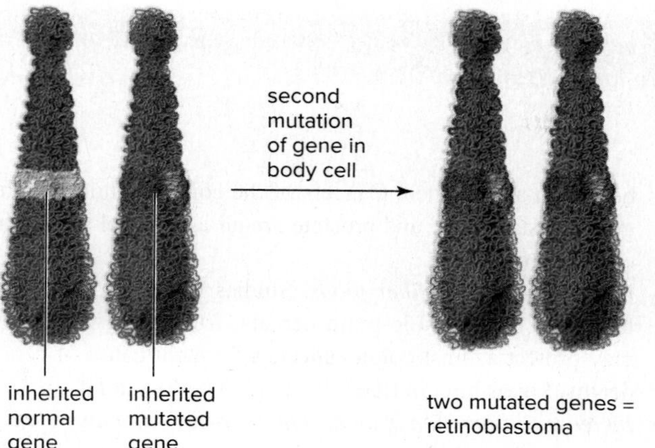

Figure 20.6 **Inheritance of retinoblastoma.**
A child is at risk for an eye tumor when a mutated copy of the *RB* gene is inherited, even though a second mutation in the normal copy is required before the tumor develops.

form is given off by cell phones, electrical lines, and appliances. Some recent studies have discovered links between these forms of radiation and rare forms of cancer.

Organic Chemicals

Certain chemicals, particularly synthetic organic chemicals, have been found to be risk factors for cancer. We will examine only two examples: the organic chemicals in tobacco and those pollutants in the environment. There are many other chemical carcinogens.

Smoking Tobacco smoke contains a number of organic chemicals that are known mutagens, including *N*-nitrosonornicotine, vinyl chloride, and benzo[a]pyrene (a known suppressor of *p53*). The greater the number of cigarettes smoked per day and the earlier the habit starts, the more likely it is that cancer will develop. Scientists estimate that about 80% of all cancers, including oral cancer and cancers of the larynx, esophagus, pancreas, bladder, kidney, and cervix, are related to the use of tobacco products or secondhand smoke. When smoking is combined with drinking alcohol, the risk of these cancers increases.

Passive smoking, or inhalation of someone else's tobacco smoke, is also dangerous. Researchers continue to collect evidence that confirms the link between passive smoking and cancer.

Pollutants Being exposed to substances such as metals, dust, chemicals, or pesticides at work can increase the risk of cancer. Asbestos, nickel, cadmium, uranium, radon, vinyl chloride, benzidine, and benzene are well-known examples of carcinogens in the workplace. For example, inhaling asbestos fibers increases the risk of lung diseases, including cancer. The cancer risk is especially high for individuals who work with asbestos who smoke.

Data show that the incidence of soft-tissue sarcomas, malignant lymphomas, and non-Hodgkin's lymphomas has increased in farmers living in Nebraska and Kansas. All those affected have used 2,4-D, a commonly used herbicidal agent, on crops and to clear weeds along railroad tracks.

Viruses

At least four types of DNA viruses—hepatitis B and C viruses, Epstein–Barr virus, and human papillomavirus (HPV)—are believed to cause human cancers.

In China, the hepatitis B virus is a significant public health problem, with high rates of infection. This correlates with the high incidence of liver cancer in that country. A combined vaccine is now available for hepatitis A and B. For a long time, circumstances suggested that cervical cancer was a sexually transmitted disease. Now, human papillomaviruses (HPVs) are routinely isolated from cervical cancers. Burkitt lymphoma occurs frequently in Africa, where the rate of Epstein–Barr virus is high.

RNA-containing retroviruses, in particular, are known to cause cancers in animals. In humans, the retrovirus HTLV-1 (human T-cell lymphotropic virus, type 1) has been shown to cause hairy cell leukemia. This disease occurs frequently in parts of Japan, the Caribbean, and Africa, particularly in regions where people are known to be infected with the virus. HIV, the virus that causes AIDS, and Kaposi sarcoma–associated herpesvirus (KSHV) are responsible for the development of Kaposi sarcoma and certain lymphomas. This occurs due to the suppression of proper immune system functions.

Dietary Choices

Nutrition is emerging as a way to help prevent cancer. The incidence of breast and prostate cancer parallels a high-fat diet, as does obesity. The Health feature "Prevention of Cancer" discusses how to protect yourself from cancer. The American Cancer Society recommends consumption of fruits and vegetables, as well as whole grains instead of processed (refined) grains, and limited consumption of red meats (especially high-fat and processed meats). Moderate to vigorous activity for 30 to 45 minutes a day, 5 or more days a week, is also recommended.

CHECK YOUR PROGRESS 20.2

1. Explain what it means when cancer is said to have a hereditary component.
2. List the environmental carcinogens known to play a role in the development of cancer.
3. Discuss the proactive steps you can take to reduce your risk of cancer.

CONNECTING THE CONCEPTS

For more information on cancer and its prevention, refer to the following discussions:

Section 4.7 describes methods of protecting yourself against skin cancer.

Section 9.5 summarizes how the components of a healthy diet reduce the risk of cancer.

Section 10.7 examines the influence of smoking on lung cancer.

BIOLOGY TODAY ▶ Health

Prevention of Cancer

While there is a genetic component to many forms of cancer, there are both preventive behaviors and dietary choices that may reduce cancer risk.

Preventive Behaviors

These behaviors help prevent cancer:

- *Don't use tobacco.* Cigarette smoking accounts for over 30% of cancer deaths. Smoking is responsible for 80% of lung cancer cases among men and 79% among women—about 87% on average. People who smoke have lung cancer mortality rates 23 times greater than those of people who do not smoke. Smokeless tobacco (chewing tobacco or snuff) increases the risk of cancers of the mouth, larynx, throat, and esophagus.
- *Don't sunbathe or use a tanning booth.* Almost all cases of basal cell and squamous cell skin cancers are considered sun-related. Sun exposure is also a major factor in the development of melanoma, and the incidence of this cancer increases for people living near the equator.
- *Avoid radiation.* Excessive exposure to ionizing radiation can increase cancer risk. Even though most medical and dental X-rays are adjusted to deliver the lowest dose possible, unnecessary X-rays should be avoided. Excessive radon exposure in homes increases the risk of lung cancer, especially for people who smoke cigarettes. It is best to test your home for radon and take the proper remedial actions.
- *Undergo cancer screening.* Do the shower check for breast cancer or testicular cancer. Have other exams done regularly by a physician. (See Table 20.1.)
- *Be aware of occupational hazards.* Exposure to several different industrial agents (nickel, chromate, asbestos, vinyl chloride, etc.) and/or radiation increases the risk of various cancers. The risk from asbestos is greatly increased when combined with cigarette smoking.
- *Get vaccinated.* Get vaccinated for HPV and hepatitis A and B. Consult with your physician or other health professional for advice regarding these vaccines and whether they are appropriate for you.

The Right Diet

Statistical studies have suggested that people who follow certain dietary guidelines are less likely to have cancer. The following dietary guidelines greatly reduce your risk of developing cancer:

- *Avoid obesity.* Obesity increases the risk for many types of cancer, especially those related to the reproductive systems in both men and women. Cancers of the colon, rectum, esophagus, breast, kidney, and prostate are all associated with being overweight.
- *Eat plenty of high-fiber foods.* Studies have indicated that a high-fiber diet (whole-grain cereals, fruits, and vegetables) may protect against colon cancer, a frequent cause of cancer deaths. Foods high in fiber also tend to be low in fat.
- *Increase consumption of foods that are rich in vitamins A and C.* Beta-carotene, a precursor of vitamin A, is found in dark-green, leafy vegetables; carrots; and various fruits. Vitamin C is present in citrus fruits. These vitamins are called antioxidants, because in cells they prevent the formation of free radicals (organic ions having an unpaired electron) that can damage DNA. Vitamin C also prevents the conversion of nitrates and nitrites into carcinogenic nitrosamines in the digestive tract.
- *Reduce consumption of salt-cured, smoked, or nitrite-cured foods.* Salt-cured or pickled foods may increase the risk of stomach and esophageal cancers. Smoked foods, such as ham and sausage, contain chemical carcinogens similar to those in tobacco smoke. Nitrites are sometimes added to processed meats (e.g., hot dogs and cold cuts) and other foods to protect them from spoilage. As mentioned previously, nitrites are converted to nitrosamines in the digestive tract.
- *Include vegetables from the cabbage family in the diet.* The cabbage family includes cabbage, broccoli, brussels sprouts, kohlrabi, and cauliflower. These vegetables may reduce the risk of gastrointestinal and respiratory tract cancers.
- *Drink alcohol in moderation.* Risks of cancer development rise as the level of alcohol intake increases. The risk increases still further for those who smoke or chew tobacco while drinking. People who drink heavily face a much greater risk for oral, pharyngeal, esophageal, and laryngeal cancer. Higher rates for cancers of the breast and liver are also linked to heavy alcohol use. Men should limit their daily alcohol consumption to two drinks or fewer. Women should have only one alcoholic drink daily. (A drink is defined as 12 oz of beer, 5 oz of wine, or 1.5 oz of distilled spirits.)

Questions to Consider

1. Why won't these changes completely protect you from the chances of developing cancer?
2. Consider your diet over the past few days and propose changes that could be made to help reduce your risk of cancer.

20.3 Diagnosis of Cancer

LEARNING OUTCOMES

Upon completion of this section, you should be able to

1. List the seven warning signs of cancer.
2. Describe the tests that may be used to diagnose cancer in an individual.

The earlier a cancer is detected, the more likely it can be effectively treated. At present, physicians have ways to detect several types of cancer before they become malignant. Researchers are always looking for new and better detection methods. A growing number of researchers now believe the future of early detection lies in testing for cancer's "fingerprints"—molecular changes caused by cancer. Several teams of scientists are working on blood, saliva, and urine tests to catch cancerous gene and protein patterns in these body fluids before a tumor develops. In the meantime, cancer is usually diagnosed by the methods discussed here.

Seven Warning Signs

At present, diagnosis of cancer before metastasis is difficult, although treatment at this stage is usually more successful. The American Cancer Society publicizes seven warning signals, which spell out the word CAUTION and of which everyone should be aware:

C	Change in bowel or bladder habits
A	A sore that does not heal
U	Unusual bleeding or discharge
T	Thickening or lump in breast or elsewhere
I	Indigestion or difficulty in swallowing
O	Obvious change in wart or mole
N	Nagging cough or hoarseness

Keep in mind that these signs do not necessarily mean you have cancer. However, they are an indication that something is wrong and a medical professional should be consulted. Unfortunately, some of these symptoms are not obvious until cancer has progressed to one of its later stages.

Routine Screening Tests

Self-examination, followed by examination by a physician, can help detect the presence of cancer. For example, the letters ABCDE can help you examine your skin for melanoma, the most serious form of skin cancer (Fig. 20.7). Breast cancer in women and testicular cancer in men can often be detected during a monthly shower check. The technique is discussed in the Health feature "Cancer Self-Examinations."

The ideal tests for cancer are relatively easy to do, cost little, and are fairly accurate. The Pap test for cervical cancer fulfills these three requirements. A physician merely takes a sample of cells from the cervix, which are then examined microscopically for signs of abnormality (see Fig. 20.1). Any woman who chooses to receive the new HPV vaccine should still get regular Pap tests, because (1) the vaccine will not protect against all types of HPV that cause cervical cancer, and (2) the vaccine does not protect against any HPV infections she may already have if she is sexually active. Regular Pap tests are credited with preventing over 90% of deaths from cervical cancer.

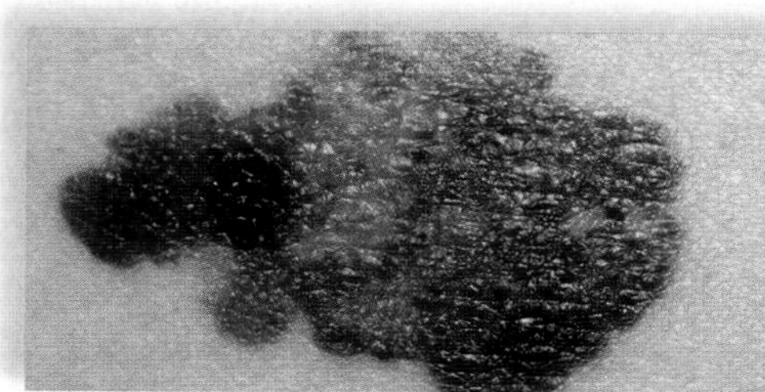

A = Asymmetry: one-half of mole does not look like the other half.

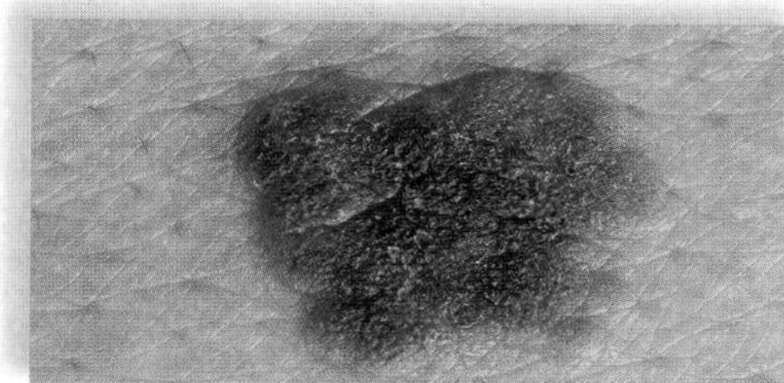

B = Border: irregular scalloped or poorly circumscribed border.

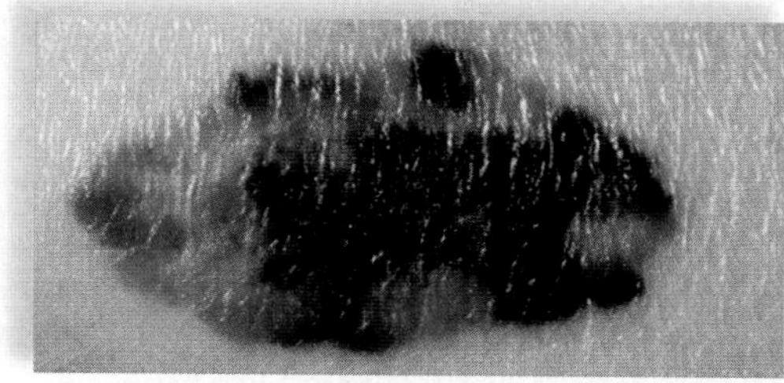

C = Color: varied from one area to another; shades of tan, brown, black, or sometimes white, red, or blue.

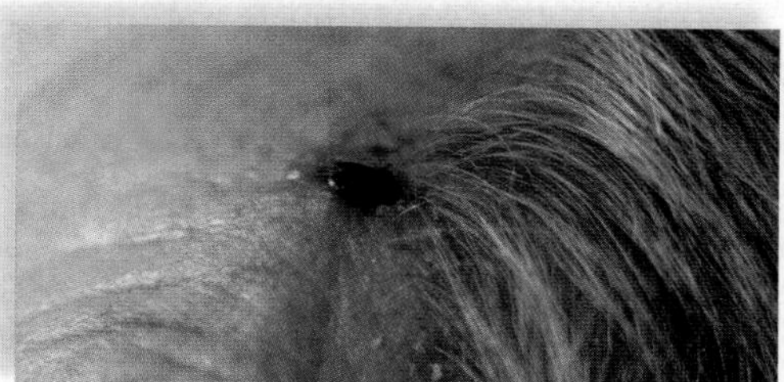

D = Diameter: larger than 6 mm (the diameter of a pencil eraser).

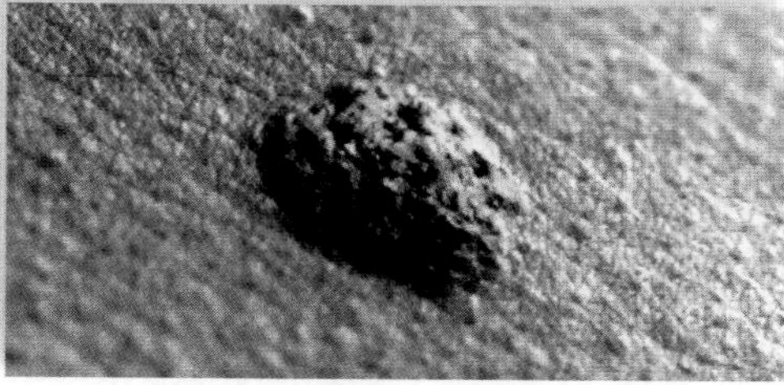

E = Elevated: above skin surface, and **evolving,** or changing over time.

Figure 20.7 **The ABCDE test for melanoma.** Suspicion of melanoma can begin by discovering a mole that has one or more of these characteristics.

(A): National Cancer Institute (NCI); (B): LYphoto/Shutterstock; (C): Dr. P. Marazzi/Science Source; (D): Image Source/Getty Images; (E): BSIP/Universal Images Group/Getty Images

Screening for colon cancer also depends on three types of testing. A digital rectal examination performed by a physician is of limited value, because only a portion of the rectum can be reached.

BIOLOGY TODAY ▶ **Health**

Cancer Self-Examinations

The American Cancer Society urges women to do a breast self-exam and men to do a testicle self-exam every month. Breast cancer and testicular cancer are far more curable if found early, and we must all take on the responsibility of checking for one or the other.

Shower Self-Exam for Women

1. Check your breasts for any lumps, knots, or changes about 1 week after your period.
2. Place your right hand behind your head. Move your *left* hand over your *right* breast in a circle. Press firmly with the pads of your fingers (Fig. 20C). Also check the armpit.
3. Now place your left hand behind your head and check your *left* breast with your *right* hand in the same manner as before. Also check the armpit.
4. Check your breasts while standing in front of a mirror right after you do your shower check. First, put your hands on your hips and then raise your arms above your head (Fig. 20D). Look for any changes in the way your breasts look: dimpling of the skin, changes in the nipple, or redness or swelling.
5. If you find any changes during your shower or mirror check, see your doctor right away.

You should know that the best check for breast cancer is a mammogram. When your doctor checks your breasts, ask about getting a mammogram.

Shower Self-Exam for Men

1. Check your testicles once a month.
2. Roll each testicle between your thumb and finger as shown in Figure 20E. Feel for hard lumps or bumps.
3. If you notice a change or have aches or lumps, tell your doctor right away so that the proper treatment can be recommended.

Cancer of the testicles can be cured if you find it early. You should also know that prostate cancer is the most common cancer in men. Men over age 50 should have an annual health checkup that includes a prostate examination.

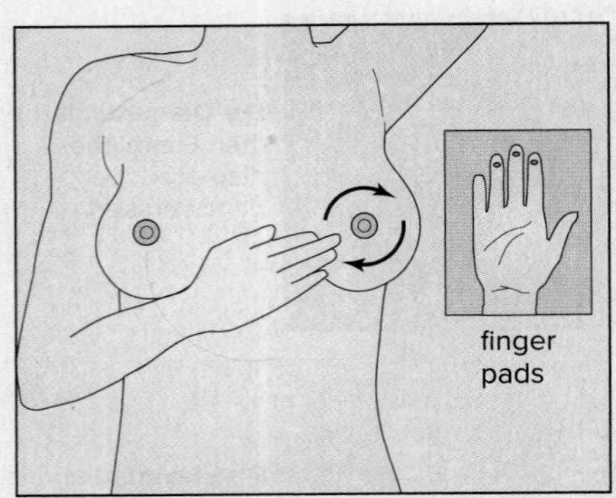

Figure 20C Shower check for breast cancer.
Source: The American Cancer Society

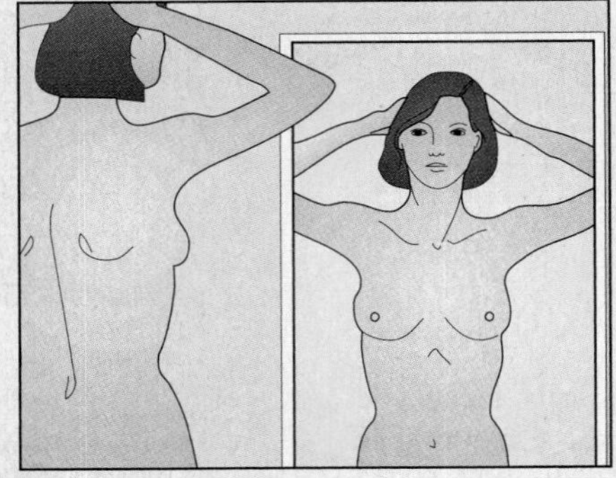

Figure 20D Mirror check for breast cancer.
Source: The American Cancer Society

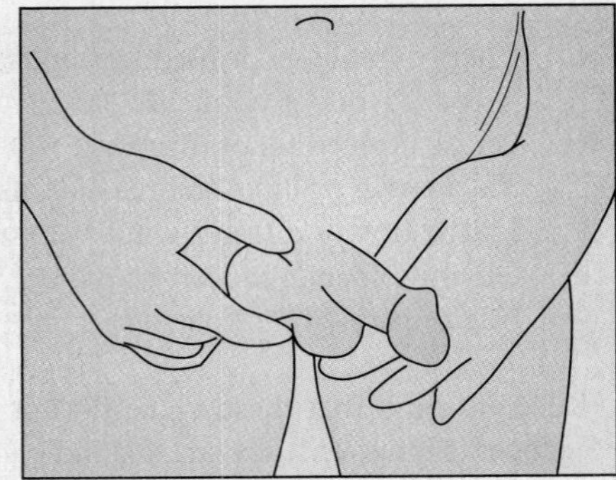

Figure 20E Shower check for testicular cancer.
Source: The American Cancer Society

With flexible sigmoidoscopy, the second procedure, a much larger portion of the colon can be examined by using a thin, pliable, lighted tube. Finally, a stool blood test (fecal occult blood test) consists of examining a stool sample to detect any hidden blood. The sample is smeared on a slide, and a chemical is added that changes color in the presence of hemoglobin. This procedure is based on the supposition that a cancerous polyp bleeds, although some polyps do not bleed. Moreover, bleeding is not always because of a polyp. Therefore, the percentage of false negatives and false positives is high. All positive tests are followed up by a colonoscopy, an examination of the entire colon, or by X-ray after a barium enema. If the colonoscopy detects polyps, they can be destroyed by laser therapy. Blood tests are used to detect leukemia. Urinalysis aids in the diagnosis of bladder cancer.

Breast cancer is not as easily detected, but three procedures are recommended. First, every woman should do a monthly breast self-examination. But this is not a sufficient screen for breast cancer. Therefore, all women should have an annual physical examination, especially women over 40, when a physician will do the same procedure. Even then, this type of examination may not detect lumps before metastasis has already taken place. That is the goal of the third recommended procedure, *mammography,* an X-ray study of the breast (Fig. 20.8). However, mammograms do not show all cancers, and new tumors may develop in the interval between mammograms. The hope is that a mammogram will reveal a lump too small to be felt, at a time when the cancer is still highly curable. Table 20.1 outlines when routine screening tests should be done for various cancers, including breast cancer.

The diagnosis of cancer in other parts of the body may involve other types of imaging. A computerized axial tomography (CT) scan uses computer analysis of scanning X-ray images to create cross-sectional pictures that portray a tumor's size and location. Magnetic resonance imaging (MRI) is another type of imaging technique that depends on computer analysis. MRI is particularly useful for analyzing tumors in tissues surrounded by bone, such as tumors of the brain or spinal cord. A radioactive scan obtained after a radioactive isotope is administered can reveal any abnormal isotope accumulation due to a tumor. During ultrasound, echoes of high-frequency sound waves directed at a part of the body are used to reveal the size, shape, and location of tissue masses. Ultrasound can confirm tumors of the stomach, prostate, pancreas, kidney, uterus, and ovary.

Aside from various imaging procedures, a diagnosis of cancer can be confirmed without major surgery by performing a *biopsy*. Needle biopsies allow removal of a few cells for examination. Sophisticated techniques, such as laparoscopy, permit viewing of body parts.

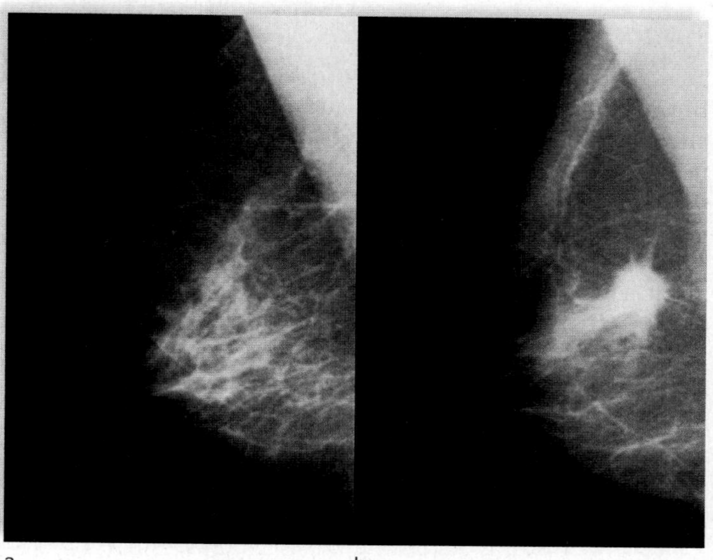

Figure 20.8 **Mammograms can detect breast cancer.** An X-ray image of the breast can find tumors too small to be felt. **a.** An image of a normal breast; (**b**) a breast with a tumor.
(both): UHB Trust/The Image Bank/Getty Images

Table 20.1 **Recommendations for the Early Detection of Cancer in Average-Risk, Asymptomatic People**

Cancer	Population	Test or Procedure	Frequency
Breast	Women, aged ≥20 years	Breast self-examination	Monthly, starting at age 20 years; see the Health feature "Cancer Self-Examinations"
		Clinical breast examination and mammography	For women in 20s and 30s, every 3 years; aged 40 years and over, preferably annually
Colorectal*	Men and women, aged ≥50 years	Fecal occult blood test (FOBT)	Annually, starting at age 50 years
		Fecal immunochemical test (FIT), flexible sigmoidoscopy, *or* double-contrast barium enema	Every 5 years, starting at age 50 years
		Colonoscopy	Every 10 years, starting at age 50 years
Prostate	Men, aged ≥50 years	Digital rectal examination and prostate-specific antigen (PSA) test	Discussion with physician annually, starting at age 50 years, for men who have a life expectancy of at least 10 more years
Cervical	Women, aged ≥21 years	Pap test	Every 3 years
	Women, aged 30–65 years	Pap test + HPV DNA test	Every 5 years, with an alternate Pap test alone every 3 years. Women aged >65 should stop screening unless they had a serious cervical precancer or cancer in the last 20 years.
Endometrial†	Women, at menopause	Report any unexpected bleeding or spotting to a physician.	
Testicular	Men, aged 20 years	Testicle, self-examination	Monthly, starting at age 20 years, see Health feature "Cancer Self-Examinations"
Other	Men and women, aged 20 years	On the occasion of a periodic health examination, a cancer-related checkup should include examination for other cancers and include counseling about tobacco, sun exposure, diet and nutrition, risk factors, and environmental and occupational exposures.	

*Follow one of the schedules.
†Average risk, increased, or high risk should contact physician.
Source: American Cancer Society website: www.cancer.org.

Tumor Marker Tests

Tumor marker tests are blood tests for antigens and/or antibodies. Blood tests are possible because tumors release substances that provoke an antibody response in the body. For example, for an individual who has already had colon cancer, it is possible to use the presence of an antigen called *carcinoembryonic antigen (CEA)* to detect any relapses. When the CEA level rises, additional tumor growth has occurred.

There are also tumor marker tests that can be used for early cancer diagnosis. They are not reliable enough to count on solely, but in conjunction with physical examination and ultrasound, they are considered useful. For example, there is a *prostate-specific antigen (PSA) test* for prostate cancer, a *CA-125 test* for ovarian cancer, and an *alpha-fetoprotein (AFP) test* for liver tumors.

Genetic Tests

Tests for genetic mutations in proto-oncogenes and tumor suppressor genes are making it possible to detect the likelihood of cancer before the development of a tumor. Tests are available that signal the possibility of colon, bladder, breast, and thyroid cancers, as well as melanoma. Physicians now believe that a mutated *RET* gene means that thyroid cancer is present or may occur in the future, and a mutated *p16* gene appears to be associated with melanoma. Genetic testing can also be used to determine if cancer cells still remain after a tumor has been removed.

A genetic test is also available for the presence of *BRCA1* (breast cancer gene 1). A woman who has inherited this gene can choose either to have prophylactic surgery or to be frequently examined for signs of breast cancer. Physicians can use microsatellites to detect chromosomal deletions that accompany bladder cancer. Microsatellites are small regions of DNA that always have two (di-), three (tri-), or four (tetra-) nucleotide repeats. They compare the number of nucleotide DNA repeats in a lymphocyte microsatellite with the number in a microsatellite of a cell found in urine. When the number of repeats is less in the cell from urine, a bladder tumor is suspected.

Telomerase, you will recall, is the enzyme that keeps telomeres a constant length in cells. The gene that codes for telomerase is turned off in normal cells but is active in cancer cells. Therefore, if the test for the presence of telomerase is positive, the cell is cancerous.

CHECK YOUR PROGRESS 20.3

1. List the seven warning signs of cancer.
2. Identify the routine screening tests that are available to detect and diagnose cancer.
3. Discuss how genetic tests and tumor marker tests may be used to prevent cancer.

CONNECTING THE CONCEPTS

For more information on the information in this section, refer to the following discussions:

Section 7.3 describes how the body generates antibodies against antigens.

Section 9.5 examines how polyps in the large intestine (colon) may lead to colon cancer.

Section 17.3 examines the structure of the female reproductive system and illustrates the location of the cervix.

20.4 Treatment of Cancer

LEARNING OUTCOMES

Upon completion of this section, you should be able to

1. Describe how radiation therapy, chemotherapy, and surgery may all be used to treat cancer.
2. Summarize some of the new advances in the treatment of cancer.

Certain therapies for cancer have been available for some time. Other methods of therapy are in clinical trials. If successful, these new therapies will become more generally available in the future.

Standard Therapies

Surgery, radiation therapy, and chemotherapy are the standard methods of cancer therapy.

Surgery

With the exception of cancers of the blood, surgery may be sufficient for cancer in situ. But because there is always the danger that some cancer cells have been left behind, surgery is often preceded by and/or followed by radiation therapy and chemotherapy.

Radiation Therapy

Ionizing radiation causes chromosomal breakage and cell cycle disruption. Therefore, rapidly dividing cells, such as cancer cells, are more susceptible to its effects than other cells. Powerful X-rays or gamma rays can be administered through an externally applied beam (Fig. 20.9). In some instances, tiny radioactive sources can be implanted directly into the patient's body. Cancer of the cervix and larynx, early stages of prostate cancer, and Hodgkin's disease are often treated with radiation therapy alone.

Although X-rays and gamma rays are the mainstays of radiation therapy, protons and neutrons also work well. Proton beams can be aimed at the tumor like a rifle bullet hitting the bull's-eye of a target.

Side effects of radiation therapy greatly depend on which part of the body is being irradiated and how much radiation is used. Weakness and fatigue are very typical. Dry mouth, nausea, and diarrhea often affect the digestive tract. Dry, red, or irritated skin or even blistering burns may occur at the treatment site. Hair loss at the treatment site, which in some situations can be permanent, can be very depressing to the patient. Fortunately, most side effects of radiation treatment are temporary.

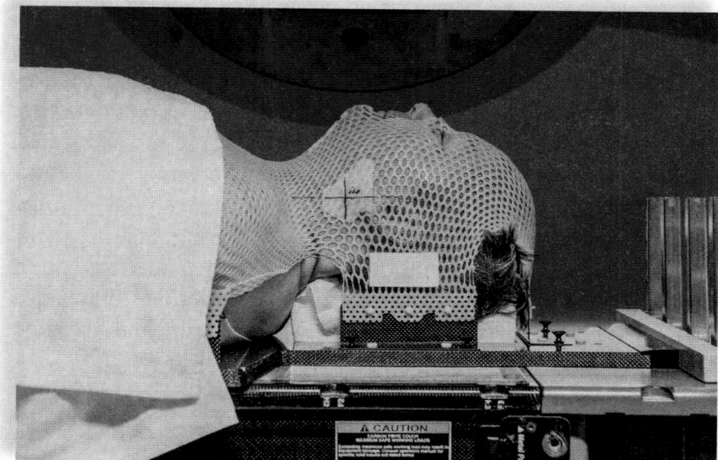

Figure 20.9 Radiation treatment for cancer.
Most people who receive radiation therapy for cancer have external radiation on an outpatient basis. The head of this patient, who has a brain tumor, has been immobilized so that radiation can be delivered to a very precise area.
Ragnar Th Sigurdsson/Arctic Images/Alamy Stock Photo

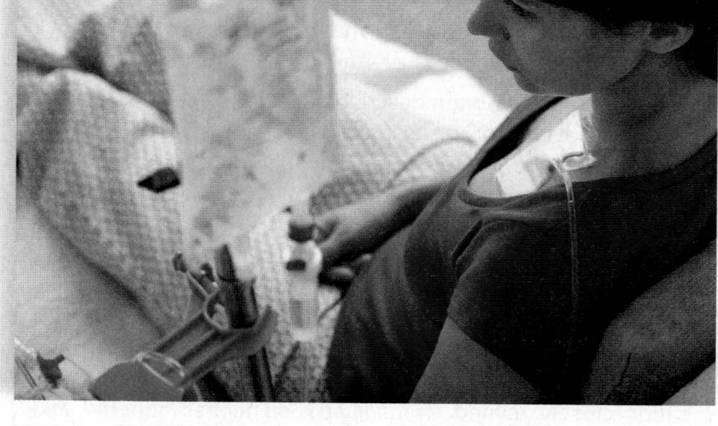

Figure 20.10 Treating cancer with chemotherapy.
The intravenous route is the most common, allowing chemotherapy drugs to spread quickly throughout the entire body by way of the bloodstream.
Image Point Fr/Shutterstock

Chemotherapy

Radiation is localized therapy, whereas chemotherapy is a way to catch cancer cells that have spread. Unlike radiation, which treats only the part of the body exposed to the radiation, chemotherapy treats the entire body (Fig. 20.10). As a result, any cells that may have escaped from where the cancer originated are treated.

Most chemotherapeutic drugs kill cells by damaging their DNA or interfering with DNA synthesis. The hope is that all cancer cells will be killed, while leaving enough normal cells untouched to allow the body to keep functioning. Combining drugs that have different actions at the cellular level may help destroy a greater number of cancer cells. Combinations may also reduce the risk of the cancer developing resistance to one particular drug. What chemicals are used is generally based on the type of cancer and the patient's age, general health, and perceived ability to tolerate potential side effects. Some of the types of chemotherapy medications commonly used to treat cancer include the following:

- *Alkylating agents.* These medications interfere with the growth of cancer cells by blocking the replication of DNA.
- *Antimetabolites.* These drugs block the enzymes needed by cancer cells to live and grow.
- *Antitumor antibiotics.* These antibiotics—different from those used to treat bacterial infections—interfere with DNA, blocking certain enzymes and cell division and changing plasma membranes.
- *Mitotic inhibitors.* These drugs inhibit cell division or hinder certain enzymes necessary in the cell reproduction process.
- *Nitrosoureas.* These medications impede the enzymes that help repair DNA.

Whenever possible, chemotherapy is specifically designed for the particular cancer. For example, in some cancers, a small portion of chromosome 9 is missing. Therefore, DNA metabolism differs in the cancerous cells compared with normal cells. Specific chemotherapy for the cancer can exploit this metabolic difference and destroy the cancerous cells.

One drug, paclitaxel (Taxol), extracted from the bark of the Pacific yew tree, was found to be particularly effective against advanced ovarian cancers, as well as breast, head, and neck tumors. Paclitaxel interferes with microtubules needed for cell division. Chemists have now synthesized a family of related drugs, called taxoids, which may be more powerful and have fewer side effects than paclitaxel.

Certain types of cancer, such as leukemias, lymphomas, and testicular cancer, are now successfully treated by combination chemotherapy alone. The survival rate for children with childhood leukemia is 80%. Hodgkin's disease, a lymphoma, once killed two out of three patients. Combination therapy, using four different drugs, can now wipe out the disease in a matter of months. Three out of four patients achieve a cure, even when the cancer is not diagnosed immediately. In other cancers—most notably, breast and colon cancer—chemotherapy can reduce the chance of recurrence after surgery has removed all detectable traces of the disease.

Chemotherapy sometimes fails, because cancer cells become resistant to one or several chemotherapeutic drugs, a phenomenon called multidrug resistance. This occurs because a plasma membrane carrier pumps the drug (or drugs) out of the cancer cell before it can be harmed. Researchers are testing drugs known to poison the pump in an effort to restore the effectiveness of the drugs. Another possibility is to use combinations of drugs with different toxic activities, because cancer cells can't become resistant to many different types at once.

BIOLOGY IN YOUR LIFE

What can be done to lessen the side effects of radiation and chemotherapy?

People with cancer often describe the side effects of treatment as the worst part of the disease. Nausea, vomiting, diarrhea, weight loss and hair loss, anxiety and/or depression, and extreme fatigue are common symptoms that may be caused by chemotherapy or radiation therapy.

However, strategies now exist to help patients deal with treatment side effects, and others continue to be devised. Antiemetic drugs alleviate nausea and vomiting. Genetically engineered erythropoietin helps stimulate red blood cell production and reduce fatigue (see Section 6.2). Dronabinol (Marinol), a medication closely related to marijuana, stimulates appetite and helps with weight loss. Hair loss can be minimized by cryotherapy, which involves applying cold packs on the scalp during treatment. Cold temperatures slow the metabolic rate of hair follicles, and more follicles survive treatment. Antidepressants and antianxiety medications help the patient deal with the psychological effects of the disease.

Increasingly, patients with cancer are also turning to alternative therapies for help in coping with the disease. Calming techniques, including yoga, meditation, and tai chi, help the patient relax. Hypnosis can have the same restful effect. Aromatherapy, massage therapy, and music therapy seem to ease tension and stress, perhaps by stimulating pleasure centers in the brain. Exercise is known to produce endorphins, the brain's pain-relieving neurotransmitters.

Bone marrow transplants are sometimes done in conjunction with chemotherapy. The red bone marrow contains large populations of dividing cells. Therefore, red bone marrow is particularly prone to destruction by chemotherapeutic drugs. In bone marrow autotransplantation, a patient's stem cells are harvested and stored before chemotherapy begins. High doses of radiation or chemotherapeutic drugs are then given within a relatively short time. This prevents multidrug resistance from occurring, and the treatment is more likely to catch every cancer cell. The stored stem cells can then be returned to the patient by injection. They automatically make their way to bony cavities, where they resume blood cell formation.

Newer Therapies

Several therapies are now in clinical trials and are expected to be increasingly used to treat cancer.

Immunotherapy

We now know that the immune system has the ability to keep some cancers under control, meaning it will slow tumor growth. However, in many cases, the cancer cells are able to avoid the immune system, even though they bear antigens that make them different from the body's normal cells. It has been possible for some time to vaccinate the body against viruses that are associated with cancer—for example, HPV—and scientists are beginning to develop vaccines against cancer cells directly. Several vaccines are in development, but currently none are available in the United States.

Another idea is to use immune cells, genetically engineered to bear the tumor's antigens (Fig. 20.11). When these cells are returned to the body, they produce cytokines. Recall that cytokines are

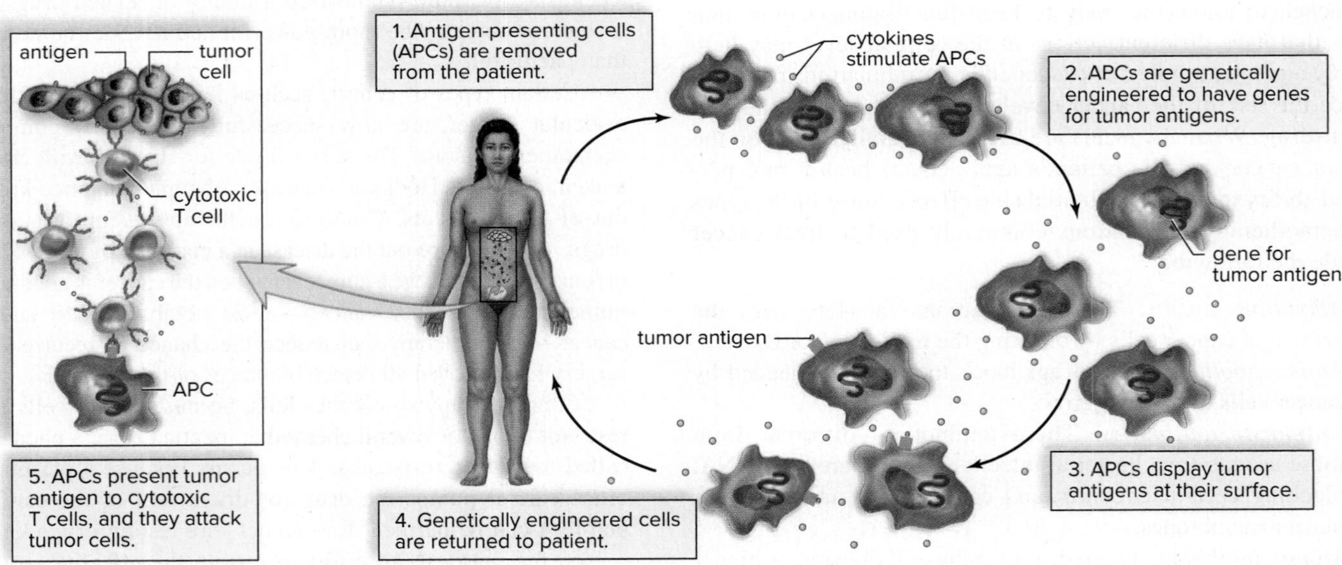

Figure 20.11 Use of immunotherapy to treat cancer.
1. Antigen-presenting cells (APCs) are removed and (**2**) are genetically engineered to (**3**) display tumor antigens. **4.** After these cells are returned to the patient, (**5**) they present the antigen to cytotoxic T cells, which then kill tumor cells.

chemical messengers for immune cells (see Section 7.2). Cytokines stimulate the body's immune cells to attack the tumor. Further, the altered immune cells present the tumor antigen to cytotoxic T cells, which then go forth and destroy tumor cells in the body.

Passive immunotherapy is also possible. Monoclonal antibodies have the same structure, because they are produced by the same plasma cell (see Fig. 7.9). Some monoclonal antibodies are designed to zero in on the receptor proteins of cancer cells. To increase the killing power of monoclonal antibodies, they are linked to radioactive isotopes or chemotherapeutic drugs. It is expected that soon they will be used as initial therapies, in addition to chemotherapy.

p53 Gene Therapy

Researchers believe that *p53* gene expression is needed for only 19 hours to trigger apoptosis, programmed cell death. And the *p53* gene seems to trigger cell death only in cancer cells—elevating the *p53* level in a normal cell doesn't do any harm, possibly because apoptosis requires extensive DNA damage.

Ordinarily, when adenoviruses infect a cell, they first produce a protein that inactivates *p53*. In a cleverly designed procedure, investigators genetically engineered an adenovirus that lacks the gene for this protein. Now, the adenovirus can infect and kill only cells that lack a *p53* gene. Which cells are those? Tumor cells, of course. Another plus to this procedure is that the injected adenovirus spreads through the cancer, killing tumor cells as it goes. This genetically engineered virus is now in clinical trials.

Genome Editing

Genome editing is the targeting of specific sequences in a DNA molecule for editing. Editing can be done via several methods. The most widely used is called CRISPR (*c*lustered *r*egularly *i*nterspaced *s*hort *p*alindromic *r*epeats). We will explore how CRISPR works in more detail in Section 22.3.

As a cancer treatment, the CRISPR system has been used to inactivate cell-cycle control genes that have lost their ability to function. The first trials were associated with fusion proteins, which as the name suggests, are the result of two proteins fusing together. Fusion proteins tend to be oncogenes, and thus act like a stuck gas pedal on a car. By using CRISPR to target the specific DNA sequence of the fusion protein, researchers have been able to inactivate the gene and "unstick" the oncogene gas pedal. Initial results have indicated that this approach has been successful in reducing the size of tumors, which can then be targeted for more traditional therapies.

In the future, genome editing may be able to go into cells and correct mutations that have set a cell on a cancer pathway, or restore the function of mutated proto-oncogenes or tumor-suppressor genes, thus restoring some of the normal regulatory mechanisms that protect against the formation of cancer.

CHECK YOUR PROGRESS 20.4

1. Describe the three types of therapy that are presently the standard ways to treat cancer.
2. Discuss why cancer treatment may involve a combination of chemotherapy, radiation therapy, and surgery.
3. Explain the rationale for antiangiogenesis therapy.

CONNECTING THE CONCEPTS

For more information on the topics presented in this section, refer to the following discussions:

Section 7.2 examines the role of chemical signals, such as cytokines, in protecting the body from infection.

Section 7.4 explores the function of cytotoxic T cells in the immune response.

Section 22.3 provides an overview of how genetic engineering can alter the genes within a virus.

CONCLUSION

In this chapter, we explored the importance of cancer in our understanding of human biology. Cancer is one of the leading causes of death in humans, and a disease that will impact most of us in some manner during our lives. However, thanks to the intensive work of scientists and medical professionals around the world, we are making tremendous progress in the prevention, detection, and treatment of cancer.

SUMMARIZE

20.1 Overview of Cancer

Characteristics of Cancer Cells

Cancer represents uncontrolled cell growth. Certain characteristics are common to cancer cells. Cancer cells

- Lack **differentiation** and do not contribute to function.
- Do not undergo **apoptosis**—they enter the cell cycle an unlimited number of times. This is often due to the presence of telomerase enzyme, which regulates the length of the **telomere.**
- Form **tumors** and do not need growth factors to signal them to divide.
- Gradually become abnormal—**carcinogenesis** is comprised of initiation, promotion, and progression.
- Undergo **angiogenesis** (the growth of blood vessels to support them) and can spread throughout the body **(metastasis).**

Cancer Results from Gene Mutation

The cell cycle contains **checkpoints** regulated by proteins, such as cyclin. In normal cells, the cell cycle functions normally due to the action of two sets of genes.

- **Proto-oncogenes** promote cell cycle activity, often using **growth factors,** and restrain apoptosis. Proto-oncogenes can mutate into **oncogenes.**
- **Tumor suppressor genes** restrain the cell cycle and promote apoptosis.

In cancer cells, the cell cycle is accelerated and occurs repeatedly.

- **Oncogenes** cause an unrestrained cell cycle and prevent apoptosis.
- **Mutated tumor suppressor genes** cause an unrestrained cell cycle and prevent apoptosis.

Types of Cancer

Oncology is the study of cancer. Cancers are classified according to their places of origin.

- **Carcinomas** originate in epithelial tissues.
- **Sarcomas** originate in muscle and connective tissues.
- **Leukemias** originate in blood.
- **Lymphomas** originate in lymphoid tissue.

Certain body organs are more susceptible to cancer than others.

20.2 Causes and Prevention of Cancer

The development of cancer is determined by a person's genetic profile, plus exposure to environmental **mutagens** and **carcinogens.**

- Cancers that run in families are most likely due to the inheritance of mutated genes (e.g., breast cancer, retinoblastoma tumor).
- Certain environmental factors are carcinogens (e.g., UV radiation, tobacco smoke, pollutants).
- Industrial chemicals (e.g., pesticides and herbicides) are carcinogenic.
- Certain viruses (e.g., hepatitis B and C, human papillomavirus, and Epstein–Barr virus) cause specific cancers.

20.3 Diagnosis of Cancer

The earlier a cancer is diagnosed, the more likely it can be effectively treated. Tests for cancer include the following:

- Pap test for cervical cancer
- Mammogram for breast cancer
- Tumor marker tests, which are blood tests that detect tumor antigens/antibodies
- Tests for genetic mutations of oncogenes and tumor suppressor genes
- Biopsy and imaging—used to confirm the diagnosis of cancer

20.4 Treatment of Cancer

Surgery, radiation, and chemotherapy are traditional methods of treating cancer. Other methods include the following:

- Chemotherapy involving bone marrow transplants
- Immunotherapy
- *p53* gene therapy, which causes cancer cells to undergo apoptosis
- Other therapies, such as inhibitory drugs for angiogenesis and metastasis

ENGAGE

THINKING CRITICALLY

1. The vaccine for HPV is recommended for both females and males between the ages of 11 and 26. There is some controversy over this vaccine. Some believe vaccination for a sexually transmitted disease might lull young adults into a false sense of security regarding safety during sexual intercourse. Others fear that vaccination will encourage young adults to engage in sex.
   a. Why would the vaccine be recommended for anyone who may not be sexually active yet?
   b. What type of immunity would individuals develop from being vaccinated for HPV? You may need to revisit Chapter 7 on immunity to answer this question.
2. Why are lymph nodes surrounding a breast with an invasive cancer often removed when a mastectomy is performed?
3. Many types of cancer (ovarian cancer, for example) show no symptoms until they are well advanced. What might be the consequence for the patient?

MAKING IT RELEVANT

1. What are some healthy lifestyle choices you could make that might prevent cancer later in your life?
2. There are a number of cancer vaccines currently in clinical trials. Would you get a cancer vaccine if it were available? Why or why not?
3. Why do you think that some forms of cancer, such as brain cancer, are harder to treat and have a higher risk of death?

Find answers to all of the chapter questions at connect.mheducation.com

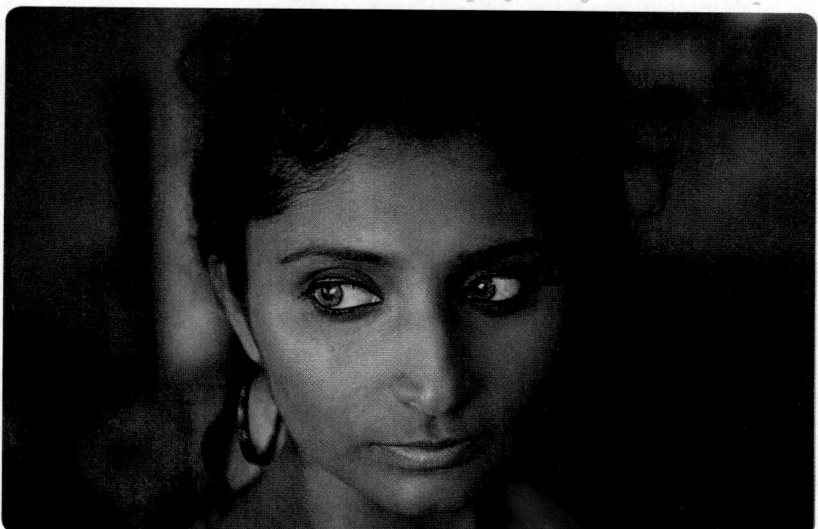
Deborah Kolb/Shutterstock

CHAPTER 21

Genetic Inheritance

Genetics of Eye Color

From an early age, we compare our eye color to those of our parents, friends, and people around us. We attempt to establish patterns to explain how we have inherited a certain eye color. However, as with many traits in humans, the real story is a little more complicated.

Eye color is determined by a gene called *OCA2*. Variations in this gene, and the interactions of up to 16 other genes, can influence whether your eyes are brown, green, hazel, or something in between. But what about blue eyes?

Blue eye color is a relatively recent development for humans. It is due to a mutation in a gene called *HERC2,* which controls the production of eye-color pigments. In some forms of *HERC2,* a mutation causes the gene to be inactive. You need only one copy of *HERC2* for *OCA2* to produce your eye color, but if both copies of *HERC2* are defective, the result is blue eyes, regardless of which *OCA2* gene you inherited.

This mutation first appears in northern Europe 6,000–7,000 years ago. Geneticists believe this may have occurred in a single individual, and then it spread across Europe and into other areas of Asia and North Africa. All blue-eyed people are thought to be able to trace their ancestry to this one human.

In this chapter, we will explore some of the fundamental principles associated with patterns of inheritance.

As you read through the chapter, think about the following questions:

1. How do both the environment and genetics influence genetic traits such as eye color?
2. What is the difference between an autosomal dominant and autosomal recessive pattern of inheritance?
3. How does meiosis help predict the probability of producing gametes and inheriting a trait?

CHAPTER OUTLINE

BEFORE YOU BEGIN

Before beginning this chapter, take a few moments to review the following discussions:

Section 2.7 What is the role of DNA in a cell?

Section 19.4 How is meiosis involved in sperm and egg production?

Section 19.4 How does meiosis produce new combinations of alleles?

21.1 Genotype and Phenotype

LEARNING OUTCOMES

Upon completion of this section, you should be able to

1. Distinguish between a genotype and a phenotype.
2. Define *allele, gene, dominant,* and *recessive* as they relate to patterns of inheritance.
3. Given the genotype of an individual, identify the phenotype.

The science of genetics explains the process of inheritance (why you are human, as are your parents) and also why there are variations between offspring from one generation to the next (why you have a different combination of traits than your parents). Virtually every culture in history has attempted to explain observed inheritance patterns. An understanding of these patterns has always been important to many aspects of human society, including agriculture, animal husbandry (the science of breeding animals), and medicine. In this section, we will explore some of the terminology associated with the study of genetics.

Genotype

The term **genotype** refers to the genes of an individual. Recall that **genes** are segments of DNA on a chromosome that code for a trait (or characteristic). These genes are the units of heredity. Each gene is located in a specific position, or **locus** (*pl.,* loci), on a chromosome. An **allele** is an alternate form of a gene. For example, if the trait the gene codes for is eye color, one allele contains the information that determines the blue eye color, while a different allele may result in brown eyes.

Alleles are often classified as being either dominant or recessive. In general, **dominant alleles** mask (hide) the expression of **recessive alleles.** Therefore, if an allele is dominant, only one copy of that allele needs to be present for that trait to appear (or be expressed). If an allele is recessive, both of the chromosomes must possess the recessive allele for it to be expressed in the individual.

The terms *dominant* and *recessive* do not indicate the prevalence (or frequency) of a trait in the population but, instead, what is happening in the cell at the level of gene expression. A dominant allele may be very rare in a population, and the recessive alleles may be the most prevalent.

Alleles are often designated by abbreviations. In many cases, a dominant allele is assigned an uppercase letter. The same letters, as lowercase, are used to indicate a recessive allele. In humans, for example, melanocytes in the skin produce pigmentation (see Section 4.7). Recessive mutation inhibits either the production of the pigmentation or its deposition into the skin cells, in either case producing albinism. A suitable key for these alleles is *A* for normal pigmentation and *a* for no pigmentation. Another example is cystic fibrosis, for which the dominant allele is designated *Cf* and the recessive allele *cf.*

For each pair of chromosomes, we receive one chromosome from each parent; therefore, we inherit one allele from each parent, resulting in a pair of alleles for each trait. Figure 21.1 shows three possible fertilization events between different alleles for the pigmentation trait and the resulting offspring of those fertilizations. In the first instance, the chromosomes of both the sperm and the egg carry the dominant trait, designated *A,* resulting in an individual with the alleles *AA.* This type of genotype is called **homozygous dominant.** In the second fertilization, the zygote has received two recessive alleles *(aa),* a genotype called **homozygous recessive.** In the third fertilization, the resulting individual has the alleles *Aa,* called a **heterozygous** genotype.

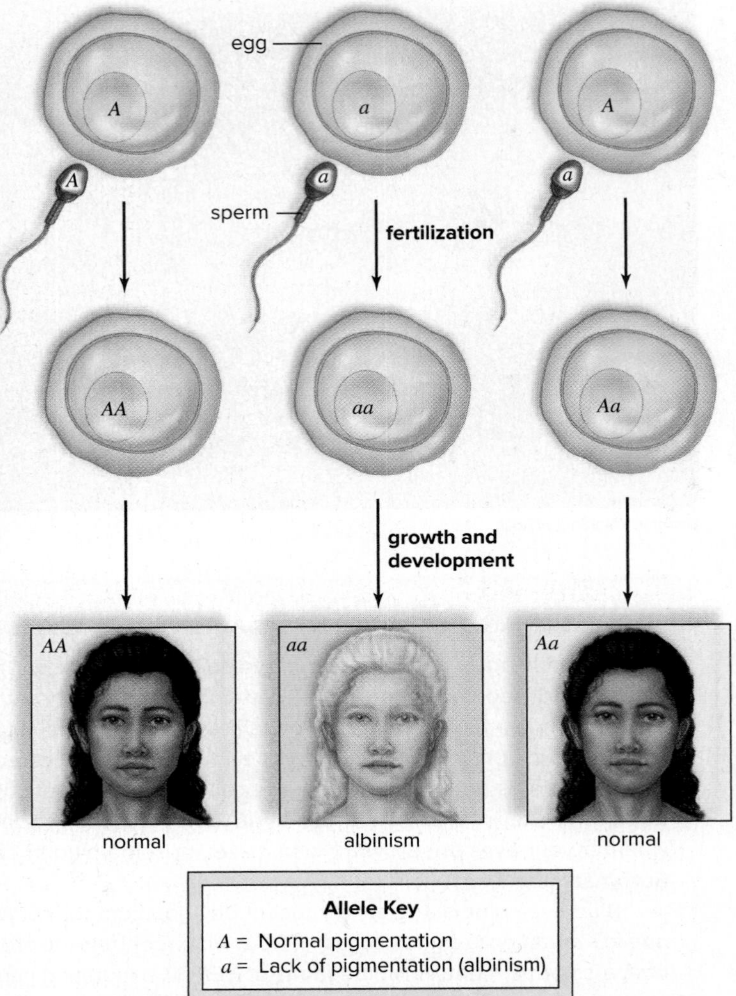

Figure 21.1 Genetic inheritance affects our characteristics. For each trait, we inherit one allele from each parent. Therefore, we possess two alleles for every trait. The inheritance of a single dominant allele (resulting in either *AA* or *Aa*) causes an individual to have normal pigmentation; two recessive alleles *(aa)* cause an individual to have albinism.

Phenotype

The physical appearance of a trait is called a phenotype. The phenotype is determined by the expression of the alleles in the genotype. Thus, we may generally state that the DNA determines the genotype and that proteins (gene products) determine the phenotype.

In Figure 21.1, the phenotypes are normal pigmentation (dominant phenotype) and no pigmentation (recessive phenotype). It is important to recognize that the genotype directs the phenotype of the individual. In most cases, the presence of a single dominant

BIOLOGY IN YOUR LIFE

Why are some alleles dominant to other alleles?

In a simple example, the dominant allele *(A)* codes for a particular protein. Let's assume this gene codes for an enzyme (protein) responsible for brown eye color. The recessive allele *(a)* is a mutated allele that no longer codes for the enzyme. At the molecular level, having the enzyme is dominant to lacking the enzyme. In other words, having brown in the eye is dominant over not having brown in the eye.

Using this example, a homozygous dominant individual *(AA)* may have twice the amount of enzyme as a heterozygous individual *(Aa)*. However, it may not be possible to detect a difference between homozygous and heterozygous, as long as there is enough enzyme to bring about the dominant phenotype. Half the amount of enzyme may still turn the eyes completely brown. Thus, a person with the genotype *Aa* would have eyes just as brown as a person with the genotype *AA*. A homozygous recessive individual *(aa)* makes no enzyme, so the brown phenotype is absent. Gene expression is discussed further in Section 22.2.

allele is all that is necessary to express the dominant phenotype (some exceptions are explained in Section 21.4). Notice that this is the case in the heterozygous individual *(Aa)* in Figure 21.1. A heterozygote shows the dominant phenotype, because the dominant allele needs only one copy to appear in the phenotype. Therefore, this individual has normal pigmentation. Homozygous recessive individuals *(aa)* have albinism, whereas homozygous dominant individuals *(AA)* have normal pigmentation.

From our example, you may get the impression that the phenotype has to be an easily observable trait. However, the phenotype can be any characteristic of the individual, including color blindness or a metabolic disorder, such as the lack of an enzyme to metabolize the amino acid phenylalanine.

CHECK YOUR PROGRESS 21.1

1. Define the following terms: *gene, allele, locus, chromosome, dominant,* and *recessive.*
2. Describe the difference between genotype and phenotype.
3. Summarize the three possible genotypes and their corresponding phenotypes.

CONNECTING THE CONCEPTS

The genotype of an individual is based on the information in the DNA of a person's cells. For more information on DNA, refer to the following discussions:

Sections 2.7 and **22.1** describe the basic structure of the DNA molecule.

Section 4.7 provides more information on the role of melanocytes in the skin.

Section 22.2 examines how the information in DNA is expressed as a protein.

21.2 One- and Two-Trait Inheritance

LEARNING OUTCOMES

Upon completion of this section, you should be able to

1. Understand how probability is involved in solving one- and two-trait crosses.
2. Calculate the probability of a specific genotype or phenotype in an offspring of a genetic cross.

A one-trait cross examines the patterns of inheritance of only a single set of alleles for a single characteristic. A two-trait cross explores the patterns of inheritance of the alleles for two different characteristics. For both types of crosses, it is first necessary to determine the gametes of both of the parents in the cross.

Forming the Gametes

During meiosis, the chromosome number of the cells that will form the gametes (egg and sperm) is divided in half (see Section 19.4). This is accomplished by the separation of homologous chromosomes. Each individual has 46 chromosomes, arranged as 23 homologous pairs. For each pair, one of the homologous chromosomes was originally from the mother, and the other was donated by the father. During meiosis, the homologous chromosomes, and the alleles they contain, are separated. Therefore, the sperm or egg has only 23 chromosomes. If reduction of the chromosome number did not occur, the new individual would have twice as many chromosomes after fertilization, which would not result in a viable embryo.

For example, let's say the gene for pigmentation is on a particular chromosome. On the homologous chromosome originally from the mother, the allele is for normal pigmentation *(A)*. On the father's paired chromosome, the allele is also an *A*. Therefore, *A* is the only option for alleles on either chromosome, so every gamete formed by this individual will carry an *A*. This occurs whether the gamete gets the mother's or the father's original chromosome. Similarly, if the homologous chromosome originally from the mother carries the recessive allele for pigmentation *(a)* and the father's chromosome also bears an *a,* then all gametes will have the *a* allele. However, if the individual is heterozygous, the combination of alleles may be different. For example, the mother's homologous chromosome may have the *A* allele, while the father's has an *a.* If this is the case, then half of the gametes formed will receive an *A* allele from the mother's homologue. The other half will get the father's homologue with the *a.*

Figure 21.2 shows the genotypes and phenotypes for a couple of observable traits in humans that have simple dominant and recessive relationships between the alleles. Although many different alleles control finger length, a dominant allele *(S)* produces a condition called brachydactyly, or shortened fingers. There are also many factors that influence freckles, but a dominant allele *(F)* causes widespread freckling patterns on the body.

One-Trait Crosses

Often, individuals may like to know the chances of having a child with a certain genotype and, therefore, a certain phenotype. To illustrate, consider a cross involving freckles. What happens when

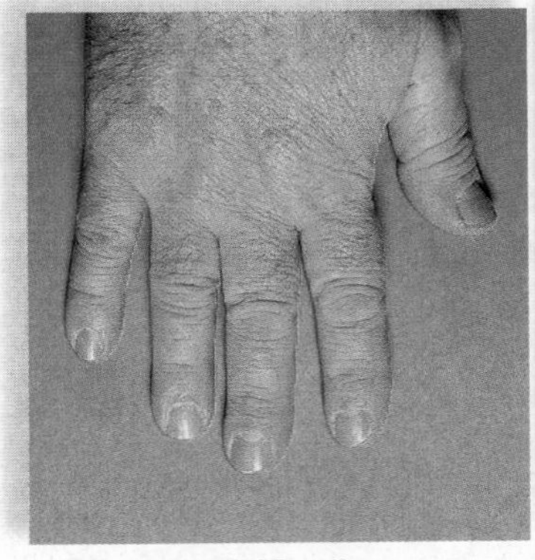

a. Short fingers: *SS* or *Ss*

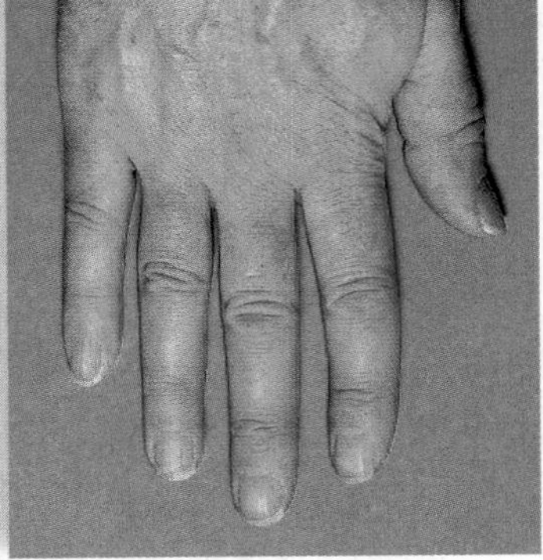

b. Long fingers: *ss*

c. Freckles: *FF* or *Ff*

d. No freckles: *ff*

Figure 21.2 Examples of dominant and recessive traits.
The allele for short fingers (brachydactyly) is dominant to long fingers. The allele for freckles is dominant to no freckles.
(a, b): Bob Coyle/McGraw Hill; (c): BananaStock/age fotostock; (d): BDLM/Cultura/Getty Images

two parents without freckles have children? Will the children of this couple have freckles? In solving the problem, we will (1) use *F* to indicate the dominant allele for freckles and use *f* to indicate the recessive allele of no freckles; (2) determine the possible gametes for each parent; (3) combine all possible gametes; and (4) finally, determine the genotypes and phenotypes of all the offspring. If both parents do not have freckles, then their genotypes are both *ff*. The only gametes they can produce contain the *f* allele. All the children will therefore be *ff* and will not have freckles. In the following diagram, the letters indicate the genotypes of the parents. Each parent has only one type of gamete with regard to freckles; therefore, all the children have a similar genotype and phenotype.

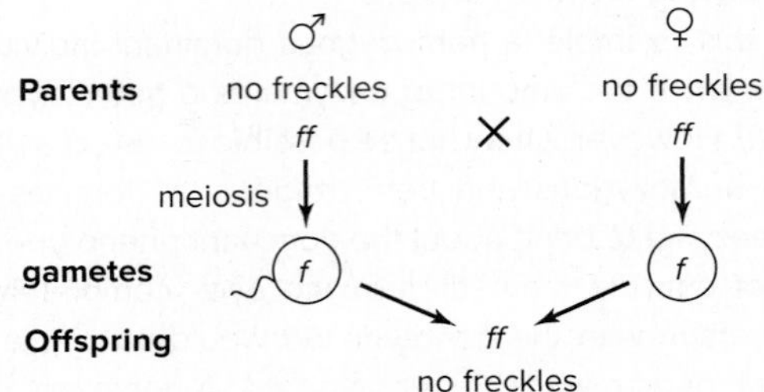

BIOLOGY IN YOUR LIFE

Aren't traits such as earlobe shape and dimples due to dominant and recessive alleles?

For a considerable amount of time, geneticists thought traits such as earlobe shape (attached or unattached), the shape of the hairline (widow's peak), and the presence of dimples were examples of simple dominant and recessive inheritance. However, as we learn more about the 20,000 or so genes that make us human, we have discovered that these traits are actually under the control of multiple genes. These interactions complicate the expression of the phenotype, and thus they are not good examples of simple dominant and recessive allele combinations.

Let's also consider the results when a homozygous dominant man with freckles has children with a woman with no freckles. Will the children of this couple have freckles? The children are heterozygous (*Ff*) and have freckles. When writing a heterozygous genotype, always put the capital letter (for the dominant allele) first to avoid confusion.

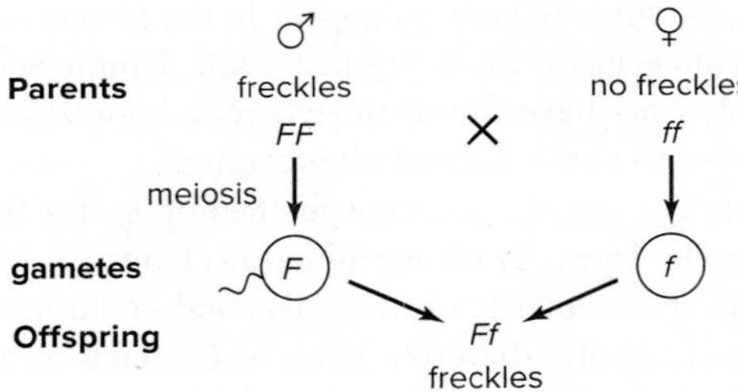

A one-trait cross is often referred to as a **monohybrid cross,** because it involves a cross between two individuals who are heterozygous for a single trait. Notice that in this example the children are heterozygous with regard to one pair of alleles. If these individuals reproduce with someone else of the same genotype, will their children have freckles? In this problem (*Ff* × *Ff*), each parent has two possible types of gametes (*F* or *f*), and we must ensure that all types of sperm have an equal chance to fertilize all possible types of eggs. One way to do this is to use a **Punnett square** (Fig. 21.3), in which all possible alleles that may be found in the sperm are lined up vertically, and all possible alleles for the eggs are lined up horizontally (or vice versa). Every possible combination of gametes occurs within the squares.

After we determine the genotypes and the phenotypes of the offspring, we can determine both the genotypic and phenotypic ratios. The genotypic ratio is 1 *FF*: 2 *Ff*: 1 *ff* or simply 1:2:1, but the phenotypic ratio is 3 freckles to 1 non-freckles, or 3:1. This is because there are three possibilities for freckles (the *FF* and the two *Ff*) and one for not having freckles (the *ff*).

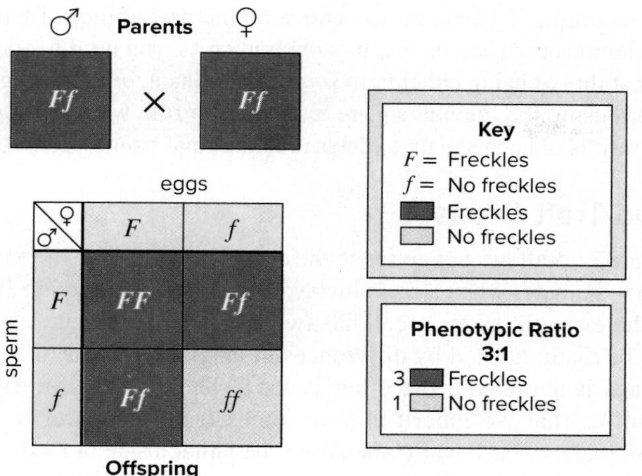

Figure 21.3 **Expected results of a monohybrid cross.** A Punnett square diagrams the results of a cross. When the parents are heterozygous, each child has a 75% chance of having the dominant phenotype and a 25% chance of having the recessive phenotype.

BIOLOGY IN YOUR LIFE

Why is it called a Punnett square?

The Punnett square was first proposed by the English geneticist Reginald Punnett. Punnett first used the diagram as a teaching tool to explain basic patterns of inheritance to his introductory genetics classes in 1909. This teaching tool has remained basically unchanged for over 100 years!

Punnett squares are useful for visualizing crosses that involve one or two traits, but they quickly become cumbersome with complex traits involving many different factors. Most geneticists rely on statistical analysis to predict the outcomes of complex crosses.

This 3:1 phenotypic ratio is always expected for a monohybrid cross between two heterozygous individuals when one allele is completely dominant over the other. The exact ratio is more likely to be observed if a large number of matings take place and if a large number of offspring result. Only then do we have the chance of seeing the results of all possible types of sperm fertilizing all possible types of eggs. Naturally, we do not routinely observe hundreds of offspring from a single type of cross in humans. The best interpretation of Figure 21.3 in humans is to say that each child has three chances out of four to have freckles, or one chance out of four to not have freckles.

Every fertilization has exactly the same chance for allele combinations as the previous fertilization. For example, if two heterozygous parents already have three children with freckles and are expecting a fourth child, this child still has a 75% chance of having freckles and a 25% chance of not having freckles, just as each of the child's siblings did. The chance of achieving a new phenotype not previously shown does not increase with each fertilization; it stays exactly the same with every fertilization. Every new fertilization is not influenced by any previous fertilizations. Each one is considered an individual occurrence, each time subject to the probabilities of the gametes of the parents.

Determining If the Genotype Is Heterozygous or Homozygous Dominant

It is not possible to tell by inspection if a person expressing a dominant allele is homozygous dominant or heterozygous. However, it is sometimes possible to tell by the results of a cross. For example, Figure 21.4 shows two possible results when a man with freckles reproduces with a woman who does not have freckles. If the man is homozygous dominant, all his children will have freckles. If the man is heterozygous, each child has a 50% chance of having freckles. The birth of just one child without freckles indicates that the man is heterozygous.

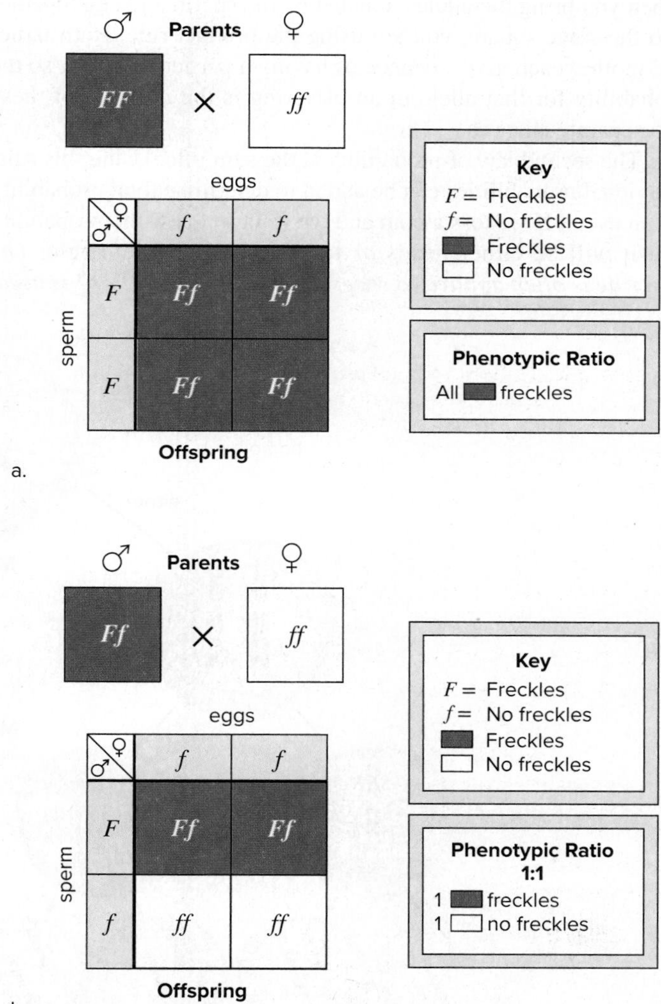

Figure 21.4 **Determining if a dominant phenotype is homozygous or heterozygous.** The offspring of a monohybrid cross indicates if an individual with a dominant phenotype is homozygous or heterozygous. **a.** All offspring show the dominant characteristic, so the individual is most likely homozygous, as shown. **b.** The offspring show a 1:1 phenotypic ratio, so the individual is heterozygous, as shown.

The Punnett Square and Probability

Two laws of probability apply to the study of genetics. Probabilities range from 0.0 (0%, or an event that will not happen) to 1.0 (100%, or an event that will always happen). The first is the product rule. According to this rule, the chance of two different events occurring simultaneously is equal to the multiplied probabilities of each event occurring separately. For example, what is the probability that a coin toss will be "heads"? There are only two options, so the probability of "heads" is 1 out of 2, or 50% (0.50). If we wanted to know what the probability was of a first coin toss being "heads" *and* a second coin toss being "heads," we would use the product rule. *The product rule is often applied to cases in which the word "and" is used.* This would be ½ × ½ = ¼, or 25% (0.25).

The Punnett square allows you to determine the probability that an offspring will have a particular genotype or phenotype. When you bring the alleles donated by the sperm and egg together into the same square, you are using the product rule. Both father and mother each give a chance of having a particular allele, so the probability for that allele in an offspring is the multiple of these two separate chances.

The second law of probability is the sum rule. Using this rule, individual probabilities can be added to determine total probability for an event. If we toss a coin and we want to know the probability that it will be either heads *or* tails, we use the sum rule. *The sum rule is often applied to cases in which the word "or" is used.* For example, if you want to determine the probability of having the dominant phenotype in a monohybrid cross, you need to add the probability of being either homozygous dominant, *or* heterozygous. When using the Punnett square, use the sum rule when adding up the results of each square to determine the final phenotypic ratio.

Two-Trait Crosses

Figure 21.5 allows you to relate the events of meiosis to the formation of gametes when a cross involves two traits (see Section 19.4). In the example given, a cell has two pairs of homologues, which can be distinguished by differences in length. One pair of homologues is short, and the other is long. The color in the figure signifies that we inherit chromosomes from our parents. One homologue of each pair comes from the father's side of the family, and is referred to as the "paternal" chromosome. The chromosome coming from the mother's side of the family is referred to as the "maternal" chromosome.

The homologues separate during meiosis I (see Section 19.4), so each gamete receives one member from each pair of homologues. The homologues separate independently, so it does not matter which member of a pair goes into which gamete. All possible combinations of alleles occur in the gametes. In the simplest of terms, a gamete in Figure 21.5 will *receive one short and one long chromosome of either color.* Therefore, all possible combinations of chromosomes and alleles are in the gametes.

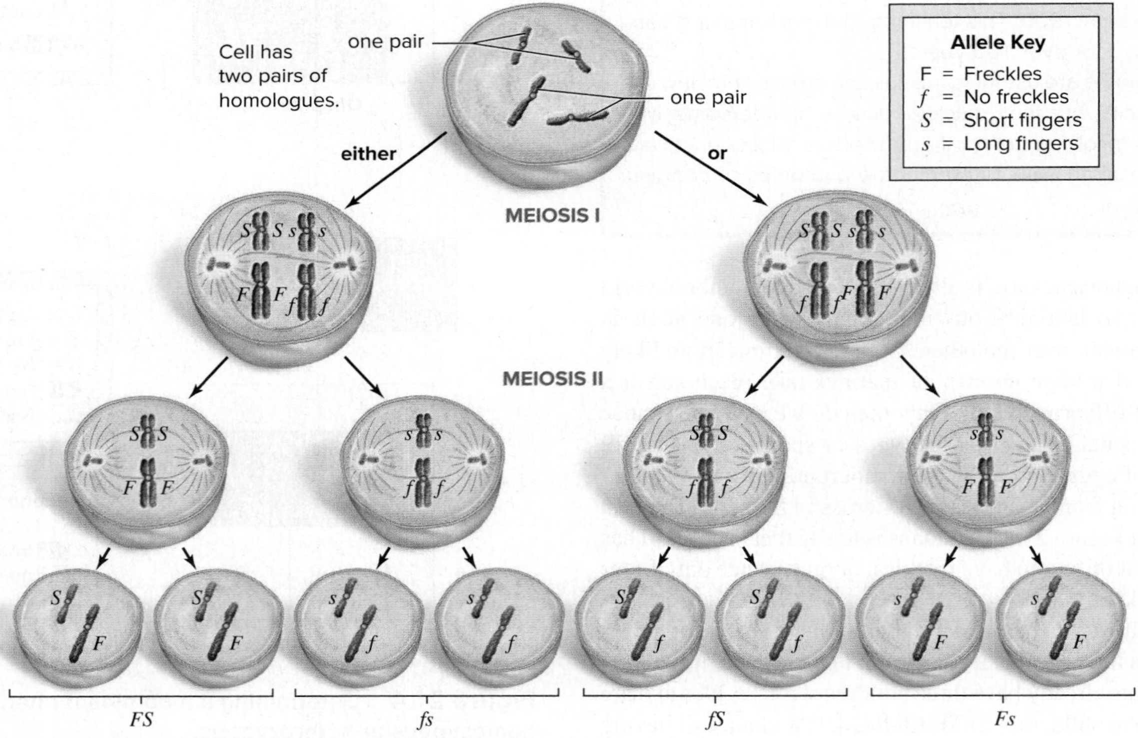

Figure 21.5 Meiosis results in genetic diversity of gametes.
A cell has two pairs of homologous chromosomes (homologues), recognized by length, not color. The long pair of homologues carries alleles for freckles, and the short pair of homologues carries alleles for finger length. The homologues, and the alleles they carry, align independently during meiosis. Therefore, all possible combinations of chromosomes and alleles occur in the gametes, as shown in the last row of cells.

Specifically, assume that the alleles for two genes are on these homologues. The alleles *S* and *s* are on one pair of homologues, and the alleles *F* and *f* are on the other pair of homologues. The homologues separate, so a gamete will have either an *S* or an *s* and either an *F* or an *f*. They will never have two of the same letter. Also, because the homologues align independently at the equator, either the paternal or maternal chromosome of each pair can face either pole.

Therefore, there are no restrictions as to which homologue goes into which gamete. A gamete can receive either an *S* or an *s* and either an *F* or an *f* in any combination. In the end, the gametes will collectively have all possible combinations of alleles. You should be able to transfer this information to any cross that involves two traits. In other words, the process of meiosis explains why a person with the genotype *FfSs* would produce the gametes *FS, fs, Fs,* and *fS* in equal number.

The Dihybrid Cross

In the two-trait cross depicted in Figure 21.6, a person homozygous for freckles and short fingers *(FFSS)* reproduces with one who has no freckles and long fingers *(ffss)*. Because this cross involves two traits, it is also referred to as a **dihybrid cross.** In this example, the gametes for the *FFSS* parent must be *FS* and the gametes for the *ffss* parent must be *fs*. Therefore, the offspring will all have the genotype *FfSs* and the same phenotype (freckles and short fingers). This genotype is called a dihybrid because the individual is heterozygous in two regards: presence of freckles and finger length.

When a dihybrid *FfSs* has children with another dihybrid who is *FfSs,* what gametes are possible? Each gamete can have only one letter of each type in all possible combinations. Therefore, these are the gametes for both dihybrids: *FS, Fs, fS,* and *fs*.

A Punnett square makes sure that all possible sperm fertilize all possible eggs. If so, these are the expected phenotypic results:

- 9 freckles and short fingers
- 3 freckles and long fingers
- 3 no freckles and short fingers
- 1 no freckles and long fingers

This 9:3:3:1 phenotypic ratio is always expected for a dihybrid cross when simple dominance is present. We can use this expected ratio to predict the chances of each child receiving a certain phenotype. For example, the chance of getting the two dominant phenotypes together is 9 out of 16. The chance of getting the two recessive phenotypes together is 1 out of 16.

Two-Trait Crosses and Probability

It is also possible to use the rules of probability discussed earlier to predict the results of a dihybrid cross. For example, we know the probable results for two separate monohybrid crosses are as follows:

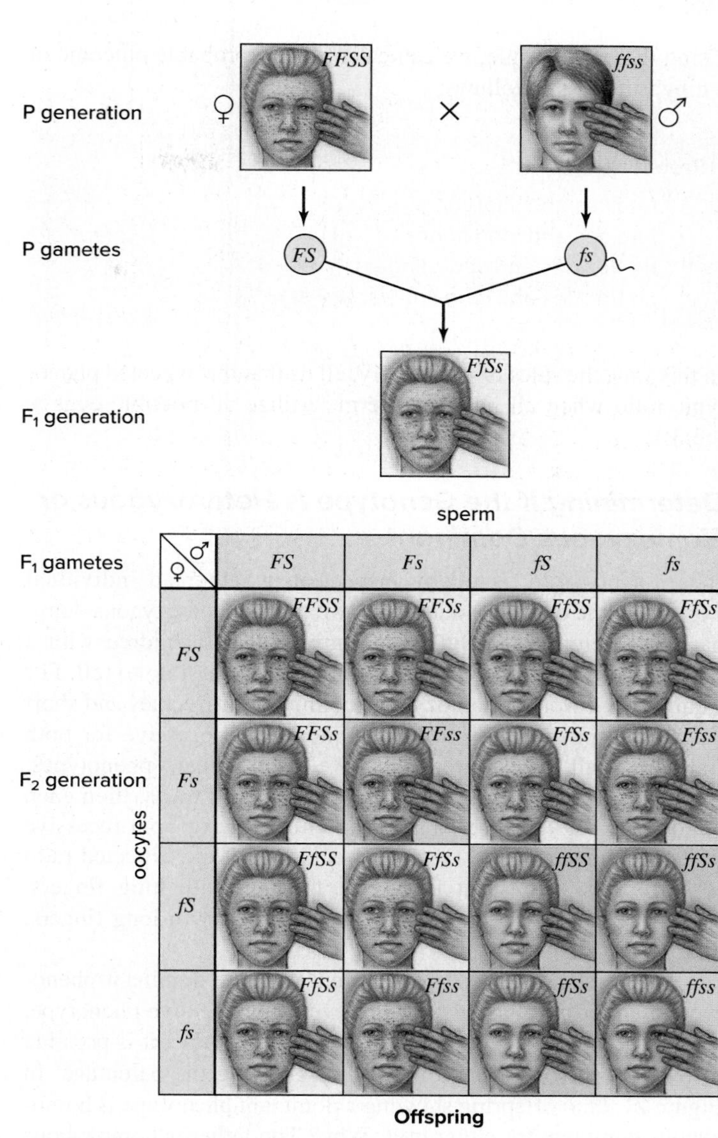

Figure 21.6 Expected results of a dihybrid cross. Each dihybrid can form four possible types of gametes, so four different phenotypes occur among the offspring in the proportions shown.

For freckles

- probability of freckles = ¾
- probability of no freckles = ¼

For finger length

- probability of short fingers = ¾
- probability of long fingers = ¼

Using the product rule, we can calculate the probable outcome of a dihybrid cross as follows:

Probability of:

- freckles and short fingers: $3/4 \times 3/4 = 9/16$
- freckles and long fingers: $3/4 \times 1/4 = 3/16$
- no freckles and short fingers: $1/4 \times 3/4 = 3/16$
- no freckles and long fingers: $1/4 \times 1/4 = 1/16$

In this way, the rules of probability tell us that the expected phenotypic ratio when all possible sperm fertilize all possible eggs is 9:3:3:1.

Determining If the Genotype Is Heterozygous or Homozygous Dominant

It is not possible to tell by inspection whether an individual expressing the dominant alleles for two traits is homozygous dominant or heterozygous. But if the individual has children with a homozygous recessive individual, it may be possible to tell. For example, if a woman homozygous dominant for freckles and short fingers reproduces with a male homozygous recessive for both traits, then all the children will have the dominant phenotypes. However, if a woman is heterozygous for both traits, then each child has a 75% chance of showing either one or both recessive traits. A Punnett square (Fig. 21.7) shows that the expected ratio is 1 freckles with short fingers: 1 freckles with long fingers: 1 no freckles with short fingers: 1 no freckles with long fingers, or 1:1:1:1.

For practical purposes, if a parent with the dominant phenotype in either trait has an offspring with the recessive phenotype, the parent has to be heterozygous for that trait. Also, it is possible to tell if a person is heterozygous by knowing the parentage. In Figure 21.7, no offspring showing a dominant phenotype is homozygous dominant for either trait. Why? The father is homozygous recessive for that trait.

Table 21.1 gives the phenotypic results for certain crosses we have been studying. These crosses always give these phenotypic results. Therefore, it is not necessary to do a Punnett square to arrive at the results. To facilitate doing crosses, study Table 21.1 so you can understand why these are the results expected for these crosses.

Table 21.1 Phenotypic Ratios of Common Crosses

Genotypes	Phenotypes
Monohybrid *Aa* × monohybrid *Aa*	3:1 (dominant to recessive)
Monohybrid *Aa* × recessive *aa*	1:1 (dominant to recessive)
Dihybrid *AaBb* × dihybrid *AaBb*	9:3:3:1 (9 both dominant: 3 dominant for one of the traits: 3 dominant for other trait: 1 both recessive)
Dihybrid *AaBb* × recessive *aabb*	1:1:1:1 (all possible combinations in equal number)

Parents

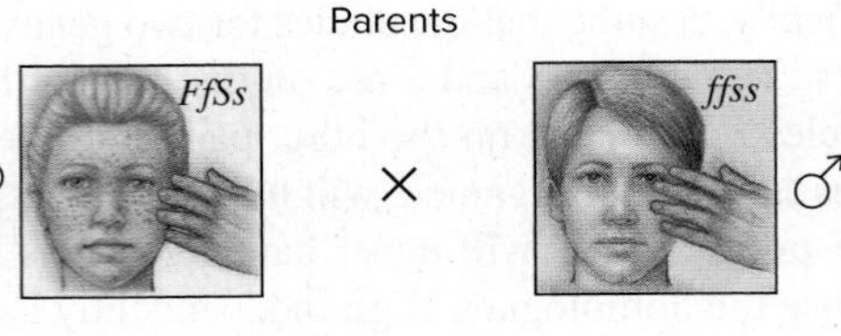

sperm

eggs

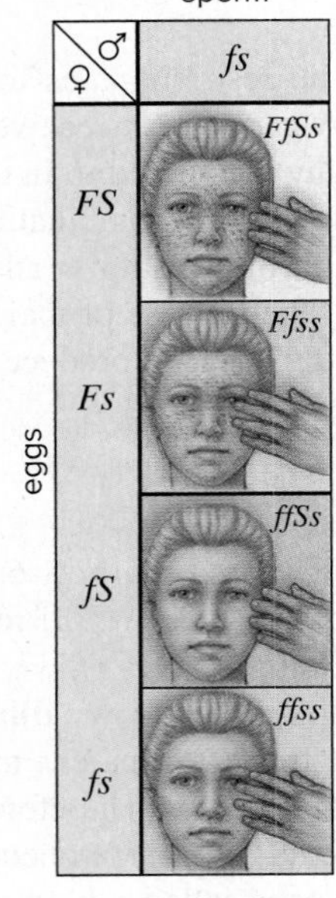

Offspring

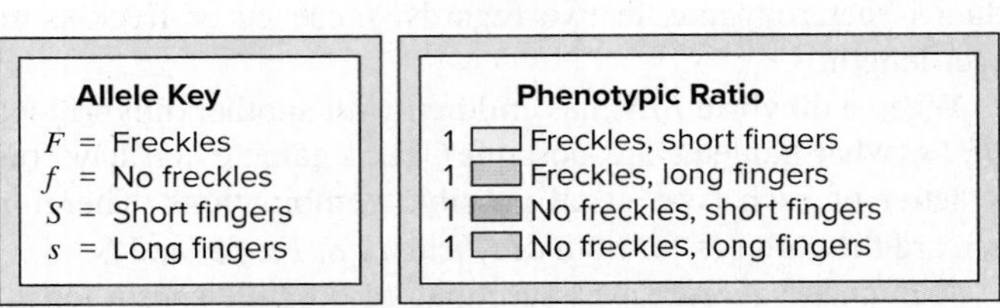

Figure 21.7 Determining if an individual is homozygous dominant or heterozygous. The results of this cross indicate that the individual with the dominant phenotypes is heterozygous for both traits, because some of the children are homozygous recessive for one or both traits. The chance of receiving any one possible phenotype is 25%.

CHECK YOUR PROGRESS 21.2

1. Explain how the results of a dihybrid cross are related to the events of meiosis.
2. Predict what genotype the children will have if one parent is homozygous recessive for no freckles and homozygous dominant for short finger length *(ffSS)* and the other parent is homozygous dominant for freckles and homozygous recessive for long fingers *(FFss)*.
3. Using a dihybrid cross as an example (see Fig. 21.6), explain how the gametes are formed by the process of meiosis.

CONNECTING THE CONCEPTS

For more information on the relationship between meiosis and patterns of inheritance, refer to the following discussions:

Section 17.2 explains gamete production in males.

Section 17.3 explores the process of gamete formation in females.

Section 19.4 describes how meiosis introduces genetic variation.

21.3 Inheritance of Genetic Disorders

LEARNING OUTCOMES

Upon completion of this section, you should be able to

1. Interpret a human pedigree to identify the pattern of inheritance for a trait.
2. Understand the genetic basis of select human autosomal dominant and autosomal recessive genetic disorders.

We inherit many different traits from our parents—not only our hair and eye color but also traits for diseases and disorders. Many of these diseases occur as a result of changes, or mutations, in our parents' genetic codes. The abnormal gene could be present in each of your parents' cells and thus passed down in the sperm or egg. Your parent may or may not have been affected by this genetic mutation. Alternatively, the genetic mutation might have occurred only in the sperm or egg that became a part of you. Some genetic diseases require two damaged alleles for the disease to manifest itself. Others need only one.

For example, for an autosomal dominant genetic disorder (represented by the allele *A*) an individual with the genotypes of *AA* or *Aa* will have the disorder. When a genetic disorder is autosomal recessive, only individuals with the genotype *aa* will have the disorder. Genetic counselors often construct pedigrees to determine whether a condition that runs in the family is dominant or recessive. A pedigree shows the pattern of inheritance for a particular condition. Consider these two possible patterns of inheritance:

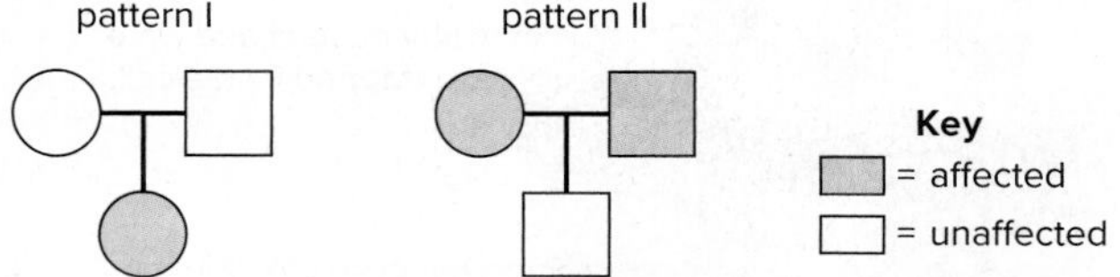

In both patterns, males are designated by squares and females by circles. Shaded circles and squares are individuals who are affected. A line between a square and a circle represents a mating. A vertical line going downward leads, in these patterns, to a single child. If there are more children, they are placed off a horizontal line. In the next sections, we will explore which of these patterns represents an autosomal recessive pattern, and which represents an autosomal dominant pattern.

Autosomal Recessive Patterns of Inheritance

In pattern I, the child is affected but neither parent is. This can happen if the condition is recessive and the parents are *Aa*. The parents are **carriers** because they carry the recessive trait in their DNA but their phenotype is dominant. Figure 21.8 shows a typical pedigree chart for a recessive genetic disorder. Other ways to recognize an autosomal recessive pattern of inheritance are also listed in the figure. If both parents are affected, all the children are affected. Why? The parents can pass on only recessive alleles for this condition. All children will be homozygous recessive, just like the parents.

Autosomal Dominant Pattern of Inheritance

In pattern II, the child is unaffected but the parents are affected. Of the two patterns, this one shows a dominant pattern of inheritance. The condition is dominant, so the parents can be *Aa* (heterozygous). The child inherited a recessive allele from each parent and, therefore, is unaffected. Figure 21.9 shows a typical pedigree for a dominant disorder. Other ways to recognize an autosomal dominant pattern of inheritance are also listed. When a disorder is dominant, an affected child must have at least one affected parent.

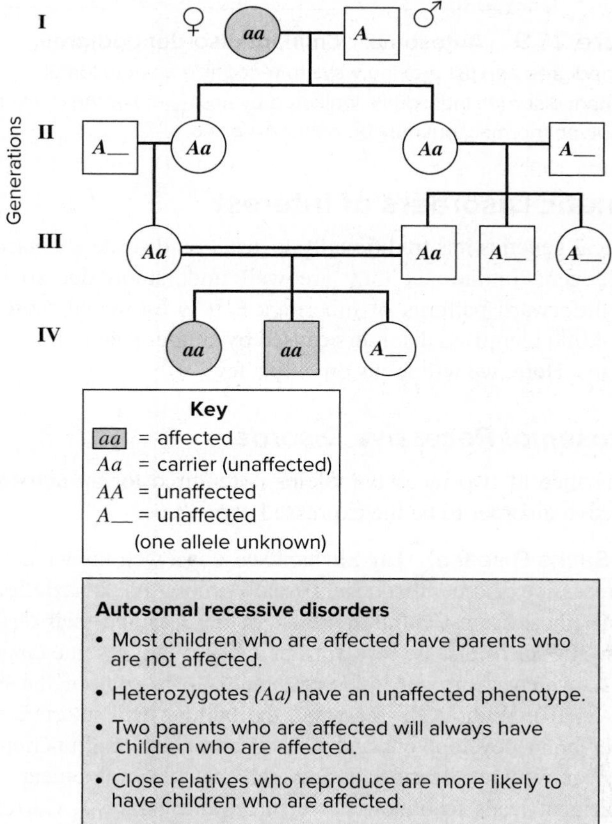

Autosomal recessive disorders

- Most children who are affected have parents who are not affected.
- Heterozygotes (*Aa*) have an unaffected phenotype.
- Two parents who are affected will always have children who are affected.
- Close relatives who reproduce are more likely to have children who are affected.

Figure 21.8 Autosomal recessive disorder pedigree. This pedigree and list provide ways to recognize an autosomal recessive disorder. Individuals indicated by an *A*__ have the dominant phenotype (normal), but may be either *AA* or *Aa*.

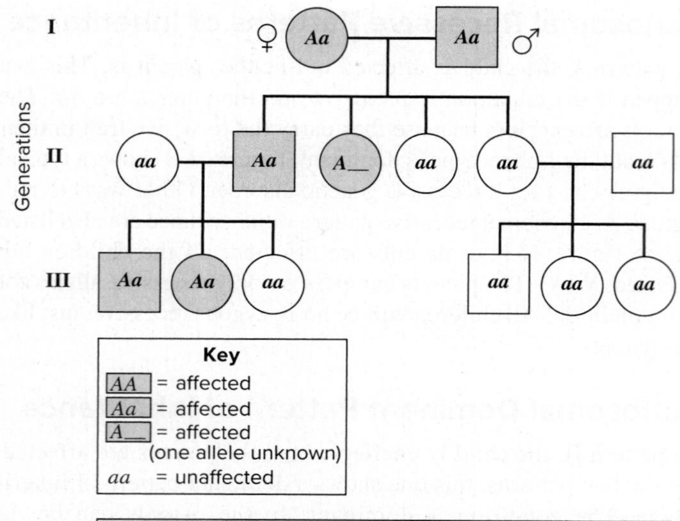

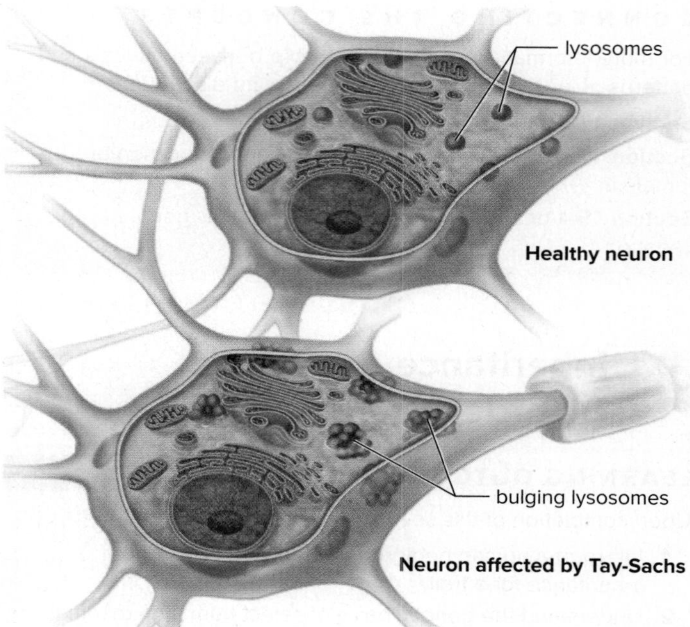

Figure 21.10 Neuron affected by Tay-Sachs disease.
In Tay-Sachs disease, a lysosomal enzyme is missing. This causes the substrate of that enzyme to accumulate within the lysosomes.

Autosomal dominant disorders

- Children who are affected will usually have a parent who is affected.
- Heterozygotes *(Aa)* are affected.
- Two parents who are affected can produce a child who is not affected.
- Two parents who are unaffected will not have children who are affected.
- Both males and females are affected with equal frequency.

Figure 21.9 Autosomal dominant disorder pedigree.
This pedigree and list provide ways to recognize an autosomal dominant disorder. Individuals indicated by an *A*__ have the dominant phenotype (normal), but may be either *AA* or *Aa*.

Genetic Disorders of Interest

Medical genetics has traditionally focused on disorders caused by single gene mutations; they are well understood due to their straightforward patterns of inheritance. It is estimated there are over 4,000 identified disorders caused by single-gene mutations in humans. Here, we will focus on only a few.

Autosomal Recessive Disorders

Inheritance of two recessive alleles is required for an autosomal recessive disorder to be the expressed phenotype.

Tay-Sachs Disease **Tay-Sachs disease** is a well-known autosomal recessive disorder that occurs usually among Ashkenazic Jewish people (those from Central and Eastern Europe) and their descendants. Tay-Sachs disease results from a lack of a lysosome enzyme, hex A, which clears out lipids that build up in cells of the brain (Fig. 21.10). Without this enzyme, the buildup will interfere with proper brain development and growth and cause malfunctions in vision, movement, hearing, and overall mental development. This impairment leads to blindness, seizures, and paralysis. Currently, there is no cure for Tay-Sachs disease; children who are affected normally die by the age of 5.

Cystic Fibrosis **Cystic fibrosis (CF)** is an autosomal recessive disorder that occurs among all ethnic groups but is most prevalent in whites. Cystic fibrosis is caused by a defective chloride ion channel that is encoded by the *c*ystic *f*ibrosis conductance *t*ransmembrane *r*egulator *(CFTR)* allele on chromosome 7. It is estimated that 1 in 29 whites in the United States carries this allele. Research has demonstrated that chloride ions (Cl^-) fail to pass through the defective version of the *CFTR* chloride ion channel (Fig. 21.11), which is located on the plasma membrane. Ordinarily, after chloride ions have passed through the channel to the other side of the membrane, sodium ions (Na^+) and water follow. It is believed that lack of water is the cause of the abnormally thick mucus in the bronchial tubes and pancreatic ducts.

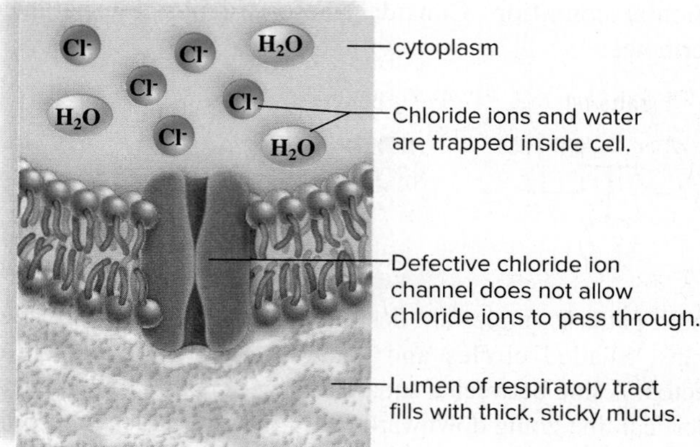

Figure 21.11 Cystic fibrosis disease.
Cystic fibrosis is due to a faulty protein that is supposed to regulate the flow of chloride ions into and out of cells through a channel protein.

By understanding the genetic basis of this disease, scientists have been able to develop treatments that have raised the average life expectancy for individuals with CF to as much as 35 years of age. Gene therapy (see Section 22.4) has also been successful in treating some forms of CF. Research has indicated that the mutated *CFTR* allele has persisted in the human population as a means of surviving the risk of potentially fatal diseases, such as cholera.

Sickle-Cell Disease **Sickle-cell disease** is an autosomal recessive disorder in which the red blood cells are not biconcave disks like normal red blood cells. Many are sickle- or boomerang-shaped, and these red blood cells live for only about 2 weeks, unlike the average 4-month life span of a normal red blood cell. The defect is caused by abnormal hemoglobin that differs from normal hemoglobin by one amino acid in the protein globin. The single amino acid change causes hemoglobin molecules to stack up and form insoluble rods. This causes the red blood cells to become sickle-shaped (see Section 6.2). This single gene defect can affect any race but is prevalent among African Americans. It is estimated that 1 in every 625 African Americans is affected by sickle-cell disease.

Sickle-shaped cells can't pass along narrow capillary passageways as disk-shaped cells can, so they clog the vessels, preventing adequate circulation. This results in anemia, tissue damage, jaundice, joint pain, and gallstones. Those affected by sickle-cell disease are also susceptible to many types of bacterial infections and have a higher incidence of stroke. Many treatment options, including blood transfusions and bone marrow transplants, are highly effective. The most common medicinal treatment, hydroxyurea, has been on the market for several decades and is considered one of the most effective daily treatments for the reduction in sickle-cell-related anemia, joint pain, and tissue damage.

Variations in the sickle-cell gene enable heterozygous individuals to express variations of the recessive phenotype. Heterozygous individuals for this disease have sickle-cell traits in which the blood cells are normal unless they experience dehydration or mild oxygen deprivation. Intense exertion may cause sickling of some red blood cells for a short period of time. These patients can experience episodes and symptoms very similar to those of patients with the autosomal recessive genotype.

Autosomal Dominant Disorders

Inheritance of only one dominant allele is necessary for an autosomal dominant genetic disorder to be displayed. Here, we discuss just a few of the known autosomal dominant disorders.

Marfan Syndrome The autosomal dominant disorder **Marfan syndrome** is caused by a defect in the production of an elastic connective tissue protein called fibrillin. This protein is normally abundant in the lens of the eye; the bones of limbs, fingers, and ribs; and the wall of the aorta and the blood vessels. This explains why a person with Marfan syndrome often has a dislocated lens, long limbs and fingers, and a caved-in chest. The wall of the aorta is weak and can burst without warning. Marfan syndrome is considered a "rare" disorder, currently affecting less than 200,000 people in the United States, or less than 1 in every 2,000 individuals. Treatments for Marfan syndrome include beta-blockers to control the cardiovascular symptoms, corrective lenses or eye surgery, and braces or orthopedic surgery for musculoskeletal symptoms.

Osteogenesis Imperfecta **Osteogenesis imperfecta** is an autosomal dominant genetic disorder that results in weakened, brittle bones. Although at least nine types of the disorder are known, most are linked to mutations in two genes necessary to the synthesis of a type I collagen—one of the most abundant proteins in the human body. Collagen has many roles, including providing strength and rigidity to bone and forming the framework for most of the body's tissues. Because the mutant collagen can cause structural defects even when combined with normal collagen I, osteogenesis imperfecta is generally considered to be dominant.

Osteogenesis imperfecta, which has an incidence of approximately 1 in 5,000 live births, affects all racial groups similarly and there have been documented cases for the last 300 years. Some historians think that the Viking chieftain Ivar Ragnarsson, who was known as Ivar the Boneless and was often carried into battle on a shield, had this condition. In most cases, the diagnosis is made in young children who visit the emergency room frequently due to broken bones. Some children with the disorder have an unusual blue tint in the sclera, the white portion of the eye; reduced skin elasticity; weakened teeth; and heart valve abnormalities. The disorder is treatable with a number of drugs that help increase bone mass, but these drugs must be taken long-term.

Huntington's Disease An autosomal dominant neurological disorder that leads to progressive degeneration of brain cells (Fig. 21.12), **Huntington's disease** is caused by a mutated copy of the gene for a protein called huntingtin. The defective gene contains segments of DNA in which the base sequence CAG repeats again and again. This type of structure, called a trinucleotide repeat, causes the huntingtin protein to have too many copies of the amino acid glutamine. The normal version of the huntingtin protein has stretches of between 10 and 25 glutamic acids. If the huntingtin protein has more than 36 glutamic acids, as is coded for in the mutated Huntington's gene,

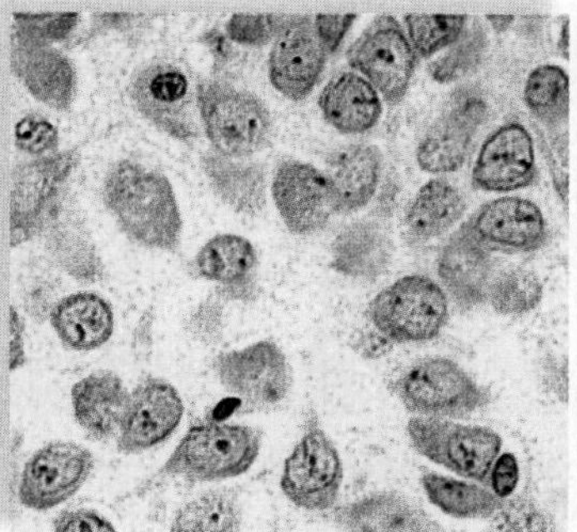

many neurons in normal brain

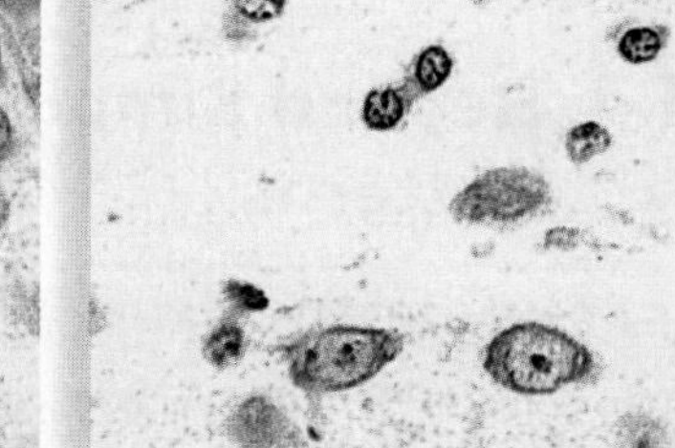

loss of neurons in Huntington's brain

Figure 21.12 **Huntington's disease.**
Huntington's disease is caused by a loss of nerve cells.
(both): ©Dr. Hemachandra Reddy, The Neurological Science Institute, Oregon Health & Science University

it changes shape and forms clumps inside neurons. These clumps attract other proteins to clump, rendering them inactive. One of these proteins that attaches itself to the clumps, called CBP, helps nerve cells survive.

The onset of symptoms for Huntington's disease is normally not seen until later in life (average age of onset is late thirties to late forties), although it is not unusual for a person with Huntington's disease to develop symptoms as early as their late teens. Huntington's disease has a range of symptoms but is normally characterized by uncontrolled movements, unsteady gait, dementia, and speech impairment. On average, patients live 15 to 20 years after the onset of symptoms, because the disease progresses rapidly. Current effective treatments include medications that slow the progression of the disease. Additionally, dopamine blockers have been found to be very effective in reducing uncontrolled movements and improving eye-hand coordination and steadiness during walking.

CHECK YOUR PROGRESS 21.3

1. Solve the following: In a pedigree, all the members of one family are affected. Based on this knowledge, list the genotypes of the parents (a) if the trait is recessive and (b) if the trait is dominant.
2. Predict the chances that homozygous normal parents for cystic fibrosis will have a child with cystic fibrosis.
3. Explain why some incidences of autosomal recessive disorders are higher in one race or culture.

CONNECTING THE CONCEPTS

Many of the diseases discussed in this section are associated with specific aspects of human physiology. For more information on these diseases (indicated in parentheses), refer to the following discussions:

Section 3.3 describes the function of proteins in the plasma membrane (cystic fibrosis).

Section 3.4 contains descriptions of the lysosomes (Tay-Sachs disease).

Section 4.2 reviews the role of connective tissue in the body (Marfan syndrome).

Section 6.2 describes the role of the red blood cells (sickle-cell disease).

21.4 Beyond Simple Inheritance Patterns

LEARNING OUTCOMES

Upon completion of this section, you should be able to

1. Summarize how polygenic inheritance, pleiotropy, codominance, and incomplete dominance differ from simple one-trait crosses.
2. Explain how a combination of genetics and the environment can influence a phenotype.
3. Predict a person's blood type based on the genotype.

Certain traits, such as those studied in Section 21.2, are controlled by one set of alleles that follows a simple dominant or recessive inheritance. However, human genetics is more complicated than can be explained by simple dominant and recessive patterns. In this section, we will explore some of the more common other types of inheritance patterns.

Polygenic Inheritance

Polygenic traits, such as skin color and height, are governed by several sets of alleles. Each individual has a copy of all allelic pairs, possibly located on many different pairs of chromosomes. Each dominant allele codes for a product; therefore, the dominant alleles have a quantitative effect on the phenotype—that is, these effects are additive. The result is a *continuous variation* of phenotypes, resulting in a distribution of these phenotypes that resembles a bell-shaped curve. The more genes involved, the more continuous the variations and distribution of the phenotypes. Also, environmental effects cause many intervening phenotypes. In the case of height, differences in nutrition bring about a bell-shaped curve (Fig. 21.13).

Skin Color

Skin color is the result of pigmentation produced by cells called melanocytes in the skin (see Section 4.7). We now know that there are over 100 different genes that influence skin color. For simplicity, skin color is an example of a polygenic trait that is likely controlled by many pairs of alleles.

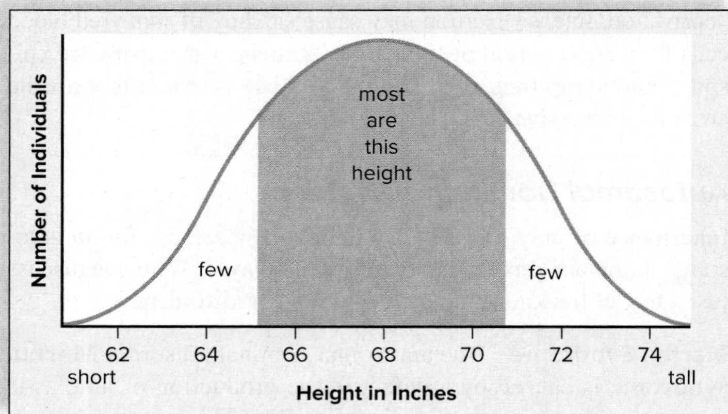

Figure 21.13 Height is a polygenic trait in humans. When you record the heights of a large group of people chosen at random, the values follow a bell-shaped curve. Such a continuous distribution is because of the control of a trait by several sets of alleles. Environmental effects are also involved.

(photo): David Hyde and Wayne Falda/McGraw Hill

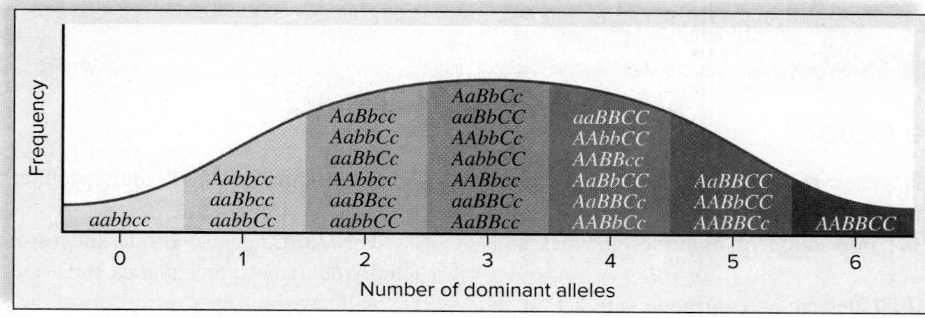

Figure 21.14 **Polygenic inheritance and skin color.**
Skin color is controlled by many pairs of alleles, which results in a range of phenotypes. The vast majority of people have skin colors in the middle range, whereas fewer people have skin colors in the extreme range.

Even so, we will use the simplest model and will assume that skin has only three pairs of alleles (*Aa* and *Bb* and *Cc*) and that each capital letter contributes pigment to the skin. When a person with very dark skin reproduces with a person with very light skin, the children have medium-brown colored skin. When two people with the genotype *AaBbCc* reproduce with one another, individuals may range in skin color from very dark to very light. The distribution of these phenotypes typically follows a bell-shaped curve, meaning that few people have the extreme phenotypes, and most people have the phenotype that lies in the middle. A bell-shaped curve is a common identifying characteristic of a polygenic trait (Fig. 21.14).

BIOLOGY IN YOUR LIFE

Is skin color a good indication of a person's race?

The simple answer to this question is no, an individual's skin color is not a true indicator of genetic heritage. People of the same skin color are not necessarily genetically related. Because only a few genes control skin color, one's skin color may not indicate the origins of one's ancestors. Scientists are actively investigating the genetic basis of race and have found some interesting relationships between a person's genetic heritage and medicine. This will be explored in greater detail in Section 23.5.

However, skin color is also influenced by the sunlight in the environment. Notice again that a range of phenotypes exists for each genotype. For example, individuals who are *AaBbCc* may vary in their skin color, even though they possess the same genotype, and several possible phenotypes fall between the two extremes. The interaction of the environment with polygenic traits is discussed below.

Environmental Influence

Many human disorders, such as cleft lip and/or palate, clubfoot, schizophrenia, diabetes, phenylketonuria, and even allergies and cancers, are most likely controlled by polygenic traits that are subject to environmental influences. These are commonly called **multifactorial traits.** The coats of Siamese cats and Himalayan rabbits are darker in color at the ears, nose, paws, and tail (Fig. 21.15). Himalayan rabbits are homozygous for the allele c^h, involved in the production of melanin. Experimental evidence suggests that the enzyme coded for by this gene is active only at a low temperature. Therefore, black fur occurs only at the extremities, where body heat is lost to the environment.

Recent studies have reported that all sorts of behavioral traits, such as alcohol use disorder, phobias, and even the risk of suicide, can be associated with particular genes. However, in almost all cases the environment plays an important role in the severity of the phenotype. Therefore, they are most likely multifactorial traits. Current research focuses on determining which percentage of the trait is due to nature (inheritance) and which percentage is due to nurture (the environment). Some studies use identical and fraternal

Figure 21.15 **Himalayan rabbit with temperature-susceptible coat color.**
The ears, nose, and feet of this rabbit are dark because those are areas of lower body temperature.
Neil Twigg/Alamy Stock Photo

BIOLOGY TODAY ▶ Science

Genetics of Eye Color

As we have already noted, genes rarely act alone to produce a phenotype. In many cases, multiple genes may be part of a metabolic pathway consisting of the interaction of multiple enzymes and proteins.

An example of a trait determined by gene interaction is human eye color (Fig. 21A) Multiple pigments are involved in producing eye color, including melanin. While a number of factors (including the structure of the eye) control minor variations in eye color (such as green or hazel eyes), a gene called *OCA2* is involved in producing the melanin that establishes the brown/blue basis of eye color. Individuals who lack *OCA2* completely (as occurs in albinism) have red eyes. A recessive form of *OCA2* results in blue eyes in homozygous recessive individuals, whereas a single dominant *OCA2* allele produces brown eyes (the most common eye color).

The *HERC2* gene overrides the instructions of the *OCA2* gene. If individuals are homozygous for a recessive allele of *HERC2*, they will have blue eyes regardless of the genotype associated with *OCA2*. Geneticists call this type of interaction, where one gene can override another, an *epistatic interaction.*

Questions to Consider

1. What would be the potential consequences if one of the genes involved in a multiple gene interaction were to develop an error?
2. How difficult would it be to use genetic engineering to modify a trait that is determined by a multiple gene interaction?

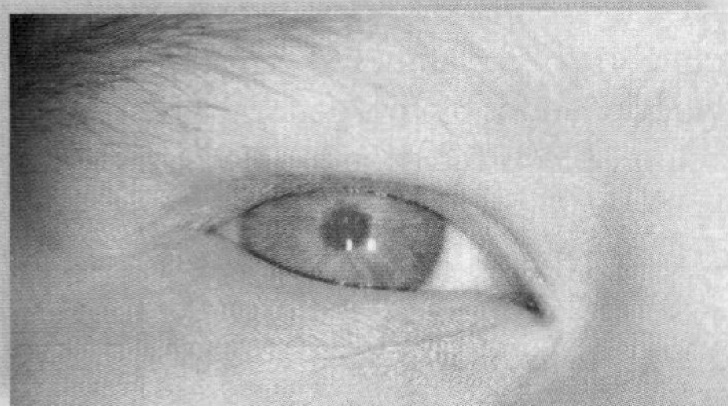
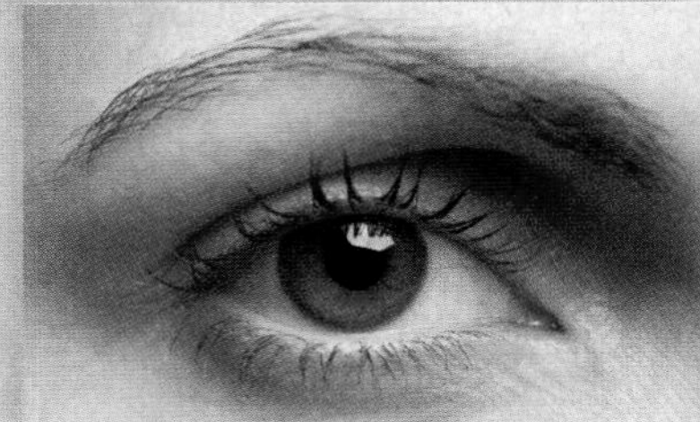
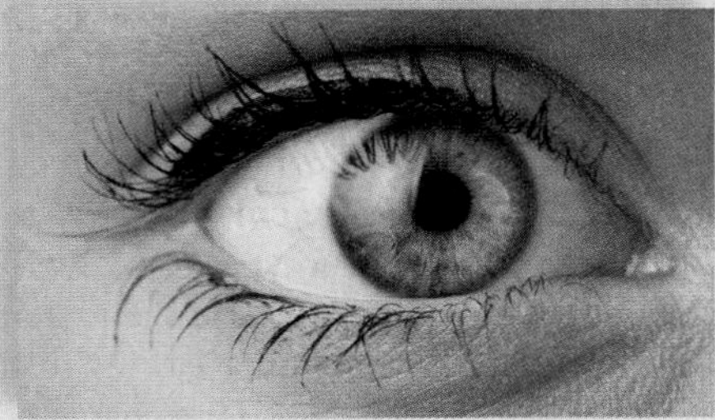

Figure 21A Genetics of eye color.
Individuals with red eyes (*left*) lack the ability to produce eye pigments. The presence of a dominant *OCA2* allele produces the common brown eye color (*center*). Blue eyes (*right*) may occur either from being homozygous recessive for an *OCA2* allele, or may be due to an interaction with a second gene, *HERC2*.
(red eye): Mediscan/Alamy Stock Photo; (brown eye): stylephotographs/123RF; (blue eye): lightpoet/123RF

twins separated at birth and raised in different environments. The supposition is that if identical twins in different environments share the same trait, that trait is most likely inherited. Identical twins separated at birth are more similar in their intellectual talents, personality traits, and levels of lifelong happiness than are fraternal twins separated from birth. This substantiates the belief that behavioral traits are partly heritable. It also supports the belief that genes exert their effects by acting together in complex combinations susceptible to environmental influences.

Pleiotropy

Pleiotropy occurs when a single mutant gene affects two or more distinct and seemingly unrelated traits. For example, persons with Marfan syndrome have disproportionately long arms, legs, hands, and feet; a weakened aorta; poor eyesight; and other characteristics (Fig. 21.16). All these characteristics are due to the production of abnormal connective tissue.

Marfan syndrome has been linked to a mutation in a gene *(FBN1)* on chromosome 15 that ordinarily specifies a functional protein called fibrillin. Fibrillin is essential for the formation of elastic fibers in connective tissue. Without the structural support of normal connective tissue, the aorta can burst, particularly if the person is engaged in a strenuous sport, such as volleyball or basketball.

Incomplete Dominance and Codominance

An example of incomplete dominance in humans is a condition called **familial hypercholesterolemia.** It is associated with a gene that controls the number of low-density lipoprotein (LDL) cholesterol receptor proteins in the plasma membrane of cells. A person with two mutated alleles lacks LDL-cholesterol receptors; a person with only one mutated allele has half the normal number of receptors; and a person with two normal alleles has the usual number of receptors. The presence of excessive cholesterol in the blood is associated with an increased risk of cardiovascular disease. Therefore, people with no receptors often die of cardiovascular disease before 30 years of age. These individuals develop cholesterol deposits in the skin, tendons, and cornea. Individuals with one-half the number of receptors may die while still young or after they have reached middle age. People with the full number of

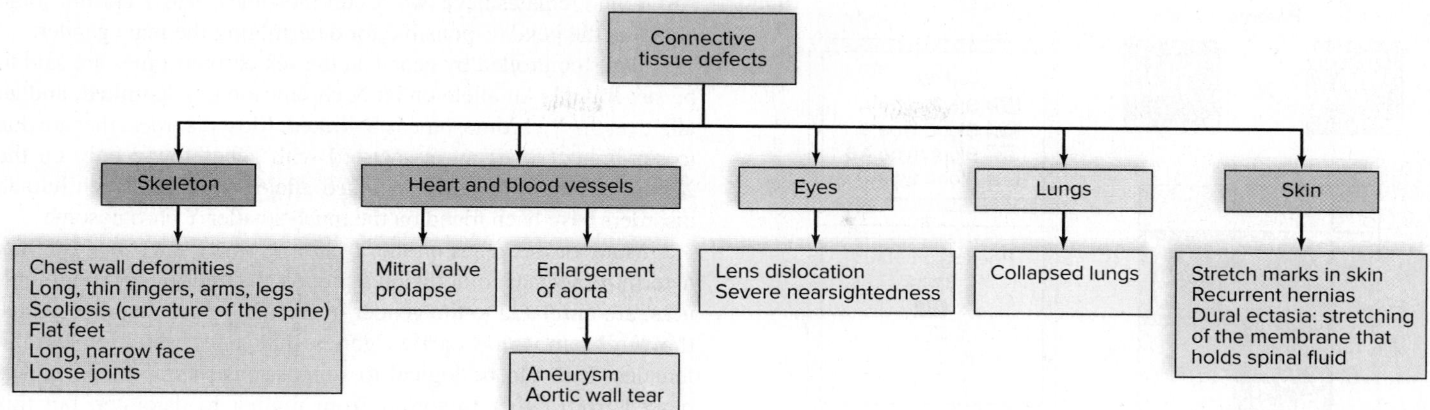

Figure 21.16 **Marfan syndrome.**
Marfan syndrome illustrates the multiple effects a single gene can have. Marfan syndrome is due to any number of connective tissue defects.

cholesterol receptors do not have familial hypercholesterolemia (Fig. 21.17).

Codominance occurs when alleles are equally expressed in a heterozygote. A familiar example is the human blood type AB, in which the red blood cells have the characteristics of both type A and type B blood. We can explain codominance by assuming that both genes code for a product, and we observe the results of both products being present. As we will see later in this section, blood type inheritance is also said to be an example of multiple alleles.

Multiple-Allele Inheritance

When a trait is controlled by **multiple alleles,** the gene exists in several allelic forms. However, each person can have only two of the possible alleles.

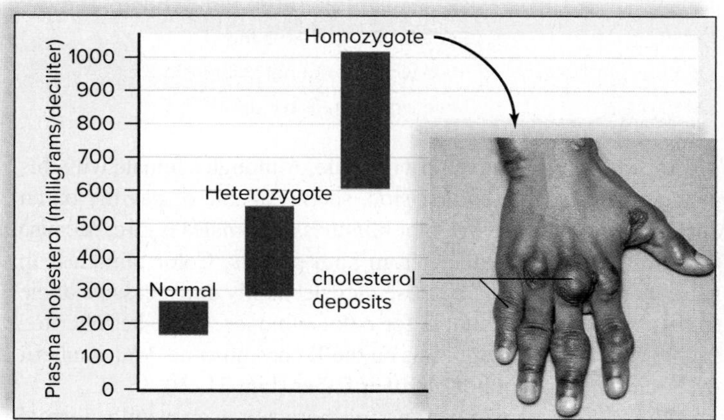

Figure 21.17 **The inheritance of familial hypercholesterolemia.**
Familial hypercholesterolemia is incompletely dominant. Persons with one mutated allele have an abnormally high level of cholesterol in the blood, and those with two mutated alleles have an even higher level still.
(photo): Medical-On-Line/Alamy Stock Photo

ABO Blood Types

Three alleles for the same gene control the inheritance of ABO blood types. These alleles determine the presence or absence of antigens on red blood cells (see Section 6.5).

Each person has only two of the three possible alleles, and both I^A and I^B are dominant over *i*. Therefore, there are two possible genotypes for type A blood and two possible genotypes for type B blood. On the other hand, I^A and I^B are fully expressed in the presence of the other. Therefore, if a person inherits one of each of these alleles, that person will have type AB blood. Type O blood can result only from the inheritance of two *i* alleles.

The possible genotypes and phenotypes for blood type are as follows:

Phenotype	Possible Genotypes
A	I^AI^A, I^Ai
B	I^BI^B, I^Bi
AB	I^AI^B
O	ii

Blood typing was traditionally used in paternity suits. However, a blood test of a supposed father can only suggest that he *might* be the father, not that he definitely *is* the father. For example, it is possible, but not definite, that a man with type A blood (genotype I^Ai) is the father of a child with type O blood. On the other hand, a blood test sometimes can definitely prove that a man is not the father. For example, a man with type AB blood cannot possibly be the father of a child with type O blood. Therefore, blood tests can be used in legal cases only to try to exclude a man from possible paternity. Modern identification relies more heavily on the analysis of patterns in the DNA, called DNA profiling (DNA fingerprinting) (see Section 22.4).

Figure 21.18 shows that matings between certain genotypes can have surprising results in terms of blood type. Parents with type A and type B blood can have offspring with all four possible blood types. Other blood types, such as Rh factor, are discussed in Section 6.5.

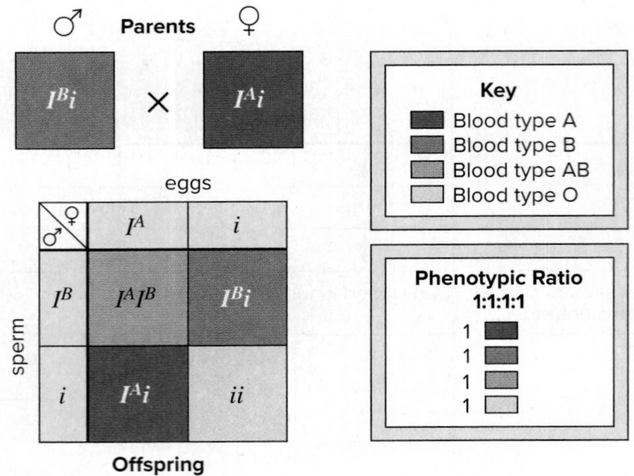

Figure 21.18 **The inheritance of ABO blood types.** Blood type exemplifies multiple-allele inheritance. The *I* gene has two codominant alleles, designated as I^A and I^B, and one recessive allele, designated by *i*. Therefore, a mating between individuals who are heterozygous for type A and type B blood can result in any one of the four blood types. Why? The parents are I^Ai and I^Bi.

CHECK YOUR PROGRESS 21.4

1. Detail why polygenic inheritance follows a bell-shaped curve.
2. Describe a multifactorial trait that could have diet and nutrition as environmental influences.
3. Discuss the potential evolutionary advantages of having multiple alleles for a trait.

CONNECTING THE CONCEPTS

For more information on the topics presented in this section, refer to the following discussions:

Section 4.7 provides more information on the melanocyte cells that control skin color.

Section 6.5 describes the basis of human blood types.

Section 23.5 explores the evolution of humans and human races.

21.5 Sex-Linked Inheritance

LEARNING OUTCOMES

Upon completion of this section, you should be able to

1. Understand the differences between autosomal and sex-linked patterns of inheritance.
2. Interpret a human pedigree to determine the sex-linked inheritance of a trait.

Normally, both males and females have 23 pairs of chromosomes; 22 pairs are called **autosomes,** and the other pair are the sex chromosomes. These are called **sex chromosomes** because they differ between the sexes. In humans, males have the sex chromosomes X and Y, and females have two X chromosomes. The Y chromosome contains the gene responsible for determining the male gender.

Traits controlled by genes on the sex chromosomes are said to be **sex-linked.** An allele on an X chromosome is **X-linked,** and an allele on the Y chromosome is **Y-linked.** Most disorders that are due to sex-linked genes are associated with genes found only on the X chromosome. Very few Y-linked alleles associated with human disorders have been found on the much smaller Y chromosome.

Many of the genes on the X chromosomes, such as those that determine normal color vision as opposed to red-green color blindness, are unrelated to the gender of the individual. In other words, the X chromosome carries genes that affect both males and females. It would be logical to suppose that a sex-linked trait is passed from father to son or from mother to daughter, but this is not the case. A male always receives an X-linked allele from the mother, from whom the X chromosome is inherited. The Y chromosome from the father does not carry the same genes as an X chromosome. Usually, the alleles associated with sex-linked genetic disorders are recessive. Therefore, a female must receive two alleles, one from each parent, to have the disorder.

X-Linked Alleles

When considering X-linked traits, the allele on the X chromosome is shown as a letter attached to the X chromosome. For example, this is the key for red-green color blindness, a well-known X-linked recessive disorder:

- $X^B =$ normal color vision
- $X^b =$ color blindness

The possible genotypes and phenotypes in both males and females follow:

Genotypes	Phenotypes
X^BX^B	Female who has normal color vision
X^BX^b	Carrier female who has normal color vision
X^bX^b	Female who is color blind
X^BY	Male who has normal color vision
X^bY	Male who is color blind

The second genotype is a carrier female. Although a female with this genotype has normal color vision, she is capable of passing on an allele for color blindness. Color blindness in females is rare, because they must receive the allele from both parents. Color blindness in males is more common, because they need only one recessive allele to be color blind. The allele for color blindness must be inherited from their mother, because it is on the X chromosome. Males inherit the Y chromosome only from their father (Fig. 21.19).

Now let us consider a mating between a man with normal vision and a heterozygous woman (Fig. 21.19). What is the chance this couple will have a daughter who is color blind? A son who is color blind? All daughters will have normal color vision, because they all receive an X^B from their father. The sons, however, have a 50% chance of being color blind, depending on whether they receive an X^B or an X^b from their mother. The inheritance of a Y chromosome from their father cannot offset the inheritance of an X^b from their mother. The Y chromosome doesn't have an allele

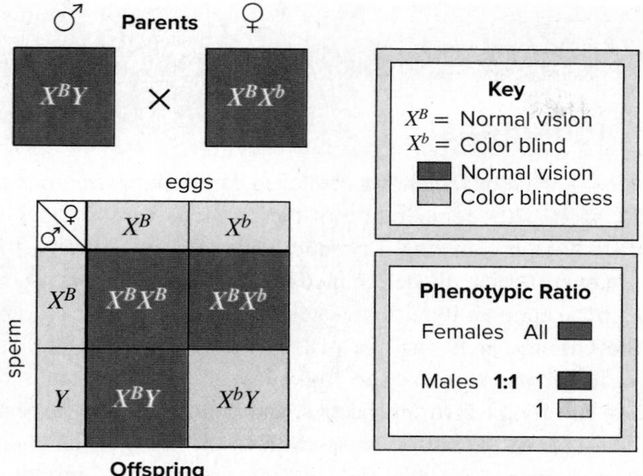

Figure 21.19 Results of an X-linked cross.
The male parent has normal vision, but the female parent is a carrier—an allele for color blindness is located on one of her X chromosomes. Therefore, each son has a 50% chance of being color blind. The daughters will have normal vision, but each one has a 50% chance of being a carrier.

for the trait, so it can't prevent color blindness in a son. Notice in Figure 21.19 that the phenotypic results for sex-linked traits are given separately for males and females.

Pedigree for X-Linked Disorders

Like color blindness, most sex-linked disorders are usually carried on the X chromosome. Figure 21.20 gives a pedigree for an *X-linked recessive disorder.* More males than females have the disorder, because recessive alleles on the X chromosome are always expressed in males. The Y chromosome lacks an allele for the disorder. X-linked recessive conditions often pass from grandfather to grandson, because the daughters of a male with the disorder are carriers. Figure 21.20 lists various ways to recognize a recessive X-linked disorder.

Only a few known traits are *X-linked dominant.* If a disorder is X-linked dominant, males with the condition pass the trait *only* to daughters, who have a 100% chance of having the condition. Females can pass an X-linked dominant allele to both sons and daughters. If a female is heterozygous and her partner has no alleles for the condition, each child has a 50% chance of not having an X-linked dominant disorder. This depends on the maternal X chromosome that is inherited.

X-Linked Recessive Disorders of Interest

Color blindness is the inability to differentiate between certain color perceptions. Some forms of color blindness (red-green) are X-linked. There is no treatment for color blindness, but the disorder itself does not lead to a significant disability for the patient. Color blindness affects about 1 in 12 males and 1 in 200 females in the United States. Most people with color blindness see brighter greens as tans, olive greens as browns, and reds as reddish-browns. A few cannot tell reds from greens at all. They see only yellows, blues, blacks, whites, and grays.

Duchenne muscular dystrophy is an X-linked recessive disorder characterized by a degeneration of the muscles. Symptoms,

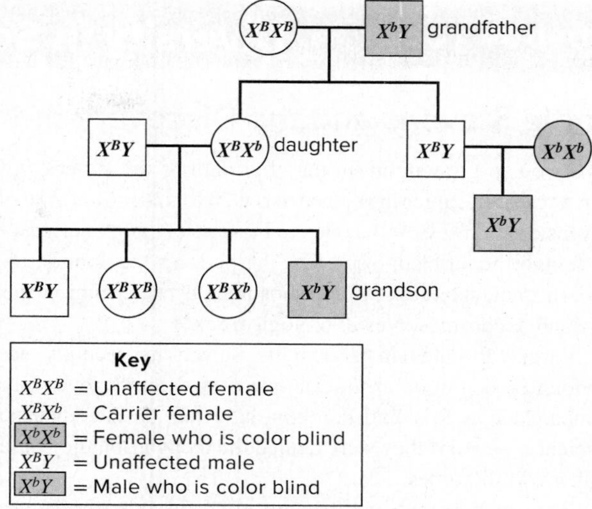

X-linked recessive disorders

- More males than females are affected.
- A son who is affected can have parents who have the normal phenotype.
- For a female to have the characteristic, her father must also have it. Her mother must have it or be a carrier.
- The characteristic often skips a generation from the grandfather to the grandson.
- If a woman has the characteristic, all of her sons will have it.

Figure 21.20 X-linked recessive disorder pedigree.
This pedigree for color blindness exemplifies the inheritance pattern of an X-linked recessive disorder. The list gives various ways of recognizing the X-linked recessive pattern of inheritance.

such as waddling gait, toe walking, frequent falls, and difficulty in rising, may appear as soon as the child starts to walk. Muscle weakness intensifies and respiratory and cardiovascular conditions progress until the individual requires the use of a wheelchair, normally by ages 7 to 10. Death usually occurs by ages 20 to 25. Therefore, males with Duchenne muscular dystrophy are rarely fathers. The recessive allele remains in the population by passage from carrier mother to carrier daughter.

The absence of a protein, now called dystrophin, is the cause of Duchenne muscular dystrophy. Much investigative work determined that dystrophin is involved in the release of calcium from the sarcoplasmic reticulum in muscle fibers. The lack of dystrophin causes calcium to leak into the cell, which promotes the action of an enzyme that dissolves muscle fibers. When the body attempts to repair the tissue, fibrous tissue forms (Fig. 21.21). This cuts off the blood supply, so that more and more cells die. Immature muscle cells can be injected into muscles, but it takes 100,000 cells for dystrophin production to increase 30–40%.

Fragile X syndrome is the most common cause of inherited intellectual disability. These impairments can range from mild learning disabilities to more severe intellectual disabilities. It is also the most common known cause of *autism spectral disorder,* a psychological disorder associated with social communication difficulties and restricted, repetitive behaviors. Fragile X syndrome affects 1 out of every 4,000 males and 1 out of every

BIOLOGY TODAY ▶ **Diversity in Science**

Nettie Stevens and the Discovery of the Sex Chromosomes

For a woman growing up in the aftermath of the American Civil War, a research career in science was next to unheard of. But Nettie Stevens didn't just beat the odds to become one of America's earliest female geneticists—she also helped set the foundation for modern understandings of chromosomes by determining the role of X and Y chromosomes in biological sex.

Largely forgotten in her own life, Stevens has recently received newfound recognition as an example of the tremendous influence women, such as Rosalind Franklin, have had on the advancement of science—even if they were denied the recognition they deserved in their own lifetimes.

Born in Vermont in 1861, Stevens held an early drive to go into higher education but lacked the financial means to make the jump from high school to college. Instead, Stevens worked as a teacher to make ends meet while studying at Westford Academy in Massachusetts, becoming one of only three women to graduate with a degree in her class. From Westford, Stevens completed degrees at the newly opened Stanford University and Bryn Mawr in Pennsylvania, where she achieved a PhD. in cellular biology at the age of 39 (Fig. 21B).

Even as Stevens was finishing her degree in 1903 at Bryn Mawr, Gregor Mendel's research on genetics was seeing a renewed burst of interest, with scientists busy diving into research on the factors behind hereditary genetics. At the same time, long-held assumptions, particularly surrounding the conditions that dictated biological sex, remained stubbornly rigid in the scientific community. For centuries, the determining factor of whether a child was biologically male or female was believed based on environmental factors, such as the temperature of the mother's womb. Even as scientists were uncovering a genetic basis for certain traits, the belief of environmentally determined sex remained stubbornly pervasive in the community.

Figure 21B **Nettie Stevens.**
Nettie Stevens conducted some of the early research on sex chromosomes.
H.S. Photos/Alamy Stock Photo

Stevens' research was one of the first to challenge this assumption. In her studies, she looked at the chromosomes of insects—mostly mealworms, beetles, and butterflies—by inspecting thousands of paper-thin cross-sections of their gonads under the microscope. After studying and cataloging the individual chromosomes, Stevens found evidence that biological sex was based on the particular assortment of chromosomes—what we now know as XY sex determination.

An Unrecognized Discovery

In 1905, Stevens published her findings, which definitively made the case for biological sex as the makeup of X and Y chromosomes. The discovery effectively made her one of the first scientists in the world to understand how chromosomes may be involved in sex determination.

However, several factors prohibited Stevens from receiving the recognition she deserved. Most prominently was the research of another scientist, Edmund Beecher Wilson, who earlier that year had published his own findings on XY sex-determination through his own independent research. While two scientists independently coming to the same conclusions in such a short amount of time would normally cause both to receive recognition, Wilson was given credit for the discovery, while Stevens' conclusions were discounted.

Even as Wilson went on to become one of the most famous geneticists of his time, Stevens faded into obscurity, dying not six years later from breast cancer in 1912.

Stevens' Legacy Today

In hindsight, Stevens' findings in the early 1900s were extremely accurate, going further than even Wilson's discovery to make the (ultimately incorrect) claim of chromosomes as being *the* determinate of biological sex, without the influence of any external or environmental factors. Between her and Wilson, the discovery of chromosomal sex determination set the foundations for generations of future geneticists to unlock the mysteries of our chromosomes, especially in how certain traits are passed along the X or Y chromosome.

Today, Stevens' name is being rediscovered, over a hundred years after her death. In 1994, Stevens was added to the National Women's Hall of Fame, and on the 155th anniversary of her birthday in 2016 she was recognized with a Google Doodle, which directed internet searches to learn more about her scientific discoveries. In time, perhaps her name will finally see its rightful place alongside Wilson's as the co-discoverer of X/Y sex determination, and she will receive the recognition she deserved over a century ago.

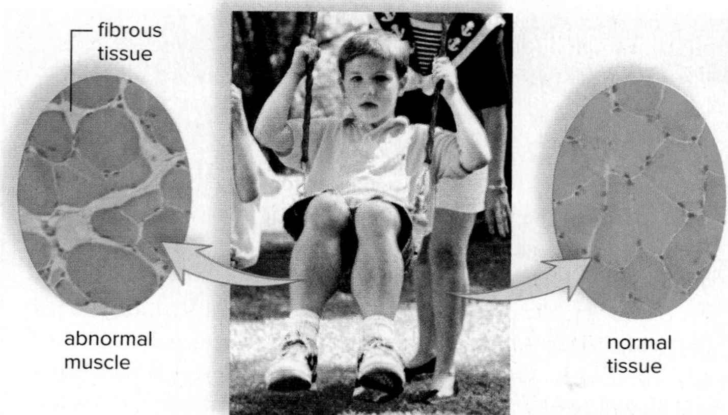

Figure 21.21 Muscular dystrophy.
In muscular dystrophy, an X-linked recessive disorder, calves enlarge because fibrous tissue develops as muscles waste away, due to lack of the protein dystrophin.
(left and right): Dr. Rabi Tawil, MD; (boy): Muscular Dystrophy Association

8,000 females, on average. In males with full symptoms, fragile X syndrome is associated with physical characteristics that include a long face, and prominent jaw, large ears, joint laxity (excessively flexible joints), and genital abnormalities. Other common characteristics include tactile defensiveness (dislike of being touched), poor eye contact, repetitive speech patterns, hand flapping, and distractibility. Females with the condition present with variable symptoms. Most of the same traits seen in males with fragile X syndrome have been reported in females as well, but often the symptoms are milder in females and present with lower frequency. There is no cure for fragile X syndrome, but early intervention services and therapies, education, and support are available to help children learn skills and build independence.

Researchers discovered that a person with fragile X syndrome does not make a specific protein, called the fragile X mental retardation protein (FMRP). Lack of this protein in the brain results in the various manifestations of the disease. As the name implies, a gene defect is found on the X chromosome. The genetic basis of fragile X syndrome is similar to that seen in Huntington's disease (see Section 21.3). In both cases, the gene in question has too many repeated copies of a DNA sequence containing three nucleotides (called a trinucleotide repeat). In fragile X syndrome, the DNA sequence is CGG. (Recall that in Huntington's disease the repeated sequence is CAG.) Fewer than 59 copies of the repeated sequence is considered normal. Between 59 and 200 copies is considered "premutation." Generally, both males and females with the premutation genotype have typical intellect and appearance, although they can have subtle intellectual or behavioral symptoms. People whose DNA has over 200 copies of the repeat have "full mutation" and show the physical and behavioral traits of fragile X syndrome.

The trinucleotide-repeat disorders, such as Huntington's disease and fragile X syndrome, exhibit what is called *anticipation.* This means that the number of repeats in the gene can increase in each successive generation. For example, a female with 100 copies of the repeat is considered to have a premutation. When this female passes her X chromosome with the premutation to her offspring, the number of repeats may expand to over 200. This would result in a full mutation in her child. In a recent study, maternal premutations of between 90 and 200 repeats resulted in an expansion to full mutation in 80–100% of the offspring.

BIOLOGY IN YOUR LIFE

Why is this disease called "fragile" X syndrome?

The name of fragile X syndrome may make you think the disease has something to do with a breakable X chromosome. Actually, the name refers to the appearance of the chromosome under a microscope. In extreme cases of fragile X syndrome, in which there are many copies of the trinucleotide repeat, a portion of the X chromosome appears to be hanging from a thread. However, the appearance of the chromosome is not a cause of the disease. Fragile X syndrome is a result of a malfunction in the fragile X mental retardation protein (FMRP).

Hemophilia is an X-linked recessive disorder. There are two common types. Hemophilia A is due to the absence or minimal presence of a clotting factor known as factor VIII, and the less common hemophilia B is due to the absence of clotting factor IX. In the United States, 1 in every 5,000 males is affected with hemophilia. Of those, 80–85% specifically have the more common hemophilia A. Rarely are females affected by hemophilia, averaging 1 in every 50 million women in the United States. Hemophilia is called the bleeder's disease, because the person's blood either does not clot or clots very slowly. Although people with hemophilia bleed externally after an injury, they also bleed internally, particularly around joints. Hemorrhages can be stopped with transfusions of fresh blood (or plasma) or concentrates of the clotting protein. Also, factors VIII and IX are now available as biotechnology products.

CHECK YOUR PROGRESS 21.5

1. Solve the following: In a given family, a man and woman have two children, a boy and a girl, and both are color blind. List the possible genotypes of the parents if both parents have normal vision.
2. Can a woman who is affected by an X-linked dominant disorder have a child who is not affected? Why or why not?
3. Discuss why X-linked disorders are more common than Y-linked disorders.

CONNECTING THE CONCEPTS

The sex-linked conditions described in this section are based on other systems of the human body. For more information, refer to the following discussions:

Section 6.4 provides more information on blood clotting and hemophilia.

Section 13.4 describes a variety of muscular disorders, including muscular dystrophy.

Section 18.3 outlines how genetics counselors obtain chromosomes to screen for diseases such as fragile X syndrome.

BIOLOGY TODAY ▶ Science

Hemophilia: The Royal Disease

The pedigree in Figure 21C shows why hemophilia is often referred to as "the Royal Disease." Queen Victoria of England, who reigned from 1837 to 1901, was the first of the royals to carry the gene. From her, the disease eventually spread to the Prussian, Spanish, and Russian royal families. In that era, monarchs arranged marriages between their children to consolidate political alliances. This practice allowed the gene for hemophilia to spread throughout the royal families. It is assumed that a spontaneous mutation arose either in Queen Victoria after her conception or in one of the gametes of her parents. However, in the book *Queen Victoria's Gene* by D. M. Potts, the author postulates that Edward Augustus, Duke of Kent, may not have been Queen Victoria's father. Potts suggests that Victoria may have instead been the illegitimate child of a male with hemophilia. Regardless of her parentage, had Victoria not been crowned, the fate of the various royal households may have been very different. The history of Europe also could have been dramatically different.

However, Victoria did become queen. Queen Victoria and her husband, Prince Albert, had nine children. Fortunately, only one son, Leopold, had hemophilia. He experienced severe hemorrhages and died in 1884 at the age of 31 as a result of a minor fall. He left behind a daughter, Alice, a carrier for the disease. Her son Rupert also had hemophilia and in 1928 died of a brain hemorrhage as a result of a car accident. Queen Victoria's eldest son, Edward VII, the heir to the throne, did not have the disease; thus, the current British royal family is free of the disease.

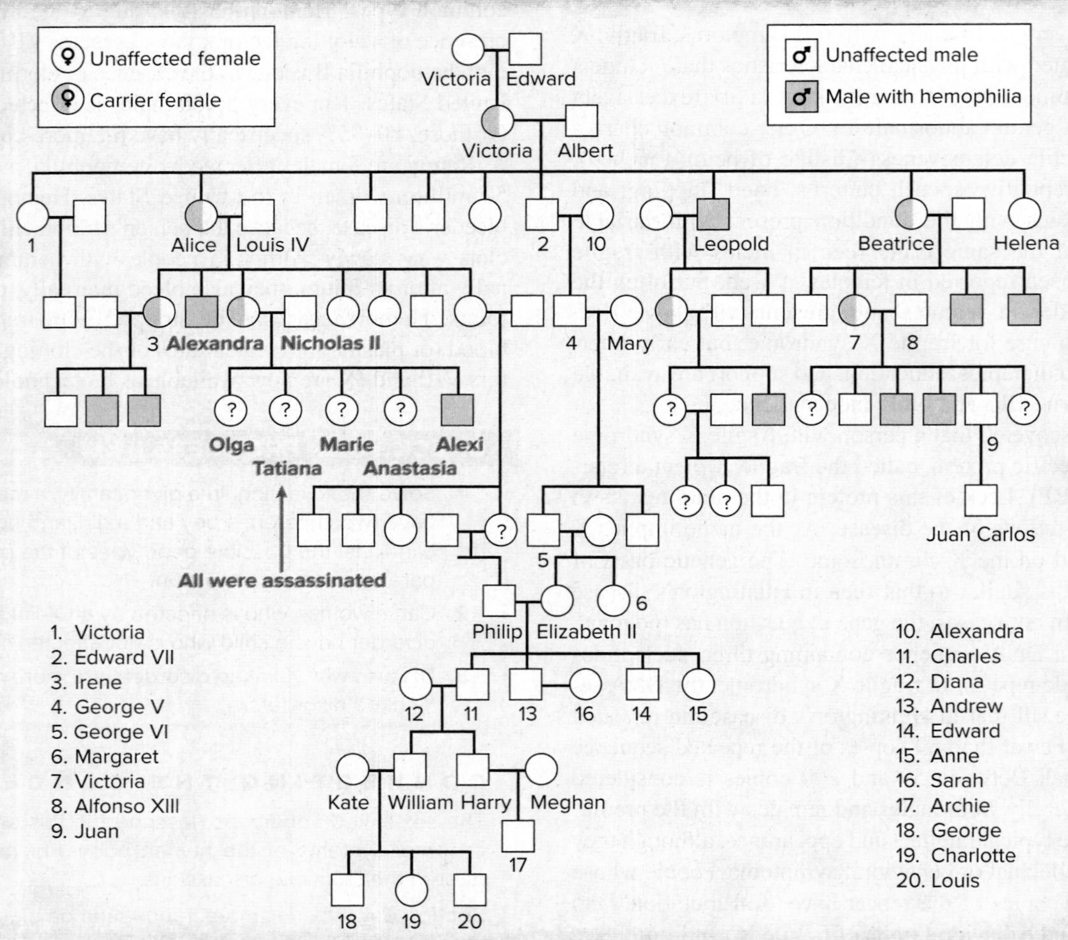

Figure 21C **X-linked inheritance of hemophilia in royal families.**
Queen Victoria was a carrier, so each of her sons had a 50% chance of having the disorder, and each of her daughters had a 50% chance of being a carrier. This pedigree shows only the affected descendants. Many others are unaffected, including the members of the present British royal family.

Two of Queen Victoria's daughters, Alice and Beatrice, were carriers of the disease. Alice married Louis IV, the Grand Duke of Hesse. Of her six children, three were affected by hemophilia. Her son Frederick died of internal bleeding from a fall. Alice's daughter Irene married Prince Henry of Prussia, her first cousin. Two of their three sons had hemophilia. One of these sons, Waldemar, died at age 56 due to the lack of blood-transfusion supplies during World War I. Henry, Alice's other son, bled to death at the age of 4.

Alice's daughter Alexandra married Nicholas II of Russia. Alexandra gave birth to four daughters before giving birth to Alexei, the heir to the Russian throne. It was obvious almost from birth that Alexei had hemophilia. Every fall caused bleeding into his joints, which led to crippling of his limbs and excruciating pain. The best medical doctors could not help Alexei. Desperate to relieve his suffering, his parents turned to the monk Rasputin. Rasputin was able to relieve some of Alexei's suffering by hypnotizing him and putting him to sleep. Alexandra and Nicholas, the czar and czarina, put unlimited trust in Rasputin. The illness of the only heir to the czar's throne, the strain Alexei's illness placed on the czar and czarina, and the power of Rasputin were all factors leading to the Russian Revolution of 1917. The czar and czarina, as well as their children, were all murdered during the revolution.

Queen Victoria's other carrier daughter, Beatrice, married Prince Henry of Battenberg. Her son Leopold had hemophilia and died at age 32 during a knee operation. Beatrice's daughter Victoria Eugenie married Alfonso XIII of Spain. Queen Ena, as Victoria Eugenie came to be known, was not popular with the Spanish people. Her firstborn son, Alfonso, the heir to the Spanish throne, did not stop bleeding on his circumcision. When it became obvious she had given her son hemophilia, it is alleged that her husband never forgave her. Like his cousin Rupert, Alfonso died in 1938 from internal bleeding after a car accident. Victoria's youngest son, Gonzalo, also had hemophilia and died in a car accident in 1934.

Today, no members of any European royal family are known to have hemophilia. Individuals with the disease gene born in the late 1800s and early 1900s have all died, eliminating the gene from the current royal houses.

Questions to Consider

1. What was the probability that Alice's and Louis' sons would have hemophilia? What was the probability for their daughters? How does that relate to the actual occurrence in their children?
2. Assume that the mutation for hemophilia did not originate with Victoria. What does this tell you about the genotypes of her parents?

CONCLUSION

Geneticists recognize that very few traits exhibit a simple recessive or dominant pattern of inheritance. For example, eye color is a complex interaction of multiple genes, and skin color involves the interaction of hundreds of genes, as well as the environment. We also know that a variety of other factors, including the sex of the individual (covered in the next chapter), may influence the expression of a trait. Still, by understanding the simple patterns of inheritance presented in this chapter, it is often easier to identify outside factors that cause the trait to deviate from a typical Mendelian pattern.

SUMMARIZE

21.1 Genotype and Phenotype

An allele is a variation of a **gene.** Each **allele** exists at a specific **locus** on a chromosome. **Genotype** refers to the alleles of the individual, and **phenotype** refers to the physical characteristics associated with these alleles. **Dominant alleles** mask the expression of **recessive alleles.**

- **Homozygous dominant** individuals have the dominant phenotype (e.g., *AA* = normal pigmentation).
- **Homozygous recessive** individuals have the recessive phenotype (e.g., *aa* = albino).
- **Heterozygous** individuals have the dominant phenotype (e.g., *Aa* = normal pigmentation).

21.2 One- and Two-Trait Inheritance

One-Trait Crosses

The first step in doing a problem with a one-trait cross, or **monohybrid cross,** is to determine the genotype and then the gametes.

- An individual has two alleles for every trait, but a gamete has one allele for every trait.

The next step is to combine all possible sperm with all possible eggs. If there are more than one possible sperm and/or egg, a **Punnett square** is helpful in determining the genotypic and phenotypic ratio among the offspring.

- For a monohybrid cross between two heterozygous individuals, a 3:1 ratio is expected among the offspring.
- For a monohybrid cross between a heterozygous and homozygous recessive individual, a 1:1 ratio is expected among the offspring.
- The expected ratio can be converted to the chance of a particular genotype or phenotype. For example, a 3:1 ratio = a 75% chance of the dominant phenotype and a 25% chance of the recessive phenotype.

Two-Trait Crosses

A problem consisting of two traits is often referred to as a **dihybrid cross.**

- If an individual is heterozygous for two traits, four gamete types are possible, as can be substantiated by knowledge of meiosis.
- For a cross between two heterozygous individuals (*AaBb* × *AaBb*), a 9:3:3:1 ratio is expected among the offspring.
- For a cross between a heterozygous and homozygous recessive individual (*AaBb* × *aabb*), a 1:1:1:1 ratio is expected among the offspring.

21.3 Inheritance of Genetic Disorders

A pedigree shows the pattern of inheritance for a trait from generation to generation of a family. This first pattern appears in a family pedigree for a recessive disorder—both parents are **carriers.** The second pattern appears in a family pedigree for a dominant disorder. Both parents are again heterozygous.

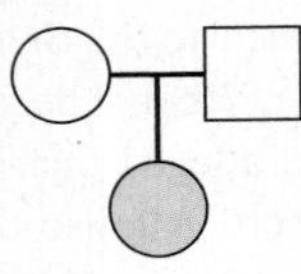

Trait is recessive.

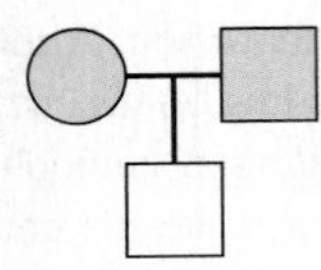

Trait is dominant.

Genetic Disorders of Interest

- **Tay-Sachs disease, cystic fibrosis (CF),** and **sickle-cell disease** are autosomal recessive disorders.
- **Marfan syndrome, osteogenesis imperfecta,** and **Huntington's disease** are autosomal dominant disorders.

21.4 Beyond Simple Inheritance Patterns

In some patterns of inheritance, the alleles are not just dominant or recessive.

Polygenic Inheritance

Polygenic traits, such as skin color and height, are controlled by more than one set of alleles. The alleles have an additive effect on the phenotype. **Multifactorial traits** are usually polygenic with an environmental influence.

Incomplete Dominance and Codominance

In **incomplete dominance** (e.g., **familial hypercholesterolemia**), the heterozygote is intermediate between the two homozygotes. In **codominance** (e.g., type AB blood), both dominant alleles are expressed equally.

Multiple-Allele Inheritance

In humans, an example of a trait involving **multiple alleles** is the ABO blood types. Every individual has two out of three possible alleles: I^A, I^B, or *i*. Both I^A and I^B are expressed. Therefore, this is also a case of codominance.

21.5 Sex-Linked Inheritance

X-Linked Alleles

Humans contain 22 pairs of **autosomes** and 1 pair of **sex chromosomes.** Traits on the sex chromosomes are said to be **sex-linked. X-linked** traits, such as those that determine normal vision as opposed to color blindness, are unrelated to the gender of the individual. Common X-linked genetic crosses are

- $X^BX^b \times X^BY$: All daughters will have normal vision, even though they have a 50% chance of being carriers, but sons will have a 50% chance of being color blind.
- $X^BX^B \times X^bY$: All children will have normal vision (daughters will be carriers).

Pedigree for X-Linked Disorders

- A pedigree for an X-linked recessive disorder shows that the trait often passes from grandfather to grandson by way of a carrier daughter. Also, more males than females have the characteristic.
- Like most X-linked disorders, **color blindness, Duchenne muscular dystrophy, fragile X syndrome,** and **hemophilia** are recessive.

ENGAGE

BioNOW

Want to know how this science is relevant to your life? Check out the BioNOW video below:

- Glowing Fish Genetics

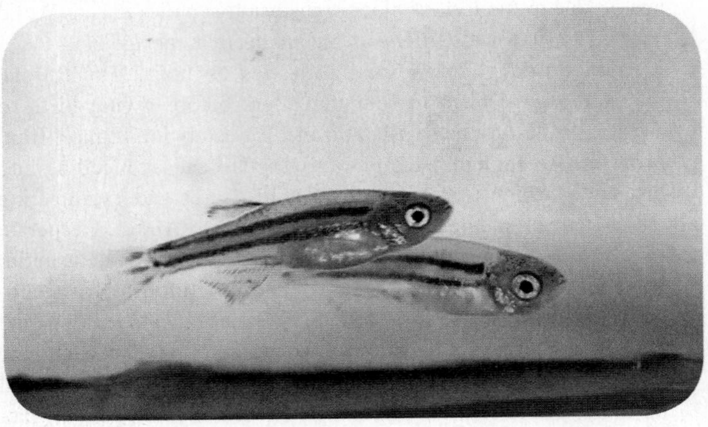

McGraw Hill

What would you conclude if a cross between an orange-colored fish and a yellow-colored fish produced all yellow-colored offspring?

THINKING CRITICALLY

The chapter detailed many autosomal recessive disorders, as well as other types of genetic inheritance, and simple one- and two-trait inheritance patterns. Think about the basics learned from this chapter when answering the following questions:

1. In the pedigree for an autosomal recessive disorder in Section 21.3, the chart depicts a skip in the generations of affected individuals. Is this always the case for autosomal recessive disorders? Why or why not?
2. In two-trait crosses, does one trait being dominant have an effect on the inheritance of the second trait?
3. Would an X-linked disorder or an autosomal disorder appear more in a family pedigree? Explain your reasoning.

MAKING IT RELEVANT

1. Variation in a trait may provide an evolutionary advantage or disadvantage for an individual, or sometimes may just be completely neutral, meaning they have no noticeable effect. Consider some variation of traits in humans that may also be considered neutral.
2. The *OCA2* gene is not only associated with eye color, but also the production of melanin associated with skin pigmentation. Consider why mutations that lighten skin and eye coloration may first develop in northern European countries.
3. At one time, geneticists believed that humans may have as many as 100,000 different genes, but now the number is believed to be closer to 19,000. How do gene interactions, such as *HERC2* and *OCA2* with eye color, help describe how complex organisms, such as humans, have so few genes?

Find answers to all of the chapter questions at connect.mheducation.com

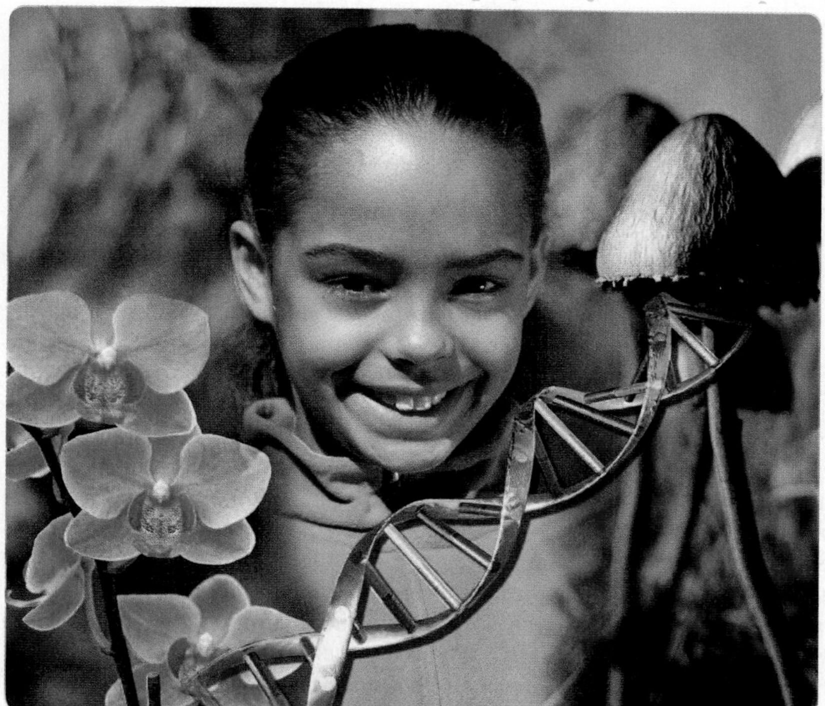

(girl): Jodi Matthews/iStock/Getty Images; (orchid): Sombat Muycheen/Shutterstock; (DNA): Radius Images/Alamy Stock Photo; (mushrooms): IT Stock/age fotostock

CHAPTER

22

DNA Biology and Technology

Next-Generation DNA

Deoxyribonucleic acid, or DNA, is the genetic material of all life on Earth. Each of the organisms in the photo above, and all of the estimated 2.3 million species currently identified on the planet, use a combination of four nucleotides (A, C, G, and T) to code for 20 different amino acids. The combination of these amino acids produces the tremendous variation that gives us the diversity of life. Recently, biotechnology companies have been able to utilize, and improve upon, DNA's characteristics in ways that may benefit us in the future.

A company named Synthorx has expanded this genetic alphabet by creating two new forms of nucleotides, called X and Y. When these nucleotides are incorporated into the DNA of *Escherichia coli* bacteria, the number of potential amino acids that can be coded for increases from 20 to 172. Because of this innovation, it may be possible to develop new drugs (including antibiotics) and vaccines that can help protect us from some diseases. It may also be possible to develop genetically modified organisms that resist pathogens, grow faster, or produce foods with higher nutritional content.

Other companies have been working on using DNA's ability to store information to build the next generation of data storage modules. A single gram of DNA contains 215 million gigabytes of information, or the equivalent of 215,000 large computer hard drives. Because information storage is critical in many industries, including medicine, DNA-based storage systems may soon make conventional hard drives obsolete.

In this chapter, we will explore the structure and function of the genetic material and examine how the instructions contained within DNA are expressed to form the proteins that create the characteristics of life.

As you read through the chapter, think about the following questions:

1. How is information contained within a molecule of DNA?
2. How does the flow of genetic information from DNA to protein to trait work?

CHAPTER OUTLINE

BEFORE YOU BEGIN

Before beginning this chapter, take a few moments to review the following discussions:

Section 2.7 What are the roles of nucleic acids in a cell?

Section 3.4 What is the structure of the nucleus?

Section 19.1 When are the chromosomes replicated in the cell cycle?

22.1 DNA and RNA Structure and Function

LEARNING OUTCOMES

Upon completion of this section, you should be able to

1. Describe the structure of a DNA molecule.
2. Explain the process of DNA replication and list the major enzymes involved.
3. Distinguish between the structures of DNA and RNA.
4. State the roles of RNA in a cell.

For life on Earth, **DNA (deoxyribonucleic acid)** is the genetic material. Within the genetic material, information is organized as **genes,** short segments of DNA that contain instructions for a specific trait. Genes are organized into structures called *chromosomes*—the mechanism by which genetic information is transmitted, at both the cellular and the organismal level, from one generation to the next (see Section 19.1). In eukaryotic cells, including those of humans, the majority of the DNA is located in the nucleus. A small amount of DNA is also found in the mitochondria, but in this chapter we will focus on the nuclear DNA.

As the genetic material, DNA must be able to do three things: (1) replicate, so it can allow for cell division, as well as be transmitted to the next generation; (2) store information; and (3) undergo change (mutation) to provide genetic variability. DNA meets all three of these criteria.

Structure of DNA

In the twentieth century, scientists discovered that the DNA molecule is a **double helix** (see the Science feature "Discovering the Structure of DNA"). DNA is composed of two strands that spiral about each other (Fig. 22.1*a*). Each strand is a polynucleotide, because it is composed of a series of nucleotides. A **nucleotide** is a molecule composed of three subunits—phosphoric acid (phosphate), a pentose sugar (deoxyribose), and a nitrogen-containing base (adenine [A], cytosine [C], guanine [G], or thymine [T]) (see Fig. 2.25). Adenine and guanine are purines (two rings), and cytosine and thymine are pyrimidines (one ring) (Fig. 22.1*c*).

Looking at just one strand of DNA, notice that the phosphate and sugar molecules make up a backbone and the bases project to one side. Put the two strands together, and DNA resembles a ladder (Fig. 22.1*b*). The sugar-phosphate backbones make up the supports of the ladder. The rungs of the ladder are the paired bases,

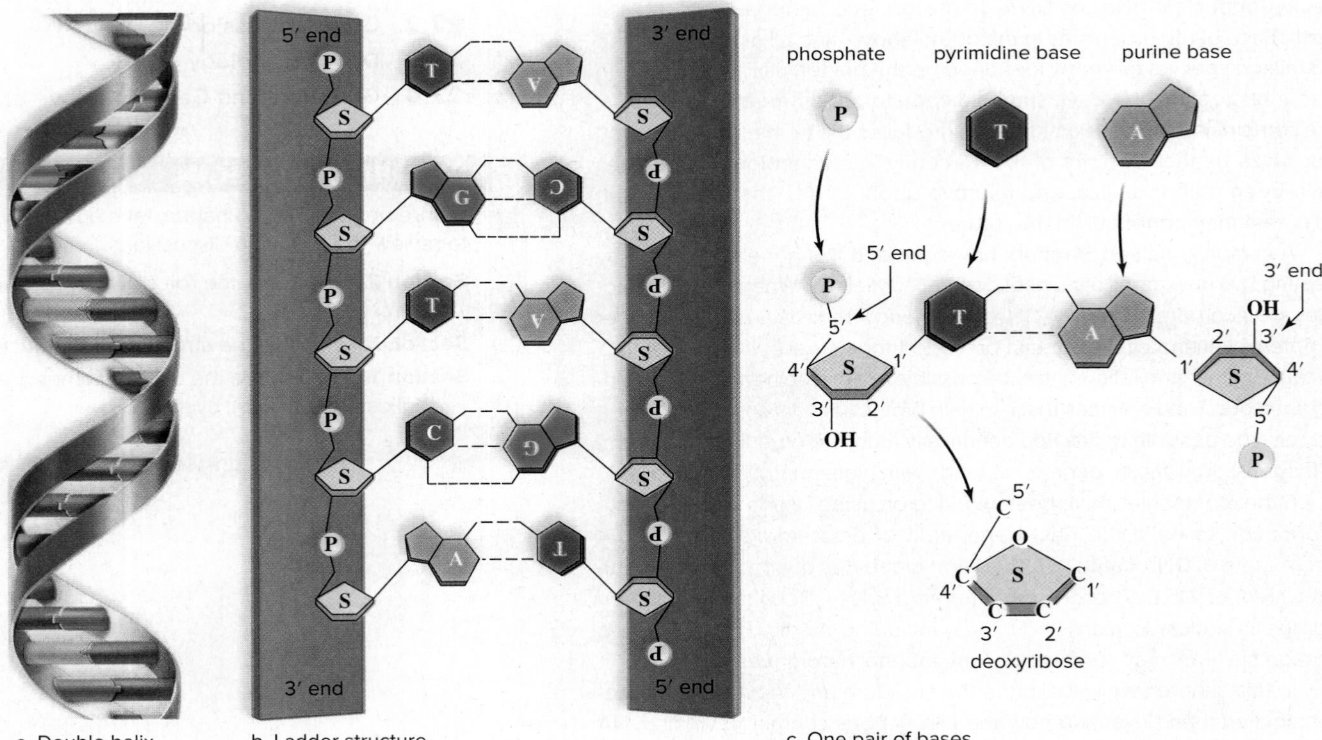

Figure 22.1 The structure of DNA.
a. DNA double helix. **b.** An unwound helix showing a ladder configuration. The supports are composed of sugar (S) and phosphate (P) molecules. The rungs are complementary bases. The DNA bases pair in such a way that the sugar-phosphate backbones are oriented in different directions. **c.** The DNA strands are antiparallel. Notice the numbering of the carbon atoms (5′–3′) in deoxyribose.

BIOLOGY TODAY ▶ **Science**

Discovering the Structure of DNA

In 1953, James Watson, an American biologist, began an internship at the University of Cambridge in England. There he met Francis Crick, a British physicist, who was interested in molecular structures. Together, they set out to predict the structure of DNA and to build a model that would explain how DNA, the genetic material, can vary from species to species and even from individual to individual. They also proposed how DNA replicates (makes a copy of itself), so that daughter cells receive an identical copy.

The bits and pieces of data available to Watson and Crick were like puzzle pieces they had to fit together. This is what they knew from others' research:

- DNA is a polymer of nucleotides, each one having a phosphate group, the sugar deoxyribose, and a nitrogen-containing base. There are four types of nucleotides, because there are four different bases: adenine (A) and guanine (G) are purines, whereas cytosine (C) and thymine (T) are pyrimidines.
- A chemist, Erwin Chargaff, had determined in the late 1940s that regardless of the species under consideration, the number of purines in DNA always equals the number of pyrimidines. Further, the amount of adenine equals the amount of thymine (A = T), and the amount of guanine equals the amount of cytosine (G = C). These findings came to be known as Chargaff's rules.
- Rosalind Franklin (Fig. 22A*a*), working with Maurice Wilkins at King's College, London, had just prepared an X-ray diffraction photograph of DNA. It showed that DNA is a double helix of constant diameter and that the bases are regularly stacked on top of one another (Fig. 22A*b*).

Using these data, Watson and Crick deduced that DNA has a twisted, ladderlike structure. The sugar-phosphate molecules make up the sides of the ladder, and the bases make up the rungs. Further, they determined that if A is normally hydrogen-bonded with T, and G is normally hydrogen-bonded with C (in keeping with Chargaff's rules), then the rungs always have a constant width, consistent with the X-ray photograph.

Watson and Crick built a model of DNA out of wire and tin. This double-helix model does indeed allow for differences in DNA structure between species, because the base pairs can be in any order. Also, the model suggests that complementary base pairing plays a role in the replication of DNA. As Watson and Crick pointed out in their original paper, "It has not escaped our notice that the specific pairing we have postulated immediately suggests a possible copying mechanism for the genetic material."

When the Nobel Prize for the discovery of the double helix was awarded in 1962, the honor went to James Watson, Francis Crick, and Maurice Wilkins. Rosalind Franklin was not listed as one of the recipients. Tragically, Franklin developed ovarian cancer in 1956, and she died in 1958 at the age of 37. Franklin had not been nominated for the award, and according to the rules at that time, was ineligible for the Nobel Prize.

Questions to Consider

1. Watson and Crick's discovery of DNA is clearly one of the most important biological discoveries in the last century. What advances in medicine and science can you think of that are built on knowing the structure of DNA?
2. Describe why the structure of DNA led Watson and Crick to point out "a possible copying mechanism for the genetic material."

a.

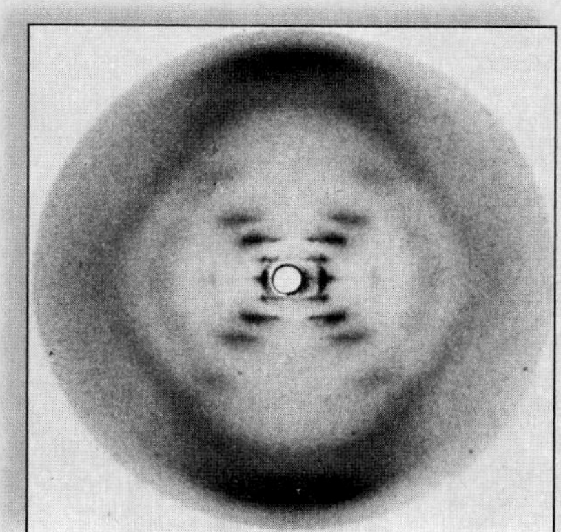

b.

Figure 22A X-ray diffraction of DNA.
a. Rosalind Franklin. **b.** The diffraction pattern of DNA produced by Rosalind Franklin. The crossed (X) pattern in the center told investigators that DNA is a helix, and the dark portions at the top and the bottom indicated that some feature is repeated over and over. Watson and Crick determined that this feature is the hydrogen-bonded bases.

(a): Photo Researchers/Science History Images/Alamy Stock Photo; (b): Omikron/Science Source

which are held together by hydrogen bonding: A pairs with T by forming two hydrogen bonds, and G pairs with C by forming three hydrogen bonds, or vice versa. This is called **complementary base pairing** (Fig. 22.1*c*).

Complementary base pairing is important to the functioning of DNA. The two strands of DNA are antiparallel, meaning they run in opposite directions. Notice in Figure 22.1*b* that in one strand the sugar molecules appear right-side up, and in the other they appear upside down. This is due to the position of carbon molecules on the deoxyribose sugar molecules. When looking at a double helix, one side will have the 5′ carbon at one end, and the other side will have the 3′ carbon (Fig. 22.1*b*). This orientation becomes important when the DNA is replicated or transcribed into mRNA.

Replication of DNA

When cells divide, each new cell gets an exact copy of DNA. The process of copying a DNA helix is called **DNA replication.** During the S phase of interphase during mitosis when DNA is replicated, the double-stranded structure of DNA allows each original strand to serve as a **template** for the formation of a complementary new strand. DNA replication is termed *semiconservative,* because each new double helix has one original strand and one new strand. In other words, one of the original strands is conserved, or present, in each new double helix. Each original strand has produced a new strand through complementary base pairing, so there are now two DNA helices identical to each other and to the original molecule (Fig. 22.2).

At the molecular level, several enzymes and proteins participate in the semiconservative replication of the new DNA strands. This process is summarized in Figure 22.3.

The major events in DNA replication include:

1. The enzyme *DNA helicase* unwinds and "unzips" double-stranded DNA by breaking the weak hydrogen bonds between the paired bases.
2. New complementary DNA nucleotides (composed of a sugar, phosphate, and one nitrogen-containing base), always present in the nucleus, are fit into place by the process of complementary base pairing. These are positioned and joined by the enzyme *DNA polymerase.*
3. Because the strands of DNA are oriented in an antiparallel configuration, and the DNA polymerase may add new nucleotides onto one end of the chain, DNA synthesis occurs in opposite directions. The *leading strand* follows the helicase enzyme, while synthesis on the *lagging strand* must wait for the DNA to unwind and results in the formation of short segments of DNA, called *Okazaki fragments.*

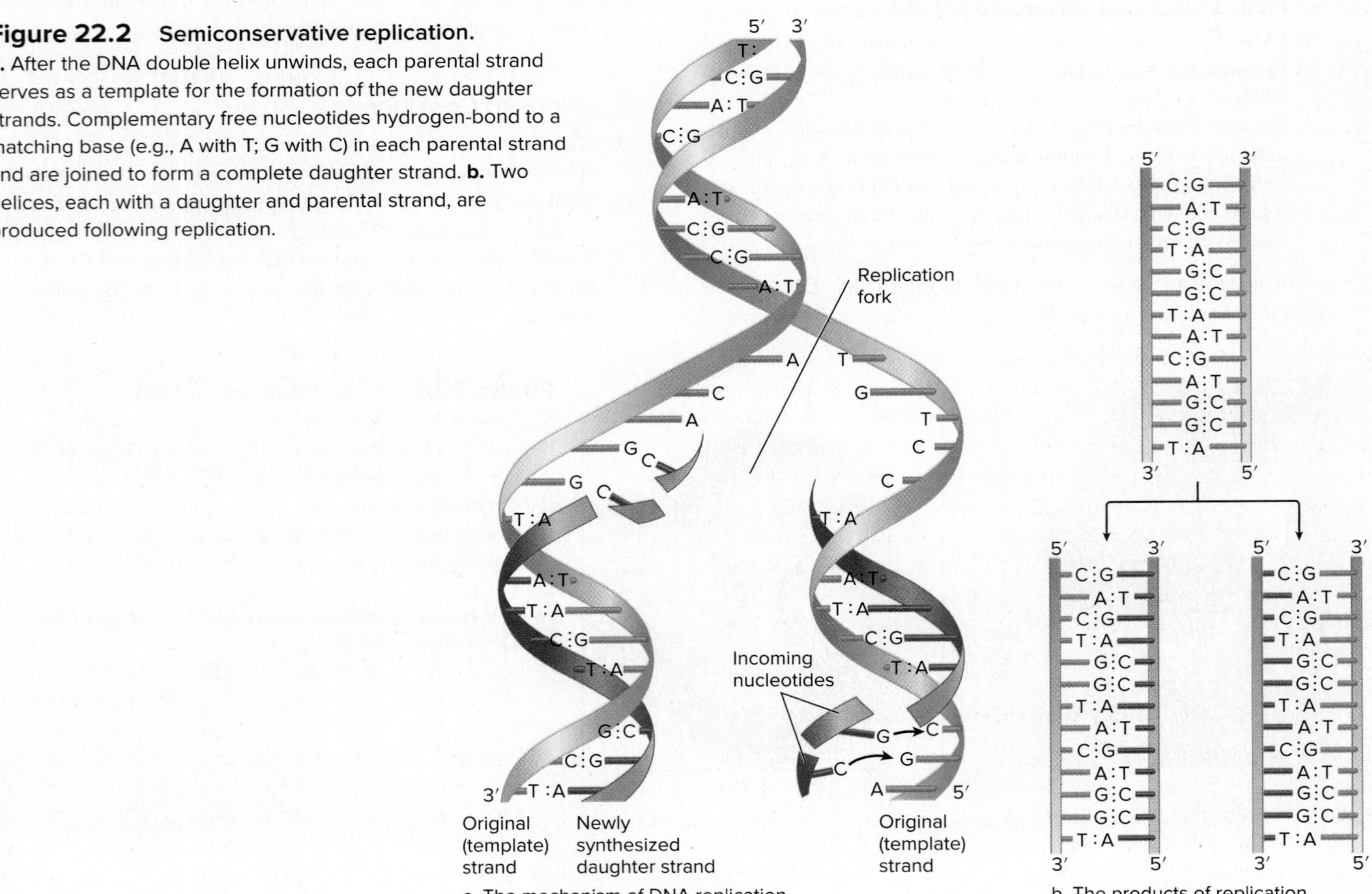

Figure 22.2 Semiconservative replication.
a. After the DNA double helix unwinds, each parental strand serves as a template for the formation of the new daughter strands. Complementary free nucleotides hydrogen-bond to a matching base (e.g., A with T; G with C) in each parental strand and are joined to form a complete daughter strand. **b.** Two helices, each with a daughter and parental strand, are produced following replication.

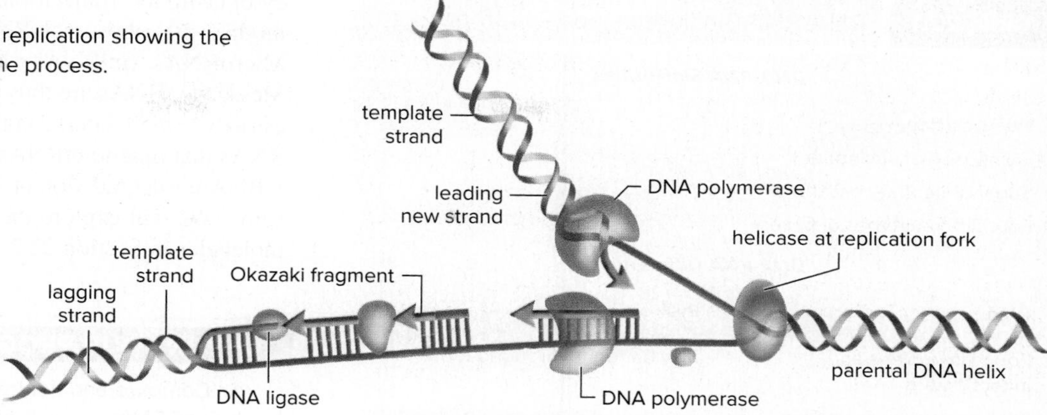

Figure 22.3 **DNA replication.**
A general diagram of the process of DNA replication showing the major enzymes and proteins involved in the process.

4. To complete replication, the enzyme *DNA ligase* seals any breaks in the sugar-phosphate backbone. The DNA returns to its coiled structure.
5. The two double-helix molecules are identical to each other and to the original DNA molecule.

BIOLOGY IN YOUR LIFE

How long does it take to copy the DNA in one human cell?

The enzyme DNA polymerase in humans can copy approximately 50 bases per second. If only one DNA polymerase were used to copy human DNA, it would take weeks! However, multiple DNA polymerases copy the human genome by starting at many different places. All of the several billion base pairs in the human genome can be copied in just a few hours in a rapidly dividing cell.

DNA replication is a relatively fast process—the DNA polymerase is able to add new nucleotides at the rate of around 50 per second. Rarely, a replication error occurs (around 1 in every 100 million nucleotides), making the sequence of the bases in the new strand different from the parental strand. But if an error does occur, the cell has repair enzymes that usually fix it. A replication error that persists is a **mutation,** a permanent change in the sequence of bases. A mutation is not always a bad thing; a mutation may introduce variability by producing a new allele that alters the amino acid sequence and the phenotype. Such variabilities make you different from your neighbor, and make humans different from other animals.

The Structure and Function of RNA

RNA (ribonucleic acid) is made up of nucleotides containing the sugar ribose. This sugar accounts for the scientific name of this polynucleotide. The four nucleotides that make up the RNA molecule have the following bases: adenine (A), uracil (U), cytosine (C), and guanine (G) (Fig. 22.4). One of the differences between RNA and DNA is the replacement of thymine with uracil. As with

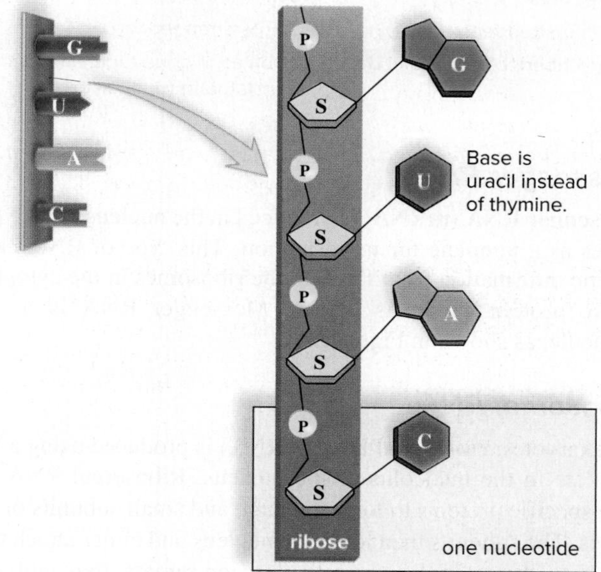

Figure 22.4 **The structure of RNA.**
Like DNA, RNA is a polymer of nucleotides. In an RNA nucleotide, the sugar ribose is attached to a phosphate molecule and to a base: G, U, A, or C. In RNA, the base uracil replaces thymine as one of the pyrimidine bases. RNA is usually single-stranded, whereas DNA is double-stranded.

DNA, complementary base pairing may occur in RNA; cytosine pairs with guanine and adenine pairs with uracil. However, unlike the double-helix structure of DNA, most RNA is single-stranded (Fig. 22.4). Table 22.1 lists the similarities and differences between DNA and RNA.

RNA is divided into coding and noncoding RNAs. The coding RNA is messenger RNA (mRNA), which is translated into protein. Noncoding RNAs are divided into ribosomal RNA (rRNA), transfer RNA (tRNA), and the small RNAs. The small RNAs are involved in the regulation of the genes that code for mRNA and rRNA.

Table 22.1 DNA-RNA Similarities and Differences

DNA-RNA Similarities	
Nucleic acids	
Composed of nucleotides	
Sugar-phosphate backbone	
Four different types of bases	
DNA-RNA Differences	
DNA	**RNA**
Found in nucleus and mitochondria	May be found throughout the cell
Stores genetic information	Assists in the processing of genetic information
Sugar is deoxyribose.	Sugar is ribose.
Bases are A, T, C, G.	Bases are A, U, C, G.
Double-stranded	Single-stranded
Transcribed to produce RNA	Involved in gene regulation and is translated to produce proteins

Messenger RNA

Messenger RNA (mRNA) is produced in the nucleus, where DNA serves as a template for its formation. This type of RNA carries genetic information from DNA to the ribosomes in the cytoplasm, where protein synthesis occurs. Messenger RNA is a linear molecule, as shown in Figure 22.4.

Ribosomal RNA

In eukaryotes, **ribosomal RNA (rRNA)** is produced using a DNA template in the nucleolus of the nucleus. Ribosomal RNA joins with specific proteins to form the large and small subunits of ribosomes. The subunits then leave the nucleus and either attach themselves to the endoplasmic reticulum or remain free within the cytoplasm. During the process of protein synthesis, the large and small ribosomal subunits combine to form a complex (the ribosome) that acts as a workbench for the manufacture of proteins.

Transfer RNA

Transfer RNA (tRNA) is produced in the nucleus, and a portion of DNA also serves as a template for its production. Appropriate to its name, tRNA transfers amino acids to the ribosomes. At the ribosomes, the amino acids are bonded together in the correct order to form a protein. There are 20 different types of amino acids used to make proteins. Each type of tRNA carries only one type of amino acid; therefore, at least 20 different tRNA molecules must be functioning in the cell to properly make a protein.

Small RNAs

There are many other types of RNAs than those mentioned above. For example, small RNAs are divided into several classes. Small nuclear RNAs (snRNAs) are involved in splicing the mRNA (see Section 22.2) before it is exported from the nucleus to the cytoplasm for translation. Small nucleolar RNAs (snoRNAs) modify the ribosomal RNAs within the nucleolus of the cell. MicroRNAs (miRNAs) attach to mRNAs in the cytoplasm. Messenger RNAs are thus prevented from being translated unnecessarily. Small interfering RNAs (siRNAs) are double-stranded RNAs that bind to mRNAs. Attachment of an siRNA prepares the mRNA for degradation or it blocks protein translation by the ribosome. We will explore the function of some of these small RNA molecules in Section 22.2.

CHECK YOUR PROGRESS 22.1

1. Compare and contrast the structure and function of DNA and RNA.
2. Explain why DNA replication is semiconservative.
3. Summarize the major steps in DNA replication.
4. Explain the roles of mRNA, tRNA, and rRNA in a cell.

CONNECTING THE CONCEPTS

For more information on DNA and RNA, refer to the following discussions:

Section 2.7 describes the role of DNA and RNA as organic molecules.

Section 19.6 examines the role of chromosomes in inheritance, as well as the consequences of changes in chromosome number and structure.

Section 23.3 explores how mitochondrial DNA is being used to study human evolution.

22.2 Gene Expression

LEARNING OUTCOMES

Upon completion of this section, you should be able to

1. Understand the structure and function of the genetic code.
2. Summarize the process of gene expression.
3. Describe the process of transcription.
4. Describe the process of translation.
5. Explain how gene expression may be regulated by a cell.

As we will explore in this section, DNA provides the cell with a blueprint for synthesizing proteins. In simplest terms, DNA acts as a template for making RNA, which in turn acts as a template for the manufacture of proteins. A gene is a linear sequence of DNA that may code for a protein, ribosomal RNA, transfer RNA, or microRNAs. For gene expression that results in protein synthesis, the process of transcription makes an RNA copy of DNA, and the process of translation makes protein from the RNA. Before discussing the mechanics of gene expression, it is important to review the structure of proteins.

Structure and Function of Proteins

Proteins are polymers composed of subunits called amino acids (see Section 2.6). There are 20 different amino acids that may be found in most proteins. Proteins differ because the number and order of their amino acids differ. The sequence of amino acids in a protein leads to its particular shape. (See Fig. 2.23 for more detail on the levels of protein structure.)

As we have seen throughout our discussions of each of the human body systems, proteins have many different functions in the body. They determine the structure and function of all the various types of cells in the body. Proteins are used as structural and regulatory components of cells. They are used as enzymes to catalyze chemical reactions, neurotransmitters to aid in the function of the nervous system, antibodies for the immune system, and hormones to change the activities of certain cells and regulate homeostasis. Proteins have this great diversity of function due to the arrangement of these 20 different amino acids in their individual structures. The order of those amino acids is determined by the information contained in the double-helix structure of DNA (see Section 22.1).

Gene Expression: An Overview

The first step in gene expression is called *transcription,* and the second step is called *translation* (Fig. 22.5). During **transcription,** a strand of mRNA forms that is complementary to the template strand of the DNA molecule. The mRNA molecule that forms (mRNA) is a *transcript* of a gene. *Transcription* means "to make a faithful copy." In this case, the sequence of nucleotides in DNA is copied to a sequence of nucleotides in mRNA.

Protein synthesis requires the process of **translation.** *Translation* means "to put information into a different language." In this case, a sequence of nucleotides (the mRNA) is translated into the sequence of amino acids (the protein). This is possible only if the bases in DNA and mRNA code for amino acids. This code is called the genetic code.

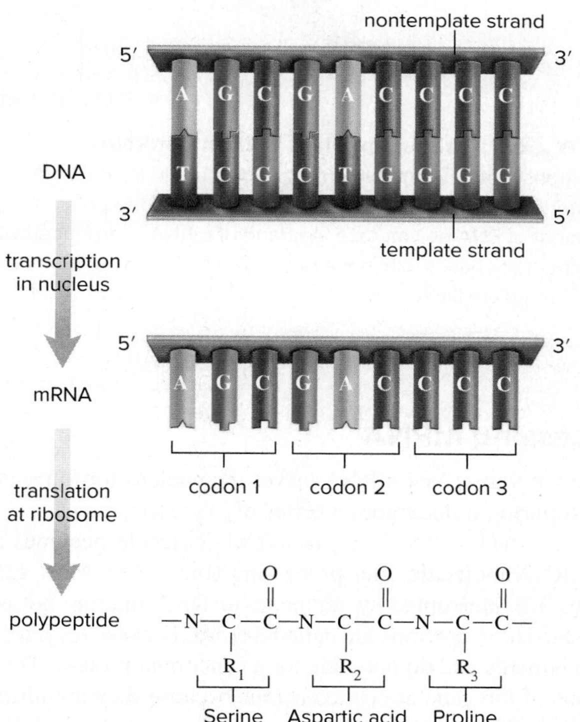

Figure 22.5 Summary of gene expression.
One strand of DNA acts as a template for mRNA synthesis, and the sequence of bases in mRNA determines the sequence of amino acids in a polypeptide.

BIOLOGY IN YOUR LIFE

Are all mutations bad?

A mutation simply means a change from the original structure of DNA during replication or cell division. As we have seen in some forms of human disease, these changes can result in a faulty or detrimental product that can negatively affect the organism. Examples are sickle-cell disease and Huntington's disease. However, mutations are the source of variation in our genetic code. Thus, all of the diversity in our traits, from eye color to our ability to eat certain foods, can be considered to be the result of mutations. From an evolutionary perspective, without the ability to change, we, as a species, would not have been able to adapt to changing environments, and *Homo sapiens* would therefore probably not exist.

The Genetic Code

The genetic code (Fig. 22.6) corresponds to a three-base sequence in the mRNA molecule called a **codon.** Each codon represents a specific amino acid. The reason that each codon contains three bases instead of one or two is a matter of mathematics. Twenty different amino acids are used to build proteins. If a codon consisted of just a single base, then 16 amino acids could not be coded for. If each codon contained two bases, only 16 amino acids would be covered. However, the use of three bases allows for 64 possible codons, more than enough to code for the 20 amino acids. A closer examination of the genetic code (Fig. 22.6) shows that each of the 61 codons corresponds to a particular amino acid. The remaining 3 are stop codons, which signal polypeptide termination. One of the codons (AUG) stands for the amino acid methionine, the amino acid used to signal the beginning of the polypeptide. Notice as well that 18 out of 20 amino acids have more than 1 codon. For example, leucine, serine, and arginine each have 6 different codons. This redundancy in the genetic code offers some protection against possibly harmful mutations that change the sequence of the bases.

The genetic code is considered to be universal, meaning it is basically the same for most living organisms (minor variations exist in some bacteria). This suggests that the code dates back to the very first organisms on Earth and that all life is related. In other words, the observation that all organisms utilize the same genetic code supports the hypothesis that all life on Earth shares an evolutionary heritage (see Section 23.2).

First Base	Second Base: U	Second Base: C	Second Base: A	Second Base: G	Third Base
U	UUU phenylalanine	UCU serine	UAU tyrosine	UGU cysteine	U
U	UUC phenylalanine	UCC serine	UAC tyrosine	UGC cysteine	C
U	UUA leucine	UCA serine	UAA *stop*	UGA *stop*	A
U	UUG leucine	UCG serine	UAG *stop*	UGG tryptophan	G
C	CUU leucine	CCU proline	CAU histidine	CGU arginine	U
C	CUC leucine	CCC proline	CAC histidine	CGC arginine	C
C	CUA leucine	CCA proline	CAA glutamine	CGA arginine	A
C	CUG leucine	CCG proline	CAG glutamine	CGG arginine	G
A	AUU isoleucine	ACU threonine	AAU asparagine	AGU serine	U
A	AUC isoleucine	ACC threonine	AAC asparagine	AGC serine	C
A	AUA isoleucine	ACA threonine	AAA lysine	AGA arginine	A
A	**AUG *(start)* methionine**	ACG threonine	AAG lysine	AGG arginine	G
G	GUU valine	GCU alanine	GAU aspartic acid	GGU glycine	U
G	GUC valine	GCC alanine	GAC aspartic acid	GGC glycine	C
G	GUA valine	GCA alanine	GAA glutamic acid	GGA glycine	A
G	GUG valine	GCG alanine	GAG glutamic acid	GGG glycine	G

Figure 22.6 The genetic code.
In this chart, each of the codons (white rectangles) is composed of three letters representing the first base, second base, and third base. For example, find the rectangle where C for the first base and A for the second base intersect. You will see that U, C, A, or G can be the third base. CAU and CAC are codons for histidine; CAA and CAG are codons for glutamine.

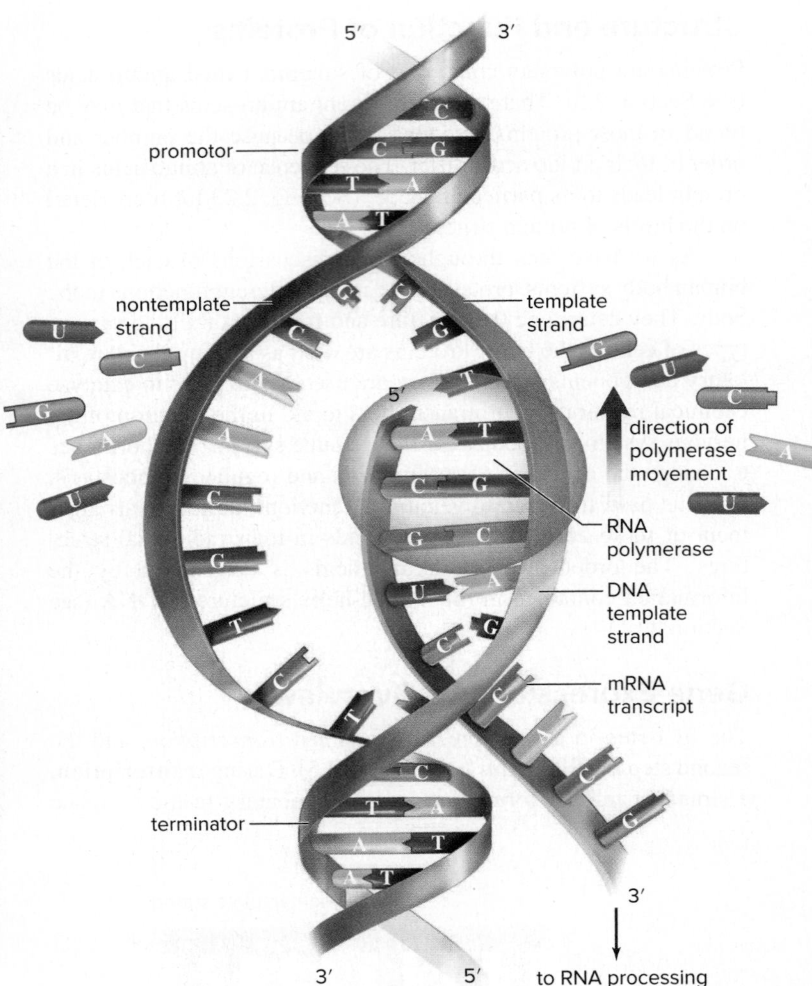

Figure 22.7 Transcription of DNA into mRNA.
During transcription, complementary RNA is made from a DNA template. A portion of DNA unwinds and unzips at the point of attachment of RNA polymerase. A strand of mRNA is produced when complementary bases join in the order dictated by the sequence of bases in template DNA.

Transcription

During transcription, a segment of the DNA serves as a template for the production of an RNA molecule. Although all classes of RNA are formed by transcription, we will focus on transcription to form mRNA.

Forming mRNA

Transcription begins in the nucleus when the enzyme **RNA polymerase** opens up the DNA helix, so that complementary base pairing can occur. Recall that RNA contains uracil instead of thymine, so base pairing between DNA and the mRNA strand will be A-U and C-G (Fig. 22.7). Then, RNA polymerase joins the RNA nucleotides, and an mRNA molecule with a sequence of bases complementary to the DNA segment results.

Processing mRNA

Before the transcribed mRNA leaves the nucleus for translation in the cytoplasm, it undergoes a series of processing steps.

The newly synthesized *pre-mRNA* molecule becomes a *mature* mRNA molecule after processing (Fig. 22.8). Most genes in humans are interrupted by segments of DNA that are not part of the gene. These portions are called *introns,* because they are intragene segments and do not code for a functional protein. The other portions of the gene are called *exons,* because they are ultimately expressed. Only exons result in a protein product.

Primary mRNA contains bases complementary to both exons and introns, but during processing, (1) one end of the mRNA is capped by the addition of an altered guanine nucleotide. The other end is given a tail, by the addition of multiple adenosine

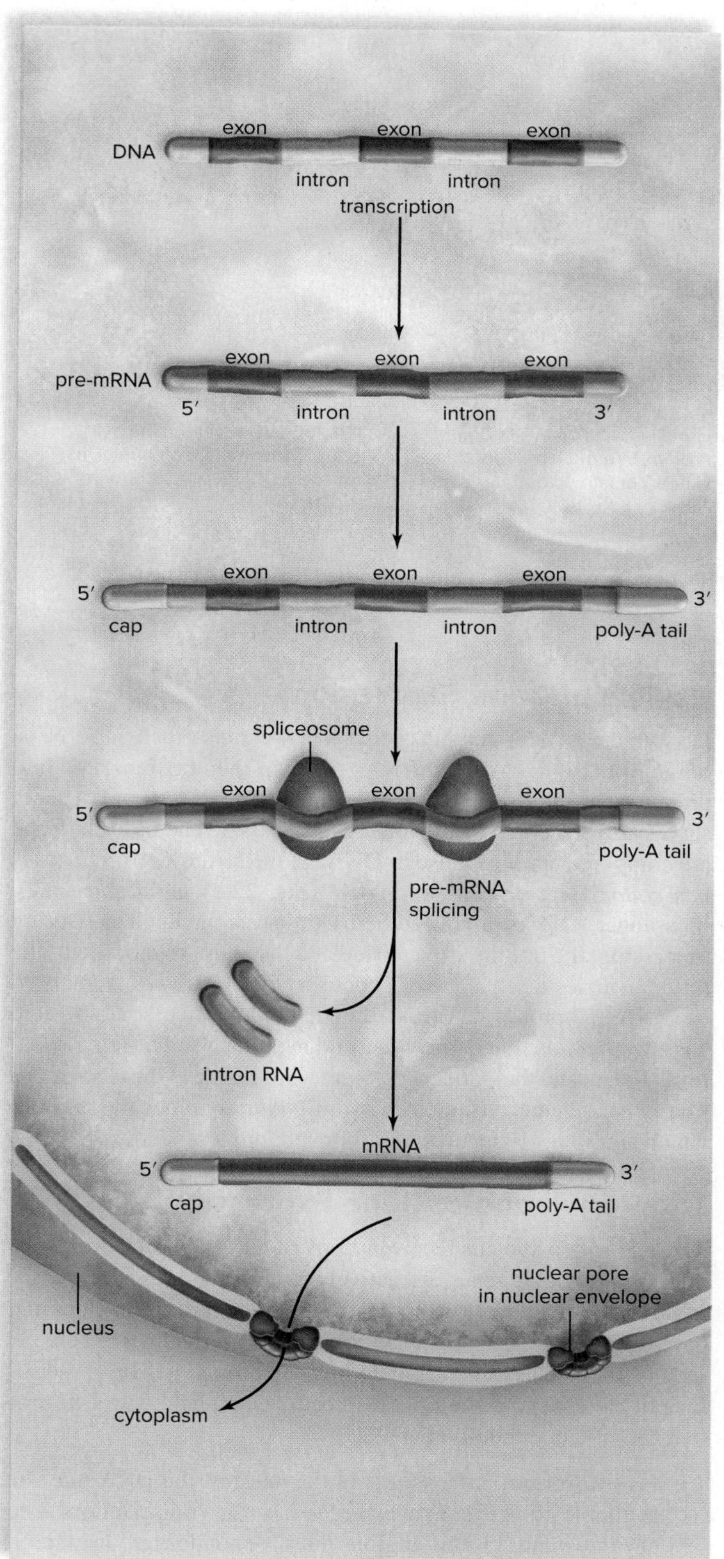

Figure 22.8 mRNA processing.
During processing, a 5′ cap and poly A tail are added to mRNA, and the introns are removed, so that only exons remain. Then, the mRNA molecule is ready to leave the nucleus.

nucleotides. (2) The introns are removed, and the exons are joined to form a mature mRNA molecule consisting of continuous exons. This *splicing* of mRNA is done by a complex called a *spliceosome*, which is composed of both RNA and protein. Surprisingly, the RNA portion, not the protein, is functioning as the enzyme, and so it is called a *ribozyme*. For this reason, not all enzymes are proteins (see Section 2.6).

Ordinarily, processing brings together all the exons of a gene. In some instances, cells use only certain exons rather than all of them to form a mature RNA transcript. This is called *alternative mRNA splicing* and accounts for the ability of a single gene to produce a variety of proteins in a cell. Due to alternative splicing, the estimated 20,000 genes of humans can encode for approximately 100,000 proteins.

Increasingly, small RNA molecules have been found that regulate not only mRNA processing but also transcription and translation. DNA codes for proteins, but RNA orchestrates the outcome.

Translation

During translation, transfer RNA (tRNA) molecules bring amino acids to the ribosomes (Fig. 22.9), where polypeptide synthesis occurs. The ribosome consists of a small and a large subunit that will join together during translation and bind to the mRNA strand. This creates a translation complex (Fig. 22.9*a*). The ribosome contains binding sites called the A (for acceptor or arrival), P (polypeptide), and E (exit) sites, where individual tRNA molecules can bind with the mRNA strand. A tRNA molecule has an almost cloverleaf shape with an area for binding onto an amino acid and a region called an **anticodon** (Fig. 22.9*c*). The anticodon is a three-base sequence on the tRNA that will complementary base pair with the codons of mRNA. This complementary base pairing between an anticodon and a codon is how the tRNA brings the correct amino acid into the correct order instructed by the mRNA strand. Each amino acid, coded by specific codons, has a tRNA molecule with a specific anticodon that carries it to the translation complex. The tRNA molecules attach to the translation complex at the A site where each anticodon pairs with the complementary codon (Fig. 22.9*b*).

The order in which tRNA molecules link to the ribosome is directed by the sequence of the mRNA codons. In this way, the order of codons in mRNA brings about a particular order of amino acids in a protein. The tRNA attached to the growing polypeptide moves from the A site to the P site of a ribosome, as shown in Figure 22.9*b*.

If the codon sequence in a portion of the mRNA is ACCGUAAAA, what will be the sequence of amino acids in a portion of the polypeptide? The genetic code chart in Figure 22.6 allows us to determine this:

mRNA Codon	tRNA Anticodon	Amino Acid
ACC	UGG	Threonine
GUA	CAU	Valine
AAA	UUU	Lysine

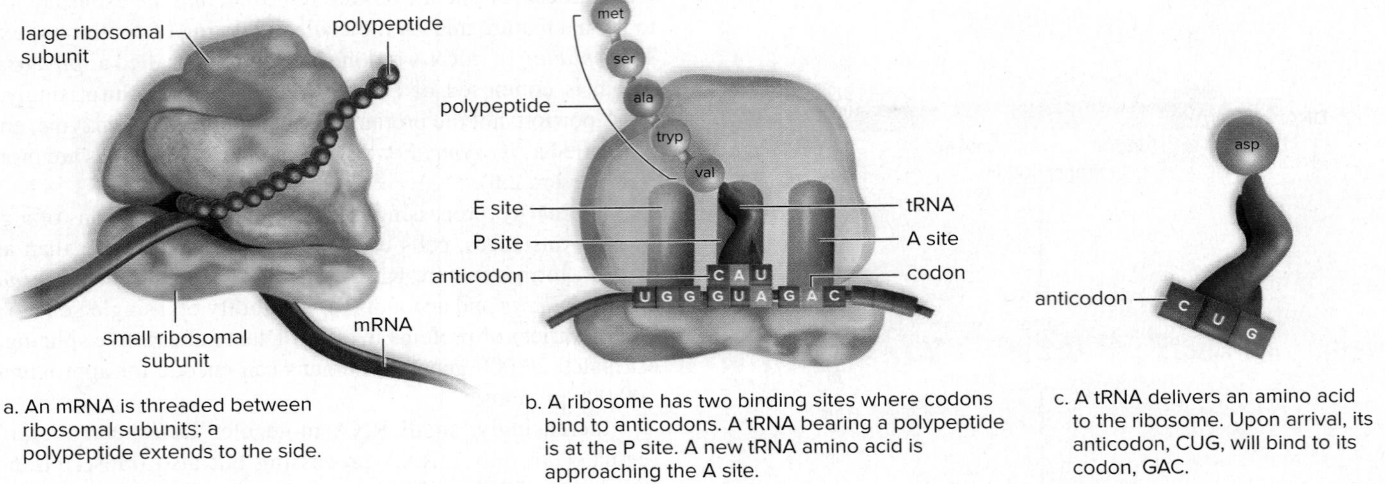

a. An mRNA is threaded between ribosomal subunits; a polypeptide extends to the side.

b. A ribosome has two binding sites where codons bind to anticodons. A tRNA bearing a polypeptide is at the P site. A new tRNA amino acid is approaching the A site.

c. A tRNA delivers an amino acid to the ribosome. Upon arrival, its anticodon, CUG, will bind to its codon, GAC.

Figure 22.9 **The roles of all three forms of RNA in translation.**
Protein synthesis occurs at a ribosome. **a.** Side view of a ribosome showing mRNA and a growing polypeptide. **b.** The large ribosomal subunit contains binding sites for tRNAs. **c.** tRNA structure and function.

Stages of Translation

The process of forming a polypeptide by translation involves three steps: initiation, elongation, and termination:

1. During *initiation* (Fig. 22.10*a*), mRNA binds to the smaller of the two ribosomal subunits. Then, the larger ribosomal subunit associates with the smaller one, forming the translation complex.
2. During *elongation* (Fig. 22.10*b*), the polypeptide lengthens, one amino acid at a time, about five amino acids per second. An incoming tRNA arrives at the A site and then receives the growing peptide chain from the outgoing tRNA. The ribosome moves laterally down the mRNA strand one codon at a time, so that again the P site is filled by a tRNA-peptide complex. The spent tRNA, now at the E site, exits the ribosome. The A site is now available to receive another incoming tRNA, as the complex has moved down one codon. In this manner, the peptide grows and the linear structure of a polypeptide is made. The particular shape of a polypeptide (see Section 2.6) begins to form as the linear structure is established.
3. Then, *termination* (Fig. 22.10*c*) of synthesis occurs when one of the three stop codons enters the A site. Termination requires a protein called a release factor, which can bind to a stop codon and cleave the polypeptide from the last tRNA. The ribosome then dissociates into its two subunits and falls off the mRNA molecule. The individual portions of the translation complex can then re-form at the beginning of the mRNA strand to repeat this process and make another polypeptide.

Additionally, many ribosomes are at work forming the same polypeptide at the same time. As soon as the initial portion of mRNA has been translated by one ribosome and the ribosome has begun to move down the mRNA, another ribosome attaches to the mRNA to begin translation. Therefore, several ribosomes, collectively called a *polyribosome,* can move along one mRNA at a time. Several polypeptides of the same type can be synthesized using one mRNA molecule.

Review of Gene Expression

DNA in the nucleus contains genes that are transcribed into RNAs. Some of these RNAs are mRNAs that will then be translated into proteins. During transcription, a segment of a DNA strand (a gene) serves as a template for the formation of RNA. The bases in RNA are complementary to those in DNA. In mRNA, every three bases is a *codon* for a certain amino acid (Fig. 22.11 and Table 22.2). Messenger RNA is processed before it leaves the nucleus. During processing, the introns are removed and the ends are modified. The mRNA carries a sequence of codons to the *ribosomes,* composed of rRNA and proteins. A tRNA bonded to a particular amino acid has an *anticodon* that pairs with a codon in mRNA. During translation, tRNAs and their attached amino acids arrive at the ribosomes. The linear sequence of codons of mRNA determines the order in which amino acids become incorporated into a protein.

The Regulation of Gene Expression

All cells with a nucleus receive a copy of all genes. However, cells differ as to which genes are actively expressed. Muscle cells, for example, have a different set of genes turned on in the nucleus and have different proteins active in the cytoplasm than nerve cells. A variety of mechanisms regulate gene expression, from pretranscriptional access to the DNA to posttranslational control of protein activity, in our cells (Fig. 22.12):

- *Pretranscriptional control:* In the nucleus, the DNA must be available to the enzymes necessary for transcription. The chromosome in the region must decondense, or uncoil. Proteins and chemical modifications that protect the DNA must be removed before transcription can begin.
- *Transcriptional control:* In the nucleus, a number of mechanisms regulate which genes are transcribed and the rate at which transcription of genes occurs. These include the use of transcription factors that initiate transcription, the first step in gene expression.

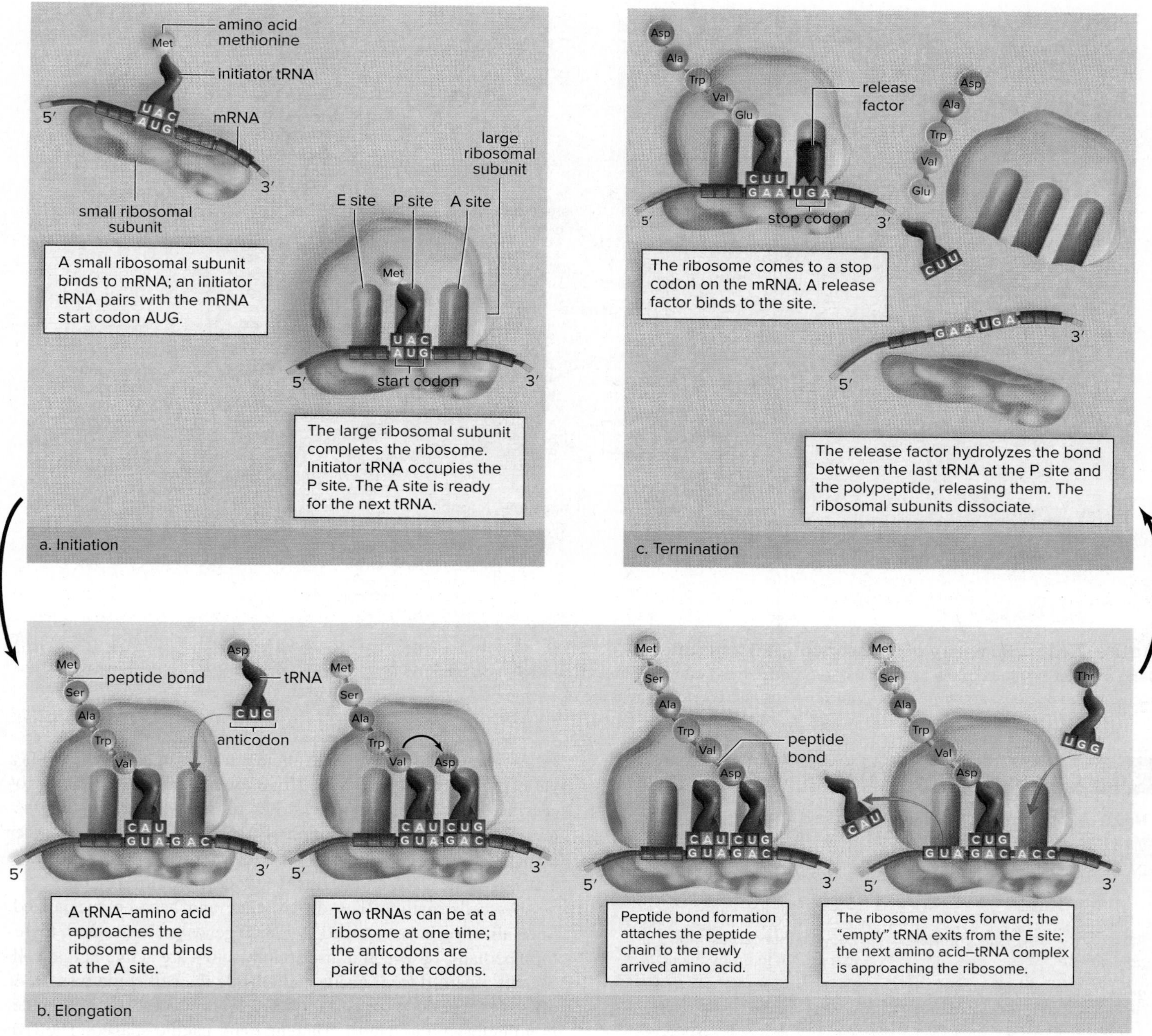

Figure 22.10 **Stages of translation.**
The synthesis of a polypeptide synthesis during translation takes place at a ribosome and has three steps: (**a**) initiation, (**b**) elongation, and (**c**) termination.

- *Posttranscriptional control:* Posttranscriptional control occurs in the nucleus after DNA is transcribed and mRNA is formed. How mRNA is processed before it leaves the nucleus and how fast mature mRNA leaves the nucleus can affect the amount of gene expression.
- *Translational control:* Translational control occurs in the cytoplasm after mRNA leaves the nucleus but before there is a protein product. Some mRNAs require additional changes before translation, and this affects not only the life expectancy of mRNA molecules in the cytoplasm but also their ability to bind to ribosomes. Two of the small RNA classes—microRNAs (miRNAs) and small interfering RNAs (siRNA)—are involved at this level of gene expression. miRNAs bind to mRNAs, inhibiting protein translation. siRNAs prevent translation by marking the mRNA for destruction by nucleases.
- *Posttranslational control:* Posttranslational control, which also happens in the cytoplasm, occurs after protein synthesis. The polypeptide product may have to undergo additional changes before it is biologically functional. Also, a functional enzyme is subject to feedback control—the binding of an enzyme's product can change its shape so it is no longer able to carry out its reaction.

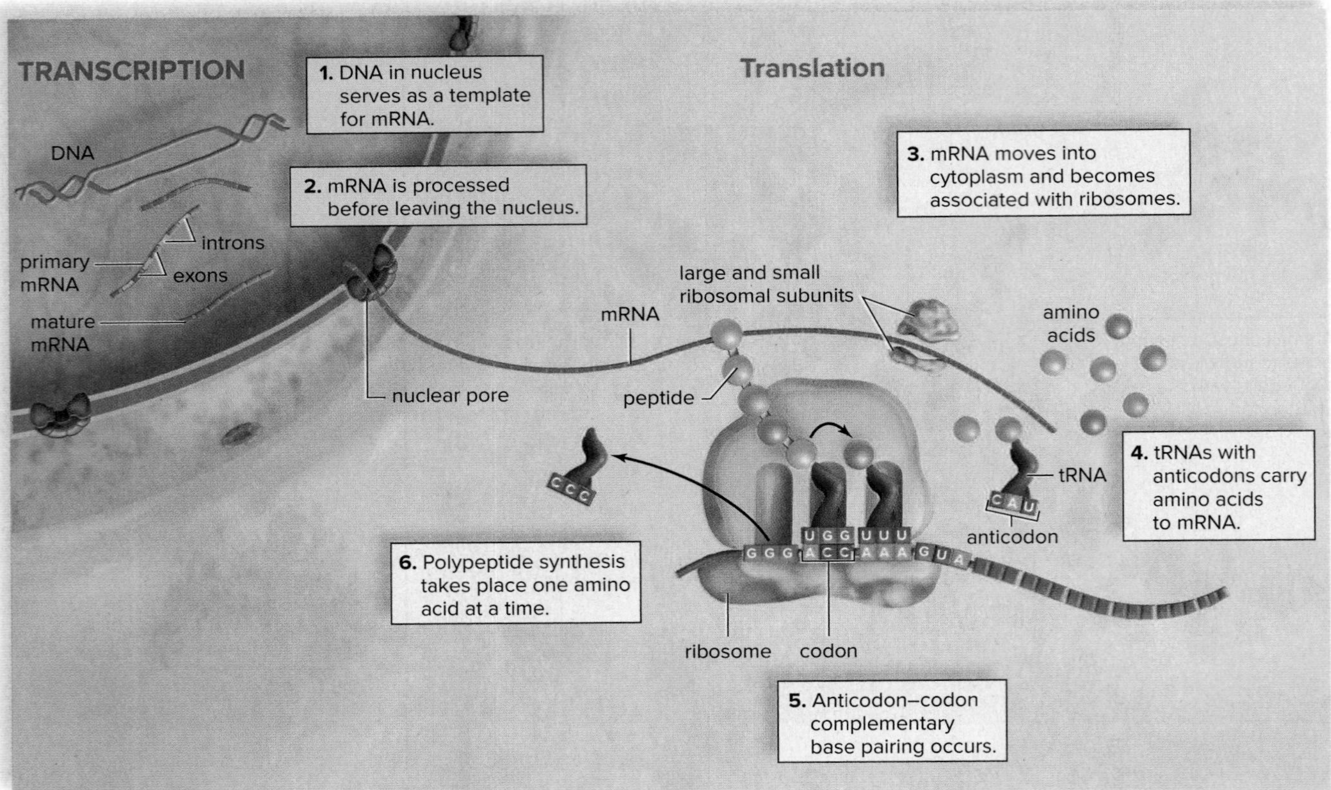

Figure 22.11 Summary of transcription and translation.
Gene expression leads to the formation of a product, most often a protein. The two steps required for gene expression are transcription, which occurs in the nucleus, and translation, which occurs in the cytoplasm at the ribosomes.

Table 22.2 Participants in Gene Expression

Name of Molecule	Stage of Gene Expression	Role
DNA	Transcription	Contains genetic information for the formation of a gene product (proteins)
RNA polymerase	Transcription	Enzyme that copies information in the DNA to produce mRNA
mRNA	Transcription/ Translation	Moves information from the DNA to the ribosome
tRNA	Translation	Translates genetic information into amino acid sequences
rRNA	Translation	Helps form the structure of the ribosome
Amino acid	Translation	Monomers used to build a polypeptide chain

Transcription Factors

In human cells, **transcription factors** are DNA-binding proteins. At one time, scientists thought that transcription factors simply act as on/off switches for genes. We now know this role of transcription factors is much more complex. A better analogy is that the level of gene expression is controlled like a variable light switch, with a variety of transcription factors fine-tuning the transcription process. Every cell contains many different types of transcription factors. After the right combination of transcription factors and other associated regulatory proteins bind to DNA, an RNA polymerase attaches to the DNA and begins the process of transcription.

As cells mature, they differentiate and become specialized. Specialization is determined by which genes are active and, therefore, perhaps, by which transcription factors are active in that cell. Signals received from inside and outside the cell could turn on or off genes that code for certain transcription factors. For example, in an embryo, the hand is flattened and paddle-shaped. The five fingers are joined by webs of skin and connective tissue. The gene for apoptosis (programmed cell death) is turned on in the embryo's hand. Separated fingers are formed when the webs of tissue die off.

CHECK YOUR PROGRESS 22.2

1. Summarize the processes of transcription and translation.
2. Explain how the genetic code is involved in gene expression.
3. Explain how mRNA, tRNA, and rRNA are involved in gene expression.
4. Identify the various means of gene regulation in a eukaryotic cell.

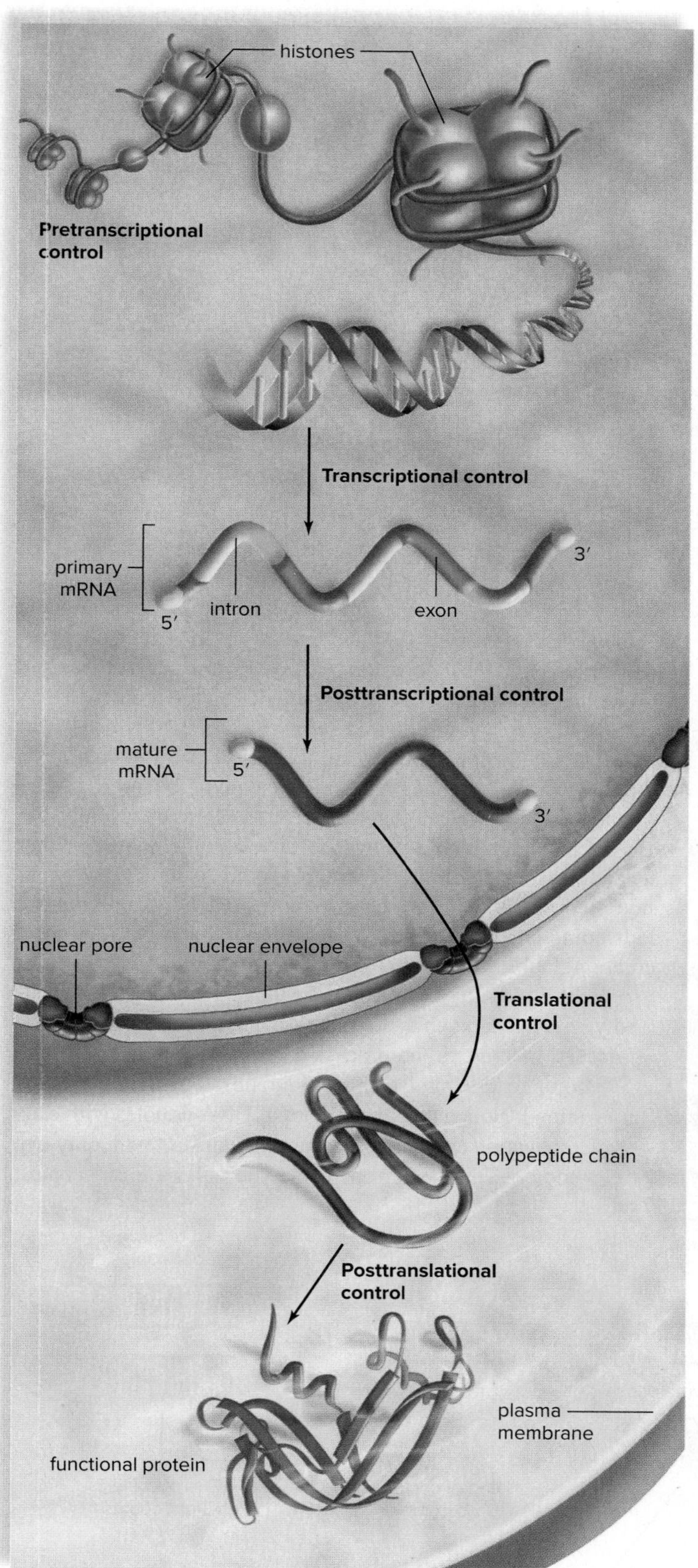

Figure 22.12 Levels of control of gene expression in eukaryotic cells.
Gene expression is controlled at various levels in eukaryotic cells. Three mechanisms pertain to the nucleus and two mechanisms pertain to the cytoplasm. An external signal (red) may also alter gene expression.

CONNECTING THE CONCEPTS

For more information on DNA, RNA, and proteins, refer to the following discussions:

Section 2.6 examines the structure of proteins and their role in the body.

Section 2.7 describes the role of DNA and RNA as organic molecules.

22.3 DNA Technology

LEARNING OUTCOMES

Upon completion of this section, you should be able to

1. Recognize the importance of DNA sequencing to the study of biology.
2. State the purpose of the polymerase chain reaction and DNA cloning.
3. Understand the goals of genome editing.
4. Summarize some of the products that have been produced using biotechnology.

The term **biotechnology** refers to the use of natural biological systems to create a product or achieve some other end desired by humans. Today, **genetic engineering** allows scientists to modify the genomes of a variety of organisms, from bacteria to plants and animals, to either improve the characteristics of the organism or make biotechnology products. Such modification is possible because decades of research on how DNA and RNA function in cells has allowed for the development of new techniques. These techniques allow scientists not only to clone genes but also to directly edit the genome of an organism. Before exploring some of the ways this has been done, we need to examine some of the DNA techniques used in biotechnology.

DNA Sequencing

DNA sequencing is a procedure that determines the order of nucleotides in a segment of DNA, often within a specific gene. DNA sequencing allows researchers to identify specific alleles associated with a genetic disorder and thus facilitate the development of medicines or treatments. This information also serves as the foundation for the study of forensic biology and even contributes to our understanding of our evolutionary history (see Chapter 23).

When DNA technology was in its inception in the early 1970s, this technique was performed manually using dye-terminator substances or radioactive tracer elements attached to each of the four nucleotides during DNA replication, with results being deciphered from their pattern on a gel plate. Modern-day sequencing involves dyes attached to the nucleotides and use of a laser to detect the different dyes by an automated sequencing machine, which then provides a digital representation of the nucleotide sequence (Fig. 22.13).

To begin sequencing a segment of DNA, many copies of the segment are made, or replicated, using a procedure called the polymerase chain reaction.

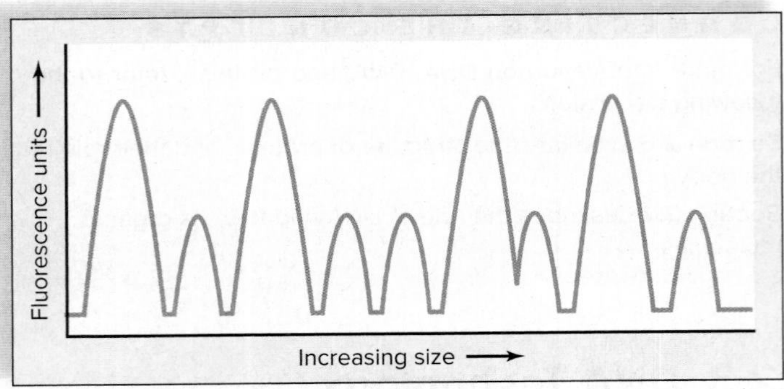

a. Automated DNA sequencing

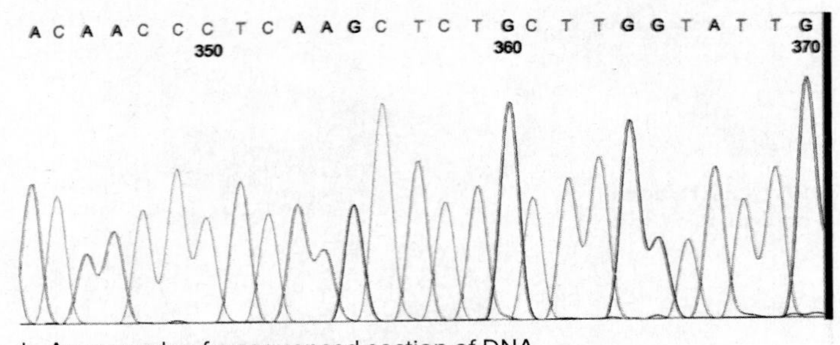

b. An example of a sequenced section of DNA

Figure 22.13 Automated DNA sequencing.
a. Modern DNA sequencing techniques use fluorescent dyes that allow researchers to determine the nucleotide sequence of a segment of DNA.
b. An example of a DNA sequence.
(b): Alan John Lander Phillips/E+/Getty Images

Polymerase Chain Reaction

The **polymerase chain reaction (PCR)** can create millions of copies of a segment of DNA in a test tube in a matter of hours. PCR is very specific—it *amplifies* (makes copies of) a targeted DNA sequence, usually a few hundred bases in length. PCR requires the use of DNA polymerase, the enzyme that carries out DNA replication, and a supply of nucleotides for the new DNA strands. PCR involves three basic steps (Fig. 22.14), which occur repeatedly, usually for about 35 to 40 cycles: (1) a denaturation step at 92–95°C, in which DNA is heated to become single-stranded; (2) an annealing step at a temperature usually between 50° and 60°C, in which an oligonucleotide primer hybridizes to each of the single DNA strands; and (3) an extension step at 72°C, in which an engineered DNA polymerase adds complementary bases to each of the single DNA strands, creating double-stranded DNA.

PCR is a chain reaction because the targeted DNA is repeatedly replicated, much in the same way natural DNA replication occurs, as long as the process continues. Figure 22.14 uses color to distinguish the old strand from the new DNA strand. Notice that the amount of DNA doubles with each replication cycle. Thus, assuming you start with only one copy of DNA, after one cycle you will have two copies,

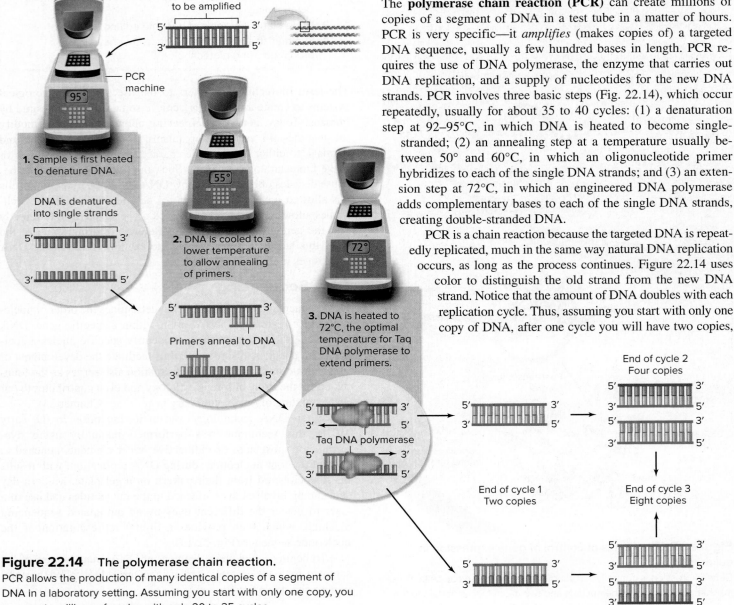

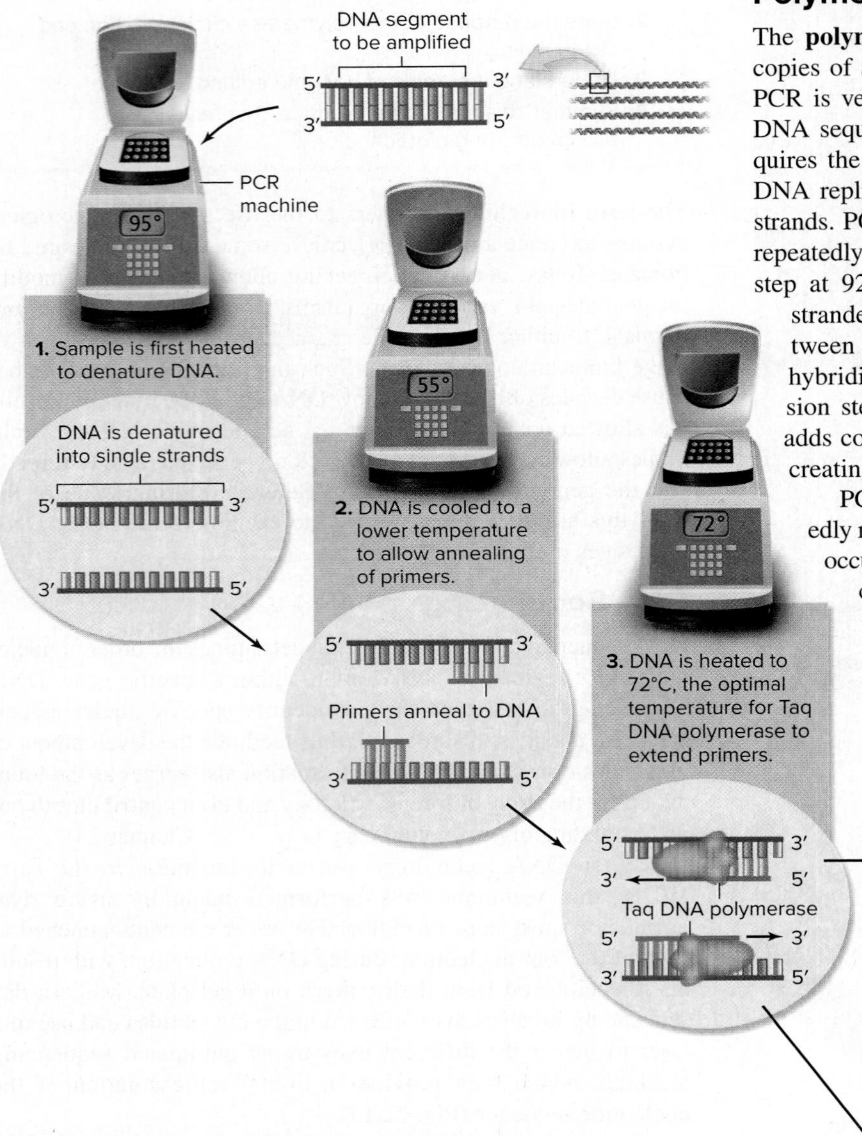

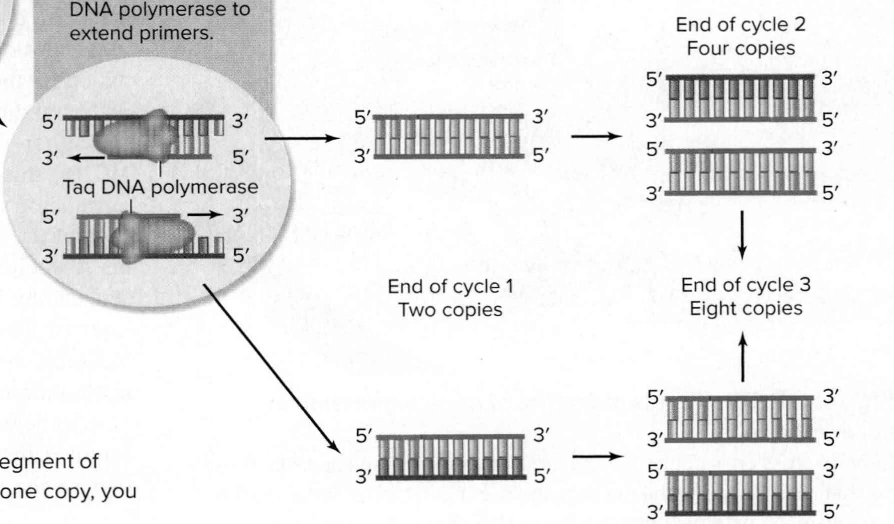

DNA segment to be amplified
5′ 3′
3′ 5′
PCR machine
95°
1. Sample is first heated to denature DNA.
DNA is denatured into single strands
5′ 3′
3′ 5′
55°
2. DNA is cooled to a lower temperature to allow annealing of primers.
5′ 3′
Primers anneal to DNA
3′ 5′
72°
3. DNA is heated to 72°C, the optimal temperature for Taq DNA polymerase to extend primers.
5′ 3′
3′ 5′
Taq DNA polymerase
5′ 3′
3′ 5′
End of cycle 1
Two copies
End of cycle 2
Four copies
End of cycle 3
Eight copies

Figure 22.14 The polymerase chain reaction.
PCR allows the production of many identical copies of a segment of DNA in a laboratory setting. Assuming you start with only one copy, you can create millions of copies with only 30 to 35 cycles.

after two cycles four copies, and so on. PCR has been in use since its development in 1985 by Kary Banks Mullis, and now almost every laboratory has automated PCR machines to carry out the procedure. Automation became possible after a heat-stable DNA polymerase was extracted from the bacterium *Thermus aquaticus,* which lives in hot springs. The enzyme can withstand the high temperature used to denature double-stranded DNA. Therefore, replication does not have to be interrupted by the need to add more enzyme. Only a small amount of DNA is required for PCR to be effective, so it has even been possible to sequence DNA from the tiniest sample at a crime scene or from mummified human brains.

Also, following PCR, DNA can be subjected to DNA fingerprinting, also called DNA profiling. Today, DNA fingerprinting is often carried out by detecting how many times a short sequence (two to five bases) is repeated. Individuals may differ by how many repeats they have at particular locations (Fig. 22.15).

Recall that PCR amplifies only particular portions of the DNA. Therefore, the greater the number of repeats at a location, the longer the section of DNA amplified by PCR. During a process called capillary gel electrophoresis, these DNA fragments can be separated according to their size; the result is a pattern of fluorescent peaks. If two DNA patterns match, there is a high probability that the DNA came from the same source. It is customary to test for the number of repeats at several locations to further define the source.

Much of the forensic DNA fingerprinting done today uses short tandem repeats (STRs)—stretches of noncoding DNA in our genome that contain repeated DNA sequences. STRs are inherited in a Mendelian fashion (see Section 21.2). Most commonly, these repeats are four bases in length—for example, CATG. You may have 11 copies of this repeat on a particular chromosome inherited from your father and only 3 copies on the homologous chromosome from your mother. When analyzed by electrophoresis, greater numbers of repeats correspond to increasing lengths on the DNA. People have unique repeat patterns, so these STRs can be used to discriminate between individuals. A particular STR pattern on a single chromosome may be shared by a number of people. However, by studying multiple STR sites, a statistically unique pattern can be developed for everyone—unless you share your DNA with an identical twin! In the United States, the FBI's Combined DNA Index System (CODIS) uses 13 STR sites (plus a marker for sex called the amelogenin gene) to identify individuals.

DNA fingerprinting has many uses. When the DNA matches that of a virus or mutated gene, it is known that a viral infection, genetic disorder, or cancer is present. Fingerprinting DNA from a single sperm is enough to identify a person suspected of rape. DNA fingerprinted from blood or tissues at a crime scene has been successfully used in convicting people of crimes.

Applications of PCR and DNA fingerprinting are limited only by our imagination. PCR analysis has been used to identify unknown soldiers and members of the royal Russian family. Paternity suits can be settled. Environmental law enforcement authorities can identify illegally poached ivory and whale meat using these technologies. These applications have shed new light on evolutionary studies by comparing DNA from fossils with that of living organisms. PCR reactions have also been used effectively as a diagnostic tool to determine if an individual has been exposed to the SARS-CoV-2 virus.

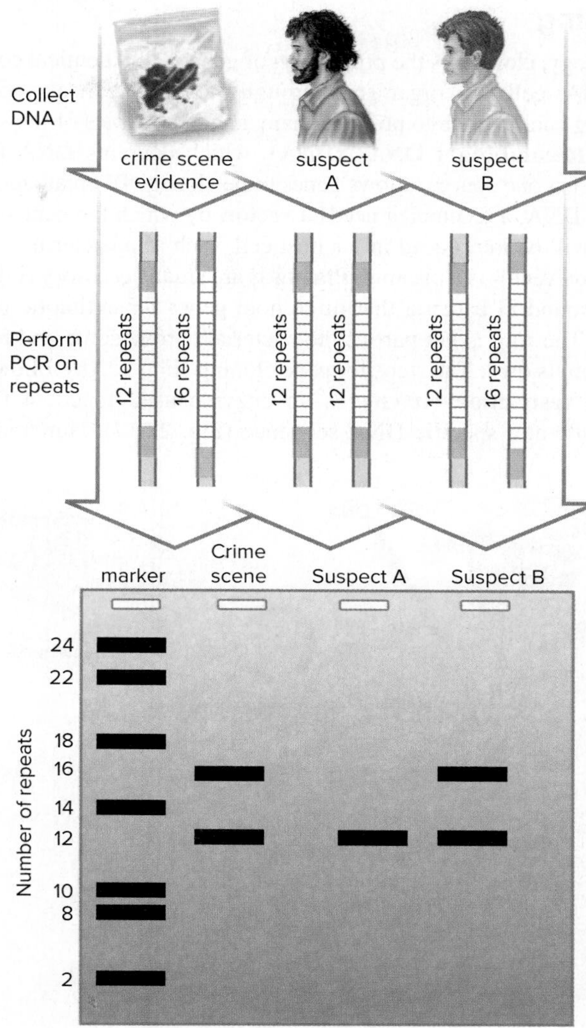

Figure 22.15 **DNA fingerprinting.**
To establish a DNA fingerprint, short segments of DNA from samples are amplified by a PCR reaction. These fragments are then separated using gel electrophoresis (or a detector) to look for small variations in the length of the fragments.

BIOLOGY IN YOUR LIFE

How do the home DNA paternity kits work?

Many laboratories now have kits allowing the collection of a sample to be done at home. The collection consists of taking a buccal swab of both the child and the possible father. This is a DNA sample from inside the mouth taken by rubbing the inside of the cheeks with a sterilized swab. This sample is then sent to the lab, where the DNA is replicated by PCR and DNA fingerprinting occurs. Most labs will look at 12 to 16 different chromosomal markers to identify paternity, and results are ready in about 3 to 5 days. Although efficient, private, and quick, these home test results are not approved by the court system as evidence.

Cloning

In biology, **cloning** is the production of genetically identical copies of DNA, cells, or organisms through an asexual means. **Gene cloning** can be done to produce many identical copies of the same gene. **Recombinant DNA (rDNA),** which contains DNA from more than one source, allows genes to be cloned. To create recombinant DNA, a technician needs a **vector,** by which the gene of interest will be introduced into a host cell, such as a bacterium. One common vector is a plasmid. **Plasmids** are small accessory rings of DNA found in bacteria that often hold genes for antibiotic resistance. The ring is not part of the bacterial chromosome and replicates on its own. The steps for gene cloning (Fig. 22.16) follow.

A **restriction enzyme** is an enzyme used to cut a DNA molecule at a specific DNA sequence (Fig. 22.17). Hundreds of restriction enzymes occur naturally in bacteria, where they cut up any viral DNA that enters the cell. They are called *restriction enzymes* because they restrict the growth of viruses. They also act as molecular scissors to cleave any piece of DNA at a specific site. For example, the restriction enzyme called *Eco*RI always cuts double-stranded DNA at this sequence of bases and in this manner:

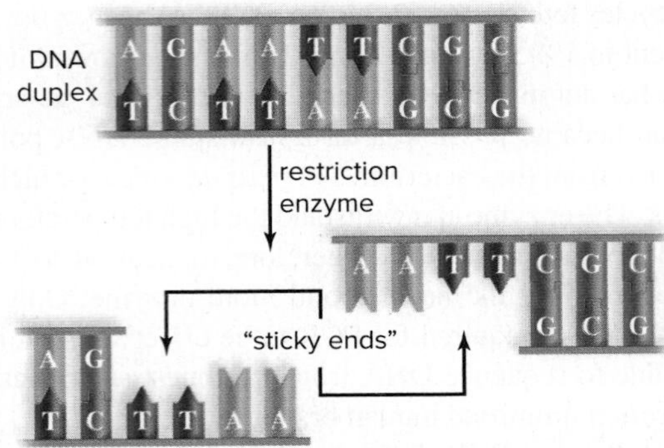

Figure 22.17 Restriction enzymes.
Each restriction enzyme recognizes a specific sequence of nucleotides. After the enzyme cuts the DNA, "sticky ends" may be formed that are useful in the cloning of DNA sequences.

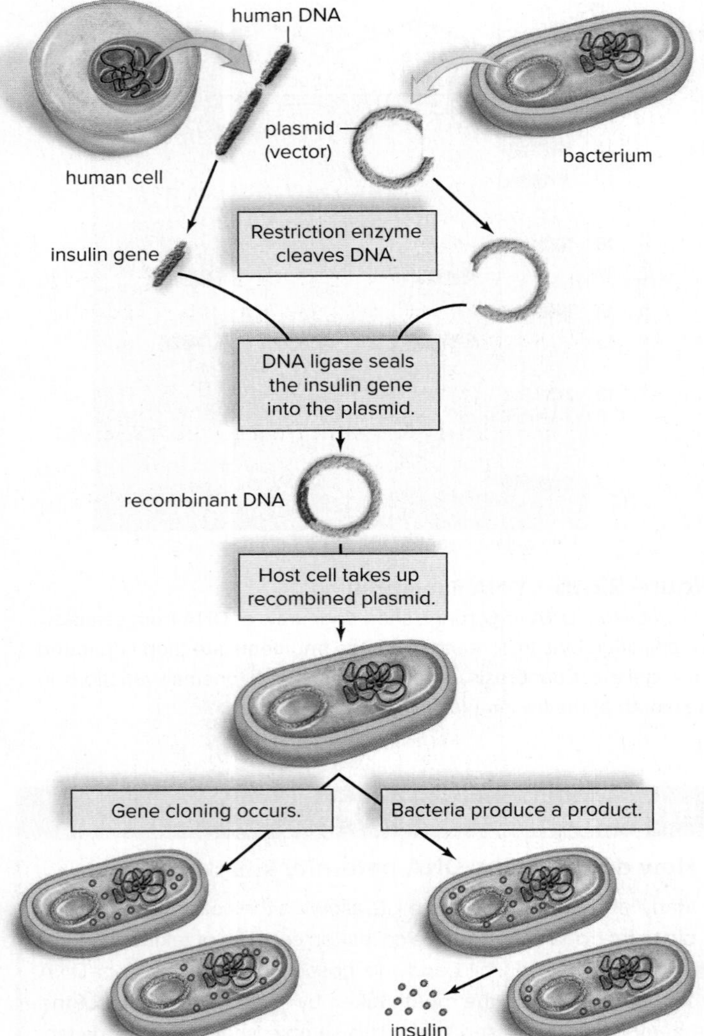

Figure 22.16 Cloning of a human gene.
This figure shows the basic steps in the cloning of a human gene. Human DNA and plasmid DNA are cleaved by a specific type of restriction enzyme. Then, the human DNA, perhaps containing the insulin gene, is spliced into a plasmid by the enzyme DNA ligase. Gene cloning is achieved after a bacterium or eukaryotic cell takes up the plasmid. If the gene functions normally as expected, the product (e.g., insulin) may also be retrieved.

The restriction enzyme creates a gap in plasmid DNA in which foreign DNA (possibly a human gene, such as the insulin gene, see Fig. 22.16) can be placed if it ends in bases complementary to those exposed by the restriction enzyme. To ensure this, it is only necessary to use the same type of restriction enzyme to cleave both human DNA containing the gene for insulin and plasmid DNA.

Next, an enzyme called *DNA ligase* is used to seal foreign DNA into the opening created in the plasmid. The single-stranded but complementary ends of a cleaved DNA molecule are called "sticky ends." This is because they can bind a piece of DNA by complementary base pairing. Sticky ends facilitate the sealing of the plasmid DNA with human DNA for the insulin gene to be cloned. Now the vector is complete, and an rDNA molecule has been prepared.

Some of the bacterial cells take up a recombinant plasmid, especially if the bacteria have been treated to make them more permeable. Gene cloning occurs as the plasmid replicates on its own. Scientists clone genes for a number of reasons. For instance, they might want to determine the difference in base sequence between a normal gene and a mutated gene, or they might use the genes to genetically modify organisms in a beneficial way.

The end result is a bacterium that can make a product (e.g., insulin) that it could not make before. For a human gene to express itself in a bacterium, the gene has to be accompanied by regulatory regions unique to bacteria. Also, the gene should not contain introns, because bacteria don't have introns. However, it is possible to make a human gene that lacks introns. The enzyme called reverse transcriptase can be used to make a DNA copy of mRNA. The DNA molecule, called **complementary DNA (cDNA),** does not contain introns. In this manner, the recombinant cells make many copies of themselves containing the new gene through mitosis, and each new cell will make the product coded for by the new gene.

The term *cloning* can be used in several different ways at the organismal level. The Science feature "Reproductive and Therapeutic Cloning" explains some of the differences between these methods.

BIOLOGY TODAY ▶ **Science**

Reproductive and Therapeutic Cloning

The term *cloning* may be used in several different ways in biology. In addition to the gene cloning shown in Figure 22.16, there is reproductive cloning—the ability to clone an adult animal from a normal body cell—and therapeutic cloning, which allows the rapid production of mature cells of a specific type. Both types of cloning are a direct result of recent discoveries about how the cell cycle is controlled.

Reproductive cloning, or the cloning of adult animals, was once thought to be impossible, because investigators found it difficult to have the nucleus of an adult cell "start over" with the cell cycle, even when it was placed in an egg cell that had its own nucleus removed.

In 1997, Dolly the sheep demonstrated that reproductive cloning is indeed possible. The donor cells were starved before the cell's nucleus was placed in an egg that had its nucleus removed (enucleated). The starvation caused them to stop dividing and go into a G_0 (resting) stage, and this made the nuclei amenable to cytoplasmic signals for initiation of development (Fig. 22B*a*). This advance has made it possible to clone all sorts of farm animals that have desirable traits and even to clone rare animals that might otherwise become extinct. Despite the encouraging results, however, there are still obstacles to be overcome, and a ban on the use of federal funds for experiments to clone human embryos past the blastocyst stage remains firmly in place.

In *therapeutic cloning,* however, the objective is to produce mature cells of various cell types rather than an individual organism. The purposes of therapeutic cloning are (1) to learn more about how specialization of cells occurs and (2) to provide cells and tissues that could be used to treat human illnesses, such as diabetes, or major injuries, such as strokes or spinal cord injuries.

There are two possible ways to carry out therapeutic cloning. The first is to use the same procedure as reproductive cloning, except that *embryonic stem cells (ESCs),* which are derived from the inner mass cells of the blastocysts, are separated and each is subjected to a treatment that causes it to develop into a particular type of cell, such as red blood cells, muscle cells, or nerve cells (Fig. 22B*b*). Some people have ethical concerns about this type of therapeutic cloning, which is still experimental, because if the embryo were allowed to continue development it would become an individual.

The second way to carry out therapeutic cloning is to use *adult stem cells.* Stem cells are found in many organs of an adult's body; for example, the bone marrow has stem cells that produce new blood cells. However, adult stem cells are limited in the number of cell types they may become. Nevertheless, scientists are beginning to overcome this obstacle. In 2006, by adding just four genes to adult skin stem cells, Japanese scientists were able to coax the cells, called fibroblasts, into becoming induced pluripotent stem cells (iPSCs), a type of stem cell that is similar to an ESC. The researchers were then able to create heart and brain cells from the adult stem cells. Other researchers have used this technique to reverse Parkinson's-like symptoms in rats.

Although questions exist about the benefits of iPSCs, these advances demonstrate that scientists are actively investigating methods of overcoming the current limitations and ethical concerns of using embryonic stem cells.

Questions to Consider

1. How might the study of therapeutic cloning benefit scientific studies of reproductive cloning?
2. What types of diseases might not be treatable using therapeutic cloning?

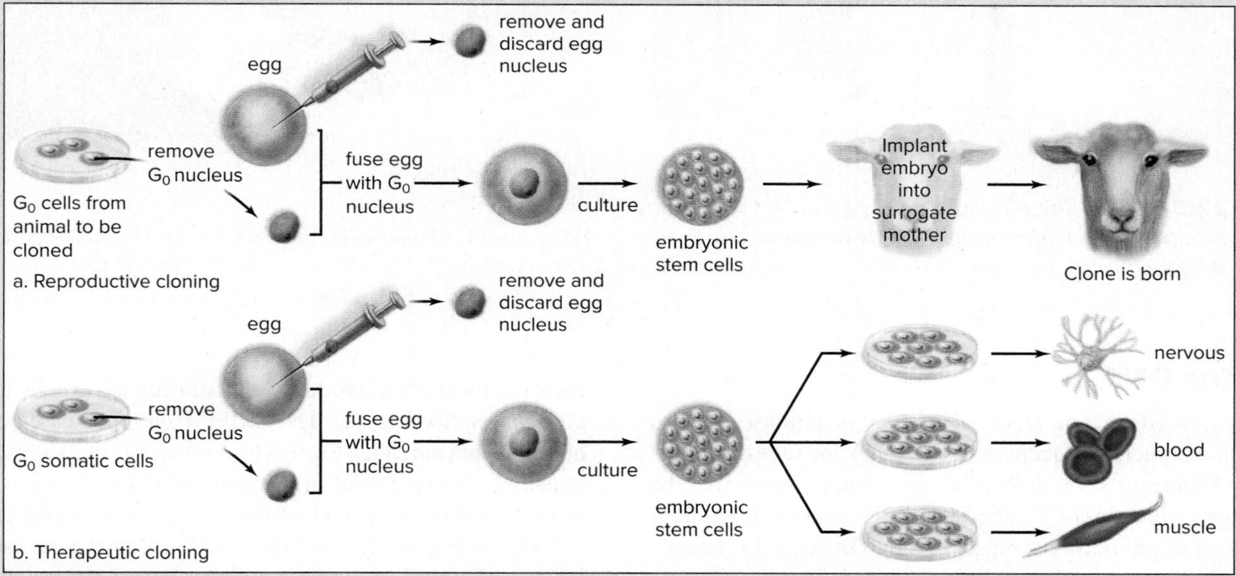

Figure 22B **Reproductive and therapeutic cloning.**
a. The purpose of reproductive cloning is to produce an individual that is genetically identical to the one that donated a nucleus. The nucleus is placed in an enucleated egg, and after several mitotic divisions, the embryo is implanted into a surrogate mother for further development. **b.** The purpose of therapeutic cloning is to produce specialized tissue cells. A nucleus is placed in an enucleated egg, and after several mitotic divisions, the embryonic cells (called embryonic stem cells) are separated and treated to become specialized cells.

BIOLOGY TODAY ▶ **Diversity in Science**

CRISPR Pioneers

Since 1901, the Nobel Prize in Chemistry has been awarded to 186 individuals. Only 7 have been women. Two were added to the list in 2020 when Emmanuelle Charpentier and Jennifer A. Doudna were awarded the prize for their pioneering work on the CRISPR method of genome editing (Fig. 22C).

Nobel Prizes are awarded to people who, according to Alfred Nobel, "have conferred the greatest benefit to humankind." Charpentier and Doudna both studied the CRISPR/Cas9 system as it related to bacterial immunity and began collaborating in 2011 after meeting at a scientific conference. Their experiments first led to important discoveries of how the system worked in bacteria to destroy the DNA of invading viruses. The big breakthrough happened when Charpentier and Doudna were able to simplify the molecules to create a "scalpel" that precisely cuts DNA at a location that could be programmed by the scientists.

The use of CRISPR gene-editing technology has since exploded. In the eight short years between the publication of the women's work and the Nobel Prize ceremony, other scientists have used the technique to benefit humankind through the development of genetically modified bacteria, plants, and animals. Trials are even underway that deploy the CRISPR scalpel into human patients in order to treat genetic disorders. CRISPR has also been proposed as a diagnostic tool for detecting the presence of viruses, such as SARS-CoV-2, in a patient.

In the wake of receiving an award that has historically gone to male scientists. Doudna reflected on its meaning, saying, "I'm proud of my gender. I think it's great, especially for younger women, to see this and to see that women's work can be recognized as much as men's."

Charpentier shared her hope for the next generation: "My wish is that this will provide a positive message to the young girls who would like to follow the path of science, and to show them that women in science can also have an impact through the research they are performing."

a.

b.

Figure 22C Nobel Prize recipients for CRISPR technology.
(a) Jennifer A. Doudna and **(b)** Emmanuelle Charpentier received the 2020 Nobel Prize in Chemistry for the development of CRISPR gene editing.
(a): Anastasiia Sapon/The New York Times/Redux Pictures; (b): Dpa picture alliance/Alamy Stock Photo

Editing the DNA

A relatively new advance in DNA technology is **genome editing,** the targeting of specific sequences in the DNA for removal or replacement. There are several methods by which editing may be done; the most widely used is called CRISPR (*c*lustered *r*egularly *i*nterspaced *s*hort *p*alindromic *r*epeats). The Diversity in Science feature "CRISPR Pioneers" highlights the two female scientists who developed the process.

CRISPR was first discovered in prokaryotes, where it acts as a form of immune defense against invading viruses. Viruses function by inserting their DNA into host cells, causing those cells to form new viruses (see Section 8.1). The CRISPR system is based on an endonuclease enzyme called Cas9, which is capable of identifying specific sequences of nucleotides in the genomic DNA of the invading virus and breaking both of the DNA strands, thus inactivating the virus.

Cas9 identifies the specific nucleotides to be cut using a guide RNA molecule that complementary base pairs to the genomic DNA sequence (Fig. 22.18).

The CRISPR system can be used by researchers to target a specific sequence of nucleotides, in almost any organism, for

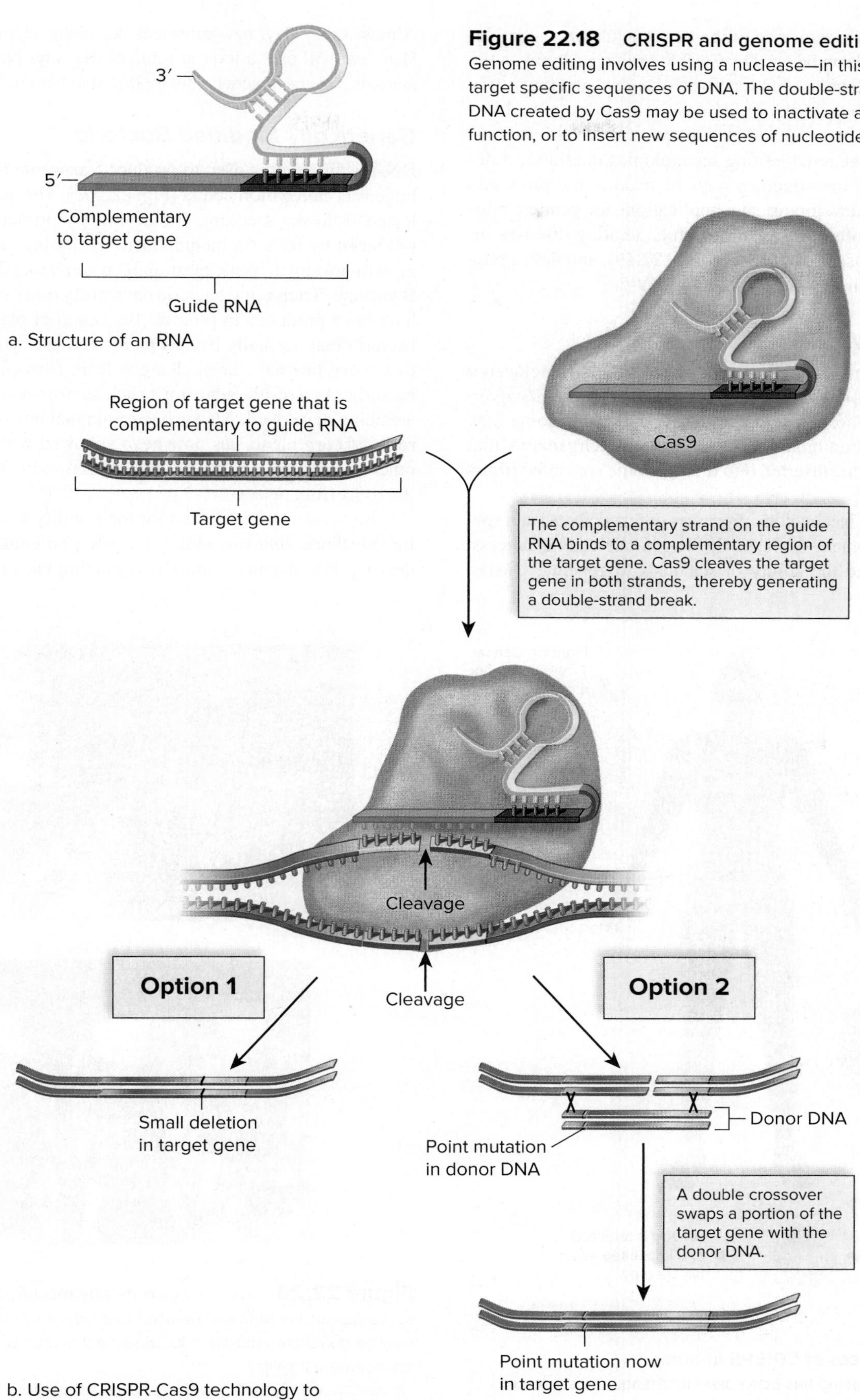
3′
5′
Complementary to target gene
Guide RNA
a. Structure of an RNA
Cas9
Region of target gene that is complementary to guide RNA
Target gene
The complementary strand on the guide RNA binds to a complementary region of the target gene. Cas9 cleaves the target gene in both strands, thereby generating a double-strand break.
Cleavage
Cleavage
Option 1
Option 2
Small deletion in target gene
Donor DNA
Point mutation in donor DNA
A double crossover swaps a portion of the target gene with the donor DNA.
Point mutation now in target gene
b. Use of CRISPR-Cas9 technology to inactivate a gene or create a point mutation

Figure 22.18 **CRISPR and genome editing.** Genome editing involves using a nuclease—in this case, Cas9—to target specific sequences of DNA. The double-stranded break in the DNA created by Cas9 may be used to inactivate a gene to study its function, or to insert new sequences of nucleotides.

editing. If the genomic sequence of the target is known, a complementary RNA strand can be used by Cas9 to produce a break in the DNA. This break can be used to inactivate the gene and thus study the role of the gene in the cell, or Cas9 can act as a form of molecular scissors to insert new nucleotides at specific DNA locations. CRISPR and other genome-editing technologies continue to develop. Scientists are investigating ways of making the processes more efficient, and developing new applications for genome editing in humans and other organisms, such as treating diseases including sickle-cell disease and cancer (Fig. 22.19), and developing new rapid tests for viruses such as SARS-CoV-2.

Biotechnology Products

Today, bacteria, plants, and animals may be genetically engineered to produce biotechnology products. A *genetically modified organism (GMO)* is one whose genome has been modified in some way, usually by using recombinant DNA technology. Organisms that have had a foreign gene inserted into their genome are called *transgenic organisms.*

The use of the biotechnology processes outlined above, and specifically the development of the CRISPR genome-editing process, has greatly facilitated the ability of scientists to generate GMOs. Almost every day, new advances are being reported by scientists. Here, we will take a look at some of the ways bacteria, plants, and animals have been genetically modified to benefit humans.

Genetically Modified Bacteria

DNA technology is used to produce transgenic bacteria, grown in huge vats called bioreactors (Fig. 22.20*a*). The gene product is collected from the medium. Biotechnology products on the market produced by bacteria include insulin, clotting factor VIII, human growth hormone, tissue plasminogen activator (tPA), and hepatitis B vaccine. Transgenic bacteria have many other uses as well. Some have been produced to promote the health of plants. For example, bacteria that normally live on plants and encourage the formation of ice crystals have been changed from frost-plus to frost-minus bacteria. As a result, new crops such as frost-resistant strawberries are being developed. Also, a bacterium that normally colonizes the roots of corn plants has now been endowed with genes (from another bacterium) that code for an insect toxin. The toxin protects the roots from insects.

Bacteria can be selected for their ability to degrade a particular substance, and this ability can then be enhanced by bioengineering. For instance, naturally occurring bacteria that eat oil can

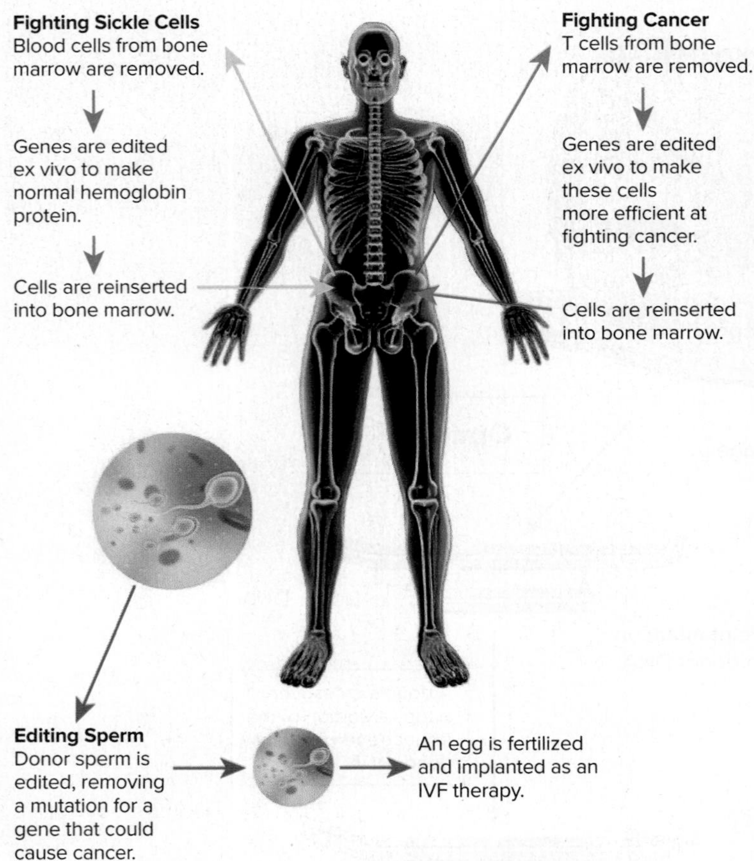
Fighting Sickle Cells
Blood cells from bone marrow are removed.
Genes are edited ex vivo to make normal hemoglobin protein.
Cells are reinserted into bone marrow.
Fighting Cancer
T cells from bone marrow are removed.
Genes are edited ex vivo to make these cells more efficient at fighting cancer.
Cells are reinserted into bone marrow.
Editing Sperm
Donor sperm is edited, removing a mutation for a gene that could cause cancer.
An egg is fertilized and implanted as an IVF therapy.

Figure 22.19 Uses of CRISPR in humans.
Direct human gene editing has been used to change the sickle-cell gene, fight cancer, and alter cancer genes in sperm.

a.

b.

Figure 22.20 Uses of genetically modified bacteria.
a. Transgenic bacteria can be used to produce medicines. **b.** Bacteria may be genetically modified to enhance their ability to clean up environmental spills.
(a): Maximilian/Prisma by Dukas Presseagentur GmbH/Alamy Stock Photo; (b): Jerry Mason/Science Source

be genetically engineered to do an even better job of cleaning up beaches after oil spills (Fig. 22.20*b*), such as the 2010 *Deepwater Horizon* spill in the Gulf of Mexico. Bacteria can also remove sulfur from coal before it is burned, resulting in cleaner emissions. One bacterial strain was given genes that allowed it to clean up levels of toxins that would have killed other bacterial strains. Further, these bacteria were given "suicide" genes that caused them to self-destruct when their job was done.

Genetically Modified Plants

Corn, potato, soybean, and cotton plants have been engineered to be resistant to either insect predation or commonly used herbicides. Some corn and cotton plants have been developed that are both insect- and herbicide-resistant. Annually, over 90% of the soybeans, corn, and cotton planted in the United States is genetically modified. If crops are resistant to a broad-spectrum herbicide and weeds are not, then the herbicide can be used to kill the weeds. When herbicide-resistant plants are planted, weeds are easily controlled, less tillage is needed, and soil erosion is minimized.

One of the main focuses of genetic engineering of plants has been the development of crops with improved qualities, especially improvements that reduce waste from food spoilage. For example, by knocking out a gene that causes browning in apples, a company called Okanagan Specialty Fruits produced the Arctic apple, a genetically modified apple with an increased shelf life (Fig. 22.21). A potato called Innate has been genetically modified using a process called *RNA interference,* which turns off the expression of genes associated with bruising.

Progress has also been made to increase the food quality of crops. Soybeans have been developed that mainly produce the monounsaturated fatty acid oleic acid, a change that may improve human health. Other types of crop plants are genetically engineered to increase their productivity. Leaves can be engineered to lose less water and take in more carbon dioxide. This type of modification helps a range of crops grow successfully in various climates, including those more likely to experience drought or have a higher average temperature than the plant's normal growing climate. Other single-gene modifications allow plants to produce various products, including human hormones, clotting factors, antibodies, and vaccines.

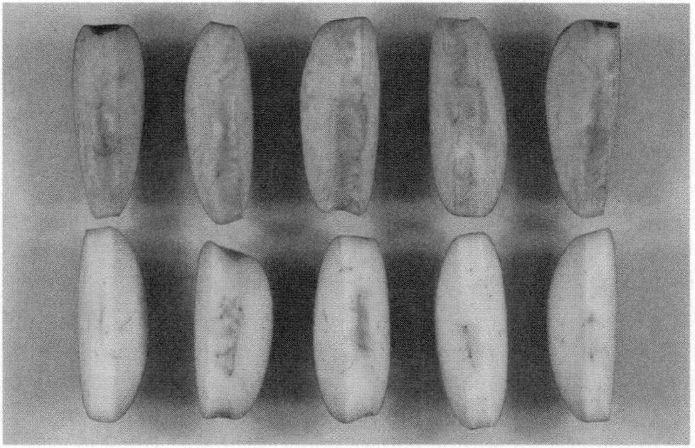

Figure 22.21 **Example of a genetically modified plant.** Genetic modification of these apples (*bottom row*) allows them to resist browning compared to other apples (*top row*).

Genetically Modified Animals

Like plants, animals can be genetically modified to increase their value as food products. A new form of transgenic salmon contains genes from two other fish species. These genes produce a growth hormone that allows the salmon to grow quicker. Interestingly, these salmon are also engineered to be triploid females, which makes them sterile and unable to transmit the growth hormone gene to future generations (Fig. 22.22*a*). The *Aedes aegypti* mosquito acts as a vector for several human diseases, including Zika and chikungunya. A transgenic form of the mosquito being released in Florida contains a genetic "kill switch," which produces proteins that kill the offspring, thus reducing the size of the population (Fig. 22.22*b*).

Gene pharming, the use of transgenic farm animals to produce pharmaceuticals, is being pursued by a number of firms. Genes that code for therapeutic and diagnostic proteins are incorporated into an animal's DNA, and the proteins appear in the

a.

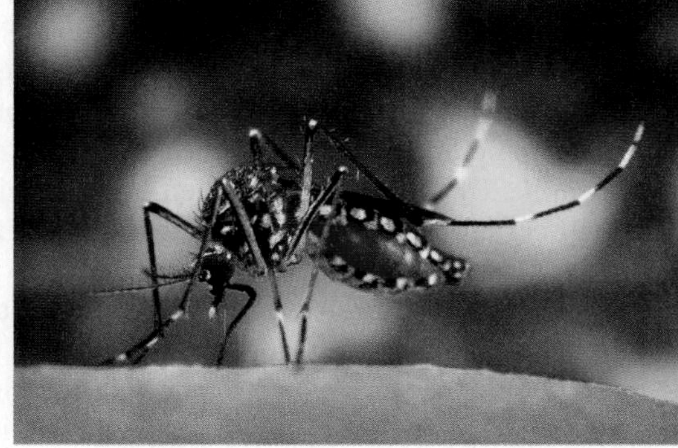

b.

Figure 22.22 **Examples of genetically modified animals.** **a.** Salmon may be genetically modified to grow faster. **b.** Pest species, such as the mosquito *Aedes egyptii,* may be genetically modified to reduce population size.

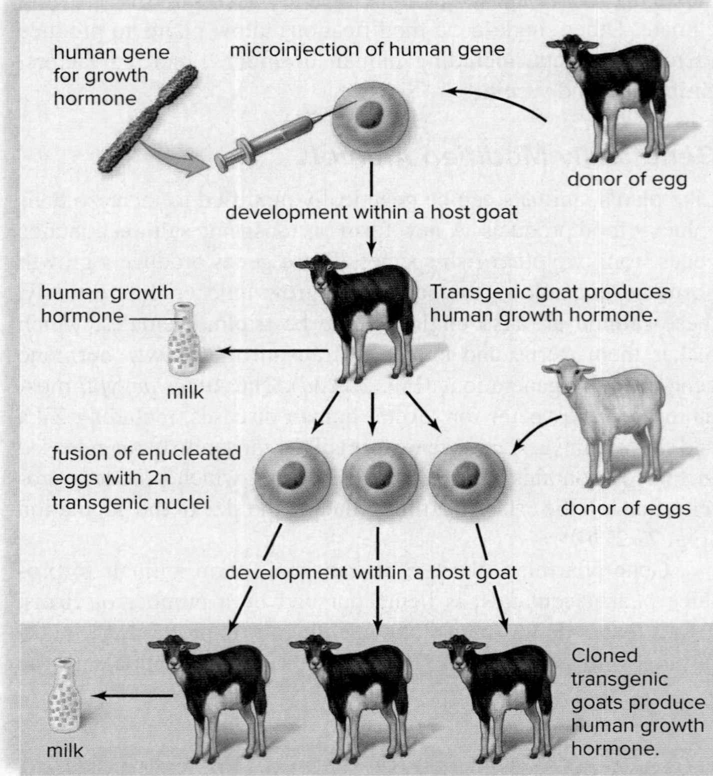

Figure 22.23 Production of a transgenic animal.
Once the desired human gene is introduced into a fertilized ovum, a single transgenic goat is produced. Using the first goat's cell nuclei and ova, a herd of transgenic goats can be developed. Each produces human growth hormone in its milk.

animal's milk (Fig. 22.23). Plans are underway to produce drugs for the treatment of cystic fibrosis, cancer, blood diseases, and other disorders by this method. Figure 22.23 outlines the procedure for producing transgenic animals. The gene of interest is microinjected into donor eggs. Following in vitro fertilization, the zygotes are placed in host females, where they develop. After transgenic female offspring mature, the product is secreted in their milk. Then, cloning can be used to produce many animals that produce the same product. Female clones produce the same product in their milk. This technique has been beneficial in producing milk with certain antibiotics or vaccines, in addition to milk with a higher nutritional value.

Mouse models have also been created to study human diseases. An allele such as the one that causes cystic fibrosis can be cloned and inserted into mice embryonic stem cells. Occasionally, a mouse embryo homozygous for cystic fibrosis will result. This embryo develops into a mutant mouse that has a phenotype similar to a human with cystic fibrosis. New drugs for the treatment of cystic fibrosis can then be tested in these mice. The same scenario is seen in the OncoMouse, which carries genes for the development of cancer.

Xenotransplantation is the use of animal organs instead of human organs in transplant patients. Currently, there are hundreds of thousands of individuals worldwide who are in need of organ transplants. Human donors are hard to match, and in most cases are not available. Scientists have chosen to use the pig because knowledge of pig breeding has a long history in animal husbandry and most pig organs match the size and structure of human organs. Additionally, the ability of pigs to express genes for human-recognition proteins means that pig organs will be more readily accepted by humans and rejection will be less likely to occur.

CHECK YOUR PROGRESS 22.3

1. Briefly describe how the polymerase chain reaction and DNA cloning are used to make copies of genes.
2. Explain how genome editing can change a nucleotide sequence.
3. Summarize the reasons genetically modified organisms (GMOs) are produced.

CONNECTING THE CONCEPTS

The procedures outlined in this section are used to study many important questions in the life sciences. For a few examples, refer to the following discussions:

Chapter 18 contains a discussion on the various forms of cloning.

Chapter 25 explores how biotechnology may be used to produce food for an increasing human population.

22.4 Genomics and Gene Therapy

LEARNING OUTCOMES

Upon completion of this section, you should be able to

1. Distinguish between functional and comparative genomics.
2. Distinguish between genomics and proteomics.
3. Explain the difference between in vivo and ex vivo gene therapy.

The Human Genome

Genetics in the twenty-first century concerns genomics, the study of genomes—our genes and the genes of other organisms. The Human Genome Project (HGP), whose purpose was to sequence the human genome, was completed in 2003 through a coordinated effort by the U.S. government and private laboratories and via contributions from many other countries, such as France, Japan, China, and Germany. During the 13-year study, many interesting facts emerged. The human genome contains approximately 3 billion bases, and 99.9% of these bases are identical in sequence in all humans. The average functional gene contains only about 3,000 bases; the number of functional genes in humans is estimated to be just under 20,000. These data were obtained through the use of advanced biotechnology, including PCR, electrophoresis, and DNA sequencing (see Section 22.3).

A surprising finding has been that genome size is not proportionate to the number of genes and does not correlate to the complexity of the organism. The flowering plant *Arabidopsis thaliana* has a genome size of 120 million bases and around 26,000 coding genes. The common house mouse, *Mus musculus,* has a genome of 2.5 billion bases and about 20,000 coding genes. When scientists first completed the DNA sequence of the human genome, they made an estimate of the number of genes based on sequences that appeared to encode proteins. Researchers have been surprised to find fewer than 20,000 genes in the human genome, surprisingly low from the original estimates of 80,000 to 140,000 genes. Furthermore, less than 2% of the entire human genome codes for functional proteins. Research suggests that the noncoding areas (the remaining 98%) of the genome may produce RNA molecules that play an important role in gene regulation.

Functional and Comparative Genomics

Goals of continuing research in the Human Genome Project are to determine how our approximately 20,000 genes function and how together they form a human. This type of study, called **functional genomics,** has already been successful in identifying the roles of many areas of noncoding DNA sequences (also called *intergenic* sequences because they occur between genes) in the production of small RNA molecules that are involved in gene regulation.

Comparative genomics is one way to determine how species have evolved and how genes and noncoding regions of the genome function. In one study, researchers compared our genome to that of chromosome 22 in chimpanzees. They found three types of genes of particular interest: a gene that is associated with speech, several for hearing, and several for smell. Genes necessary for speech development are thought to have played an important role in human evolution. You can suppose that changes in hearing may also have facilitated using language for communication between people. To explain differences in smell genes, investigators speculated that the olfaction genes may have affected dietary changes or sexual selection. Or they may have been involved in other traits, rather than just smell. The researchers who did this study were surprised to find that many of the other genes they located and studied are known to cause human diseases. They wondered if comparing genomes would be a way of finding other genes associated with human diseases. Investigators are taking all sorts of avenues to link human base sequence differences to illnesses.

Another surprising discovery has been how very similar the genomes of all vertebrates are. Researchers weren't surprised to learn that the base sequence of chimpanzees and humans is 95–98% alike. However, they didn't expect to find that our sequence is also 85% similar to that of a mouse, for example. So the quest is on to discover how the regulation of genes explains why we have one set of traits, while mice have another set, despite the similarity of our base sequences. One possibility is alternative gene splicing. We may differ from mice in the types of proteins we manufacture and/or by when and where certain proteins are present.

Proteomics and Bioinformatics

Proteomics is the study of the structure, function, and interaction of cellular proteins. Many of our genes are translated into proteins at some time, in some of our cells. The translation of all coding genes results in a collection of proteins called the human proteome. The analysis of proteomes is more challenging than the analysis of genomes. A single gene can code for several hundred different proteins, and protein concentrations can differ widely in cells. Researchers have to be able to identify proteins, regardless of whether there is one copy or thousands of copies of a protein in a cell. Any particular protein differs minute by minute in concentration, interactions, cellular location, and chemical modifications, among other features. But to understand a protein, all these features must be analyzed. Computer modeling of the three-dimensional shape of cellular proteins is an important part of proteomics. The study of cellular proteins and how they function is essential to understanding the causes of certain diseases and disorders. This study is also important in the discovery of better drugs, because most drugs are proteins or molecules that affect the function of proteins.

Bioinformatics is the application of computer technologies to the study of the genome. Specifically, it is the process of creating databases of information, and then mapping and analyzing the information gained from DNA sequencing and proteomics. Genomics and proteomics produce raw data. These fields depend on computer analysis to find significant patterns in the data. As a result of bioinformatics, scientists hope to find cause-and-effect relationships between various genetic profiles and genetic disorders caused by multifactorial genes. By correlating any sequence changes with resulting phenotypes, one current focus of bioinformatics research is discovering if noncoding regions of the genome do have functions, and if so, what effect those functions may have on homeostasis.

Gene Therapy

Gene therapy is the insertion of genetic material into human cells for the treatment of a disorder. Gene therapy has been used to cure inborn errors of metabolism and to treat more generalized disorders, such as cardiovascular disease and cancer. Most recently, several clinical trials have shown that gene therapy can successfully treat a type of inherited blindness. Both ex vivo (outside the body) and in vivo (inside the body) gene therapy methods are used.

Ex Vivo Gene Therapy

Figure 22.24 describes the methodology for treating children who have severe combined immunodeficiency disease (SCID). These children lack the enzyme adenosine deaminase (ADA), which is involved in the maturation of T and B cells. To carry out ex vivo gene therapy, stem cells are removed from bone marrow. These cells are mixed with a normal gene for the enzyme contained in a vector, or "carrier" molecule. The most successful vectors are viruses that have been altered for safety that are infectious, but not pathogenic. The combined cells are then returned to the patient. Bone marrow stem cells are preferred for this procedure because they divide to produce more cells with the same genes. Patients

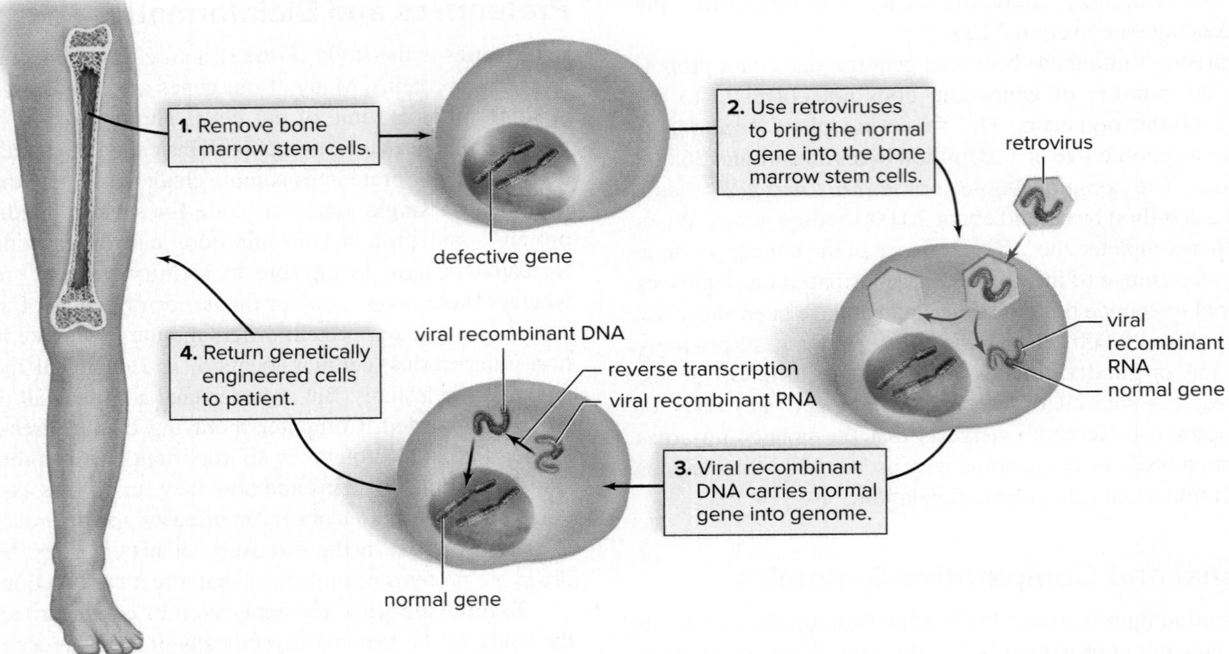

Figure 22.24 Gene therapy.
Bone marrow stem cells are withdrawn from the body, an RNA retrovirus is used to insert a normal gene into them, and they are then returned to the body.

with SCID who have undergone this procedure show significantly improved immune function and a sustained rise in ADA enzyme activity in the blood. Ex vivo gene therapy has also been proven effective for hemophilia A, Alzheimer's disease, Parkinson's disease, Crohn's disease, and certain cancers.

In Vivo Gene Therapy

Patients with cystic fibrosis (CF) lack a functional gene that codes for the transmembrane carrier of the chloride ion. They often have numerous and potentially deadly infections of the respiratory tract. For in vivo gene therapy, the therapeutic DNA is injected straight into the body cells. As in ex vivo therapy, the use of a vector is needed. For in vivo therapy, a retrovirus or an adenovirus is used as the vector that carries the corrective gene. For patients with CF, the adenovirus with the functioning gene is either sprayed into the nose or injected into the lower respiratory tract. This type of gene therapy is minimally invasive and gives quick results, but the effects are not as long lasting as ex vivo therapy. In vivo gene therapy has been used for cardiovascular diseases, endocrine disorders, and Huntington's disease.

CHECK YOUR PROGRESS 22.4

1. Describe how an understanding of genomics influences everyday life.
2. Discuss the differences between the study of genomics and proteomics.
3. Explain why gene therapy might be used over medication, and list some advantages and disadvantages.

CONNECTING THE CONCEPTS

The study of genomics and proteomics plays an important role in our understanding of evolutionary change. For more information, refer to the following discussions:

Section 23.2 examines how biochemical evidence, including the analysis of DNA, helps us understand biological evolution.

Section 23.3 explores how DNA evidence enables a deeper understanding of human evolution.

CONCLUSION

As we have learned in this chapter, DNA is the genetic information that contains the instructions required for the production of the proteins (and enzymes) involved in the majority of body functions. Scientists are now learning how to use the properties of DNA to develop solutions for society. For example, the development of synthetic DNA, with its unique collection of genetic information, may result in the capability to produce proteins with a number of benefits to humans. In addition, the use of DNA-based information storage devices may revolutionize the technology industry by providing the ability to store large amounts of information in a very small space.

BIOLOGY TODAY ▶ **Science**

Testing for Genetic Disorders

Prospective parents know if either of them has an autosomal dominant disorder because the person shows it. However, genetic testing is required to detect if either is a carrier for an autosomal recessive disorder. If a woman is already pregnant, the parents may want to know if the unborn child has the disorder. If the woman is not pregnant, the parents may opt for testing of an embryo or egg before she does become pregnant. One way to detect genetic disorders is to test the DNA for mutated genes.

Testing the DNA

Two types of DNA testing are possible: testing for a genetic marker and using DNA microarrays.

Genetic Markers

Testing for a genetic marker is similar to the traditional procedure for DNA fingerprinting (see Section 22.3). As an example, consider that individuals with Huntington's disease have an abnormality in the sequence of their bases at a particular location on a chromosome. This abnormality in sequence is a *genetic marker.* Huntington's disease, specifically, results from a trinucleotide repeat that is so long it causes a frameshift mutation within the gene. In this and similar cases, the length of the repeat can be detected with PCR and analysis on an automated DNA sequencer.

DNA Microarrays

With advances in robotic technology, it is possible to place the entire human genome onto a single microarray (Fig. 22D). The mRNA from the organism or the cell to be tested is labeled with a fluorescent dye and added to the chip. When the mRNAs bind to the microarray, a fluorescent pattern results and is recorded by a computer. Now the investigator knows what DNA is active in that cell or organism. A researcher can use this method to determine the difference in gene expression between two different cell types, such as between liver cells and muscle cells.

A *mutation microarray,* the most common type, can be used to generate a person's genetic profile. The microarray contains hundreds to thousands of known disease-associated mutant gene alleles. Genomic DNA from the individual to be tested is labeled with a fluorescent dye and then added to the microarray. The spots on the microarray fluoresce if the individual's DNA binds to the mutant genes on the chip, indicating that the individual may have a particular disorder or is at risk of developing it later in life. This technique can generate a genetic profile much more quickly and inexpensively than older methods involving DNA sequencing.

DNA microarrays also promise to hasten the identification of genes associated with diseased tissues. In the first instance, mRNA derived from diseased tissue and normal tissue is labeled with different fluorescent dyes. The normal tissue serves as a control.

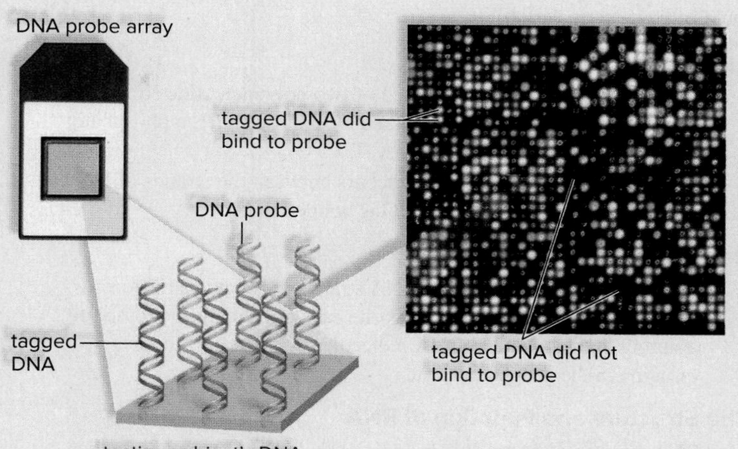

Figure 22D Use of a DNA microarray to test for a genetic disorder.
This DNA chip contains rows of DNA sequences for mutations that indicate the presence of particular genetic disorders. If DNA fragments derived from an individual's DNA bind to a sequence representing a mutation on the DNA chip, that sequence fluoresces, and the individual has the mutation.
(photo): Deco/Alamy Stock Photo

The investigator applies the mRNA from both normal and abnormal tissue to the microarray. The relative intensities of fluorescence from a spot on the microarray indicate the amount of mRNA originating from that gene in the diseased tissue relative to the normal tissue. If a gene is activated in the disease, more copies of mRNA will bind to the microarray than from the control tissue, and the spot will appear more red than green.

Genomic microarrays are also used to identify links between disease and chromosomal variations. In this instance, the chip contains genomic DNA that is cut into fragments. Each spot on the microarray corresponds to a known chromosomal location. Labeled genomic DNA from diseased tissues and control tissues bind to the DNA on the chip, and the relative fluorescence from both dyes is determined. If the number of copies of any particular target DNA has increased, more sample DNA will bind to that spot on the microarray relative to the control DNA, and a difference in fluorescence of the two dyes will be detected.

Questions to Consider

1. What benefits are there when using a DNA microarray over a genetic marker such as an STR?
2. Why might a researcher want to know which genes are being expressed in different cell types?
3. How might the information from a DNA microarray be used to develop new drugs to treat disease?

SUMMARIZE

22.1 DNA and RNA Structure and Function

DNA (deoxyribonucleic acid) is the genetic material. It is organized as **genes,** located on chromosomes. DNA replicates, stores information, and mutates for genetic variability.

Structure of DNA

- DNA is a **double helix** composed of two polynucleotide strands. Each **nucleotide** is composed of a deoxyribose sugar, a phosphate, and a nitrogen-containing base (A, T, C, G).
- **Complementary base pairing** occurs between the strands of DNA. The base A is bonded to T, and G is bonded to C.

Replication of DNA

- During **DNA replication,** the DNA strands unzip, and a new complementary strand forms opposite each old strand (the **template**), resulting in two identical DNA molecules. **Mutations** produce variation in the genetic material.

The Structure and Function of RNA

- **RNA (ribonucleic acid)** is a single-stranded nucleic acid in which the base U (uracil) occurs instead of T (thymine).
- The four primary forms of RNA are **ribosomal RNA (rRNA), messenger RNA (mRNA), transfer RNA (tRNA),** and several types of small RNAs.

22.2 Gene Expression

Gene expression leads to the formation of a product, either an RNA or a protein. Proteins differ by the sequence of their amino acids. Gene expression for proteins requires transcription and translation.

Transcription

Transcription occurs in the nucleus using an enzyme called **RNA polymerase.** The three-base DNA **codon** is passed to an mRNA that contains codons. Introns are removed from mRNA during mRNA processing.

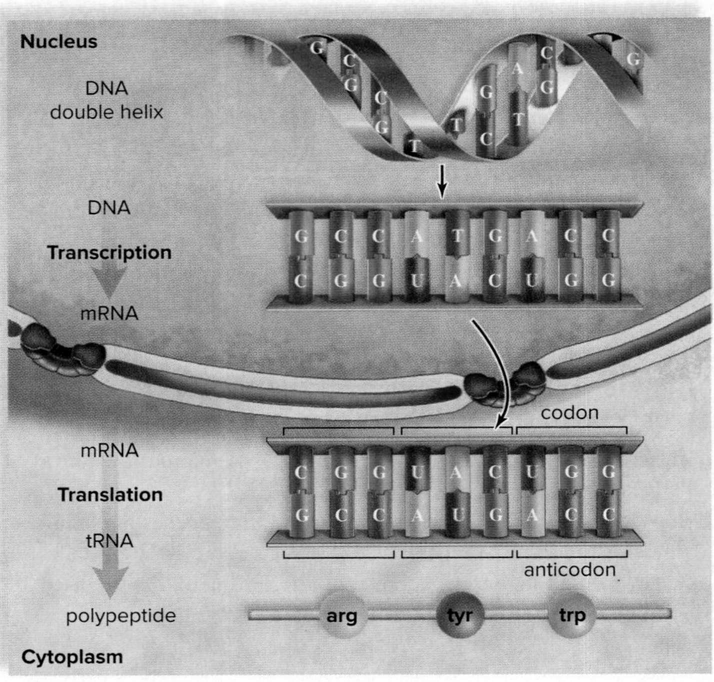

Translation

Translation occurs in the cytoplasm at the ribosomes. The tRNA molecules bind to their amino acids, and then their **anticodons** pair with mRNA codons.

The Regulation of Gene Expression

Regulation of gene expression occurs at five levels in a human cell.

- *Pretranscriptional control:* In the nucleus; the DNA is made available to transcription factors and enzymes.
- *Transcriptional control:* In the nucleus; the degree to which a gene is transcribed into mRNA determines the amount of gene product. **Transcription factors** are involved at this stage.
- *Posttranscriptional control:* In the nucleus; involves mRNA processing and how fast mRNA leaves the nucleus.
- *Translational control:* In the cytoplasm; affects when translation begins and how long it continues; includes inactivation and degradation of mRNA.
- *Posttranslational control:* In the cytoplasm; occurs after protein synthesis.

22.3 DNA Technology

Cloning is the production of genetically identical copies of DNA, cells, and organisms. **Gene cloning** has a variety of applications in biology.

- **Recombinant DNA (rDNA)** contains DNA from two different sources. The foreign gene and vector DNA are cut by the same **restriction enzyme** and then the foreign gene is sealed into **vector** DNA, such as bacterial **plasmids.** The reverse transcriptase enzyme may be used to make **complementary DNA (cDNA).**
- The **polymerase chain reaction (PCR)** uses DNA polymerase to make multiple copies of a specific piece of DNA. Following PCR, DNA can be subjected to DNA fingerprinting.
- **Genome editing** is a form of DNA technology that targets specific sequences in a genome for inactivation or the insertion of nucleotides. CRISPR is one of the leading methods of genome editing.

Some applications of DNA technology allow for **genetic engineering** and the production of transgenic organisms.

- **Transgenic organisms** (bacteria, plants, and animals that have had a foreign gene inserted into them) can produce **biotechnology products,** such as hormones and vaccines.
- Transgenic bacteria can promote plant health, remove sulfur from coal, clean up toxic waste and oil spills, extract minerals, and produce chemicals.
- Transgenic crops can resist herbicides and pests.
- Transgenic animals can be given growth hormone to produce larger animals, can supply transplant organs **(xenotransplantation),** and can produce pharmaceuticals.

22.4 Genomics and Gene Therapy

Genomics is the study of the genomes of humans and other organisms.

Functional and Comparative Genomics

- **Functional genomics** is the study of how the estimated 19,000 genes in a human genome function.
- **Comparative genomics** is a way to determine how species have evolved and how genes and noncoding regions of the genome function.

Proteomics and Bioinformatics

- **Proteomics** is the study of the structure, function, and interaction of cellular proteins.
- **Bioinformatics** is the application of computer technologies to the study of the genome.

Gene Therapy

Gene therapy allows for the treatment of several human diseases.

- In ex vivo gene therapy, cells are removed from the body for treatment, then reintroduced back into the body.
- In in vivo therapy, the vector is introduced directly into the body.

ENGAGE

BioNOW

Want to know how this science is relevant to your life? Check out the BioNOW video below:

- Glowing Fish Genetics

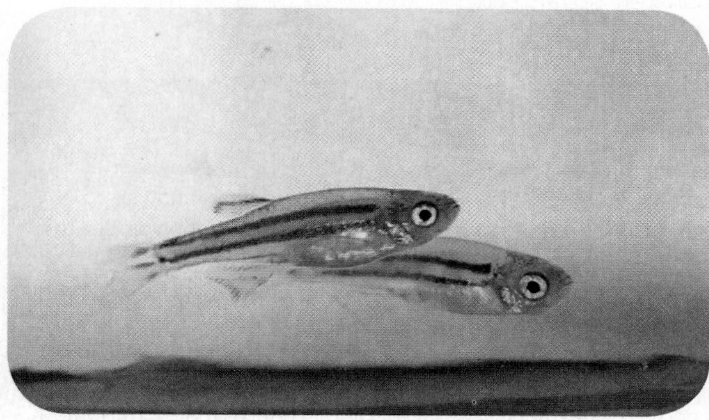

McGraw Hill

The U.S. Food and Drug Administration (FDA) had to grant approval for the fluorescent fish to be sold in the United States as pets. Some groups were opposed to this approval. What concerns exist regarding genetically modified organisms such as the fluorescent zebrafish?

THINKING CRITICALLY

The advances in biotechnology since the 1970s have made a huge impact on medicine and the treatment and management of certain diseases. The ability to combine DNA from two different organisms has given us the means to produce substances the body needs. It has also given doctors the ability to insert properly functioning genes into patients lacking those genes. With certain advances in biotechnology, ethical issues arise. Think about both sides when answering the following questions:

1. What are the advantages of using a recombinant DNA human product instead of a product isolated from another organism? (For example, what advantage would there be to using human recombinant insulin versus insulin produced from cows or pigs?)
2. Are there any disadvantages to using a recombinant DNA product? (*Hint:* You may want to think about how the product is produced and then purified.)
3. Recombinant human growth hormone is available for children and adults with growth hormone deficiency.
   a. When would use of the hormone be appropriate? Under what circumstances would hormone use be improper?
   b. How would a physician know that the hormone treatment was completely effective? What further information might you need to answer this question?
4. In general, diseases caused by a single protein deficiency are more easily treated with a recombinant DNA–produced product, yet certain cancers can be treated in this manner. What aspects of cancer can be treated with a product created using recombinant DNA?
5. What types of regulations should be placed on advances in DNA technology, and who should be responsible for these regulations?

MAKING IT RELEVANT

1. In what ways would the integration of DNA-based information storage systems into consumer devices, such as phones, computers, and even household appliances, change the way your life functioned on a daily basis?
2. How might synthetic DNA be used to fight human diseases, such as cancer? How about communicable diseases such as the flu?
3. From an evolutionary perspective, what concerns do you have about the development of organisms that include synthetic DNA?

Find answers to all of the chapter questions at connect.mheducation.com

CHAPTER 23 Human Evolution

(Neanderthal): Clément Philippe/ArTerra Picture Library/age fotostock; (smiling man): 4x6/iStockphoto/Getty Images

CHAPTER OUTLINE

BEFORE YOU BEGIN

Before beginning this chapter, take a few moments to review the following discussions:

Section 1.1 What is the definition of the term *evolution*?

Section 2.7 What are the differences between RNA and DNA?

Section 3.1 What are the basic principles of the cell theory?

The Neanderthal Within Us

Human evolution is a complex topic with a body of knowledge that is constantly growing. With advances in molecular analysis, DNA evidence has been able to provide important information about the relatedness between Neanderthals *(Homo neanderthalensis)* and modern humans *(Homo sapiens)*.

Starting around 100,000 years ago, evidence indicates that *H. sapiens* migrated into the *H. neanderthalensis* territory. Molecular studies have revealed that as recently as 47,000 years ago modern humans and Neanderthals were inbreeding. Neanderthals contributed 1–4% of the genes found in modern humans of Eurasian descent. For example, the SPAG17 protein helps move sperm, PCD16 assists in wound healing, TTF1 is involved in the transcription process, and RPTN is a protein found in the hair, skin, and sweat glands.

These discoveries, among others, have renewed interest in discovering the genes that distinguish us from our closest ancestors and, in the process, in developing a greater understanding of the evolutionary history of our species.

In this chapter, we will explore the basic principles of evolution, and then apply these to develop an understanding of our evolutionary past.

As you read through the chapter, think about the following questions:

1. What was the last common ancestor of both Neanderthals and *Homo sapiens*?
2. What is the current thinking on the evolutionary relationship of the Neanderthals to modern humans?
3. How does the evidence for evolution support the concept of human evolution?

23.1 Origin of Life

LEARNING OUTCOMES

Upon completion of this section, you should be able to

1. Describe the conditions of the early Earth's atmosphere.
2. Distinguish between chemical and biological evolution.
3. Discuss how the first organic monomers and polymers may have evolved.
4. Summarize how the first true cell evolved.

In Section 1.1, we explored the basic characteristics shared by all living organisms. Living organisms acquire energy through metabolism, or the chemical reactions that occur within cells. They also respond to and interact with their environment, self-replicate, and are subject to the forces of natural selection that drive adaptation to the environment. The first living organisms on Earth would have had all of these characteristics, yet early Earth was very different from the Earth we know today and was comprised mainly of inorganic substances. The molecules of life, called *biomolecules,* are organic molecules (see Section 2.3). How, then, did life get started on our planet?

Advances and discoveries in chemistry, evolutionary biology, paleontology, microbiology, and other branches of science have helped scientists develop new, and test old, hypotheses about the origin of life. These studies contribute to an ever-growing body of scientific evidence that life originated 3.5 to 4 billion years ago (BYA) from nonliving matter over a series of four stages (Fig. 23.1):

- *Stage 1: Small organic molecules.* Simple organic molecules, called *monomers,* evolved from inorganic compounds prior to the existence of cells. Amino acids (the basis of proteins) and nucleotides (the building blocks of DNA and RNA) are examples of organic monomers.
- *Stage 2: Macromolecules.* Organic monomers were joined to form larger macromolecules *(polymers),* such as DNA, RNA, and proteins.
- *Stage 3: Protocells.* Organic polymers became enclosed in a membrane to form the first cell precursors, called protocells or protobionts.
- *Stage 4: Living cells.* Protobionts acquired the ability to self-replicate, as well as other cellular properties.

Scientists have performed experiments to test hypotheses at each stage of the origin of life. Stages 1–3 involve the processes of **chemical evolution** and occurred before the origin of life. Stage 4 is when life first evolved through the processes of **biological evolution.** In this section, we will examine the hypotheses and supporting scientific evidence for each stage of chemical and biological evolution: the origin of life from nonliving matter.

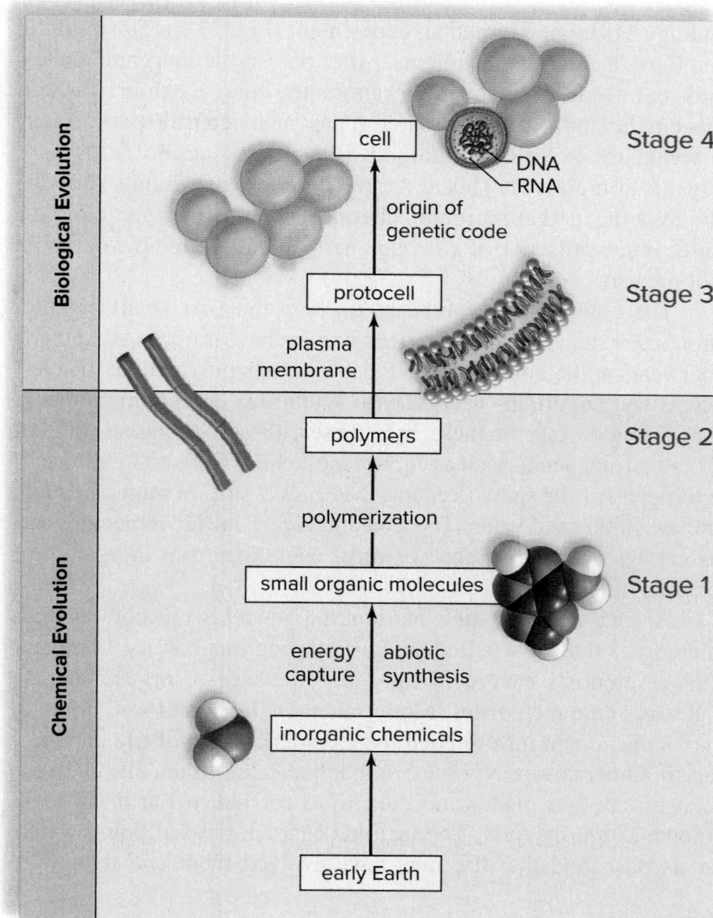

Figure 23.1 **Chemical and biological evolution.** The first organic molecules (*bottom*) originated from chemically altered inorganic molecules present on early Earth (Stage 1). More complex organic macromolecules were synthesized to create polymers (Stage 2), which were then enclosed in a plasma membrane to form the protocells, or protobionts (Stage 3). The protocell underwent biological evolution to produce the first true, self-replicating, living cell (Stage 4).

Small Organic Molecules

The early Earth's atmosphere was not the same as today's atmosphere. Most likely, the first atmosphere was formed by gases escaping from volcanoes. If so, the primitive atmosphere would have consisted mostly of water vapor (H_2O), nitrogen (N_2), and carbon dioxide (CO_2), with only small amounts of hydrogen (H_2) and carbon monoxide (CO). The primitive atmosphere had little, if any, free oxygen.

At first, the Earth and its atmosphere were extremely hot. Water, existing only as a gas, formed dense, thick clouds. Then, as the Earth cooled, water vapor condensed to liquid water, and rain began to fall. The rain washed gases, and other chemicals, into the oceans. Rain fell in such enormous quantities over hundreds of millions of years that the Earth's oceans were produced.

The primitive Earth had many sources of energy. These included volcanoes, meteorites, radioactive isotopes, lightning, and ultraviolet radiation. In the presence of so much available energy, the primitive gases may have reacted with one another. This may have produced small organic compounds, such as nucleotides and amino acids (Stage 1 of Fig. 23.1). In 1953,

Stanley Miller performed an experiment (Fig. 23.2). To simulate the Earth's early environment, Miller placed the inorganic materials believed to have been present on the early Earth in a closed system, heated it, and circulated it past an electrical spark. After a week, the solution contained a variety of amino acids and organic compounds. This and other similar experiments support the hypothesis that inorganic chemicals can form organic molecules in the presence of a strong energy source, even if oxygen is not present.

There are other hypotheses on how the first small organic monomers may have evolved. Researchers have proposed that thermal vents at the bottom of the Earth's oceans provided all the elements and conditions necessary to synthesize organic monomers. According to one of these hypotheses, dissolved gases emitted from thermal vents, such as carbon monoxide (CO), ammonia, and hydrogen sulfide, pass over iron and nickel sulfide minerals, also present at thermal vents. The iron and nickel sulfide molecules act as catalysts that drive the chemical evolution from inorganic to organic molecules.

A very different line of thinking involves the comets and meteorites that have pelted the Earth throughout history. In recent years, scientists have confirmed the presence of organic molecules in some meteorites. Many scientists feel that these organic molecules could have seeded the chemical origin of life on early Earth. Others even hypothesize that bacterium-like cells evolved first on another planet and then were carried to Earth, an idea known as *panspermia.* The fact that Mars possessed liquid water in its past, and that life may have evolved there and then was carried to Earth, is one hypothesis that is being examined. Another event that lends evidence to panspermia is the discovery of glycerine and phosphorus found in the Churyumov–Gerasimenko comet in 2015. Glycerine is important because it is found in fat and is necessary for metabolic processes. The discovery of phosphorus is significant because it is an important element in so many biological molecules, such as ATP, DNA, RNA, and phospholipids.

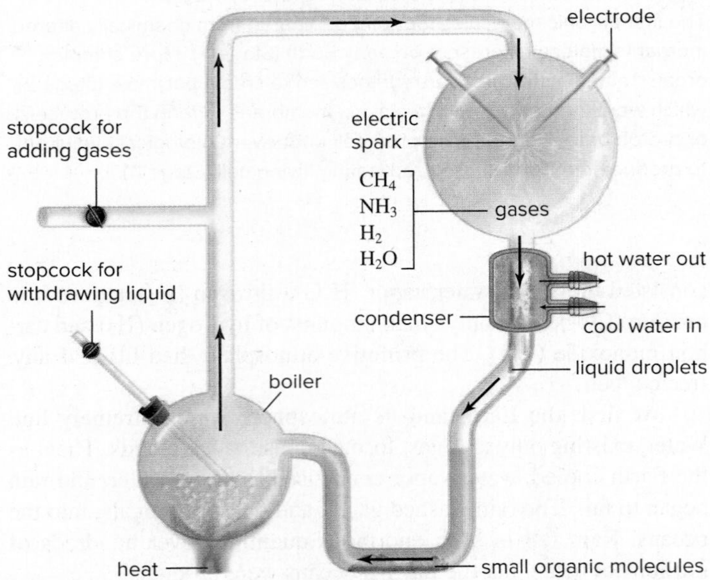

Figure 23.2 **The Stanley Miller experiment.**
Gases thought to be present early in the Earth's atmosphere were admitted to the apparatus, circulated past an energy source (electrical spark), and cooled to produce a liquid that could be withdrawn. Upon chemical analysis, the liquid was found to contain various small organic molecules.

Macromolecules

The newly formed small organic molecules likely joined to produce larger polymers (Stage 2 of Fig. 23.1). There are two hypotheses of special interest concerning this stage in the origin of life. One is the **RNA-first hypothesis.** This suggests that only the macromolecule RNA was needed at this time to progress toward formation of the first cell or cells. This hypothesis was formulated after the discovery that RNA can sometimes be both a substrate and an enzyme during RNA processing (see Section 22.2). At that time, the splicing of mRNA to remove introns (internal portions of a gene that do not code for proteins) was done by a complex composed of both RNA and protein. The RNA, not the protein, is the enzyme. RNA enzymes are called *ribozymes.* Then, too, ribosomes where protein synthesis occurs contain rRNA. Perhaps, then, RNA could have carried out the processes of life commonly associated with DNA and proteins. Scientists who support this hypothesis are fond of saying it was an "RNA world" some 3.5 BYA. However, DNA, being a double helix, is more stable than RNA. In the RNA-first hypothesis, RNA would have served as the first genetic material, with a transition to DNA occurring later. As far as we know, all organisms on the planet use DNA as their genetic material, but scientists continue to look for evidence to support the RNA-first hypothesis.

Another hypothesis is termed the **protein-first hypothesis.** Sidney Fox, an American biochemist, demonstrated that amino acids join together when exposed to dry heat. He suggested that amino acids collected in shallow puddles along rocky shores. The heat of the sun caused them to form proteinoids, small polypeptides that have some catalytic properties. When these proteinoids were then returned to water, they formed microspheres. Microspheres are structures composed only of protein and have many of the properties of a cell.

The Protocell

A cell has a lipid–protein membrane. Fox demonstrated that if lipids are made available to microspheres, the two tend to become associated, producing a lipid–protein membrane. A **protocell** (see Stage 3 of Fig. 23.1), which could carry on metabolism but could not reproduce, could have come into existence in this manner.

The protocell would have been able to use the still-abundant small organic molecules in the ocean as food. Therefore, the protocell was, most likely, a **heterotroph,** an organism that takes in organic material as food. Further, the protocell would have run anaerobic respiration, because there was no free oxygen.

The First True Cell

Reproduction, in the form of cell division, is an important characteristic of all cells. In today's cells, DNA replicates before cell division occurs. Enzymatic proteins carry out the replication process.

How did the first cell (see Stage 4 of Fig. 23.1) acquire both DNA and enzymatic proteins? Scientists who support the RNA-first hypothesis propose a series of steps. According to this hypothesis, the first cell had RNA genes that, like messenger RNA, could have specified protein synthesis. Some of the proteins formed would have been enzymes. Perhaps one of these enzymes, such as reverse transcriptase found in retroviruses, could use RNA as a template to form DNA. Replication of DNA then would have proceeded normally.

By contrast, supporters of the protein-first hypothesis suggest that some of the proteins in the protocell would have evolved the enzymatic ability to synthesize DNA from nucleotides in the ocean. Then, DNA would have gone on to specify protein synthesis. In this way, the cell could have acquired all of its enzymes, even the ones that replicated DNA.

Several scientists have proposed that polypeptides and RNA evolved simultaneously. Therefore, the first true cell would have contained RNA genes that could have replicated because of the presence of proteins. This eliminates the baffling chicken-and-egg paradox: Assuming a plasma membrane, which came first, proteins or RNA? It means, however, that two unlikely events would have had to happen at the same time.

After DNA formed, the genetic code had to evolve before DNA could store genetic information. The present genetic code is subject to fewer errors than a million other possible codes. Also, the present code is among the best at minimizing the effect of mutations. A single-base change in a present codon is likely to result in the substitution of a chemically similar amino acid and, therefore, minimal changes in the final protein. This evidence suggests that the genetic code, like all other cellular processes, underwent natural selection before finalizing into today's code.

CHECK YOUR PROGRESS 23.1

1. Discuss why chemical evolution was necessary before biological evolution could occur.
2. Explain what the Miller experiment demonstrated about the formation of the first organic molecules.
3. Discuss the importance of RNA in the formation of the first protocells.

CONNECTING THE CONCEPTS

For more information on the topics presented in this section, refer to the following discussions:

Section 3.1 describes the principles of the cell theory.

Section 3.3 examines the structure of the plasma membrane of cells.

Section 22.1 describes the structure and function of RNA.

23.2 Biological Evolution

LEARNING OUTCOMES

Upon completion of this section, you should be able to

1. Explain the relationship between adaptation and the process of biological evolution.
2. Describe how the process of natural selection supports the concept of biological evolution.
3. Discuss how the fossil record, biogeography, and anatomical and biochemical evidence all support the concept of biological evolution.
4. Distinguish between homologous and analogous structure.

The first true cells were the simplest forms of life. These first cells were **prokaryotic cells,** which lack a nucleus (see Section 8.1). From these simple cells evolved the eukaryotic cells (see Fig. 1.5), which have a nucleus and membrane-bound organelles. These first eukaryotic cells were the single-celled protists. From the protists evolved the multicellular eukaryotes, such as fungi, plants, and animals.

Evidence suggests that all life on Earth has an evolutionary history and has undergone biological evolution, or change over time. Biological evolution has two important aspects: descent from a common ancestor and adaptation to the environment. Descent from the original cell or cells explains why all life has a common chemical and cellular structure. An **adaptation** is a characteristic that makes an organism able to survive and reproduce in its environment. Adaptations to different environments help explain the diversity of life—why there are so many different types of living organisms.

Mechanism of Biological Evolution

Charles Darwin was an English naturalist who first presented the concept that the mechanism of biological evolution was the process of **natural selection,** or descent with modification. Darwin formulated his ideas while sailing around the world as the naturalist on board the HMS *Beagle.* Between 1831 and 1836, the ship sailed in the tropics of the Southern Hemisphere.

Darwin's most significant contribution was to describe a mechanism for adaptation: natural selection. During adaptation, a species becomes suited to its environment. On his trip, Darwin visited the Galápagos Islands and saw a number of finches that resembled one another, but which had different ways of life. Some were seed-eating ground finches, some cactus-eating ground finches, and some insect-eating tree finches. A warbler-type finch had a beak that could take honey from a flower. A woodpecker-type finch lacked the long tongue of a woodpecker but could use a cactus spine or twig to pull insects from cracks in the bark of a tree. Darwin thought the finches were all descended from a mainland ancestor whose offspring had spread out among the islands and had become adapted to different environments.

To emphasize the nature of Darwin's natural selection process, it is often contrasted with a process described by Jean-Baptiste Lamarck, another nineteenth-century naturalist. Lamarck's explanation for the long neck of the giraffe was based on the assumption that the ancestors of the modern giraffe were trying to reach into the trees to browse on high-growing vegetation (Fig. 23.3). Continual stretching of the neck caused it to become longer, and this acquired characteristic was passed on to the next generation. In reality, Lamarck's mechanism would not work, because acquired characteristics cannot be inherited (Fig. 23.3).

When Darwin returned home, he spent the next 20 years gathering data to support the principle of biological evolution. In 1859, he published *On the Origin of Species,* which outlined his thoughts on natural selection and biological evolution. The following are the critical elements of the natural selection process:

- *Variation.* Individual members of a species vary in physical characteristics. Physical variations can be passed from generation to generation. (Darwin was never aware of genes, but we know today that the inheritance of the genotype determines the phenotype.)

Lamarck's hypothesis
Darwin's hypothesis
Originally, giraffes had short necks.
Originally, giraffe neck length varied.
Giraffes stretched their necks in order to reach food.
Competition for resources causes long-necked giraffes to have the most offspring.
With continual stretching, most giraffes now have long necks.
Due to natural selection, most giraffes now have long necks.

Figure 23.3 The two major mechanisms for evolutionary change in the nineteenth century.
This diagram contrasts Jean-Baptiste Lamarck's process of acquired characteristics with Charles Darwin's process of natural selection.

- *Competition for limited resources.* Even though each individual could eventually produce many descendants, the overall population size typically stays about the same. Why? Resources are limited, and competition for resources results in unequal reproduction rates among members of a population.
- *Adaptation.* Those members of a population with advantageous traits capture more resources and are more likely to reproduce and pass on these traits. Thus, over time, the environment "selects" for the better-adapted traits. Each subsequent generation includes more individuals adapted in the same way to the environment.

Darwin noted that when humans help carry out **artificial selection,** they breed selected animals with particular traits to reproduce. For example, prehistoric humans probably noted desirable variations among wolves and selected particular individuals for breeding. Therefore, the desired traits increased in frequency in the next generation. The same process was repeated many times, resulting in today's numerous varieties of dogs, all descended from the wolf. In a similar way, several varieties of vegetables can be traced to a single ancestor. Chinese cabbage, brussels sprouts, and kohlrabi are all derived from a single species, *Brassica oleracea.*

Natural selection can account for the great diversity of life. Environments differ widely; therefore, adaptations are varied. From vampire bats to sea turtles to the many finches observed by Darwin, all the different organisms are adapted to their way of life.

Evidence of Evolution

From the time Darwin first proposed the concept of natural selection, scientists have accumulated many different lines of evidence to support the concept that organisms are related through descent from a common ancestor. This is significant because the more varied and abundant the evidence supporting a hypothesis, the more certain it becomes. Scientists widely recognize evolution as one of the core theories in the biological sciences due to the overwhelming amount of supportive evidence.

Fossil Evidence

Fossils remain one of the best sources of evidence for evolution. They are the actual remains of species that lived on Earth at least

BIOLOGY IN YOUR LIFE

How does artificial selection relate to human society?

Almost all animals currently used in modern agriculture are the result of thousands of years of artificial selection by humans. But perhaps the longest-running experiment in artificial selection is the modern dog. Analysis of canine DNA indicates that dogs *(Canis familiaris)* are a direct descendant of the gray wolf *(Canis lupus).* This domestication, and the subsequent selection for desirable traits, now appears to have begun around 130,000 years ago! Artificial selection of dogs continues to this day, with over 190 variations (breeds) currently known.

> **BIOLOGY IN YOUR LIFE**
>
> **What is intelligent design?**
>
> Evolution is a scientific theory. Sometimes we use the word *theory* when we mean a hunch or a guess. But in science, the term *theory* is reserved for those ideas that scientists have found to be all-encompassing because they are based on evidence (data) collected in a number of different fields. In other words, evolutionary theory has been supported by repeated scientific experiments and observations.
>
> Some people advocate the teaching of ideas that run contrary to the theory of evolution in schools. The emphasis is currently placed on intelligent design, a belief system that maintains that the diversity of life could never have arisen without the involvement of an "intelligent agent." Many scientists, and some religions, argue that intelligent design is faith-based and not science-based. It would not be possible to test in a scientific way whether an intelligent agent exists.

10,000 years ago and up to billions of years ago. Fossils can be the traces of past life or any other direct evidence that past life existed. Traces include trails, footprints, burrows, worm casts, and even preserved droppings. Fossils can also be such items as pieces of bone, impressions of plants pressed into shale, and insects trapped in tree resin (which we know as amber). Most fossils, however, are found embedded in or recently eroded from sedimentary rock. Sedimentation, a process that has been going on since the Earth was formed, can take place on land or in bodies of water. Weathering and erosion of rocks produce an accumulation of particles. These particles vary in size and nature and are called sediment. Sediment becomes a stratum (*pl.,* strata), a recognizable layer in a sequence of layers. Any given stratum is older than the one it is beneath, and younger than the one it is on top of. This allows fossils to be dated.

Usually, when an organism dies, the soft parts are either consumed by scavengers or decomposed by bacteria. This means that most fossils consist only of hard parts, such as shells, bones, or teeth. These are usually not consumed or destroyed. When a fossil is found encased by rock, it indicates that the remains were first buried in sediment. The hard parts were then preserved by a process called mineralization. Finally, the surrounding sediment hardened to form rock. Subsequently, the fossil has to be found by a human. Most estimates suggest that less than 1% of past species have been preserved as fossils. Only a small fraction of these have been found.

More and more fossils have been found because researchers, called paleontologists, and their assistants have been out in the field looking for them. Usually, paleontologists remove fossils from the strata to study them in the laboratory. They then may decide to exhibit them. The **fossil record** is the history of life recorded by fossils. *Paleontology* is the science of discovering the fossil record. Decisions about the history of life, ancient climates, and environments can be made using the fossil record. The fossil record is the most direct evidence we have that evolution has occurred. The species found in ancient sedimentary rock are not the species we see today.

Darwin relied on fossils to formulate his theory of evolution. Today, we have a far more complete record than was available to Darwin. It is complete enough to tell us that, in general, life has progressed from the simple to the complex. Single-celled prokaryotes are the first signs of life in the fossil record. These were followed by single-celled eukaryotes, and then multicellular eukaryotes. Among the latter, fishes evolved before terrestrial plants and animals. On land, nonflowering plants preceded the flowering plants. Amphibians preceded the reptiles, including the dinosaurs. Dinosaurs are directly linked to the birds, but they are only indirectly linked to the evolution of mammals, including humans.

Transitional fossils are those that have characteristics of two different groups. In particular, they tell us who is related to whom and how evolution occurred. In 2004, a team of paleontologists discovered fossilized remains of *Tiktaalik roseae,* nicknamed the "fishapod" because it is the transitional form between fish and four-legged animals, the tetrapods (Fig. 23.4). Tiktaalik fossils are

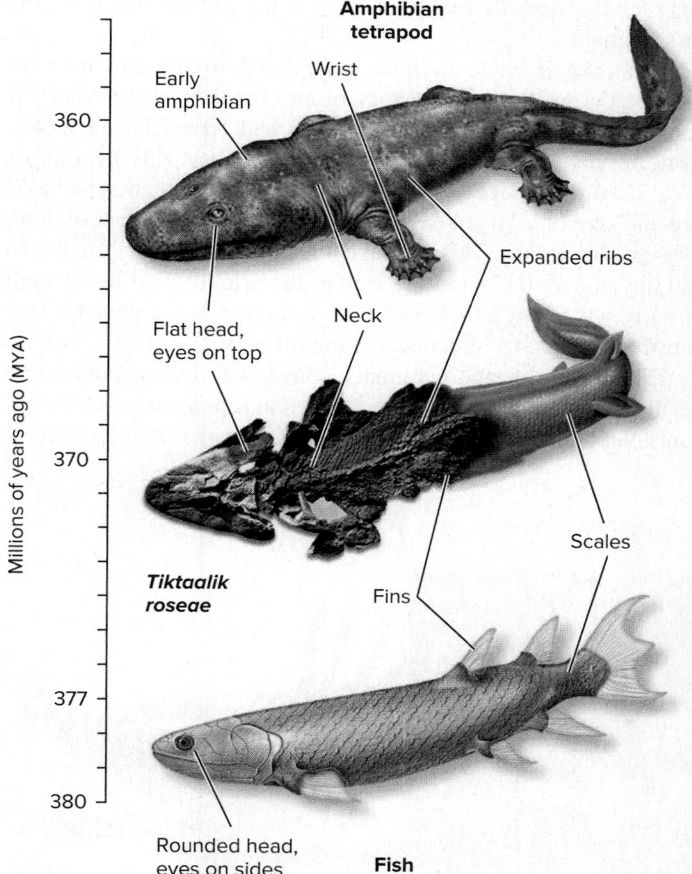

Figure 23.4 Transitional fossils.
Tiktaalik roseae had a mix of fishlike and tetrapod-like features. Fossils such as *Tiktaalik* provide evidence that the evolution of new groups involves the modification of preexisting features in older groups. The evolutionary transition from one form to another, such as from a fish to a tetrapod, can be gradual, with intermediate forms having a suite of adapted, fully functional features.
(photo): Corbin17/Alamy Stock Photo

estimated to be 375 million years old and are from a time when the transition from fish to tetrapods is likely to have occurred. As expected of an intermediate fossil, Tiktaalik has a mix of fishlike and tetrapod-like features that illustrate the steps in the evolution of tetrapods from a fishlike ancestor (Fig. 23.4). For example, Tiktaalik has a very fishlike set of gills and fins, with the exception of the pectoral (front) fins, which have the beginnings of wrist bones similar to a tetrapod. Unlike a fish, Tiktaalik has a flat head, a flexible neck, eyes on the top of its head like a crocodile, and interlocking ribs that suggest it had lungs. These transitional features suggest it had the ability to push itself along the bottom of shallow rivers and see above the surface of the water—features that would have come in handy in the river habitat where it lived.

Even in Darwin's day, scientists knew of the Archaeopteryx fossils, which are intermediate to reptiles and birds. The dinosaur-like skeleton of these fossils had reptilian features, including jaws with teeth, and a long, jointed tail. But Archaeopteryx also had feathers and wings. Figure 23.5 shows both a fossil of Archaeopteryx and an artist's representation of the animal based on the fossil remains.

Another example of how transitional fossils can be used to trace the evolutionary history of an organism is the whale. It had always been thought that whales had terrestrial ancestors. Now, fossils have been discovered that support this hypothesis (Fig. 23.6). *Ambulocetus natans* ("the walking whale that swims") was the size of a large sea lion, with broad, webbed feet on both fore- and hindlimbs. This animal could both walk and swim. It also had tiny hooves on its toes, as well as the primitive skull and teeth of early whales. It is believed that *A. natans* was a predator that patrolled freshwater streams, looking for prey.

The origin of land mammals is also well documented in the fossil record. Synapsids are mammal-like reptiles whose descendants were wolflike and bearlike predators, as well as several types of piglike herbivores. The fossil record shows that such mammalian-like animals slowly acquired features, such as a palate, that would have enabled them to breathe and eat at the same time. They also acquired a muscular diaphragm and rib cage that would have helped them breathe efficiently. The earliest true

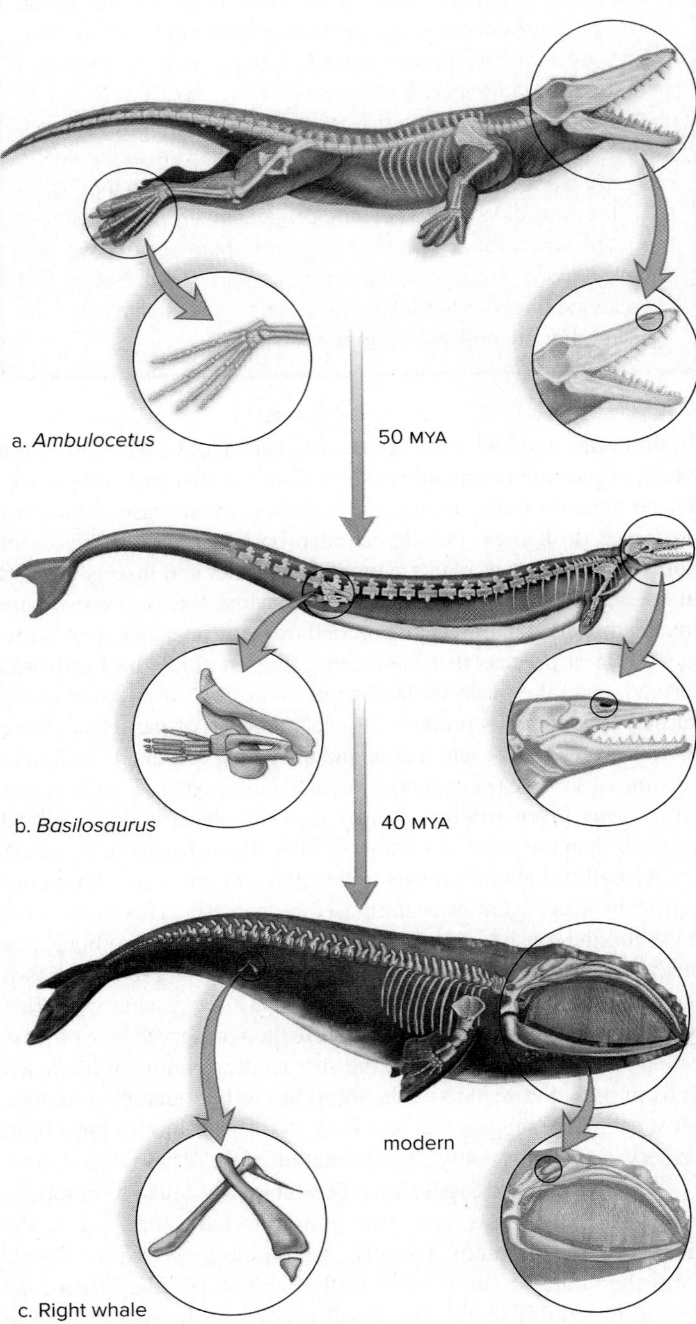

Figure 23.6 **The evolution of whales.**
Transitional fossils such as *Ambulocetus* and *Basilosaurus* support the hypothesis that modern whales evolved from terrestrial ancestors that walked on four limbs. These fossils show a gradual reduction in the hindlimb, as well as a movement of the nasal opening from the tip of the nose to the top of the head—both of them adaptations to living in water.

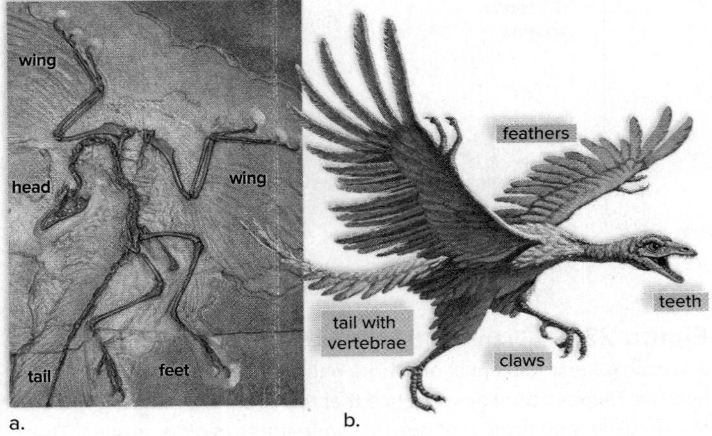

Figure 23.5 **Archaeopteryx.**
Archaeopteryx had a combination of reptilian and bird characteristics.
(fossil): Jason Edwards/National Geographic/Getty Images; (drawing): Joe Tucciarone/Interstellar Illustrations

mammals were shrew-size creatures found in fossil beds that are about 200 million years old.

Biogeographical Evidence

Biogeography is the study of the distribution of plants and animals in different places throughout the world. Such distributions are consistent with the hypothesis that life-forms evolved in particular locales before they spread out. Therefore, you would expect a different mix of plants and animals whenever geography separates continents, islands, or seas. For example, Darwin noted that South America lacks a diversity of rabbits, even though the environment is suitable for them. He concluded that few rabbits lived in South America because rabbits evolved somewhere else and had no means of reaching South America. Instead, the Patagonian hare lives in South America and resembles a rabbit in anatomy and behavior, but has the face of a guinea pig, from which it probably evolved.

As another example, both cacti and euphorbia are plants adapted to a hot, dry environment. Both are succulent, spiny, flowering plants. Why do cacti grow in North American deserts and euphorbia grow in African deserts, when each would do well on the other continent? They just happened to evolve on their respective continents.

The islands of the world are home to many unique species of animals and plants found no place else, even when the soil and climate are the same. Why do so many species of finches live on the Galápagos Islands, while the same species are not on the mainland? The reasonable explanation is that finches from the ancestral species migrated to all the different islands. Then, geographic isolation allowed the ancestral finches to evolve into a different species on each island.

Earlier in Earth's history, South America, Antarctica, and Australia were originally connected. Marsupials (pouched mammals) arose at this time, and today are found in both South America and Australia. But when Australia separated and drifted away, the marsupials diversified into many different forms suited to various environments of Australia (Fig. 23.7). They were free to do so because there were few, if any, placental mammals in Australia. In South America, which does have placental mammals, marsupials are not as diverse. This supports the hypothesis that evolution is influenced by the mix of plants and animals on a particular continent—by biogeography.

Anatomical Evidence

Darwin was able to show that a hypothesis that features common descent offers a plausible explanation for anatomical similarities among organisms. Vertebrate forelimbs are used for flight (birds and bats), orientation during swimming (whales and seals), running (horses), climbing (arboreal lizards), or swinging from tree branches (monkeys). However, all vertebrate forelimbs contain the same sets of bones organized in similar ways, despite their dissimilar functions (Fig. 23.8). The most plausible explanation

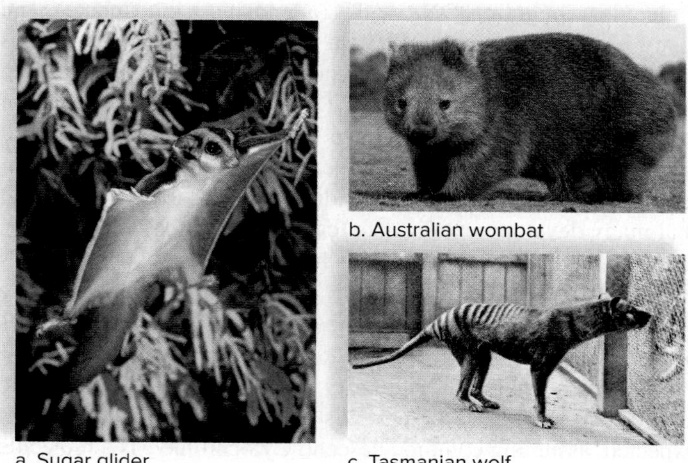

Figure 23.7 Biogeography.
Each type of marsupial in Australia is adapted to a different way of life. **a.** The sugar glider *(Petaurus breviceps)* is a tree-dweller that resembles the placental flying squirrel. **b.** The Australian wombat *(Vombatus)* is nocturnal and lives in burrows. It resembles the placental woodchuck. **c.** The Tasmanian wolf *(Thylacinus cynocephalus)* is an extinct species that resembled the placental American wolf.
(sugar glider): ANT Photo Library/Science Source; (wombat): Marco Tomasini/Shutterstock; (Tasmanian wolf): World History Archive/Alamy Stock Photo

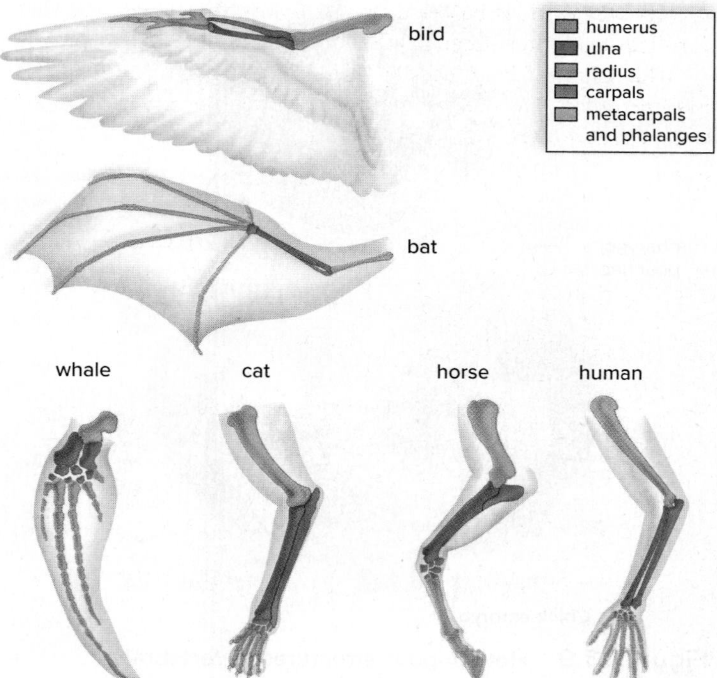

Figure 23.8 Vertebrate forelimbs are homologous structures.
Despite differences in function, vertebrate forelimbs have the same bones.

for this unity is that the basic forelimb plan belonged to a common ancestor. This basic plan was then modified in succeeding groups as each continued along its own evolutionary pathway. Structures that are anatomically similar because they are inherited from a common ancestor are called **homologous structures.** In contrast, **analogous structures** serve the same function but are not constructed similarly, nor do they share a common ancestry. The wings of birds and insects are analogous structures, as are the jointed appendages of a lobster and a human. The presence of homology, not analogy, is evidence that organisms are related.

Vestigial structures are anatomical features that are fully developed in one group of organisms, but that are reduced and may have no function in similar groups. Modern whales have a vestigial pelvic girdle and legs. The ancestors of whales walked on land, but whales are totally aquatic animals today. Most birds have well-developed wings used for flight. Some bird species (e.g., ostrich), however, have greatly reduced wings and do not fly. Similarly, snakes have no use for hindlimbs, yet some have remnants of a pelvic girdle and legs. Humans have a tailbone but no tail. The presence of vestigial structures can be explained by common descent: Vestigial structures occur because organisms inherit their anatomy from their ancestors. They are traces of an organism's evolutionary history.

The homology shared by vertebrates extends to their embryological development (Fig. 23.9). At some time during development, all vertebrates have a postanal tail and exhibit paired pharyngeal pouches. In fish and amphibian larvae, these pouches develop into functioning gills. In humans, the first pair of pouches becomes the cavity of the middle ear and the auditory tube. The second pair becomes the tonsils. The third and fourth pairs become the thymus and parathyroid glands, respectively. There is a question as to why terrestrial vertebrates develop and then modify structures, such as pharyngeal pouches, even though the structures have lost their original function. Studies of evolutionary relationships have determined that this is because fish are ancestral to all other vertebrate groups, and during development, the genes associated with these structures are expressed but then overwritten by other genes.

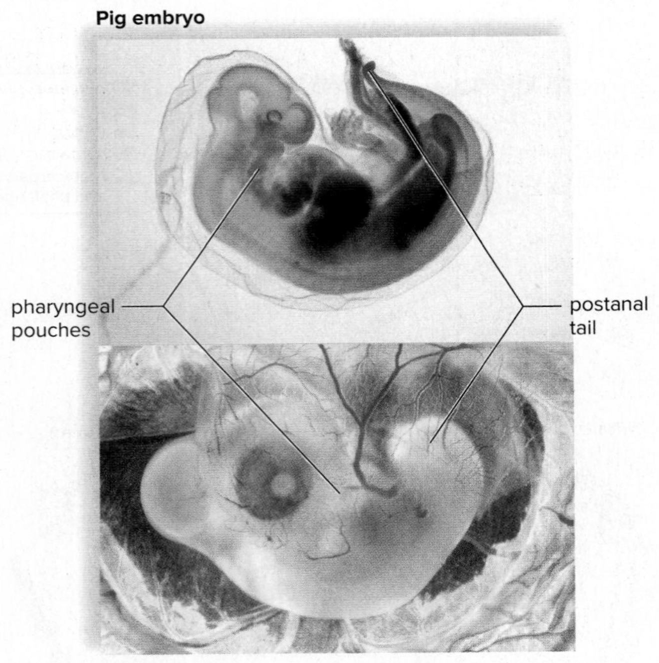

Figure 23.9 Homologous structures in vertebrate embryos.
Vertebrate embryos have features in common, such as pharyngeal pouches, despite different ways of life as adults.
Carolina Biological/Medical Images/DIOMEDIA

BIOLOGY IN YOUR LIFE

What are some examples of vestigial organs in humans?

The human body is littered with vestigial organs from our evolutionary past. One example is the tiny muscles (called piloerectors) that surround each hair follicle. During times of stress, these muscles cause the hair to stand straight up—a useful protection mechanism for small mammals trying to escape predators, but one that has little function in humans. Wisdom teeth are also considered to be vestigial organs because most people now retain their original teeth for the majority of their lives.

Biochemical Evidence

Almost all living organisms use the same basic biochemical molecules, including DNA, ATP (adenosine triphosphate), and many identical or nearly identical enzymes. Further, organisms use the same DNA triplet code and the same 20 amino acids in their proteins. The sequences of DNA bases in the genomes of many organisms are now known, so it has become clear that humans share a large number of genes with much simpler organisms. Evolutionists who study development have also found that many developmental genes (called *Hox* genes) are shared in animals ranging from worms to humans. It appears that life's vast diversity has come about by only slight differences in the regulation of genes. The result has been widely divergent types of bodies.

When the degree of similarity in DNA base sequences or in amino acid sequences of proteins is examined, the data are as expected, assuming common descent. Cytochrome *c* is a molecule used in the electron transport chain of many organisms. Data regarding differences in the amino acid sequence of cytochrome *c* show that the sequence in a human differs from that in a monkey by only 2 amino acids. The human sequence differs from that in a duck by 11 amino acids, and from that in a yeast by 51 amino acids (Fig. 23.10). These data are consistent with other data regarding the anatomical similarities of these organisms and, therefore, their relatedness.

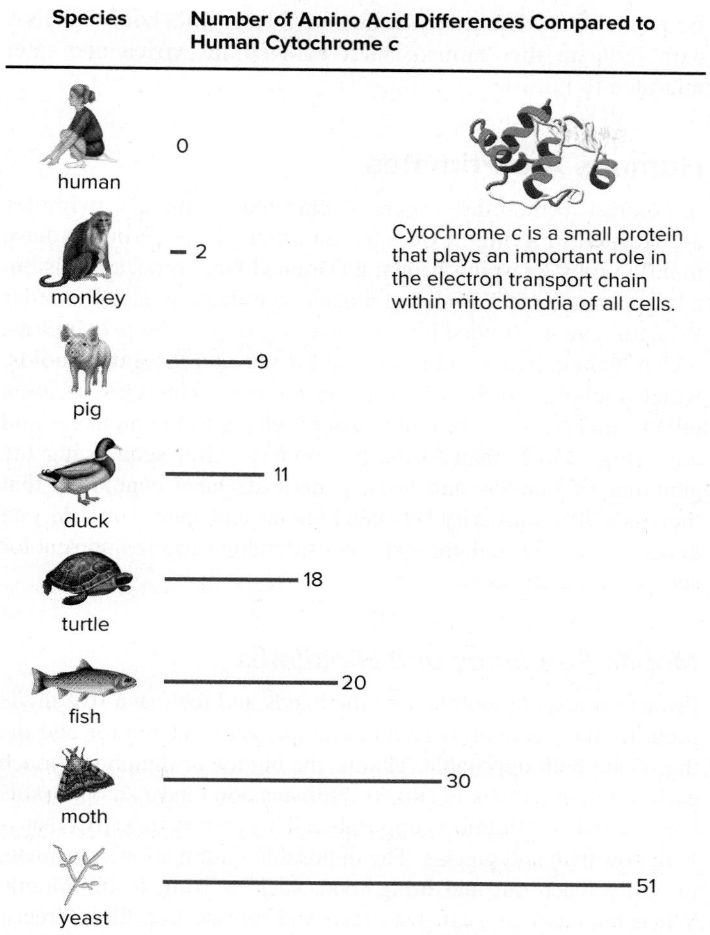

Species	Number of Amino Acid Differences Compared to Human Cytochrome *c*
human	0
monkey	2
pig	9
duck	11
turtle	18
fish	20
moth	30
yeast	51

Cytochrome *c* is a small protein that plays an important role in the electron transport chain within mitochondria of all cells.

Figure 23.10 **Biochemical evidence describes evolutionary relationships.**
The number of amino acid differences in cytochrome *c* between humans and other species is indicated.

CHECK YOUR PROGRESS 23.2

1. Define *biological evolution* and explain its two most important aspects.
2. Describe the types of evidence that support Darwin's theory of biological evolution.
3. Discuss why natural selection is the mechanism for biological evolution.

CONNECTING THE CONCEPTS

For more information on the content provided in this section, refer to the following discussions:

Section 1.1 explains why evolutionary change is the core concept of the study of biology.

Section 19.4 describes how meiosis introduces the variation that is the basis of evolutionary change.

Section 22.3 explores how scientists study changes in DNA and proteins.

23.3 Classification of Humans

LEARNING OUTCOMES

Upon completion of this section, you should be able to

1. Describe how DNA analysis is used to study primate evolution.
2. Describe the evolutionary trends that occur in primates.
3. Compare the structure of chimpanzee and human skeletons and list the adaptations in humans that make upright walking possible.

To begin a study of human evolution, we will first explore the biological classification of humans. This classification is an indication of the evolutionary relatedness of humans to other species. In Section 1.2, we examined the different levels of classification, from domains down to species. Table 23.1 applies these levels to humans. In this section, we will focus primarily on the genus and **binomial names** of the species that are most closely related to our species, *Homo sapiens*.

DNA Data and Human Evolution

We are accustomed to using the characteristics given in Table 23.1 to determine evolutionary relationships, but researchers are increasingly depending on DNA data to trace the history of life. DNA data are particularly useful when anatomical differences are unavailable.

For example, in the late 1970s Carl Woese and his colleagues at the University of Illinois decided to use ribosomal RNA (rRNA) sequence data to discover how prokaryotes are related. They knew that the DNA coding for rRNA changes slowly during evolution. Ribosomal RNA genes may change only when there is a major evolutionary event. Woese reported, on the basis of

Table 23.1 **Evolution and Classification of Humans**

Classification Category	Characteristics
Domain Eukarya	Possess a membrane-bound nucleus
Supergroup Opisthokonta	Possess cells with flagella
Kingdom Animalia	Multicellular, motile, heterotrophic
Phylum Chordata	At some points in their life history, organisms possess a dorsal tubular nerve cord, notochord, and pharyngeal pouches.
Class Mammalia	Vertebrates with hair and mammary glands
Order Primates	Well-developed brain and adapted to live in trees
Family Hominidae	Adapted to upright stance and bipedal locomotion
Genus *Homo*	Highly developed brain. Able to make and use tools.
Species *Homo sapiens*	Modern humans. Speech centers of brain are well developed.

rRNA sequence data, that there are three domains of life and that members of Archaea are more closely related to members of Eukarya than to those of Bacteria (Fig. 23.11). (See Fig. 1.6 for a description of these domains.) In other words, major decisions regarding the history of life are now being made on the basis of DNA/rRNA/protein sequencing data. For example, studies of rRNA sequences indicate that among the major groups of eukaryotes, animals are more closely related to fungi than to plants. For this reason, fungi and animals are assigned to the same supergroup (see Section 1.2).

Scientists have used a variety of techniques, including DNA sequence data, to calculate when the last common ancestor for the apes and humans must have existed. While paleontologists and archaeologists are getting closer to discovering this ancestor, the DNA data indicate that this ancestor must have existed about 7 MYA. For more recent events, mitochondrial DNA (mtDNA) is often used, because mtDNA changes occur more frequently than changes to the nuclear DNA. Mitochondrial DNA data indicate that humans first evolved in Africa and later migrated to Eurasia.

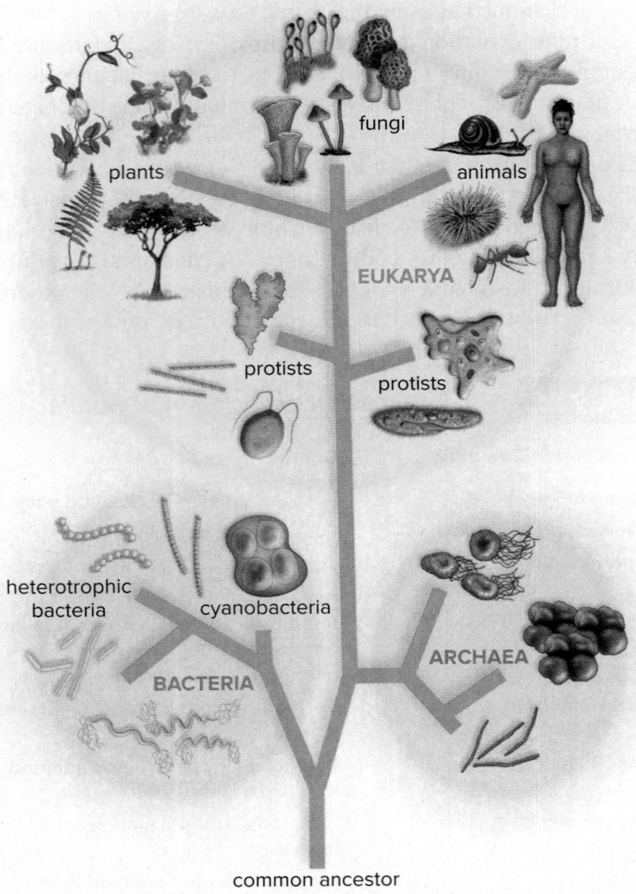

Figure 23.11 **The three domains of life.** Representatives of each domain are depicted in the ovals. The evolutionary tree of life shows that domain Archaea is more closely related to domain Eukarya than either is to domain Bacteria.

Humans Are Primates

In contrast to the other orders of placental mammals, **primates** are adapted to living in trees, or an arboreal life. Primates have mobile limbs; grasping hands; a flattened face; binocular vision; a large, complex brain; and a reduced reproductive rate. The order Primates can be divided into two major groups—the **prosimians,** which include lemurs, tarsiers, and lorises, and the **anthropoids,** which include monkeys, apes, and humans. This classification tells us that humans are more closely related to the monkeys and apes (Fig. 23.12) than to the prosimians. After sequencing the genomes of humans and apes, geneticists have concluded that there is a 90% similarity between humans and apes. Thus, despite genetic similarities, there is still considerable variation present for specific adaptations.

Mobile Forelimbs and Hindlimbs

Primate limbs are mobile, and the hands and feet have five digits each. In many primates, such as chimpanzees, the big toe and the thumb are both opposable. That is, the big toe or thumb can touch each of the other toes or fingers. Humans don't have an opposable big toe, but our thumb is opposable. This results in a grip that is both powerful and precise. The opposable thumb allows a primate to easily reach out and bring food, such as fruit, to the mouth. When locomoting, primates grasp and release tree limbs freely, because nails have replaced claws.

Binocular Vision

In chimps, like other primates, the snout is shortened considerably, allowing the eyes to move to the front of the head. The resulting stereoscopic vision (depth perception) permits primates to accurately judge the distance and position of adjoining tree limbs. Humans and the apes have three different kinds of cone cells, which are able to discriminate among greens, blues, and reds (see Section 15.4). Cone cells require bright light, but the image is sharp and in color. The lens of the eye focuses light directly on the fovea, a region of the retina where cone cells are concentrated.

Large, Complex Brain

The evolutionary trend among primates is generally toward a larger and more complex brain. The brain size is smallest in prosimians and largest in humans and Neanderthals. The cerebral cortex, with many association areas, expands so much that it becomes extensively folded in humans. The portion of the brain devoted to smell is smaller. The portions devoted to sight have increased in size and complexity during primate evolution. Also, more of the brain is involved in controlling and processing information received from the hands and the thumb. The result is good hand-eye coordination in chimpanzees and humans.

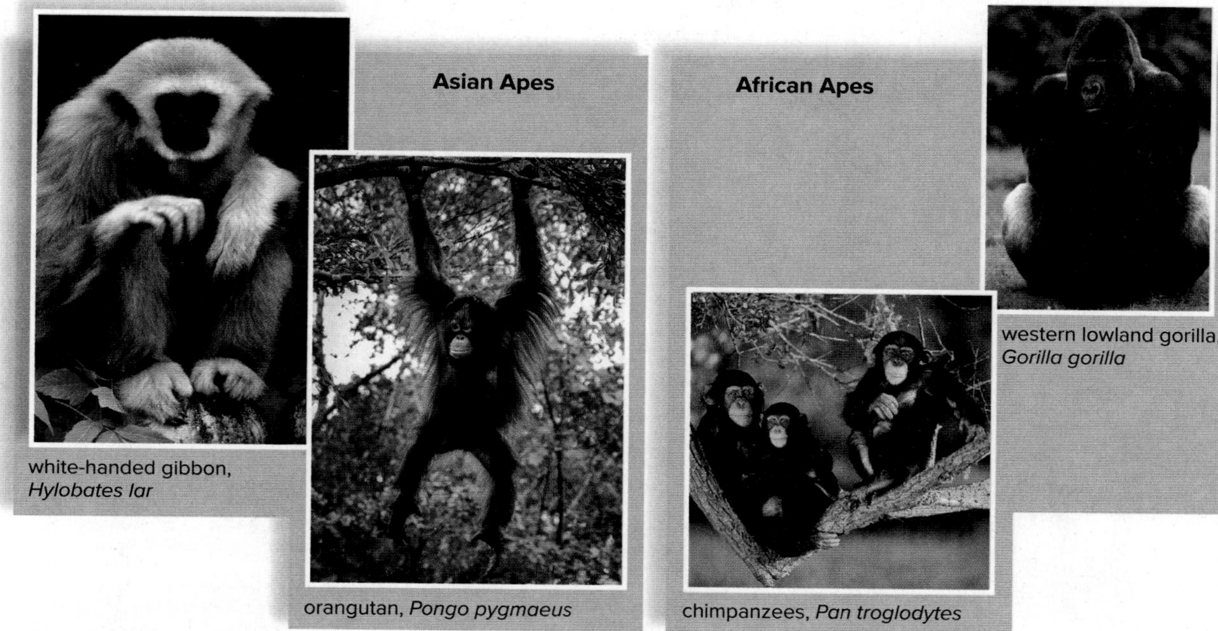

Figure 23.12 **Asian and African apes.**
The apes can be divided into the Asian apes (gibbons and orangutans) and the African apes (chimpanzees and gorillas). Molecular data and the location of early fossil remains tell us we are more closely related to African apes than Asian apes.
(gibbon): Photodisc/Getty Images; (orangutan): jeep2499/Shutterstock; (chimpanzees): Fuse/Getty Images; (gorilla): Erni/Shutterstock

Reduced Reproductive Rate

It is difficult to care for several offspring while moving among tree branches, and one birth at a time is the norm in primates. The juvenile period of dependency is extended, and there is an emphasis on learned behavior and complex social interactions.

Comparing the Human Skeleton to the Chimpanzee Skeleton

Figure 23.13 compares the anatomical differences between chimpanzees and humans, which relate to the upright stance of humans when they walk compared to the chimpanzees' practice of knuckle-walking. When chimpanzees walk, their forearms rest on their knuckles.

These differences in anatomy between chimpanzees and humans determine that humans—but not chimps—are adapted for an upright stance. This includes:

- In humans, the spine exits inferior to the center of the skull, and this places the skull in the midline of the body.
- The longer, S-shaped spine of humans places the trunk's center of gravity squarely over the feet.
- The broader pelvis and hip joint of humans keep them from swaying when they walk.
- The longer neck of the femur in humans causes the femur to angle inward at the knees.
- The human knee joint is modified to support the body's weight; the femur is larger at the bottom, and the tibia is larger at the top.
- Finally, the human toe is not opposable; instead, the foot has an arch. The arch enables humans to walk long distances and run with less chance of injury.

CHECK YOUR PROGRESS 23.3

1. List the general characteristics of primates.
2. Discuss the benefits of binocular vision and a complex brain structure.
3. Summarize the major differences between the chimpanzee skeleton and the human skeleton.

CONNECTING THE CONCEPTS

For more information on the material in this section, refer to the following discussions:

Section 3.6 discusses the structure and function of the mitochondria in a eukaryotic cell.

Section 14.2 examines the function of the cerebral cortex in the human brain.

Section 22.1 explores the structure and function of DNA and RNA molecules.

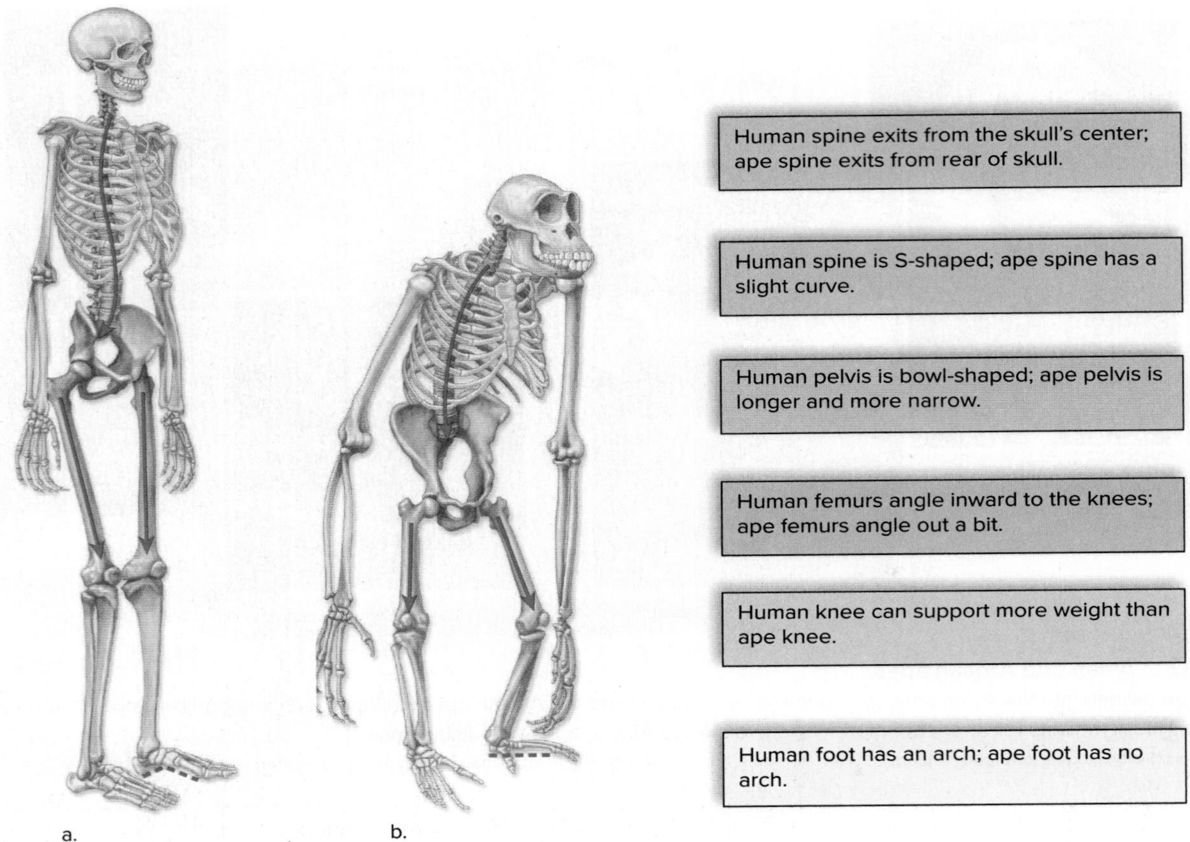

Human spine exits from the skull's center; ape spine exits from rear of skull.
Human spine is S-shaped; ape spine has a slight curve.
Human pelvis is bowl-shaped; ape pelvis is longer and more narrow.
Human femurs angle inward to the knees; ape femurs angle out a bit.
Human knee can support more weight than ape knee.
Human foot has an arch; ape foot has no arch.
a.
b.

Figure 23.13 **Adaptations in the human skeleton allow upright locomotion.** **a.** Human skeleton compared to (**b**) chimpanzee skeleton.

23.4 Evolution of Hominins

LEARNING OUTCOMES

Upon completion of this section, you should be able to

1. Describe the major events in the evolution of the hominins.
2. Summarize the significance of the australopithecines in the study of human evolution.

Once biologists have studied the characteristics of a group of organisms, they can construct an **evolutionary tree,** which represents a working hypothesis of their history. The evolutionary tree in Figure 23.14 shows that all primates share one common ancestor and that the other types of primates diverged from the human line of descent over time. When any two lines of descent, called a *lineage,* first diverge from a common ancestor, the genes and proteins of the two lineages are nearly identical. As time goes by, each lineage accumulates genetic changes, which lead to RNA and protein changes. Many genetic changes are neutral (not tied to adaptation) and accumulate at a fairly constant rate. Such changes can be used as a type of **molecular clock** to indicate the relatedness of two groups and when they diverged from each other. Molecular data also suggest that hominids split from the ape line of descent about 7 MYA.

The anthropoids include all of the hominids, as well as the gibbons, Old World monkeys, and New World monkeys. Old World monkeys, native to Africa and Asia, lack prehensile tails and have protruding noses. Some of the better-known Old World monkeys are the baboon, a ground dweller, and the rhesus monkey, which has been used extensively in medical research. New World monkeys, which often have long, prehensile tails and flat noses, evolved in South America and are now also found in Central America and parts of Mexico. Two of the well-known New World monkeys are the spider monkey and the capuchin, the "organ grinder's monkey."

The **hominids** include our closest primate relatives, such as chimpanzees, gorillas, and orangutans. The designation **hominins** includes humans and species very closely related to humans. Molecular evidence suggests that humans and chimpanzees shared a common ancestor between 5 and 7 MYA and have been evolving separately from that ancestor since that time. Similar to our relationship with chimpanzees, humans and apes shared a common apelike ancestor which our two species branched off from 7 MYA. Following that split, different environments selected for the different traits that apes and humans have now.

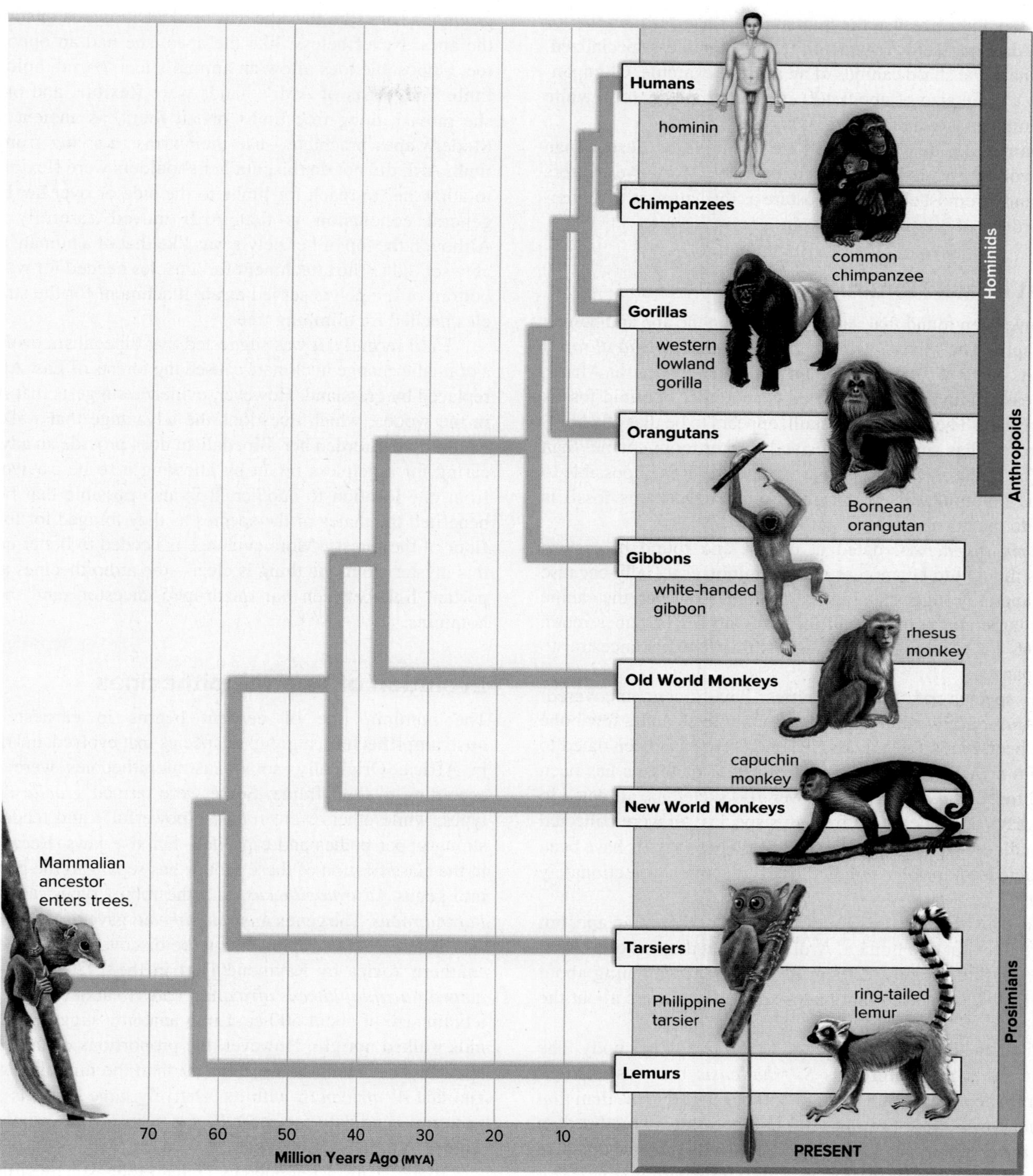

Figure 23.14 **The evolutionary tree of the primates.**
Humans are related to all other primates through a common ancestor.

One of the most unfortunate misconceptions concerning human evolution is the belief that Darwin and others suggested that humans *evolved* from apes. Today's apes are our distant cousins, and we couldn't have evolved from our cousins because we are contemporaries—living on Earth at the same time.

The First Hominins

Paleontologists use certain anatomical features when they try to determine if a fossil is a hominin. These features include **bipedal posture** (walking on two feet), the shape of the face, and brain size. Today's humans have a flatter face and a more pronounced chin than the apes, because the human jaw is shorter than that of the apes. Also, our teeth are generally smaller and less specialized. We don't have the sharp canines of an ape, for example. Chimpanzees have a brain size of about 400 cubic centimeters (cc), while modern humans have a brain size of about 1,360 cc.

It's hard to decide which fossils are hominins, because human features evolved gradually and at different rates. Most investigators rely first and foremost on bipedal posture as the hallmark of a hominin, regardless of the size of the brain.

Earliest Fossil Hominins

Fossils have been found that date back to when the ape and human lineages split. The oldest of these fossils, called *Sahelanthropus tchadensis,* dated at 7 MYA, was found in Chad, in central Africa, far from eastern and southern Africa where other hominid fossils were excavated. The only find, a skull, appears to be that of a hominin because it has smaller canines and thicker tooth enamel than an ape. The braincase, however, is very apelike. It is impossible to tell if this hominin walked upright. Some suggest this fossil is ancestral to the gorilla.

Orrorin tugenensis, dated at 6 MYA and found in eastern Africa, is thought to be another early hominin, especially because the limb anatomy suggests a bipedal posture. However, the canine teeth are large and pointed, and the arm and finger bones retain adaptations for climbing. Some suggest this fossil is ancestral to the chimpanzee.

Two species of **ardipithecines** have been uncovered: *Ardipithecus kadabba* and *A. ramidus.* Only teeth and a few bone bits have been found for *A. kadabba,* and these have been dated to around 5.6 MYA. A more extensive collection of fossils has been collected for *A. ramidus.* To date, over 100 skeletons, all dated to 4.4 MYA, have been identified from this species; all were collected near a small town in Ethiopia, East Africa. These fossils have been reconstructed to form a female fossil specimen affectionately called Ardi.

Some of Ardi's features are primitive, like that of an ape, but others are like that of a human. Ardi was about the size of a chimpanzee, standing roughly 120 cm (4 ft) tall and weighing about 55 kg (110 lb). It appears that males and females were about the same size.

Ardi had a small head compared to the size of her body. The skull had the same features as *S. tchadensis* but was smaller. Ardi's brain size was around 300 to 350 cc, slightly less than that of a chimpanzee brain (around 400 cc), and much smaller than that of a modern human (1,360 cc). The muzzle (area of the nose and mouth) projects forward, and the forehead is low with heavy eyebrow ridges, a combination that makes the face more primitive than that of the australopithecines (discussed next). However, the projection of the face is less than that of a chimpanzee, because Ardi's teeth were small and like those of an omnivore. She lacked the strong, sharp canines of a chimpanzee, and her diet probably consisted mostly of soft, rather than tough, plant material.

Ardi could walk erect, but she spent a lot of time in trees. Her feet had a bone, missing in apes, that kept them squarely on the ground, a sure sign that she was bipedal and not a quadruped like the apes. Nevertheless, like the apes, she had an opposable big toe. Opposable toes allow an animal's feet to grab hold of a tree limb. The wrists of Ardi's hands were flexible, and most likely she moved along tree limbs on all fours, as ancient apes did. Modern apes brachiate—use their arms to swing from limb to limb. Ardi did not do this, but her shoulders were flexible enough to allow her to reach for limbs to the side or over her head. The general conclusion is that Ardi moved carefully in trees. Although the top of her pelvis was like that of a human, and probably served as the attachment for muscles needed for walking, the bottom of the pelvis served as an attachment for the strong muscles needed for climbing trees.

Until recently, it was suggested that bipedalism evolved when a dramatic change in climate caused the forests of East Africa to be replaced by grassland. However, evidence suggests that Ardi lived in the woods, which questions the advantage that walking erect would have afforded her. Bipedalism does provide an advantage in caring for a helpless infant by allowing it to be carried by hand from one location to another. It is also possible that bipedalism benefited the males of the species as they foraged for food on the floor of the forests. More evidence is needed to better understand this mystery, but one thing is clear—the ardipithecines are an important link between our quadruped ancestors and the bipedal hominins.

Evolution of Australopithecines

The hominin line of descent begins in earnest with the **australopithecines,** a group of species that evolved and diversified in Africa. Originally, some australopithecines were classified according to their frame. Some were termed *gracile* ("slender") types, while others were *robust* ("powerful") and tended to have strong upper bodies and especially massive jaws. Recent changes in the classification of these groups has separated the gracile types into genus *Australopithecus,* and the robust types into the genus *Paranthropus*. The genus *Australopithecus* gave rise to genus *Homo*.

The first australopithecine to be discovered was unearthed in southern Africa by Raymond Dart in the 1920s. This hominin, named *Australopithecus africanus,* dates to about 2.9 MYA and had a brain size of about 500 cc. Limb anatomy suggests these hominids walked upright. However, the proportions of the limbs were apelike. The forelimbs were longer than the hindlimbs. Some argue that *A. africanus,* with its relatively large brain, is a possible ancestral candidate for early *Homo,* whose limb proportions are similar to those of this fossil.

In the 1970s, a team led by Donald Johanson unearthed nearly 250 fossils of a hominin called *A. afarensis.* A now-famous female skeleton dated at 3.18 MYA is known worldwide by its field name, Lucy. Although her brain was small (400 cc), the shapes and relative proportions of her limbs indicate that Lucy stood upright and walked bipedally (Fig. 23.15*a*). Even better evidence of bipedal locomotion comes from a trail of footprints in Laetoli dated about 3.7 MYA. The larger prints are double, as though a smaller being was stepping in the footfalls of another. Additional small prints are evident off to the side, within hand-holding distance (Fig. 23.15*b*).

a.

b.

Figure 23.15 ***Australopithecus afarensis.***
a. A reconstruction of Lucy on display at the St. Louis Zoo. **b.** These fossilized footprints occur in ash from a volcanic eruption some 3.7 MYA. The larger footprints are double (one followed behind the other), and a third, smaller individual was walking to the side. (A female holding the hand of a youngster may have been walking in the footprints of a male.) The footprints suggest that *A. afarensis* walked bipedally.
(a): ©Dreyfus and Associates Photography; (b): John Reader/Science Source

BIOLOGY IN YOUR LIFE

Why did Johanson name his fossil Lucy?

The evening of the discovery, there was a party in camp. The team gathered to celebrate the find of what appeared to be an almost complete hominid skeleton. The Beatles' song "Lucy in the Sky with Diamonds" was played over and over, and the name Lucy was given to the skeleton.

The fact that the australopithecines were apelike above the waist (small brain) and humanlike below the waist (walked erect) shows that human characteristics did not evolve all at one time. The term **mosaic evolution** is applied when different body parts change at different rates and, therefore, at different times.

Australopithecus afarensis is most likely ancestral to the *Paranthropus* genus found in eastern Africa: *P. robustus* and *P. boisei. Paranthropus boisei* had a powerful upper body and the largest molars of any hominin. This genus died out; therefore, it is possible that *A. afarensis* is ancestral to both *A. africanus* and early *Homo* species (see Section 23.5).

CHECK YOUR PROGRESS 23.4

1. Distinguish between a hominid and a hominin and give an example of each.
2. Name three features characteristic of hominins.
3. Discuss why the discovery of Lucy was an important event in the study of human evolution.

CONNECTING THE CONCEPTS

For additional information on the topics in this section, refer to the following discussions:

Section 9.2 describes the types of teeth found in modern humans.
Figure 12.3 illustrates the skeletal structure of a modern human.
Section 14.2 examines the brain structure of modern humans.

23.5 Evolution of Humans

LEARNING OUTCOMES

Upon completion of this section, you should be able to

1. Explain the adaptations of *Homo erectus.*
2. Distinguish among the different theories regarding *Homo sapiens* evolution.
3. Describe the differences between Neanderthals and Cro-Magnons.

The study of our genus, *Homo,* has undergone considerable scrutiny in the past several years. Increasingly, there is evidence that what were once considered separate species are, in fact, variations of a single species. Notice in Figure 23.16 that a number of the members of the genus *Homo* are indicated by hash marks to indicate areas under debate. For our purposes, we will focus on the more traditional classification of the members of our genus.

Fossils are assigned to the genus *Homo* if (1) the brain size is 600 cc or greater, (2) the jaw and teeth resemble those of humans, and (3) tool use is evident. In this section, we will discuss early *Homo*—*Homo habilis* and *Homo erectus*—and later *Homo*—the Neanderthals, Denisovans, and Cro-Magnons, the first modern humans.

Early *Homo* Species

Homo habilis is a ancestor of modern humans that lived between 2.0 and 1.9 MYA (Fig. 23.16). Some of these fossils have a brain size as large as 775 cc, about 45% larger than that of *A. afarensis.* The cheek teeth are smaller than even those of the gracile australopithecines. Therefore, it is likely these early members of the genus *Homo* were omnivores who ate meat in addition to plant material. Bones at their campsites bear cut marks, indicating that *H. habilis* used tools to strip meat from bones.

The stone tools made by *H. habilis,* whose name means "handyman," are rather crude. It is possible these are the cores from which they took flakes sharp enough to scrape away hide, cut tendons, and easily remove meat from bones.

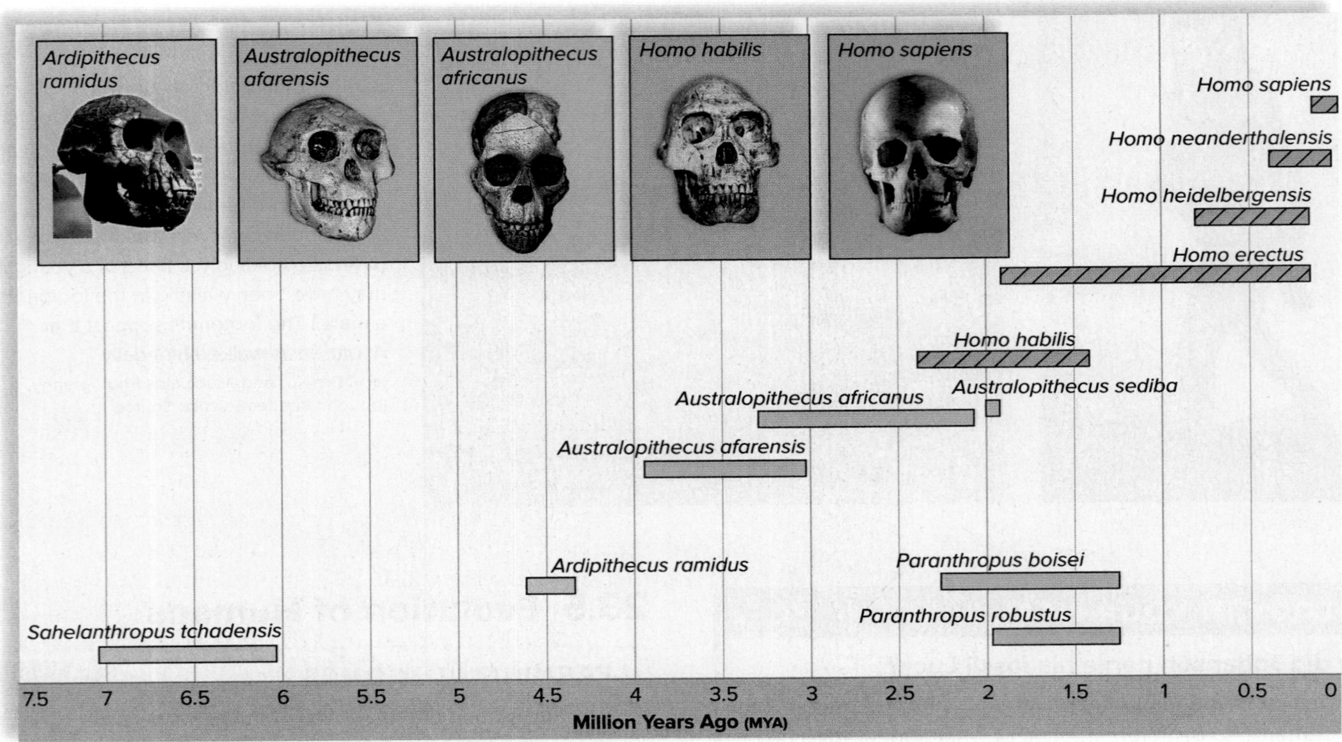

Figure 23.16 **Human evolution.**
Several groups of extinct hominins preceded the evolution of modern humans. The groups have been divided into the early humanlike hominins (orange), later humanlike hominins (green), early *Homo* species (lavender), and finally the later *Homo* species (blue). The hash marks indicate areas where current research is focusing on combining groups into a single species.
(*Ardipithecus ramidus*): Danny Ye/Shutterstock; (*Australopithecus afarensis*): Scott Camazine/Alamy Stock Photo; (*Australopithecus africanus* skull): Philippe Plailly/Science Source; (*Homo habilis*): Kike Calvo/Visual & Written/SuperStock; (*Homo sapiens*): Kenneth Garrett/Getty Images

Early *Homo* skulls suggest that the portions of the brain associated with speech were enlarged. We can speculate that the ability to speak may have led to hunting cooperatively. Other members of the group may have remained plant gatherers. If so, both hunters and gatherers most likely ate together and shared their food. In this way, society and culture could have begun.

Culture, which encompasses both behavior and examples of intellectual achievement (e.g., technology and the arts), depends on the capacity to speak and transmit knowledge. We can further speculate that the advantages of a culture to *H. habilis* may have hastened the extinction of the australopithecines.

Homo erectus

Homo erectus and similar fossils have been found in Africa, Asia, and Europe and been dated between 1.9 and 0.3 MYA. A Dutch anatomist named Eugene Dubois was the first to unearth *H. erectus* bones, in Java in 1891. Since that time, many other fossils have been found in the same area. Although all fossils assigned the name *H. erectus* are similar in appearance, enough discrepancy exists to suggest that several different species have been included in this group. In particular, some experts suggest that the Asian form is *H. erectus,* while the African form is *Homo ergaster* (Fig. 23.17).

Compared with *H. habilis, H. erectus* had a larger brain (about 1,000 cc) and a flatter face. The nose projected, however. This type of nose is adaptive for a hot, dry climate, because it permits water to be removed before air leaves the body. The recovery of an almost complete skeleton of a 10-year-old boy indicates that *H. ergaster* was much taller than the hominids discussed thus far. Males were 1.8 m tall (about 6 ft), and females were 1.55 m (approaching 5 ft). Indeed, these hominids were erect and most likely had a striding gait like ours. The robust and most likely heavily muscled skeleton still retained some australopithecine features. Even so, the size of the birth canal indicates that infants were born in an immature state that required an extended period of care.

H. erectus may have first appeared in Africa and then migrated into Asia and Europe (see Fig. 23.19). The migration was once thought to have occurred about 1 MYA. Recently, *H. erectus* fossil remains in Java and the Republic of Georgia have been dated at 1.9 and 1.6 MYA, respectively. These remains push the evolution of *H. erectus* in Africa to an earlier date that has not yet been determined. In any case, such an extensive population movement is a first in the history of our genus and a tribute to the intellectual and physical skills of the species.

H. erectus was the first hominid to use fire, and members of this group fashioned more advanced tools than earlier *Homo* species. These hominids used heavy, teardrop-shaped axes and cleavers. Flake tools were probably used for cutting and scraping. It could be that *H. ergaster* was a systematic hunter and brought kills to the same site over and over. In one location, researchers

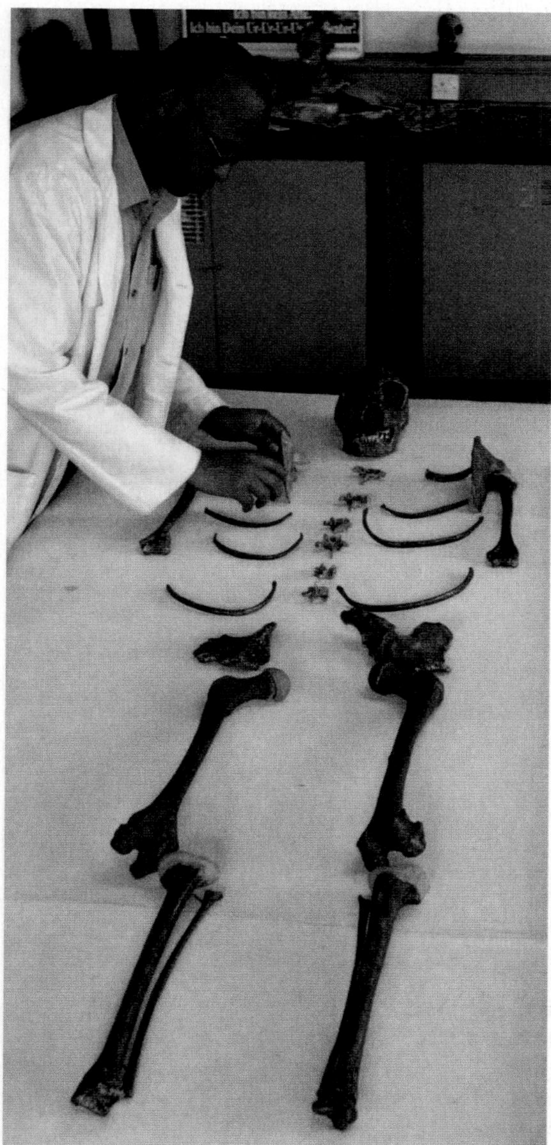

Figure 23.17 *Homo ergaster.*
This skeleton of a 10-year-old boy who lived 1.6 MYA in eastern Africa shows angled femurs because the femur neck is quite long.
Sayyid Azim/AP Images

have found more than 40,000 bones and 2,647 stones. These sites could have been "home bases," where social interaction occurred and a prolonged childhood allowed time for learning. Perhaps a language evolved and a culture more like our own developed.

Evolution of Modern Humans

Later *Homo* species are represented by blue-colored bars in Figure 23.16. The evolution of these species from older *Homo* species has been the subject of much debate. While most researchers believe that modern humans *(Homo sapiens)* evolved from an *H. erectus* lineage in Africa, they differ as to the details of when this occurred. Furthermore, recent discoveries of fossil remains, most notably of *H. erectus,* Neanderthals, Denisovans and yet to be classified species, is challenging much of what we know about this period in human evolution.

More than any other time period, it is difficult to talk in terms of species beyond *H. erectus* because of fuzzy dividing lines, wide geographic movement, and the presence of multiple species. Keep in mind that between 100,000 and 200,000 years ago, there may have been multiple human lineages existing on the planet, including *H. erectus, H. neanderthalensis, H. sapiens,* and as the Evolution feature "The Complexity of Our Evolutionary Past" presents, several recently discovered new species.

The most widely accepted hypothesis for the evolution of modern humans from archaic humans is referred to as the **replacement model,** or out-of-Africa hypothesis (Fig. 23.18), which proposes that modern humans evolved from earlier *Homo* species only in Africa (Fig. 23.19), and then modern humans migrated to Asia and Europe, where they replaced the early *Homo* species about 100,000 years BP (before the present).

A hypothesis opposing the replacement model does exist. This hypothesis, called the *multiregional continuity hypothesis,* proposes that modern humans arose from earlier *Homo* species in essentially the same manner in Africa, Asia, and Europe. The hypothesis is multiregional, because it applies equally to Africa, Asia, and Europe, and it proposes that in these regions genetic continuity will be found between modern populations and early *Homo*. The discovery of new species, such as *H. florensiensis, H. naledi,* and the Denisovans, is bringing attention back to this hypothesis, or possibly a combination of the multiregional and replacement models.

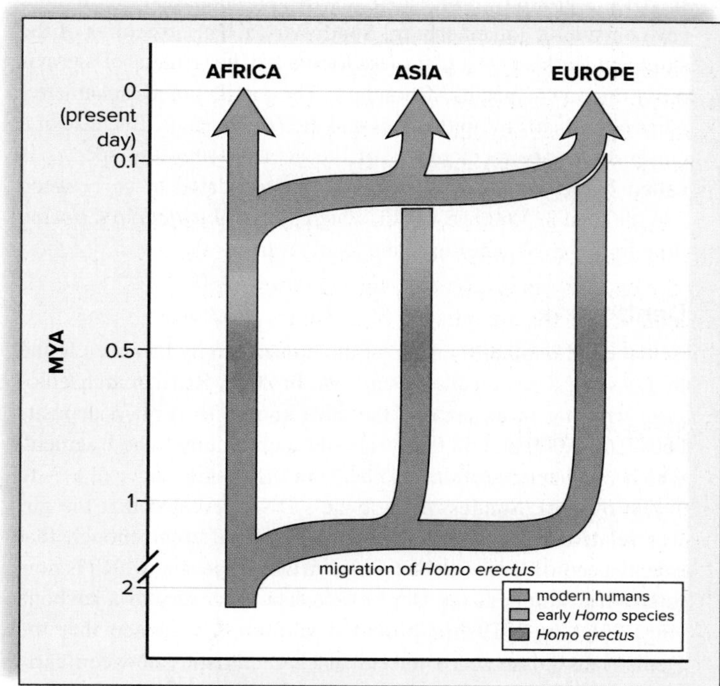

Figure 23.18 **Replacement model.**
According to the replacement model, modern humans evolved in Africa and then replaced early *Homo* species in Asia and Europe.

BIOLOGY TODAY ▶ Science

The Complexity of Our Evolutionary Past

Over the past several years, fossil and genetic evidence has indicated that rather than a simple linear transition from *Homo erectus* to *H. neanderthalensis* to *H. sapiens*, there may have been a period of several hundred thousand years when multiple species of *Homo* occupied what is now Europe and Asia.

Homo floresiensis

In 2004, scientists announced the discovery of the fossil remains of *Homo floresiensis*. The approximately 80,000-year-old fossil of a 1-m-tall, 25-kg adult female was discovered on the island of Flores in the South Pacific. The specimen was the size of a 3-year-old *H. sapiens* but possessed a braincase only one-third the size of a modern human (Fig. 23A). Due to its small size, this species has been nicknamed "Hobbits," after characters in the books by J. R. R. Tolkien. How *H. floresiensis* evolved is still under investigation. Scientists hypothesize the population split from *H. erectus* after being isolated on the island. Their small size may have evolved on the island or originated in their *H. erectus* ancestors. Interestingly, *H. floresiensis* existed as modern *H. sapiens* evolved and spread across Africa, Europe, and Asia, but is believed to have gone extinct around 12,000 years ago before *H. sapiens* arrived at the island.

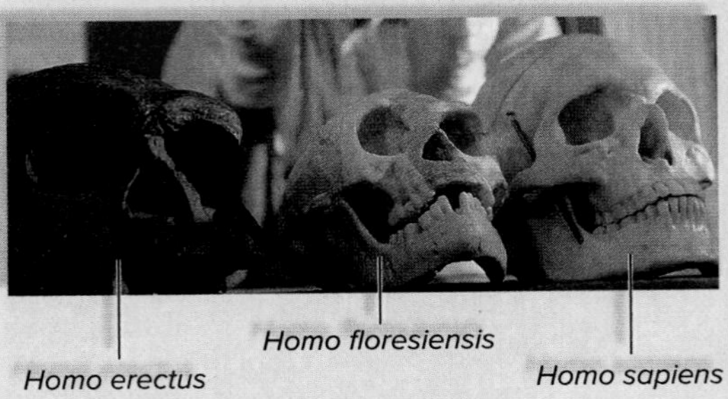

Figure 23A ***Homo floresiensis*.**
The *H. floresiensis* skull is smaller than that of *H. erectus* and that of *H. sapiens*.
Richard Lewis/AP Images

Homo naledi

In 2013, a group of researchers discovered humanlike fossils in a cave outside of Johannesburg, South Africa. The structures of the skull and teeth suggest that these fossils are the remains of a previously unknown species of hominin. The fossils possess characteristics of both australopithecines and the *Homo* genus. Because of a closer similarity to members of the genus *Homo,* the species is called *Homo naledi*. The fossils have been dated to be between 236,000 and 335,000 years old, which places *H. naledi* in the same time frame as Neanderthals and Denisovans.

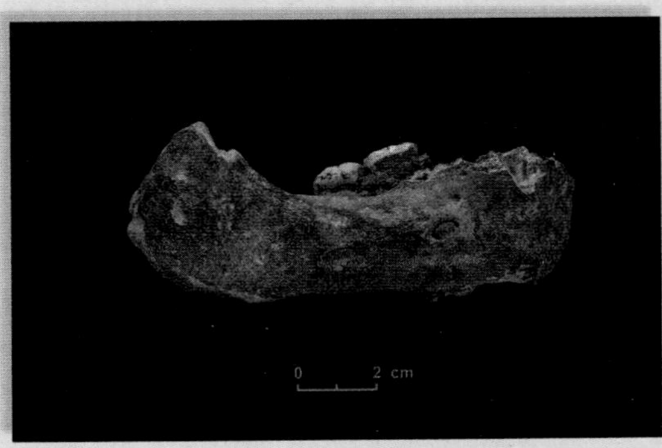

Figure 23B **Evidence of Denisovans.**
This jawbone of a Denisovan was found high in the Tibetan plateaus.
Lanzhou University/Dongju Zhang

Denisovans

Evidence of another member of the human family has been found in a cave in Russia, called Denisova. In 2008, Russian archaeologists working in an area of the cave known to contain deposits between 30,000 and 50,000 years old found a tiny bone fragment, which was later determined to be from the pinkie finger of a 5- to 7-year-old girl. Studies of the bone's DNA revealed that the girl was related to Neanderthals, but she was different enough that scientists consider her to be from a different species, which is now referred to simply as the Denisovans. The discovery of a jawbone (Fig. 23B) in 2019 has provided additional evidence that the Denisovans possessed a hybrid of characteristics between early *Homo* species and what is found in modern humans. Their lineages diverged some 200,000 years ago from *H. heidelbergensis* ancestors in the Middle East.

By comparing Denisovan DNA to that of present-day humans, researchers have discovered that people living in East Asia, and especially the Pacific Islands, share 3–5% of their genome with Denisovans. In addition, Neanderthal DNA has been found when analyzing Denisovans. This indicates that Neanderthals, Denisovans, and early *Homo sapiens* likely coexisted for a period of time and interbred.

Questions to Consider

1. What does the discovery of these species tell you about what we know regarding human evolution?
2. Do you think other species of *Homo* have yet to be discovered? Where would you look?

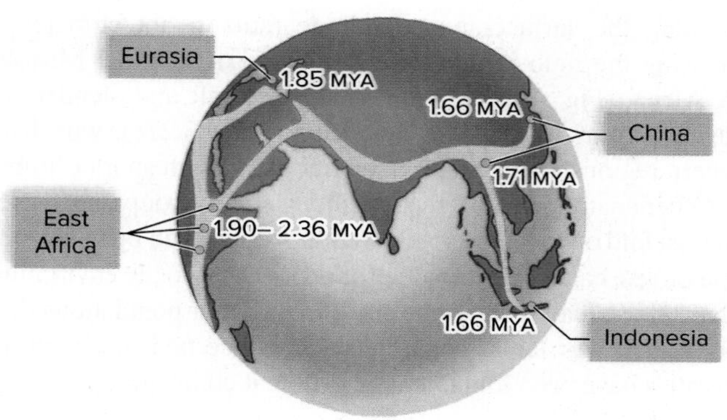

Figure 23.19 **Migration of early *Homo* from Africa.** The dates indicate the migration of early *Homo erectus* from Africa.
Source: Derived from Antón, S. et al., "Evolution of Early Homo: An Integrated Biological Perspective," *Science*, 4 July, 2014, vol. 345, no. 6192

Neanderthals

Neanderthals *(Homo neanderthalensis)* take their name from Germany's Neander Valley, where one of the first Neanderthal skeletons, dated some 200,000 years BP, was discovered. The Neanderthals had massive brow ridges, and their nose, jaws, and teeth protruded far forward. The forehead was low and sloping, and the lower jaw lacked a chin. New fossils show that the pubic bone was long, compared to ours.

According to the replacement model, Neanderthals were eventually supplanted by modern humans. However, this traditional view is being challenged by studies of the Neanderthal genome (completed in 2010), which suggest not only that Neanderthals interbred with *Homo sapiens* but that 1–4% of the genomes of non-African *H. sapiens* contain remnants of the Neanderthal genome. Some scientists are suggesting that Neanderthals were not a separate species but simply a race of *H. sapiens* that was eventually absorbed into the larger population. Research continues into these and other hypotheses that explain these similarities.

Physiologically, the Neanderthal brain was, on average, slightly larger than that of *H. sapiens* (1,400 cc, compared with 1,360 cc in most modern humans). The Neanderthals were heavily muscled, especially in the shoulders and neck. The bones of the limbs were shorter and thicker than those of modern humans. It is hypothesized that a larger brain than that of modern humans was required to control the extra musculature. The Neanderthals lived in Europe and Asia during the last Ice Age, and their sturdy build could have helped conserve heat.

The Neanderthals show evidence of being culturally advanced. Most lived in caves, but those living in the open may have built houses. They manufactured a variety of stone tools, including spear points, which could have been used for hunting. Scrapers and knives could have helped in food preparation. They most likely successfully hunted bears, woolly mammoths, rhinoceroses, reindeer, and other contemporary animals. They used and could control fire, which probably helped them cook meat and keep themselves warm. They even buried their dead with flowers and tools and may have had a religion. Perhaps they believed in life after death. If so, they were capable of thinking symbolically.

Cro-Magnons

Cro-Magnons are the oldest fossils to be designated ***Homo sapiens*** and are named for a fossil location in France. Scientists recognize that Cro-Magnons were the modern humans who entered Asia and Europe from Africa around 100,000 years ago (or even earlier). Cro-Magnons had a thoroughly modern appearance (Fig. 23.20). Analysis of Neanderthal DNA indicates it is so different from Cro-Magnon DNA that these two groups of people did not interbreed. Instead, Cro-Magnons seem to have replaced the Neanderthals in the Middle East and then spread to Europe 40,000 years ago. There, they lived side by side with the Neanderthals for several thousand years. If so, the Neanderthals are cousins, not ancestors, to us.

Cro-Magnons made advanced stone tools, including compound tools, as when stone flakes were fitted to a wooden handle. They may have been the first to make knifelike blades and throw spears, enabling them to kill animals from a distance. They were such accomplished hunters that some researchers suggest they were responsible for the extinction of many larger mammals, such as the giant sloth, mammoth, saber-toothed tiger, and giant ox, during the late Pleistocene epoch.

Cro-Magnons hunted cooperatively, and perhaps they were the first to have a language. Most likely, they lived in small groups, with the men hunting by day while the women remained at home with the children. It's possible that this hunting way of life among prehistoric people influences our behavior today. The Cro-Magnon culture included art. They sculpted small figurines out of reindeer bones and antlers. They also painted beautiful drawings of animals on cave walls in Spain and France (Fig. 23.20).

Figure 23.20 **The Cro-Magnons.** Cro-Magnon people are one of the earliest groups to be designated *Homo sapiens*. Their tool-making ability and other cultural attributes, including artistic talents, are legendary.
Tomas Abad/age fotostock/SuperStock

Human Variation

Humans have been widely distributed about the globe since they evolved. As with any other species that has a wide geographic distribution, phenotypic and genotypic variations are noticeable among populations. Today, we say that people have different ethnicities (Fig. 23.21*a*).

It has been hypothesized that human variations evolved as adaptations to local environmental conditions. One obvious difference among people is skin color. A darker skin is protective against the high ultraviolet (UV) intensity of bright sunlight. On the other hand, a white skin ensures vitamin D production in the skin when the UV intensity is low. Harvard University geneticist Richard Lewontin points out, however, that this hypothesis concerning the survival value of dark and light skin has never been tested.

Two correlations between body shape and environmental conditions have been noted since the nineteenth century. The first, Bergmann's rule, states that animals in colder regions of their range have a bulkier body build. The second, Allen's rule, states that animals in colder regions of their range have shorter limbs, digits, and ears. Both of these effects help regulate body temperature by increasing the surface-area-to-volume ratio in hot climates and decreasing the ratio in cold climates. For example, the Maasai of East Africa (Fig. 23.21*b*) tend to be very tall and slender, with elongated limbs. By contrast, the Inuit (Fig. 23.21*c*), who live in northern regions, tend to have a bulkier build, with shorter limbs.

Other anatomical differences among ethnic groups, such as hair texture, a fold on the upper eyelid (common in Asian peoples), or the shape of lips, cannot be explained as adaptations to the environment. Perhaps these features became fixed in different populations due to genetic drift. As far as intelligence is concerned, no significant disparities have been found among different ethnic groups.

a.

b.

c.

Figure 23.21 Ethnic variations in modern humans.
a. Some of the differences among the diverse ethnic groups may be due to adaptations to their original environment. **b.** The Maasai live in East Africa. **c.** The Inuit live near the Arctic Circle.

(a): Anderson Ross/Photodisc/Getty Images; (b): Sylvia S. Mader; (c): Sue Flood/Stone/Getty Images

Genetic Evidence for a Common Ancestry

The replacement model for the evolution of humans (see Fig. 23.18) also pertains to the origin of ethnic groups. This hypothesis proposes that all modern humans have a relatively recent common ancestor (Cro-Magnon) who evolved in Africa and then spread into other regions. Paleontologists tell us that the variation among modern populations is considerably less than among human populations some 250,000 years ago. This would mean that all ethnic groups evolved from the same single, ancestral population.

A comparative study of mitochondrial DNA shows that the differences among human populations are consistent with their having a common ancestor no more than a million years ago. The evolutionary biologist Richard Lewontin found that the genotypes of different modern populations are extremely similar. He examined variations in 17 genes, including blood groups and various enzymes, among seven major geographic groups: Caucasians, black Africans, mongoloids, south Asian Aborigines, Amerinds, Oceanians, and Australian Aborigines. He found that the great majority of genetic variation—85%—occurs within ethnic groups, not among them. In other words, the amount of genetic variation between individuals of the same ethnic group is greater than the variation between ethnic groups.

CHECK YOUR PROGRESS 23.5

1. Discuss the difference between australopithecines and early *Homo* species.
2. Name the hominin that is believed to be the first to migrate out of Africa.
3. Discuss how *H. habilis* might have differed from the australopithecines.
4. Describe how the replacement model hypothesis relates to the evolution of modern humans.
5. Describe the relationship between Neanderthals, Cro-Magnons, and *H. sapiens*.

CONNECTING THE CONCEPTS

For more information on the topics presented in this section, refer to the following discussions:

Section 3.6 describes the structure and function of mitochondria.

Section 24.1 examines the major terrestrial ecosystems occupied by humans.

BIOLOGY TODAY ▶ Science

The Effects of Biocultural Evolution on Population Growth

Humans today undergo biocultural evolution, because culture has developed to the point that adaptation to the environment is dependent not on genes but on the passage of culture from one generation to the next.

Tool Use and Language Begins

The first step toward biocultural evolution began when *Homo habilis* made primitive stone tools. *Homo erectus* continued the tradition and most likely was a hunter of sorts. It's possible the campsites for these species were home bases, where the women stayed with the children while the men went out to hunt. Hunting was an important event in the development of culture, especially because it encouraged the development of language. If *H. erectus* didn't have the use of language, certainly Cro-Magnons did. People who have the ability to speak a language would have been able to cooperate better as they hunted, and even as they sought places to gather plants. Among animals, only humans have a complex language that allows them to communicate their experiences. Words are not objects and events. They stand for objects and events that can be pictured in the mind.

Agriculture Begins

About 10,000 years ago, people gave up being full-time hunter-gatherers and became at least part-time farmers. What accounts for the rise of agriculture? The answer is not known, but several explanations have been put forth. About 12,000 years ago, a warming trend occurred as the Ice Age came to a close. A variety of big-game animals became extinct, including the saber-toothed cats, mammoths, and mastodons. This may have made hunting less productive. As the weather warmed, the glaciers retreated and left fertile valleys, where rivers and streams were full of fish and the soil was good. The Fertile Crescent in Mesopotamia is one such example. Here, fishing villages may have sprung up, causing people to settle down.

The people were probably already knowledgeable about what crops to plant. Most likely, as hunter-gatherers, people had already selected seeds with desirable characteristics for propagation. Then, a chance mutation may have made these plants particularly suitable as a source of food. They began to till the good soil where they had settled and to systematically plant crops (Fig. 23C).

As people became more sedentary, they may have had more children, especially because the men were home more often. Population increases may have tipped the scales and caused them to adopt agriculture full-time, especially if agriculture could be counted on to provide food for hungry mouths. The availability of agricultural tools must have contributed to making agriculture worthwhile. The digging stick, the hoe, the sickle, and the plow were improved when iron tools replaced bronze in the stone-bronze-iron sequence of ancient tools. Irrigation began as a way to control the water supply, especially in semiarid areas and regions of periodic rainfall.

Figure 23C **Primitive Agriculture.** Agriculture began in several locations across the globe about 10,000 years ago.
Barry Barker/McGraw Hill

If evolutionary success is judged by population size, agriculture was extremely beneficial to our success, because it caused a rapid increase of human numbers all over the Earth. Also, agriculture ushered in civilization as we know it. When crops became bountiful, some people were freed from raising their own food. They began to specialize in particular trades in towns and then cities. Some became shopkeepers, bakers, traders, and teachers, to name a few. Others became the nobility, priests, and soldiers. Today, farming is highly mechanized and cities are extremely large. However, we are on a treadmill. As the human population increases, we need new innovations to produce greater amounts of food. As soon as food production increases, populations grow once again, and the demand for food becomes still greater. Will there be a point when the population is greater than the food capacity? Is that time already upon us?

The Industrial Revolution Begins

The Industrial Revolution began in England during the eighteenth century, and with it arose a demand for energy in the form of coal and oil that today seems unlimited. Our ability to construct any number of tools, including high-tech computers, is not stored in our genes. We learn it from the previous generation. Our modern civilization that began due to the advent of agriculture is now altering the global environment in a way that affects the evolution of other species. Species are becoming extinct unless they can adapt to the presence of our civilization. It could be that biocultural evolution will be so harmful to the biosphere that the human species also will eventually be driven to extinction.

Questions to Consider

1. Can technology be used to help us not pollute the environment? How?
2. Should the extinction of other species be prevented? If so, how?
3. Should the human population be reduced in size? How might this be brought about?

CONCLUSION

Neanderthals and modern humans shared a common ancestor approximately 550,000 to 690,000 years ago before the populations became geographically isolated. It wasn't until around 100,000 years ago that modern humans migrated into the range of Neanderthals and the populations began to interbreed.

Molecular evidence shows that individuals of Eurasian descent inherited 1–4% of their genes from our Neanderthal cousins. This is the result of our ancestral populations interbreeding with each other prior to the extinction of Neanderthals. Many of these genes played a role in the survival of Neanderthals but are not necessarily beneficial for modern humans. Further comparative studies of the Neanderthal and modern human genomes will undoubtedly reveal more information about what our species' interactions may have been with the other hominins.

SUMMARIZE

23.1 Origin of Life

The processes of **chemical evolution** and **biological evolution** contributed to the formation of the first cells.

- Using an outside energy source, small organic molecules were produced by reactions between early Earth's atmospheric gases.
- Macromolecules evolved and interacted.
- The **RNA-first hypothesis** proposed that only macromolecule RNA was needed for the first cell or cells.
- The **protein-first hypothesis** proposed that amino acids join to form polypeptides when exposed to dry heat.
- The **protocell,** a **heterotroph,** which obtained energy by anaerobic respiration, lived on preformed organic molecules in the ocean.

The protocell eventually became a true cell once it had genes composed of DNA and could reproduce.

23.2 Biological Evolution

Biological evolution explains both the unity and the diversity of life. **Prokaryotic cells** are the simplest form of life. Eukaryotic cells evolved from prokaryotic cells.

- Descent from a common ancestor explains the unity (sameness) of living organisms.
- **Adaptation** to different environments explains the great diversity of life.

Darwin's theory of evolution by **natural selection** explains the process of biological evolution. **Artificial selection** occurs when humans select for specific traits in a species. Natural selection is supported by the following:

- *Fossil evidence:* **Fossils** and the **fossil record** provide the history of life in general and allow us to trace the descent of a particular group.
- *Biogeographical evidence:* **Biogeography** is the distribution of organisms on Earth and is explainable by assuming that organisms evolved in one locale.
- *Anatomical evidence:* The common anatomies and development of a group of organisms are explainable by descent from a common ancestor. **Homologous structures** are inherited from a common ancestor. **Analogous structures** are adaptations that evolved independently. **Vestigial structures** have no function in current organisms but may have had function in an ancestral group.
- *Biochemical evidence:* All organisms have similar biochemical molecules.

Darwin developed a mechanism for adaptation known as natural selection

- The result of natural selection is a population adapted to its local environment.

23.3 Classification of Humans

The classification of humans can be used to trace their ancestry. Humans, like other species, are assigned a **binomial name:** *Homo sapiens.*

- Humans are **primates.** Primates can be divided into two groups, the **prosimians** and the **anthropoids.** Humans belong to the anthropoid group.
- Primates have the characteristics of mobile limbs, binocular vision, complex brains, and a reduced reproductive rate.

23.4 Evolution of Hominins

- The evolutionary tree of humans is supported by DNA evidence, which can be used as a molecular clock to indicate when the groups diverged.
- **Hominids** are a classification that includes apes, chimpanzees, and humans. **Hominin** refers only to members of the genus *Homo* and their close relatives. The first hominins (a group that includes humans) most likely lived about 6 to 7 MYA.
- Certain features (**bipedal posture,** flat face, and brain) are used to identify fossil hominins.
- **Ardipithecines** and **australopithecines** are examples of early hominins. The features of australopithecines support the concept of **mosaic evolution.**

23.5 Evolution of Humans

Fossils are classified as *Homo* with regard to brain size (over 600 cc), jaws and teeth (which resemble modern humans'), and evidence of tool use.

- ***Homo habilis*** made and used tools. They were among the first to display evidence of **culture.**
- ***Homo erectus*** was the first *Homo* to have a brain size of more than 1,000 cc.
- *H. erectus* migrated from Africa into Europe and Asia.
- *H. erectus* used fire and may have been big-game hunters.

Evolution of Modern Humans

- The **replacement model** hypothesis says that *H. sapiens* evolved in Africa but then migrated to Asia and Europe.

Neanderthals

- The **Neanderthals** were already living in Europe and Asia before modern humans arrived.
- They had a culture but did not have the physical traits of modern humans.

Denisovans

- The **Denisovans** lived in the area that is now Siberia, but they interacted with early *H. sapiens.*

Cro-Magnons

- **Cro-Magnons** are the oldest fossil to be designated ***Homo sapiens.***
- Their tools were sophisticated, and they had a culture.

ENGAGE

THINKING CRITICALLY

1. Bipedalism has many selective advantages, including the increased ability to spot predators and prey. However, bipedalism has one particular disadvantage—upright posture leads to a smaller pelvic opening, which makes giving birth to an offspring with a large head very difficult. This situation results in a higher percentage of deaths (of both mother and child) during birth in humans compared to other primates. How can you explain the selection for a trait, such as bipedalism, that has both positive and negative consequences for fitness?
2. In studying recent fossils of the genus *Homo,* such as Cro-Magnon, biologists have determined that modern humans have not undergone much biological evolution in the past 50,000 years. Rather, cultural anthropologists argue that cultural evolution has been far more important than biological evolution in the recent history of modern humans. What do they mean by this? Support your argument with some examples.
3. Some modern ethnic groups (white Europeans, Asians) have apparently inherited genes from Neanderthals that may influence resistance to cold temperatures. What types of genes might these be?

MAKING IT RELEVANT

1. How does genetic analyses of fossils help us understand human evolution better than just a comparison of skulls?
2. Some scientists suggest that the Neanderthals, and possibly the Denisovans, never went extinct, but instead were assimilated into *H. sapiens*. What evidence would you look for to support this hypothesis?
3. Assuming the Denisovans, Neanderthals, and humans were able to interbreed, what does this tell you about their species status according to the biological species concept?

Find answers to all of the chapter questions at connect.mheducation.com

CHAPTER

24

Ecology and the Nature of Ecosystems

Charoenchai Tothaisong/123RF

CHAPTER OUTLINE

BEFORE YOU BEGIN

Before beginning this chapter, take a few moments to review the following discussions:

Section 1.1 What is the relationship between populations and ecosystems in the levels of biological organization?

Section 1.1 Why must living organisms acquire materials and energy?

Section 1.4 What are some of the major challenges facing science?

The Origins of COVID-19

In 2019, a novel coronavirus strain, SARS-CoV-2, emerged, leading to the disease COVID-19. In a short period of time, COVID-19 quickly escalated into a global pandemic. In the first year of the pandemic, over 100 million people were infected and over 2 million died. The earliest human cases of COVID-19 were traced back to a seafood and wet animal market in Wuhan, China. While there have been claims that COVID-19 was created in a laboratory, overwhelmingly the scientific evidence points to horseshoe bats as the most likely origin of this strain. Uncertainty remains about the intermediate host that enabled the strain to make its way into the human population.

Previous versions of COVID were found to have been transmitted to humans through civet cats and dromedary camels. The only other animals currently known to transmit COVID-19 to humans are minks. We do know humans were able to transmit COVID-19 to a tiger at a New York zoo, domesticated cats and dogs, along with numerous other animal species.

With an estimated 70% of emerging and reemerging pathogens having animal origins, being able to identify the origin and intermediate host for a virus is a crucial step in preventing future transmissions. As humans continue to alter ecosystems and harvest new sources of animal-based food, we expose ourselves to novel strains of viruses that would otherwise remain hidden.

As you read through the chapter, think about the following questions:

1. Which ecosystems are most likely to contain emerging pathogens?
2. Why is an understanding of ecology important to the protection of our species against emerging pathogens?

24.1 The Nature of Ecosystems

LEARNING OUTCOMES

Upon completion of this section, you should be able to

1. Identify the relationship between ecosystems and the biosphere.
2. Identify ways in which autotrophs and heterotrophs obtain nutrients.
3. Interpret the energy flow and biogeochemical cycling within and among ecosystems.

The **biosphere** is the portion of the Earth that contains living organisms, from the atmosphere to the ocean depths to everything in between. Specific areas of the biosphere where organisms interact among themselves, and also with the physical and chemical environment, are called **ecosystems.** The interactions between the living and nonliving factors within an ecosystem help maintain stability within the ecosystem. One ecosystem can affect the next, which in turn affects the stability of the biosphere. Human activities change the interactions between organisms and their environments in ways that alter the abundance and diversity of life in an ecosystem. It is important to understand how ecosystems function, so we can repair past damage and predict how human activities will lead to future damage.

Types of Ecosystems

Scientists recognize several distinctive major types of terrestrial ecosystems, also called **biomes** (Fig. 24.1). Regional climate conditions, such as average temperature and rainfall levels, define a biome. Within each biome are a variety of organisms adapted to the regional climate.

A few examples of terrestrial biomes are shown in Figure 24.2. For example, the tropical rain forest, which occurs at the equator, is dominated by large, evergreen, broad-leaved trees. The savanna is a tropical grassland that supports many types of grazing animals. Temperate grasslands receive less rainfall than temperate forests, which are populated by trees that lose their leaves during the winter. Deserts receive scant rainfall and therefore lack trees. The taiga is a very cold northern forest of conifers such as pine, spruce, hemlock, and fir. Bordering the North Pole is the frigid tundra, which has long winters and a short growing season. A permafrost persists even during the summer in the tundra and prevents large plants from becoming established.

Aquatic ecosystems are divided into two broad categories: fresh water systems and salt water (marine) systems. Examples are shown in Figure 24.3. Freshwater ecosystems are those with standing water, such as lakes and ponds, and those with running water, such as rivers and streams. They can further be divided based upon the amount of nutrients they contain. The ocean is a marine ecosystem that covers 70% of the Earth's surface. Estuaries are where

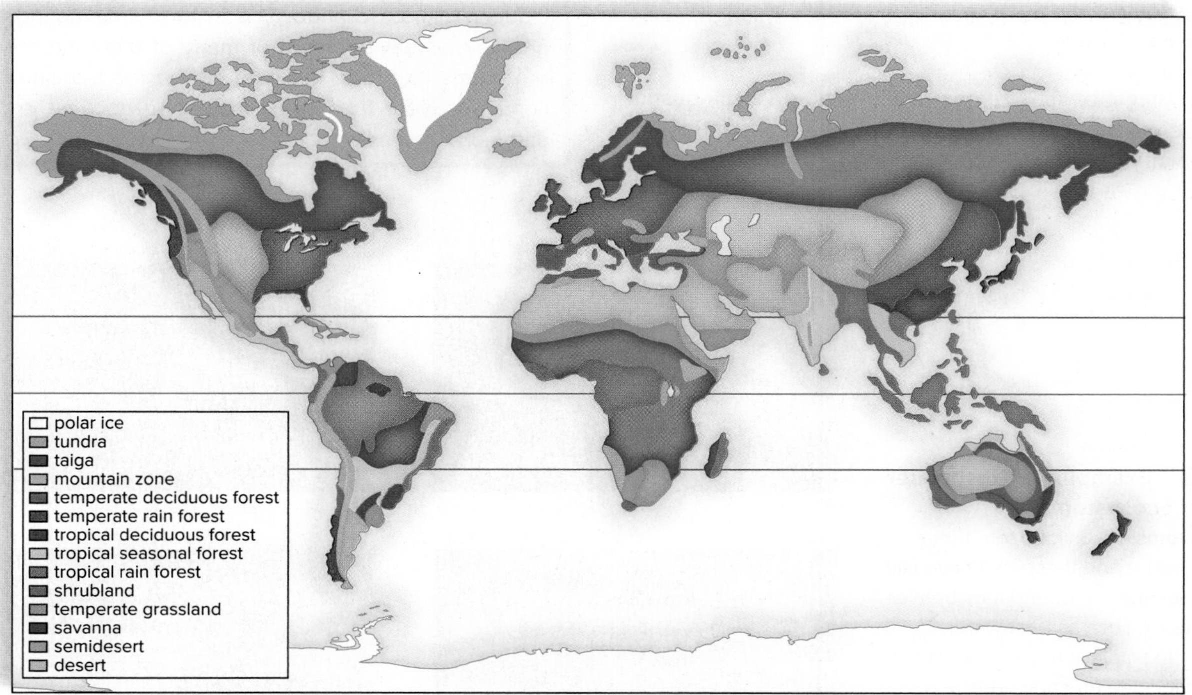

Figure 24.1 The distribution of the major terrestrial biomes.
The general distribution of the major terrestrial ecosystems, or biomes, is shown here. The characteristics of each biome are largely determined by temperature and precipitation.

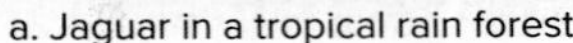
a. Jaguar in a tropical rain forest

b. Tall-grass prairie

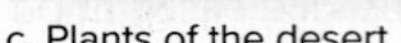
c. Plants of the desert

d. Spruce trees in the taiga biome

Figure 24.2 Examples of terrestrial biomes.
a. Jaguars are a predator in the tropical rain forest. **b.** A tall-grass prairie is an example of a temperate grassland. **c.** The plants of the desert either retain or are shrubs with woody stems and small leaves. **d.** Taigas are dominated by spruce trees and swampy conditions.
(a): ©Sandy Windelspecht/Ricochet Creative Productions, LLC; (b): Jim Steinberg/Science Source; (c): Kevin Burke/Corbis/Getty Images; (d): Perry Mastrovito/Creatas Images/Jupiterimages

fresh and saltwater mix and are one of the most diverse aquatic ecosystems. Coral reefs are located offshore, and are home to an incredible diversity of marine life.

Biotic Components of an Ecosystem

Ecosystems contain both biotic (living) and abiotic (nonliving) components. Examples of abiotic components are nutrients in the soil, water, and the weather. The biotic components of an ecosystem can be categorized according to how they obtain their energy (Fig. 24.4). Biotic species are generally organized as autotrophs and/or heterotrophs.

Autotrophs

Autotrophs require only inorganic nutrients and an outside source of energy to produce organic nutrients for their own use and for all the other members of a community. Therefore, they are called **producers,** meaning they produce food (Fig. 24.4*a*). Photosynthetic organisms produce most of the organic nutrients for the biosphere. Algae of all types possess chlorophyll and carry on photosynthesis in freshwater and marine ecosystems. Green plants are the primary photosynthesizers in terrestrial ecosystems.

BIOLOGY IN YOUR LIFE

Why should I care about phytoplankton?

The producer base of the ocean is made up of single-celled organisms called phytoplankton. They are eaten by other microscopic organisms called zooplankton. These feed the next level of the food chain, which eventually makes its way up to top-level producers such as sharks, dolphins, and tuna.

The pH of the ocean is becoming more acidic due to human-induced climate change. This in turn is disrupting the normal growth and development of many of the microscopic marine organisms that form the base of the food chain. If this trend continues, your tuna steak may soon become less available and more expensive.

a.

c.

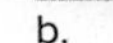
b.

d.

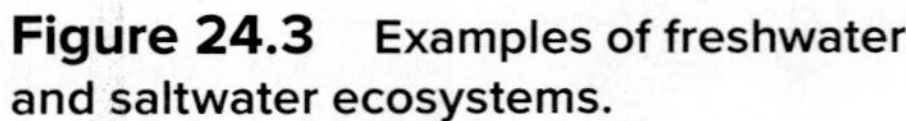
Figure 24.3 Examples of freshwater and saltwater ecosystems.

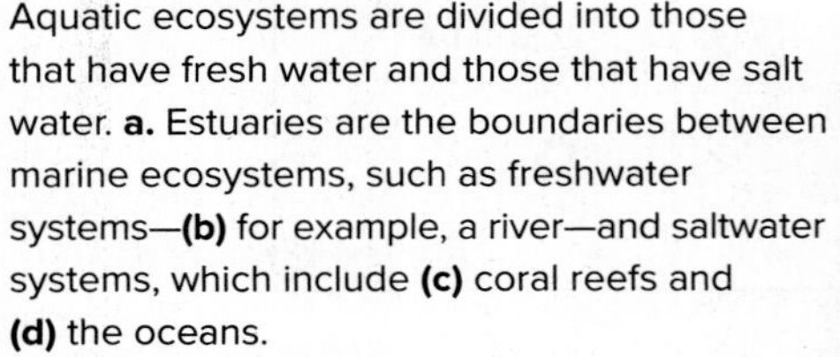
Aquatic ecosystems are divided into those that have fresh water and those that have salt water. **a.** Estuaries are the boundaries between marine ecosystems, such as freshwater systems—**(b)** for example, a river—and saltwater systems, which include **(c)** coral reefs and **(d)** the oceans.
(a): Carlyn Iverson/McGraw Hill; (b): Victor Ovies Arenas/Getty Images; (c): adokon/iStock/Getty Images; (d): Francois Gohier/Science Source

a. Producers

b. Herbivores

c. Carnivores

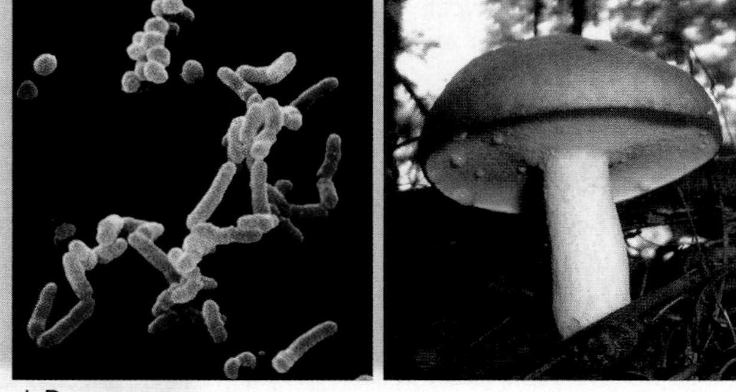

d. Decomposers

Figure 24.4 **The biotic components of an ecosystem.** **a.** Diatoms and green plants are autotrophs (producers). **b.** Caterpillars and rabbits are herbivores (heterotrophs). **c.** Snakes and hawks are carnivores (heterotrophs). **d.** Some bacteria and some mushrooms are decomposers (heterotrophs).

(a) (diatom): ©Ed Reschke; (tree): Alexander Dunkel/Sieboldianus/E+/Getty Images; (b) (caterpillar): Ken Cavanagh/McGraw Hill; (rabbit): Jose A. Bernat Bacete/Moment/Getty Images; (c) (bullsnake): Derrick Hamrick/imagebroker/Getty Images; (hawk): Tze-hsin Woo/Flickr/Getty Images; (d) (bacteria): Image Source/Getty Images; (mushroom): Denise McCullough

Heterotrophs

Heterotrophs need a source of organic nutrients. They are **consumers,** meaning they consume food. **Herbivores** are organisms that feed directly on producers such as plants and algae (Fig. 24.4*b*). Deer, rabbits, and caterpillars are herbivores found in terrestrial habitats. Some birds are herbivores, too. In aquatic ecosystems, some protists are herbivores. **Carnivores** feed on other animals. Examples are snakes and hawks (Fig. 24.4*c*). **Omnivores** are animals that feed on both plants and animals. Humans are considered omnivores.

There are often multiple levels of consumers in an ecosystem. A consumer's level depends on where it is in the food chain in relation to the producers. Examples are primary consumers (e.g., plant-eating insects); secondary consumers (e.g., insect-eating frogs); and tertiary consumers (e.g., frog-eating snakes). The top-level consumers are called top predators.

Detritus feeders are organisms that feed on detritus, decomposing particles of organic matter. Marine fan worms take detritus from the water, and crayfish take it from the substratum. Earthworms, various beetles, termites, and ants are terrestrial detritus feeders. Bacteria and fungi, including mushrooms, are decomposers. They acquire nutrients by breaking down dead organic matter, including animal wastes. Decomposers perform a valuable service because they release inorganic substances that can be taken up by plants for their growth (Fig. 24.4*d*). Otherwise, plants would be completely dependent on physical processes, such as the release of minerals from rocks, to supply them with inorganic nutrients.

Niche

A **niche** is the role of an organism in an ecosystem. Being a producer or a carnivore is an example of a niche. Generally, descriptions of a niche include how an organism gets its food, and how it interacts with other populations in the community and its physical habitat. Humans have a niche in most ecosystems because we interact with both the biotic and abiotic components.

Energy Flow and Chemical Cycling

When we diagram the interactions of all the populations in an ecosystem, it is possible to illustrate two phenomena that characterize every ecosystem. One of these phenomena is energy flow, which begins when producers absorb solar (and in some cases, chemical) energy. The second, nutrient cycling, occurs when producers take in inorganic chemicals from the physical environment. Thereafter, producers make organic nutrients that can be used by them, as well as by other populations of the ecosystem. Energy flow occurs when nutrients pass from one population to another. Eventually, all the energy content is converted to heat. The heat then dissipates into the environment. Therefore, most ecosystems cannot exist without a continual input of solar energy. Chemicals cycle when inorganic nutrients are returned to the producers from the atmosphere or soil (Fig. 24.5).

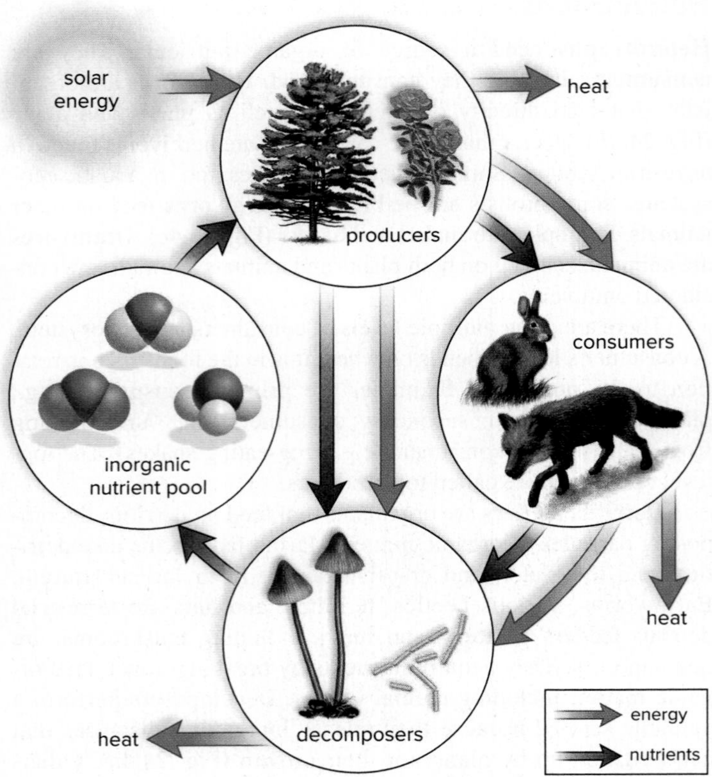

Figure 24.5 Energy flow and chemical cycling in an ecosystem.
Chemicals cycle, but energy flows through an ecosystem. As energy transformations occur repeatedly, all the energy derived from the sun eventually dissipates as heat.

Only a portion of the organic nutrients made by autotrophs is passed on to heterotrophs, because plants use some of the organic molecules to fuel their cellular respiration (see Fig. 3.22). Similarly, only a small percentage of nutrients taken in by heterotrophs is available to higher-level consumers. Figure 24.6 shows why. Some of the food eaten by a herbivore is never digested and is eliminated as feces. Metabolic wastes are excreted in urine. Of the assimilated energy, a large portion is used during metabolism and thereafter becomes heat. Only a small fraction of the food energy is converted into increased body weight (or additional offspring), which become available to carnivores. Plants carry on cellular respiration, too, so only about 55% of the original energy absorbed by plants is available to an ecosystem. Further, as organisms feed on one another, less and less of this 55% is available in a usable form.

The elimination of wastes and the deaths of all organisms do not mean substances are lost to an ecosystem. Instead, they are nutrients made available to decomposers. Decomposers convert organic nutrients, such as glucose, back into inorganic chemicals, such as carbon dioxide and water. The inorganic chemicals are then released to the soil or atmosphere. Chemicals complete their cycle in an ecosystem when the producers absorb inorganic chemicals from the atmosphere or soil.

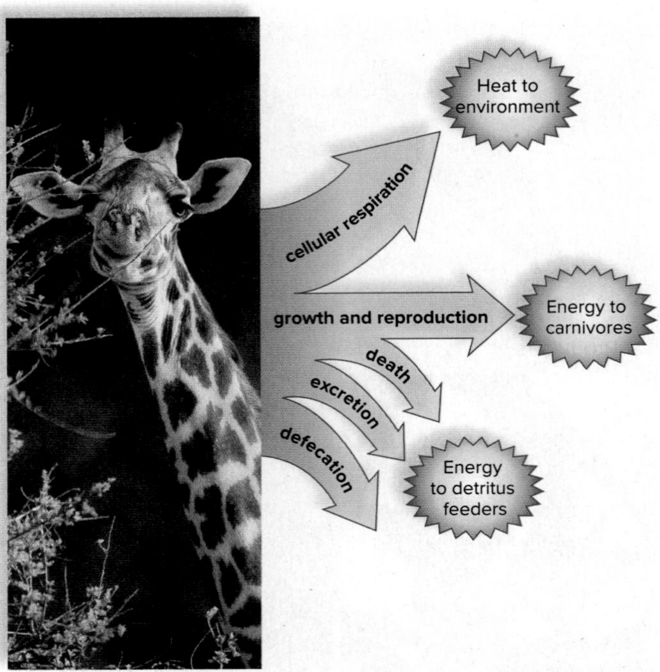

Figure 24.6 The fate of food energy taken in by a herbivore.
Only about 10% of the food energy taken in by a herbivore is passed on to carnivores. A large portion goes to detritus feeders via defecation, excretion, and death. Another large portion is used for metabolism.
(photo): fStop Images GmbH/Shutterstock

CHECK YOUR PROGRESS 24.1

1. Why can the biosphere be considered a giant ecosystem?
2. Explain why autotrophs are called producers and heterotrophs are called consumers.
3. Explain the characteristics used to identify biomes.
4. Distinguish between the movement of energy and the movement of chemicals in an ecosystem.

CONNECTING THE CONCEPTS

For more information on the topics presented in this section, refer to the following discussions:

Section 1.1 describes the relationship among populations, the ecosystems on the planet, and the biosphere.

Section 3.6 examines how organisms release the energy stored in organic nutrients by cellular respiration.

24.2 Energy Flow in Ecosystems

LEARNING OUTCOMES

Upon completion of this section, you should be able to

1. Recognize the differences between a grazing food web and a detrital food web.
2. Explain the energy flow among populations through food webs and ecological pyramids.

The ecological principles we have been discussing can now be applied using a forest ecosystem as an example. The various interconnecting paths of energy flow are represented by a **food web,** which is a diagram that describes trophic, or feeding, relationships. Figure 24.7*a* is a **grazing food web,** because it begins with an oak tree and grass. Caterpillars feed on oak leaves; mice, rabbits, and deer feed on leaves and grass at or near the ground. Certain species of birds, chipmunks, and mice feed on seeds and nuts, but they are omnivores, because they also feed on caterpillars. These herbivores and omnivores are then food for a number of different carnivores.

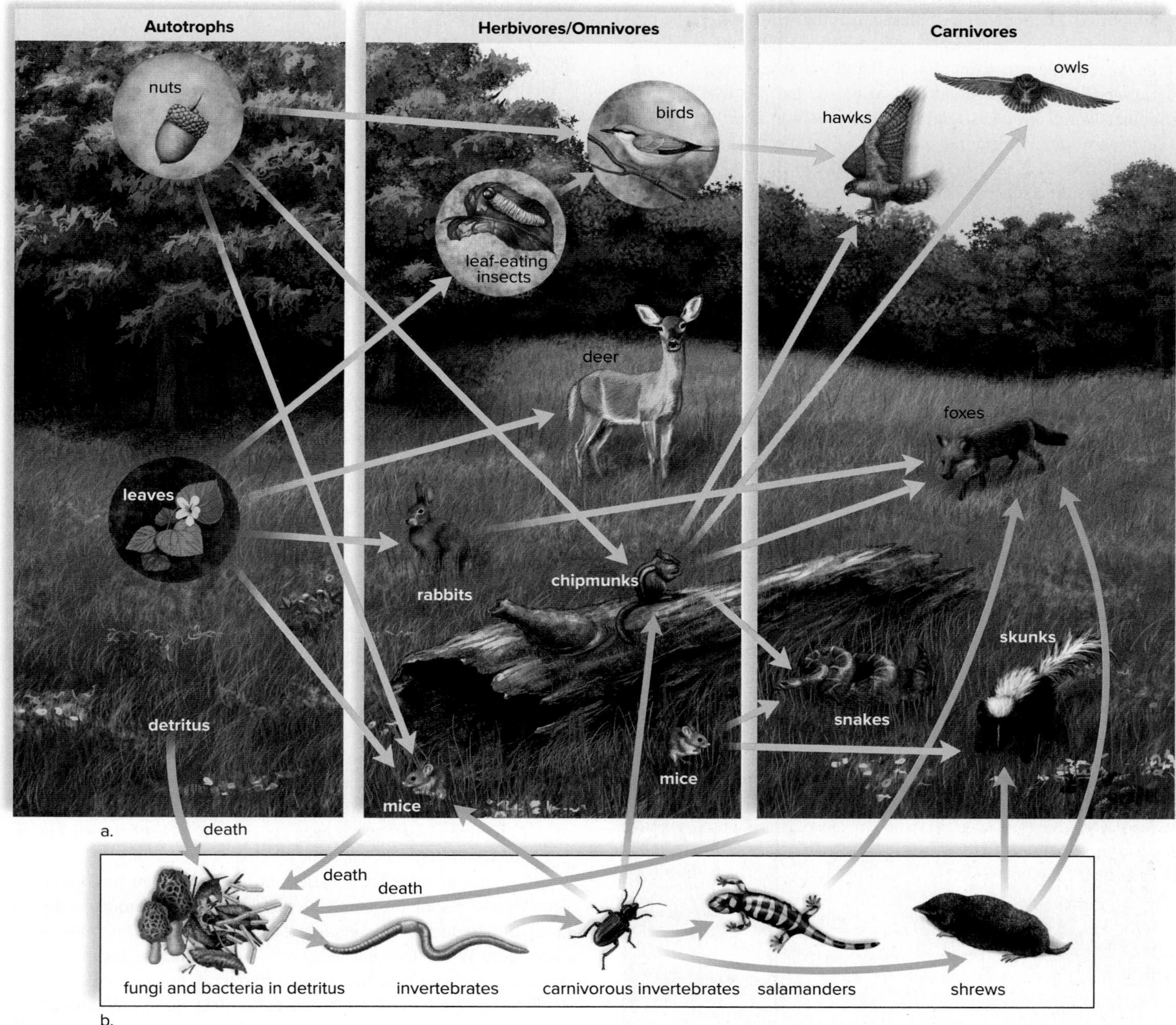

Figure 24.7 Food webs.
Food webs are descriptions of who eats whom. **a.** Tan arrows illustrate possible grazing food webs. The tree and other producers convert sun energy into food energy at the first trophic level. Mice and other animals that eat the producers are primary consumers (second trophic level). Carnivores that rely on primary consumer animals for energy (the hawk, fox, skunk, snake, and owl) are secondary consumers (third trophic level). **b.** Green arrows illustrate possible detrital food webs. These begin with detritus: organic waste and the remains of dead organisms. Decomposers and detritus feeders recycle these organic nutrients. The organisms in the detrital food web may be prey for animals in the grazing food web, as when chipmunks feed on bugs. Thus, the grazing food web and detrital food web are interconnected.

BIOLOGY TODAY ▶ Science

How Much Plastic Are You Eating?

The earliest plastics date back to 1856 when Alexander Parkes patented the first synthetic plastic. In 1869, John Wesley Hyatt simplified the production of plastic, making industrial plastic production possible. Large-scale production decreased human reliance on the material constraints and availability of resources in the natural world. The mass production of plastic has changed the consumer world. Products that were previously in short supply and expensive quickly become available to the average consumer. In today's world, plastic is everywhere. It can be found lining our soup cans, in cosmetics, and wrapping our food, as well as countless other products.

Plant cellulose provided the foundation for the earliest plastics, whereas today's plastics are composed of hydrocarbon molecules derived from refining oil and natural gas. Other components of modern plastic are chemicals that can disrupt the actions of human hormones. Several of these have been linked to obesity, reproductive harm, organ problems, and developmental delays in children. Animal studies have shown that microplastic can cross the membrane that protects the brain from foreign particles, as well as the barrier that separates the placenta and the fetus.

Since the 1950s, we have produced over 8 billion tons of plastic. Sadly, less than 10% has been recycled. What many of us don't realize is that plastic doesn't decompose. Instead, it breaks down into microscopic forms called microplastics (Fig. 24A). While the chemicals contained within plastics are of concern, the microplastics also have scientists worried. It is estimated that Americans ingest over 74,000 microplastic particles each year. These particles can be found in the food we eat, the water we drink, and even the air we breathe. A study commissioned by the World Wildlife Fund estimated that people consume approximately 5 grams of plastic per week—roughly the amount found in a credit card.

Figure 24A Microplastics.
The human diet contains a significant amount of microplastics.
Pcess609/Shutterstock

Figure 24B Plastic pollution in the oceans.
Plastic waste in the ocean can disrupt marine food chains and impact threatened species.
Rich Carey/Shutterstock

Plastic pollution has been rated as the number one problem in the marine environment. Over 8 million tons of plastic make their way into the ocean from land-based sources. This constitutes over 80% of all marine debris and can range from the surface of the ocean to the sediments found in the deep sea. Millions of marine animals mistake plastic for their natural food sources. A plastic bag floating in the water resembles a jellyfish, a favorite food of many turtles. Seabirds will consume bottle caps and other bright bits of plastic, mistaking it for a source of food as well. Once ingested, the animals die of starvation because their stomachs are filled with plastic debris (Fig. 24B). It is estimated that by the year 2050, plastic will outweigh the marine life in the ocean.

Exposure to seawater leaches the toxic chemicals out of plastic and into the bodies of the marine animals that consume the plastic. Over time, the chemicals accumulate and magnify as they make their way up the food chain. The transfer of pollutants to humans as a result of consumption of seafood has been identified as a health hazard, but rigorous scientific research into the problem is still lacking.

Fortunately, there are a variety of things that can be done to decrease our personal risk. These things are also environmentally beneficial. Reducing, reusing, or not using plastic at all will make a difference. While humans recognize the destructive nature and ecological consequences that come with our dependence on plastic, it will be up to us to work together to collectively make a difference.

Questions to Consider

1. Would you support a ban on single-use plastic items such as grocery bags?
2. Are there any species in an ecosystem that are capable of biodegrading plastic into completely harmless molecules?
3. Is there a way to limit the movement of plastic from one ecosystem to the next?

Figure 24.7*b* is a **detrital food web.** This type of food web begins with wastes and the remains of dead organisms. Detritus is food for decomposers and soil organisms such as earthworms. Earthworms may be food for carnivorous insects. In turn, salamanders and shrews may consume the carnivorous insects. The members of detrital food webs may become food for aboveground carnivores, so the detrital and grazing food webs are connected.

We naturally tend to think that aboveground plants, such as trees, are the largest storage form of organic matter and energy. This is not necessarily the case. In this particular forest, the organic matter lying on the forest floor and mixed into the soil contains more than twice as much energy as the leaves of living trees. Therefore, more energy in a forest may be funneling through the detrital food web than through the grazing food web.

Trophic Levels

The arrangement of the species in Figure 24.7 suggests that organisms are linked to one another in a straight line, according to feeding or predator–prey relationships. Diagrams that show a single path of energy flow are called **food chains.** For example, in the grazing food web, we might find this **grazing food chain:**

oak leaves → caterpillars → mice → hawks

And in the detrital food web (Figure 24.7*b*), we might find this **detrital food chain:**

detritus → earthworms → beetles → shrews

A **trophic level** is composed of all the organisms that feed at a particular link in a food chain. In the grazing food web in Figure 24.7*a*, going from left to right, the trees, grass, and flowers are producers (first trophic level); the first series of animals are primary consumers (second trophic level); and the next group of animals are secondary consumers (third trophic level). Some food chains can go beyond three trophic levels if there is enough energy available at the producer base.

Ecological Pyramids

The shortness of food chains can be attributed to the loss of energy between trophic levels. Only about 10% of the energy of one trophic level is available to the next trophic level. Therefore, if a herbivore population consumes 1,000 kg of plant material, only about 100 kg is converted to herbivore tissue, 10 kg to first-level carnivores, and 1 kg to second-level carnivores. This general 10% rule explains why so few carnivores can be supported in a food web. The flow of energy with large losses between successive trophic levels is sometimes depicted as an **ecological pyramid** (Fig. 24.8).

Energy losses between trophic levels also result in pyramids based on the number of organisms in each trophic level. When constructing a pyramid based on number of organisms, problems arise, however. For example, in Figure 24.7*a*, each tree would contain numerous caterpillars. Therefore, there would be more herbivores than autotrophs. The explanation has to do with size.

Figure 24.8 **The influence of trophic level on biomass.** The biomass, or dry weight (g/m^2), for trophic levels in a grazing food web in a bog at Silver Springs, Florida. There is a sharp drop in biomass between the producer level and the herbivore level. This is consistent with the common knowledge that the detrital food web plays a significant role in bogs.

An autotroph can be as tiny as a microscopic alga or as big as a beech tree. Similarly, a herbivore can be as small as a caterpillar or as large as an elephant.

Pyramids of biomass eliminate size as a factor, because **biomass** is the number of organisms multiplied by the weight of organic matter contained in one organism. You would certainly expect the biomass of the producers to be greater than the biomass of the herbivores, and that of the herbivores to be greater than that of the carnivores. In aquatic ecosystems, such as lakes and open seas, the herbivores may have a greater biomass than the producers. This is because algae are the only producers. Over time, algae are able to provide enough energy for the consumers because they reproduce so rapidly.

These types of problems are making some ecologists hesitant about using pyramids to describe ecological relationships. Another issue concerns the role played by decomposers. These organisms are rarely included in pyramids, even though a large portion of energy becomes detritus in many ecosystems.

CHECK YOUR PROGRESS 24.2

1. Explain the difference between a grazing food web and a detrital food web, and give an example of each.
2. Describe what is meant by a trophic level.
3. Explain why a diagram of the trophic levels in most ecosystems resembles a pyramid.

CONNECTING THE CONCEPTS

For more information on the topics presented in this section, refer to the following discussion:

Section 25.1 examines how human population growth is threatening the structure of many ecological pyramids.

24.3 Global Biogeochemical Cycles

LEARNING OUTCOMES

Upon completion of this section, you should be able to

1. Define the term *biogeochemical cycle.*
2. Identify the steps of the water cycle, carbon cycle, nitrogen cycle, and phosphorus cycle.
3. Identify how human activities can alter each of the biogeochemical cycles.

In this section, we will examine in more detail how chemicals cycle through ecosystems. All organisms require a variety of organic and/or inorganic nutrients. For example, carbon dioxide and water are necessary nutrients for photosynthetic organisms. Nitrogen is a component of all the structural and functional proteins and nucleic acids that sustain living tissues. Phosphorus is essential for ATP and nucleotide production.

The pathways by which chemicals circulate through ecosystems involve both living (biotic) and nonliving (abiotic) components. Therefore, they are known as **biogeochemical cycles.** A biogeochemical cycle can be gaseous or sedimentary. In a gaseous cycle, such as the carbon and nitrogen cycles, the element returns to and is withdrawn from the atmosphere as a gas. The phosphorus cycle is a sedimentary cycle. Phosphorus is absorbed from the soil by plant roots, passed to heterotrophs, and eventually returned to the soil by decomposers.

Chemical cycling involves the components of ecosystems shown in Figure 24.9. A *reservoir* is a source of chemicals normally unavailable to producers, such as the carbon found in calcium carbonate shells on ocean bottoms. An *exchange pool* is a source from which organisms generally have the ability to take chemicals, such as the atmosphere or soil. Chemicals move along food chains in a *biotic community.*

Human activities (purple arrows in Figure 24.9) remove various chemicals from reservoirs and exchange pools and make them available to the biotic community. In this way, human activities upset the normal balance of nutrients in the environment, resulting in pollution.

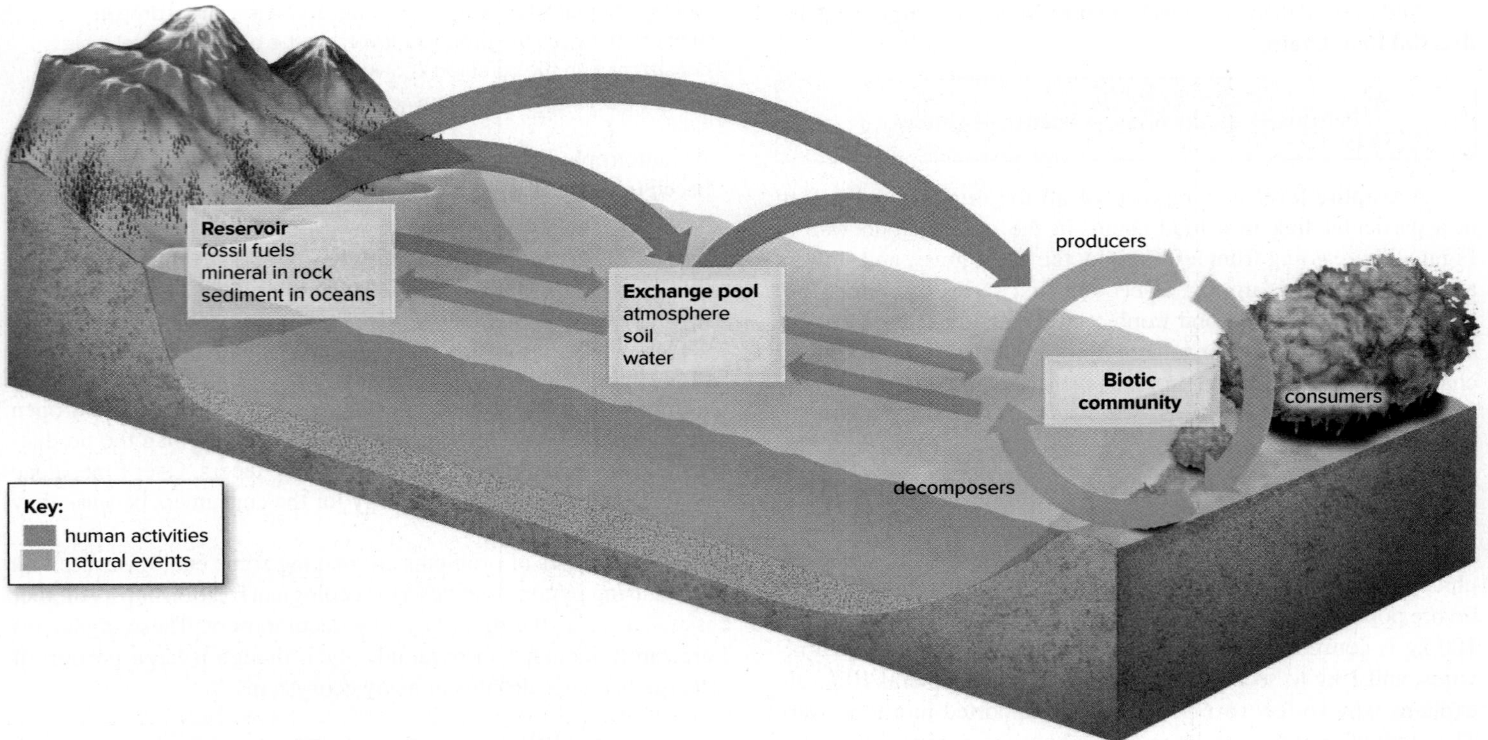

Figure 24.9 The cycling of nutrients.
Reservoirs, such as fossil fuels, minerals in rocks, and sediments in oceans, are normally relatively unavailable sources of nutrients for the biotic community. Nutrients in exchange pools, such as the atmosphere, soil, and water, are available sources of chemicals for the biotic community. When human activities (purple arrows) remove chemicals from a reservoir or an exchange pool and make them available to the biotic community, pollution can result. This is because not all the nutrients are used. For example, when humans burn fossil fuels, CO_2 increases in the atmosphere and contributes to climate change.

The Water Cycle

The width of the arrows in the following cycles represents the approximate transfer rate of the substances between the components of an ecosystem. The **water cycle,** also called the *hydrologic cycle,* is shown in Figure 24.10.

During **evaporation** in the water cycle, the sun's rays cause freshwater to evaporate from seawater, leaving the salts behind. Water also evaporates from land and from plants. In the case of plants, evaporation is called *transpiration.* As the water enters the atmosphere, condensation may occur. During condensation, a gas is changed into a liquid. The condensed water may then fall as **precipitation** (e.g., rain, snow, sleet, hail, and fog) over the oceans and the land.

The water that precipitates over the land may have a number of different routes. However, because land lies above sea level, gravity eventually returns all fresh water to the sea. Some of the water remains temporarily within standing waters (lakes and ponds) and flowing water (streams and rivers) sources. If the precipitation does not enter the ground, but flows directly into nearby streams, lakes, wetlands, or the ocean, it is called **runoff.**

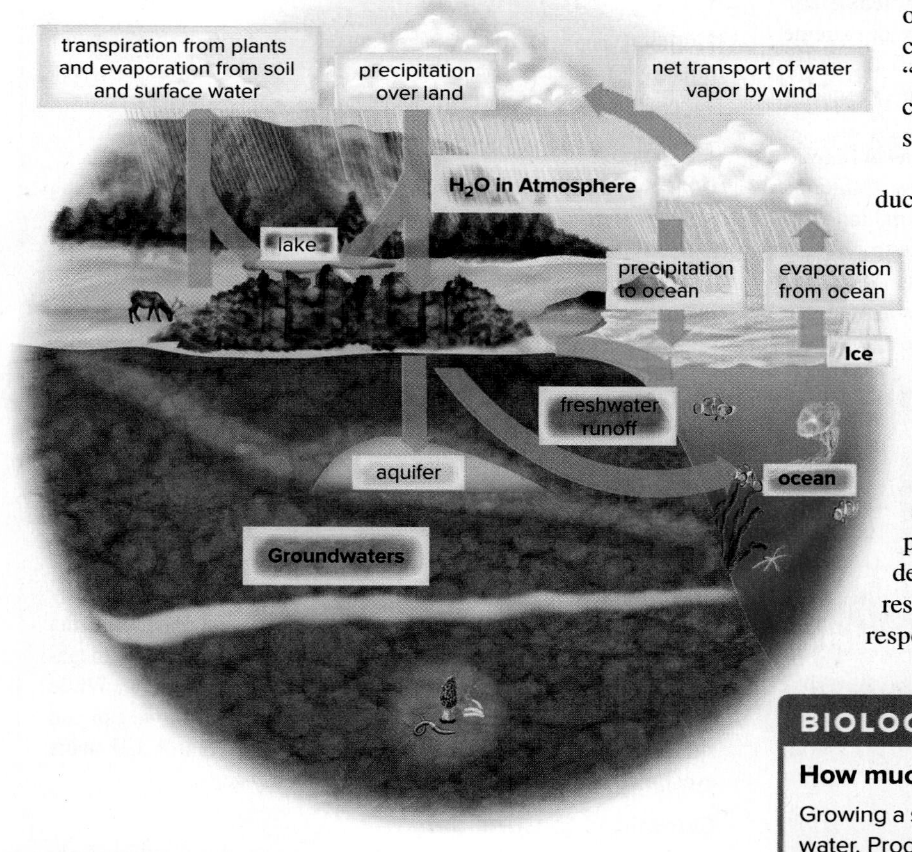

transpiration from plants and evaporation from soil and surface water
precipitation over land
net transport of water vapor by wind
H_2O in Atmosphere
lake
precipitation to ocean
evaporation from ocean
Ice
freshwater runoff
aquifer
ocean
Groundwaters

Figure 24.10 The water cycle.
Evaporation from the ocean exceeds precipitation, so there is a net movement of water vapor onto land. There, precipitation results in surface water and groundwater, which flow back to the sea. On land, transpiration by plants contributes to evaporation.

Instead of running off, some precipitation sinks, or percolates, into the ground. This saturates the earth to a certain level and forms *groundwater.* The top of the saturation zone is called the groundwater table, or the water table. Sometimes, groundwater is also located in **aquifers,** rock layers that contain water and release it in appreciable quantities to wells and springs. Aquifers are recharged when rainfall and melted snow percolate into the soil.

Human Activities

Humans interfere with the water cycle in three ways. First, we withdraw water from aquifers. Second, we clear vegetation from land and build roads and buildings that prevent percolation and increase runoff. Third, we interfere with the natural processes that purify water and instead add pollutants such as sewage and chemicals to water.

In some parts of the United States, especially the arid West and southern Florida, withdrawals from aquifers exceed any possibility of recharge. This is called "groundwater mining." In these locations, the groundwater is dropping. Residents may run out of groundwater, at least for irrigation purposes, within a few years. Fresh water, which makes up only about 3% of the world's supply of water, is called a renewable resource because a new supply is always being produced. However, it is possible to run out of fresh water when the available supply runs off instead of entering bodies of fresh water and aquifers. Fresh water may also become so polluted it is not usable. The Science feature "The Wildfires of California" explores how long-term changes in precipitation have influenced the rate and severity of wildfires in California.

Increasing the water supply is also difficult. Aquaducts, canals, and pipelines are expensive and take considerable time to build. Desalinization plants, which remove the salt from ocean water, require a significant amount of energy, and often supply water for only a small percentage of the population. For example, the new desalinization plant in San Diego, the largest in the world, will supply around only 10% of the local population with water.

Water usage is a complex problem that requires efforts across all aspects of our society to solve. One single solution will not adequately address the entire problem. New technologies in the areas of water desalinization may help, as will more research in how reservoirs are recharged in the water cycle. Californians responded to the drought with a significant effort to

BIOLOGY IN YOUR LIFE

How much water is required to produce your food?

Growing a single serving of lettuce takes about 6 gallons (gal) of water. Producing an 8-oz glass of milk requires 49 gal of water. That includes the amount of water the cow drinks, the water used to grow the cow's food, and the water needed to process the milk. Producing a single serving of steak consumes more than 2,600 gal of water.

BIOLOGY TODAY ▶ Science

The Wildfires of California

Coastal mountain ranges, fertile valleys, and giant redwood and sequoia forests are just a few of the many ecosystems that can be found in California. It has taken millions of years for these ecosystems to evolve into the rich centers of biodiversity they are today. Sadly, the impact humans are having upon these ecosystems is damaging them beyond what they may be able to recover from.

The industrial activities we rely upon to support our way of life have raised the levels of carbon dioxide and other greenhouse gases in the atmosphere to historic levels (Fig. 24C). These increases are contributing to an increase in global temperatures, contributing to climate change. Increasing global temperatures, a warming ocean, decreased snow cover, and extreme weather events are all part of the consequences of climate change.

From 2011 to 2017, California experienced one of the worst multiyear droughts in its history. In April 2017, California governor Edmund G. Brown credited water conservation efforts by the citizens of California, along with an abundance of winter rain and snow, as the reason for lifting the drought state of emergency for most of the state. This respite from drought was only temporary. Over 70% of California ended 2020 in a state of severe or extreme drought conditions. The record-setting drought was off the charts when compared to previous years; 2020 was an extreme example of a shortened rainy season and an expanded fire season.

The 2020 conditions helped propel the state into a record-breaking year, but not in a good way. During the course of the year, California experienced over 9,600 wildfires that burned close to 4.2 million acres of land. California had 10,488 structures damaged or destroyed, and 31 fatalities, as a result of its historic fire season (Fig. 24D). The 4.2 million acres burned set a record for the most acres burned in a state in a single year. The economic damage was estimated to be over $2 billion. The year 2020 also holds the record for 5 of the 6 biggest fires in California's history. The level of destruction experienced during 2020 was greater than the previous 3 years combined.

Figure 24D California wildfires.
Wildfires in the western United States, especially in California, have caused significant damage to fragile ecosystems.
Bloomberg Creative/Getty Images

Figure 24C Greenhouse gases.
Modern agriculture, especially cattle farming, makes a significant contribution to annual carbon dioxide emissions globally.
Design Pics Inc/Alamy Stock Photo

Taking Responsibility for Our Actions

While wildfires have always been a part of California's history, the concern is how frequent and catastrophic they have become. It is believed there are four key factors contributing to the frequency and destructive nature of the fires. Warmer temperatures, due to human-induced climate change, is making the vegetation drier and more prone to burning. Fireworks at parties, downed power lines, or other ways people have accidentally started fires are other contributing factors. Fire suppression and improper forest management at the local and federal level has led to an accumulation of dried vegetation. This causes the fires to be more destructive and uncontrollable once they start. The Santa Ana Winds blow dry air from the Great Basin area into Southern California, causing the vegetation to dry out even further. All of these factors combine to create a worrisome future for California. Unfortunately, computer models created by scientists suggest that the worst is yet to come, and that California and large parts of the Southwest are likely to experience a "mega-drought" (an event lasting more than 35 years) before 2080. While not all of the factors are ones that humans can control, we can and should take responsibility for the ones we can control and make every effort to help preserve California's ecosystems.

Questions to Consider

1. Do you think the government should be able to enact measures that reduce our individual contribution to climate change? If so, what type of measures should be required?
2. Should federal dollars be allocated to California to help manage climate change–induced disasters?

reduce and conserve their water supplies. Urban water use, across the state, was reduced by nearly 25%. California also enacted the Sustainable Groundwater Management Act to improve the management of its water resources. While this drought has come to an end, most scientists agree that there will be more in the future. Water conservation must become a standard way of life not only for Californians, but all people.

The Carbon Cycle

The carbon dioxide (CO_2) in the atmosphere is the exchange pool for the carbon cycle. In this cycle, organisms in both terrestrial and aquatic ecosystems exchange carbon dioxide with the atmosphere (Fig. 24.11). On land, plants take up carbon dioxide from the air.

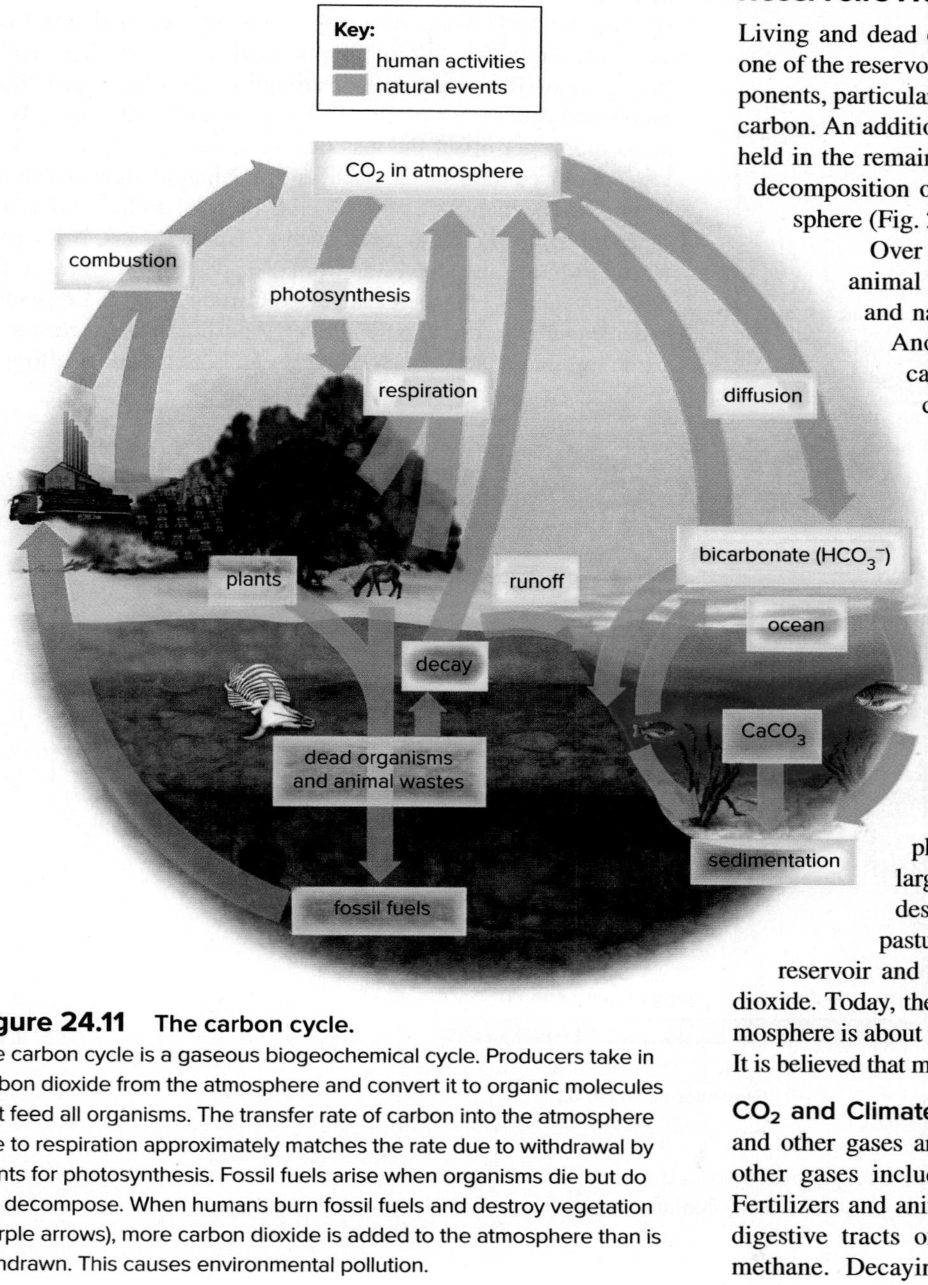

Figure 24.11 **The carbon cycle.**
The carbon cycle is a gaseous biogeochemical cycle. Producers take in carbon dioxide from the atmosphere and convert it to organic molecules that feed all organisms. The transfer rate of carbon into the atmosphere due to respiration approximately matches the rate due to withdrawal by plants for photosynthesis. Fossil fuels arise when organisms die but do not decompose. When humans burn fossil fuels and destroy vegetation (purple arrows), more carbon dioxide is added to the atmosphere than is withdrawn. This causes environmental pollution.

Through photosynthesis, they incorporate carbon into nutrients used by autotrophs and heterotrophs. When organisms, including plants, conduct cellular respiration, carbon is returned to the atmosphere as carbon dioxide. Therefore, carbon dioxide recycles back to plants by way of the atmosphere.

In aquatic ecosystems, the exchange of carbon dioxide with the atmosphere is indirect. Carbon dioxide from the air combines with water to produce bicarbonate ion (HCO_3^-). This is a source of carbon for aquatic producers that create food for themselves and for heterotrophs. Similarly, when aquatic organisms respire, the carbon dioxide they give off becomes bicarbonate ions. The amount of bicarbonate in the water is in equilibrium with the amount of carbon dioxide in the air.

Reservoirs Hold Carbon

Living and dead organisms contain organic carbon and serve as one of the reservoirs for the carbon cycle. The world's biotic components, particularly trees, contain over 800 billion tons of organic carbon. An additional 1,000–3,000 billion tons are estimated to be held in the remains of plants and animals in the soil. Ordinarily, decomposition of plants and animals returns CO_2 to the atmosphere (Fig. 24.11).

Over the past 300 million years on Earth, plant and animal remains have been transformed into coal, oil, and natural gas. We call these materials **fossil fuels.** Another reservoir for carbon is the inorganic carbonate that accumulates in limestone and in calcium carbonate shells. Many marine organisms have calcium carbonate shells that remain in ocean sediments long after the organisms have died. Geological forces change these sediments into limestone.

Human Activities

The natural transfer rates of carbon dioxide between the storage of carbon during photosynthesis and the release of carbon during cellular respiration and decomposition are just about even. However, more carbon dioxide is being deposited in the atmosphere due to human activities than can be removed through photosynthesis (Fig. 24.11). This increase is largely due to the burning of fossil fuels and the destruction of forests to make way for farmland and pasture. When we do away with forests, we reduce a reservoir and lose the organisms that take up excess carbon dioxide. Today, the amount of carbon dioxide released into the atmosphere is about twice the amount that remains in the atmosphere. It is believed that much of this has been absorbed by the ocean.

CO_2 and Climate Change Large amounts of carbon dioxide and other gases are being emitted due to human activities. The other gases include nitrous oxide (N_2O) and methane (CH_4). Fertilizers and animal wastes are sources of nitrous oxide. In the digestive tracts of animals, bacterial decomposition produces methane. Decaying sediments and flooded rice paddies are methane sources as well. In the atmosphere, nitrous oxide and methane are known as **greenhouse gases,** because they act just like the panes of a greenhouse. They allow solar radiation to penetrate to Earth but hinder the escape of infrared rays (heat) back into space—a phenomenon called the **greenhouse effect.** The greenhouse gases are contributing significantly to an overall rise in the Earth's ambient temperature. This phenomenon is called **global warming** and is contributing to the **climate change** of the Earth.

BIOLOGY IN YOUR LIFE

What are some other greenhouse gases?

In addition to carbon dioxide, these gases also play a role in the greenhouse effect:

- *Methane (CH_4):* A single molecule of methane has 21 times the warming potential of a molecule of carbon dioxide, making it a powerful greenhouse gas. Methane is a natural byproduct of the decay of organic material but is also released by landfills and the production of coal, natural gas, and oil.
- *Nitrous oxide (N_2O):* Nitrous oxide is released from the combustion of fossil fuels and as gaseous waste from many industrial activities.
- *Hydrofluorocarbons:* These were initially produced to reduce the levels of ozone-depleting compounds in the upper atmosphere. Unfortunately, although present in very small quantities, they are potent greenhouse gases.

Figure 24.12 shows how the average temperature in the United States has steadily increased over the past two centuries. If the Earth's temperature continues to rise, more water will evaporate, forming more clouds. This sets up a positive feedback effect that could increase global warming even more. The global climate has already warmed about 0.6°C (1.1°F) since the Industrial Revolution. Enhancements in computer science are allowing scientists to explore the majority of the variables that influence the global climate. Most climate scientists agree that the Earth's temperature may rise 1.5–4.5°C (2.0–8.1°F) by 2100 if greenhouse emissions continue at the current rates.

As climate change continues, other effects will possibly occur. It is predicted that, as the oceans warm, temperatures in the polar regions will rise to a greater degree than in other regions. As a result, sea levels will rise, because glaciers will melt, and water expands as it warms. Water evaporation will increase, and most likely there will be increased rainfall along the coasts and dryer conditions inland. The occurrence of droughts will reduce agricultural yields and cause trees to die off. Expansion of forests into Arctic areas might not offset the loss of forests in the temperate zones. Coastal agricultural lands, such as the deltas of Bangladesh and China, will be inundated with water. Billions of dollars will have to be spent to keep coastal cities such as New Orleans, New York, Boston, Miami, and Galveston from disappearing into the sea. The Science feature "Climate Change and Carbon Dioxide Emissions" provides more information on the relationship between carbon dioxide emissions and climate change, and international efforts to reduce the production of greenhouse gases.

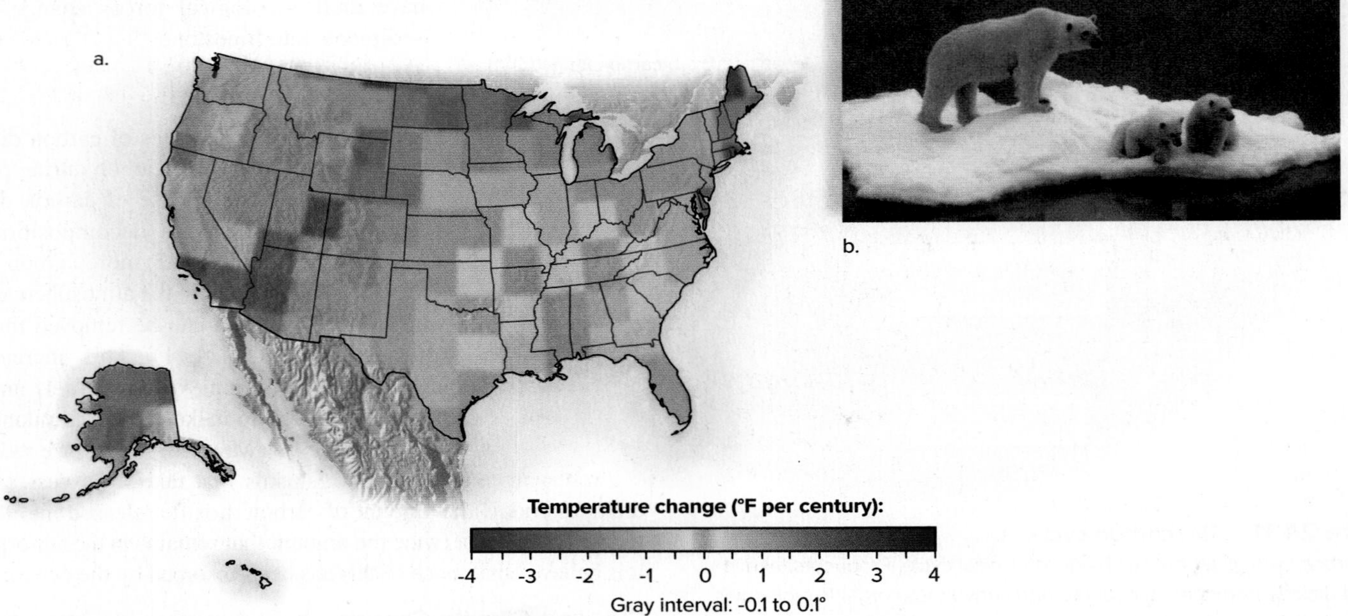

Figure 24.12 Global warming and climate change.
a. The average temperature in the United States has steadily increased over the past two centuries, leading to more severe droughts and more erratic periods of precipitation that are altering the composition of many communities. **b.** Increased risks of extinction for many species are just one of the consequences of climate change.
(b): Russell Millner/Alamy Stock Photo

BIOLOGY TODAY ▶ Science

Climate Change and Carbon Dioxide Emissions

Over 97% of actively publishing climate scientists support the consensus that climate change is occurring and is primarily due to human activities. Changes in the average temperature of a region, precipitation patterns, sea levels, and greenhouse gas concentrations are all indicators that our climate is changing. Scientists are actively collecting and interpreting environmental indicators that help us understand how and why the Earth's climate is changing.

Since 1901, the average temperature across the United States has risen, with 2000–2009 being the warmest decade on record worldwide. The year 2016 was the warmest year on record, with 2020 ranking among the top three warmest years on record. We have experienced 16 of the 17 warmest years on record since 2001.

Average precipitation rates have also increased by 6% over the past century, with 30–60% of the United States experiencing drought conditions. Since 1990, the United States has experienced eight of the top ten years of extreme precipitation events in its history. In line with this, increases in sea surface temperatures produce more active hurricane seasons. The year 2019 marked the fourth consecutive above-normal Atlantic hurricane season, with 2017 being ranked among the top ten all-time most active hurricane seasons, as well as the most expensive in history.

Sea levels worldwide have risen an average of 1 inch per decade due to the overall increase in the surface temperature of the world's oceans. Climate models suggest we will see a rise in sea levels of 3 to 4 feet over the next century, leading to more flooding and increasingly severe storms and storm surges that could cause significant economic losses.

Since 1900, atmospheric carbon dioxide levels have steadily increased (Fig. 24E). In 2021, carbon dioxide concentrations in the atmosphere were 419 parts per million (ppm). This is the highest average over the past 800,000 years.

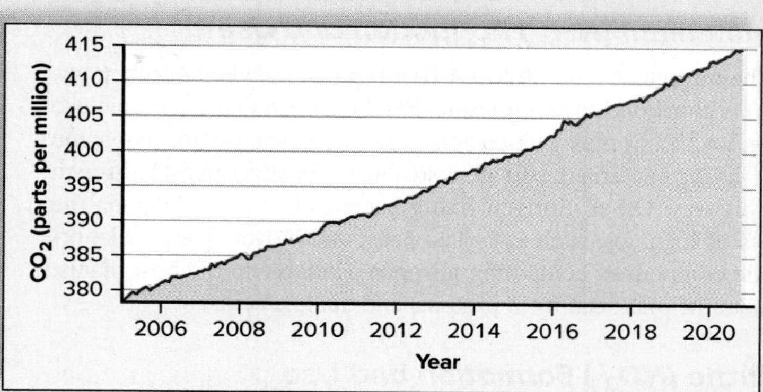

Figure 24E **Atmospheric carbon dioxide concentrations.** Increases in atmospheric carbon dioxide concentrations. The global average carbon dioxide concentration now exceeds 415 ppm and is the major contributing factor to climate change and global warming.

NOAA, "Global Climate Change: Facts." http://climate.nasa.gov/vital-signs/carbon-dioxide/.

International Efforts to Reduce Carbon Emissions

Over the past decade, a number of international treaties have attempted to address limiting global carbon dioxide emissions.

- The Kyoto Protocol was adopted on December 11, 1997, and initiated in force on February 16, 2005. The goal of the protocol was to achieve stabilization and reduction of greenhouse gas concentrations in the atmosphere. As of November 2009, 187 countries had ratified the protocol, with the goal of reducing emissions by an average of 5.2% by the year 2012. Unfortunately, the United States never ratified the agreement, even though it is responsible for roughly 19% of the global CO_2 emissions from fossil-fuel combustion and is the largest per-capita emission producer in the world.
- The Copenhagen conference in 2009 ended without any binding agreement for long-term action against climate change, but it did produce a collective commitment to raise $30 billion to help developing nations cope with and combat the effects of climate change.
- The 2010 Cancun summit on climate change helped solidify this agreement. Because deforestation produces about 15% of global carbon emissions, many developing countries can receive incentives to prevent the destruction of their rain forests.
- The 2013 UN Climate Change Conference in Warsaw was successful in establishing ways to help developing nations reduce greenhouse emissions as a result of deforestation, and generated finance commitments to assist developing nations. The conference also helped keep governments on track toward a universal climate agreement that was presented in 2015 and will be implemented in 2020.
- The Paris Agreement was adopted on November 4, 2016, and commits all the world's nations into undertaking efforts to adapt to and combat climate change. The central goal is to strengthen efforts in keeping the global rise in temperature to under 2 degrees Celsius. The agreement requires all nations to report their emissions and implementation efforts to achieve the agreement's goals.

While the United States had initially withdrawn from the Paris Agreement, it is in the process of rejoining and strengthening the accord. One of the goals is to have companies net carbon neutral by 2050, while creating millions of new jobs in the green energy sector and improving the quality of life for all Americans. The rest of the world's nations, who remain part of the agreement, are continuing to make efforts in combating climate change as well.

Questions to Consider

1. Should the United States and other developed countries pay developing nations to preserve these nations' forests?
2. Do you think economic incentives will be effective in preventing deforestation, or should another strategy be used?

The Nitrogen Cycle

Nitrogen gas (N_2) makes up about 78% of the atmosphere, in a form that is unusable by plants. Therefore, nitrogen can be a nutrient that limits the amount of growth in an ecosystem.

Ammonium (NH_4^+) Formation and Use

In the nitrogen cycle, **nitrogen fixation** occurs when nitrogen gas (N_2) is converted to ammonium (NH_4^+), a form that plants can use (Fig. 24.13). Some cyanobacteria in aquatic ecosystems and some free-living bacteria in soil are also able to fix atmospheric nitrogen in this way. Other nitrogen-fixing bacteria live in nodules on the roots of legumes, such as beans, peas, and clover. They make organic compounds containing nitrogen available to the host plants, so that the plant can form proteins and nucleic acids.

Nitrate (NO_3^-) Formation and Use

Plants can also use nitrates (NO_3^-) as a source of nitrogen. The production of nitrates during the nitrogen cycle is called **nitrification.** Nitrification can occur in various ways:

- Nitrogen gas (N_2) is converted to nitrate (NO_3^-) in the atmosphere, where high energy is available for nitrogen to react with oxygen. This energy may be supplied by cosmic radiation, meteor trails, or lightning.
- Ammonium (NH_4^+) in the soil from various sources, including decomposition of organisms and animal wastes, is converted to nitrate by soil bacteria.
- Nitrite-producing bacteria can convert ammonium to nitrite (NO_2^-). Nitrate-producing bacteria have the ability to convert nitrite to nitrate.

During the process of *assimilation,* plants take up ammonia and nitrate from the soil and use these ions to produce proteins and nucleic acids. In Figure 24.13, observe the biotic community subcycles occurring on land and in water. Those subcycles do not depend on the presence of nitrogen gas.

Formation of Nitrogen Gas from Nitrate

Denitrification (Fig. 24.13) is the conversion of nitrate back to nitrogen gas, which enters the atmosphere. Denitrifying bacteria living in the anaerobic mud of lakes, bogs, and estuaries carry out this process during their metabolism. In the nitrogen cycle, denitrification would counterbalance nitrogen fixation if human activities were not involved.

Human Activities

Human activities, some of which are shown in Figure 24.13, significantly alter the transfer rates in the nitrogen cycle by producing fertilizers from N_2. They nearly double the fixation rate. Fertilizer, which also contains phosphate, often runs off into lakes and rivers. This results in an overgrowth of algae and rooted aquatic plants, a process called eutrophication. This may lead to an algal boom. When the algae die off, enlarged decomposer populations use up all the oxygen in the water. The result is a massive fish kill. A similar process may occur with excess phosphorus (see below).

Acid deposition occurs because nitrogen oxides (NO_x) and sulfur dioxide (SO_2) enter the atmosphere from the burning of fossil fuels (Fig. 24.14*a*). Both of these gases combine with water vapor to form acids that eventually return to the Earth in acid rain. Acid deposition has drastically affected forests and lakes in northern Europe, Canada, and the northeastern United States. The soil in these forests is naturally acidic, whereas the surface water is only mildly alkaline (basic). Soil pH is made even more acidic by acid rain. The increased acidity kills trees (Fig. 24.14*b*) and

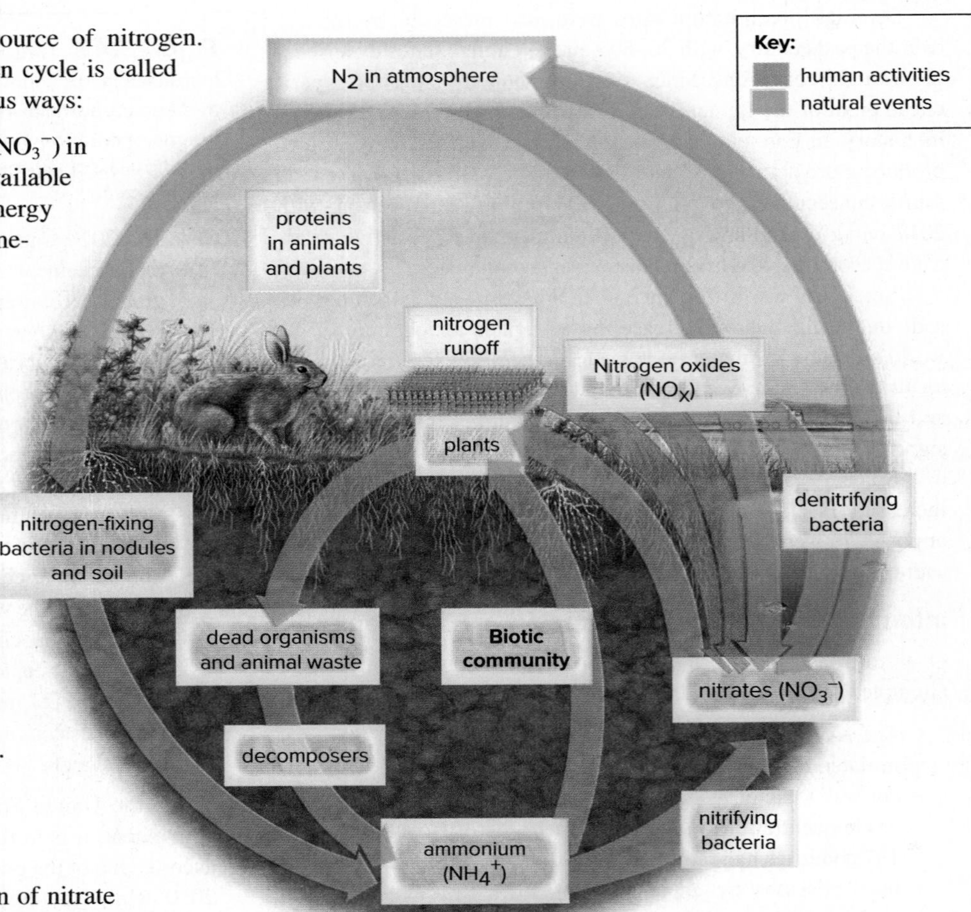

Figure 24.13 The nitrogen cycle.
Nitrogen is primarily made available to biotic communities by the internal cycling of the element. Without human activities, the amount of nitrogen returned to the atmosphere (denitrification in terrestrial and aquatic communities) exceeds withdrawal from the atmosphere (N_2 fixation and nitrification). Human activities (dark purple arrow) result in an increased amount of NO_3^- in terrestrial communities, with resultant runoff to aquatic biotic communities.

a.

b.

c.

Figure 24.14 **The effects of acid deposition.**
a. Air pollution due to fossil-fuel burning in factories and modes of transportation is the major cause of acid deposition. **b.** Many forests in higher elevations of northeastern North America and northern Europe are dying due to acid deposition. **c.** Acid deposition damages architectural features.
(a): Larry Lee Photography/Corbis/Getty Images; (b): Oxford Scientific/Photolibrary/Getty Images; (c): julof90/iStock/Getty Images

reduces agricultural yields. Marble, metal, and stonework are corroded by acid deposition, which results in the loss of architectural features (Fig. 24.14*c*).

Nitrogen oxides and hydrocarbons (HCs) from the burning of fossil fuels react with one another in the presence of sunlight to produce *photochemical smog*. Smog contains dangerous pollutants. Warm air near the Earth usually escapes into the atmosphere, taking pollutants with it. However, during a thermal inversion, pollutants are trapped near the Earth beneath a layer of warm, stagnant air. The air does not circulate, so pollutants can build up to dangerous levels. Areas surrounded by hills are particularly susceptible to the effects of a thermal inversion. This is because the air tends to stagnate, preventing the pollution from diffusing into the atmosphere (Fig. 24.15).

BIOLOGY IN YOUR LIFE

How acidic is acid rain?

The pH of normal rain varies from 4.5 to 5.6 (see Fig. 2.10). That's about the acidity of tomatoes or black coffee, and neither of these is particularly corrosive or harmful to the body. Rain collected in the eastern United States during the summer has an average pH of 3.6, similar to the acidity of vinegar. Can you imagine watering trees or house plants with vinegar? Fog with a pH of 2 has been measured in some locations. A solution with pH 2 is only slightly less acidic than stomach acid or battery acid. It is easy to imagine the damage such a solution could do to the environment.

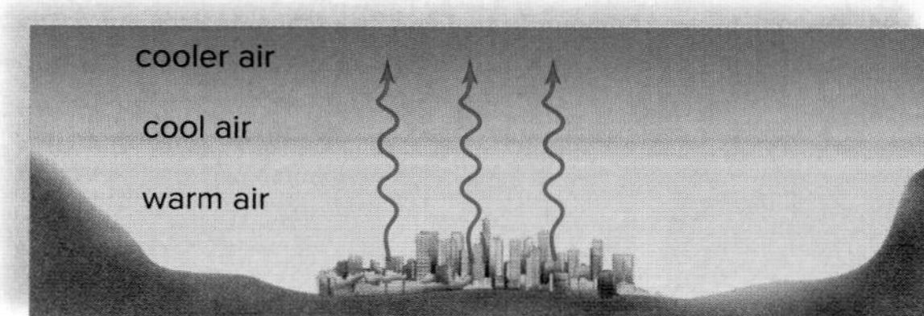

a. Normal pattern

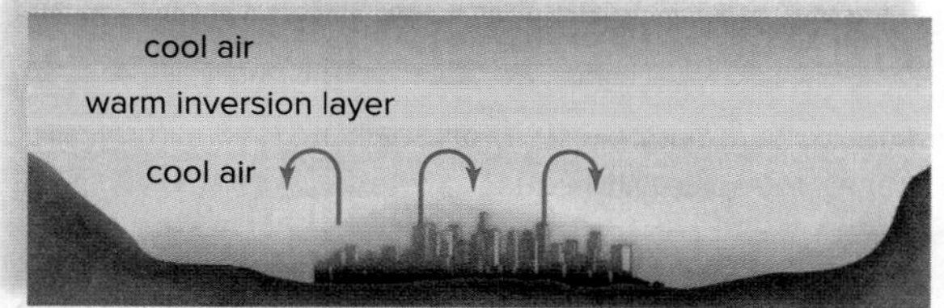

b. Thermal inversion

Figure 24.15 **Thermal inversions.**
a. Normally, pollutants escape into the atmosphere when warm air rises. **b.** During a thermal inversion, a layer of warm air (warm inversion layer) overlies and traps pollutants in cool air below.

The Phosphorus Cycle

In the phosphorus cycle (Fig. 24.16), the phosphorus trapped in oceanic sediments moves onto land after a geological upheaval. Once on land, the very slow weathering of rocks moves phosphate ions (PO_4^{3-} and HPO_4^{2-}) into the soil. Some of this soil becomes available to plants, which then incorporate phosphate into a variety of molecules. Molecules requiring phosphate include phospholipids, ATP, and the nucleotides that become a part of DNA and RNA. In the food web, animals eat producers and incorporate some of the phosphate into their teeth, bones, and shells. However, the eventual death and decomposition of all organisms and their wastes do make phosphate ions available to producers once again. All of the available phosphate in a community is generally being used in various food chains. The lack of phosphate will limit the size of populations in ecosystems.

Some phosphate naturally runs off into aquatic ecosystems, enabling the algae to acquire it before it becomes trapped in sediments. Phosphate in marine sediments will not become available to producers on land until a geological upheaval exposes sedimentary rocks on land, allowing the cycle to begin again. Phosphorus does not enter the atmosphere. Therefore, the phosphorus cycle is called a sedimentary cycle.

Phosphorus and Water Pollution

Human activities are directly responsible for the increasing levels of phosphates in our environment. Activities like the mining of phosphate ores, used in the production of fertilizers, as well as detergent use, can lead to excessive levels of phosphates in the environment. Fertilizers are applied to agricultural fields to increase the yield. If the fields experience a heavy rain shortly after the fertilizers have been applied, it can lead to a high level of runoff that will wash the phosphates into nearby aquatic ecosystems (Fig. 24.16). With climate change disrupting rainfall patterns, we can expect to see more periods of heavy precipitation in various areas of the country, resulting in more runoff. The discharge of phosphates, nitrates, contamination from livestock facilities, and other forms of pollution into aquatic ecosystems is leading to **cultural eutrophication** (overenrichment) of waterways. The excessive nutrient load causes a rapid increase in bacterial and algae growth within the aquatic ecosystems. When these organisms die off, decomposition will remove the oxygen from the water, leading to an aquatic system known as a dead zone. This phenomenon occurs yearly in the Gulf of Mexico because of runoff from the Midwest, creating a dead zone off the coast of Louisiana and Mississippi that is over 2,000 square miles in size.

CHECK YOUR PROGRESS 24.3

1. Explain the role of reservoirs in the cycling of chemicals in the biosphere.
2. Are the carbon, water, nitrogen, and phosphorus cycles examples of gaseous or sedimentary biogeochemical cycles?
3. Discuss the roles of bacteria in the nitrogen cycle.
4. Summarize the ecological problems associated with the water, carbon, nitrogen, and phosphorus cycles.
5. Discuss the potential consequences of climate change.

CONNECTING THE CONCEPTS

For more information on the material presented in this section, refer to the following discussions:

Section 25.2 describes some of the problems associated with the overexploitation of natural resources.

Section 25.4 explores some of the ways humans can move toward a sustainable society.

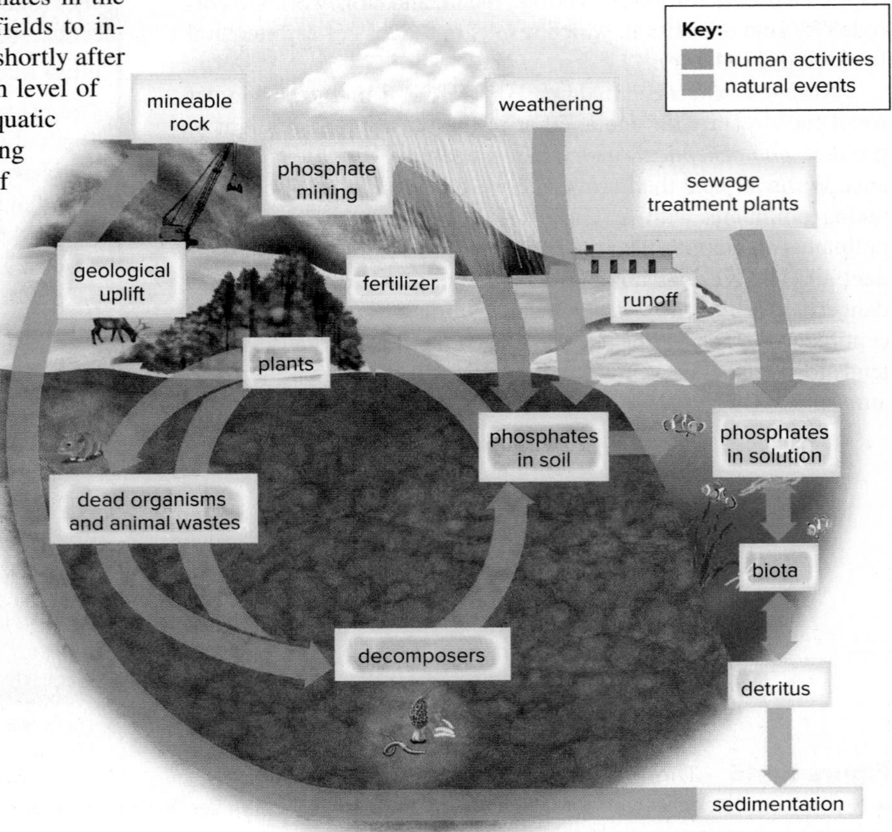

Figure 24.16 **The phosphorus cycle.** The weathering of rocks provides phosphorus, which cycles locally in both terrestrial and aquatic biota. Human activities (purple arrows) produce fertilizers, which add to the amount of phosphorus available to biotic communities. Eventually, fertilizers become a part of the runoff that enriches waters. Sewage treatment plants directly add phosphorus to local waters. When phosphorus becomes a part of oceanic sediments, it is lost to biotic communities for many years.

CONCLUSION

As the human population continues to grow, we will be forced to continue expanding our ecological footprint into nearly every ecosystem on Earth. We will be looking for new sources of agricultural land, minerals, and sources of food. This will inevitably increase our risk of exposure to emerging pathogens and the organisms that can transmit them to humans. While COVID-19 has proven to be a terrible pandemic that has impacted everyone on Earth, scientists predict it won't be the last one we experience. Open and honest communication among countries, and trust in the scientific method, are just two of the things we need to focus on in order to prepare for and deal with the next global pandemic.

SUMMARIZE

24.1 The Nature of Ecosystems

Ecology is the study of the interactions of organisms with each other and with the physical environment.

- **Ecosystems** are where living organisms interact with the physical and chemical environment.
- The sum of the ecosystems on the planet is called the **biosphere.**

Types of Ecosystems

- Terrestrial ecosystems, also called **biomes,** are forests (tropical rain forests, coniferous forests, temperate deciduous forests); grasslands (savannas and prairies); and deserts, including the tundras.
- Aquatic ecosystems are either salt water (seashores, oceans, coral reefs, estuaries) or fresh water (lakes, ponds, rivers, and streams).

Biotic Components of an Ecosystem

- In a community, each population has a habitat (place it lives) and a **niche** (its role in the community).
- **Autotrophs (producers)** produce organic nutrients for themselves and others from inorganic nutrients and an outside energy source.
- **Heterotrophs (consumers)** consume organic nutrients.
- Consumers are **herbivores** (eat plants/algae), **carnivores** (eat other animals), and **omnivores** (eat both plants/algae and animals).
- **Detritus feeders** feed on detritus, releasing inorganic substances back into the ecosystem.

Energy Flow and Chemical Cycling

Ecosystems are characterized by energy flow and chemical cycling.

- Energy flows through the populations of an ecosystem.
- Chemicals cycle within and among ecosystems.

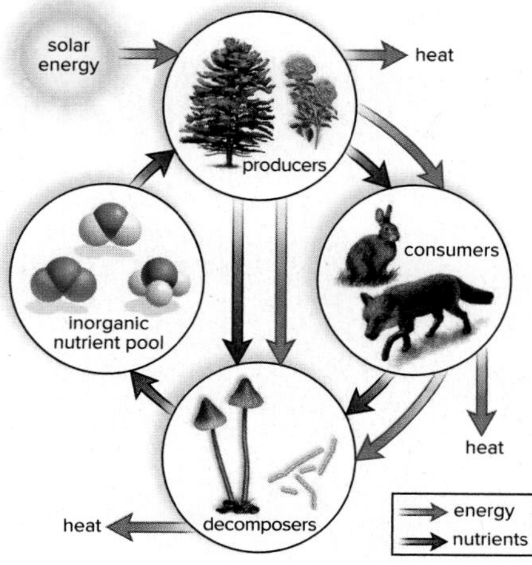

24.2 Energy Flow in Ecosystems

Various interconnecting paths of energy flow are called a **food web.**

- A food web is a diagram showing how various organisms are connected by eating relationships.
- **Grazing food webs** begin with vegetation eaten by a herbivore that becomes food for a carnivore.
- **Detrital food webs** begin with detritus, food for decomposers and for detritivores.
- Members of detrital food webs can be eaten by aboveground carnivores, joining the two food webs.

Trophic Levels

A **trophic level** is all the organisms that feed at a particular link in a **food chain.** There are two primary types of food chains: **grazing food chains** and **detrital food chains.**

Ecological Pyramids

- **Ecological pyramids** illustrate that **biomass** and energy content decrease from one trophic level to the next because of energy loss.

24.3 Global Biogeochemical Cycles

Chemicals circulate through ecosystems via **biogeochemical cycles,** pathways involving both biotic and geological components. Biogeochemical cycles

- Can be gaseous or sedimentary
- Have reservoirs (e.g., ocean sediments, the atmosphere, and organic matter) that contain inorganic nutrients available to living organisms on a limited basis

Exchange pools are sources of inorganic nutrients.

- Nutrients cycle among the biotic communities (producers, consumers, decomposers) of an ecosystem.

The Water Cycle

- The **water (hydrologic) cycle** is characterized by **evaporation, precipitation,** and **runoff** from the surface to lakes, rivers, and oceans.
- The primary reservoir of the water cycle is the ocean, although freshwater reserves may be located in **aquifers.**

The Carbon Cycle

- The reservoirs of the carbon cycle are organic matter (e.g., forests and dead organisms for **fossil fuels**), limestone, and the ocean (e.g., calcium carbonate shells).
- The exchange pool is the atmosphere.
- Photosynthesis removes carbon dioxide from the atmosphere. Respiration and combustion add carbon dioxide to the atmosphere.
- Imbalances in the cycling of **greenhouses gases,** such as carbon dioxide, are causing an increase in the **greenhouse effect.** These changes account for an increase in **global warming** and **climate change.**

The Nitrogen Cycle

- The reservoir of the nitrogen cycle is the atmosphere.
- Nitrogen gas must be converted to a form usable by plants (nitrates). The conversion is called **nitrification.**
- Nitrogen-fixing bacteria perform **nitrogen fixation** (in root nodules), which converts nitrogen gas to ammonium, a form producers can use.
- Nitrifying bacteria convert ammonium to nitrate.
- Some bacteria convert nitrate back to nitrogen gas **(denitrification).**
- Imbalances in the nitrogen cycle can cause **acid deposition** and acid rain.

The Phosphorus Cycle

- The reservoir of the phosphorus cycle is ocean sediments.
- Phosphate in ocean sediments becomes available through geological upheaval, which exposes sedimentary rocks to weathering. Weathering slowly makes phosphate available to the biotic community.
- Phosphate is a limiting nutrient in ecosystems.
- Imbalances in the phosphorus cycle may lead to **cultural eutrophication.**

ENGAGE

THINKING CRITICALLY

Throughout this chapter, we have seen that human activity has a negative impact on many of the world's ecosystems. In response, many people are making efforts to reduce the environmental impact of their lifestyles. Across the country, state agencies, businesses, local organizations, and educational institutions are developing environmental projects and/or increasing their conservation methods. Many colleges and universities have initiatives that make the campuses more environmentally friendly. Our own contributions help, too. Just a few of the many ideas you can consider are conserving water, recycling trash, replacing paper or plastic containers with cloth, conserving electricity, starting a compost pile, and collecting rainwater for plants in rain barrels.

1. Visit https://www.nature.org/en-us/get-involved/how-to-help/carbon-footprint-calculator/ to determine the size of your ecological footprint. Then, discuss ways you can reduce your footprint.
2. What impact might fungicides and pesticides have on detrital food webs? How would the nutrient cycles be affected by the use of fungicides and pesticides?
3. What types of things can you do at home to facilitate the cycling of nutrients such as carbon and nitrogen? What types of things can you do at home to conserve water or improve the quality of a nearby body of water?

MAKING IT RELEVANT

1. With most emerging pathogens having animal origins, do you support the continued alteration of native habitat for human use?
2. Explain why consuming less meat would help decrease the potential for the transmission of another novel virus.
3. Would you support a law prohibiting keeping an exotic animal as a pet if that animal could possibly transmit a novel virus to humans?

Find answers to all of the chapter questions at connect.mheducation.com

(wildfires): Kevin Key/Slworking/Getty Images; (drought): Jasper Suijten/Shutterstock; (flooding): Sk Hasan Ali/Shutterstock; (polar bear): Jan Martin Will/Shutterstock

CHAPTER

25 Human Interactions with the Biosphere

The Reality of Climate Change

Over 97% of active climate researchers agree that human actions are the cause of global warming, which is contributing to climate change. The burning of fossil fuels, the destruction of natural habitats, and the large-scale farming of livestock are some of the activities contributing to climate change.

Over the next century, we can expect to see an increase of 2.5–10°F to the average global temperature, leading to more extreme weather events. Fire seasons will be more destructive, and hurricanes will be stronger and more intense. Whereas some regions will experience extreme flooding, others will suffer extended droughts and heat waves. Sea levels are predicted to rise by 3 to 4 feet, flooding many coastal communities.

The year 2020 produced a record number of wildfires, hurricanes, and floods. These events, magnified by climate change, led to over $210 billion in damages globally. The impact on human welfare and health, and the resulting loss of lives, is even more difficult to measure.

To decrease the impact of climate change, everyone needs to take responsibility for their actions. We need to recognize that fundamental changes to our society are required if we wish to minimize the consequences of climate change. Small changes such as recycling, eating less meat, and driving fuel-efficient vehicles are just a few of the actions each of us can take to collectively make a difference.

In this chapter, we will explore how humans are interacting with their ecosystems, and how those interactions can sometimes have negative consequences.

As you read through the chapter, think about the following questions:

1. What type of lifestyle changes can you make that will lessen climate change?
2. Should each country be responsible for their own climate change strategy or should there be a global plan?

CHAPTER OUTLINE

BEFORE YOU BEGIN

Before beginning this chapter, take a few moments to review the following discussions:

Section 22.3 How has biotechnology been applied to plants such as corn and potatoes to produce increases in food production?

Section 24.1 How does the cycling of energy and chemicals differ in an ecosystem?

Section 24.3 How are human activities influencing the water cycle?

25.1 Human Population Growth

LEARNING OUTCOMES

Upon completion of this section, you should be able to

1. Define the terms *exponential growth* and *carrying capacity* and explain how each relates to human population growth.
2. Explain the relationship among birthrate, death rate, and the annual growth rate of a population.
3. Compare and contrast the difference between more-developed countries (MDCs) and less-developed countries (LDCs) with regard to population growth.

The world's population has risen steadily to a present size of slightly over 7.8 billion people (Fig. 25.1). Prior to 1750, the growth of the human population was relatively slow. As more individuals reproduced, population growth began to increase rapidly, indicating that the population was undergoing **exponential growth.** The number of people added annually to the world population peaked at about 90 million around 1990. Currently, it is a little over 81 million per year.

The **growth rate** of the human population is determined by considering the difference between the number of persons born per year (birthrate, or natality) and the number who die per year (death rate, or mortality). It is customary to record these rates per 1,000 persons. For example, the world at the present time has a birthrate of 18.0 per 1,000 per year, but it has a death rate of 7.6 per 1,000 per year. This means that the world's population growth, or its growth rate, is

$$\frac{18.0 - 7.6}{1{,}000} = \frac{10.4}{1{,}000} = 0.0104 \times 100 = 1.04\%$$

Note that the birthrate and death rate are expressed in terms of 1,000 persons, whereas the growth rate is expressed per 100 persons, or as a percentage.

After 1750, the world population growth rate steadily increased, until it peaked at 2% in 1965. It has since fallen to its present level of under 1.1%, yet the world population is still steadily growing because of its past exponential growth. However, it is projected that the world's population may level off over the next 50 years due to reductions in the birthrate in many countries.

BIOLOGY IN YOUR LIFE

How do population growth rates vary among countries?

In 2020, the country with the highest projected fertility rate was Niger (7.00 children born per woman), followed by Angola (5.96 children per woman) and the Democratic Republic of the Congo (5.77 children per woman), whereas Singapore was the country with the lowest fertility rate (0.87 children born per woman). For death rates, Lesotho had the highest rate (15.4 deaths per 1,000 people) and Qatar had one of the lowest (1.60 deaths per 1,000). For overall annual growth rates, the fastest-growing countries are projected to be Syria (4.25%) and Niger (3.66%). Several areas are expected to experience declines, including the territory of Puerto Rico (–1.59%) and the country of Lebanon (–6.68%). In comparison, in the United States the projected fertility rate is 1.84 births per woman, the death rate 8.3 per 1,000 people, and the annual growth rate is 0.72%.

Source: www.cia.gov.

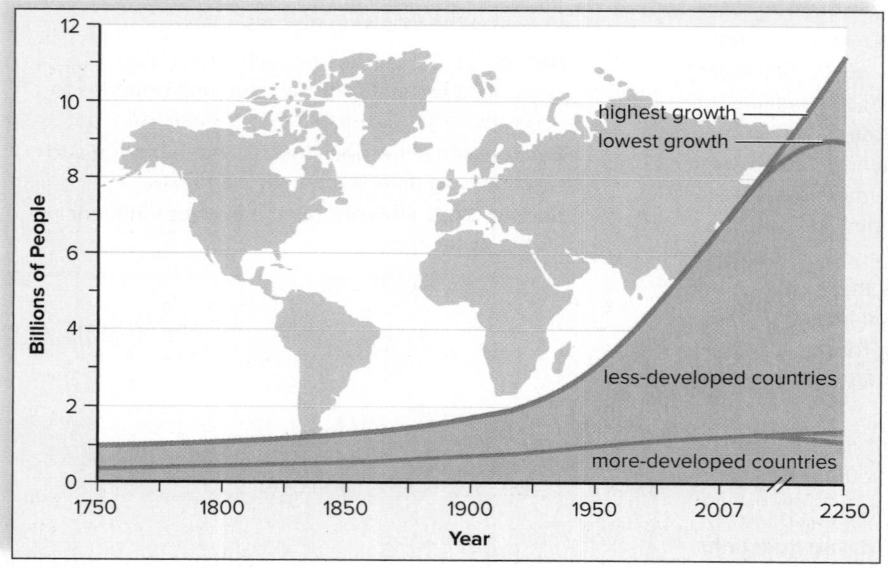

Figure 25.1 Projections for human population growth.
The world population is approaching 8 billion humans. It is predicted that the world's population size may reach 11 billion by 2100.

In the wild, exponential growth indicates that a population is enjoying its **biotic potential.** This is the maximum growth rate under ideal conditions. Growth begins to decline because of limiting factors, such as food and space. Finally, the population levels off at the **carrying capacity,** the maximum population the environment can support for an extended period. The carrying capacity of the Earth for humans has not been determined. Some authorities think the Earth may be able to sustain 50 to 100 billion people. Others think we already have more humans than the Earth can adequately support.

The MDCs Versus the LDCs

The countries of the world can be broadly divided into two groups. The more-developed countries (MDCs), typified by countries in North America and Europe, are those in which population growth is modest. The people in these countries often enjoy a high standard of living. The less-developed countries

(LDCs), typified by some countries in Asia, Africa, and Latin America, are those in which population growth is dramatic. The majority of people in these countries live in poverty. Many countries are in a transitional stage between being an LDC and being an MDC. Their population growth is decreasing and their standard of living is on the rise.

The MDCs

The MDCs did not always have low population increases. Between 1850 and 1950, they doubled their populations. This was largely because of a decline in the death rate due to development of modern medicine and improvements in public health and socioeconomic conditions. The decline in the death rate was followed shortly thereafter by a decline in the birthrate. As a result, the MDCs have experienced only modest growth since 1950 (Fig. 25.1).

The growth rate for the MDCs as a whole is about 0.3%. In some countries, the population is not increasing but, rather, decreasing. While the population of the MDCs are expected to increase until 2050, their total population should stabilize at just around 1.2–1.5 billion. In contrast to the other MDCs, growth in the United States has not leveled off. The U.S. population is now above 331 million and continues to increase. Though the birthrate in the United States has increased slightly, much of the continued population growth is due to immigration.

The LDCs

The death rate began to decline steeply in the LDCs following World War II due to the introduction of modern medicine. However, the birthrate remained high. The growth rate of the LDCs peaked at 2.5% between 1960 and 1965. Since that time, the collective growth rate for the LDCs has declined. However, the growth rate has not declined in all LDCs. In many countries in sub-Saharan Africa, women give birth to more than five children each.

By 2050, the population of the LDCs may jump to around 8–9 billion. Some of this increase will occur in Africa, but most will occur in Asia. Many deaths from AIDS are slowing the growth of the African population. Continued growth in Asia is expected to cause acute water scarcity, a significant loss of biodiversity, and more urban pollution. Twelve of the world's 15 most polluted cities are in Asia.

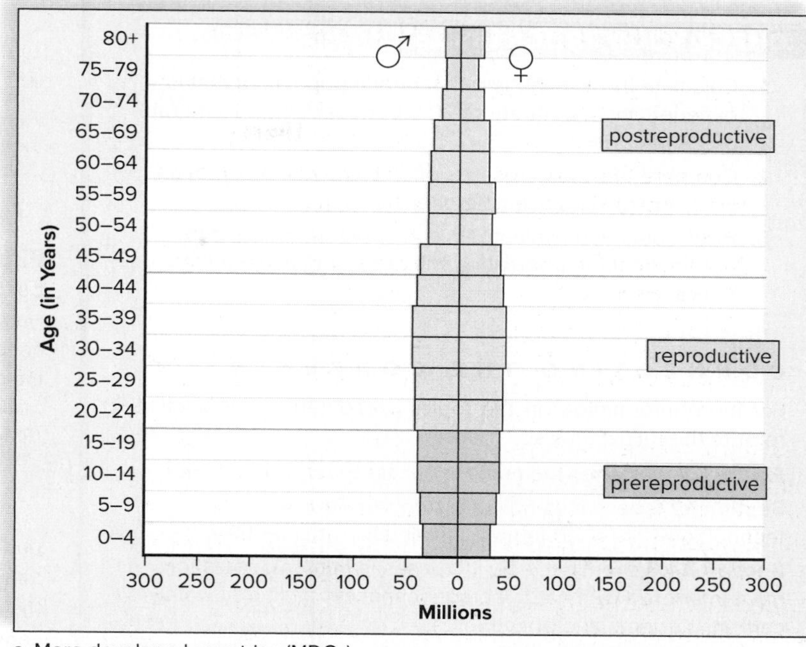

a. More-developed countries (MDCs)

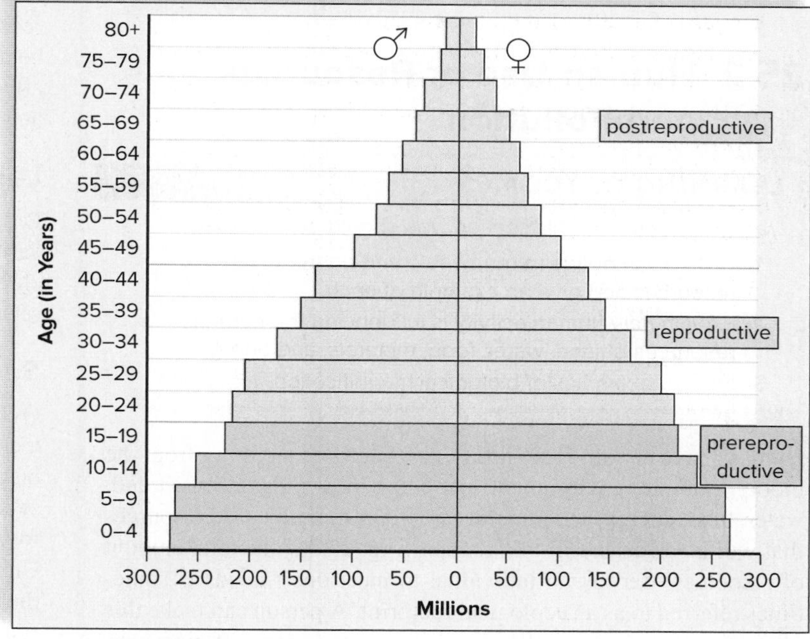

b. Less-developed countries (LDCs)

Figure 25.2 **Age structure diagrams of MDCs and LDCs.** The shape of these age structure diagrams allows us to predict that **(a)** the populations of MDCs are approaching stabilization and **(b)** the populations of LDCs will continue to increase for some time.

Comparing Age Structure

The LDCs are experiencing a population increase because they have more women entering the reproductive years than older women leaving them. Populations have three age groups: prereproductive, reproductive, and postreproductive. This is best visualized by plotting the proportion of individuals in each group on a bar graph, producing an age structure diagram (Fig. 25.2).

Laypeople are sometimes under the impression that if each couple has two children, zero population growth will take place immediately. However, **replacement reproduction,** as this practice is called, will still cause populations to increase in size because of our life expectancy. Most people will live long enough to become grandparents or even great-grandparents, thus resulting in an increase in the population.

CHECK YOUR PROGRESS 25.1

1. Calculate the annual growth rate of a population that is experiencing a birthrate of 20.5 per year and a death rate of 9.8 per year.
2. Compare the characteristics of an MDC with those of an LDC, and give an example of each.
3. How would you evaluate an age structure diagram to determine if the population will grow or decline in the future?

CONNECTING THE CONCEPTS

For more information on the topics presented in this section, refer to the following discussions:

Figure 8.7 illustrates the number of cases worldwide of HIV.

Section 17.5 describes how assisted reproductive technologies are used to treat individuals with infertility.

Section 24.3 examines how increases in human population have interfered with natural biogeochemical cycling of water, carbon, nitrogen, and phosphorus.

25.2 Human Use of Resources and Pollution

LEARNING OUTCOMES

Upon completion of this section, you should be able to

1. Distinguish between renewable and nonrenewable resources and give an example of each.
2. Explain how human activity is influencing the natural resources of land, water, food, minerals, and energy.
3. Identify examples of biological magnification.

Humans have certain basic needs. A resource is anything from the biotic or abiotic environment that helps meet those needs. Land, water, food, energy, and minerals are the commonly used resources that will be discussed in this chapter (Fig. 25.3). The total amount of resources used by an individual to meet one's needs is sometimes referred to as an ecological footprint. A person can make this ecological footprint smaller by driving an energy-efficient car, living in a smaller house, owning fewer possessions, eating vegetables as opposed to meat, and so forth.

Some resources are nonrenewable, and some are renewable. **Nonrenewable resources** are limited in supply. For example, the amount of land, fossil fuels, and minerals is finite and can be exhausted. Efficient use, recycling, or substitution can make the supply last longer, but eventually these resources will run out. **Renewable resources** are capable of being naturally replenished. We can use water and certain forms of energy (e.g., solar energy) or harvest plants and animals for food. A new supply will always be forthcoming. However, even with renewable resources, we have to be careful not to overuse them before they can replenish themselves.

Figure 25.3 The five classes of resources needed to meet basic human needs.
Humans use land, water, food, energy, and minerals to meet their basic needs, such as a place to live, food to eat, and products that make their lives easier.
(land): Budimir Jevtic/Shutterstock; (water): ©Evelyn Jo Johnson; (food): John Thoeming/McGraw Hill; (energy): Geniusksy/Shutterstock; (minerals): TTstudio/Shutterstock

Unfortunately, a side effect of resource consumption can be pollution. **Pollution** is any undesired alteration of the environment and is often caused by human activities. The effect of humans on the environment is proportional to the human population size and consumption levels. As the population grows, so does the need for resources and the amount of pollution caused by using these resources. Seven people adding waste to the ocean may not be alarming, but over 7.8 billion people doing so would certainly affect its cleanliness. In modern times, the consumption of mineral and energy resources has grown faster than population size.

Land

People need a place to live. Naturally, land is also needed for a variety of uses aside from homes. Land is used for agriculture, electrical power plants, manufacturing plants, highways, hospitals, schools, and so on.

Beaches and Human Habitation

Over 40% of the world population lives within 100 km (60 mi) of a coastline, and this number is expected to increase. Living right on the coast is an unfortunate choice because it leads to beach erosion, loss of habitat for marine organisms, and loss of a buffer zone for storms. Figure 25.4 shows how severe the problem can be in the United States. Coastal wetlands are also impacted when people fill them in. One reason to protect coastal wetlands is that they are spawning areas for fish and other forms of marine life. They are also habitats for certain terrestrial species, including many types of birds. Wetlands also protect coastal areas from storms. The level of storm damage to New Orleans during Hurricanes Katrina (2005) and Isaac (2012) is largely attributed to the lack of protective wetlands along the coast. Wetlands are also particularly subject to pollution, because toxic substances placed in freshwater lakes, rivers, and streams can eventually find their way to these areas.

Semiarid Lands and Human Habitation

Forty percent of the Earth's lands are already deserts. Land adjacent to a desert is in danger of becoming unable to support human life if it is improperly managed by humans (Fig. 25.5). **Desertification** is the conversion of semiarid land to desertlike conditions.

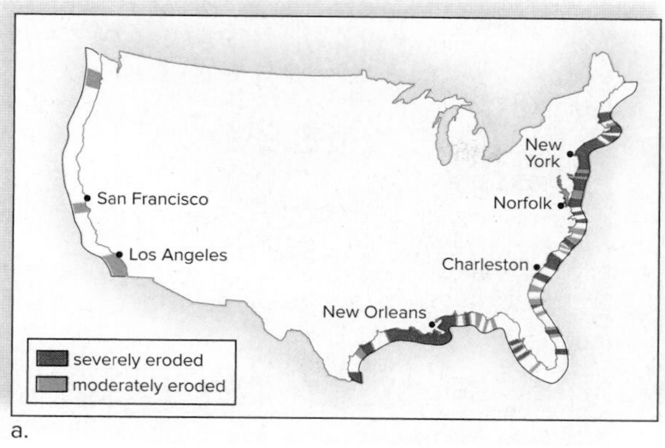

a.

b.

Figure 25.4 Beach erosion and coastal development.
a. Most of the U.S. coastline is subject to beach erosion. **b.** Therefore, people who choose to live near the coast may eventually lose their homes.
(b): xuanhuongho/Shutterstock

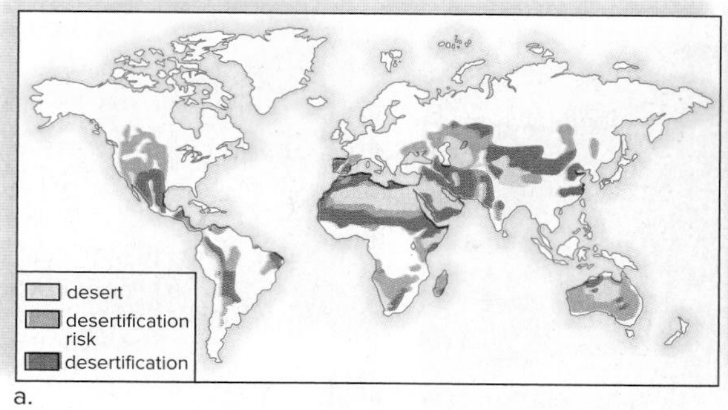

a.

b.

Figure 25.5 Desertification.
a. Desertification is a worldwide occurrence that **(b)** reduces the amount of land suitable for human habitation.
(b): Mangiwau/Moment/Getty Images

Often, desertification begins when humans allow animals to overgraze the land. The soil can no longer hold rainwater, and it runs off instead of keeping the remaining plants alive or replenishing wells. Humans then remove whatever vegetation they can find to use as fuel or as fodder for their animals. The result is a lifeless desert. That area is then abandoned as people move on to continue the process someplace else. Some ecologists estimate that nearly three-quarters of all rangelands worldwide are in danger of desertification. Many famines are due, at least in part, to degradation of the land to the point that it can no longer support humans and their livestock.

Tropical Rain Forests and Human Habitation

Deforestation, the removal of trees, has long allowed humans to live in areas where forests once covered the land (Fig. 25.6). This land, too, is subject to desertification. Soil in the tropics is often thin and nutrient-poor, because all the nutrients are tied up in the trees and other vegetation. When the trees are felled and the land is used for agriculture or grazing, it quickly loses its fertility. It is then subject to desertification.

Water

In the water-poor areas of the world, people may not have ready access to drinking water, and if they do, the water may be unsafe. It's considered a human right for people to have clean drinking water. In reality, most fresh water is used by industry and agriculture (Fig. 25.7). Worldwide, 70% of fresh water is used to irrigate crops! Much of a recent surge in demand for water stems from increased industrial activity and irrigation-intensive agriculture. This type of agriculture now supplies about 40% of the world's food crops. In the MDCs, more water is usually used for bathing, flushing toilets, and watering lawns than for drinking and cooking.

Increasing Water Supplies

Globally, the needs of the human population do not exceed the renewable supply of fresh water. However, this is not the case in certain regions of the United States and the world. About 40% of the world's land is desert, and deserts are bordered by semiarid land. To live in these regions, humans increase the availability of fresh water by damming rivers and withdrawing water from aquifers.

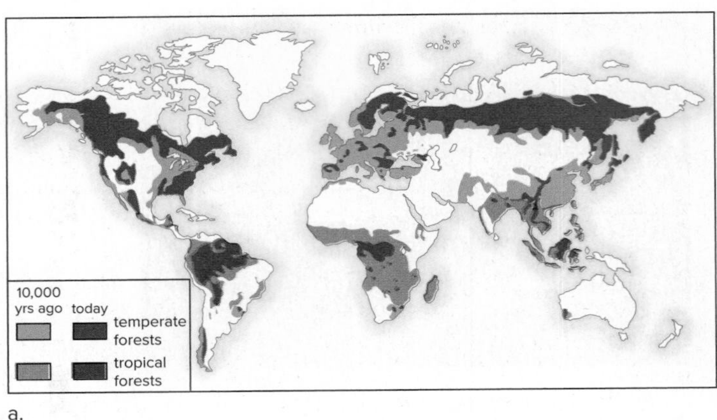

a.

b.

Figure 25.6 Deforestation.

a. Nearly half of the world's forestlands have been cleared for farming, logging, and urbanization. **b.** The soil of tropical rain forests cannot sustain long-term farming.

(b): luoman/E+/Getty Images

a. Agriculture uses most of the fresh water consumed.

b. Industrial use of water is about half that of agricultural use.

c. Domestic use of water is about half that of industrial use.

Figure 25.7 Water use by agriculture, industries, and households.

a. Agriculture primarily uses water for irrigation. **b.** Industry uses water in a variety of ways. **c.** Households use water to drink, shower, flush toilets, and water lawns.

(a): Comstock Images/Alamy Stock Photo; (b): David Birkbeck/Getty Images; (c): Stockbyte/PunchStock/Getty Images

Dams The world's 57,000 large dams catch 14% of all precipitation runoff and provide water for up to 40% of irrigated land. They also give some 65 countries more than half their electricity. Damming of certain rivers has been so extensive that the rivers no longer flow as they once did. The Yellow River in China fails to reach the sea most years. The Colorado River barely makes it to the Gulf of California. During the past few decades, even the Rio Grande has occasionally dried up before it reaches the Gulf of Mexico. The Nile in Egypt and the Ganges in India are also so overexploited they hardly make it to the ocean at some times of the year.

Dams have other drawbacks as well, not the least of which is losing water by evaporation and seepage into underlying rock beds. The amount of water lost sometimes equals the amount made available! The salt left behind by evaporation and agricultural runoff increases salinity and can make a river's water unusable farther downstream. Dams hold back less water with time because of sediment buildup. Some reservoirs become so full of silt they are no longer useful for storing water.

Aquifers To meet their freshwater needs, people are pumping vast amounts of water from **aquifers.** These are reservoirs that are anywhere from just below ground to as much as 1 km beneath the surface of the Earth. Aquifers hold about 1,000 times the amount of water that falls on land as precipitation each year. This water accumulates from rain that has fallen in far-off regions. In the past 50 years, groundwater depletion has become a problem in many areas of the world. In substantial portions of the High Plains Aquifer (stretching from South Dakota to Texas), more than half of the water has been pumped out. Section 24.3 explores some of the challenges in addressing aquifer depletion in California.

Consequences of Groundwater Depletion Removal of water from aquifers is causing land **subsidence,** a settling of the soil as it dries out. An area in California's San Joaquin valley has subsided at least 30 cm due to groundwater depletion. In the worst spot, the surface of the ground has dropped more than 9 m! Subsidence damages canals, buildings, and underground pipes. Withdrawal of groundwater can cause **sinkholes,** which form when an underground cavern collapses because water no longer supports the roof (Fig. 25.8).

Saltwater intrusion is another consequence of aquifer depletion. The flow of water from streams and aquifers usually keeps them fairly free of seawater. As water is withdrawn, the water table can lower to the point that seawater backs up into streams and aquifers. Saltwater intrusion reduces the supply of fresh water along the coast.

Water Pollution There are two different ways that sources of water pollution are classified. *Point* sources of pollution can be traced to a specific source, whereas *nonpoint* sources are those sources that cannot be specifically identified. Industrial wastes can include heavy metals and organochlorides, such as DDT and PCBs. These materials are not readily degraded under natural conditions or in conventional sewage treatment plants. Biological magnification occurs as these toxic chemicals pass along a food chain. Pollutants become increasingly concentrated with each higher consumer level, because they remain in the body and are not excreted. Aquatic food chains are more likely to experience biological magnification, because there are more links than in a terrestrial food chain. Mercury levels can be high in some of the fish we eat (top consumers such as shark, swordfish, and tuna) for this reason.

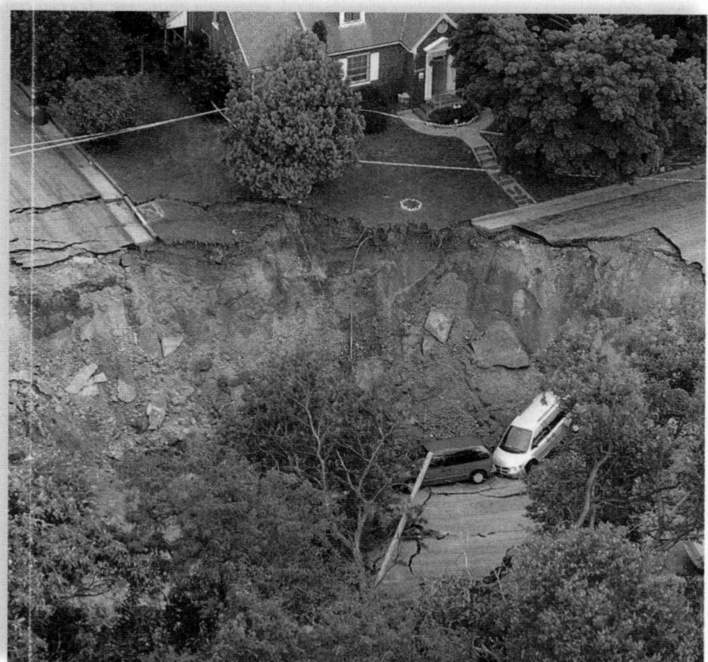

Figure 25.8 **Sinkholes and groundwater depletion.** Sinkholes occur when an underground cavern collapses after groundwater has been withdrawn.
Mark Gormus/Richmond Times-Dispatch/AP Images

Coastal regions are the immediate receptors for local pollutants and the final receptors for pollutants from watersheds that drain into rivers that empty at a coast. Waste dumping occurs at sea. However, ocean currents sometimes transport both trash and pollutants back to shore. Offshore mining and shipping add pollutants to the oceans. Some 5 million metric tons of oil a year end up in the oceans. Large oil spills kill plankton, fish, and shellfishes, as well as birds and marine mammals.

In the last 50 years, humans have polluted the seas and exploited their resources to the point that many species are on the brink of extinction. Fisheries once rich and diverse, such as George's Bank off the coast of New England, are in severe decline. Haddock was once the most abundant species in this fishery, but now it accounts for less than 2% of the total catch. Cod and bluefin tuna have suffered a 90% reduction in population size. In warm, tropical regions, many areas of coral reefs are now overgrown with algae. This is because the fish that normally keep the algae under control have been overharvested.

Conservation of Water

By 2025, two-thirds of the world's population may be living in countries facing serious water shortages. Some solutions for expanding water supplies have been suggested. Planting drought- and salt-tolerant crops would help a lot. Using drip irrigation delivers more water to crops and increases crop yields as well (Fig. 25.9). Although the first drip systems were developed in 1960, they're used on less than 1% of irrigated land. Most governments subsidize irrigation so heavily that farmers have little incentive to invest in drip systems or other water-saving methods. Reusing water and adopting conservation measures could help the world's industries cut their water demands by more than half.

Food

In 1950, the human population numbered 2.5 billion. Only enough food was produced to provide less than 2,000 calories per person per day. Today's food production supplies nearly 2,700 calories per person per day to support the 7.8 billion people on Earth. Generally speaking, food comes from three activities: growing crops, raising animals, and fishing the seas. The increase in the food supply has largely been possible because of modern farming methods. Unfortunately, many of these methods include some harmful practices:

- *Planting of a few genetic varieties.* The majority of farmers practice monoculture. Wheat farmers plant the same type of wheat, and corn farmers plant the same type of corn. With a *monoculture,* a single type of parasite can destroy an entire crop.
- *Heavy use of fertilizers, pesticides, and herbicides.* Fertilizer production is energy-intensive, and fertilizer runoff contributes to water pollution. Pesticides reduce soil fertility, because they kill off beneficial soil organisms, as well as pests. Some pesticides and herbicides are linked to the development of cancer. **Agricultural runoff** places these chemicals in our water supply.
- *Generous irrigation.* As already discussed, water is sometimes withdrawn from aquifers for crop irrigation. In the

a.

b.

c.

Figure 25.9 Measures that can be taken to conserve water. **a.** Planting drought-resistant crops in the fields, as well as drought-resistant plants in parks and gardens, cuts down on the need to irrigate. **b.** When irrigation is necessary, drip irrigation is preferable to using sprinklers. **c.** Wastewater can be treated and reused instead of withdrawing more water from a river or an aquifer.

(a): Bruno Barbier/Getty Images; (b): Milan Stojanovic/iStock/Getty Images; (c): View Stock/Alamy Stock Photo

future, the water content of these aquifers may become so reduced that it may not be available to pump out any more.

- *Excessive fuel consumption.* Irrigation pumps remove water from aquifers. Large farming machines are used to spread fertilizers, pesticides, and herbicides, as well as to sow and harvest the crops. In effect, modern farming uses large amounts of fossil fuels to produce food.

Figure 25.10 shows ways to minimize the harmful effects of modern farming practices. *Polyculture* is the planting of two or more different crops in the same area. In Figure 25.10*a,* a farmer has planted alfalfa in between strips of corn. The alfalfa replenishes the nitrogen content of the soil so that fertilizer doesn't have to be added. In Figure 25.10*b,* contour farming with no-till farming conserves topsoil, because it reduces agricultural runoff. Contour farming is planting and plowing according to the slope of the land. No-till farming allows the previous crop to remain on the land, recycling nutrients and preventing soil erosion. Biological control (Fig. 25.10*c*) relies on the use of natural predators to destroy organisms that harm crops. This reduces the need for pesticides.

Soil Loss

Land suitable for farming and grazing animals is being degraded worldwide. Topsoil is the richest in organic matter and the most capable of supporting grass and crops. When bare soil is acted on by water and wind, soil erosion occurs and topsoil is lost. As a result, marginal rangeland is often lost to desert, and farmland loses its productivity.

The custom of planting the same crop in straight rows, which facilitates the use of large farming machines, has caused the United States and Canada to have one of the highest rates of soil erosion in the world. Conserving soil nutrients by altering farming practices could save farmers billions of dollars annually in fertilizer costs. Much of the eroded sediment ends up in lakes and streams where it creates problems in the aquatic ecosystem.

Green Revolutions

About 50 years ago, researchers began to breed tropical wheat and rice varieties specifically for farmers in the LDCs. The dramatic increase in yield due to the introduction of these new varieties around the world was called "the green revolution." These plants helped the world food supply keep pace with the rapid increase in world population. Unfortunately, most green revolution plants are called "high responders," because they need high levels of fertilizer, water, and pesticides to produce a high yield. They require the same subsidies and create the same ecological problems as modern farming methods do.

Genetic Engineering As discussed in Section 22.3, genetic engineering can produce transgenic plants with new and different traits. For example, resistance to both insects and herbicides are traits that can be inserted into plant DNA. When herbicide-resistant crops are planted, weeds are controlled more easily, less tillage is needed, and soil erosion is minimized. Researchers also want to produce crops that tolerate salt, drought, and cold. Some progress has also been made in increasing the food quality of crops so they will supply more of the proteins, vitamins, and minerals people need. Genetically engineered crops could result in still another green revolution.

Domestic Livestock

A low-protein, high-carbohydrate diet consisting only of grains such as wheat, rice, or corn can lead to malnutrition. In the LDCs, kwashiorkor, a disease caused by a severe protein deficiency, is

a. Polyculture

b. Contour farming

c. Biological pest control

Figure 25.10 Methods that make farming more friendly to the environment.
a. Polyculture reduces the ability of one parasite to wipe out an entire crop and reduces the need to use an herbicide to kill weeds. This farmer has planted alfalfa in between strips of corn, which also replenishes the nitrogen content of the soil (instead of adding fertilizers). Alfalfa, a legume, has root nodules that contain nitrogen-fixing bacteria. **b.** Contour farming with no-till conserves topsoil, because water has less tendency to run off. **c.** Instead of pesticides, it is possible to use natural predators. Here, ladybugs are feeding on aphids, an insect pest species.
(a): David R. Frazier/Science Source; (b): Inga Spence/Alamy Stock Photo; (c): Perennou Nuridsany/Science Source

seen in infants and children ages 1 to 3 years old. It usually occurs after a new arrival in the family and the older children are no longer fed milk. The diet then consists of protein-poor starches. Such children are lethargic and irritable and have bloated abdomens. Problems associated with intellectual development may also occur.

In the MDCs, many people tend to have more than enough protein in their diet. Almost two-thirds of United States cropland is devoted to producing livestock feed. This means that a large percentage of the fossil fuels, fertilizer, water, herbicides, and pesticides used are for the purpose of raising livestock. Typically, cattle are range-fed for about 4 months. They are then taken to crowded feedlots, where they may receive growth hormones and antibiotics. At the feedlots, they feed on grain or corn. Many animals, including cows (Fig. 25.11) and pigs, spend their entire lives in crowded pens and cages.

Because livestock eat a large proportion of the crops in the United States, raising livestock accounts for much of the pollution associated with the farming industry. Fossil-fuel energy is used to produce herbicides, pesticides, grow food, and to grow feed used for livestock. Raising livestock is extremely energy-intensive. In addition, water is used to wash livestock wastes into nearby bodies of water, where it adds significantly to water pollution. Whereas human wastes are sent to sewage treatment plants, raw animal wastes are not.

For these reasons, it is prudent to recall the ecological energy pyramid (see Fig. 24.8), which shows that as you move up the food chain, not all of the energy is transferred. As a rule of thumb, for every 10 calories of energy from a plant, only 1 calorie is available for the production of animal tissue in a herbivore. A great deal of energy is wasted when the human diet contains more protein than is needed to maintain good health. It is possible to feed ten times as many people on grain as on meat.

Figure 25.11 Environmental effects of raising livestock.
Raising livestock requires the use of more fossil fuels and water than raising crops. Livestock waste often washes into nearby bodies of water, creating water pollution.
Photo by Tim McCabe, U.S. Department of Agriculture Natural Resources Conservation Service

Energy

Modern society runs on various sources of energy. Some are renewable, whereas others are nonrenewable. The consumption of nonrenewable energy supplies results in environmental degradation, which is one of the reasons renewable energy is expected to be used more in the future.

Nonrenewable Sources

Presently, about 10% of the world's energy supply comes from nuclear power, approximately 63%

comes from fossil fuels, and the remainder from hydropower or renewable sources. Both of these are finite, nonrenewable sources. It was once predicted that the nuclear power industry would fulfill a significant portion of the world's energy needs. However, this has not happened for two reasons. One is that people are very concerned about nuclear power dangers, such as the Fukushima nuclear power plant disaster in Japan in 2011. Further, radioactive wastes from nuclear power plants remain a threat to the environment for thousands of years. We still have not decided how best to store them safely.

Fossil fuels (oil, natural gas, and coal) are derived from the compressed remains of plants and animals that died millions of years ago. While oil remains the most widely used fossil fuel, the U.S. production of natural gas reached a record high in 2019. Coal has continued to decline for a variety of reasons. Regardless of which fossil fuel is used, all contribute to environmental problems because of the pollutants released when they're burned. Current research into new extraction and combustion methods are underway.

Fossil Fuels and Global Climate Change In 1850, the level of carbon dioxide in the atmosphere was about 280 parts per million (ppm); currently, it is over 409 ppm. This increase is largely due to the burning of fossil fuels and the clearing and burning of forests. Human activities are causing the emission of other gases as well. These gases are known as **greenhouse gases.** Just like the panes of a greenhouse, they allow solar radiation to pass through but hinder the escape of infrared heat back into space.

Computer models predict the Earth may warm to temperatures never before experienced by living organisms. The global climate has already warmed about 0.6°C, and it may rise as much as 1.5–4.5°C by 2100 (see Section 24.3). If so, sea levels will rise as glaciers melt and warm water expands. Major coastal cities of the United States could eventually be threatened. The present wetlands will be inundated. Great losses of aquatic habitat will occur wherever wetlands cannot move inward because of coastal development and levees. Coral reefs, which prefer shallow waters, will most likely "drown" as the waters rise.

On land, regions of suitable climate for various species will shift toward the poles and higher elevations. Plants migrate when seeds disperse and growth occurs in a new locale. The present assemblages of species in ecosystems will be disrupted as some species migrate northward faster than others. Trees, for example, cannot migrate as fast as nonwoody plants. Also, too many species of organisms are isolated to relatively small habitat patches surrounded by agricultural or urban areas. Even if such species have the capacity to disperse to new sites, suitable habitats may not be available.

Renewable Energy Sources

Renewable types of energy include hydropower, geothermal, wind, and solar.

Hydropower Hydroelectric plants convert the energy of falling water into electricity (Fig. 25.12*a*). Hydropower accounts for about 6.6% of the electrical power generated in the United States and approximately 24% of the total renewable energy used. Worldwide, hydropower generates 17% of all electricity used. This percentage is expected to continue to rise because of increased use in certain countries.

Much of the hydropower development in recent years has been due to the construction of enormous dams. These are known to have detrimental environmental effects, however. The better choice is believed to be small-scale dams that generate less power per dam but do not have the same environmental impact.

Geothermal Energy Elements such as uranium, thorium, radium, and plutonium undergo radioactive decay below the Earth's surface. This heats the surrounding rocks to hundreds of degrees Celsius. When the rocks are in contact with underground streams or lakes, huge amounts of steam and hot water are produced. This steam can be piped up to the surface to supply hot water for home heating or to run steam-driven turbogenerators. California's Geysers Recharge Project is the world's largest geothermal electricity-generating complex.

Wind Power Wind power is expected to fulfill a significant percentage of our energy needs in the future. A common belief is that a huge amount of land is required for the "wind farms" that produce commercial electricity; however, the amount of land needed for a wind farm compares favorably with the amount of land required by a coal-fired power plant or a solar thermal energy system (Fig. 25.12*b*).

A community generating its own electricity by using wind power can solve the problem of uneven energy production. Electricity can be sold to a local public utility when an excess is available. Then, electricity is bought from the same facility when wind power is in short supply.

Energy and the Solar–Hydrogen Revolution Solar energy is diffuse energy that must be collected, converted to another form, and stored if it is to compete with other available forms of energy. Passive solar heating of a house is successful when the windows of the house face the sun and the building is well insulated. Successful heating also requires that heat be stored in water tanks, rocks, bricks, or some other suitable material.

In a **photovoltaic (solar) cell,** a wafer of an electron-emitting metal is in contact with another metal that collects the electrons. Electrons are then passed along into wires in a steady stream. Spurred by the oil shocks of the 1970s, the U.S. government has been supporting the development of photovoltaics ever since. As a result, the price of a photovoltaic cell has dropped from about $100 per kilowatt (in the 1970s) to around $3 per kilowatt today. Photovoltaic cells placed on roofs generate electricity that can be used inside a building and/or sold back to a power company (Fig. 25.12*c*).

Several types of solar power plants are now operational in California. In one type, huge reflectors focus sunlight on a pipe containing oil. The heated pipes boil water, generating steam that drives a conventional turbogenerator. In another type, 1,800 sun-tracking mirrors focus sunlight onto a molten salt receiver mounted on a tower. The hot salt generates steam that drives a turbogenerator (Fig. 25.12*d*).

a.

c.

b.

d.

Figure 25.12 Sources of renewable energy.

a. Hydropower dams provide a clean form of energy but can be ecologically disastrous in other ways. **b.** Wind power requires land on which to place enough windmills to generate energy. **c.** Photovoltaic cells on rooftops and **(d)** sun-tracking mirrors on land can collect diffuse solar energy more cheaply than could be done formerly.

(a): Jeffrey Schreier/iStock/Getty Images; (b): Glen Allison/Photodisc/Getty Images; (c): Danita Delimont/Getty Images; (d): Darren Baker/Alamy Stock Photo

Scientists are working on the possibility of using solar energy to extract hydrogen from water via electrolysis. The hydrogen can then be used as a clean-burning fuel. When it burns, water is produced. Presently, cars have internal combustion engines that run on gasoline. In the future, more vehicles, including airplanes, are expected to be powered by fuel cells that use hydrogen to produce electricity (Fig. 25.13). The electricity runs a motor that propels the vehicle. Fuel cells are now powering buses in Vancouver and Chicago, with additional buses planned. Hyundai, Honda, and Toyota are just a few of the automakers that have fuel-cell vehicles on the roads today.

Hydrogen fuel can be produced locally or in central locations, using energy from photovoltaic cells. The fuel produced in central locations can be piped to filling stations using the natural gas pipes already plentiful in the United States. However, two major hurdles are storage and production. The advantages of a solar–hydrogen revolution are decreased dependence on oil and fewer environmental problems.

Minerals

Minerals are nonrenewable raw materials in the Earth's crust that can be mined (extracted) and used by humans. Nonmetallic raw materials, such as sand, gravel, and phosphate, are considered minerals. Metals, such as aluminum, copper, iron, lead, and gold, fall into this category as well.

One of the greatest threats to the maintenance of ecosystems and biodiversity is surface mining, called strip mining. In the

a.

b.

Figure 25.13 Alternate fuel-source vehicles.
a. This bus is powered by natural gas. **b.** Hydrogen fuel cells reduce air pollution and dependence on fossil fuels.
(a): LusoEnvironment/Alamy Stock Photo; (b): Abaca Press/Alamy Stock Photo

United States, huge machines can go as far as removing mountaintops to reach a mineral. The land devoid of vegetation takes on a surreal appearance, and rain washes toxic waste deposits into nearby streams and rivers.

The metals that are most dangerous to human health are the heavy metals. These include lead, mercury, arsenic, cadmium, tin, chromium, zinc, and copper. They are used to produce batteries, electronics, pesticides, medicines, paints, inks, and dyes. In the ionic form, they enter the body and inhibit vital enzymes. That's why these items should be discarded carefully and taken to hazardous waste sites.

Hazardous Wastes

The consumption of minerals and the use of synthetic organic chemicals contribute to the buildup of hazardous waste in the environment. Every year, countries around the world discard billions of tons of solid waste on land and in fresh water and salt water. In the United States, the Environmental Protection Agency (EPA) oversees the cleanup of hazardous waste disposal sites. An EPA program called the Superfund helps pay for this cleanup. Commonly found contaminants include heavy metals (such as lead, mercury, and arsenic) and chlorine-containing organic chemicals (such as chloroform and polychlorinated biphenyls, or PCBs). Some of these contaminants interfere with hormone activity and proper endocrine system functioning.

Organic chemicals made by humans play a role in the production of plastics, pesticides, herbicides, cosmetics, and hundreds of other products. For example, *halogenated hydrocarbons* are compounds made from carbon and hydrogen and include halogen atoms such as chlorine and fluorine. These compounds, **chlorofluorocarbons (CFCs),** have been shown to damage the Earth's ozone shield. This shield protects terrestrial life from harmful UV radiation and has recently been depleted by the use of CFCs.

Further, these types of synthetic compounds pose a threat to the health of living organisms, including humans, because they can undergo **biological magnification.** Such chemicals are not excreted and can accumulate in an organism's body. Therefore, they become more concentrated as they pass from organism to organism along a food chain. Biological magnification is more apt to occur in aquatic food chains, which have more links than terrestrial food chains. Rachel Carson's book *Silent Spring,* published in 1962, made the public aware of the harmful effects of pesticides, such as DDT. These substances accumulate in the mud of deltas and estuaries of highly polluted rivers and cause environmental problems if disturbed. After working their way up the food chain, high concentrations of DDT in predatory birds such as bald eagles and pelicans interfered with their ability to reproduce (Fig. 25.14). There are health advisories about eating certain types of fish due to the high levels of mercury they contain. Humans are often the final consumers in a variety of food chains

BIOLOGY IN YOUR LIFE

Microplastics in our seafood

The majority of plastic we use in our daily life does not decompose. Instead, it breaks down into smaller and smaller pieces called microplastics. As these fragments move through the ecosystem, they eventually enter the food chain. Marine ecosystems are of extreme concern. With over 250,000 tons of plastic in our ocean, it is no surprise that some of it will make its way into the seafood that many humans rely upon for their source of protein. Microplastics enter the body of marine animals through direct consumption, as well as passive water filtration. After ingestion, the plastics are absorbed into various body tissues that are then consumed by humans. Atlantic cod, mackerel, mussels, oysters, crustaceans, and various other marine species have been found to contain detectable levels of microplastics. Unfortunately, our knowledge about the health consequences of consuming microplastics is limited. Further research is necessary for us to determine the overall risk to human health that this new pollutant is having.

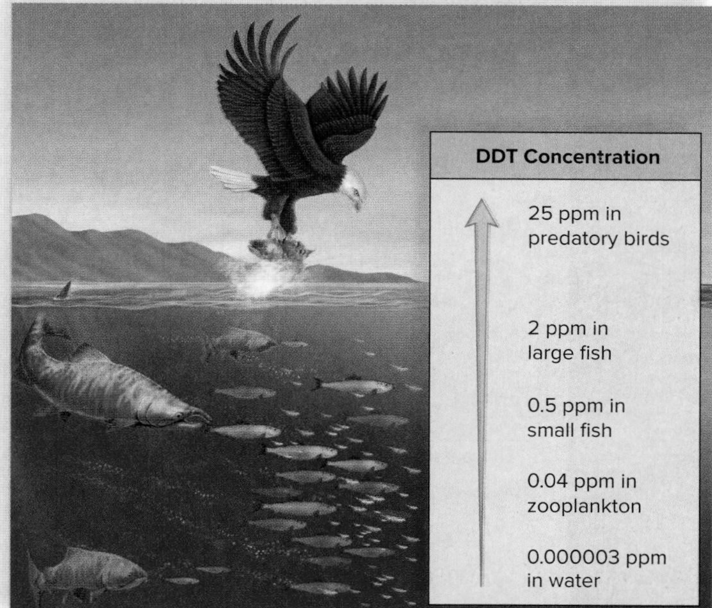

Figure 25.14 **Biological magnification concentrates chemicals in the food chain.**
Various synthetic organic chemicals, such as DDT, accumulate in animal fat. Therefore, the chemicals become increasingly concentrated at higher trophic levels. By the time DDT was banned in the United States, it had interfered with predatory bird reproduction by causing eggshell thinning.

and are affected by biological magnification as well. Human breast milk has been found to contain significant levels of DDT, PCBs, solvents, and heavy metals.

Raw sewage causes oxygen depletion in lakes and rivers. As the oxygen level decreases, the diversity of life is greatly reduced. Also, human feces can contain pathogenic microorganisms that cause cholera, typhoid fever, and dysentery. In regions of the LDCs where sewage treatment is practically nonexistent, many children die each year from these diseases. Typically, sewage treatment plants use bacteria to break down organic matter to inorganic nutrients, such as nitrates and phosphates, which then enter surface waters. The result can be cultural eutrophication (see Section 24.3).

CHECK YOUR PROGRESS 25.2

1. List the five main classes of resources.
2. Describe how humans have increased the availability of groundwater and food resources, and summarize the problems these activities may be creating.
3. Summarize why it is better for humans to use renewable rather than nonrenewable sources of energy.
4. Discuss the consequences of using fossil fuels as an energy source.
5. Describe how hazardous wastes may interfere with natural environmental processes.

CONNECTING THE CONCEPTS

For more information on the topics in this section, refer to the following discussions:

Section 24.1 examines the interactions of organisms in a food web.

Section 24.2 explores the flow of energy in an ecosystem.

Section 24.3 examines the water and carbon cycles and explores the influence of human activity on these cycles.

25.3 Biodiversity

LEARNING OUTCOMES

Upon completion of this section, you should be able to

1. Describe the factors that are contributing to the current biodiversity crisis.
2. Identify the direct values to society for conserving biodiversity.
3. Discuss the indirect values to society for conserving biodiversity.

Biodiversity can be defined as the variety of life on Earth and described in terms of the number of different species. For a number of reasons, including climate change and human population growth, we are presently in a biodiversity crisis. The number of current extinctions (loss of species) and those expected to occur in the near future is unparalleled in the history of the Earth.

Loss of Biodiversity

Figure 25.15 identifies the major causes of extinction.

Habitat Loss

Human occupation and alteration of nearly every biome on Earth have contributed to the loss of biodiversity. Scientists are especially concerned about the tropical rain forests and coral reefs, because these are particularly rich in species. Already, tropical rain forests have been reduced from their original 14% of global landmass to around 6% today. Also, over 60% of coral reefs have been destroyed or are on the verge of destruction.

Exotic Species

Exotic species, sometimes called *invasive species,* are nonnative members of an ecosystem. Humans have introduced exotic species into new ecosystems via colonization, horticulture and agriculture, and accidental transport. For example, the Pilgrims brought the dandelion to the United States as a familiar salad green. Japanese honeysuckle is a woody shrub from Japan that the U.S. Department of Agriculture thought would help prevent soil erosion, but the plant has overtaken many of the forests in the Midwest. The zebra mussel from the Caspian Sea was accidentally introduced into the Great Lakes in 1988 and is now found in many U.S. rivers, where it forms dense beds that squeeze out native mussels. One way to counteract invasive species is to support native (original to the area) species.

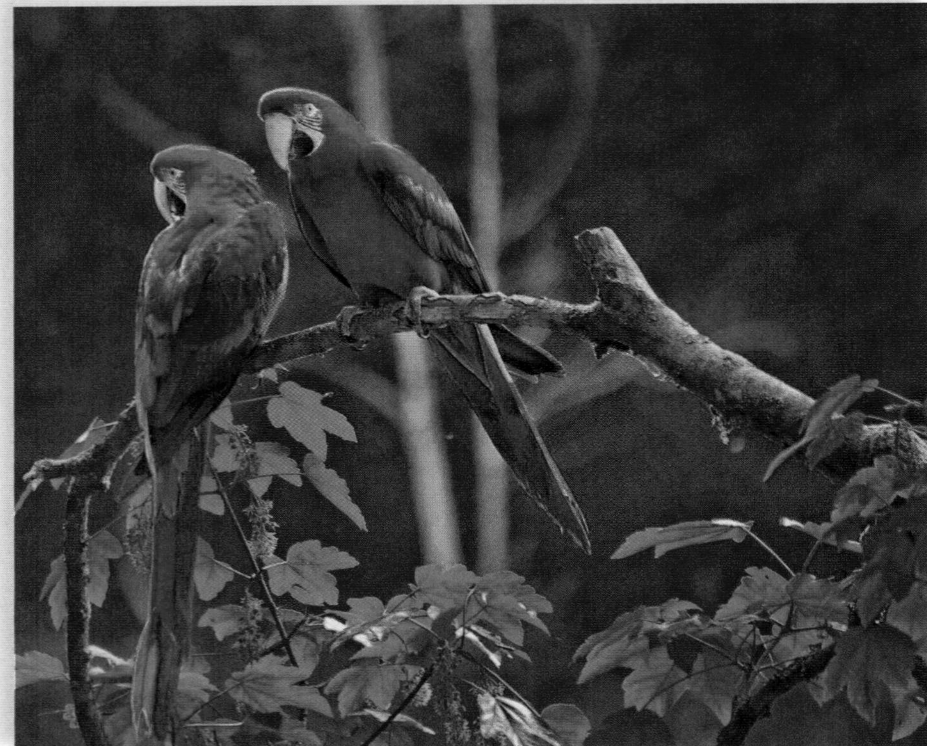

b. Macaws

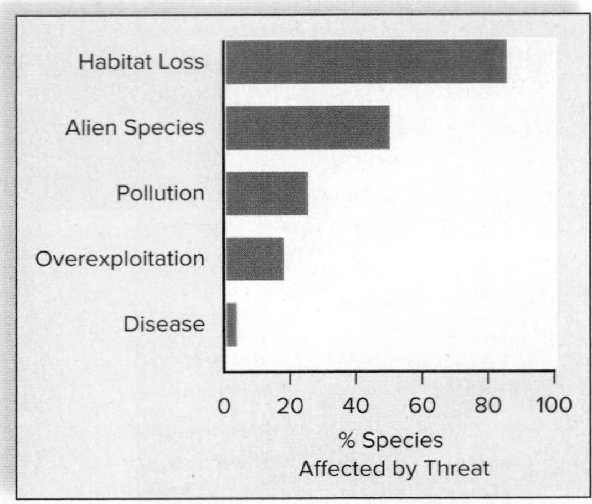

a. Threats to wildlife

Figure 25.15 Causes for the loss of biodiversity.
a. Habitat loss, alien species, pollution, overexploitation, and disease have been identified as causes of extinction of organisms. **b.** Macaws that reside in South American tropical rain forests are endangered for the reasons listed in the graph.
(photo) (b): Charan Reddy/EyeEm/Getty Images

BIOLOGY IN YOUR LIFE

Why are there dogs at the customs area in an international airport?

The dogs working at an airport's customs checkpoint are trained to detect agricultural items (foodstuffs, plants, animals, and the like) that are not allowed into the United States. Importing foreign species is prohibited by law. The goal of this law is to prevent the introduction of exotic life and diseases that might affect crops or animals in the United States. Over $2 million worth of illegal articles are seized yearly. Dogs assist in about 10% of those cases. Beagles are used because of their keen sense of smell and good-natured temperament.

Pollution

Pollution brings about environmental change that adversely affects the lives and health of living organisms. Pollution has been identified as the third main cause of extinction. Pollution can also weaken organisms and lead to disease. Biodiversity is particularly threatened by acid deposition, eutrophication, ozone depletion, and synthetic organic chemicals. Acid deposition weakens trees and increases their susceptibility to disease and insects, which can decimate a forest. Commercial and industrial organic chemicals released into the environment may interfere with hormone function and affect the reproductive ability of various species.

Climate Change

Climate change refers to recent changes in the Earth's climate (see Section 24.3). Our planet is experiencing erratic temperature patterns, more severe storms, and melting glaciers as a result of an increase in the Earth's temperature. Climate change is predicted to cause habitat loss due to global temperature shifts. For example, coral reefs die off as ocean temperatures increase. Coastal wetlands may be lost as sea levels increase. The depletion of the ozone shield limits crop and tree growth and kills the plankton that sustain ocean life.

Overexploitation

Overexploitation occurs when the number of individuals taken from a wild population is so great that the population cannot replace itself and becomes severely reduced. A positive feedback cycle explains overexploitation: The smaller the population, the more valuable its members are, resulting in a greater incentive to exploit the few remaining individuals.

Markets for decorative plants and exotic pets support both legal and illegal trade in wild species. Rustlers dig up rare cacti, such as the single-crested saguaro, and sell them to gardeners. Parakeets and macaws are among the birds taken from the wild for sale to pet owners. For every bird delivered alive, many have died during collection and transportation. The same holds true for tropical fish, which often come from the coral reefs of Indonesia and the Philippines. Divers dynamite reefs or use plastic squeeze bottles of cyanide to stun them. During the collection process, many fish die.

Declining species of mammals are still hunted for their hides, tusks, horns, or bones. A single Siberian tiger is now worth more than $500,000 because of its rarity. Its bones are pulverized and used as a medicinal powder. The horns of rhinoceroses become ornate carved daggers, and their bones are ground up to sell as a medicine. The ivory of an elephant's tusk is used to make art objects, jewelry, and piano keys. The fur of a Bengal tiger sells for as much as $100,000 in Tokyo.

Fish are a renewable resource if harvesting does not exceed the ability of the fish to reproduce. Today, larger and more efficient fishing fleets decimate fishing stocks (Fig. 25.16). Tuna and similar fish are captured by purse seining. A very large net surrounds a school of fish, and then the net is closed in the same manner as a drawstring purse. Dolphins that accompany the tuna are killed by this type of net. Other fishing boats drag huge trawling nets, large enough to accommodate 12 jumbo jets, along the seafloor to capture bottom-dwelling fish. Trawling has been called the marine equivalent of clear-cutting trees, because after the net goes by, the sea bottom is devastated. Only large fish are kept; undesirable small fish and sea turtles are discarded, dying, back into the ocean. Cod and haddock were once the most abundant bottom-dwelling fish along the Northeast Coast. Now, they are often outnumbered by dogfish and skate.

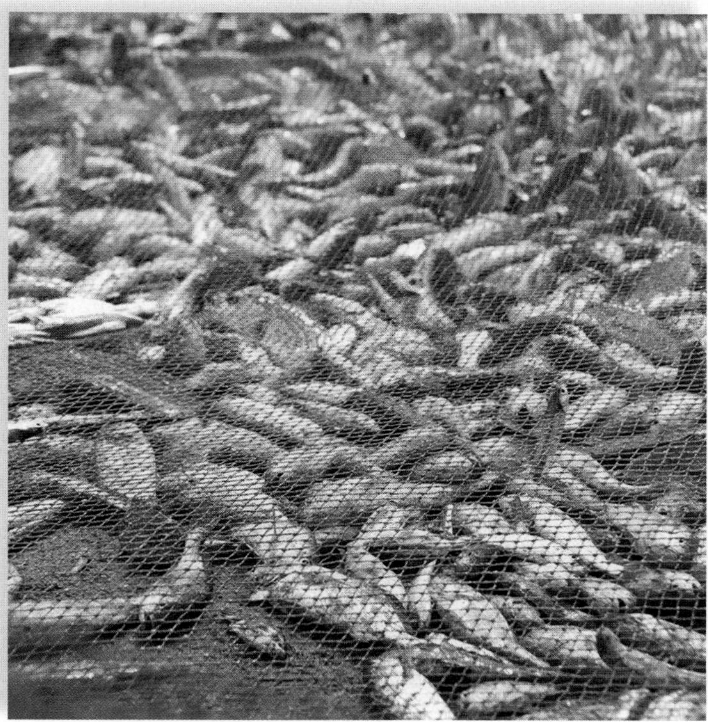

a. Fishing by use of a drag net

b. Result of drag net fishing

Figure 25.16 **The impact of modern fishing practices.**
a. These fish were caught by dragging a net along the seafloor.
b. Appearance of the seafloor after the net passed.
(a): StrahilDimitrov/360/iStock/Getty Images; (b): Peter Auster

BIOLOGY IN YOUR LIFE

How do you choose the best fish to eat?

Before you include fish in your meal plan, you should take a moment to consider your choice. You may want to determine if it is a sustainable species, one that is being overfished, or one that contains high levels of pollutants. Pacific halibut is usually caught with environmentally friendly techniques that won't harm other species of marine life. U.S. farm–raised tilapia is a good choice because it is grown in closed inland systems that decrease exposure of the fish to pollutants. Farm-raised salmon or trout supplies high concentrations of omega-3 acids (thought to protect against heart disease) and contains little or no mercury or other pollutants. Shark, sole, haddock, and swordfish are poor choices due to unsustainable fishing and/or because they likely contain high levels of mercury.

What many people don't often consider is the safety of eating locally caught fish. The Department of Public Health in each state issues fish advisories indicating which species are safe to eat and which are of concern. Predatory and long-lived species are often flagged with advisories for high levels of methylmercury, chlordane, dioxin, and PCBs. The advisories are meant to protect sensitive populations, which include women who are pregnant or nursing, as well as children younger than 15. Overall, fish are a great choice for dinner, but consumers need to be cautious about which species they are eating.

A marine ecosystem can be disrupted by overfishing, as exemplified on the U.S. West Coast. In one study, when sea otters began to decline in numbers, investigators found that they were being eaten by orcas (killer whales). Usually, orcas prefer seals and sea lions to sea otters, but they began eating sea otters when seals and sea lions could not be found. The decline in seal and sea lion populations was due to the decline in the perch and herring populations as a result of overfishing. Sea otters ordinarily keep the population of sea urchins, which feed on kelp, under control. But with fewer sea otters around, the sea urchin population exploded and decimated the kelp beds. Thus, overfishing set in motion a chain of events that detrimentally altered the food web of an ecosystem.

Disease

Emerging diseases affect not just humans but also wildlife. Domestic animals expose wildlife to their pathogens when humans encroach on wildlife habitats. Wildlife can also be infected by other wild animals that are foreign to their habitats. For example, African elephants carry a strain of herpes virus that is fatal to Asian elephants. Asian elephants can die if the two types of elephants are housed together.

The significant effect of diseases on biodiversity is underscored by a National Wildlife Health Center study, which found that, off the coast of California, almost half of sea otter deaths that were not due to predation occurred due to infectious diseases. Scientists tell us that the number of pathogens that cause disease is on the rise, threatening the health of both humans and wildlife. There may be extinctions due to disease.

Direct Value of Biodiversity

Various species perform useful services for humans and contribute greatly to the value of biodiversity. The direct value of wildlife species is related to their medicinal value, agricultural value, and consumptive use value.

Medicinal Value

Most of the prescription drugs used in the United States, valued at over $200 billion, were originally derived from living organisms. The rosy periwinkle (Fig. 25.17*a*) from Madagascar is an excellent example of a tropical plant that has provided us with useful medicines.

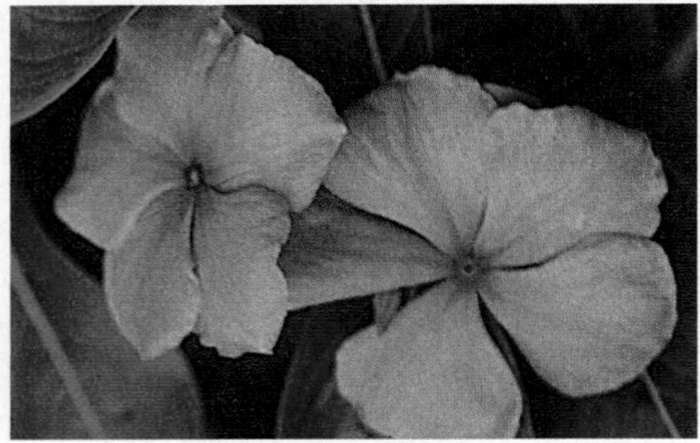

a.

b.

Figure 25.17 **Direct value of wildlife.**
Many wild species have a significant monetary value to humans.
a. The rosy periwinkle *(Catharansus roseus)* is a source of medicine.
b. The nine-banded armadillo *(Dasypus novemcinctus)* is used in medical research. The challenge is to manage these species correctly to ensure their continued survival.
(a): Steven P. Lynch; (b): Steve Bower/Shutterstock

Potent chemicals from this plant are now used to treat two forms of cancer: leukemia and Hodgkin's disease. Because of these drugs, the survival rate for childhood leukemia has risen from 10% to 90%, and Hodgkin's disease is now usually curable. Researchers estimate that hundreds of new drugs are yet to be found in tropical rain forests, and they may have an economic value of over $100 billion.

The antibiotic penicillin is derived from a fungus, and certain species of bacteria produce the antibiotics tetracycline and streptomycin. These drugs have proved to be indispensable in the treatment of bacterial infections.

Leprosy is among those diseases for which no cure is currently available. The bacterium that causes leprosy will not grow in laboratories, but scientists have discovered that it grows naturally in the nine-banded armadillo (Fig. 25.17*b*). Having a source for the bacterium may make it possible to find a cure for leprosy. The blood of horseshoe crabs, *Limulus,* contains a substance called limulus amoebocyte lysate, which is used to ensure that medical devices, such as pacemakers, surgical implants, and prosthetic devices, are free of bacteria.

The antibiotic penicillin is derived from a fungus, whereas certain species of bacteria produce the antibiotics tetracycline and streptomycin. These drugs have proved to be indispensable in the treatment of various diseases.

Agricultural Value

Crops such as wheat, corn, and rice are derived from wild plants that have been modified to be high producers. The same high-yield, genetically similar strains tend to be grown worldwide. At one time, rice crops in Africa were being devastated by a virus. Researchers grew wild rice plants from thousands of seed samples until they found one that contained a gene for resistance to the virus. These wild plants were then used in a breeding program to transfer the gene into high-yield rice plants. If this variety of wild rice had become extinct before being discovered, rice cultivation in Africa could have collapsed.

Animals are the main pollinators for flowering plants. The domesticated honeybee, *Apis mellifera,* pollinates billions of dollars' worth of food crops annually in the United States. Bats and other animals also contribute as pollinators (Fig. 25.18*a*). This dependency on a single species has inherent dangers: Colony collapse disorder has wiped out more than 30% of the commercial honeybee population in the United States. The USDA estimates that honeybee pollination supports $15 billion worth of agricultural production, including more than 130 different types of fruits and vegetables, per year. In order to find honeybees resistant to the mites, researchers must look to the wild populations.

Using natural pest controls is preferable to using chemical pesticides. When a rice pest called the brown planthopper became resistant to pesticides through natural selection, farmers began to use spiders, the natural predator of the brown planthopper, as a way of controlling population size. The economic savings were calculated at well over a billion dollars. Similarly, cotton growers in Cañete Valley, Peru, found that pesticides were no longer working against the cotton aphid because resistance had evolved in the aphid population. Researchers have identified the aphids' natural predators and are using them with great success (Fig. 25.18*b*).

a.

b.

Figure 25.18 Examples of the agricultural value of biodiversity.

a. Many species, including the long-nosed bat *(Leptonycteris curasoae),* are important pollinators. **b.** Ladybugs play a critical role in pest control.

(a): MerlinTuttle.org/Science Source; (b): D. Hurst/Alamy Stock Photo

Consumptive Use Value

We have had much success cultivating crops, keeping domesticated animals, growing trees in plantations, and so forth. However, aquaculture, the growing of fish and shellfish for human consumption, has contributed only minimally to our supply of seafood (Fig. 25.19). Instead, most freshwater and marine harvests depend on the harvesting of wild fish (e.g., trout and tuna), crustaceans (e.g., shrimps and crabs), and mammals (e.g., whales). These aquatic organisms are an invaluable source of biodiversity.

The environment provides all sorts of other products that are sold in the marketplace worldwide. Wild fruits and vegetables, skins, fibers, beeswax, and seaweed are only a few examples. Also, some people obtain their meat directly from the environment. The economic value of wild pigs in the diet of indigenous hunters in Sarawak, East Malaysia, has been calculated to be approximately $40 million per year.

Figure 25.19 The consumptive value of biodiversity.

Many wild species, such as these fish, are used as sources of food.

Monty Rakusen/Cultura/Getty Images

Similarly, many trees are still felled in the natural environment for their wood. Researchers have calculated that a species-rich forest in the Peruvian Amazon is worth far more if the forest is used for fruit and rubber production than for timber production. Fruit and the latex needed to produce rubber can be brought to market for an unlimited number of years. Once the trees are gone, fruit and latex cannot be harvested until new trees replace those that have been taken.

Indirect Value of Biodiversity

To bring about the preservation of wildlife, it is necessary to make more people aware of the indirect or unseen value of biodiversity, as well as the direct value. If we want to preserve wildlife, it is more economical to save ecosystems than to focus on individual species. Ecosystems perform many useful services for humans. These services are said to be indirect because they are pervasive, and it is not easy to calculate a dollar amount associated with them. Our very survival depends on the functions that ecosystems perform for us. The indirect value of biodiversity can be associated with the following services.

Waste Disposal

Decomposers break down dead organic matter and other types of wastes into inorganic nutrients. The nutrients are then used by the producers within ecosystems. This function aids humans immensely, because we dump millions of tons of waste material into natural ecosystems each year. Waste would soon cover the entire surface of our planet without decomposition. We can build expensive sewage treatment plants, but few of them break down solid wastes completely to inorganic nutrients. It is less expensive and more efficient to water plants and trees with partially treated wastewater and let soil bacteria cleanse it completely.

Biological communities are also capable of breaking down and immobilizing pollutants such as heavy metals and pesticides that humans release into the environment.

BIOLOGY TODAY ▶ Science

Bees Now Officially Listed as an Endangered Species

In 2017, the rusty patched bumble bee *(Bombus affinis)* was listed as endangered under the Endangered Species Act. This made it the first wild bee species in the continental United States to be listed as such. The listing comes in response to nearly a 90% decline in the bee's population and distribution since the late 1990s. Seven varieties of masked bees in Hawaii were also recently listed as endangered.

Rusty patched bumble bees, like their domesticated counterparts, are major pollinators of domesticated crops such as blueberries, cranberries, clover, and tomatoes, as well as many native plant species. Due to their importance as pollinators, they are considered a keystone species in a multitude of ecosystems. It is estimated that native insects, mostly bees, contribute nearly $3 billion worth of pollinating services per year in the United States.

Figure 25A Asian giant hornet.
The Asian giant hornet is a predator of many bee pollinator species.
Scott Camazine/Science Source

Changes in farming practices, diseases, pesticide use, habitat loss, and degradation, as well as climate change, are contributing to declining bee populations. In 2019, *Vespa mandarinia,* the Asian giant hornet, made its first appearance in North America. Asian giant hornets are equipped with biting mouthparts that enable them to decapitate their prey (Fig. 25A). They will also mark the entrance to a honeybee hive with a pheromone to attract other giant hornets. A band of hornets can quickly overwhelm a bee colony, killing all of the adult bees, and saving the bee larvae to use as a food source for the larvae of the hornets.

Scientists believe it is not just one, but rather a combination of factors that are stressing bee colonies. Stress makes the bees vulnerable to infection by different parasites and pathogens. The indiscriminate use of pesticides (specifically, neonicotinoids), the strain of being moved from place to place to pollinate crops, and/or poor nutrition (because genetically engineered plants don't provide as much food for the bees) may also be contributing to colony losses among bees.

A wide variety of efforts are underway to help reverse the potential extinction of both wild and domesticated bee populations. Service programs are working on ways to assess, protect, and restore the bee populations along with their habitats. The planting of pollinator-friendly vegetation, providing natural habitat areas, and decreasing the use of pesticides and chemical fertilizers are ways in which individuals can make a difference. Ideally, with enough global effort, bee populations will be stabilized and increased.

Within the honeybee industry, there is an effort to crossbreed various strains of honeybees. The goal is to produce bees that have increased honey production and are resistant to many of the pathogens decimating bee populations. The negative of crossbreeding is that it may lead to an increase in aggressive behavior and the tendency to swarm. The original genetics of the bee strain may also be lost if crossbreeding occurs too often.

The extinction of bees will lead to a decrease in food security for humans, as well as a significant disruption to the stability of native ecosystems. If everyone makes a small effort to help bees, the environment and human society will both benefit.

Questions to Consider

1. Is it more important to conserve the wild bee or domesticated bee populations?
2. What threat facing honeybees should be dealt with first?

Provision of Fresh Water

Few terrestrial organisms are adapted to living in a salty environment. They need fresh water. The water cycle continually supplies fresh water to terrestrial ecosystems. Humans use fresh water in innumerable ways, including for drinking and irrigation of crops. Freshwater ecosystems, such as rivers and lakes, also provide us with fish and other types of organisms for food.

Unlike other commodities, there is no substitute for fresh water. We can remove salt from seawater to obtain fresh water, but the cost of desalinization is about four to eight times the average cost of fresh water acquired via the water cycle.

BIOLOGY TODAY ▶ Science

Using Science to Save Jaguars

Jaguars *(Panthera onca)* (Fig. 25B) are the third-largest cats in the world, behind lions and tigers. They are the largest cats in the Western Hemisphere. Historically, they have ranged from the southwestern United States through the Amazon basin and south to Argentina. Currently, jaguars are estimated to occupy only 51% of their historic range, with only Central American countries and the Amazon making up their current range.

Detailed genetic analysis of jaguar DNA has indicated that whether they live in Mexico, Argentina, or anywhere in between, jaguars are all the same species. Previous studies based on their physical features indicated that there were several subspecies of jaguars across their range. This new genetic analysis shows that, historically, jaguars have had a large-scale gene flow across their range. This gene flow helps decrease the potential for speciation to occur. Jaguars are the only wide-ranging carnivore in the world that shows genetic continuity across their entire range. This genetic information led to the formation of the Jaguar Corridor Initiative (JCI), whose goal is to create a genetic corridor (a habitat corridor that allows gene flow) that links jaguar populations in all of the 18 countries in Latin America, from Mexico to Argentina, in the hope of ensuring the survival of this species.

They are classified as Near Threatened by the International Union for Conservation of Nature (IUCN) due to a 20–25% decline in their population over the past three generations. Jaguars are top-level predators that require extensive territories and a large diversity of prey. Their diet has been found to contain over 85 prey species that include mammals, reptiles, and birds. Unfortunately, if their natural prey base declines or if the cats are injured, jaguars will often turn to killing domestic livestock. This is when they frequently become "conflict jaguars," which are often killed by ranchers.

Sharon Matola, the founding director of the Belize Zoo, established the Problem Jaguar Rehabilitation Program. When a jaguar becomes a conflict jaguar, the Belize Zoo, the government of Belize, and the U.S. Fish and Wildlife Service will work together to trap the big cat. The jaguar is then transferred to the zoo where it enters the Problem Jaguar Rehabilitation Program. The cats will move through a series of phases to acclimate them to life in captivity. Once successfully trained, some of the cats are used as "ambassadors" of their species to help educate the tens of thousands of visitors to the Belize Zoo every year.

Figure 25B **DNA analysis helps preserve biodiversity.** Conservation of jaguars is being aided by DNA analysis.
Photodisc/Getty Images

Preserving habitat is a critical step in preventing species from extinction. Matola and the Belize Zoo, through a fundraising campaign, were able to purchase 950 acres of critical habitat in the Mayan Forest Corridor. This habitat surrounds the Belize Zoo and adjoins a 1,700-acre conservation parcel comprised of over 2,800 acres of protected habitat. With deforestation and encroachment by humans increasing, these protected areas provide important habitats for a wide variety of rare and endangered wildlife, including the jaguar.

1. How might DNA analysis be used to prevent the poaching of endangered species?
2. Should international groups be responsible for preserving habitat in developing countries in order to save endangered species?

Forests and other natural ecosystems exert a "sponge effect." They soak up water and then release it at a steady rate. When rain falls in a natural area, plant foliage and dead leaves lessen its impact, and the soil slowly absorbs it, especially if it has been aerated by soil organisms. The water-holding capacity of forests reduces the possibility of flooding. The value of a marshland outside Boston, Massachusetts, has been estimated at $72,000 per hectare per year, solely for its ability to reduce floods. Forests release water slowly for days or weeks after the rains have ceased. Rivers flowing through forests in West Africa release twice as much water halfway through the dry season, and between three and five times as much at the end of the dry season, as do rivers from agricultural lands.

Prevention of Soil Erosion

Intact ecosystems naturally retain soil and prevent soil erosion. The importance of this ecosystem attribute is especially observed following deforestation. The world's largest earth-filled dam, the Tarbela Dam in Pakistan, is losing its storage capacity of 12 billion cubic meters (m^3) many years sooner than expected. Deforestation is causing silt to build up behind the dam, decreasing its storage capacity. Similarly, the Republic of the Philippines used to export

$100 million worth of oysters, mussels, clams, and cockles each year. Now, silt carried down rivers following deforestation is smothering the mangrove ecosystem that serves as a nursery for these shellfish. Because of deforestation and myriad other environmental problems, most coastal ecosystems are not as bountiful as they once were.

Biogeochemical Cycles

We saw in Section 24.2 that ecosystems are characterized by energy flow and chemical cycling. The biodiversity within ecosystems contributes to the workings of the water, phosphorus, nitrogen, carbon, and other biogeochemical cycles. We depend on these cycles for fresh water, the provision of phosphate, uptake of excess soil nitrogen, and the removal of carbon dioxide from the atmosphere. When human activities upset the usual workings of biogeochemical cycles, the dire environmental consequences include the release of excess pollutants that are harmful to us. Technology is unable to substitute for any of the biogeochemical cycles.

Regulation of Climate

At the local level, trees provide shade and reduce the need for fans and air conditioners during the summer, decreasing a homeowner's electric bill. In a rain forest, transpiration from the trees helps maintain area rainfall. The trees form an important part of the water cycle (see Section 24.3), and without them, the disruptions would result in the transformation of the rain forest into a more arid ecosystem.

Globally, forests stabilize the climate, because they take up carbon dioxide. The leaves of trees use carbon dioxide when they photosynthesize, and the bodies of the trees store carbon. When trees are cut and burned, carbon dioxide is released into the atmosphere. Carbon dioxide makes a significant contribution to climate change, which is expected to be stressful for many plants and animals. Only a small percentage of wildlife will be able to move to new areas where the weather will be suitable for them.

Ecotourism

Almost everyone prefers to vacation in the beauty of a natural ecosystem. In the United States, nearly 100 million people vacation in natural settings every year. To do so, they spend billions of dollars annually on fees, travel, lodging, and food. Many tourists want to go sport fishing, whale watching, boating, hiking, birdwatching, and the like. With 1,200 miles of sandy beaches and over 86 million tourists a year, tourism generates $67 billion a year for Florida's economy. Many underdeveloped countries in tropical regions take advantage of this by offering "ecotours" of the local biodiversity. Providing guided tours of forests is more profitable than destroying them.

CHECK YOUR PROGRESS 25.3

1. Describe the factors contributing to the current extinction crisis.
2. Summarize the direct and indirect benefits of preserving wildlife.
3. Discuss the importance of biodiversity to human society.

CONNECTING THE CONCEPTS

For more information on the topics presented in this section, refer to the following discussions:

Section 24.1 explores the importance of biodiversity to terrestrial food webs.

Section 24.3 examines the water, carbon, nitrogen, and phosphorus cycles.

25.4 Working Toward a Sustainable Society

LEARNING OUTCOMES

Upon completion of this section, you should be able to

1. Describe the characteristics of a sustainable society.
2. Identify methods of developing sustainability in rural and urban environments.
3. List the methods of determining economic well-being and quality of life.

A society is said to be **sustainable** if it can provide the same level of goods and services for future generations as it does for the current one, while maintaining biodiversity.

To achieve a sustainable society, resource consumption cannot be greater than resource replenishment. In particular, future generations need clean air and water, an adequate amount of food, and enough space to live in. This goal is not possible unless we carefully regulate our consumption of resources today, taking into consideration that the human population is still increasing.

Today's Unsustainable Society

Together, population growth in the LDCs and the excessive resource consumption of the MDCs have created a strain on the environment. Sustainability is incompatible with the current level of consumption of resources and the level of waste produced by the MDCs. Population growth in the LDCs and overconsumption of resources by the MDCs account for many of the problems we are facing today (Fig. 25.20).

At present, a considerable proportion of land is being used for human purposes (such as homes, agriculture, and factories). Agriculture uses large inputs of fossil fuels, fertilizer, and pesticides, which create a large amount of pollution. More fresh water is used for agriculture than in homes. Almost half the agricultural yield in the United States goes toward feeding animals. According to the ten-to-one rule of thumb, it takes 10 lb of grain to grow 1 lb of meat for consumption. Therefore, it is environmentally unsustainable for citizens in MDCs to eat as much meat as they do.

Humans obtain fresh water from surface water and groundwater to raise animals and crops. Available supplies of fresh water are dwindling, and the remaining groundwater is in danger of being contaminated. Sewage and animal wastes wash into bodies of surface water and cause overenrichment, which robs aquatic animals of the oxygen they need to survive.

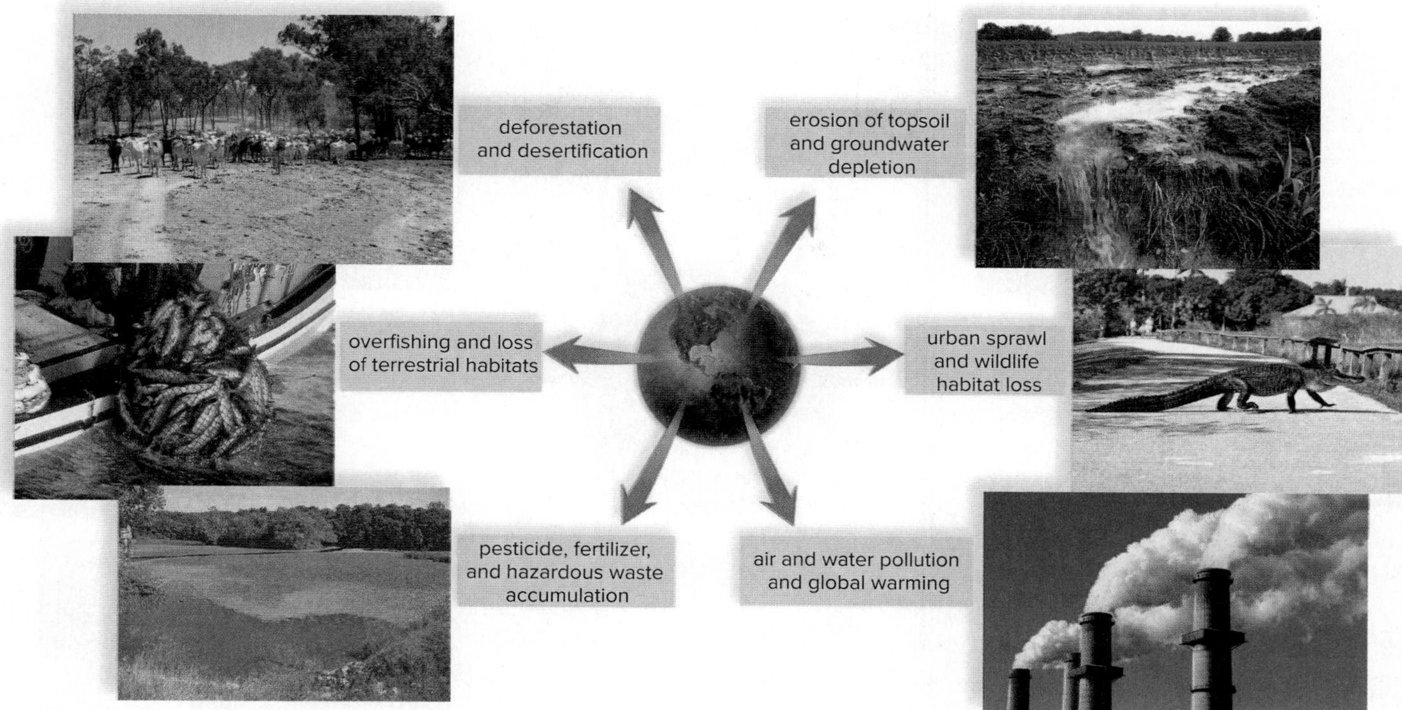

Figure 25.20 Characteristics of an unsustainable society.
Arrows point outward to signify that these types of activities reduce the sustainability of the Earth's ecosystems.
(deforestation): Mangiwau/Moment/Getty Images; (overfishing): Kevin Fleming/Corbis/VCG/Getty Images; (pond): Pat Watson/McGraw Hill; (erosion): Photo by Lynn Betts, USDA Natural Resources Conservation Service; (habitat loss): Alexander Yates/Moment Open/Getty Images; (pollution): Larry Lee Photography/Corbis/Getty Images

Our society primarily uses nonrenewable fossil-fuel energy, which leads to climate change, acid deposition, and smog, resulting in weakened ecosystems. The demand for goods has increased to the point that facilities are strained trying to meet the demand. Construction of improved infrastructure to support increased transportation needs only increases the use of nonrenewable energy resources. LDCs have increased needs for energy, making it imperative for the MDCs to develop renewable energy sources.

The human population is expanding into all regions of the planet, so habitats for other species are being lost, resulting in a significant extinction of wildlife.

Characteristics of a Sustainable Society

A natural ecosystem can offer clues about how to make today's society sustainable. A natural ecosystem uses only solar energy, which is renewable. Its materials cycle through the various populations back to the producer once again. For example, coral reefs have been sustaining themselves for millions of years. At the same time, the reefs have provided sustenance to the LDCs. The value of coral reefs has been assessed at over $300 billion a year, and their aesthetic value is immeasurable.

It is clear that if we want to develop a sustainable society, we need to use renewable energy sources and recycle materials. We should protect natural ecosystems that help sustain our modern society. While coral reefs may be more highly protected near the coasts of MDCs due to a greater availability of conservation resources, unsustainable practices remain a threat. The good news is that reefs are remarkably regenerative and will return to their former condition if left alone for a long enough period of time. The message of today's environmentalists is about what can be done to improve matters and use sustainable practices (Fig. 25.21). There is still time to make changes and improvements.

Sustainability should be practiced in as many areas of human endeavor as possible, from agriculture to business enterprises. Efficiency is the key to sustainability. For example, an efficient car should be ultralight and fuel efficient. Efficient cars could be just as durable and speedy as today's inefficient cars. Only through efficiency and conservation can we meet the challenges of limited resources and a growing human population in the future.

People generally live in either the country or the city, but rural and urban systems are interdependent. Achieving sustainability requires that we understand how the two kinds of regions are interconnected. Because they are linked, one region can be sustainable only if the other is. What happens in one ultimately affects the other. Let's consider, therefore, the importance of both rural and urban sustainability.

Rural Sustainability

In rural areas, we must put the emphasis on preservation. We need to preserve both terrestrial ecosystems (such as forests and prairies) and aquatic ecosystems (freshwater ecosystems and brackish ones along the coast). We should also preserve agricultural lands and other areas that provide us with renewable resources.

It is imperative that we take all possible steps to preserve what remains of our topsoil and replant areas with native plants. Native grasses stabilize the soil, restore soil nutrients, and can serve as a

Figure 25.21 **Characteristics of a sustainable society.**
Arrows point inward to signify that these types of activities increase the carrying capacity of the Earth.
(farming): Inga Spence/Alamy Stock Photo; (wetland preservation): Peter DeJong/AP Images; (recycling): Rawpixel.com/Shutterstock; (pest management): Perennou Nuridsany/Science Source; (temperature control): Emilio Ambasz (American architect born 1943)/Kenichi Yamada/yyama3270/123RF; (mass transit): LusoEnvironment/Alamy Stock Photo

source of renewable biofuel. Native trees can be planted as a wind break, to protect the soil from erosion, and provide habitat for wildlife. Creative solutions are needed to help solve today's ecological problems.

Here are some other ways to help make rural areas sustainable:

- Plant *cover crops,* which often are a mixture of legumes and grasses, to stabilize the soil between rows of cash crops or between seasonal plantings of cash crops.
- Use *multi-use farming* by planting a variety of crops and use a variety of farming techniques to increase the amount of organic matter in the soil.
- Replenish soil nutrients through composting, organic gardening, or other self-renewable methods.
- Use low-flow or trickle irrigation, retention ponds, and other water-conserving methods.
- Increase the planting of *cultivars* (plants that have undergone selective breeding for desirable traits) that are resistant to blight, rust, insect damage, salt, drought, and encroachment by noxious weeds.
- Use *precision farming (PF)* techniques that rely on accumulated knowledge to reduce habitat destruction and improve crop yields.
- Use *integrated pest management (IPM),* which encourages the growth of competitive beneficial insects and uses biological controls to reduce the abundance of pest populations.
- Plant a variety of species, including native plants, to reduce dependence on traditional crops.
- Plant *multipurpose trees*—trees with the ability to provide numerous products and perform a variety of functions, in addition to serving as windbreakers (Fig. 25.22). Remember that mature trees can provide many types of products. For example, mature rubber trees provide rubber, and tagua nuts are an excellent substitute for ivory.

Figure 25.22 **The roles of trees in a sustainable society.**
Trees planted by a farmer as a wind break and to prevent soil erosion can also have other purposes, such as supplying nuts and fruits.
Photo by Erwin Cole, USDA Natural Resources Conservation Service

- Maintain and restore wetlands, especially in hurricane- or tsunami-prone areas. Protect deltas from storm damage. By protecting wetlands, we protect the spawning grounds for many valuable fish nurseries.
- Use renewable forms of energy, such as wind and biofuels.
- Support local farmers to reduce the environmental impact of transporting goods over long distances.

Urban Sustainability

More and more people are moving to urban environments. Much thought needs to be given to how to serve the needs of new arrivals without increasing urban spread. Resources need to be shared in a way that will allow urban sustainability. Here are some other ways to help make a city sustainable:

- Design an energy-efficient transportation system to rapidly move people about.
- Heat buildings using solar or geothermal energy. Cool them with an air-conditioning system that uses seawater. In general, use conservation methods to regulate the temperature of buildings.
- Use *green roofs*. Grow a garden of grasses, herbs, and vegetables on the tops of buildings. This will assist with temperature control, supply food, reduce the amount of rainwater runoff, and be visually appealing (Fig. 25.23).
- Improve storm-water management by using storm-drain sediment traps, artificial wetlands, and holding ponds. For walking paths, parking lots, and roads, replace concrete and asphalt with porous surfaces that reflect less heat and help rainwater soak into the ground, reducing runoff.
- Replace grass with native plant species that attract bees and butterflies and require less water and fewer fertilizers.

Figure 25.23 A green roof.
A green roof has plants growing on it that help control temperature, supply food, and reduce water runoff.
Diane Cook and Len Jenshel/Getty Images

- Create *greenbelts*. Include plenty of paths for walking and bicycling.
- Revitalize old sections of a city before developing new sections.
- Use lighting fixtures that hug the walls or ground and send light downward, to reduce light pollution at night. Control noise levels by designing quiet motors and sound-absorbing construction materials.
- Promote sustainability by encouraging the recycling of business equipment. Use low-maintenance building materials rather than wood.

Assessing Economic Well-Being and Quality of Life

The gross national product (GNP) is a measure of the flow of money from consumers to businesses in the form of goods and services purchased. It can also be considered the total costs of all manufacturing, production, and services. Costs include salaries and wages, mortgage and rent, interest and loans, taxes, and profit within and outside the country. In other words, GNP pertains solely to economic activities.

When calculating GNP, economists do not necessarily consider whether an activity is environmentally or socially harmful. For example, destruction of forests due to clear-cutting, strip mining, or land development is not a part of the GNP. In the same way, the cost of medical services does not include the pain or suffering caused by illness.

Our quality of life is most likely better revealed by measures that include noneconomic indicators other than by the GNP. The index of sustainable economic welfare (ISEW) includes real per capita income, distributional equity, natural resources depletion, environmental damage, and the value of unpaid labor. The ISEW *does* take into account other forms of value, beyond the purely monetary value of goods and services. Another such index is called the genuine progress indicator (GPI). This indicator attempts to consider quality of life, an attribute that does not necessarily depend on worldly goods. For example, the quality of life might depend on how much respect we give other humans. The Grameen Bank in Bangladesh decided to loan women small amounts of money to start up small businesses. The loans give women the opportunity to make choices that can improve the quality of their lives. For these women, a loan is a way to sustain their lives while, in part, fulfilling their dreams.

It is difficult to assign a value to well-being or happiness, but some economists are trying to devise ways to do so. The following criteria, among others, can be used.

- *Use value:* the monetary price we pay to use or consume a resource, such as the entrance fees into national parks
- *Option value:* preserving options for the future, such as saving a wetland or a forest
- *Existence value:* saving things we might not yet realize exist. This might be flora and fauna in a tropical rain forest that could be the source of new drugs in the future.
- *Aesthetic value:* appreciating an area or a creature for its beauty and/or contribution to biodiversity

- *Cultural value:* factors such as language, mythology, and history that are important for cultural identity
- *Scientific and educational value:* valuing the knowledge of naturalists, or even an experience of nature, as a type of rational fact

Humans will continue to develop the environment. If we are wise, we can use these values to help us direct future development. Growth creates increases in demand, but smart development includes sustainable growth. If we permit unbridled growth, resources will become depleted. If development restrains resource consumption while promoting economic growth, perhaps a balance can be reached. We can then preserve resources for future generations.

Each person has a particular comfort level, and humans do not like to make sacrifices that reduce their particular comfort level. Thus, despite our knowledge of the need to protect fisheries and forests, we continue to exploit them. People in LDCs directly depend on these resources to survive and therefore have much to lose, so it is difficult for them to sacrifice today for the sake of the future. There is still hope, though, because nature is incredibly resilient. One solution to deforestation is reforestation—for example, Costa Rica has been successfully reforesting its country since the early 1980s. Also, declining fisheries can be restocked and then managed for sustainability. It will take an informed citizenry, creativity, and a willingness to bring about change for the better to move toward sustainability.

BIOLOGY IN YOUR LIFE

What simple things can you do to conserve energy or water and help decrease environmental problems, such as global warming?

The following are a few easy things you can do:

- Change the lightbulbs in your home to compact fluorescent CFC (bulbs) and LED lights. They use 75–80% less electricity than incandescent bulbs.
- Walk, ride your bike, carpool, or use mass transit.
- Get cloth or mesh bags for groceries and other purchases. Plastic bags may take 10–20 years to degrade. They're also dangerous to wildlife that mistake the bags for food and consume them.
- Turn off the water while you brush your teeth. If you don't finish a bottle of water, use it to water your plants. In dry climates, plant native plants that won't require frequent watering.

CHECK YOUR PROGRESS 25.4

1. Describe the characteristics of today's society that make it unsustainable.
2. Discuss what changes are needed to convert today's society into one that is sustainable.
3. Summarize how scientists assess economic well-being and quality of life.

CONNECTING THE CONCEPTS

For more information on the material presented in this section, refer to the following discussions:

Section 24.2 describes how the 10% rule relates to energy flow in an ecosystem.

Section 24.3 examines human influence on the major biogeochemical cycles.

CONCLUSION

Climate change is considered an existential threat to humankind. It is having an impact upon every region of the planet and all human life will be affected by it.

The scientific community has identified the major challenges we will face as a society in the near future. The average global temperature will rise by 2.5–10 degrees Fahrenheit, leading to more extreme weather events. Coastal regions will be more likely to flood while experiencing more intense hurricanes. The interior of continents are projected to experience more extreme precipitation events, along with more severe droughts.

Overall, climate change is projected to cost humans hundreds of billions of dollars annually. Each of us needs to take an individual responsibility and make small changes to our lifestyles that will have environmental benefits. Collectively, we can make a difference and preserve the planet for future generations.

SUMMARIZE

25.1 Human Population Growth

- The **growth rate** of the human population displays **exponential growth,** which is represented on a graph by a steep curve upward.
- The **biotic potential** is the maximum growth rate for a population. The biotic potential is normally held in check by environmental resistance. This determines the **carrying capacity** of an ecosystem.
- Age structure diagrams can be used to predict population growth. MDCs are approaching a stable population size. LDC populations will continue to increase in size even if they experience **replacement reproduction.**

25.2 Human Use of Resources and Pollution

The ecological footprint of an individual represents the total resources needed to meet their needs. Five resources are maximally used by humans:

(land): Budimir Jevtic/Shutterstock; (water): ©Evelyn Jo Johnson; (food): John Thoeming/McGraw Hill; (energy): Geniusksy/Shutterstock; (minerals): TTstudio/Shutterstock

Resources are either nonrenewable or renewable.

- **Nonrenewable resources** are not replenished and are limited in quantity (e.g., land, **fossil fuels,** minerals).
- **Renewable resources** are replenished but still are limited in quantity (e.g., water, solar energy, food).

Land

Human activities, such as habitation, farming, and mining, contribute to erosion, **pollution, desertification, deforestation,** and loss of biodiversity.

Water

Industry and agriculture use most of the freshwater supply. Water supplies are increased by damming rivers and drawing from **aquifers.** As aquifers are depleted, **subsidence, sinkhole** formation, and **saltwater intrusion** can occur. If used by industries, water conservation methods could cut world water consumption by half.

Food

Food comes from growing crops, raising animals, and fishing.

- Modern farming methods increase the food supply, but some methods harm the land, pollute water, and consume fossil fuels excessively.
- Genetically engineered plants increase the food supply and reduce the need for chemicals.
- Raising livestock contributes to water pollution and uses fossil-fuel energy.
- The increased number and high efficiency of fishing boats have caused the world fish catch to decline.

Energy

Fossil fuels (oil, natural gas, coal) are nonrenewable sources. Burning fossil fuels and burning to clear land for farming cause pollutants and gases to enter the air.

- **Greenhouse gases** include CO_2 and other gases. Greenhouse gases cause global warming, because solar radiation can pass through them but infrared heat cannot escape back into space.
- Renewable resources include hydropower, and geothermal, wind, and solar power.

Minerals

Minerals are nonrenewable resources that can be mined. These raw materials include sand, gravel, phosphate, and metals. Mining causes destruction of the land by erosion, loss of vegetation, and toxic **agricultural runoff** into bodies of water. Some metals are dangerous to health. Land ruined by mining can take years to recover.

Hazardous Wastes

Billions of tons of solid waste are discarded on land and in water.

- Heavy metals include lead, arsenic, cadmium, and chromium.
- Synthetic organic chemicals include **chlorofluorocarbons (CFCs),** which are involved in the production of plastics, pesticides, herbicides, and other products.
- Ozone shield destruction is associated with CFCs.
- Other synthetic organic chemicals enter the aquatic food chain, where the toxins become more concentrated **(biological magnification).**

25.3 Biodiversity

Biodiversity is the variety of life on Earth.

Loss of Biodiversity

The five major causes of biodiversity loss and extinction are:

- Habitat loss
- Introduction of **alien species** and **invasive** species
- Pollution
- Overexploitation of plants and animals
- Disease

Direct Value of Biodiversity

Direct values of biodiversity are:

- Medicinal value (medicines derived from living organisms)
- Agricultural value (crops derived from wild plants, biological pest controls, and animal pollinators)
- Consumptive use values (food production)

Indirect Value of Biodiversity

Biodiversity in ecosystems contributes to:

- Waste disposal (through the action of decomposers and the ability of natural communities to purify water and take up pollutants)
- Freshwater provision through the water biogeochemical cycle
- Prevention of soil erosion, which occurs naturally in intact ecosystems
- Function of biogeochemical cycles
- Climate regulation (plants take up carbon dioxide)
- Ecotourism (human enjoyment of a beautiful ecosystem)

25.4 Working Toward a Sustainable Society

A **sustainable** society would use only renewable energy sources, would reuse heat and waste materials, and would recycle almost everything. It would also provide the same goods and services presently provided and would preserve biodiversity.

BioNOW

Want to know how this science is relevant to your life? Check out the BioNOW video below.

- Biodiversity

McGraw Hill

What was the effect of the exotic (alien) species on the biodiversity? Why do you think this was the case?

THINKING CRITICALLY

1. What environmental reasons would you give a friend for becoming a vegetarian?
2. How would failure to recycle items that can be recycled (they end up in a landfill) affect the nutrient cycles, such as the carbon cycle covered in Section 24.3?
3. a. What types of environmental activities or initiatives (Earth Day festivities, recycling program, etc.) are in place at your school?
   b. How could you increase awareness of environmental issues on your campus?

MAKING IT RELEVANT

1. With human population growth being one of the most important contributing factors to climate change, do you think people should be limited to the number of children they should be allowed to have?
2. What level of recycling does your household, workplace, and community participate in? Is there a cost to recycle or do you receive payment for recycling certain items?
3. Is it more important to protect biodiversity or allow humans to develop native ecosystems for economic gain?

Find answers to all of the chapter questions at connect.mheducation.com

Periodic Table of the Elements

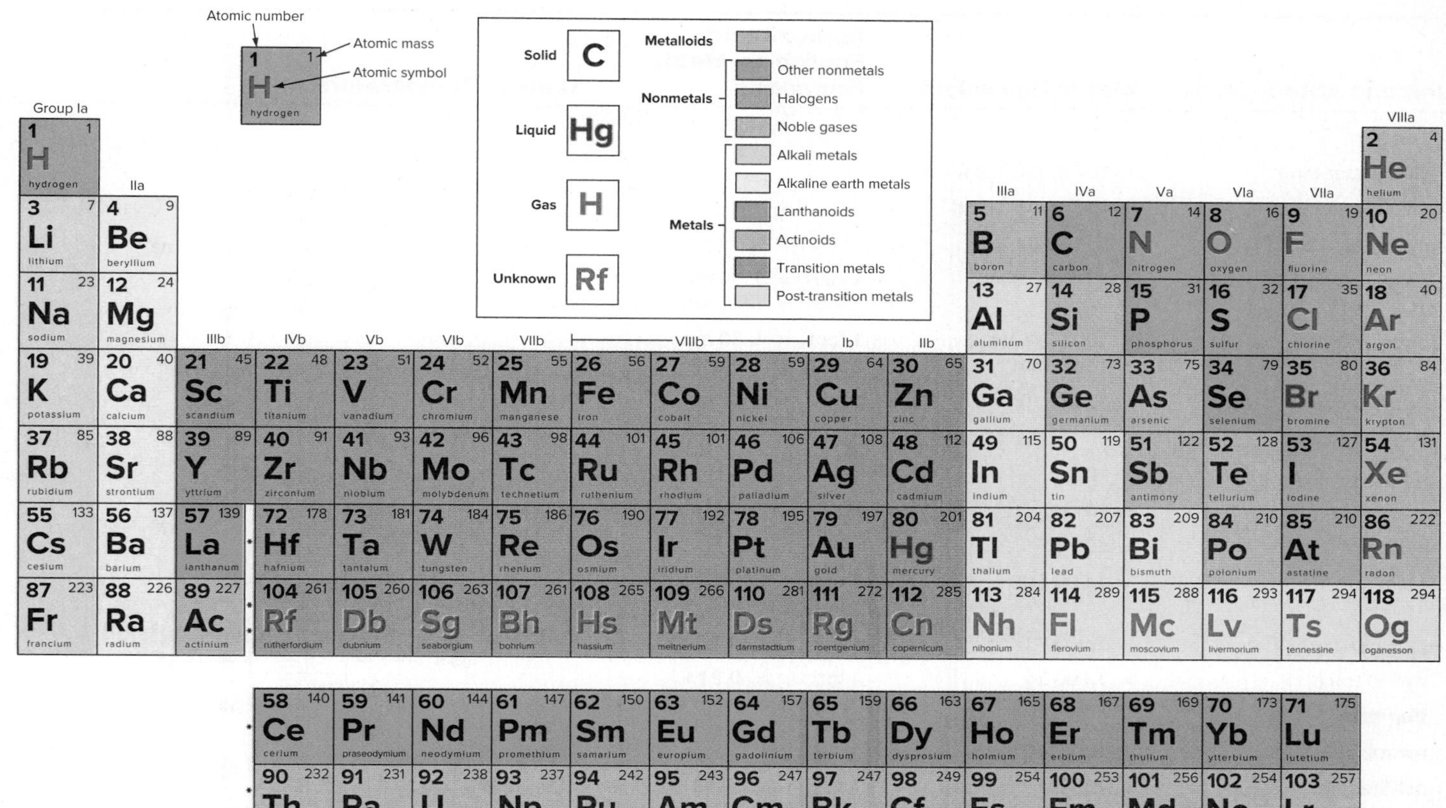

Metric System

Unit and Abbreviation	Metric Equivalent	Approximate English-to-Metric Equivalents
Length		
nanometer (nm)	$= 10^{-9}$ m (10^{-3} µm)	
micrometer (µm)	$= 10^{-6}$ m (10^{-3} mm)	
millimeter (mm)	= 0.001 (10^{-3}) m	
centimeter (cm)	= 0.01 (10^{-2}) m	1 inch = 2.54 cm 1 foot = 30.5 cm
meter (m)	= 100 (10^{2}) cm = 1,000 mm	1 foot = 0.30 m 1 yard = 0.91 m
kilometer (km)	= 1,000 (10^{3}) m	1 mi = 1.6 km
Weight (mass)		
nanogram (ng)	$= 10^{-9}$ g	
microgram (µg)	$= 10^{-6}$ g	
milligram (mg)	$= 10^{-3}$ g	
gram (g)	= 1,000 mg	1 ounce = 28.3 g 1 pound = 454 g
kilogram (kg)	= 1,000 (10^{3}) g	= 0.45 kg
metric ton (t)	= 1,000 kg	1 ton = 0.91 t
Volume		
microliter (µl)	$= 10^{-6}$ l (10^{-3} ml)	
milliliter (ml)	$= 10^{-3}$ l = 1 cm^3 (cc) = 1,000 mm^3	1 tsp = 5 ml 1 fl oz = 30 ml
liter (l)	= 1,000 ml	1 pint = 0.47 l 1 quart = 0.95 l 1 gallon = 3.79 l
kiloliter (kl)	= 1,000 l	

°C	°F	
100	212	Water boils at standard temperature and pressure.
71	160	Flash pasteurization of milk
54	130	Highest recorded temperature in the world, Death Valley, August 2020
41	105.8	Average body temperature of a marathon runner in hot weather
37	98.6	Human body temperature
13.7	56.66	Human survival is still possible at this body temperature.
0	32.0	Water freezes at standard temperature and pressure.

Units of Temperature

To convert temperature scales:

$$°C = \frac{(°F - 32)}{1.8}$$

$$°F = 1.8(°C) + 32$$

Glossary

A

absorption Taking in of substances by cells or membranes.

acetylcholine (ACh) Neurotransmitter active in both the peripheral and central nervous systems.

acetylcholinesterase (AChE) Enzyme that breaks down acetylcholine bound to postsynaptic receptors within a synapse.

acid Molecules that raise the hydrogen ion concentration in a solution and lower its pH numerically.

acid deposition The return to Earth in rain or snow of sulfate or nitrate salts of acids produced by commercial and industrial activities.

acidosis Excessive accumulation of acids in body fluids typically characterized by a fluid pH of less than 7.35.

acquired immunodeficiency syndrome (AIDS) Disease caused by HIV and transmitted via body fluids; characterized by failure of the immune system.

acromegaly Condition resulting from an increase in growth hormone production after adult height has been achieved.

actin One of two major proteins of muscle; makes up thin filaments in myofibrils of muscle fibers. *See also* **myosin.**

actin filament Cytoskeletal filaments of eukaryotic cells composed of the protein actin; also refers to the thin filaments of muscle cells.

action potential Electrochemical changes that take place across the axon membrane; the nerve impulse.

active immunity Resistance to disease due to the immune system's response to a microorganism or a vaccine.

active site Region of an enzyme where the substrate binds and where the reaction occurs.

active transport Movement of a molecule across a plasma membrane from an area of lower concentration to one of higher concentration; uses a carrier protein and energy.

acute bronchitis Infection of the primary and secondary bronchi.

adaptation Organism's modification in structure, function, or behavior suitable to the environment.

Addison's disease Condition resulting from a deficiency of adrenal cortex hormones; characterized by low blood glucose, weight loss, weakness, and bronzing of the skin.

adenine (A) One of four nitrogen bases in nucleotides composing the structure of DNA and RNA.

adhesion The ability of water molecules to adhere to polar surfaces due to hydrogen bonding.

adipocyte Cell that stores fat.

adipose tissue Connective tissue in which fat is stored.

ADP (adenosine diphosphate) Nucleotide with two phosphate groups that can accept another phosphate group and become ATP.

adrenal cortex Outer portion of the adrenal gland; secretes mineralocorticoids, such as aldosterone, and glucocorticoids, such as cortisol.

adrenal gland An endocrine gland that lies atop a kidney; consisting of the inner adrenal medulla and the outer adrenal cortex.

adrenal medulla Inner portion of the adrenal gland; secretes the hormones epinephrine and norepinephrine.

adrenocorticotropic hormone (ACTH) Hormone secreted by the anterior lobe of the pituitary gland that stimulates activity in the adrenal cortex.

aerobic Chemical process that requires oxygen.

afterbirth Placenta and the extraembryonic membranes, which are delivered (expelled) during the third stage of parturition.

agglutination Clumping of red blood cells due to a reaction between antigens on red blood cell plasma membranes and antibodies in the plasma.

aging Progressive changes over time, leading to loss of physiological function and eventual death.

agranular leukocyte White blood cell that does not contain distinctive granules.

agricultural runoff Water from precipitation and irrigation that flows over fields into bodies of water or aquifers.

albumin Plasma protein of the blood having transport and osmotic functions.

aldosterone Hormone secreted by the adrenal cortex that decreases sodium and increases potassium excretion; raises blood volume and pressure.

alkalosis Excessive accumulation of bases in body fluids typically characterized by a fluid pH of over 7.45.

allantois Extraembryonic membrane that contributes to the formation of umbilical blood vessels in humans.

allele Alternative form of a gene; alleles occur at the same locus on homologous chromosomes.

allergen Foreign substance capable of stimulating an allergic response.

allergy Immune response to substances, such as pollen, food, or animal hair, that ordinarily would do no harm to the body.

alveoli (sing., alveolus) Microscopic air sacs in a lung; site of gas exchange.

amino acid Organic molecule having an amino group and an acid group, which covalently bonds to produce peptide molecules.

amnion Extraembryonic membrane that forms an enclosing, fluid-filled sac.

amygdala Portion of the limbic system that functions to add emotional overtones to memories.

amylase Enzyme that breaks down carbohydrates.

anabolic steroid Synthetic steroid that mimics the effect of testosterone.

anaerobic Chemical reaction that occurs in the absence of oxygen; examples are the fermentation reactions.

analogous structure Structure that has a similar function in separate lineages but differs in anatomy and ancestry.

anaphase Mitotic phase during which daughter chromosomes move toward the poles of the spindle.

anaphylactic shock Severe systemic form of allergic reaction involving bronchiolar constriction, impaired breathing, vasodilation, and a rapid drop in blood pressure with a threat of circulatory failure.

androgen General term for a male sex hormone (e.g., testosterone).

anemia Inefficient oxygen transport by the blood due to a shortage of hemoglobin.

aneurysm Saclike expansion of a blood vessel wall.

angina pectoris Condition characterized by thoracic pain resulting from occluded coronary arteries; precedes a heart attack.

angiogenesis Formation of new blood vessels; one characteristic of cancer.

angioplasty Surgical procedure for treating clogged arteries in which a plastic tube is threaded through a major blood vessel toward the heart and then a balloon at the end of the tube is inflated, forcing open the vessel. A stent is then placed in the vessel.

animals Multicellular eukaryotes that undergo development to achieve their final form. In general, animals are mobile organisms, characterized by the presence of muscular and nervous tissue. Animals acquire energy by ingesting other organisms.

anorexia nervosa Eating disorder characterized by a morbid fear of gaining weight.

anterior pituitary Portion of the pituitary gland controlled by the hypothalamus and that produces seven types of hormones, some of which control other endocrine glands.

anthropoid Group of primates that includes monkeys, apes, and humans.

antibiotic resistance A characteristic of pathogens that causes them to survive treatment with chemicals (antibiotics) that normally would kill them.

antibody Protein produced in response to the presence of an antigen; each antibody combines with a specific antigen.

antibody-mediated immunity Form of adaptive immunity where B lymphocytes (B cells) produce antibodies against specific antigens in the fluids of the body.

anticodon Three-base sequence in a tRNA molecule base that pairs with a complementary codon in mRNA.

antidiuretic hormone (ADH) Hormone secreted by the posterior pituitary that increases the permeability of the collecting ducts in a kidney.

antigen Foreign substance, usually a protein or a polysaccharide, that stimulates the immune system to produce antibodies.

antigen-presenting cell (APC) Cell that displays the antigen to the cells of the immune system so they can defend the body against that particular antigen.

anus Outlet of the digestive tract.

aorta Major systemic artery that receives blood from the left ventricle.

apoptosis Programmed cell death involving a cascade of specific cellular events leading to death and destruction of the cell.

appendicular skeleton Portion of the skeleton forming the pectoral girdles and upper extremities and the pelvic girdle and lower extremities.

appendix In humans, small, tubular appendage that extends outward from the cecum of the large intestine; composed of lymphoid tissue.

aquaporin Protein membrane channel through which water can diffuse.

aqueous humor Clear, watery fluid between the cornea and the lens of the eye.

aquifer Rock layers that contain water released in appreciable quantities to wells or springs.

ardipithecines Common name for species in the genus *Ardipithecus*, an early hominin.

arteriole Vessel that takes blood from an artery to capillaries.

arteriovenous shunt A pathway, usually abnormal, that connects an artery directly to a vein.

artery Vessel that transports blood from the heart.

artificial selection The intentional breeding of organisms for the selection of certain traits.

association area One of several regions of the cerebral cortex related to memory, reasoning, judgment, and emotional feelings.

asthma Condition in which bronchioles constrict and cause difficulty in breathing.

astigmatism Blurred vision due to an irregular curvature of the cornea or the lens.

atherosclerosis Condition in which fatty substances accumulate abnormally beneath the inner linings of the arteries.

atom Smallest particle of an element that displays the properties of the element.

atomic mass Mass of an atom equal to the number of protons plus the number of neutrons within the nucleus.

atomic number Number of protons within the nucleus of an atom.

ATP (adenosine triphosphate) Nucleotide with three phosphate groups. The breakdown of ATP into ADP + P_i makes energy available for energy-requiring processes in cells.

atria (sing. atrium) The upper chambers of the heart, either the left atrium or the right atrium, that receive blood.

atrial natriuretic hormone (ANH) Hormone secreted by the heart that increases sodium excretion and, therefore, lowers blood volume and pressure.

atrioventricular (AV) valve Valve located between the atrium and the ventricle.

auditory canal Curved tube extending from the pinna to the tympanic membrane that is lined with fine hairs and sweat glands.

auditory tube Extension from the middle ear to the nasopharynx that equalizes air pressure on the eardrum; also called the eustachian tube or pharyngotympanic tube.

australopithecine Any of the early hominins; classified into several species of *Australopithecus*.

autoimmune disease Disease that results when the immune system mistakenly attacks the body's tissues.

autonomic system Branch of the peripheral nervous system that regulates the activity of cardiac and smooth muscles, organs, and glands; consists of the sympathetic and parasympathetic systems.

autosome Any chromosome other than the sex chromosomes.

autotroph Organism that can capture energy and synthesize organic nutrients from inorganic nutrients.

AV (atrioventricular) node Small region of neuromuscular tissue that transmits impulses received from the sinoatrial node to the ventricles.

axial skeleton Portion of the skeleton that supports and protects the organs of the head, the neck, and the trunk.

axon Elongated portion of a neuron that conducts nerve impulses typically from the cell body to the synapse.

axon terminal Small swelling at the end of an axon. Location of vesicles that contain the neurotransmitters.

B

B cell (B lymphocyte) Lymphocyte that matures in the bone marrow and, when stimulated by the presence of a specific antigen, gives rise to antibody-producing plasma cells.

bacteria Members of one of three domains of life; prokaryotic cells other than archaea with unique genetic, biochemical, and physiological characteristics.

Barr body Dark-staining body (discovered by M. Barr) in the nuclei of female mammals that contains a condensed, inactive X chromosome.

basal nuclei Nerve cells that integrate motor commands to ensure balance and coordination.

base Molecule that lowers the hydrogen ion concentration in a solution and raises the pH numerically.

basement membrane Layer of nonliving material that anchors epithelial tissue to underlying connective tissue.

basophil White blood cell with granular cytoplasm; able to be stained with a basic dye.

bicarbonate ion Ion that participates in buffering the blood; the form in which carbon dioxide is transported in the bloodstream.

bile Secretion of the liver temporarily stored and concentrated in the gallbladder before being released into the small intestine, where it emulsifies fat.

bilirubin The yellow-orange bile pigment produced from the breakdown of hemoglobin.

binge-eating disorder Condition characterized by overeating episodes that are not followed by purging.

binomial name Two-part scientific name of an organism. The first part designates the genus, the second part the specific epithet.

biodiversity Total number of species, the variability of their genes, and the communities in which they live.

biogeochemical cycle Circulating pathway of elements such as carbon and nitrogen, involving abiotic exchange pools, storage areas, and biotic communities.

biogeography Study of the geographic distribution of organisms.

bioinformatics Computer technologies used to study the genome.

biological evolution Change in life that has taken place in the past and will take place in the future; includes descent from a common ancestor and adaptation to the environment.

biological magnification Process by which substances become more concentrated in organisms in the higher trophic levels of a food web.

biology Scientific study of life.

biomass The number of organisms multiplied by their weight.

biome A major regional community of organisms, characterized primarily by climate and the types of plant species present.

biosphere Zone of air, land, and water at the surface of the Earth in which living organisms are found.

biotechnology Scientific research that involves researching and producing commercial or agricultural products that are made with or derived from transgenic organisms.

biotic potential Maximum reproductive rate of an organism, given unlimited resources and ideal environmental conditions.

bipedal posture Ability to walk upright on two feet; characteristic of the hominins.

birth control method Prevents either fertilization or implantation of an embryo in the uterine lining.

birth control pill Oral contraceptive containing a combination of estrogen and/or progesterone.

blastocyst Early stage of human embryonic development that consists of a hollow, fluid-filled ball of cells.

blind spot Region of the retina lacking rods or cones where the optic nerve leaves the eye.

blood Type of connective tissue in which cells are separated by a liquid called plasma.

blood pressure Force of blood pushing against the inside wall of a vessel; measured as a ratio of systolic to diastolic pressure.

blood transfusion Introduction of whole blood or a blood component directly into the bloodstream.

body mass index (BMI) Calculation that uses an individual's height and weight to determine whether the individual is overweight or obese.

bolus Small lump of food that forms in the oral cavity before being swallowed.

bone remodeling Ongoing mineral deposits and withdrawals from bone that adjust bone strength and maintain levels of calcium and phosphorus in blood.

Boyle's Law Physical law that defines the relationship between pressure of a gas and the volume of the container.

brain Enlarged superior portion of the central nervous system located in the cranial cavity of the skull.

brain stem Portion of the brain consisting of the medulla oblongata, pons, and midbrain.

Braxton Hicks contractions Strong, late-term uterine contractions prior to cervical dilation; also called false labor.

Broca's area Region of the left frontal lobe that coordinates complex muscular actions of the mouth, tongue, and larynx, making speech possible.

bronchi (sing., bronchus) The two major divisions of the trachea leading to the lungs.

bronchioles Smaller air passages in the lungs that begin at the bronchi and terminate in alveoli.

buffer Substance or group of substances that tend to resist pH changes of a solution, thus stabilizing its relative acidity and basicity.

bulbourethral gland Either of two small structures located below the prostate gland in males; each adds secretions to semen.

bulimia nervosa Eating disorder characterized by binge eating followed by purging via self-induced vomiting or use of a laxative.

bursae (sing., bursa) Saclike, fluid-filled structures, lined with synovial membrane, that occur near a joint.

bursitis Inflammation of any of the friction-easing sacs called bursae within many types of synovial joints.

C

calcitonin Hormone secreted by the thyroid gland that increases the blood calcium level.

calorie Amount of heat energy required to raise the temperature of 1 g of water 1°C.

cancer Malignant tumor whose nondifferentiated cells exhibit loss of contact inhibition, uncontrolled growth, and the ability to invade tissue and metastasize.

capillaries Smallest of the blood vessels in the circulatory system; site of the majority of nutrient and fluid exchange with tissues.

capsule Gelatinous layer surrounding the cells of blue-green algae and certain bacteria.

carbaminohemoglobin Hemoglobin carrying carbon dioxide.

carbohydrate Class of organic compounds that includes monosaccharides, disaccharides, and polysaccharides.

carbonic anhydrase Enzyme in red blood cells that speeds the formation of carbonic acid from the reactants water and carbon dioxide.

carcinogen Environmental agent that causes mutations leading to the development of cancer.

carcinogenesis Development of cancer.

carcinoma Cancer arising in epithelial tissue.

cardiac cycle One complete cycle of systole and diastole for all heart chambers.

cardiac muscle Striated, involuntary muscle found only in the heart.

cardiovascular system Organ system in which blood vessels distribute blood powered by the pumping action of the heart.

carnivore Consumer in a food chain that eats other animals.

carrier Heterozygous individual who has no apparent abnormality but can pass on an allele for a recessively inherited genetic disorder.

carrying capacity Maximum number of individuals of any species that can be supported by a particular ecosystem on a long-term basis.

cartilage Connective tissue in which the cells lie within lacunae separated by a flexible proteinaceous matrix.

cecum Small pouch that lies below the entrance of the small intestine and is the blind end of the large intestine.

cell Fundamental unit of life. Smallest unit of biological organization that displays all the properties of life.

cell body Portion of a neuron that contains a nucleus and from which dendrites and an axon extend.

cell cycle Repeating sequence of cellular events that consists of interphase, mitosis, and cytokinesis.

cell theory One of the major theories of biology; states that all organisms are made up of cells and cells come only from preexisting cells.

cell wall Rigid, outermost layer of plant cells, bacteria, fungi, and some protists. Composed of complex carbohydrates such as cellulose.

cell-mediated immunity Form of adaptive immunity during which T lymphocytes (T cells) target cells that are presenting specific antigens.

cellular respiration Metabolic reactions that use the stored energy in carbohydrates, but also from fats or amino acids, to produce ATP molecules.

cellulose Polysaccharide that is the major complex carbohydrate in plant cell walls.

central nervous system (CNS) Portion of the nervous system consisting of the brain and spinal cord.

centriole Cellular structure, existing in pairs, that possibly organizes the mitotic spindle for chromosomal movement during mitosis and meiosis.

centromere Area of a chromosome where sister chromatids are held together.

centrosome Central microtubule organizing center of cells. In animal cells, it contains two centrioles.

cerebellum Part of the brain located under the occipital lobe of the cerebrum that coordinates skeletal muscles to produce smooth, graceful motions.

cerebral cortex Outer layer of cerebral hemispheres; receives sensory information and controls motor activities.

cerebral hemisphere One of the large, paired structures that together constitute the cerebrum of the brain.

cerebrospinal fluid Fluid found in the ventricles of the brain, in the central canal of the spinal cord, and in association with the meninges.

cerebrum Main part of the brain consisting of two large masses, or cerebral hemispheres; the largest part of the brain in mammals.

cervix Narrow end of the uterus, which projects into the vagina.

checkpoint Regulatory location in the cell cycle at which the cell assesses whether to proceed with cell division.

chemical evolution Increase in the complexity of chemicals over time that could have led to the first protocells.

chemoreceptor Sensory receptor sensitive to chemical stimuli—for example, receptors for taste and smell.

chlorofluorocarbons (CFCs) Organic compounds containing carbon, chlorine, and fluorine atoms. CFCs, such as Freon, can deplete the ozone shield by releasing chlorine atoms in the upper atmosphere.

chondrocyte Type of cell found in the lacunae of cartilage.

chorion Extraembryonic membrane that contributes to placenta formation.

chorionic villi Treelike extensions of the chorion that project into the maternal tissues at the placenta.

choroid Vascular, pigmented middle layer of the eye.

chromatin Network of fine threads in the nucleus composed of DNA and proteins.

chromosome Chromatin condensed into a compact structure.

chronic bronchitis Obstructive pulmonary disorder that tends to recur; marked by inflamed airways filled with mucus and degenerative changes in the bronchi, including loss of cilia.

chyme Thick, semiliquid food material that passes from the stomach to the small intestine.

cilia (sing., cillium) Short, hairlike projections from the plasma membrane; may be involved in movement.

circadian rhythm Biological rhythm with a 24-hour cycle.

circumcision Removal of the prepuce (foreskin) of the penis.

cirrhosis Chronic, irreversible injury to liver tissue; commonly caused by frequent alcohol consumption.

citric acid cycle Cycle of reactions in mitochondria that begins with citric acid; it breaks down an acetyl group as CO_2, ATP, NADH, and $FADH_2$ are given off; also called the Krebs cycle.

cleavage Cell division without cytoplasmic addition or enlargement; occurs during the first stage of animal development.

cleavage furrow Indentation that begins the process of cleavage, by which human cells undergo cytokinesis.

climate change Changes in weather patterns over periods of time; currently used to indicate changes in climate (global warming, desertification, etc.) associated with human activities on the planet.

cloning Production of identical copies; can be either the production of identical individuals or, in genetic engineering, the production of identical copies of a gene.

clotting Process of blood coagulation, usually when injury occurs.

coagulation Homeostatic mechanism that forms blood clots in response to injury.

cochlea Portion of the inner ear that resembles a snail's shell and contains the spiral organ, the sense organ for hearing.

cochlear nerve Either of two cranial nerves that carry nerve impulses from the spiral organ to the brain; also called the auditory nerve.

codominance Inheritance pattern in which both alleles of a gene are equally expressed.

codon Three-base sequence in mRNA that causes the insertion of a particular amino acid into a protein or termination of translation.

coenzyme Nonprotein organic molecule that aids the action of the enzyme to which it is loosely bound.

cohesion The ability of water molecules to bind to each other due to the abundance of hydrogen bonds between water molecules.

collagen fiber White fiber in the matrix of connective tissue; gives flexibility and strength.

collecting duct Duct within the kidney that receives fluid from several nephrons; the reabsorption of water occurs here.

colon Major portion of the large intestine, consisting of the ascending colon, the transverse colon, and the descending colon.

color blindness Deficiency in one or more of the three types of cone cells responsible for color vision.

columnar epithelium Type of epithelial tissue in which the cells have a shape similar to a vertical column or pillar.

community Assemblage of populations interacting with one another within the same environment.

compact bone Type of bone that contains osteons consisting of concentric layers of matrix and osteocytes in lacunae.

comparative genomics Study of the evolutionary relationship of species based on differences in the structure of their genomes.

complement system Series of proteins in plasma that form a nonspecific defense mechanism against a microbe invasion; it complements the antigen–antibody reaction.

complementary base pairing Hydrogen bonding between particular bases. In DNA, thymine (T) pairs with adenine (A), and guanine (G) pairs with cytosine (C). In RNA, uracil (U) pairs with A, and G pairs with C.

complementary DNA (cDNA) DNA that has been synthesized from mRNA by the action of reverse transcriptase.

compound Substance having two or more different elements united chemically in a fixed ratio.

conclusion Statement made following an experiment as to whether the results support the hypothesis.

condom For females, a large polyurethane tube with a flexible ring that fits onto the cervix. For males, a sheath used to cover the penis; used as a contraceptive and, if latex, to minimize the risk of transmitting infection.

cone cell Photoreceptor in retina of eye that responds to bright light; detects color and provides visual acuity.

congenital hypothyroidism Condition resulting from improper development of the thyroid in an infant; characterized by stunted growth and intellectual disability.

connective tissue Type of tissue that binds structures together, provides support and protection, fills spaces, stores fat, and forms blood cells; adipose tissue, cartilage, bone, and blood are types of connective tissue.

constipation Delayed and difficult defecation caused by insufficient water in the feces.

consumer Organism that feeds on another organism in a food chain; primary consumers eat plants, and secondary consumers eat animals.

contraceptive Medication or device used to reduce the chance of pregnancy.

control group Sample that goes through all the steps of an experiment but lacks the factor or is not exposed to the factor being tested; a standard against which results of an experiment are checked.

convulsion Sudden attack characterized by a loss of consciousness and severe, sustained, rhythmic contractions of some or all voluntary muscles.

cornea Transparent, anterior portion of the outer layer of the eye.

coronary artery Artery that supplies blood to the wall of the heart.

corpus callosum Bridge of nerve tracts that connects the two cerebral hemispheres.

corpus luteum Yellow body that forms in the ovary from a follicle that has discharged its secondary oocyte. It secretes progesterone and some estrogen.

cortisol Glucocorticoid secreted by the adrenal cortex that responds to stress on a long-term basis; reduces inflammation and promotes protein and fat metabolism.

covalent bond Chemical bond in which atoms share one pair of electrons.

cramp Muscle contraction that causes pain.

cranial nerve Nerve that is attached to the brain.

creatinine Nitrogenous waste; the end product of creatine phosphate metabolism.

Cro-Magnon Common name for first fossils to be designated *Homo sapiens*.

crossing-over Exchange of genetic material between nonsister chromatids of a tetrad during meiosis.

cuboidal epithelium Type of epithelial tissue with cube-shaped cells.

cultural eutrophication Enrichment of water by inorganic nutrients used by phytoplankton. Often, overenrichment caused by human activities leads to excessive bacterial growth and oxygen depletion.

culture Total pattern of behavior that depends upon the capacity to speak and transmit knowledge; includes examples of intellectual achievement (technology, arts, etc.).

Cushing's syndrome Condition resulting from hypersecretion of glucocorticoids; characterized by a loss of muscle protein and an increase in subcutaneous fat in the midsection. In women, it may result in increased masculinization.

cutaneous receptor Sensory receptor for pressure, touch, pain, and temperature that is found in the dermis of the skin.

cyclic adenosine monophosphate (cAMP) ATP-related compound that acts as the second messenger in peptide hormone transduction; it initiates activity of the metabolic machinery.

cystic fibrosis (CF) A generalized, autosomal recessive disorder of infants and children in which there is widespread dysfunction of the exocrine glands.

cystitis Inflammation of the urinary bladder.

cytokine Type of protein secreted by a T cell that stimulates cells of the immune system to perform their various functions.

cytokinesis Division of the cytoplasm following mitosis and meiosis.

cytoplasm Contents of a cell between the nucleus and the plasma membrane that contains the organelles.

cytosine (C) One of four nitrogen bases in nucleotides composing the structure of DNA and RNA.

cytoskeleton Internal framework of the cell, consisting of microtubules, actin filaments, and intermediate filaments.

cytotoxic T cell T cell that attacks and kills antigen-bearing cells.

D

data Facts or pieces of information collected through observation and/or experimentation.

daughter cell Cell that arises from a parent cell by mitosis or meiosis.

dead air space Volume of inspired air that cannot be exchanged with blood.

deductive reasoning Use of general principles to predict specific outcomes. Often uses "if . . . then" statements.

defecation Discharge of feces from the rectum through the anus.

deforestation Removal of trees from a forest in a way that continuously reduces the size of the forest.

dehydration reaction Chemical reaction resulting in a covalent bond with the accompanying loss of a water molecule.

dehydroepiandrosterone (DHEA) Precursor to testosterone, the male sex hormone.

delayed allergic response Allergic response initiated at the site of the allergen by sensitized T cells, involving macrophages and regulated by cytokines.

deletion Change in chromosome structure in which the end of a chromosome breaks off or two simultaneous breaks lead to the loss of an internal segment; often causes abnormalities (e.g., cri du chat syndrome).

denaturation Loss of normal shape by an enzyme so that it no longer functions; caused by a less-than-optimal pH or temperature.

dendrite Branched ending of a neuron that conducts signals toward the cell body.

dendritic cell Specialized epidermal cell that assists the immune system; previously called Langerhans cells.

denitrification Conversion of nitrate or nitrite to nitrogen gas by bacteria in soil.

dense fibrous connective tissue Type of connective tissue containing many collagen fibers packed together; found in tendons and ligaments, for example.

dental caries Tooth decay that occurs when bacteria within the mouth metabolize sugar and give off acids that erode teeth; a cavity.

deoxyhemoglobin Hemoglobin not carrying oxygen.

depolarization When the charge inside the axon changes from negative to positive.

dermis Region of skin that lies beneath the epidermis.

desertification Denuding and degrading a once-fertile land, initiating a desert-producing cycle that feeds on itself and causes long-term changes in the soil, climate, and biota of an area.

detrital food chain Straight-line linking of organisms according to who eats whom, beginning with detritus.

detrital food web Complex pattern of interlocking and crisscrossing food chains, beginning with detritus.

detritus feeder Any organism that obtains most of its nutrients from the detritus in an ecosystem.

development Group of stages by which a zygote becomes an organism or by which an organism changes during its life span; includes puberty and aging, for example.

diabetes mellitus Condition characterized by a high blood glucose level and the appearance of glucose in the urine, due to a deficiency of insulin production and the failure of cells to take up glucose.

diaphragm 1. Dome-shaped horizontal sheet of muscle and connective tissue that divides the thoracic cavity from the abdominal cavity. 2. A birth control device consisting of a soft rubber or latex cup that fits over the cervix.

diarrhea Excessively frequent, watery bowel movements.

diastole Relaxation period of a heart chamber during the cardiac cycle.

diastolic pressure Arterial blood pressure during the diastolic phase of the cardiac cycle.

diencephalon Portion of the brain in the region of the third ventricle that includes the thalamus and hypothalamus.

differentiation Development of an unspecialized cell into one with a more specialized structure and function.

diffusion Movement of molecules or ions from a region of higher to lower concentration; it requires no energy and stops when the distribution is equal.

digestion Breaking down of large nutrient molecules into smaller molecules that can be absorbed.

digestive system Organ system including the mouth, esophagus, stomach, small intestine, and large intestine (colon) that receives food and digests it into nutrient molecules. Also has associated organs: teeth, tongue, salivary glands, liver, gallbladder, and pancreas.

dihybrid cross Genetic cross that involves two traits; often involves individuals that are heterozygous for the traits and produces a 9:3:3:1 phenotypic ratio.

diploid (2n) Cell condition in which two of each type of chromosome are present in the nucleus.

disaccharide Sugar that contains two units of a monosaccharide (e.g., maltose).

distal convoluted tubule Final portion of a nephron that joins with a collecting duct; associated with tubular secretion.

diuretic Drug used to counteract hypertension by causing the excretion of water.

diverticulosis A condition in which portions of the digestive tract mucosa have pushed through other layers of the tract, forming pouches where food may collect.

DNA (deoxyribonucleic acid) Nucleic acid polymer produced from covalent bonding of nucleotide monomers that contain the sugar deoxyribose; the genetic material of nearly all organisms.

DNA replication Synthesis of a new DNA double helix prior to mitosis and meiosis in eukaryotic cells and during prokaryotic fission in prokaryotic cells.

domain The primary taxonomic group above the kingdom level; all living organisms may be placed in one of three domains.

dominant allele Allele that exerts its phenotypic effect in the heterozygote; it masks the expression of the recessive allele.

double helix Double spiral; describes the three-dimensional shape of DNA.

Duchenne muscular dystrophy Chronic progressive disease affecting the shoulder and pelvic girdles, commencing in early childhood. Characterized by increasing weakness of the muscles, followed by atrophy and a peculiar swaying gait with the legs kept wide apart. Transmitted as an X-linked trait; affected individuals, predominantly males, rarely survive to maturity. Death is usually due to respiratory weakness or heart failure.

duplication Change in chromosome structure in which a particular segment is present more than once in the same chromosome.

E

ecological pyramid Pictorial graph based on the biomass, number of organisms, or energy content of various trophic levels in a food web—from the producer to the final consumer populations.

ecosystem Biological community together with the associated abiotic environment; characterized by energy flow and chemical cycling.

effacement During the first stage of labor, the uterine contractions of labor occur in such a way that the cervical canal slowly disappears as the lower part of the uterus is pulled upward toward the baby's head.

effector A muscle, gland, or organ that carries out the responses of the nervous system to external or internal stimuli.

egg Female gamete having the haploid number of chromosomes; fertilized by a sperm, the male gamete.

elastic cartilage Type of cartilage composed of elastic fibers, allowing greater flexibility.

elastic fiber Yellow fiber in the matrix of connective tissue, providing flexibility.

electrocardiogram (ECG) Recording of the electrical activity associated with the heartbeat.

electron Negative subatomic particle, moving about in an energy level around the nucleus of an atom.

electron shell Average location, or energy level, of an electron in an atom.

electron transport chain Passage of electrons along a series of membrane-bound carrier molecules from a higher to lower energy level; the energy released is used for the synthesis of ATP.

element Substance that cannot be broken down into substances with different properties; composed of only one type of atom.

elimination Process of expelling substances from the body.

embryo Immature developmental stage not recognizable as a human.

embryonic development Period of development from the second through eighth weeks.

emerging diseases Infectious diseases that are either occurring for the first time in human populations, are rapidly increasing in incidence, or are entering into new geographic regions. Examples are SARS and MERS.

emphysema Degenerative lung disorder in which the bursting of alveolar walls reduces the total surface area for gas exchange.

emulsification Breaking up of fat globules into smaller droplets by the action of bile salts or any other emulsifier.

endemic goiter Condition in which a deficiency of iodine in the diet results in an enlarged thyroid gland. The condition is called endemic because it tends to occur in specific geographic regions.

endochondral ossification Ossification that begins as hyaline cartilage and is subsequently replaced by bone tissue.

endocrine gland Ductless organ that secretes a hormone or hormones into the bloodstream.

endocrine system Organ system involved in the coordination of body activities; uses hormones as chemical signals secreted into the bloodstream.

endomembrane system A collection of membranous structures involved in transport within the cell.

endometriosis Condition in which cells of the endometrium (uterus) migrate outside the reproductive tract.

endometrium Mucous membrane lining the interior surface of the uterus.

endoplasmic reticulum (ER) System of membranous saccules and channels in the cytoplasm, often with attached ribosomes.

energy The capacity to do work. Energy can exist in many forms, such as potential and kinetic energy.

energy of activation (E_a) Energy that must be added to a chemical reaction in order for molecules to react with one another.

enzymes Metabolic assistants, usually proteins, that accelerate the rate of chemical reactions.

eosinophil White blood cell containing cytoplasmic granules that stain with acidic dye.

epidemic More cases of a disease than expected in a certain area for a certain period of time.

epidermis Region of skin that lies above the dermis.

epididymis (pl., epididymides) Coiled tubule next to the testes where sperm mature and may be stored for a short time.

epiglottis Structure that covers the glottis during the process of swallowing.

epinephrine Hormone secreted by the adrenal medulla in times of stress; also called adrenaline.

epiphyseal plate Growth plate of a long bone; allows for increase in the length of a long bone during childhood.

episiotomy Surgical procedure performed during childbirth in which the opening of the vagina is enlarged to avoid tearing.

episodic memory Capacity of the brain to store and retrieve information with regard to persons and events.

epithelial tissue Type of tissue that lines hollow organs and covers surfaces; also called epithelium.

erectile dysfunction (ED) Failure of the penis to achieve or maintain erection.

erythrocyte Red blood cell; contains hemoglobin and is involved in the transport of oxygen in the respiratory system.

erythropoietin (EPO) Hormone, produced by the kidneys, that speeds red blood cell formation.

esophagus Muscular tube for moving swallowed food from the pharynx to the stomach.

estradiol Sex hormone; form of estrogen.

estrogen Female sex hormone that helps maintain sex organs and secondary sex characteristics.

eukaryotic cell Type of cell that has a membrane-bound nucleus and membranous organelles.

evaporation Conversion of a liquid or a solid into a gas.

evolution Descent of organisms from common ancestors with the development of genetic and phenotypic changes over time that make them more suited to the environment.

evolutionary tree Diagram that describes the evolutionary relationship of groups of organisms; a common ancestor is presumed to have been present at points of divergence.

excretion Removal of metabolic wastes from the body.

exocrine gland Gland that secretes its product to an epithelial surface directly or through ducts.

exophthalmic goiter Enlargement of the thyroid gland accompanied by an abnormal protrusion of the eyes.

exotic species nonnative members of an ecosystem

experiment Artificial situation devised to test a hypothesis.

experimental design Study in which a controlled set of experiments is used to test the cause-and-effect relationship between variables and/or observations.

experimental variable Value expected to change as a result of an experiment; represents the factor being tested by the experiment.

expiration Act of expelling air from the lungs; also called exhalation.

expiratory reserve volume Volume of air that can be forcibly exhaled after normal exhalation.

exponential growth Growth at a constant rate of increase per unit of time; can be expressed as a constant fraction or exponent.

external respiration Exchange of oxygen and carbon dioxide between alveoli and blood.

exteroceptor Sensory receptor that detects stimuli from outside the body (e.g., taste, smell, vision, hearing, and equilibrium).

extinction Total disappearance of a species or higher group.

extracellular matrix (ECM) Meshwork of polysaccharides and proteins that provides support for an animal cell and regulates movement of materials into the cell.

extraembryonic membrane Membrane that is not a part of the embryo but is necessary to the continued existence and health of the embryo.

F

facial tic Involuntary muscle movement of the face.

facilitated transport Use of a plasma membrane carrier to move a substance into or out of a cell from higher to lower concentration; no energy required.

familial hypercholesterolemia Genetic disorder characterized by an inability to remove cholesterol from the bloodstream; predisposes individual to heart attack.

farsighted Vision abnormality due to a shortened shape of the eye causing light rays to focus in back of retina when viewing close objects.

fat Organic molecule that contains glycerol and fatty acids; found in adipose tissue.

fatty acid Molecule that contains a hydrocarbon chain and ends with an acid group.

fermentation Anaerobic breakdown of glucose that results in a gain of two ATP and end products, such as alcohol and lactate.

fertilization Union of a sperm nucleus and an egg nucleus, which creates a zygote.

fetal development Period of development from the ninth week through birth.

fetus Developmental stage of humans between the embryo and newborn.

fiber Structure resembling a thread; also, plant material that is nondigestible.

fibrin Insoluble protein threads formed from fibrinogen during blood clotting.

fibrinogen Plasma protein that is converted into fibrin threads during blood clotting.

fibroblast Cell in connective tissues that produces fibers and other substances.

fibrocartilage Cartilage with a matrix of strong collagenous fibers.

fibromyalgia Chronic, widespread pain in muscles and soft tissues surrounding joints.

fibrous connective tissue Tissue composed mainly of closely packed collagenous fibers and found in tendons and ligaments.

fimbriae (sing., fimbria) In bacteria, small, bristle-like fibers on the exterior of the cell that attach bacteria to a surface. In mammals, fingerlike projections on the uterine tubes that receive the ovum from the ovaries.

flagella (sing., flagellum) Long extensions of the cytoskeleton (microtubules) that serve to propel a cell through a fluid medium.

fluid-mosaic model Model for the plasma membrane based on the changing location and pattern of protein molecules in a fluid phospholipid bilayer.

focus Bending of light rays by the cornea, lens, and humors so that they converge and create an image on the retina.

follicle Structure in the ovary that produces a secondary oocyte and the hormones estrogen and progesterone.

follicle-stimulating hormone (FSH) Hormone secreted by the anterior pituitary gland that stimulates the development of an ovarian follicle in a female or the production of sperm in a male.

fontanel Membranous region located between certain cranial bones in the skull of a fetus or infant.

food chain Order in which one population feeds on another in an ecosystem, from detritus (detrital food chain) or producer (grazing food chain) to final consumer.

food web In ecosystems, a complex pattern of interlocking and crisscrossing food chains.

foramen magnum Opening in the occipital bone of the vertebrate skull through which the spinal cord passes.

formed element Constituent of blood that is either cellular (red blood cells and white blood cells) or at least cellular in origin (platelets).

fossil Any past evidence of an organism that has been preserved in the Earth's crust.

fossil fuel Fuel, such as oil, coal, or natural gas, that is the result of partial decomposition of plants and animals coupled with exposure to heat and pressure for millions of years.

fossil record History of life recorded from fossilized remains from the past.

fovea centralis Region of the retina consisting of densely packed cones; responsible for the greatest visual acuity.

fragile X syndrome Most common form of inherited intellectual disability; results from mutation to a single gene and results in deficiency of a protein critical to brain development.

functional genomics Study of all the nucleotide sequences, including structural genes, regulatory sequences, and noncoding DNA segments, in the chromosomes of an organism.

fungi Multicellular eukaryotes that acquire energy by decomposing organic material.

G

gallbladder Organ attached to the liver that serves to store and concentrate bile.

gallstones Crystalline bodies formed by concentration of normal and abnormal bile components within the gallbladder.

gamete Haploid sex cell; the egg or sperm, which join in fertilization to form a zygote.

ganglia (sing., ganglion) Collections of nerve cell bodies found outside the central nervous system in the peripheral nervous system.

gastric gland Gland within the stomach wall that secretes gastric juice.

gastrulation Stage of animal development during which germ layers form, at least in part, by invagination.

gene Unit of heredity existing as alleles on the chromosomes; in diploid organisms, typically two alleles are inherited—one from each parent.

gene cloning Production of one or more copies of the same gene.

genetic engineering Human-induced changes in the genome of an organism, often performed for the benefit of humans.

genome editing Form of DNA technology that uses nucleases that can target specific sequences of nucleotides in the genome of an organism for inactivation or insertion of new nucleotides.

genotype Genes of an individual for a particular trait or traits; often designated by letters, for example, *BB* or *Aa*.

gerontology Study of aging.

gigantism Condition that results in individuals having excessive height compared to individuals of the same sex, age, and ethnic background.

gingivitis Inflammation of the gums in the oral cavity (mouth).

gland Epithelial cell or group of epithelial cells specialized to secrete a substance.

glaucoma Increasing loss of field of vision; caused by blockage of the ducts that drain the aqueous humor, creating pressure buildup and nerve damage.

global warming The increase in global atmospheric temperatures due to increases in the concentration of greenhouse gases.

globulin Type of protein in blood plasma. There are alpha, beta, and gamma globulins.

glomerular capsule Double-walled cup that surrounds the glomerulus at the beginning of the nephron.

glomerular filtrate The contents of the glomerular capsule following the process of glomerular filtration.

glomerular filtration Movement of small molecules from the glomerulus into the glomerular capsule due to the action of blood pressure.

glomerulus Cluster; for example, the cluster of capillaries surrounded by the glomerular capsule in a nephron, where glomerular filtration takes place.

glottis Opening for airflow in the larynx.

glucagon Hormone secreted by the pancreas that causes the liver to break down glycogen and raises the blood glucose level.

glucocorticoid Type of hormone secreted by the adrenal cortex that influences carbohydrate, fat, and protein metabolism; *see also* **cortisol**.

glucose Six-carbon sugar that organisms degrade as a source of energy during cellular respiration.

glycemic index (GI) Blood glucose response of a given food.

glycogen Storage polysaccharide composed of glucose molecules joined in a linear fashion but having numerous branches.

glycolysis Anaerobic breakdown of glucose that results in a gain of two ATP molecules.

Golgi apparatus Organelle, consisting of saccules and vesicles, that processes, packages, and distributes molecules about or from the cell.

gonad Organ that produces gametes; the ovary produces eggs, and the testis produces sperm.

gonadocorticoids Sex hormones produced by the adrenal cortex that include androgens and estrogen.

gonadotropic hormone Chemical signal secreted by the anterior pituitary that regulates the activity of the ovaries and testes; principally, follicle-stimulating hormone (FSH) and luteinizing hormone (LH).

gout Joint inflammation caused by accumulation of uric acid.

granular leukocyte White blood cell with prominent granules in the cytoplasm.

gravitational equilibrium Maintenance of balance when the head and body are in motion.

gray matter Nonmyelinated axons and cell bodies in the central nervous system.

grazing food chain Straight-line linking of organisms according to who eats whom, beginning with a producer.

grazing food web Complex pattern of interlocking and crisscrossing food chains that begins with populations of autotrophs serving as producers.

greenhouse effect Reradiation of solar heat toward the Earth because gases, such as carbon dioxide, methane, nitrous oxide, and water vapor, allow solar energy to pass through toward the Earth but block the escape of heat back into space.

greenhouse gases Gases involved in the greenhouse effect.

growth Increase in the number of cells and/or the size of these cells.

growth factor Chemical signal that regulates mitosis and differentiation of cells that have receptors for it; important in such processes as fetal development, tissue maintenance and repair, and hematopoiesis; sometimes a contributing factor in cancer.

growth hormone (GH) Substance secreted by the anterior pituitary; controls size of individual by promoting cell division, protein synthesis, and bone growth; also called a somatotropic hormone.

growth rate A percentage that reflects the difference between the number of persons in a population who are born and the number who die each year.

guanine (G) One of four nitrogen-containing bases in nucleotides composing the structure of DNA and RNA; pairs with cytosine.

H

hair cell Cell with stereocilia (long microvilli) that is sensitive to mechanical stimulation; mechanoreceptor for hearing and equilibrium in the inner ear.

hair follicle Tubelike depression under the skin in which a hair develops. Formed from epithelial tissue.

haploid (n) The n number of chromosomes—half the diploid number; the number characteristic of gametes that contain only one set of chromosomes.

heart Muscular organ located in the thoracic cavity whose rhythmic contractions maintain blood circulation.

heart attack Damage to the myocardium due to blocked circulation in the coronary arteries; also called a myocardial infarction.

heartburn Burning pain in the chest that occurs when part of the stomach contents escape into the esophagus.

helper T cell T cell that secretes cytokines that stimulate all types of immune system cells.

hemodialysis Cleansing of blood by using an artificial membrane that causes substances to diffuse from blood into a dialysis fluid.

hemoglobin (Hb) Iron-containing pigment in red blood cells that combines with and transports oxygen.

hemolysis Rupture of red blood cells accompanied by the release of hemoglobin.

hemophilia Genetic disorder in which the affected individual is subject to uncontrollable bleeding.

hemorrhoid Abnormally dilated blood vessels of the rectum.

hepatic portal vein Vein leading to the liver and formed by the merging blood vessels leaving the small intestine.

hepatic vein Vein that runs between the liver and the inferior vena cava.

hepatitis Inflammation of the liver. Viral hepatitis occurs in several forms.

herbivore Primary consumer in a grazing food chain; a consumer of plants or algae.

heterotroph Organism that cannot synthesize organic molecules from inorganic nutrients and therefore must take in organic nutrients (food).

heterozygous Possessing unlike alleles for a particular trait.

hippocampus Portion of the limbic system where memories are stored.

histamine Substance, produced by basophils in blood and mast cells in connective tissue, that causes capillaries to dilate.

homeostasis Maintenance of normal internal conditions in a cell or an organism by means of self-regulating mechanisms.

hominid Member of the family Hominidae, which contains australopithecines and humans.

hominin An extinct or modern species of humans.

Homo erectus Hominid who used fire and migrated out of Africa to Europe and Asia.

Homo habilis Hominid of 2 MYA who is believed to have been the first tool user.

Homo sapiens Modern humans.

homologous chromosome Member of a pair of chromosomes that are alike and come together in synapsis during prophase of the first meiotic division.

homologous structure Structure similar in two or more species because of common ancestry.

homozygous dominant Possessing two identical dominant alleles, such as *AA*, for a particular trait.

homozygous recessive Possessing two identical recessive alleles, such as *aa*, for a particular trait.

hormone A protein or steroid produced by a cell that affects a different cell, the so-called target cell.

human chorionic gonadotropin (HCG) Hormone produced by the chorion that functions to maintain the uterine lining.

human immunodeficiency virus (HIV) The virus responsible for AIDS.

human leukocyte antigen (HLA) Protein in a plasma membrane that identifies the cell as belonging to a particular individual and acts as an antigen in other organisms.

Huntington's disease Genetic disease marked by progressive deterioration of brain and nerve cells in the nervous system due to deficiency of a neurotransmitter.

hyaline cartilage Cartilage whose cells lie in lacunae separated by a white, translucent matrix containing very fine collagen fibers.

hydrogen bond Weak bond that arises between a slightly positive hydrogen atom of one molecule and a slightly negative atom of another, or between parts of the same molecule.

hydrolysis reaction Splitting of a compound by the addition of water, with the H^+ being incorporated in one fragment and the OH^- in the other.

hydrolyze To break a chemical bond between molecules by insertion of a water molecule.

hydrophilic Type of molecule that interacts with water by dissolving in water and/or forming hydrogen bonds with water molecules.

hydrophobic Type of molecule that does not interact with water because it is nonpolar.

hypertension Elevated blood pressure, particularly the diastolic pressure.

hyperthyroidism Condition where the thyroid gland overproduces thyroid hormone.

hypothalamus Part of the brain located below the thalamus that helps regulate the internal environment of the body and produces releasing factors that control the anterior pituitary.

hypothesis Supposition that is formulated after making an observation; it can be tested by obtaining more data, often by experimentation.

I

immediate allergic response Allergic response that occurs within seconds of contact with an allergen, caused by the attachment of the allergen to IgE antibodies.

immunity Ability of the body to protect itself from foreign substances and cells, including disease-causing agents.

immunization Use of a vaccine to protect the body against specific disease-causing agents.

immunosuppressive Inactivating the immune system to prevent organ rejection, usually via a drug.

implantation Attachment and penetration of the embryo into the lining of the uterus (endometrium).

in vitro fertilization (IVF) Form of assisted reproductive technology in which the egg is fertilized outside the body, and then is placed within the uterus.

incomplete dominance Inheritance pattern in which the offspring has an intermediate phenotype, as when a red-flowered plant and a white-flowered plant produce pink-flowered offspring.

incus The middle of three ossicles of the ear that serve to conduct vibrations from the tympanic membrane to the oval window of the inner ear.

inductive reasoning Using specific observations and the process of logic and reasoning to arrive at a hypothesis.

infectious diseases Diseases caused by pathogens such as bacteria, viruses, fungi, parasites, protozoans, and prions.

infertility Failure to achieve pregnancy after 1 year of attempts.

inflammatory response Tissue response to injury that is characterized by redness, swelling, pain, and heat.

ingestion The taking of food or liquid into the body by way of the mouth.

inner cell mass An aggregation of cells at one pole of the blastocyst, destined to form the embryo proper.

inner ear Portion of the ear consisting of a vestibule, semicircular canals, and the cochlea, where equilibrium is maintained and sound is transmitted.

insertion End of a muscle attached to a movable bone.

inspiration Act of taking air into the lungs; also called inhalation.
inspiratory reserve volume Maximum volume of air that the lungs can contain.
insulin Hormone secreted by the pancreas that lowers the blood glucose level by promoting the uptake of glucose by cells, and the conversion of glucose to glycogen by the liver and skeletal muscles.
integration Summing up of excitatory and inhibitory signals by a neuron or by some part of the brain.
integumentary system Organ system consisting of skin and structures, such as nails, found in skin.
intercalated disc Region that holds adjacent cardiac muscle cells together; discs appear as dense bands at right angles to the muscle striations.
interferon Antiviral agent produced by an infected cell that blocks the infection of another cell.
interkinesis Period between meiosis I and meiosis II, during which no DNA replication takes place.
interleukin Cytokine produced by macrophages and T cells that functions as a metabolic regulator of the immune response.
intermediate filament Ropelike assemblies of fibrous polypeptides in the cytoskeleton that provide support and strength to cells; so called because they are intermediate in size between actin filaments and microtubules.
internal respiration Exchange of oxygen and carbon dioxide between blood and interstitial fluid.
interneuron Neuron located within the central nervous system that conveys messages between parts of the central nervous system.
interoceptor Sensory receptor that detects stimuli from inside the body (e.g., pressoreceptors, osmoreceptors, and chemoreceptors).
interphase Cell cycle stage during which growth and DNA synthesis occur when the nucleus is not actively dividing.
interstitial cell Hormone-secreting cell located between the seminiferous tubules of the testes.
interstitial fluid Fluid that surrounds the body's cells; consists of dissolved substances that leave the capillaries of the circulatory system by diffusion and filtration.
intervertebral disc Layer of cartilage located between adjacent vertebrae.
intramembranous ossification Ossification that forms from membranelike layers of primitive connective tissue.
intrauterine device (IUD) Birth control device consisting of a small piece of molded plastic (and sometimes copper) that is inserted into the uterus; believed to alter the uterine environment so fertilization does not occur.
inversion Change in chromosome structure in which a segment of a chromosome is turned around 180°; this reversed sequence of genes can lead to altered gene activity and abnormalities.
ion Charged particle that carries a negative or positive charge.
ionic bond Chemical bond in which ions are attracted to one another by opposite charges.
iris Muscular ring that surrounds the pupil and regulates the passage of light through this opening.
isotope Atoms with the same atomic number but a different atomic mass due to a different number of neutrons.

J

jaundice Yellowish tint to the skin caused by an abnormal amount of bilirubin (bile pigment) in the blood, indicating liver malfunction.
joint Articulation between two bones of a skeleton.
juxtaglomerular apparatus Structure located in the walls of arterioles near the glomerulus; regulates renal blood flow.

K

kidney Organ in the urinary system that produces and excretes urine.
kingdom One of the categories used to classify organisms; the category above phylum.

L

lacteal Lymphatic vessel in an intestinal villus; it aids in the absorption of lipids.
lactose intolerance Inability to digest lactose because of an enzyme deficiency.
lacuna (pl., lacunae) Small pit or hollow cavity, as in bone or cartilage, where a cell or cells are located.
lanugo Short, fine hair that is present during the later portion of fetal development.
large intestine Last major portion of the digestive tract, extending from the small intestine to the anus and consisting of the cecum, the colon, the rectum, and the anal canal.
laryngitis Infection of the larynx with accompanying hoarseness.
larynx Cartilaginous organ located between the pharynx and the trachea that contains the vocal cords; also called the voice box.
law Universal principle that describes the basic functions of the natural world.
learning Relatively permanent change in behavior that results from practice and experience.
lens Clear, membranelike structure found in the eye behind the iris; brings objects into focus.
leptin Hormone produced by adipose tissue; acts on the hypothalamus to signal satiety.
leukemia Cancer of the blood-forming tissues leading to the overproduction of abnormal white blood cells.
ligament Tough cord or band of dense fibrous connective tissue that joins bone to bone at a joint.
limbic system System of associations among various brain centers, including the amygdala and hippocampus; governs learning, memory, and various emotions such as pleasure, fear, and happiness.
lipase Enzyme that digests fats and lipids; secreted by the pancreas.
lipid Class of organic compounds that tend to be soluble only in nonpolar solvents such as alcohol; includes fats and oils.
liver Large, dark-red internal organ that produces urea and bile, detoxifies the blood, stores glycogen, and produces the plasma proteins, among other functions.
locus (pl., loci) Particular site where a gene is found on a chromosome. Homologous chromosomes have corresponding gene loci.
long-term memory Retention of information that lasts longer than a few minutes.
loop of the nephron Portion of the nephron lying between the proximal convoluted tubule and the distal convoluted tubule that functions in water reabsorption; also called the loop of Henle.
loose fibrous connective tissue Tissue composed mainly of fibroblasts widely separated by a matrix containing collagen and elastic fibers.
lumen Cavity inside any tubular structure, such as the lumen of the digestive tract.
lung cancer Malignant growth that often begins in the bronchi.
lungs Paired, cone-shaped organs within the thoracic cavity; function in internal respiration and contain moist surfaces for gas exchange.
luteinizing hormone (LH) Hormone that controls the production of testosterone by interstitial cells in males and promotes the development of the corpus luteum in females.
lymph Fluid, derived from interstitial fluid, that is carried in lymphatic vessels.
lymph node Mass of lymphatic tissue located along the course of a lymphatic vessel.
lymphatic organ Organ other than a lymphatic vessel that is part of the lymphatic system; includes lymph nodes, tonsils, spleen, thymus, and bone marrow.
lymphatic system Organ system consisting of lymphatic vessels and lymphatic organs that transport lymph and lipids; aids the immune system.
lymphatic vessel System of vessels and ducts that transport lymph from the tissues of the body to the cardiovascular system.
lymphocyte Specialized white blood cell that functions in specific defense; occurs in two forms—T cell and B cell.
lymphoma Cancer of lymphatic tissue.
lysosome Membrane-bound vesicle that contains hydrolytic enzymes for digesting macromolecules.
lysozyme Enzyme found in tears, milk, saliva, mucus, and other body fluids that destroys bacteria by digesting their cell walls.

M

macromolecule Extremely large biological molecule; refers specifically to proteins, nucleic acids, polysaccharides, lipids, and complexes of these.
macrophage Large phagocytic cell derived from a monocyte that ingests microbes and debris.
major histocompatibility complex (MHC) Cluster of genes on chromosome 6 concerned with self-antigen production; matching these is critical to success of organ transplants. The MHC includes the human leukocyte antigen (HLA) genes.
malleus The first of three ossicles of the ear that serve to conduct vibrations from the tympanic membrane to the oval window of the inner ear.
Marfan syndrome Congenital disorder of connective tissue characterized by abnormal length of the extremities and weakness of the aorta.
mass number The sum of the number of protons and neutrons in the nucleus of an atom.
mast cell Cell to which antibodies, formed in response to allergens, attach, causing it to release histamine, thus producing allergic symptoms.
matrix Unstructured semifluid substance that fills the space between cells in connective tissues or inside organelles.

matter Anything that takes up space and has mass.

mechanoreceptor Sensory receptor that responds to mechanical stimuli, such as that from pressure, sound waves, and gravity.

medulla oblongata Part of the brain stem that is continuous with the spinal cord; controls heartbeat, blood pressure, breathing, and other vital functions.

megakaryocyte Large cell that gives rise to blood platelets.

meiosis Type of nuclear division that occurs as part of sexual reproduction in which the daughter cells receive the haploid number of chromosomes in varied combinations.

melanocyte Melanin-producing cell found in skin.

melanocyte-stimulating hormone Substance that causes melanocytes to secrete melanin in lower vertebrates.

melatonin Hormone secreted by the pineal gland that is involved in biorhythms.

memory Capacity of the brain to store and retrieve information about past sensations and perceptions; essential to learning.

memory B cell Cell of the immune system that is involved in the secondary response to an antigen. Derived from cloned B cells.

memory T cell T cell that differentiates during an initial infection and responds rapidly during subsequent exposure to the same antigen.

meninges (sing., meninx) Protective membranous coverings about the central nervous system.

menopause Termination of the ovarian and uterine cycles in older women.

menstruation Loss of blood and tissue from the uterus at the start of a uterine cycle.

messenger RNA (mRNA) Type of RNA formed from a DNA template that bears coded information for the amino acid sequence of a polypeptide.

metabolism All the chemical reactions that occur in a cell.

metaphase Mitotic phase during which chromosomes are aligned at the equator of the mitotic spindle.

metastasis Spread of cancer from the place of origin throughout the body; caused by the ability of cancer cells to migrate and invade tissues.

microtubule Small cylindrical structure that contains 13 rows of the protein tubulin around an empty central core; component of the cytoskeleton; present in the cytoplasm, centrioles, cilia, and flagella.

microvilli Small projections that extend from the epithelial cells of a villus; they increase the surface area of the cell.

midbrain Part of the brain located below the thalamus and above the pons; contains reflex centers and tracts.

middle ear Portion of the ear consisting of the tympanic membrane, the oval and round windows, and the ossicles; where sound is amplified.

mineral Naturally occurring inorganic substance containing two or more elements; certain minerals are needed in the diet.

mineralocorticoid Type of hormone secreted by the adrenal cortex that regulates water-salt balance, leading to increases in blood volume and blood pressure.

mitochondria (sing., mitochondrion) Membrane-bound organelles in which ATP molecules are produced during the process of cellular respiration.

mitosis Type of cell division in which daughter cells receive the exact chromosomal and genetic makeup of the parent cell; occurs during growth and repair; sometimes referred to as duplication division.

mitotic spindle Structure consisting of centrosomes and microtubules that brings about chromosomal movement during nuclear division.

model Simulation of a process that aids conceptual understanding until the process can be studied in more detail; a hypothesis that describes how a specific process might be carried out.

mole A unit of scientific measurement for atoms, ions, and molecules.

molecular clock Mutational changes that accumulate at a presumed constant rate in regions of DNA not involved in adaptation to the environment.

molecule Union of two or more atoms of the same element; also, the smallest part of a compound that retains the properties of the compound.

monoclonal antibody One of many antibodies produced by a clone of hybridoma cells that all bind to the same antigen.

monocyte Type of agranular white blood cell that functions as a phagocyte and an antigen-presenting cell.

monohybrid cross Genetic cross that involves individuals that are heterozygous for one trait; shows the phenotype of the dominant allele but carries the recessive allele.

monosaccharide Simple sugar; a carbohydrate that cannot be decomposed by hydrolysis (e.g., glucose).

monosomy Condition that is characterized by a diploid cell that has only one copy of a chromosome as a result of a nondisjunction event during cell division.

morphogenesis Emergence of shape in tissues, organs, or entire embryo during development.

morula Spherical mass of cells resulting from cleavage during animal development, prior to the blastula stage.

mosaic evolution Concept that human characteristics did not evolve at the same rate; for example, some body parts are more humanlike than others in early hominids.

motor neuron Nerve cell that conducts nerve impulses away from the central nervous system and innervates effectors such as muscles, glands, and organs.

motor unit Motor neuron and all the muscle fibers it innervates.

mouth Oral cavity; location where mechanical and chemical digestion begin.

movement Motion. This may be at the level of the organism, at the organ level (movement of materials within the digestive tract), or the transport of materials within a cell.

MRSA Methicillin-resistant *Staphylococcus aureus,* a type of bacterium that causes "staph" infections that is no longer susceptible to certain antibiotics, including methicillin.

mucosa Membrane that lines tubes and body cavities that open to the outside of the body; also called mucous membrane.

mucous membrane Membrane that lines tubes and body cavities that open to the outside of the body; also called mucosa.

multifactorial trait A trait controlled by several allelic pairs; each dominant allele contributes to the phenotype in an additive and like manner.

multiple allele Inheritance pattern in which there are more than two alleles for a particular trait; each individual has only two of all possible alleles.

multiple sclerosis (MS) Disease in which the outer myelin layer of nerve fiber insulation becomes scarred, interfering with normal conduction of nerve impulses.

muscle dysmorphia Mental state in which a person considers their body to be underdeveloped and becomes preoccupied with bodybuilding and diet; affects more men than women.

muscle fiber Muscle cell.

muscle tone Continuous, partial contraction of muscle.

muscle twitch Contraction of a whole muscle in response to a single stimulus.

muscular dystrophy Progressive muscle weakness and atrophy caused by deficient dystrophin protein.

muscular system System of muscles that produces movement, both within the body and of its limbs; principal components are skeletal, smooth, and cardiac muscle.

muscular tissue Type of tissue composed of fibers that can shorten and thicken.

muscularis Two layers of muscle in the gastrointestinal tract.

mutagen Agent, such as radiation or a chemical, that brings about a mutation.

mutation Alteration in chromosome structure or number and also an alteration in a gene due to a change in DNA composition.

myalgia Muscular pain.

myasthenia gravis Chronic disease characterized by muscles that are weak and easily fatigued. It results from the immune system's attack on neuromuscular junctions so that stimuli are not transmitted from motor neurons to muscle fibers.

myelin sheath White, fatty material derived from the membrane of Schwann cells; forms a covering for nerve fibers.

myocardium The middle of the three layers of the wall of the heart; composed of cardiac muscle.

myocyte Cell that is the main component of muscle tissue.

myofibril Contractile portion of muscle cells that contains a linear arrangement of sarcomeres and shortens to produce muscle contraction.

myofilament Component of a muscle fiber that is responsible for muscle contraction.

myoglobin Pigmented molecule in muscle tissue that stores oxygen.

myosin One of two major proteins of muscle; makes up thick filaments in myofibrils of muscle fibers. *See also* **actin.**

myxedema Condition resulting from a deficiency of thyroid hormone in an adult.

N

NAD^+ (nicotinamide adenine dinucleotide) Coenzyme that functions as a carrier of electrons and hydrogen ions, especially in cellular respiration.

nail Protective covering of the distal part of fingers and toes.

nasal cavity One of two canals in the nose, separated by a septum.

natural selection Mechanism of evolutionary change resulting in adaptation to the environment.

Neanderthal Hominin with a sturdy build who lived during the last Ice Age in Europe and the Middle East; hunted large game and left evidence of being culturally advanced.

nearsighted Vision abnormality due to an elongated eyeball from front to back; light rays focus in front of retina when viewing distant objects.

negative feedback Mechanism of homeostatic response in which a stimulus initiates reactions that reduce the stimulus.

nephron Microscopic kidney unit that regulates blood composition by glomerular filtration, tubular reabsorption, and tubular secretion.

nerve Bundle of long axons outside the central nervous system.

nerve impulse Action potential (electrochemical change) traveling along a neuron.

nervous system Organ system consisting of the brain, spinal cord, and associated nerves that coordinates the other organ systems of the body.

nervous tissue Tissue that contains nerve cells (neurons), which conduct impulses, and neuroglia, which support, protect, and provide nutrients to neurons.

neuroglia Nonconducting nerve cells that are intimately associated with neurons and function in a supportive capacity.

neuromuscular junction Region where an axon terminal approaches a muscle fiber; the synaptic cleft separates the axon terminal from the sarcolemma of a muscle fiber.

neuron Cell of the nervous system that transmits nerve impulses; consists of three parts: dendrites, cell body, and axon.

neurotransmitter Chemical stored at the ends of axons that is responsible for transmission across a synapse.

neutron Neutral subatomic particle, located in the nucleus and having a weight of approximately one atomic mass unit.

neutrophil Granular leukocyte that is the most abundant of the white blood cells; first to respond to infection.

niche Role an organism plays in its community, including its habitat and its interactions with other organisms.

nitrification Process by which nitrogen in ammonia and organic molecules is oxidized to nitrites and nitrates by soil bacteria.

nitrogen fixation Process whereby free atmospheric nitrogen is converted into compounds, such as ammonium and nitrates, usually by bacteria.

nociceptor Sensory receptor that is sensitive to chemicals released by damaged tissues or excess stimuli of heat or pressure; pain receptors.

node of Ranvier Gap in the myelin sheath around a nerve fiber.

nondisjunction Failure of homologous chromosomes or daughter chromosomes to separate during meiosis I and meiosis II, respectively.

nonpolar Molecules in which the electrons are evenly shared between the atoms in the molecule.

nonrenewable resource Minerals, fossil fuels, and other materials present in essentially fixed amounts (within human timescales) in our environment.

norepinephrine Neurotransmitter of the postganglionic fibers in the sympathetic division of the autonomic system; also, a hormone produced by the adrenal medulla; also called noradrenaline.

nose External structure of the respiratory system where air enters the respiratory tract. Contains hairs to filter the incoming air.

nuclear envelope Double membrane that surrounds the nucleus and is connected to the endoplasmic reticulum; has pores that allow substances to pass between the nucleus and the cytoplasm.

nuclear pore Opening in the nuclear envelope that permits the passage of proteins into the nucleus and ribosomal subunits out of the nucleus.

nucleic acid Polymer of nucleotides; DNA and RNA are both examples.

nucleolus Dark-staining, spherical body in the cell nucleus that produces ribosomal subunits.

nucleotide Monomer of DNA and RNA consisting of a 5-carbon sugar bonded to a nitrogen-containing base and a phosphate group.

nutrient Chemical substance in foods that is essential to the diet and contributes to good health.

O

obesity Excess adipose tissue; exceeding ideal weight by more than 20%.

oblique layer Muscle layer of the stomach that is responsible for mixing the food with gastric juice and mechanical digestion.

observation Step in the scientific method by which information is collected so that a hypothesis may be developed.

oil Substance, usually of plant origin and liquid at room temperature, formed when a glycerol molecule reacts with three fatty acid molecules.

oil gland Gland of the skin associated with hair follicle; secretes sebum; also called sebaceous gland.

olfactory cell Modified neuron that is a sensory receptor for the sense of smell.

omnivore Organism in a food chain that feeds on both plants and animals.

oncogene Gene that disrupts the normal cell cycle, causing cancer.

oncology The study of cancer.

oocyte Immature egg cell that undergoes meiosis for reproduction.

oogenesis Production of an egg in females by the process of meiosis and maturation.

opportunistic infection Infection that has an opportunity to occur because the immune system has been weakened.

optic chiasma X-shaped structure on the underside of the brain formed by a partial crossing-over of optic nerve fibers.

optic nerve Either of two cranial nerves that carry nerve impulses from the retina of the eye to the visual cortex, thereby contributing to the sense of sight.

optic tract Group of neurons from the optic nerve that sweep around the hypothalamus. Most fibers synapse with neurons in nuclei within the thalamus.

organ Combination of two or more different tissues performing a common function.

organ system Group of related organs working together.

organelle Small membranous structure in the cytoplasm of eukaryotic cells having a specific structure and function.

organic molecule Type of molecule that contains carbon and hydrogen—and often contains oxygen also.

organism Individual living thing.

origin End of a muscle attached to a relatively immovable bone.

osmosis Diffusion of water from an area of high concentration to low concentration through a selectively permeable membrane.

osmotic pressure Measure of the tendency of water to move across a selectively permeable membrane; visible as an increase in liquid on the side of the membrane with higher solute concentration.

ossicle One of the small bones of the middle ear—malleus, incus, and stapes.

ossification Formation of bone tissue.

osteoblast Bone-forming cell.

osteoclast Cell that causes the breakdown of bone.

osteocyte Mature bone cell located within the lacunae of bone.

osteogenesis imperfecta Genetic condition that results in very weak bones.

osteoporosis Condition in which bones break easily because calcium is removed from them faster than it is replaced.

otolith Calcium carbonate granule associated with ciliated cells in the utricle and the saccule.

outbreak A disease epidemic that is confined to a local area.

outer ear Portion of ear consisting of the pinna and auditory canal.

oval window Membrane-covered opening between the stapes and the inner ear.

ovarian cycle Monthly follicle changes occurring in the ovary that control the level of sex hormones in the blood and the uterine cycle.

ovaries Female gonads that produce eggs and the female sex hormones.

ovulation Release of a secondary oocyte from the ovary. If fertilization occurs, the secondary oocyte becomes an egg.

oxygen debt Amount of oxygen needed to metabolize lactate, a compound that accumulates during vigorous exercise.

oxyhemoglobin Compound formed when oxygen combines with hemoglobin.

oxytocin Hormone released by the posterior pituitary that causes contraction of uterus and milk letdown.

P

pacemaker Another name for the SA (sinoatrial) node; establishes the electrical rhythm of the heart.

pancreas Internal organ that produces digestive enzymes and the hormones insulin and glucagon.

pancreatic islets (islets of Langerhans) Masses of cells that constitute the endocrine portion of the pancreas.

parasympathetic division That part of the autonomic system that is active under normal conditions; uses acetylcholine as a neurotransmitter.

parathyroid gland Gland embedded in the posterior surface of the thyroid gland; it produces parathyroid hormone.

parathyroid hormone (PTH) Hormone secreted by the four parathyroid glands that increases the blood calcium level and decreases the blood phosphate level.

parent cell Cell that divides to form daughter cells.

Parkinson's disease Progressive deterioration of the central nervous system due to a deficiency in the neurotransmitter dopamine.

parturition Processes that lead to and include birth and the expulsion of the afterbirth.

passive immunity Protection against infection acquired by transfer of antibodies to a susceptible individual.

pathogen Disease-causing agent.

pectoral girdle Portion of the skeleton that provides support and attachment for an arm; consists of a scapula and a clavicle.

pelvic girdle Portion of the skeleton to which the legs are attached; consists of the coxal bones.

pelvis Bony ring formed by the sacrum, coxae, and pelvic girdle.

penis External organ in males through which the urethra passes; also serves as the organ of sexual intercourse.

pepsin Enzyme secreted by gastric glands that digests proteins to peptides.

peptide bond Type of covalent bond that joins two amino acids.

peptide hormone Type of hormone that is a protein, a peptide, or is derived from an amino acid.

pericardium Protective serous membrane that surrounds the heart.

periodontitis Inflammation of the periodontal membrane that lines tooth sockets, causing loss of bone and loosening of teeth.

peripheral nervous system (PNS) Nerves and ganglia that lie outside the central nervous system.

peristalsis Wavelike contractions that propel substances along a tubular structure such as the esophagus.

peritubular capillary network Capillary network that surrounds a nephron and functions in reabsorption during urine formation.

pH scale Measurement scale for hydrogen ion concentration; logarithmic scale.

pharynx Portion of the digestive tract between the mouth and the esophagus that serves as a passageway for food and also for air on its way to the trachea.

pheromone Chemical signal released by an organism that affects the metabolism or influences the behavior of another individual of the same species.

phospholipid Lipid molecule that forms the bilayer of the cell's membranes; has a polar, hydrophilic head bonded to two nonpolar, hydrophobic tails.

photoreceptor Sensory receptor in retina that responds to light stimuli.

photosynthesis Process by which plants, algae, and some bacteria harvest the energy of the sun and convert it to chemical energy.

photovoltaic (solar) cell Energy-conversion device that captures solar energy and converts it to an electrical current.

pilus Elongated, hollow appendage on bacteria used to transfer DNA from one cell to another.

pineal gland Endocrine gland located in the third ventricle of the brain; produces melatonin.

pinna Part of the ear that projects on the outside of the head.

pituitary dwarfism Condition that results in individuals having reduced height compared to individuals of the same sex, age, and ethnic background.

pituitary gland Endocrine gland that lies just inferior to the hypothalamus; consists of the anterior pituitary and posterior pituitary.

placebo Treatment that is an inactive substance (pill, liquid, etc.) administered as if it were a therapy in an experiment but that has no therapeutic value.

placenta Structure that forms from the chorion and the uterine wall and allows the embryo and then the fetus to acquire nutrients and rid itself of wastes.

plants Multicellular eukaryotes that acquire energy through the process of photosynthesis.

plaque Accumulation of soft masses of fatty material, particularly cholesterol, beneath the inner linings of the arteries.

plasma Liquid portion of blood; contains nutrients, wastes, salts, and proteins.

plasma cell Cell derived from a B lymphocyte specialized to mass-produce antibodies.

plasma membrane Membrane surrounding the cytoplasm that consists of a phospholipid bilayer with embedded proteins; functions to regulate the entrance and exit of molecules from the cell.

plasma protein Protein dissolved in blood plasma.

plasmid Self-replicating ring of accessory DNA in the cytoplasm of bacteria.

platelet (thrombocyte) Fragment of a cell found in the blood that is necessary for blood clotting.

pleurae (sing., pleura) Serous membranes that enclose the lungs.

pneumonectomy Surgical removal of all or part of a lung.

pneumonia Infection of the lungs that causes alveoli to fill with mucus and pus.

polar Combination of atoms in which the electrical charge is not distributed symmetrically.

polar body In oogenesis, a nonfunctional product; two to three meiotic products are of this type.

pollution Any environmental change that adversely affects the lives and health of living organisms.

polygenic trait Trait that is controlled by several allelic pairs; each dominant allele contributes to the phenotype in an additive and like manner.

polymerase chain reaction (PCR) Technique that uses the enzyme DNA polymerase to produce millions of copies of a particular piece of DNA.

polyp Small, abnormal growth that arises from the epithelial lining.

polypeptide Polymer of three or more amino acids linked by peptide bonds.

polysaccharide Polymer made from sugar monomers; the polysaccharides starch and glycogen are polymers of glucose monomers.

pons Portion of the brain stem above the medulla oblongata and below the midbrain; assists the medulla oblongata in regulating the breathing rate.

population Organisms of the same species occupying a certain area.

positive feedback Mechanism in which the stimulus initiates reactions that lead to an increase in the stimulus.

posterior pituitary Portion of the pituitary gland that stores and secretes oxytocin and antidiuretic hormone, which are produced by the hypothalamus.

pre-embryonic development Development of the zygote in the first week, including fertilization, the beginning of cell division, and the appearance of the chorion.

precipitation Water deposited on the Earth in the form of rain, snow, sleet, hail, or fog.

prediction Step in the scientific process that follows the formation of a hypothesis and assists in the creating of the experimental design.

prefrontal area Association area in the frontal lobe that receives information from other association areas and uses it to reason and plan actions.

primary germ layer One of the three layers (ectoderm, mesoderm, and endoderm) of embryonic cells that develop into specific tissues and organs.

primary motor area Area in the frontal lobe where voluntary commands begin; each section controls a part of the body.

primary somatosensory area Area dorsal to the central sulcus where sensory information arrives from skin and skeletal muscles.

primate Animal that belongs to the order Primates; includes prosimians, monkeys, apes, and humans.

principle Theory generally accepted by an overwhelming number of scientists; a law.

prion An infectious particle that is the cause of diseases such as scrapie in sheep, mad cow disease, and Creutzfeldt–Jakob disease in humans. It has a protein component, but no nucleic acid has been detected.

producer Photosynthetic organism at the start of a grazing food chain that makes its own food (e.g., green plants on land and algae in water).

progesterone Female sex hormone that helps maintain sex organs and secondary sex characteristics.

prokaryotic cell Type of cell that lacks a membrane-bound nucleus and organelles.

prolactin Hormone secreted by the anterior pituitary that stimulates the production of milk from the mammary glands.

prometaphase Stage of mitosis where the spindle fibers attach to the centromeres of the chromosomes before entering metaphase.

prophase Phase of nuclear division during which chromatin condenses so that chromosomes appear and the nuclear envelope dissolves.

prosimian Member of a group of primates that includes lemurs, tarsiers, and lorises; may resemble the first primates to have evolved.

prostaglandin Hormone that has various and powerful local effects; examples are prostaglandins that are produced by damaged tissues to indicate pain and by the uterus for contraction.

prostate gland Gland located around the male urethra below the urinary bladder; adds secretions to semen.

protease Enzyme capable of breaking peptide bonds in a protein or polypeptide.

protein Molecule consisting of one or more polypeptides.

protein-first hypothesis In chemical evolution, the proposal that protein originated before other macromolecules and allowed the formation of protocells.

proteomics The study of the structure, function, and interactions of the proteins in a cell.

prothrombin Plasma protein converted to thrombin during the steps of blood clotting.

protists Single-celled or multicellular eukaryotes from which the other kingdoms of eukaryotes evolved.

proto-oncogene Normal gene that can become an oncogene through mutation; involved in the regulation of the cell cycle.

protocell In biological evolution, a possible cell forerunner that became a cell once it could reproduce.

proton Positive subatomic particle, located in the nucleus and having a weight of approximately one atomic mass unit.

provirus Latent form of a virus in which the viral DNA is incorporated into the chromosome of the host.

proximal convoluted tubule Highly coiled region of a nephron near the glomerular capsule, where tubular reabsorption takes place.

pseudostratified columnar epithelium Appearance of layering in some epithelial cells when, actually, each cell touches a baseline and true layers do not exist.

pulmonary artery Blood vessel that takes blood away from the heart to the lungs.

pulmonary circuit Circulatory pathway that consists of the pulmonary trunk, the pulmonary arteries, and the pulmonary veins; takes oxygen-poor blood from the heart to the lungs and oxygen-rich blood from the lungs to the heart.

pulmonary fibrosis Accumulation of fibrous connective tissue in the lungs; caused by inhaling irritating particles, such as silica, coal dust, or asbestos.

pulmonary vein Blood vessel that takes blood from the lungs to the heart.

pulse Vibration felt in arterial walls due to expansion of the aorta following ventricle contraction.

Punnett square Gridlike guide used to calculate the expected results of simple genetic crosses.

pupil Opening in the center of the iris of the eye.

pyelonephritis Inflammation of the kidney due to bacterial infection.

R

radioisotope Unstable form of an atom that spontaneously emits radiation in the form of radioactive particles or radiant energy.

recessive allele Allele that exerts its phenotypic effect only in the homozygote; its expression is masked by a dominant allele.

recombinant DNA (rRNA) DNA that contains genes from more than one source.

rectum Terminal end of the digestive tube between the sigmoid colon and the anus.

red blood cell (erythrocyte) Formed element of the blood that contains hemoglobin and carries oxygen from the lungs to the tissues.

red bone marrow Blood-cell-forming tissue located in the spaces within spongy bone.

reflex Automatic, involuntary response of an organism to a stimulus.

refractory period Time following an action potential during which the axon is unable to conduct another nerve impulse.

renal artery Vessel that originates from the aorta and delivers blood to the kidney.

renal cortex Outer portion of the kidney that appears granular.

renal medulla Inner portion of the kidney that consists of renal pyramids.

renal pelvis Hollow chamber in the kidney that lies inside the renal medulla and receives freshly prepared urine from the collecting ducts.

renal vein Vessel that takes blood from the kidney to the inferior vena cava.

renewable resource Resources normally replaced or replenished by natural processes; resources not depleted by moderate use. Examples include solar energy, biological resources such as forests and fisheries, biological organisms, and some biogeochemical cycles.

renin Enzyme released by kidneys that leads to the secretion of aldosterone and a rise in blood pressure.

replacement model Proposal that modern humans originated only in Africa, then migrated out of Africa and supplanted populations of early *Homo* in Asia and Europe about 100,000 years ago; also called the out-of-Africa hypothesis.

replacement reproduction Population in which each person is replaced by only one child.

repolarization When the charge inside the axon resumes a negative charge.

reproduce To produce a new individual of the same type.

reproductive system Organ system that contains male or female organs and specializes in the production of offspring.

residual volume Amount of air remaining in the lungs after a forceful expiration.

respiratory control center Group of nerve cells in the medulla oblongata that sends out nerve impulses on a rhythmic basis, resulting in involuntary inspiration on an ongoing basis.

respiratory system Organ system consisting of the lungs and tubes that bring oxygen into the lungs and take carbon dioxide out.

responding variable Result or change that occurs when an experimental variable is varied in an experiment; also called the dependent variable.

resting potential Polarity across the plasma membrane of a resting neuron due to an unequal distribution of ions.

restriction enzyme Bacterial enzyme that stops viral reproduction by cleaving viral DNA; used to cut DNA at specific points during production of recombinant DNA.

reticular fiber Very thin collagen fiber in the matrix of connective tissue, highly branched and forming delicate supporting networks.

reticular formation Complex network of nerve fibers within the central nervous system that arouses the cerebrum.

retina Innermost layer of the eye that contains the rod cells and the cone cells.

retinal Light-absorbing molecule that is a derivative of vitamin A and a component of rhodopsin.

retrovirus RNA virus containing the enzyme reverse transcriptase that carries out RNA to DNA transcription.

rheumatic fever Disease caused by bacterial infection, characterized by fever, swelling and pain in the joints, sore throat, and cardiac involvement.

rheumatoid arthritis Persistent inflammation of synovial joints, often causing cartilage destruction, bone erosion, and joint deformities.

rhodopsin Light-absorbing molecule in rod cells and cone cells that contains a pigment called retinal and the protein opsin.

ribosomal RNA (rRNA) Type of RNA found in ribosomes where protein synthesis occurs.

ribosome RNA and protein in two subunits; site of protein synthesis in the cytoplasm.

RNA (ribonucleic acid) Nucleic acid produced from covalent bonding of nucleotide monomers that contain the sugar ribose; its three major forms are messenger RNA, ribosomal RNA, and transfer RNA.

RNA polymerase During transcription, an enzyme that joins nucleotides complementary to a DNA template.

RNA-first hypothesis In chemical evolution, the proposal that RNA originated before other macromolecules and allowed the formation of the first cell or cells.

rod cell Photoreceptor in retina of eye that responds to dim light.

rotational equilibrium Maintenance of balance when the head and body are suddenly moved or rotated.

round window Membrane-covered opening between the inner ear and the middle ear.

rugae Deep folds, as in the wall of the stomach.

runoff Water—from rain, snowmelt, or other sources—that flows over the land surface, adding to the water cycle.

S

SA (sinoatrial) node Small region of neuromuscular tissue that initiates the heartbeat; also called the pacemaker.

saccule Saclike cavity in the vestibule of the inner ear; contains sensory receptors for gravitational equilibrium.

salivary amylase Secreted from the salivary glands; the first enzyme to act on starch.

salivary gland Gland associated with the mouth that secretes saliva.

saltatory conduction Movement of nerve impulses from one neurofibral node to another along a myelinated axon.

saltwater intrusion Movement of salt water into freshwater aquifers in coastal areas where groundwater is withdrawn faster than it is replenished.

sarcolemma Plasma membrane of a muscle fiber; also forms the tubules of the T system involved in muscular contraction.

sarcoma Cancer that arises in muscles and connective tissues.

sarcomere One of many units arranged linearly within a myofibril whose contraction produces muscle contraction.

sarcoplasm Cytoplasm of a muscle fiber that contains the organelles.

sarcoplasmic reticulum Smooth endoplasmic reticulum of skeletal muscle cells; surrounds the myofibrils and stores calcium ions.

saturated fatty acid Fatt acid molecule that lacks double bonds between the atoms of its carbon chain.

Schwann cell Cell that surrounds a fiber of a peripheral nerve and forms the myelin sheath.

science Development of concepts about the natural world, often by using the scientific method.

scientific method Process of attaining knowledge by making observations, testing hypotheses, and coming to conclusions.

scientific theory Concept supported by a broad range of observations, experiments, and conclusions.

sclera White, fibrous, outer layer of the eyeball.

scrotum Pouch of skin that encloses the testes.

second messenger Chemical signal such as cyclic AMP that causes the cell to respond to the first messenger—a hormone bound to a receptor protein in the plasma membrane.

selectively permeable Having degrees of permeability; the cell is impermeable to some substances and allows others to pass through at varying rates.

semantic memory Capacity of the brain to store and retrieve information with regard to words or numbers.

semen Thick, whitish fluid consisting of sperm and secretions from several glands of the male reproductive tract.

semicircular canal One of three tubular structures within the inner ear that contain sensory receptors responsible for the sense of rotational equilibrium.

semilunar valve Valve resembling a half moon located between the ventricles and their attached vessels.

seminal vesicle Convoluted structure attached to the vas deferens near the base of the urinary bladder in males; adds secretions to semen.

seminiferous tubule Long, coiled structure contained within chambers of the testis; where sperm are produced.

sensation Conscious awareness of a stimulus due to nerve impulses sent to the brain from a sensory receptor by way of sensory neurons.

sensory adaptation Phenomenon of a sensation becoming less noticeable once it has been recognized by constant repeated stimulation.

sensory neuron Nerve cell that transmits nerve impulses to the central nervous system after a sensory receptor has been stimulated.

sensory receptor Structure that receives either external or internal environmental stimuli and is a part of a sensory neuron or transmits signals to a sensory neuron.

septum Wall between two cavities; in the human heart, a septum separates the right side from the left side.

serosa Membrane that covers internal organs and lines cavities without an opening to the outside of the body.

serotonin Neurotransmitter derived from the amino acid tryptophan; involved in functions such as thermoregulation, sleeping, emotions, and perception.

serous membrane Membrane that covers internal organs and lines cavities without an opening to the outside of the body; also called serosa.

Sertoli cell Cell associated with developing germ cells in seminiferous tubule; secretes fluid into seminiferous tubule and mediates hormonal effects on tubule.

severe combined immunodeficiency disease (SCID) Congenital illness in which both antibody- and cell-mediated immunity are lacking or inadequate.

sex chromosome Chromosome that determines the sex of an individual; in humans, females have two X chromosomes and males have both an X and Y chromosome.

sex-linked Refers to an allele that occurs on the sex chromosomes, but may control a trait that has nothing to do with the sex characteristics of an individual.

short-term memory Retention of information for only a few minutes, such as remembering a telephone number.

sickle-cell disease Genetic disorder in which the affected individual has sickle-shaped red blood cells subject to hemolysis.

sinkhole Large surface crater caused by the collapse of an underground channel or cavern; often triggered by groundwater withdrawal.

sinus Cavity or hollow space in an organ such as the skull.

sinusitis Infection of the sinuses, caused by blockage of the openings to the sinuses and characterized by postnasal discharge and facial pain.

sister chromatids One of two genetically identical chromosomal units that are the result of DNA replication and are attached to each other at the centromere.

skeletal muscle Striated, voluntary muscle tissue found in muscles that move the bones.

skeletal system System of bones, cartilage, and ligaments that works with the muscular system to protect the body and provide support for locomotion and movement.

skill memory Capacity of the brain to store and retrieve information necessary to perform motor activities, such as riding a bike.

skin Outer covering of the body; can be called the integumentary system because it contains organs such as sense organs.

skull Bony framework of the head, composed of cranial bones and the bones of the face.

sliding filament model An explanation for muscle contraction based on the movement of actin filaments in relation to myosin filaments.

small intestine Long, tubelike chamber of the digestive tract between the stomach and large intestine.

smooth muscle Nonstriated, involuntary muscle tissue found in the walls of internal organs; also called visceral muscle.

sodium–potassium pump Carrier protein in the plasma membrane that moves sodium ions out of, and potassium ions into, cells; important in nerve and muscle cells.

somatic system That portion of the peripheral nervous system containing motor neurons that serve the skin, skeletal muscles, and tendons.

spasm Sudden, involuntary contraction of one or more muscles.

species Group of similarly constructed organisms capable of interbreeding and producing fertile offspring; organisms that share a common gene pool.

sperm Male gamete having a haploid number of chromosomes and the ability to fertilize an egg, the female gamete.

spermatogenesis Production of sperm in males by the process of meiosis and maturation.

sphincter Muscle that surrounds a tube and closes or opens the tube by contracting and relaxing.

spinal cord Part of the central nervous system; the nerve cord that is continuous with the base of the brain plus the vertebral column that protects the nerve cord.

spinal nerve Nerve that arises from the spinal cord.

spiral organ Organ in the cochlear duct of the inner ear responsible for hearing; also called the organ of Corti.

spleen Large, glandular organ located in the upper left region of the abdomen; stores and purifies blood.

spongy bone Porous bone found at the ends of long bones where red bone marrow is sometimes located.

sprain Injury to a ligament caused by abnormal force applied to a joint.

squamous epithelium Type of epithelial tissue that contains flat cells.

stapes The last of three ossicles of the ear that serve to conduct vibrations from the tympanic membrane to the oval window of the inner ear.

starch Storage polysaccharide found in plants; composed of glucose molecules joined in a linear fashion with few side chains.

stereocilia (sing., stereocilium) Long, flexible microvilli that superficially resemble cilia. Within the inner ear, these signal changes in body position and help to maintain balance and equilibrium.

steroid Type of lipid molecule having a complex of four carbon rings; examples are cholesterol, progesterone, and testosterone.

steroid hormone One of a group of hormones derived from cholesterol.

stimulus Change in the internal or external environment that a sensory receptor can detect, leading to nerve impulses in sensory neurons.

stomach Muscular sac that mixes food with gastric juices to form chyme, which enters the small intestine.

strain Injury to a muscle resulting from overuse or improper use.

striated Having bands; in cardiac and skeletal muscle, alternating light and dark crossbands produced by the distribution of contractile proteins.

stroke Condition resulting when an arteriole in the brain bursts or becomes blocked by an embolism; also called cerebrovascular accident.

subcutaneous layer Tissue layer that lies just beneath the skin and contains adipose tissue.

submucosa Layer of connective tissue underneath a mucous membrane.

subsidence Occurs when a portion of the Earth's surface gradually settles downward.

substance use disorder Dependence on a drug, which assumes an "essential" biochemical role in the body following habituation and tolerance.

substrate Reactant in a reaction controlled by an enzyme.

supergroup Classification term used to classify the major groups of eukaryotes based on DNA similarities.

surfactant Agent that reduces the surface tension of water. In the lungs, a surfactant prevents the alveoli from collapsing.

sustainable Ability of a society or ecosystem to maintain itself while also providing services to humans.

suture Type of immovable joint articulation found between bones of the skull.

sweat gland Skin gland that secretes a fluid substance for evaporative cooling; also called sudoriferous gland.

sympathetic division The part of the autonomic system that usually promotes activities associated with emergency (fight-or-flight) situations; uses norepinephrine as a neurotransmitter.

synapse Junction between neurons consisting of the presynaptic (axon) membrane, the synaptic cleft, and the postsynaptic (usually dendrite) membrane.

synapsis Pairing of homologous chromosomes during prophase I of meiosis I; allows for crossing-over to occur.

synaptic cleft Small gap between presynaptic and postsynaptic membranes of a synapse.

syndrome Group of symptoms that appear together and tend to indicate the presence of a particular disorder.

synovial joint Freely movable joint having a cavity filled with synovial fluid.

synovial membrane Membrane that forms the inner lining of the capsule of a freely movable joint.

systemic circuit Blood vessels that transport blood from the left ventricle and back to the right atrium of the heart.

systemic lupus erythematosus Syndrome involving the connective tissues and various organs, including the kidneys.

systole Contraction period of the heart during the cardiac cycle.

systolic pressure Arterial blood pressure during the systolic phase of the cardiac cycle.

T

T (transverse) tubule Membranous channel that extends inward.

T cell (T lymphocyte) Lymphocyte that matures in the thymus. Cytotoxic T cells kill antigen-bearing cells outright; helper T cells release cytokines that stimulate other immune system cells.

T-cell receptor (TCR) Molecule on the surface of a T lymphocyte to which an antigen binds.

taste bud Sense organ containing the receptors associated with the sense of taste.

Tay-Sachs disease Lethal genetic disease in which the newborn has a faulty lysosomal digestive enzyme.

technology The science or study of the practical or industrial arts.

telomere Tip of the end of a chromosome.

telophase Mitotic phase during which daughter chromosomes are located at each pole.

template Pattern or guide used to make copies; parental strand of DNA serves as a guide for the production of daughter DNA strands, and DNA also serves as a guide for the production of messenger RNA.

tendinitis An inflammation of muscle tendons and their attachments. Also spelled as tendonitis.

tendon Strap of fibrous connective tissue that connects skeletal muscle to bone.

testes (sing., testis) Male gonads that produce sperm and the male sex hormones.

testosterone Male sex hormone that helps maintain sexual organs and secondary sex characteristics.

tetanus Sustained muscle contraction without relaxation; an infection caused by the bacterium *Clostridium tetani.*

thalamus Part of the brain located in the lateral walls of the third ventricle that serves as the integrating center for sensory input; it plays a role in arousing the cerebral cortex.

thermoreceptor Sensory receptor that is sensitive to changes in temperature.

threshold Electrical potential level (voltage) at which an action potential or nerve impulse is produced.

thrombin Enzyme that converts fibrinogen to fibrin threads during blood clotting.

thrombocytopenia Insufficient number of platelets in the blood.

thromboembolism Obstruction of a blood vessel by a thrombus that has dislodged from the site of its formation.

thymine (T) One of four nitrogen-containing bases in nucleotides composing the structure of DNA; pairs with adenine.

thymosin Peptide secreted by the thymus that increases production of certain types of white blood cells.

thymus Lymphatic organ, located along the trachea behind the sternum, involved in the maturation of T lymphocytes in the thymus gland. Secretes hormones called thymosins, which aid the maturation of T cells and perhaps stimulate immune cells in general.

thyroid gland Endocrine gland in the neck that produces several important hormones, including thyroxine, triiodothyronine, and calcitonin.

thyroid-stimulating hormone (TSH) Substance produced by the anterior pituitary that causes the thyroid to secrete thyroxine and triiodothyronine.

thyroxine (T_4) Hormone secreted from the thyroid gland that promotes growth and development. In general, it increases the metabolic rate in cells.

tidal volume Amount of air normally moved in the human body during an inspiration or expiration.

tissue Group of similar cells that perform a common function.

tonsillectomy Surgical removal of the tonsils.

tonsillitis Infection of the tonsils that causes inflammation and can spread to the middle ears.

tonsils Partially encapsulated lymph nodules located in the pharynx.

toxin Poisonous substance produced by living cells or organisms. Toxins are nearly always proteins that are capable of causing disease on contact.

trachea Passageway that conveys air from the larynx to the bronchi; also called the windpipe.

tract Bundle of myelinated axons in the central nervous system.

trans fat Fats, which occur naturally in meat and dairy products of ruminants, that are also industrially created through partial hydrogenation of plant oils and animal fats.

transcription Process whereby a DNA strand serves as a template for the formation of mRNA.

transcription factor In eukaryotes, protein required for the initiation of transcription by RNA polymerase.

transfer RNA (tRNA) Type of RNA that transfers a particular amino acid to a ribosome during protein synthesis; at one end, it binds to the amino acid, and at the other end it has an anticodon that binds to an mRNA codon.

translation Process whereby ribosomes use the sequence of codons in mRNA to produce a polypeptide with a particular sequence of amino acids.

translocation Movement of a chromosomal segment from one chromosome to another nonhomologous chromosome, leading to abnormalities (e.g., Down syndrome).

triglyceride Neutral fat composed of glycerol and three fatty acids; also known as fats and lipids.

triiodothyronine (T_3) Hormone produced by the thyroid gland that contains three iodine atoms; the metabolically active form of the thyroid hormones.

trisomy Condition that is characterized by a diploid cell that has three copies of a chromosome as a result of a nondisjunction event during cell division.

trophic level Feeding level of one or more populations in a food web.

tropomyosin Protein that functions with troponin to block muscle contraction until calcium ions are present.

troponin Protein that functions with tropomyosin to block muscle contraction until calcium ions are present.

tubal ligation Method for preventing pregnancy in which the uterine tubes are cut and sealed.

tuberculosis Infection of the lungs, caused by the bacteria *Mycobacterium tuberculosis.*

tubular reabsorption Movement of primarily nutrient molecules and water from the contents of the nephron into blood at the proximal convoluted tubule.

tubular secretion Movement of certain molecules from blood into the distal convoluted tubule of a nephron so they are added to urine.

tumor Cells derived from a single mutated cell that has repeatedly undergone cell division; benign tumors remain at the site of origin, and malignant tumors metastasize.

tumor suppressor gene Gene that codes for a protein that ordinarily suppresses cell division; inactivity can lead to a tumor.

tympanic membrane Located between the outer and middle ear where it receives sound waves; also called the eardrum.

U

umbilical cord Cord connecting the fetus to the placenta through which blood vessels pass.

unsaturated fatty acid Fatty acid molecule that has one or more double bonds between the atoms of its carbon chain.

uracil (U) The base in RNA that replaces thymine found in DNA; pairs with adenine.

urea Primary nitrogenous waste of humans derived from amino acid breakdown.

uremia High level of urea nitrogen in the blood.

ureter One of two tubes that take urine from the kidneys to the urinary bladder.

urethra Tubular structure that receives urine from the bladder and carries it to the outside of the body.

urethritis Inflammation of the urethra.

uric acid Waste product of nucleotide metabolism.

urinary bladder Organ where urine is stored before being discharged by way of the urethra.

urinary system Organ system consisting of the kidneys and urinary bladder; rids the body of nitrogenous wastes and helps regulate the water-salt balance of the blood.

uterine cycle Monthly occurring changes in the characteristics of the uterine lining (endometrium).

uterine tubes Structures of the female reproductive system that transport the egg from the ovary to the uterus; location of fertilization; also called the oviducts or fallopian tubes.

uterus Organ located in the female pelvis where the fetus develops; also called the womb.

utricle Saclike cavity in the vestibule of the inner ear that contains sensory receptors for gravitational equilibrium.

V

vaccine Antigens prepared in such a way that they can promote active immunity without causing disease.

vagina Organ that leads from the uterus to the vestibule and serves as the birth canal and organ of sexual intercourse in females.

valence shell The outermost energy shell of an atom; the location of electrons that participate in chemical reactions.

vas deferens (pl., vasa deferentia) Tube that leads from the epididymis to the urethra in males.

vasectomy Method for preventing pregnancy in which the vasa deferentia are cut and sealed.

vector In genetic engineering, a means to transfer foreign genetic material into a cell (e.g., a plasmid). In the study of disease, a vector is a living organism that transfers the disease between hosts, usually of different species.

vein Vessel that transports blood back to the heart; often has valves due to the low pressure of the blood.

vena cava Major vein of the body; returns blood from the systemic circuit to the right atrium.

ventilation Process of moving air into and out of the lungs; also called breathing.

ventricle Cavity in an organ, such as a lower chamber of the heart or the ventricles of the brain.

venule Vessel that takes blood from capillaries to a vein.

vernix caseosa Cheeselike substance covering the skin of the fetus.

vertebral column Series of joined vertebrae that extends from the skull to the pelvis.

vesicle Small, membrane-bound sac that stores substances within a cell.

vestibule Space or cavity at the entrance of a canal, such as the cavity that lies between the semicircular canals and the cochlea.

vestigial structure Remains of a structure that was functional in some ancestor but is no longer functional in the organism in question.

villi (sing., villus) Small, fingerlike projections of the inner small intestinal wall.

virus Noncellular, parasitic agent consisting of an outer capsid and an inner core of nucleic acid.

visual accommodation Ability of the eye to focus at different distances by changing the curvature of the lens.

vital capacity Maximum amount of air moved into or out of the human body with each breathing cycle.

vitamin Essential requirement in the diet, needed in small amounts. Vitamins are often part of coenzymes.

vitreous humor Clear, gelatinous material between the lens of the eye and the retina.

vocal cord Fold of tissue within the larynx; creates vocal sounds when it vibrates.

vulva External genitals of the female that surround the opening of the vagina.

water cycle Interdependent and continuous circulation of water from the ocean to the atmosphere, to the land, and back to the ocean. Also called the hydrologic cycle.

Wernicke's area Brain area involved in language comprehension; located in the posterior part of the left temporal lobe.

white blood cell (leukocyte) Type of blood cell that is transparent without staining and protects the body from invasion by foreign substances and organisms.

white matter Myelinated axons in the central nervous system.

X-linked Refers to an allele located on an X chromosome, but may control a trait that has nothing to do with the sex characteristics of an individual.

XDR TB Extensively drug-resistant tuberculosis, a type of bacterium that causes tuberculosis (TB) that is no longer susceptible to almost all of the drugs normally used to treat TB.

xenotransplantation Use of animal organs, instead of human organs, in human transplant patients.

Y-linked A trait located on the Y chromosome.

yolk sac Extraembryonic membrane that encloses the yolk of birds; in humans, it is the first site of blood cell formation.

zygote Diploid cell formed by the union of sperm and egg; the product of fertilization.

Index

Note: Page numbers followed by *f* or *t* represent figures or tables, respectively.

A

C

F

G

H

I

J

K

L

M

O

P

T

U

V